P9-BIH-022

METABOLISM

METABOLISM

COMPILED AND EDITED BY

Philip L. Altman and Dorothy S. Dittmer

PREPARED UNDER THE AUSPICES OF THE Committee on Biological Handbooks

Federation of American Societies for Experimental Biology

BETHESDA, MARYLAND

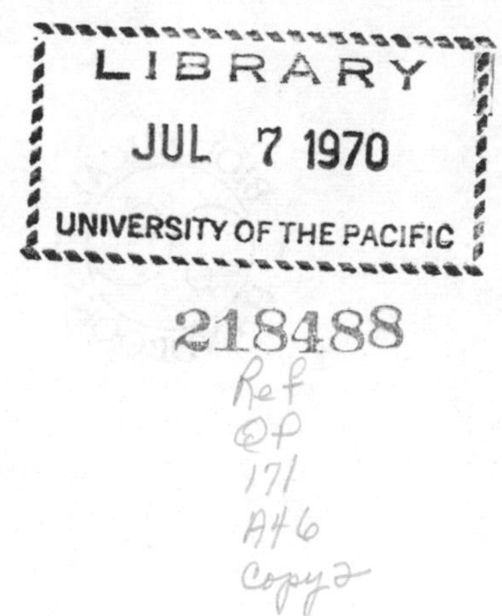

MADE IN THE UNITED STATES OF AMERICA

Library of Congress Catalog Card Number: 68–8919

FOREWORD

All the chemical processes that are constantly taking place in living organisms are included under the term metabolism. In some cases energy is used to convert simple substances into more complex cell and tissue components (anabolism). At the same time, complex substances are being changed to simple ones, often with the release of energy (catabolism). The composition of materials taken into the plant or animal, the ways in which these nutritional materials become part of the organism, the energy exchange, and metabolic end products are dealt with in various sections of this data book. Some tables show how too much or too little of some apparently minor component may profoundly influence a life process: the ancient "have" and "have not" of all living things. Metabolic pathways with intermediate products are diagrammed to show as clearly as possible the multiple steps that may occur in several ways and over very short periods of time. Certain internal and external modifiers of metabolism are included in this volume, which is an extensively revised successor to the 1954 *Standard Values in Nutrition and Metabolism.*

This volume on *METABOLISM* is one of a series of handbooks prepared for the use of specialists and published by the Federation of American Societies for Experimental Biology (FASEB): *Blood and Other Body Fluids,* 1961; *Growth, Including Reproduction and Morphological Development,* 1962; and *Environmental Biology,* 1966. In addition, the *Biology Data Book,* published in 1964, was derived in part from the series of specialized handbooks and was designed for use by persons at all levels of biological study. Earlier biological data compilations were prepared under the auspices of the National Academy of Sciences - National Research Council Committee; the first of these appeared in 1952.

J. W. Heim, former technical director of the Biomedical Laboratory, Wright-Patterson Air Force Base, upon his retirement from the Committee on Biological Handbooks in December 1967 was praised for his role in proposing the handbooks project in 1947 to the NAS - NRC, and in having it initiated in 1949. Dr. T. C. Byerly, as chairman of the first Handbooks Committee, commented that Dr. Heim is in a very real sense the father of the handbooks undertaking, and that it was through Dr. Heim's inspiration and determination that the project has flourished. It has been a privilege for the current Handbooks Committee chairman to have been associated with Drs. Heim and Byerly in this activity for the past 20 years.

Responsibility for general guidance and for selection of fields to be covered by the data books rests with the Committee on Biological Handbooks. In order to have the knowledge of experts available, a special Advisory Committee is chosen for each book planned. To help select the Advisory Committee, the Chairman and the staff Director in February 1966 called on James Waddell, executive secretary of the American Institute of Nutrition, and the late Wendell H. Griffith, former director of the Life Sciences Research Office (FASEB). Their assistance in selecting the experts to serve on the Metabolism Advisory Committee is gratefully acknowledged by the Committee on Biological Handbooks.

The Advisory Committee (listed on the following page) met to determine what should be included and what should be excluded from this volume. On the basis of their extensive research and teaching experience, committee members then made suggestions as to authorities in particular fields who should be asked to contribute their services in the preparation of a table or part of a table. Original tables may be sent in by more than one contributor. When necessary, these are integrated by the staff and sent to two or more reviewers for critical evaluation. With the aid of Committee and Advisory Committee members, the staff have been able to obtain remarkable cooperation in securing data for this and previous volumes. The staff compile the data into tables that conform to established standards, and after review the tables are edited and final drafts prepared. Because of the nature of the project, it has been found more efficient to have composition, editing, indexing, and preparation of camera-ready copy done entirely within the Office of Biological Handbooks.

The Committee on Biological Handbooks acknowledges with thanks the contributions made by 302 botanists, zoologists and basic medical research scientists who have given so generously of their time and advice. The Committee also wishes to thank the National Library of Medicine, the National Aeronautics and Space Administration, the United States Air Force, and the United States Department of Agriculture for the generous support and cooperation which have made possible the production of this book. Participation in this undertaking was fulfilled under National Library of Medicine Grant No. 5 RO1 LM 00334, National Aeronautics and Space Administration Contract No. NASr-238, Air Force Contract No. F33615-67-C-1081 and Department of Agriculture Contract No. 12-14-110-3159-20.

2 August 1968
Bethesda, Maryland

Raymund L. Zwemer, *Chairman*
Committee on Biological Handbooks

COMMITTEE ON BIOLOGICAL HANDBOOKS

ADVISORY COMMITTEE ON METABOLISM

HANDBOOK STAFF

* *ex officio*
† *emeritus*

CONTRIBUTORS AND REVIEWERS

ADOLPH, EDWARD F.
University of Rochester School of Medicine and Dentistry
Rochester, New York 14620

ALLEN, MARY BELLE
University of Alaska
College, Alaska 99735

ALLGEIER, R. J.
284 Bloomsbury Avenue
Catonsville, Maryland 21228

ALMQUIST, H. J.
The Grange Company
Modesto, California 95352

ALTSCHUL, AARON M.
USDA, International Agricultural Development Service
Washington, D.C. 20250

AMBROSE, CHARLES TESCH
Harvard Medical School
Boston, Massachusetts 02115

BADEER, HENRY S.
Creighton University School of Medicine
Omaha, Nebraska 68131

BAICH, ANNETTE
Oregon State University
Corvallis, Oregon 97331

BARKER, S. B.
University of Alabama Medical Center
Birmingham, Alabama 35233

BARNETT, H. L.
West Virginia University
Morgantown, West Virginia 26506

BARNETT, HENRY L.
Albert Einstein College of Medicine
Bronx, New York 10461

BARRETT, HAROLD W.
Jacksonville University
Jacksonville, Florida 32211

BARTGIS, I. LOUISE
National Institutes of Health
Bethesda, Maryland 20014

BASSHAM, JAMES A.
University of California
Berkeley, California 94720

BEAR, FIRMAN E.
Rutgers-State University
New Brunswick, New Jersey 08903

BECK, STANLEY D.
University of Wisconsin
Madison, Wisconsin 53706

BEESON, W. M.
Purdue University
Lafayette, Indiana 47907

BENJAMIN, C. R.
USDA, National Fungus Collection
Beltsville, Maryland 20705

BENSON, ANDREW A.
University of California
La Jolla, California 92038

BIERI, JOHN G.
National Institutes of Health
Bethesda, Maryland 20014

BIRD, H. R.
University of Wisconsin
Madison, Wisconsin 53706

BISHOP, DAVID W.
Marine Biological Laboratory
Woods Hole, Massachusetts 02543

BLISS, DOROTHY E.
American Museum of Natural History
New York, New York 10024

BONNER, JAMES
California Institute of Technology
Pasadena, California 91109

BOOKER, WALTER M.
Howard University
Washington, D.C. 20001

BRESSANI, RICARDO
Instituto de Nutricion de Centro America y Panama
Guatemala City, Guatemala

BRIGGS, WINSLOW R.
Stanford University
Stanford, California 94305

BROWN, ELEANOR S.
University of Wisconsin Medical Center
Madison, Wisconsin 53706

BROWN, GENE M.
Massachusetts Institute of Technology
Cambridge, Massachusetts 02139

BROWN, GEORGE B.
Sloan-Kettering Institute for Cancer Research
New York, New York 10021

BRUN, ROBERT
Hopital Cantonal
Geneva, Switzerland

BUCHHOLTZ, KENNETH PAUL
University of Wisconsin
Madison, Wisconsin 53706

BUTLER, WARREN L.
University of California
La Jolla, California 92037

CALHOUN, WILLIAM K.
U.S. Army Natick Laboratories
Natick, Massachusetts 01760

CALVIN, MELVIN
University of California
Berkeley, California 94720

CAMPBELL, JACK J. R.
University of British Columbia
Vancouver, British Columbia, Canada

CAROLUS, ROBERT L.
Michigan State University
East Lansing, Michigan 48823

CARTWRIGHT, GEORGE E.
University of Utah School of Medicine
Salt Lake City, Utah 84112

CHARALAMPOUS, F. C.
University of Pennsylvania School of Medicine
Philadelphia, Pennsylvania 19104

CHEW, ROBERT M.
University of Southern California
Los Angeles, California 90007

CHITWOOD, MAY BELLE H.
USDA Parasitological Laboratory
Beltsville, Maryland 20705

CLARK, F. M.
University of Illinois
Urbana, Illinois 61801

CLARK, HUGH
University of Connecticut
Storrs, Connecticut 06268

CLAYTON, RAYMOND B.
Stanford University School of Medicine
Palo Alto, California 94304

*COCHRAN, DORIS M.

COMBE, ETIENNETTE
University of Kentucky Medical Center
Lexington, Kentucky 40506

COMMON, R. H.
MacDonald College
Montreal, Quebec, Canada

CORLISS, JOHN O.
University of Illinois at Chicago Circle
Chicago, Illinois 60680

CORNELIUS, C. E.
Kansas State University
Manhattan, Kansas 66502

COTZIAS, GEORGE C.
Brookhaven National Laboratory
Upton, Long Island, New York 11973

COUCH, J. R.
Texas A & M University
College Station, Texas 77843

CRAMPTON, E. W.
MacDonald College
Montreal, Quebec, Canada

CRAWFORD, EUGENE C.
University of Kentucky
Lexington, Kentucky 40506

CUMMINS, ALVIN J.
University of Tennessee
Memphis, Tennessee 38103

CUNHA, T. J.
University of Florida
Gainesville, Florida 32601

*Deceased

DADD, R. H.
University of California
Berkeley, California 94720
DARBY, RICHARD T.
U.S. Army Natick Laboratories
Natick, Massachusetts 01760
DAVEY, R. J.
USDA, Animal Husbandry Research Division
Beltsville, Maryland 20705
DAWSON, WILLIAM R.
University of Michigan
Ann Arbor, Michigan 48104
DIAMOND, LOUIS S.
National Institutes of Health
Bethesda, Maryland 20014
DIANZANI, MARIO U.
University of Turin
Turin, Italy
DORFMAN, RALPH I.
Syntex Corporation
Palo Alto, California 94304
DOWNS, ROBERT J.
North Carolina State University
Raleigh, North Carolina 27607
*DuBOIS, EUGENE F.
DUPREE, HARRY K.
USDI, Southeastern Fish Cultural Laboratory
Marion, Alabama 36756

EDELMANN, CHESTER M., JR.
Albert Einstein College of Medicine
Bronx, New York 10461
EDWARDS, HARDY M., JR.
University of Georgia
Athens, Georgia 30601
EIK-NES, KRISTEN B.
University of Utah College of Medicine
Salt Lake City, Utah 84112
ELLIS, ELDON E.
Eleven Birch Street
Redwood City, California 94062
ELTON, NORMAN W.
Binghamton General Hospital
Binghamton, New York 13903
ELWYN, DAVID H.
Hektoen Institute for Medical Research
Chicago, Illinois 60612

FARNER, DONALD S.
University of Washington
Seattle, Washington 98105
FINCKE, MARGARET L.
Oregon State University
Corvallis, Oregon 97331
FISHER, LESTER E.
Lincoln Park Zoological Gardens
Chicago, Illinois 60614
FITZGERALD, LAURENCE R.
University of Tennessee Medical Units
Memphis, Tennessee 38103
FITZHUGH, O. G.
Food and Drug Administration
Washington, D.C. 20204
FLEMISTER, LAUNCE J.
Swarthmore College
Swarthmore, Pennsylvania 19081
FLOCK, EUNICE V.
Mayo Clinic
Rochester, Minnesota 55902
FORD, J. E.
National Institute for Research in Dairying
Shinfield, Reading, England
FORREST, ANDREW P. M.
Welsh National School of Medicine
Cardiff, South Wales
FORWARD, DOROTHY F.
University of Toronto
Toronto, Canada
FRAENKEL, GOTTFRIED S.
University of Illinois
Urbana, Illinois 61801
FRANKLIN, MARGERY H.
Cornell University
Ithaca, New York 14850
FRAZER, A. C.
The University
Birmingham, England
FREE, ALFRED H.
Ames Company
Elkhart, Indiana 46514
FREE, HELEN M.
Ames Company
Elkhart, Indiana 46514
FREGLY, MELVIN J.
University of Florida College of Medicine
Gainesville, Florida 32601
FRIEDEN, EARL
Florida State University
Tallahassee, Florida 32306
FRIEND, BERTA
USDA, Consumer and Food Economics Research Division
Hyattsville, Maryland 20782
FRIES, NILS
University of Uppsala
Uppsala, Sweden
FROST, DOUGLAS V.
Dartmouth Medical School
Brattleboro, Vermont 05301
FULLER, WALLACE H.
University of Arizona
Tucson, Arizona 85721

GALE, GEORGE O.
American Cyanamide Company
Princeton, New Jersey 08540
GAUCH, HUGH G.
University of Maryland
College Park, Maryland 20742
GERGELY, J.
Retina Foundation
Boston, Massachusetts 02114
GERSHOFF, STANLEY N.
Harvard University School of Public Health
Boston, Massachusetts 02115
GHADIMI, H.
State University of New York
Brooklyn, New York 11203
GIBSON, QUENTIN H.
Cornell University
Ithaca, New York 14850
GIERE, FREDERIC A.
Lake Forest College
Lake Forest, Illinois 60045
GLAZER, A. N.
University of California
Los Angeles, California 90024
GOLDSMITH, DALE P. J.
University of Nebraska College of Medicine
Omaha, Nebraska 68105
GOLDSMITH, GRACE A.
Tulane University School of Medicine
New Orleans, Louisiana 70112
GOODWIN, T. W.
University of Liverpool
Liverpool, England
GORDON, H. A.
University of Kentucky Medical Center
Lexington, Kentucky 40506
GORDON, H. T.
University of California
Berkeley, California 94720
GOULD, BERNARD S.
Massachusetts Institute of Technology
Cambridge, Massachusetts 02139
GRAD, BERNARD
McGill University
Montreal, Quebec, Canada
GRANICK, S.
Rockefeller University
New York, New York 10021
GROSSMAN, MORTON I.
Veterans Administration Center
Los Angeles, California 90073

HALVER, JOHN E.
USDI, Western Fish Nutrition Laboratory
Cook, Washington 98605
HANDLEY, CHARLES O., JR.
Smithsonian Institution
Washington, D.C. 20560
HARPER, A. E.
University of Wisconsin
Madison, Wisconsin 53706
HARRIS, LORIN E.
Utah State University
Logan, Utah 84321
HART, J. SANFORD
National Research Council
Ottawa, Canada
HAVELL, EDWARD
University of Notre Dame
Notre Dame, Indiana 46556

*Deceased

HAYES, WAYLAND J., JR.
National Communicable Disease Center
Atlanta, Georgia 30333
HENDERSON, LAVANIEL L., SR.
Texas Southern University
Houston, Texas 77004
HENDERSON, L. M.
University of Minnesota
St. Paul, Minnesota 55101
HENDRICKS, STERLING B.
USDA, Soil and Water Conservation Research Division
Beltsville, Maryland 20705
HOCK, RAYMOND J.
Northrop Space Laboratories
Hawthorne, California 90250
*HOLLANDER, FRANKLIN
HOUSE, H. B.
New York Zoological Society
Bronk, New York 10460
HOUSE, H. L.
Canada Department of Agriculture
Belleville, Ontario, Canada
HUDSON, JACK W.
Cornell University
Ithaca, New York 14850
HULL, HERBERT M.
USDA, Crops Research Division
Tucson, Arizona 85719
HURSH, JOHN B.
University of Rochester School of Medicine and Dentistry
Rochester, New York 14620

JENNISON, MARSHALL W.
Syracuse University
Syracuse, New York 13210
JOHNSON, HERMAN L.
Fitzsimons General Hospital
Denver, Colorado 80240
JOHNSON, PAUL E.
National Research Council
Washington, D.C. 20418
JUDKINS, WESLEY P.
Virginia Polytechnic Institute
Blacksburg, Virginia 24061
JUKES, THOMAS H.
University of California
Berkeley, California 94720

KIBLER, HUDSON H.
University of Missouri
Columbia, Missouri 65201
KING, C. G.
St. Lukes Hospital Center
New York, New York 10025
KING, KENDALL W.
Virginia Polytechnic Institute
Blacksburg, Virginia 24061
KLEIBER, MAX
University of California
Davis, California 95616
KOFT, BERNARD W.
Rutgers-State University
New Brunswick, New Jersey 08903
KOSER, STEWART A.
University of Chicago
Chicago, Illinois 60637
KOTTKE, FREDERIC J.
University of Minnesota
Minneapolis, Minnesota 55455
KROMBEIN, KARL V.
Smithsonian Institution
Washington, D.C. 20560
KUEHN, GARY
San Diego Zoological Garden
San Diego, California 92112

LACHNER, ERNEST
Smithsonian Institution
Washington, D.C. 20560
LA DU, BERT N.
New York University School of Medicine
New York, New York 10016
LANSFORD, EDWIN M., JR.
University of Texas
Austin, Texas 78712
LARSEN, SIGURD
Levington Research Station
Ipswich, Suffolk, England
LASIEWSKI, ROBERT C.
University of California
Los Angeles, California 90024
LAUSON, HENRY D.
Albert Einstein College of Medicine
Bronx, New York 10461
LECOQ, RAOUL
Centre Hospitalier de Saint-Germain-en-Laye
Seine-et Oise, France
LEE, JOHN J.
American Museum of Natural History
New York, New York 10024
LEITCH, ISABELLA
30 Ashgrove Road West
Aberdeen, Scotland
LEMON, EDGAR R.
USDA, Plant, Soil and Nutrition Laboratory
Ithaca, New York 14850
LEPKOVSKY, SAMUEL
University of California
Berkeley, California 94720
LESSEL, ERWIN F.
American Type Culture Collection
Rockville, Maryland 20852
*LEVEY, STANLEY
LIEBOWITZ, DANIEL
Eleven Birch Street
Redwood City, California 94062
LILLY, VIRGIL GREENE
West Virginia University
Morgantown, West Virginia 26506
LIVERMORE, GEORGE R., JR.
910 Madison Avenue
Memphis, Tennessee 38103
LOCKER, A.
Österreichische Studiengesellschaft für Atomenergie
Vienna, Austria
LOFTFIELD, ROBERT B.
University of New Mexico
Albuquerque, New Mexico 87106
LUCKEY, T. D.
University of Missouri Medical Center
Columbia, Missouri 65202

MACFADYEN, AMYAN
New University of Ulster
Coleraine, Northern Ireland
MANDELS, GABRIEL R.
U.S. Army Natick Laboratories
Natick, Massachusetts 01760
MANNING, RAYMOND B.
Smithsonian Institution
Washington, D.C. 20560
MARION, JAMES E.
Georgia Experiment Station
Experiment, Georgia 30212
MARSHALL, C. R.
Weybridge Park House
Weybridge, Surrey, England
MAYER, JEAN
Harvard University School of Public Health
Boston, Massachusetts 02115
McBRIDE, LANDY J.
International Minerals & Chemical Corporation
Libertyville, Illinois 60048
McCHESNEY, E. W.
Sterling-Winthrop Research Institute
Rensselaer, New York 12144
MEAD, JAMES F.
University of California
Los Angeles, California 90024
MEISTER, ALTON
Cornell University Medical College
New York, New York 10021
MERTZ, EDWIN T.
Purdue University
Lafayette, Indiana 47907
METCALF, ROBERT L.
University of California
Riverside, California 92502
MEYERS, EDWARD
Squibb Institute for Medical Research
New Brunswick, New Jersey 08903
MICKELSEN, OLAF
Michigan State University
East Lansing, Michigan 48823
MILNER, MAX
United Nations Children's Fund
United Nations, New York
MILNER, REID T.
University of Illinois
Urbana, Illinois 61801

*Deceased

MITCHELL, J. E.
University of Wisconsin
Madison, Wisconsin 53706
MITCHELL, ROBERT L.
Macaulay Institute for Soil Research
Aberdeen, Scotland
MITTLER, THOMAS E.
University of California
Berkeley, California 94720
MOMENT, GAIRDNER B.
Goucher College
Baltimore, Maryland 21204
MONAGLE, J. E.
Department of National Health and Welfare
Ottawa, Ontario, Canada
*MORGAN, AGNES FAY
MORRISON, PETER R.
University of Alaska
College, Alaska 99735
MYERS, JACK
University of Texas
Austin, Texas 78712

NADLER, KENNETH
Rockefeller University
New York, New York 10021
NELSON, LESTER S.
San Diego Zoological Garden
San Diego, California 92112
NESHEIM, M. C.
Cornell University
Ithaca, New York 14850
NEUMANN, RICHARD L.
Cornell University
Ithaca, New York 14850
NICHOL, CHARLES A.
Roswell Park Memorial Institute
Buffalo, New York 14203
NIEDERMEIER, WILLIAM
University of Alabama Medical Center
Birmingham, Alabama 35233
NIRENBERG, MARSHALL W.
National Institutes of Health
Bethesda, Maryland 20014
NORD, F. F.
Fordham University
New York, New York 10458

OACE, SUSAN
University of California
Berkeley, California 94720
O'DELL, BOYD L.
University of Missouri
Columbia, Missouri 65202
OKUNZUA, G.
The University
Birmingham, England
OLSON, JAMES A.
University of Medical Sciences
Bangkok, Thailand
OSBALDISTON, G. W.
Kansas State University
Manhattan, Kansas 66502

PAGE, LOUISE
USDA, Consumer and Food Economics Research Division
Hyattsville, Maryland 20782
PASSMORE, R.
University of Edinburgh
Edinburgh, Scotland
PEARSON, A. M.
Michigan State University
East Lansing, Michigan 48823
PEARSON, PAUL B.
Nutrition Foundation, Inc.
New York, New York 10016
PEARSON, W. N.
Vanderbilt University
Nashville, Tennessee 37203
PERLMAN, D.
University of Wisconsin
Madison, Wisconsin 53706
PESCHEL, ERNST
Duke University Medical Center
Durham, North Carolina 27706
PETTIBONE, MARIAN HOPE
Smithsonian Institution
Washington, D.C. 20560
PHILLIPSON, A. T.
School of Veterinary Medicine
Cambridge, England
PLEASANTS, JULIAN R.
University of Notre Dame
Notre Dame, Indiana 46556
PORTER, J. W. G.
National Institute for Research in Dairying
Shinfield, Reading, England
PRATT, P. F.
University of California
Riverside, California 92502
PRITHAM, GORDON H.
Kansas City College of Osteopathy and Surgery
Kansas City, Missouri 64124
PROVASOLI, LUIGI
Haskins Laboratories
New York, New York 10017

QUASTEL, J. H.
University of British Columbia
Vancouver, British Columbia, Canada

RAMAMURTHI, R.
University of Oregon
Eugene, Oregon 97403
RANDALL, WALTER C.
Loyola University Stritch School of Medicine
Chicago, Illinois 60612
RATCLIFFE, HERBERT L.
Philadelphia Zoological Garden
Philadelphia, Pennsylvania 19104
REBER, ELWOOD F.
University of Massachusetts
Amherst, Massachusetts 01003

REUTHER, WALTER
University of California
Riverside, California 92502
RHYNE, CHARLES F.
Smithsonian Institution
Washington, D.C. 20560
ROBBINS, W. REI
Rutgers-State University
New Brunswick, New Jersey 08902
ROBBINS, WILLIAM E.
USDA, Entomology Research Division
Beltsville, Maryland 20705
ROBINSON, WILLARD B.
Cornell University
Geneva, New York 14456
ROSE, WILLIAM C.
710 West Florida Avenue
Urbana, Illinois 61801
ROSENFIELD, DANIEL
Union Carbide Corporation
Tarrytown, New York 10591
ROSEWATER, JOSEPH
Smithsonian Institution
Washington, D.C. 20560
RUNNELS, TOM D.
University of Delaware
Newark, Delaware 19711
RUSSELL, E. W.
The University
Reading, England

SALLACH, H. J.
University of Wisconsin
Madison, Wisconsin 53706
SAMMONS, H. G.
East Birmingham Hospital
Birmingham, England
SAVARD, F. G. Kenneth
University of Miami School of Medicine
Miami, Florida 33134
SCHEER, BRADLEY T.
University of Oregon
Eugene, Oregon 97403
SCHULTZ, H. W.
Oregon State University
Corvallis, Oregon 97331
SELKURT, EWALD E.
Indiana University Medical Center
Indianapolis, Indiana 46207
SENIOR, JOHN R.
Philadelphia General Hospital
Philadelphia, Pennsylvania 19104
SHANTON, JOHN LYNN
Mead Johnson Research Center
Evansville, Indiana 47721
SHEMIN, DAVID
College of Physicians & Surgeons of Columbia University
New York, New York 10032
SHIH, THOMAS Y.
California Institute of Technology
Pasadena, California 91109
SIEGELMAN, H. W.
Brookhaven National Laboratory
Upton, New York 11973

*Deceased

SKINNER, DOROTHY M.
Oak Ridge National Laboratory
Oak Ridge, Tennessee 37831
SLUD, PAUL
Smithsonian Institution
Washington, D.C. 20560
SMART, GROVER C., JR.
University of Florida
Gainesville, Florida 32601
SMITH, LUCILE
Dartmouth Medical School
Hanover, New Hampshire 03755
SMITH, NATHAN R.
322 South Washington Drive
Sarasota, Florida 33577
SNELL, ESMOND E.
University of California
Berkeley, California 94720
SNELL, J. F.
Ohio State University
Columbus, Ohio 43210
SOMERS, G. FRED
University of Delaware
Newark, Delaware 19711
SPRAGUE, HOWARD B.
National Research Council
Washington, D.C. 20418
STARR, RICHARD C.
Indiana University
Bloomington, Indiana 47401
STEWART, WILLIAM D. P.
University of London
London, England
STORVICK, CLARA A.
Oregon State University
Corvallis, Oregon 97331
STUMPF, PAUL K.
University of California
Davis, California 95616
SUNDE, M. L.
University of Wisconsin
Madison, Wisconsin 53706
SWANSON, ERIC W.
University of Tennessee
Knoxville, Tennessee 37901
SWENDSEID, MARIAN E.
University of California
Los Angeles, California 90024

TANNER, FRED W., JR.
Charles Pfizer & Co., Inc.
New York, New York 10017
TAYLOR, FLOYD B.
National Center for Urban and Industrial Health
Boston, Massachusetts 02203
THOMAS, MOYER D.
2321 Elsinore Road
Riverside, California 92506
THOMAS, WILLIAM H.
University of California
La Jolla, California 92038
THOMPSON, S. Y.
National Institute for Research in Dairying
Shinfield, Reading, England
TOBIE, ELEANOR JOHNSON
National Institutes of Health
Bethesda, Maryland 20014
TOVE, SAMUEL B.
North Carolina State University
Raleigh, North Carolina 27607
TRUOG, EMIL
University of Wisconsin
Madison, Wisconsin 53706
TSAMASFYROS, CONSTANTINE
University of Missouri Medical Center
Columbia, Missouri 65202
TYZNIK, W. J.
Ohio State University
Columbus, Ohio 43210

UMBREIT, WAYNE W.
Rutgers-State University
New Brunswick, New Jersey 08903
UNDERKOFLER, L. A.
Miles Laboratories, Inc.
Elkhart, Indiana 46514
UNGLAUB, WALTER G.
Tulane University School of Medicine
New Orleans, Louisiana 70112

VAN BAVEL, CORNELIUS H. M.
Texas A & M University
College Station, Texas 77843
VAN BRUGGEN, JOHN T.
University of Oregon Medical School
Portland, Oregon 97201
VANDERZANT, ERMA S.
Texas A & M University
College Station, Texas 77843
VAN LANEN, J. M.
Hiram Walker & Sons, Inc.
Peoria, Illinois 61601
VAN PILSUM, JOHN F.
University of Minnesota
Minneapolis, Minnesota 55455
VERNBERG, F. JOHN
Duke University Marine Laboratory
Beaufort, North Carolina 28516
VERNBERG, WINONA B.
Duke University Marine Laboratory
Beaufort, North Carolina 28516
VINYARD, ELIZABETH
University of California
Los Angeles, California 90024
VISHNIAC, WOLF
University of Rochester
Rochester, New York 14627
von BERTALANFFY, LUDWIG
University of Alberta
Edmonton, Alberta, Canada
von BRAND, THEODOR
National Institutes of Health
Bethesda, Maryland 20014
VORIS, LEROY
National Academy of Sciences
Washington, D.C. 20418

WAINIO, WALTER W.
Rutgers-State University
New Brunswick, New Jersey 08903
WAISMAN, HARRY A.
University of Wisconsin Medical Center
Madison, Wisconsin 53706
WALKER, RICHARD B.
University of Washington
Seattle, Washington 98105
WARNER, R. G.
Cornell University
Ithaca, New York 14850
WASSERMAN, ROBERT H.
Cornell University
Ithaca, New York 14850
WATT, BERNICE K.
USDA, Consumer and Food Economics Research Division
Hyattsville, Maryland 20782
WATTS, ALVA BURL
Louisiana State University
Baton Rouge, Louisiana 70803
WAYMOUTH, CHARITY
Jackson Laboratory
Bar Harbor, Maine 04609
WECKEL, K. G.
University of Wisconsin
Madison, Wisconsin 53706
WEISS, MARGARET L.
University of Rochester
Rochester, New York 14627
WELCH, C. D.
Texas A & M University
College Station, Texas 77841
WHEATLEY, VICTOR R.
New York University Medical Center
New York, New York 10016
WHERRY, EDGAR T.
University of Pennsylvania
Philadelphia, Pennsylvania 19104
*WHITE, PHILIP R.
WICKERHAM, LYNFERD J.
USDA, Northern Utilization Research and Development Division
Peoria, Illinois 61604
WILD, ALAN
Ahmadu Bello University
Zaria, Northern Nigeria
WILLIAMS, A. P.
National Institute for Research in Dairying
Shinfield, Reading, England

*Deceased

WILLOUGHBY, HARVEY
USDI, Bureau of Sport Fisheries and Wildlife
Washington, D.C. 20240

WOLF, FREDERICK T.
Vanderbilt University
Nashville, Tennessee 37203

WOSTMANN, BERNARD S.
University of Notre Dame
Notre Dame, Indiana 46556

WRIGHT, LEMUEL D.
Cornell University
Ithaca, New York 14850

WRIGHT, STANLEY W.
University of California Medical Center
Los Angeles, California 90024

ZBARSKY, S. H.
University of British Columbia
Vancouver, British Columbia, Canada

ZELITCH, ISRAEL
Connecticut Agricultural Experiment Station
New Haven, Connecticut 06504

ZoBELL, CLAUDE E.
University of California
La Jolla, California 92037

CONTENTS

III. PLANT NUTRITION

IV. DIGESTION AND ABSORPTION

V. NUTRIENT FUNCTION, DEFICIENCY, AND EXCESS

VI. ANIMAL ENERGY EXCHANGE

VII. METABOLIC PATHWAYS

VIII. PLANT METABOLISM

IX. METABOLIC END PRODUCTS

APPENDIXES

INTRODUCTION

METABOLISM is an extensive revision and updating of *Standard Values in Nutrition and Metabolism,* published in 1954 and out of print since 1962. Between 1954 and 1968, much additional information has been generated in biology, requiring major alteration and expansion of the data in the old tables, plus the inclusion of many new references to the literature. At the suggestion of the Metabolism Advisory Committee, 23 entirely new tables and diagrams, required to fill gaps in coverage, have been added to this revised handbook.

METABOLISM is arranged in nine sections for the convenience of the user, with the data organized in the form of 117 quantitative and descriptive tables, diagrams, and graphs. Contents of the volume have been verified by 302 outstanding authorities in the fields of biology and medicine. The review process to which the data have been subjected was designed to eliminate, insofar as possible, material of questionable validity and errors of transcription.

An explanatory headnote, serving as an introduction to the subject matter, may precede a table. More frequently, tables have been prefaced by a short headnote containing such important information as units of measurement, abbreviations, definitions, and estimate of the range of variation. To interpret the data, it is essential to read the related headnote.

The main conventions used throughout this handbook have been adapted from the second edition of the *Style Manual for Biological Journals,* published in 1964 for the Conference of Biological Editors by the American Institute of Biological Sciences. Terminology has been checked against *Webster's Third New International Dictionary,* published in 1961 by G. & C. Merriam Company.

Appended to the tables are the names of the contributors, and a list of the literature citations arranged in alphabetical sequence. The reference abbreviations conform, insofar as possible, to the *1961 Chemical Abstracts List of Periodicals,* and the 1962-1967 supplements thereto, published by the American Chemical Society.

In the tables, a synonym following the scientific name of an organism indicates that the synonym, although cited in the reference, is no longer the preferred name. No other attempt has been made to provide taxonomic synonymy. With few exceptions, scientific names have been verified in the standard taxonomic checklists and classification lists. Those names which could not be verified were submitted for authentication to the appropriate experts at the Smithsonian Institution, the U.S. Department of Agriculture, or the American Type Culture Collection.

To aid the user in identifying an organism, the index includes the taxonomic orders for animals, and the families for plants; two appendixes provide cross-reference to scientific and equivalent common names.

. . . .

Values are generally presented as either the mean plus and minus the standard deviation, or the mean and the lower and upper limit of the range of individual values about the mean. The several methods used to estimate the range--depending on the information available--are designated by the letters "a, b, c, or d" to identify the type of range in descending order of accuracy.

"a"--When the group of values is relatively large, a 95% range is derived by curve fitting. A recognized type of normal frequency curve is fitted to a group of measured values, and the extreme 2.5% of the area under the curve at each end is excluded *(see illustration).*

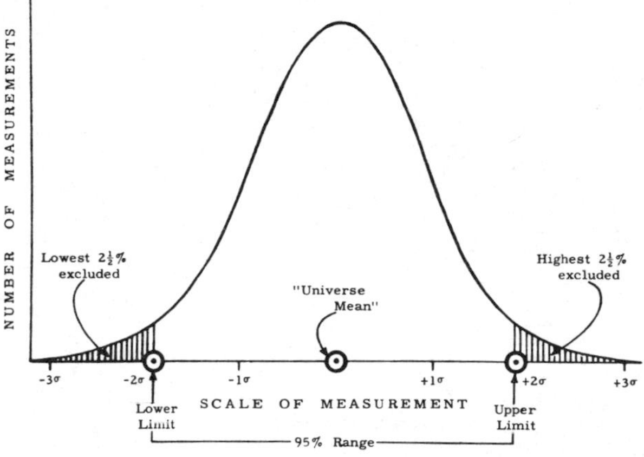

"b"--When the group of values is too small for curve fitting, as is usually the case, a 95% range is estimated by a simple statistical calculation. Assuming a normal symmetrical distribution, the standard deviation is multiplied by a factor of 2, then subtracted from and added to the mean to give the lower and upper range limits.

"c"--A less dependable, but commonly applied, procedure takes as range limits the lowest value and the highest value of the reported sample group of measurements. It underestimates the 95% range for small samples and overestimates for larger sample sizes, but where there is marked asymmetry in the position of the mean within the sample range, this method may be used in preference to the preceding one.

"d"--Another estimate of the lower and upper limits of the range of variation is based on the judgment of an individual experienced in measuring the quantity in question. The trustworthiness of such limits should not be underestimated.

ABBREVIATIONS AND SYMBOLS

Only those abbreviations and symbols not generally defined in the headnote of a table are included in this list.

Measurements

yr = year
mo = month
wk = week
hr = hour
min = minute
sec = second

ht = height
ha = hectare
m = meter
km = kilometer
dm = decimeter
cm = centimeter
mm = millimeter
μ = micron
nm = nanometer
in. = inch
ft = foot
mi = mile

wt = weight
g = gram
kg = kilogram
mg = milligram
μg = microgram
mEq = milliequivalent
μEq = microequivalent
M = mole
mM = millimole
μM = micromole
mμM = millimicromole
oz = ounce
lb = pound

vol = volume
d = density
ml = milliliter
μl = microliter
mμl = millimicroliter
% = parts per hundred
$^0/_{00}$ = parts per thousand
ppm = parts per million
tsp = teaspoon
tbsp = tablespoon
gal = gallon

λ = wavelength
E = electrode potential
mv = millivolt
$\mu\mu$c = micromicrocurie
mb = millibar
ft-c = footcandle

temp = temperature
°C = degrees Celsius
cal = calorie
kcal = kilocalorie
Q_{O_2} = oxygen quotient
Q_{CO_2} = carbon dioxide quotient

no. = number
$\pm$ = plus or minus (standard deviation)
SE = standard error
P = probability (statistical)
$\sim$ = equivalent
$>$ = more than
$<$ = less than
$\ngtr$ = not more than
$\nless$ = not less than
min. = minimum
max. = maximum
avg = average
ca. or approx = approximately

Biological and Chemical Specifications

♂ = male
♀ = female
sp. = species (singular)
spp. = species (plural)
GI = gastrointestinal
Tm = maximal tubular capacity
iv = intravenous
I.U. = international unit
I.C.U. = international chick unit
N.F. = National Formulary
U.S.P. = United States Pharmacopeia
LD_{50} = lethal dose for 50% of test subjects
pH = hydrogen ion concentration (negative log)

DL or *dl* = racemic mixture
D = *dextro* (configuration)
L = *levo* (configuration)
d = *dextro* (rotation)
l = *levo* (rotation)
i = optically inactive
m = *meta*
o = *ortho*
p = *para*
n = normal
M = molar
N = normal, or *nitro*
O = *oxy*
S = *sulf* or *sulfo*

ACTH = adrenocorticotropin
EDTA = ethylenediaminetetra-acetic acid
PAH = *para*-aminohippuric acid
AMP = adenosine phosphate
NADP$^+$ = nicotinamide adenine dinucleotide phosphate (oxidized form)
NADPH = nicotinamide adenine dinucleotide phosphate (reduced form)
DNA = deoxyribonucleic acid
RNA = ribonucleic acid
mRNA = messenger ribonucleic acid
sRNA = soluble ribonucleic acid
tRNA = transfer ribonucleic acid

Ala = alanine
Arg = arginine
Asn = asparagine
Asp = aspartic acid
Cit = citrulline
Cys = cysteine
CyS = cystine
Gln = glutamine
Glu = glutamic acid
Gly = glycine
His = histidine
Hyp = hydroxyproline
Ile = isoleucine
Leu = leucine
Lys = lysine
Met = methionine
Orn = ornithine
Phe = phenylalanine
Pro = proline
Ser = serine
Thr = threonine
Trp = tryptophan
Tyr = tyrosine
Val = valine

Ara = arabinose
Fru = fructose
Gal = galactose
Glc = glucose
Lac = lactose
Mal = maltose
Man = mannose
Rib = ribose
Sor = sorbose
Suc = sucrose
Xyl = xylose

METABOLISM

I. FOOD COMPOSITION AND ENERGY VALUES

1. COMPOSITION OF MILK

Part I. General Constituents: Various Mammals

Values are grams per 100 grams mature whole milk. Values in parentheses are ranges, estimate "c" (*see* Introduction).

	Animal	Water	Ash	Fat	Carbo-hydrate	Protein	Refer-ence
1	Man	87.2[1]	0.33[1]	2.9[1]	5.3[1]	2.7[1]	2
2		86.4[2]	0.24[2]	3.6[2]	6.6[2]	1.6[2]	2
3		87.6	0.21	3.8	7.0	1.2	2
4		86.5	......	4.6	6.9	1.2	24
5		88.6	0.2	3.5	6.5	1.3	39
6		87.4	0.3	3.8	6.3	2.2	13
7		87.5	0.2	3.5	7.5	1.25	19
8	Anteater	63	0.8	20	2.8	11	8
9	Ass	89.9	0.49	(1.4-1.5)	(6.09-6.19)	(1.00-2.04)	10
10		90.4	0.4	1.2	6.2	1.8	32
11		91.2	0.4	1.2	6.0	1.5	44
12		89.7	0.3	1.5	6.4	2.1	46
13	Bison	86.9	0.9	1.7	5.7	4.8	27
14	Buffalo	82.7	0.76	7.9	4.5	5.9	44
15		81.6	0.8	7.87	4.9	5.9	17
16	Chinese	76.8	0.86	12.6	3.7	6.0	46
17	Egyptian	82.8	0.8	8.0	4.9	4.2	32
18		83.1	0.83	7.3	4.47	4.4	16
19	Philippine	78.5	0.84	10.4	4.3	5.9	46
20	Camel	87.6	0.7	5.4	3.3	3.0	46
21		87.1	0.7	2.8	5.4	3.9	32
22		88.3	0.65	2.5	5.0	3.6	44
23		88.4	0.8	4.0	3.4	3.0	23
24	Cat	ca. 73	......	10.9	3.4	11.1	13
25		81.6	0.5	3.3	4.9	9.1	44
26	Cattle	87.3	0.72	3.7	4.8	3.3	2
27	Ayrshire	87.1	0.6	4.1	4.8	3.3	4
28	Brown Swiss	87.0	0.7	3.8	4.9	3.5	4
29	Guernsey	85.5	0.7	5.0	4.9	3.9	4
30	Holstein	88.0	0.7	3.5	4.7	3.1	4
31	Jersey	85.6	0.7	5.2	4.6	3.8	4
32		(85.7-88.2)	0.7	(3.4-5.3)	(4.6-4.7)	(3.2-3.8)	15
33	Coypu	53.6	3.3	......	......	18.3	45
34	Deer	65.9	1.4	19.7(18.8-23.0)	2.6	10.4	32
35	Dog	75.4	1.35	9.5	......	10.1	17
36		76.1	1.2	10.0	2.7	10.0	27
37		75.8	......	10.5	2.7	9.3	11
38		77.0	0.91	9.3	3.1	9.7	44
39		77.4	1.2	8.3	3.7	7.5	3
40		......	......	8.45	4.16	6.65	3
41	Beagle	......	......	13±0.70	3.5±0.11	8.7±0.32	29
42	Dachshund	......	......	9.7	2.8	5.4	3
43	Fox terrier & airedale	......	......	8.3	3.7	7.5	3
44	Pointer & large poodle	......	......	10.6	2.49	9.17	3
45	Russian wolfhound	......	......	10.0	2.6	10.6	3
46	Dolphin	(67.4-75.5)	......	(11-18)	(0.4-0.8)	(9.4-11.1)	12
47		41.1	0.6	45.8	1.3	11.2	17
48		48.8	0.46	43.71	......	......	44

[1] Colostrum. [2] Transitional milk.

continued

1. COMPOSITION OF MILK

Part I. General Constituents: Various Mammals

	Animal	Water	Ash	Fat	Carbo-hydrate	Protein	Refer-ence
49	Elephant	(67.9-73.7)	(0.6-0.7)	(15.0-19.6)	(3.2-7.7)	(3.0-3.1)	10
50		68.1	0.7	20.6	7.2	3.5	44
51		73.1	0.76	15.1	3.4	4.8	35
52		......	0.4	6.7	6.4	3.4	18
53	Fox	81.9	0.9	5.4	5.1	6.7	26
54		81.9	1.0	6.3	4.6	6.4	48
55	Giraffe	77.1	0.9	12.5	3.41	5.76	5
56	Goat	86.9	0.85	4.1	4.4	3.8	44
57		85.7	0.8	4.8	4.5	4.3	32
58		87.9	0.8	3.7	4.6	3.2	13
59		88.3	0.8	3.5	4.55	3.1	15
60	Guinea pig	......	......	8.3	3.0	8.8	13
61		81.7	0.8	7.9	2.6	7.0	27
62		......	0.8	7.1	2.2	5.2	1
63		82.1	0.95	5.5	2.93	8.55	34
64	Hamster	80-87	0.3-0.8	2.0	4.2-4.9	7.0-10.1	31
65	Hippopotamus	90.4	0.1	4.5	4.4	......	17
66	Horse	......	......	1.2	7.9	2.4	13
67		89.9	0.4	1.3	6.3	2.1	10
68		90.1	0.3	1.1	6.7	3.8	32
69		90.2	0.35	0.6	6.73	2.14	44
70	Kangaroo	79.5(76.2-82.7)	1.6(1.4-1.9)	8.3(3.9-12.8)	3.3(2.7-4.1)	7.6(5.4-9.4)	14
71	Kangaroo rat	50.42	......	23.48	......	......	25
72	Llama	86.5	0.8	3.2	5.6	3.9	44
73	Monkey	87.7	0.26	3.9	5.9	2.1	43
74		89.1	0.1	1.5	7.0	2.3	27
75	Mouse	......	......	10.2	......	......	27,28
76	Mule	89.2	0.5	1.9	5.7	2.1	32
77		(89.1-91.6)	(0.38-0.53)	(1.59-1.98)	(4.80-6.04)	(1.6-2.3)	17
78	Orangutan	88.5	0.24	3.5	6.02	1.43	41
79	Rabbit	69.5	2.6	10.5	2.0	15.5	17
80		73.1	2.0	12.1	1.8	10.9	7
81		......	......	16.7	2.0	10.4	10
82	Rat	69.3	1.5	14.8	2.83	11.8	9
83		77.8	......	12.4	3.39	7.0	30
84		72.1	......	13.8	......	......	20
85		71.0	1.2	9.3	3.74	8.7	28
86	Reindeer	63.3	1.4	22.5	2.5	10.3	46
87		(66.3-68.2)	(1.2-1.5)	(17.1-18.7)	(2.1-2.7)	(5.2-11.1)	47
88		62.0	1.4	23.6	2.5	10.4	32
89		64.3	1.4	19.7	2.6	10.9	44
90	Rhinoceros, African Black	91.2	0.34	0.2	6.6	1.4	5
91	Sea lion, California	47.3	......	36.5	......	13.8	38
92	Seal	46.0(43.8-50.0)	0.86(0.80-0.91)	42.0(40.4-42.8)	......	9.7(6.7-12.0)	42
93	Harp	43.79	......	48.82	......	11.98	38
94	Hooded	49.85	......	40.43	......	6.65	38
95	Sheep	80.1	0.9	6.9	4.9	6.5	32
96		83.6	0.9	6.2	4.2	5.2	17
97		......	......	2.6	5.4	5.0	13
98		83.9	0.93	6.2	4.2	5.2	44
99	Awassi	......	0.928	6.88	5.75	6.18	33
100	Clun Forest	......	0.87	6.2	4.7	5.3	6
101	Mountain	81.1	0.83	7.1	5.1	5.7	44
102	Swine	(83.5-84.0)	(1.0-1.1)	(3.7-5.0)	(3.5-4.0)	(7.0-7.9)	32
103		......	......	4.6	3.1	7.2	10
104		81.0	1.07	7.06	4.25	6.20	44
105		......	......	4.34	......	14.98	40

continued

1. COMPOSITION OF MILK

Part I. General Constituents: Various Mammals

	Animal	Water	Ash	Fat	Carbo-hydrate	Protein	Reference
106		81.8	1.12	5.8	4.0	7.2	22
107		82.0	0.97	6.8	....	6.2	21
108		78.8	0.92	9.6	4.6	6.1	36
109		83.0	0.97	6.0	4.9	5.1	37
110	Whale	....	(1.0-1.7)	(31-39)	....	(10-14)	42
111		62.4	1.6	22.0	2.0	12.0	27
112		70.2	0	19.4	1.0	9.4	32
113		61.7	1.7	22.2	1.8	11.95	44
114	Blue	47.17	....	38.13	....	12.79	38
115	Finback	54.10	....	30.60	....	13.14	38
116	Zebra	86.2	0.7	4.8	5.3	3.0	44

Contributors: Luckey, T. D., and Tsamasfyros, Constantine

References

[1] Abderhalden, E. 1899. Z. Physiol. Chem. 27:408.

[2] American Academy of Pediatrics, Committee on Nutrition. 1960. Pediatrics 26:1039.

[3] Anderson, H. D., B. C. Johnson, and A. Arnold. 1940. Am. J. Physiol. 129:631.

[4] Armstrong, T. V. 1959. J. Dairy Sci. 42:1.

[5] Aschaffenburg, R., et al. 1962. Proc. Zool. Soc. London 139:359.

[6] Ashton, W. M., J. B. Owen, and J. W. Ingleton. 1964. J. Agr. Sci. 63:85.

[7] Bergman, A. J., and C. W. Turner. 1937. J. Biol. Chem. 120:21.

[8] Brody, S. 1945. Bioenergetics and growth. Reinhold, New York.

[9] Cox, W. W., Jr., and A. J. Mueller. 1937. J. Nutr. 13:429.

[10] Davies, W. L. 1939. The chemistry of milk. Van Nostrand, New York.

[11] Dengies, G. 1937. Bull. Soc. Pharm. Bordeaux 73:241.

[12] Eichelberger, L., et al. 1940. J. Biol. Chem. 134:171.

[13] Folin, O., W. Denis, and A. S. Minot. 1919. Ibid. 37:349.

[14] Ford, J. E., and S. Y. Thompson. 1965. Ann. Rept. Natl. Inst. Res. Dairying (Reading), p. 154.

[15] Gamble, J. A., N. R. Ellis, and A. K. Beslay. 1939. U.S. Dept. Agr. Tech. Bull. 671.

[16] Ghoneim, A., and M. T. El-Katib. 1947. Nature 159:273.

[17] Grimmer, W. 1925. Tabulae Biol. 2:536.

[18] Hindle, E. M. 1950. Zoo Life 5(1):7.

[19] Holt, L. E., and R. McIntosh. 1933. Diseases of infancy and childhood. Ed. 10. Appleton-Century, New York. p. 147.

[20] Houston, J., and S. K. Kon. 1939. Biochem. J. 33:1655.

[21] Hughes, E. M., and M. G. Hart. 1935. J. Nutr. 9:311.

[22] Jax, P. 1953. Oesterr. Milchwirtsch. 8:346.

[23] Kiselera, N. T. 1957. Chem. Abstr. 51:2198d.

[24] Kon, S. K., and E. H. Mawson. 1950. Med. Res. Council Spec. Rept. Ser. 296.

[25] Kooyman, G. L. 1963. Science 142:1467.

[26] Laxa, O. 1930. Ann. Fals. Fraudes 23:404.

[27] Luckey, T. D. Unpublished. Univ. Missouri, Medical Center, Columbia, 1967.

[28] Luckey, T. D., T. J. Mende, and J. Pleasants. 1954. J. Nutr. 54:345.

[29] Luick, J. R., H. R. Parker, and A. C. Anderson. 1960. Am. J. Physiol. 199:731.

[30] Mayer, D. T. 1935. J. Nutr. 10:343.

[31] Miller, C. 1965. Gnotobiotics Newsletter 1(3):3.

[32] Monjonnier, T., and H. C. Troy. 1926. The technical control of dairy products. Ed. 2. Caspar, Krueger Dory; Milwaukee, Wis.

[33] Nejim, H. T. 1963. J. Dairy Res. 30:81.

[34] Neymork, M. 1937. Skand. Arch. Physiol. 76:158.

[35] Nottbohm, F. E. 1939. Vorratspflege Lebensmittelforsch. 2:150.

[36] Perrin, D. R. 1954. J. Dairy Res. 21:55.

[37] Perrin, D. R. 1958. Ibid. 25:215.

[38] Pilson, M. E. Q., and A. L. Kelley. 1962. Science 135:104.

[39] Plimmer, E., and J. Londes. 1937. Biochem. J. 31:1751.

[40] Puyaoan, R. B., and L. S. Castillo. 1963. Philippine Agriculturist 47:141.

[41] Schumacher, H. M. 1934. Z. Kinderheilk. 56:415.

[42] Sivertsen, E. Unpublished. Royal Norwegian Society of Sciences, Trondheim, Norway, 1954.

[43] Van Wagenen, G., H. E. Himwich, and H. R. Catchpole. 1941. Proc. Soc. Exptl. Biol. Med. 48:133.

[44] Winkler, W. 1930. Handbuch der Milch Wirtschaft. J. Springer, Vienna. v. 1, p. 21.

[45] Wojcik, S., and Z. Zdybicki. 1954. Ann. Univ. Mariae Curie-Sklodowska Lublin-Polonia, E, 9:321.

[46] Wright, P. A., E. F. Deysher, and C. A. Cary. 1939. Yearbook Agr. (U.S. Dept. Agr.), p. 639.

[47] Yippo, A. 1927. Z. Kinderheilk. 43:225.

[48] Young, E. G., and G. A. Grant. 1931. J. Biol. Chem. 93:805.

continued

Part II. Chemical Constituents of Colostrum: Man and Cattle

Values are for human colostrum secreted during the first five days, and for bovine colostrum secreted during the first 24 hours, after parturition. For additional information on human colostrum, consult reference 2, and on bovine colostrum, references 2 and 5.

	Constituent	Animal	Value	Reference
	General Constituents			
1	Ash, g/100 g	Man	0.32	2
2		Cow	0.97	5
3	Protein (N X 6.38), g/100 g	Man	2.6	2
4		Cow	14.3	5
5	Casein, g/100 g	Man	1.2	2
6		Cow	0.8	5
7	Fat, g/100 g	Man	2.8	2
8		Cow	3.6	5
9	Nonfat solids, g/100 g	Man	9.6	2
10		Cow	18.5	5
11	Lactose, anhydrous, g/100 g	Man	5.1	2
12		Cow	3.1	5
	Minerals			
13	Calcium, g/100 g	Man	0.030	2
14		Cow	0.147	5
15	Chlorine, g/100 g	Man	0.087	2
16		Cow	0.109	5
17	Magnesium, g/100 g	Man	0.004	2
18	Phosphorus, g/100 g	Man	0.014	2
19		Cow	0.133	5
20	Potassium, g/100 g	Man	0.071	2
21	Sodium, g/100 g	Man	0.046	2
	Vitamins			
	Water-soluble			
22	Thiamine, µg/100 g	Man	15	2
23		Cow	60	2
24	Riboflavin, µg/100 g	Man	29	2
25		Cow	500	2
26	Nicotinic acid, µg/100 g	Man	75	2
27		Cow	100	2
28	B_6, µg/100 g	Cow	50	2
29	Biotin, µg/100 g	Man	0.1	2
30		Cow	4	2
31	Pantothenic acid, µg/100 g	Man	180	2
32		Cow	220	2
33	Folic acid, µg/100 g	Cow	2	2
34	B_{12}, µg/100 g	Man	0.04	2
35		Cow	1	2
36	Ascorbic acid, mg/100 g	Man	4.3	2
37		Cow	2.5	2
	Fat-soluble			
38	A, µg/g fat	Man	23	2
39		Cow	42	2
40	Carotenoids, µg/g fat	Man	30	2
41		Cow	39	2
42	D, I.U./100 g	Cow	4	2
	Carbohydrates			
43	Galactosamine, g/100 g	Man	0.07	1
44		Cow	0.04	1
45	Glucosamine, g/100 g	Man	0.4	1
46		Cow	0.2	1
47	Lactose, g/100 g	Man	5.1	2
48		Cow	3.1	5
	Protein-bound carbohydrate, mg/g protein			
49	Hexosamine	Man	71	4
50		Cow	4	4
51	Hexose	Man	288	4
52		Cow	102	4
53	Sialic acid	Man	31	4
54		Cow	7	4
	Nitrogenous Substances			
	Nitrogen distribution, g/100 g			
55	Total N	Man	0.515	2
56		Cow	2.23	5
57	Protein N	Man	0.424	2
58		Cow	2.17	5
59	Nonprotein N	Man	0.091	2
60		Cow	0.055	5
	Protein distribution, g/100 g			
61	Total protein	Man	2.6	2
62		Cow	14.3	5
63	Casein	Man	1.2	2
64		Cow	0.8	5
65	α-	Cow	3.9	3,5
66	β-	Cow	0.9	3,5
67	γ-	Cow	0.4	3,5
68	Whey protein	Man	1.6	2
69	Albumin	Cow	1.45	5
70	Serum albumin	Cow	0.1	3,5
71	α-Lactalbumin	Cow	0.7	3,5
72	β-Lactoglobulin	Cow	0.7	3,5
73	Immune globulins	Cow	6.8	3,5
74	Proteose-peptone	Cow	0.39	5

Contributors: Porter, J. W. G.; Ford, J. E.; Thompson, S. Y.; and Williams, A. P.

continued

1. COMPOSITION OF MILK

Part II. Chemical Constituents of Colostrum: Man and Cattle

References

[1] Bigwood, E. J. 1963. World Rev. Nutr. Dietet. 4:95.
[2] Kon, S. K., and A. T. Cowie, ed. 1961. Milk: the mammary gland and its secretion. Academic Press, New York. v. 2.
[3] Larson, B. L., and K. A. Kendall. 1957. J. Dairy Sci. 40:377.
[4] Nagasawa, T., et al. 1964. Eiyo To Shokuryo 17:217.
[5] Rowland, S. J., et al. 1953. J. Dairy Res. 20:16.

Part III. Physical Properties and Chemical Constituents of Mature Milk: Man, Cattle, and Goat

The composition of milk from individual animals of any species varies with the stage of lactation; in milch animals, the composition may also vary according to breed, season, and intake and type of feed. Values are for good quality milk. For additional information on human milk, consult references 17 and 18, and on bovine milk, references 11, 17, and 30.

	Property or Constituent	Animal	Value	Reference
	Physical Properties			
1	Fat melting point, °C	Man	31	17
2		Cow	28-33	17
3	Freezing point depression, °C	Cow	0.545	17
4		Goat	0.582	6
5	pH	Man	7.0	27
6		Cow	6.7	27
7		Goat	6.33-6.52	34
8	Specific gravity	Man	1.031	17
9		Cow	1.032	17
10		Goat	1.030	37
11	Surface tension, dynes/cm	Cow	53	19
12		Goat	52	9
13	Viscosity at 15°C, centipoises	Cow	2	7
	General Constituents			
14	Ash, g/100 g	Man	0.21	17
15		Cow	0.75	17
16		Goat	0.80	17
17	Fat, g/100 g	Man	3.7	17
18		Cow	3.5	17
19		Goat	4.5	17
20	Lactose, anhydrous, g/100 g	Man	6.8	17
21		Cow	4.6	17
22		Goat	4.4	17
23	Nonfat solids, g/100 g	Man	8.4	17
24		Cow	8.6	17
25		Goat	8.7	17
26	Protein (N × 6.38), g/100 g	Man	1.2	17
27		Cow	3.25	17
28		Goat	3.3	17
29	Casein, g/100 g	Man	0.36	17
30		Cow	2.6	17
31		Goat	2.5	17
	Major Minerals			
32	Calcium, g/100 g	Man	0.032	17
33		Cow	0.12	17
34		Goat	0.14	17
35	Chlorine, g/100 g	Man	0.042	17
36		Cow	0.11	17
37		Goat	0.15	17
38	Magnesium, g/100 g	Man	0.004	17
39		Cow	0.01	17
40		Goat	0.02	17
41	Phosphorus, g/100 g	Man	0.015	17
42		Cow	0.10	17
43		Goat	0.12	17
44	Potassium, g/100 g	Man	0.054	17
45		Cow	0.15	17
46		Goat	0.17	17
47	Sodium, g/100 g	Man	0.015	17
48		Cow	0.05	17
	Minor Minerals			
49	Aluminum, ppm	Man	0.33	10
50		Cow	<0.008	17
51	Boron, ppm	Cow	0.5-1.0	17
52		Goat	0.18	15
53	Bromine, ppm	Cow	0.18-0.24	17
54	Cobalt, ppm	Man	0.001	17
55		Cow	0.0002-0.0011	17
56	Copper, ppm	Man	0.04	17
57		Cow	0.05-0.45	17
58		Goat	0.2	29
59	Fluorine, ppm	Cow	0.2	17
60	Iodine, ppm	Man	0.007	17
61		Cow	0.0007-0.0500	17
62	Iron, ppm	Man	0.15	17
63		Cow	0.15-0.7	17
64		Goat	0.02	32

continued

1. COMPOSITION OF MILK

Part III. Physical Properties and Chemical Constituents of Mature Milk: Man, Cattle, and Goat

	Property or Constituent	Animal	Value	Reference
65	Manganese, ppm	Man	0.01	24
66		Cow	0.037-0.370	17
67	Molybdenum, ppm	Cow	0.05-0.15	17
68	Silicon, ppm	Man	0.34	10
69		Cow	<1	17
70	Silver, ppm	Cow	0.015-0.037	17
71	Strontium, ppm	Cow	0.0075-0.0750	17
72	Zinc, ppm	Man	0.53	17
73		Cow	0.22-5.0	17
	Vitamins			
	Water-soluble			
74	Thiamine, μg/100 g	Man	14	17
75		Cow	45	27
76		Goat	49	27
77	Riboflavin, μg/100 g	Man	51	27
78		Cow	180	27
79		Goat	140	27
80	Nicotinic acid, μg/	Man	190	27
81	100 g	Cow	75	27
82		Goat	250	27
83	B_6, μg/100 g	Man	4	27
84		Cow	40	27
85		Goat	60	27
86	Biotin, μg/100 g	Man	1.1	27
87		Cow	2.5	27
88		Goat	3.8	27
89	Pantothenic acid,	Man	260	27
90	μg/100 g	Cow	320	27
91		Goat	360	27
92	Folic acid, μg/100 g	Man	5.3	27
93		Cow	6.3	27
94		Goat	0.4	27
95	*p*-Aminobenzoic acid, μg/100 g	Cow	10	17
96	Inositol, mg/100 g	Man	40	17
97		Cow	18	17
98	B_{12}, μg/100 g	Man	0.02	27
99		Cow	0.35	27
100		Goat	0.07	27
101	Choline, mg/100 g	Man	9	17
102		Cow	20	17
103	Ascorbic acid, mg/	Man	4.3	17
104	100 g	Cow	2.0	17
105		Goat	2.0	17
	Fat-soluble			
106	A, μg/g fat	Man	14	17
107		Cow	8	17
108		Goat	8	17
109	Carotenoids, μg/g	Man	3.5	18
110	fat	Cow	7	17
111		Goat	Trace	17
112	D, I.U./100 g	Man	0.4	17
113		Cow	1.8	17
114		Goat	2.3	17
115	E, mg/100 g	Man	1.1	12
116		Cow	0.08	17
117	K, Dam-Glavind	Man	26	17
118	units/100 g	Cow	100	17
	Lipids			
	Fatty acid distribution, g/100 g fat			
	Saturated			
119	Butyric	Man	Trace	13
120		Cow	3	13
121		Goat	3	13
122	Capric	Man	2	13
123		Cow	3	13
124		Goat	9	13
125	Caproic	Man	Trace	13
126		Cow	1	13
127		Goat	2	13
128	Caprylic	Man	Trace	13
129		Cow	1	13
130		Goat	3	13
131	Lauric	Man	6	13
132		Cow	2	13
133		Goat	5	13
134	Myristic	Man	9	13
135		Cow	9	13
136		Goat	11	13
137	Palmitic	Man	23	13
138		Cow	27	13
139		Goat	28	13
140	Stearic	Man	7	13
141		Cow	10	13
142		Goat	7	13
143	Others	Man	1	13
144		Cow	2	13
145		Goat	Trace	13
	Unsaturated			
146	Dec-9-enoic	Man	Trace	13
147		Cow	Trace	13
148		Goat	Trace	13
149	Dodec-9-enoic	Man	0.2	13
150		Cow	Trace	13
151		Goat	Trace	13
152	Tetradec-9-enoic	Man	0.7	13
153		Cow	1	13
154		Goat	1	13
155	Hexadec-9-enoic	Man	5	13
156		Cow	4	13
157		Goat	2	13
158	Oleic	Man	36	13
159		Cow	32	13
160		Goat	25	13

continued

1. COMPOSITION OF MILK

Part III. Physical Properties and Chemical Constituents of Mature Milk: Man, Cattle, and Goat

	Property or Constituent	Animal	Value	Reference
161	Octadecadienoic	Man	8	13
162		Cow	4	13
163		Goat	4	13
164	Others	Man	3	13
165		Cow	1	13
166		Goat	Trace	13
167	Cholesterol, g/100 g	Man	0.020	17
168		Cow	0.012	17
169	Lecithin, g/100 g	Man	0.076	17
170		Cow	0.056	17
171	Triglyceride fat, g/	Man	3.7	17
172	100 g	Cow	3.5	17
173		Goat	4.5	17
	Carbohydrates & Citric Acid			
174	Galactosamine, g/	Man	0.05	3
175	100 g	Cow	Trace	3
176	Glucosamine, g/100 g	Man	0.1	3
177		Cow	Trace	3
178	Lactose, g/100 g	Man	6.8	17
179		Cow	4.6	17
180		Goat	4.4	17
181	Oligosaccharides, g/	Man	0.3	25
182	100 g	Cow	0.1	1,35
	Protein-bound carbohydrate, mg/g protein			
183	Hexosamine	Man	37	23,26
184		Cow	3	23,26
185	Hexose	Man	187	23,26
186		Cow	84	23,26
187	Sialic acid	Man	16	23,26
188		Cow	4	23,26
189	Citric acid, g/100 g	Man	0.035-0.125	8
190		Cow	0.17	17
191		Goat	0.15	5
	Nitrogenous Substances			
	Nitrogen distribution, g/100 g			
192	Total N	Man	0.220	22
193		Cow	0.534	22
194		Goat	0.522	22
195	Protein N	Man	0.182	22
196		Cow	0.503	22
197		Goat	0.475	22
198	Nonprotein N	Man	0.038	22
199		Cow	0.031	22
200		Goat	0.047	22
	Protein distribution, g/100 g			
201	Total protein	Man	1.07	22
202		Cow	3.2	17
203		Goat	3.2	22
204	Casein	Man	0.39	22
205		Cow	2.5	17

	Property or Constituent	Animal	Value	Reference
206		Goat	2.4	22
207	α-	Cow	1.75	20
208	β-	Cow	0.675	20
209	γ-	Cow	0.075	20
210	κ-	Cow	0.3	36
211	Globulin	Man	0.19	22
212	Albumin	Man	0.29	22
213		Cow	0.31	17
214		Goat	0.39	22
215	Serum albumin	Cow	0.02-0.05	16,20
216	α-Lactalbumin	Cow	0.07-0.15	16,20
217	β-Lactoglobulin	Cow	0.2-0.4	16,20
218		Cow	0.11	17
219		Goat	0.29	22
220	Euglobulin	Cow	0.05	16
221	Pseudoglobulin	Cow	0.11	16
222	Proteose-peptone	Cow	0.13	31
	Amino acids, g/16 g total N			
223	Alanine	Man	3.6	3,27,33
224		Cow	3.4	2,4,27,28
225		Goat	3.7	14,27
226	Arginine	Man	3.4	3,27,33
227		Cow	3.5	2,4,27,28
228		Goat	3.0	14,27
229	Aspartic acid	Man	8.4	3,27,33
230		Cow	7.9	2,4,27,28
231		Goat	8.6	14,27
232	Cystine	Man	1.7	3,27,33
233		Cow	0.8	2,4,27,28
234		Goat	1.1	14,27
235	Glutamic acid	Man	15.5	3,27,33
236		Cow	21.9	2,4,27,28
237		Goat	19.0	14,27
238	Glycine	Man	2.3	3,27,33
239		Cow	2.0	2,4,27,28
240		Goat	2.0	14,27
241	Histidine	Man	2.3	3,27,33
242		Cow	2.7	2,4,27,28
243		Goat	3.0	14,27
244	Isoleucine	Man	4.4	3,27,33
245		Cow	5.9	2,4,27,28
246		Goat	5.3	14,27
247	Leucine	Man	8.6	3,27,33
248		Cow	9.7	2,4,27,28
249		Goat	10.0	14,27
250	Lysine	Man	6.5	3,27,33
251		Cow	8.1	2,4,27,28
252		Goat	8.6	14,27
253	Methionine	Man	1.7	3,27,33
254		Cow	2.6	2,4,27,28
255		Goat	2.8	14,27

continued

1. COMPOSITION OF MILK

Part III. Physical Properties and Chemical Constituents of Mature Milk: Man, Cattle, and Goat

	Property or Constituent	Animal	Value	Reference
256	Phenylalanine	Man	3.4	3,27,33
257		Cow	4.9	2,4,27,28
258		Goat	5.5	14,27
259	Proline	Man	7.3	3,27,33
260		Cow	9.9	2,4,27,28
261		Goat	10.9	14,27
262	Serine	Man	4.6	3,27,33
263		Cow	5.6	2,4,27,28
264		Goat	5.8	14,27
265	Threonine	Man	4.5	3,27,33
266		Cow	4.6	2,4,27,28
267		Goat	5.9	14,27
268	Tryptophan	Man	1.7	3,27,33
269		Cow	1.4	2,4,27,28
270		Goat	1.6	14,27
271	Tyrosine	Man	3.7	3,27,33
272		Cow	5.1	2,4,27,28
273		Goat	5.1	14,27
274	Valine	Man	4.8	3,27,33
275		Cow	6.6	2,4,27,28
276		Goat	7.6	14,27
	Nonprotein nitrogenous substances, g/100 g			
277	Creatine	Man	0.003	22
278		Cow	0.003	22
279	Creatinine	Man	0.031	22
280		Cow	0.001	22
281	Urea	Man	0.005	22
282		Cow	0.015	22
283		Goat	0.035	21
284	Uric acid	Cow	0.002	22
285		Goat	0.001	21

Contributors: Porter, J. W. G.; Ford, J. E.; Thompson, S. Y.; and Williams, A. P.

References

[1] Barker, S. A., and M. Stacey. 1963. Dairy Sci. Abstr. 25:445.

[2] Bigwood, E. J. 1960. Compt. Rend. Inst. Encour. Rech. Bruxelles 26.

[3] Bigwood, E. J. 1963. World Rev. Nutr. Dietet. 4:95.

[4] Block, R. J., and K. W. Weiss. 1956. Amino acid handbook. C. C. Thomas, Springfield, Ill.

[5] Bosworth, A. W., and L. L. Van Slyke. 1916. J. Biol. Chem. 24:177.

[6] Chakraborty, R. K. 1935. Indian J. Med. Res. 23:347.

[7] Cox, C. P. 1952. J. Dairy Res. 19:72.

[8] Denis, W., and A. S. Minot. 1919. J. Biol. Chem. 37:353.

[9] Gamble, J. A., N. R. Ellis, and A. K. Besley. 1939. U.S. Dept. Agr. Tech. Bull. 671.

[10] Grebennikov, E. P., V. R. Soroka, and E. V. Sabadash. 1963. Vopr. Pitaniya 22:87.

[11] Hartman, A. M., and L. P. Dryden. 1965. Vitamins in milk and milk products. American Dairy Science Association, White Plains, N.Y.

[12] Herre, H. D. 1965. Monatsschr. Kinderheilk. 113: 95.

[13] Hilditch, T. P., and P. N. Williams. 1964. The chemical constitution of natural fats. Ed. 4. Spottiswoode, Ballantyne; London.

[14] Höller, H. 1962. Milchwissenschaft 17:485.

[15] Hove, E., C. A. Elvehjem, and E. B. Hart. 1939. Am. J. Physiol. 127:689.

[16] Jenness, R., et al. 1956. J. Dairy Sci. 39:536.

[17] Kon, S. K., and A. T. Cowie, ed. 1961. Milk: the mammary gland and its secretion. Academic Press, New York. v. 2.

[18] Kon, S. K., and E. H. Mawson. 1950. Med. Res. Council Spec. Rept. Ser. 269.

[19] Kopaczewski, W. 1936. Lait 16:356.

[20] Larson, B. L., and K. A. Kendall. 1957. J. Dairy Sci. 40:377.

[21] Livrea, G., A. Cambria, and S. Campanella. 1963. Boll. Soc. Ital. Biol. Sper. 39:1294.

[22] Macy, I. G., H. J. Kelly, and R. E. Sloan. 1953. Natl. Acad. Sci. Natl. Res. Council Publ. 254.

[23] Malpress, F. H., and F. E. Hytten. 1964. Biochem. J. 91:130.

[24] Medvedeva, V. I. 1965. Dokl. Akad. Nauk Belorussk. SSR 9:563.

[25] Montreuil, J., and S. Mullet. 1960. Bull. Soc. Chim. Biol. 42:365.

[26] Nagasawa, T., et al. 1964. Eiyo To Shokuryo 17: 217.

[27] National Institute for Research in Dairying. Unpublished. Analyses of composite samples of freshly drawn milk. Shinfield, Reading, England, 1967.

[28] Orr, L. M., and B. K. Watt. 1957. U.S. Dept. Agr. Home Econ. Res. Rept. 4.

[29] Quam, G. N., and A. Hellwig. 1928. J. Biol. Chem. 76:681.

[30] Rook, J. A. F. 1961. Dairy Sci. Abstr. 23:251, 303.

[31] Rowland, S. J. 1938. J. Dairy Res. 9:47.

[32] Schäfer, K. H., A. M. Breyer, and H. Karte. 1955. Z. Kinderheilk. 76:501.

[33] Schwerdtfeger, E. 1965. Naturwissenschaften 52: 162.

[34] Trout, G. M. 1941. Mich. State Univ. Agr. Expt. Sta. Quart. Bull. 23:254.

[35] Trucco, R. E., P. Verdier, and A. Rega. 1954. Biochim. Biophys. Acta 15:582.

[36] Waugh, D. F., and P. H. von Hippel. 1956. J. Am. Chem. Soc. 78:4576.

[37] Winton, A. L., ed. 1920. Leach's Food inspection and analysis. Ed. 4. J. Wiley, Philadelphia. p. 113.

continued

1. COMPOSITION OF MILK

Part IV. Amino Acid Content of Milk Proteins: Cattle

Values are grams amino acid/16 grams nitrogen.

	Amino Acid	Casein	Serum Albumin	α-Lactalbumin	β-Lactoglobulin	Immune Globulins
1	Alanine	3.1	7.0	2.2	7.0	4.8
2	Arginine	4.2	3.1	1.2	2.8	4.1
3	Aspartic acid	6.5	11.1	18.8	11.3	9.4
4	Cystine	0.4	2.7	6.6	3.3	3.2
5	Glutamic acid	23.6	17.7	13.0	19.8	12.3
6	Glycine	2.1	2.5	3.2	1.4	5.2
7	Histidine	3.0	1.8	2.9	1.6	2.1
8	Isoleucine	6.6	6.7	6.9	7.0	3.0
9	Leucine	10.1	12.0	11.6	15.5	9.6
10	Lysine	8.2	9.7	11.6	11.8	6.8

	Amino Acid	Casein	Serum Albumin	α-Lactalbumin	β-Lactoglobulin	Immune Globulins
11	Methionine	3.3	1.9	1.0	3.1	0.9
12	Phenylalanine	5.8	4.0	4.5	3.5	3.9
13	Proline	12.3	4.7	1.5	5.2	10.0
14	Serine	6.3	4.8	4.8	3.8	11.5
15	Threonine	4.5	5.2	5.6	5.1	10.5
16	Tryptophan	1.5	1.8	7.1	2.7	2.7
17	Tyrosine	6.3	3.2	5.4	3.8	6.7
18	Valine	7.4	5.3	4.8	6.1	9.6
	Reference	1	1	3	2, 5	4

Contributors: Porter, J. W. G.; Ford, J. E.; Thompson, S. Y.; and Williams, A. P.

References

[1] Block, R. J., and K. W. Weiss. 1956. Amino acid handbook. C. C. Thomas, Springfield, Ill.

[2] Gordon, W. G., J. J. Basch, and E. B. Kalan. 1961. J. Biol. Chem. 236:2908.

[3] Gordon, W. G., and J. Ziegler. 1955. Arch. Biochem. Biophys. 57:80.

[4] Hansen, R. G., and D. M. Carlson. 1956. J. Dairy Sci. 39:663.

[5] Piez, K. A., et al. 1961. J. Biol. Chem. 236:2912.

2. COMPOSITION OF FOODS, RAW AND PROCESSED: ANIMAL ORIGIN

Values are for 100 grams edible portion of the more common foods in their simplest form (i.e., without added salt, sugar, fats, fillers, mineral or vitamin enrichment), unless otherwise specified. For information on foods less commonly used or in combined forms, consult the reference. For data on the effect of radiation on foods, *see* Table 7. Dots instead of a value denote lack of reliable data for a constituent believed to be present in measurable amount.

Part I. General Constituents and Energy Values

	Food	Specification	Water %	Ash g	Fat g	Carbohydrates Total g	Carbohydrates Fiber g	Protein g	Food Energy cal
1	Abalone	Raw	75.8	1.6	0.5	3.4	0	18.7	98
2		Canned	80.2	1.2	0.3	2.3	0	16.0	80
3	Bacon	Uncooked	19.3	2.0	69.3	1.0	0	8.4	665
4		Broiled or fried, drained	8.1	6.3	52.0	3.2	0	30.4	611
5	Canadian	Unheated	61.7	3.6	14.4	0.3	0	20.0	216
6		Broiled or fried, drained	49.9	4.7	17.5	0.3	0	27.6	277
7	Bass, small- & largemouth	Raw	77.3	1.2	2.6	0	0	18.9	104
8	striped	Raw	77.7	1.2	2.7	0	0	18.9	105
9	Beef, chuck, 82% lean & 18% fat	Raw	60.8	0.9	19.6	0	0	18.7	257
10	81% lean & 19% fat	Braised or pot-roasted	49.4	0.7	23.9	0	0	26.0	327
11	arm, 86% lean & 14% fat	Raw	64.2	0.9	15.5	0	0	19.4	223
12	85% lean & 15% fat	Braised or pot-roasted	53.0	0.7	19.2	0	0	27.1	289
13	flank, 100% lean	Raw	71.7	1.0	5.7	0	0	21.6	144
14		Braised	61.4	0.8	7.3	0	0	30.5	196
15	porterhouse, 63% lean & 37% fat	Raw	48.3	0.7	36.2	0	0	14.8	390
16	57% lean & 43% fat	Broiled	37.2	0.9	42.2	0	0	19.7	465
17	T-bone, 62% lean & 38% fat	Raw	47.5	0.7	37.1	0	0	14.7	397
18	56% lean & 44% fat	Broiled	36.4	0.9	43.2	0	0	19.5	473

continued

2. COMPOSITION OF FOODS, RAW AND PROCESSED: ANIMAL ORIGIN

Part I. General Constituents and Energy Values

	Food	Specification	Water %	Ash g	Fat g	Carbohydrates Total g	Carbohydrates Fiber g	Protein g	Food Energy cal
19	sirloin, 73% lean & 27% fat	Raw	55.7	0.8	26.7	0	0	16.9	313
20	66% lean & 34% fat	Broiled	43.9	1.1	32.0	0	0	23.0	387
21	rib, 64% lean & 36% fat	Raw	47.2	0.6	37.4	0	0	14.8	401
22		Roasted	40.0	0.7	39.4	0	0	19.9	440
23	round, 89% lean & 11% fat	Raw	66.6	0.9	12.3	0	0	20.2	197
24	81% lean & 19% fat	Broiled	54.7	1.3	15.4	0	0	28.6	261
25	rump, 75% lean & 25% fat	Raw	56.5	0.8	25.3	0	0	17.4	303
26		Roasted	48.1	1.0	27.3	0	0	23.6	347
27	hamburger, lean	Raw	68.3	1.0	10.0	0	0	20.7	179
28		Cooked	60.0	1.3	11.3	0	0	27.4	219
29	regular	Raw	60.2	0.7	21.2	0	0	17.9	268
30		Cooked	54.2	1.3	20.3	0	0	24.2	286
31	chipped	Dried, uncooked	47.7	11.6	6.3	0	0	34.3	203
32	corned, medium-fat	Uncooked	54.2	5.0	25	0	0	15.8	293
33		Cooked	43.9	2.9	30.4	0	0	22.9	372
34		Canned	59.3	3.4	12	0	0	25.3	216
35	Bluefish	Raw	75.4	1.2	3.3	0	0	20.5	117
36		Broiled or baked[1/]	68.0	1.4	5.2	0	0	26.2	159
37	Bologna, all meat	....	57.4	2.8	22.8	3.7	0	13.3	277
38	Bonito, Atlantic, Pacific, & striped	Raw	67.6	1.4	7.3	0	0	24.0	168
39	Brains, beef, calf, hog, & sheep	Raw	78.9	1.4	8.6	0.8	0	10.4	125
40	Butter, salted	....	15.5	2.5	81	0.4	0	0.6	716
41	Butterfish, northern waters	Raw	71.4	1.4	10.2	0	0	18.1	169
42	gulf waters	Raw	78.2	2.9	2.9	0	0	16.2	95
43	Buttermilk	Cultured, from skim milk	90.5	0.7	0.1	5.1	0	3.6	36
44		Dried	2.8	7.6	5.3	50.0	0	34.3	387
45	Catfish, freshwater	Raw	78.0	1.3	3.1	0	0	17.6	103
46	Caviar, sturgeon	Granular	46.0	8.8	15.0	3.3	......	26.9	262
47		Pressed	36.0	8.0	16.7	4.9	......	34.4	316
48	Cheese, American	Pasteurized process	40	4.9	30.0	1.9	0	23.2	370
49	blue or Roquefort	Natural	40	6.0	30.5	2.0	0	21.5	368
50	brick	Natural	41.0	4.4	30.5	1.9	0	22.2	370
51	Camembert, domestic	Natural	52.2	3.8	24.7	1.8	0	17.5	299
52	cheddar, domestic	Natural	37	3.7	32.2	2.1	0	25.0	398
53	cottage, creamed	Natural	78.3	1.0	4.2	2.9	0	13.6	106
54	uncreamed	Natural	79.0	1.0	0.3	2.7	0	17.0	86
55	cream	Natural	51	1.2	37.7	2.1	0	8.0	374
56	Limburger	Natural	45	3.6	28.0	2.2	0	21.2	345
57	Parmesan	Natural	30	5.1	26.0	2.9	0	36.0	393
58	pimiento	Pasteurized process	40	5.0	30.2	1.8	Trace	23.0	371
59	Swiss, domestic	Natural	39	3.8	28.0	1.7	0	27.5	370
60		Pasteurized process	40	5.1	26.9	1.6	0	26.4	355
61	Chicken, flesh only	Canned	65.2	1.4	11.7	0	0	21.7	198
62	light meat, all classes	Raw	73.7	1.0	1.9	0	0	23.4	117
63		Roasted	63.8	1.2	3.4	0	0	31.6	166
64	dark meat, all classes	Raw	73.7	1.0	4.7	0	0	20.6	130
65		Roasted	64.4	1.2	6.3	0	0	28.0	176
66	Clams	Canned, solids & liquid	86.3	2.3	0.7	2.8	......	7.9	52
67	soft	Raw, drained	80.8	2.0	1.9	1.3	......	14.0	82
68	hard	Raw, drained	79.8	2.3	0.9	5.9	......	11.1	80
69	Cod	Raw	81.2	1.2	0.3	0	0	17.6	78
70		Broiled	64.6	. . .	5.3	0	0	28.5	170
71		Canned	78.6	1.0	0.3	0	0	19.2	85
72	Crab	Canned	77.2	1.8	2.5	1.1	......	17.4	101
73	blue, Dungeness, rock, & king	Steamed	78.5	1.8	1.9	0.5	......	17.3	93

[1/] Prepared with butter or margarine.

continued

2. COMPOSITION OF FOODS, RAW AND PROCESSED: ANIMAL ORIGIN

Part I. General Constituents and Energy Values

	Food	Specification	Water %	Ash g	Fat g	Carbohydrates Total g	Carbohydrates Fiber g	Protein g	Food Energy cal
74	Crayfish, freshwater, & spiny lobster	Raw	82.5	1.2	0.5	1.2	......	14.6	72
75	Cream, light	....	71.5	0.6	20.6	4.3	0	3.0	211
76	heavy whipping	....	56.6	0.4	37.6	3.1	0	2.2	352
77	Croaker, Atlantic	Raw	79.2	1.3	2.2	0	0	17.8	96
78		Baked	71.3	1.2	3.2	0	0	24.3	133
79	Duck, domesticated, flesh only	Raw	68.8	1.2	8.2	0	0	21.4	165
80	Eel	Smoked	50.2	2.4	27.8	0	0	18.6	330
81	American	Raw	64.6	1.0	18.3	0	0	15.9	233
82	Eggs, chicken, whole	Fresh & frozen, raw	73.7	1.0	11.5	0.9	0	12.9	163
83		Hard-cooked	73.7	1.0	11.5	0.9	0	12.9	163
84		Poached	73.3	1.4	11.6	0.8	0	12.7	163
85		Dried	4.1	3.6	41.2	4.1	0	47.0	592
86	whites	Fresh & frozen, raw	87.6	0.7	Trace	0.8	0	10.9	51
87		Dried (powder)	8.8	5.1	0.2	5.7	0	80.2	372
88	yolks	Fresh 2/, raw	51.1	1.7	30.6	0.6	0	16.0	348
89		Frozen 3/, raw	55.5	1.6	26.9	0.6	0	15.4	312
90		Dried	4.5	3.2	56.6	2.5	0	33.2	664
91	duck, whole	Raw	70.4	1.1	14.5	0.7	0	13.3	191
92	goose, whole	Raw	70.4	1.1	13.3	1.3	0	13.9	185
93	turkey, whole	Raw	72.6	0.8	11.8	1.7	0	13.1	170
94	Fish flour, from whole fish	....	2.0	19.7	0.3	0	......	78.0	336
95	Flounder	Baked	58.1	2.2	8.2	0	0	30.0	202
96	Frankfurters, all meat	Raw	56.5	2.4	25.5	2.5	0	13.1	296
97	Frog legs	Raw	81.9	1.1	0.3	0	0	16.4	73
98	Goose, domesticated, flesh only	Raw	68.3	1.1	7.1	0	0	22.3	159
99		Roasted	54.8	1.5	9.8	0	0	33.9	233
100	Haddock	Raw	80.5	1.4	0.1	0	0	18.3	79
101		Smoked (finnan haddie)	72.6	3.1	0.4	0	0	23.2	103
102	Halibut, Atlantic & Pacific	Raw	76.5	1.4	1.2	0	0	20.9	100
103		Broiled	66.6	1.7	7.0	0	0	25.2	171
104		Smoked	49.4	15.0	15.0	0	0	20.8	224
105	Heart, beef, lean	Raw	77.5	1.1	3.6	0.7	0	17.1	108
106		Braised	61.3	1.1	5.7	0.7	0	31.3	188
107	calf	Raw	76.2	1.1	5.9	1.8	0	15.0	124
108		Braised	60.3	1.0	9.1	1.8	0	27.8	208
109	chicken, all classes	Raw	74.3	1.0	6.0	0.1	0	18.6	134
110		Simmered	66.7	0.8	7.2	0.1	0	25.3	173
111	hog	Raw	77.4	1.0	4.4	0.4	0	16.8	113
112		Braised	61.0	1.0	6.9	0.3	0	30.8	195
113	lamb	Raw	71.6	1.0	9.6	1.0	0	16.8	162
114		Braised	54.1	0.9	14.4	1.0	0	29.5	260
115	turkey, all classes	Raw	71.3	1.1	11.2	0.2	0	16.2	171
116		Simmered	63.2	0.8	13.2	0.2	0	22.6	216
117	Herring	Canned, solids and liquid	62.9	3.7	13.6	0	0	19.9	208
118	Atlantic	Raw	69.0	2.1	11.3	0	0	17.3	176
119	Pacific	Raw	79.4	1.2	2.6	0	0	17.5	98
120	Kidneys, beef	Raw	75.9	1.1	6.7	0.9	0	15.4	130
121		Braised	53.0	1.2	12.0	0.8	0	33.0	252
122	calf	Raw	77.4	1.3	4.6	0.1	0	16.6	113
123	hog	Raw	77.8	1.2	3.6	1.1	0	16.3	106
124	lamb	Raw	77.7	1.3	3.3	0.9	0	16.8	105
125	Lamb, leg, 83% lean & 17% fat	Raw	64.8	1.3	16.2	0	0	17.8	222
126		Roasted	54.0	1.7	18.9	0	0	25.3	279
127	loin, 72% lean & 28% fat	Raw	57.7	1.3	24.8	0	0	16.3	293
128	66% lean & 34% fat	Broiled	47.0	1.7	29.4	0	0	22.0	359

2/ Small amount of white included. 3/ Considerable amount of white included.

continued

2. COMPOSITION OF FOODS, RAW AND PROCESSED: ANIMAL ORIGIN

Part I. General Constituents and Energy Values

	Food	Specification	Water %	Ash g	Fat g	Carbohydrates Total g	Carbohydrates Fiber g	Protein g	Food Energy cal
129	rib, 68% lean & 32% fat	Raw	53.4	1.1	30.4	0	0	15.1	339
130	62% lean & 38% fat	Broiled	42.9	1.4	35.6	0	0	20.1	407
131	shoulder, 74% lean & 26% fat	Raw	59.6	1.1	23.9	0	0	15.3	281
132		Roasted	49.6	1.4	27.2	0	0	21.7	338
133	Liver, beef	Raw	69.7	1.3	3.8	5.3	0	19.9	140
134		Fried	56.0	1.7	10.6	5.3	0	26.4	229
135	calf	Raw	70.7	1.3	4.7	4.1	0	19.2	140
136		Fried	51.4	1.9	13.2	4.0	0	29.5	261
137	chicken, all classes	Raw	72.2	1.5	3.7	2.9	0	19.7	129
138		Simmered	65.0	1.0	4.4	3.1	0	26.5	165
139	hog	Raw	71.6	1.5	3.7	2.6	0	20.6	131
140		Fried	54.0	2.1	11.5	2.5	0	29.9	241
141	lamb	Raw	70.8	1.4	3.9	2.9	0	21.0	136
142		Broiled	50.4	2.1	12.4	2.8	0	32.3	261
143	turkey, all classes	Raw	70.4	1.5	4.0	2.9	0	21.2	138
144		Simmered	63.3	1.0	4.8	3.1	0	27.9	174
145	Liverwurst	Fresh	53.9	2.5	25.6	1.8	0	16.2	307
146		Smoked	52.6	2.9	27.4	2.3	0	14.8	319
147	Lobster, northern	Raw	78.5	2.2	1.9	0.5	......	16.9	91
148		Cooked or canned	76.8	2.7	1.5	0.3	......	18.7	95
149	Lungs, beef	Raw	78.8	1.0	2.3	0	0	17.6	96
150	calf	Raw	77.4	1.2	3.8	0	0	16.8	106
151	lamb	Raw	76.7	1.2	2.3	0	0	19.3	103
152	Mackerel	Smoked	59.4	2.0	13.0	0	0	23.8	219
153	Atlantic	Raw	67.2	1.6	12.2	0	0	19.0	191
154		Canned, solids & liquid	66.0	3.2	11.1	0	0	19.3	183
155	Pacific	Raw	69.8	1.4	7.3	0	0	21.9	159
156		Canned, solids & liquid	66.4	2.5	10.0	0	0	21.1	180
157	Milk[4/], whole	Pasteurized & raw	87.2	0.7	3.7	4.9	0	3.5	66
158		Dried	2.0	5.9	27.5	38.2	0	26.4	502
159	skim	Pasteurized & raw	90.5	0.7	0.1	5.1	0	3.6	36
160	nonfat solids, instant	Dried	4.0	7.9	0.7	51.6	0	35.8	359
161	evaporated	Canned	73.8	1.6	7.9	9.7	0	7.0	137
162	Mussels, Pacific	Canned, drained	74.6	2.4	3.3	1.5	......	18.2	114
163	Atlantic & Pacific	Raw, drained	78.6	1.5	2.2	3.3	......	14.4	95
164	Octopus	Raw	82.2	1.5	0.8	0	0	15.3	73
165	Oysters	Canned, solids & liquid	82.2	2.2	2.2	4.9	0.1	8.5	76
166		Frozen, solids & liquid	87.4	0.8	......	....	......	6.1	.....
167	eastern	Raw, drained	84.6	1.8	1.8	3.4	......	8.4	66
168	western	Raw, drained	79.1	1.7	2.2	6.4	......	10.6	91
169	Perch, white	Raw	75.7	1.2	4.0	0	0	19.3	118
170	yellow	Raw	79.2	1.2	0.9	0	0	19.5	91
171	Pickerel, chain	Raw	79.7	1.2	0.5	0	0	18.7	84
172	Pike, blue	Raw	78.8	1.2	0.9	0	0	19.1	90
173	northern	Raw	80.0	1.1	1.1	0	0	18.3	88
174	walleye	Raw	78.3	1.2	1.2	0	0	19.3	93
175	Pollock	Raw	77.4	1.3	0.9	0	0	20.4	95
176	Pompano	Raw	70.9	1.1	9.5	0	0	18.8	166
177	Porgy & scup	Raw	76.2	1.3	3.4	0	0	19.0	112
178	Pork, ham	Cured, canned (contents of can)	65.0	3.5	12.3	0.9	0	18.3	193
179	74% lean & 26% fat	Raw	56.5	0.7	26.6	0	0	15.9	308
180		Roasted	45.5	0.9	30.6	0	0	23.0	374
181	76% lean & 24% fat	Cured, uncooked	56.5	3.0	23.0	0	0	17.5	282
182	84% lean & 16% fat	roasted	53.6	3.4	22.1	0	0	20.9	289

[4/] Cow; for information on other milk, *see* Table 1.

continued

Part I. General Constituents and Energy Values

	Food	Specification	Water %	Ash g	Fat g	Carbohydrates Total g	Carbohydrates Fiber g	Protein g	Food Energy cal
183	loin, 80% lean & 20% fat	Raw	57.2	0.9	24.9	0	0	17.1	298
184		Roasted	45.8	1.2	28.5	0	0	24.5	362
185	Boston butt, 79% lean & 21% fat	Raw	59.3	0.7	24.5	0	0	15.5	287
186		Roasted	48.1	0.9	28.5	0	0	22.5	353
187	75% lean & 25% fat	Cured, uncooked	55.7	3.0	24.1	0	0	17.2	291
188	83% lean & 17% fat	roasted	47.7	3.7	25.7	0	0	22.9	330
189	picnic, 74% lean & 26% fat	Raw	58.9	0.7	24.7	0	0	15.8	290
190		Simmered	45.7	0.6	30.5	0	0	23.2	374
191	70% lean & 30% fat	Cured, uncooked	56.7	2.9	23.6	0	0	16.8	285
192	82% lean & 18% fat	roasted	48.8	3.6	25.2	0	0	22.4	323
193	spareribs, medium-fat	Raw	51.8	0.7	33.2	0	0	14.5	361
194		Braised	39.7	0.6	38.9	0	0	20.8	440
195	Quail, flesh & skin	Raw	66.3	1.4	7.0	0	0	25.4	172
196	Rabbit, domesticated, flesh only	Raw	70	1	8	0	0	21	162
197		Stewed	59.8	0.8	10.1	0	0	29.3	216
198	Rockfish, black, canary, yellowtail, rasphead, & bocaccio	Raw	78.9	1.2	1.8	0	0	18.9	97
199	Salami	Dry	29.8	7.1	38.1	1.2	0	23.8	450
200		Cooked	51.0	4.5	25.6	1.4	0	17.5	311
201	Salmon	Broiled or baked	63.4	1.6	7.4	0	0	27.0	182
202		Smoked	58.9	9.4	9.3	0	0	21.6	176
203	Atlantic	Raw	63.6	1.4	13.4	0	0	22.5	217
204		Canned, solids & liquid	64.2	1.6	12.2	0	0	21.7	203
205	chinook (king)	Raw	64.2	1.1	15.6	0	0	19.1	222
206		Canned, solids & liquid	64.4	2.0	14.0	0	0	19.6	210
207	chum	Raw	.....	.....	......	......	......	......	.....
208		Canned, solids & liquid	70.8	2.6	5.2	0	0	21.5	139
209	coho (silver)	Raw	.....	.....	......	......	......	......	.....
210		Canned, solids & liquid	69.3	2.4	7.1	0	0	20.8	153
211	humpback (pink)	Raw	76.0	1.2	3.7	0	0	20.0	119
212		Canned, solids & liquid	70.8	2.3	5.9	0	0	20.5	141
213	sockeye (red)	Raw	.....	.....	......	......	......	......	.....
214		Canned, solids & liquid	67.2	2.7	9.3	0	0	20.3	171
215	Sardines, Atlantic	Canned in oil, drained	61.8	3.1	11.1	......	......	24.0	203
216	Pacific	Raw	70.7	2.4	8.6	0	0	19.2	160
217	Sausage, pork	Raw	38.1	1.7	50.8	Trace	0	9.4	498
218		Cooked	34.8	2.9	44.2	Trace	0	18.1	476
219	Vienna	Canned	63.0	2.9	19.8	0.3	0	14.0	240
220	Scallops, bay & sea	Raw	79.8	1.4	0.2	3.3	......	15.3	81
221		Steamed	73.1	.....	1.4	......	......	23.2	112
222	Shad	Raw	70.4	1.3	10.0	0	0	18.6	170
223		Canned, solids & liquid	71.1	2.8	8.8	0	0	16.9	152
224	Shrimp	Raw	78.2	1.4	0.8	1.5	......	18.1	91
225		Canned, solids & liquid	78.2	4.0	0.8	0.8	......	16.2	80
226	Smelt, Atlantic, jack, & bay	Raw	79.0	1.1	2.1	0	0	18.6	98
227		Canned, solids & liquid	62.7	5.4	13.5	0	......	18.4	200
228	Snail	Raw	79.2	1.3	1.4	2.0	......	16.1	90
229	Snapper, red & gray	Raw	78.5	1.3	0.9	0	0	19.8	93
230	Squab, flesh only	Raw	72.8	1.2	7.5	0	0	17.5	142
231	Squid	Raw	80.2	1.0	0.9	1.5	......	16.4	84
232	Sturgeon	Raw	78.7	1.4	1.9	0	0	18.1	94
233		Steamed	67.5	.....	5.7	0	0	25.4	160
234		Smoked	63.7	1.9	1.8	0	0	31.2	149
235	Sweetbreads (thymus), beef	Raw	67.8	1.6	16.0	0	0	14.6	207
236		Braised	49.6	1.3	23.2	0	0	25.9	320

continued

2. COMPOSITION OF FOODS, RAW AND PROCESSED: ANIMAL ORIGIN

Part I. General Constituents and Energy Values

	Food	Specification	Water %	Ash g	Fat g	Carbohydrates Total g	Carbohydrates Fiber g	Protein g	Food Energy cal
237	calf	Raw	78.4	1.8	2.0	0	0	17.8	94
238		Braised	62.7	1.5	3.2	0	0	32.6	168
239	lamb	Raw	79.5	1.3	3.8	0	0	14.1	94
240		Braised	64.6	1.2	6.1	0	0	28.1	175
241	Swordfish	Raw	75.9	1.3	4.0	0	0	19.2	118
242		Canned, solids & liquid	78.0	1.5	3.0	0	0	17.5	102
243	Tautog (blackfish)	Raw	79.3	1.1	1.1	0	0	18.6	89
244	Terrapin, diamondback	Raw	77.0	1.0	3.5	0	0	18.6	111
245	Tongue, beef, medium-fat	Raw	68	0.9	15	0.4	0	16.4	207
246		Braised	60.8	0.6	16.7	0.4	0	21.5	244
247	calf	Raw	74.3	1.0	5.3	0.9	0	18.5	130
248		Braised	68.5	0.7	6.0	1.0	0	23.9	160
249	hog	Raw	66.1	1.0	15.6	0.5	0	16.8	215
250		Braised	59.4	0.7	17.4	0.5	0	22.0	253
251	lamb	Raw	69.5	0.8	15.3	0.5	0	13.9	199
252		Braised	60.2	0.7	18.2	0.5	0	20.5	254
253	Tripe, beef	Commercial	79.1	0.4	2.0	0	0	19.1	100
254		Pickled	86.5	0.3	1.3	0	0	11.8	62
255	Trout, brook	Raw	77.7	1.2	2.1	0	0	19.2	101
256	rainbow	Raw	66.3	1.3	11.4	0	0	21.5	195
257		Canned	63.2	2.4	13.4	0	0	20.6	209
258	Tuna	Canned in water, solids & liquid	70.0	1.2	0.8	0	0	28.0	127
259		Canned in oil, drained	60.6	2.0	8.2	0	0	28.8	197
260	bluefin	Raw	70.5	1.3	4.1	0	0	25.2	145
261	yellowfin	Raw	71.5	1.4	3.0	0	0	24.7	133
262	Turkey, flesh only	Canned	64.9	1.7	12.5	0	0	20.9	202
263	light meat, all classes	Raw	73.0	1.2	1.2	0	0	24.6	116
264		Roasted	62.1	1.2	3.9	0	0	32.9	176
265	dark meat, all classes	Raw	73.6	1.1	4.3	0	0	20.9	128
266		Roasted	60.5	1.2	8.3	0	0	30.0	203
267	Turtle, green	Raw	78.5	1.2	0.5	0	0	19.8	89
268		Canned	75.0	0.9	0.7	0	0	23.4	106
269	Veal, chuck, 86% lean & 14% fat	Raw	70	1.0	10	0	0	19.4	173
270	85% lean & 15% fat	Braised	58.5	0.8	12.8	0	0	27.9	235
271	flank, 61% lean & 39% fat	Raw	56	0.8	27	0	0	16.5	314
272	60% lean & 40% fat	Stewed	43.8	0.7	32.3	0	0	23.2	390
273	loin, 85% lean & 15% fat	Raw	69	1.0	11	0	0	19.2	181
274	77% lean & 23% fat	Broiled	58.9	1.3	13.4	0	0	26.4	234
275	rib, 82% lean & 18% fat	Raw	66	1.0	14	0	0	18.8	207
276		Roasted	54.6	1.3	16.9	0	0	27.2	269
277	round[5/], 87% lean & 13% fat	Raw	70	1.0	9	0	0	19.5	164
278	79% lean & 21% fat	Broiled	60.4	1.4	11.1	0	0	27.1	216
279	Venison, lean	Raw	74	1	4	0	0	21	126
280	Weakfish	Raw	76.6	1.2	5.6	0	0	16.5	121
281		Broiled	61.4	2.6	11.4	0	0	24.6	208
282	Whey	Fluid	93.1	0.6	0.3	5.1	0	0.9	26
283		Dried	4.5	8.0	1.1	73.5	0	12.9	349
284	Whitefish, lake	Raw	71.7	1.2	8.2	0	0	18.9	155
285		Smoked	68.2	3.7	7.3	0	0	20.9	155
286	Yoghurt, from whole milk	....	88.0	0.7	3.4	4.9	0	3.0	62
287	from partially skimmed milk	....	89.0	0.7	1.7	5.2	0	3.4	50

[5/] With rump.

Contributor: Watt, Bernice K.

Reference: Watt, B. K., and A. L. Merrill. 1963. U.S. Dept. Agr. Handbook 8.

continued

2. COMPOSITION OF FOODS, RAW AND PROCESSED: ANIMAL ORIGIN

Part II. Minerals

	Food	Specification	Calcium mg	Phosphorus mg	Iron mg	Sodium mg	Potassium mg
1	Abalone	Raw	37	191	2.4	....	....
2		Canned	14	128	......	....	....
3	Bacon	Uncooked	13	108	1.2	680	130
4		Broiled or fried, drained	14	224	3.3	1021	236
5	Canadian	Unheated	12	180	3.0	1891	392
6		Broiled or fried, drained	19	218	4.1	2555	432
7	Bass, small- & largemouth	Raw	....	192	......	....	....
8	striped	Raw	....	212	......	....	....
9	Beef, chuck, 82% lean & 18% fat	Raw	11	188	2.8	65[1]	355[1]
10	81% lean & 19% fat	Braised or pot-roasted	11	140	3.3	60[1]	370[1]
11	arm, 86% lean & 14% fat	Raw	12	180	2.9	65[1]	355[1]
12	85% lean & 15% fat	Braised or pot-roasted	12	134	3.4	60[1]	370[1]
13	flank, 100% lean	Raw	13	201	3.2	65[1]	355[1]
14		Braised	14	150	3.8	60[1]	370[1]
15	porterhouse, 63% lean & 37% fat	Raw	8	136	2.2	65[1]	355[1]
16	57% lean & 43% fat	Broiled	9	168	2.6	60[1]	370[1]
17	T-bone, 62% lean & 38% fat	Raw	8	135	2.2	65[1]	355[1]
18	56% lean & 44% fat	Broiled	8	166	2.6	60[1]	370[1]
19	sirloin, 73% lean & 27% fat	Raw	10	155	2.5	65[1]	355[1]
20	66% lean & 34% fat	Broiled	10	191	2.9	60[1]	370[1]
21	rib, 64% lean & 36% fat	Raw	9	151	2.2	65[1]	355[1]
22		Roasted	9	186	2.6	60[1]	370[1]
23	round, 89% lean & 11% fat	Raw	12	203	3.0	65[1]	355[1]
24	81% lean & 19% fat	Broiled	12	250	3.5	60[1]	370[1]
25	rump, 75% lean & 25% fat	Raw	10	160	2.6	65[1]	355[1]
26		Roasted	10	197	3.1	60[1]	370[1]
27	hamburger, lean	Raw	12	192	3.1	....	....
28		Cooked	12	230	3.5	48	558
29	regular	Raw	10	156	2.7	....	236
30		Cooked	11	194	3.2	47	450
31	chipped	Dried, uncooked	20	404	5.1	4300	200
32	corned, medium-fat	Uncooked	9	125	2.4	1300	60
33		Cooked	9	93	2.9	1740	150
34		Canned	20	106	4.3	....	....
35	Bluefish	Raw	23	243	0.6	74	....
36		Broiled or baked[2]	29	287	0.7	104	....
37	Bologna, all meat	....	....	....	......	....	....
38	Bonito, Atlantic, Pacific, & striped	Raw	....	....	......	....	....
39	Brains, beef, calf, hog, & sheep	Raw	10	312	2.4	125	219
40	Butter, salted	....	20	16	0	987	23
41	Butterfish, northern waters	Raw	....	....	......	....	....
42	gulf waters	Raw	....	....	......	....	....
43	Buttermilk	Cultured, from skim milk	121	95	Trace	130	140
44		Dried	1248	970	0.6	507	1606
45	Catfish, freshwater	Raw	....	....	0.4	60	330
46	Caviar, sturgeon	Granular	276	355	11.8	2200	180
47		Pressed	....	....	......	....	....
48	Cheese, American	Pasteurized process	697	771[3]	0.9	1136[3]	80
49	blue or Roquefort	Natural	315	339	0.5[1]	....	....
50	brick	Natural	730	455	0.9[1]	....	....
51	Camembert, domestic	Natural	105	184	0.5	....	111
52	cheddar, domestic	Natural	750	478	1.0	700	82
53	cottage, creamed	Natural	94	152	0.3	229	85
54	uncreamed	Natural	90	175	0.4	290	72
55	cream	Natural	62	95	0.2	250	74
56	Limburger	Natural	590	393	0.6	....	....

1/ Imputed, usually from another form of the food or from a similar food. 2/ Prepared with butter or margarine.

3/ Based on the use of 1.5% anhydrous disodium phosphate as the emulsifying agent.

continued

2. COMPOSITION OF FOODS, RAW AND PROCESSED: ANIMAL ORIGIN

Part II. Minerals

	Food	Specification	Calcium mg	Phosphorus mg	Iron mg	Sodium mg	Potassium mg
57	Parmesan	Natural	1140	781	0.4	734	149
58	pimiento	Pasteurized process	....	....	......	....	....
59	Swiss, domestic	Natural	925	563	0.9	710	104
60		Pasteurized process	887	867[3/]	0.9[1/]	1167[3/]	100
61	Chicken, flesh only	Canned	21	247	1.5	....	138
62	light meat, all classes	Raw	11	218	1.1	50	320
63		Roasted	11	265	1.3	64	411
64	dark meat, all classes	Raw	13	188	1.5	67	250
65		Roasted	13	229	1.7	86	321
66	Clams	Canned, solids & liquid	55	137	4.1	....	140
67	soft	Raw, drained	....	183	3.4	36	235
68	hard	Raw, drained	69	151	7.5	205	311
69	Cod	Raw	10	194	0.4	70	382
70		Broiled	31	274	1.0	110	407
71		Canned	....	....	......	....	....
72	Crab	Canned	45	182	0.8	1000	110
73	blue, Dungeness, rock, & king	Steamed	43	175	0.8	....	....
74	Crayfish, freshwater, & spiny lobster	Raw	77	201	1.5	....	....
75	Cream, light	....	102	80	Trace	43	122
76	heavy whipping	....	75	59	Trace	32	89
77	Croaker, Atlantic	Raw	....	....	......	87	234
78		Baked	....	....	......	120	323
79	Duck, domesticated, flesh only	Raw	12[1/]	203[1/]	1.3[1/]	74	285
80	Eel	Smoked	....	....	......	....	....
81	American	Raw	18	202	0.7	....	....
82	Eggs, chicken, whole	Fresh & frozen, raw	54	205	2.3	122	129
83		Hard-cooked	54	205	2.3	122	129
84		Poached	55	203	2.2	271	128
85		Dried	187	800	8.7	427	463
86	whites	Fresh & frozen, raw	9	15	0.1	146	139
87		Dried (powder)	66	110	1.0	1103	1000
88	yolks	Fresh[4/], raw	141	569	5.5	52	98
89		Frozen[5/], raw	125	502	4.9	63	100
90		Dried	275	1109	10.8	100	186
91	duck, whole	Raw	56	195	2.8	122[1/]	129[1/]
92	goose, whole	Raw	....	....	......	....	....
93	turkey, whole	Raw	....	....	......	....	....
94	Fish flour, from whole fish	....	4610	3100	41.0	170	430
95	Flounder	Baked	23	344	1.4	237	587
96	Frankfurters, all meat	Raw	....	....	......	....	....
97	Frog legs	Raw	18	147	1.5	....	....
98	Goose, domesticated, flesh only	Raw	12[1/]	203[1/]	1.3[1/]	86	420
99		Roasted	14[1/]	277[1/]	1.7[1/]	124	605
100	Haddock	Raw	23	197	0.7	61	304
101		Smoked (finnan haddie)	....	....	......	....	....
102	Halibut, Atlantic & Pacific	Raw	13	211	0.7	54	449
103		Broiled	16	248	0.8	134	525
104		Smoked	....	....	......	....	....
105	Heart, beef, lean	Raw	5	195	4.0	86	193
106		Braised	6	181	5.9	104	232
107	calf	Raw	3	160	3.0	94	208
108		Braised	4	148	4.4	113	250
109	chicken, all classes	Raw	4	158	3.3	79	159
110		Simmered	4	107	3.6	69	140
111	hog	Raw	3	131	3.3	54	106
112		Braised	4	121	4.9	65	128

[1/] Imputed, usually from another form of the food or from a similar food. [3/] Based on the use of 1.5% anhydrous disodium phosphate as the emulsifying agent. [4/] Small amount of white included. [5/] Considerable amount of white included.

continued

2. COMPOSITION OF FOODS, RAW AND PROCESSED: ANIMAL ORIGIN

Part II. Minerals

	Food	Specification	Calcium mg	Phosphorus mg	Iron mg	Sodium mg	Potassium mg
113	lamb	Raw	11	249	......	....	....
114		Braised	14	231	......	....	....
115	turkey, all classes	Raw	....	....	......	69	240
116		Simmered	....	....	......	61	211
117	Herring	Canned, solids & liquid	147	297	1.8	....	....
118	Atlantic	Raw	....	256	1.1	....	....
119	Pacific	Raw	....	225	1.3	74	420
120	Kidneys, beef	Raw	11	219	7.4	176	225
121		Braised	18	244	13.1	253	324
122	calf	Raw	....	....	4.0	....	....
123	hog	Raw	11	218	6.7	115	178
124	lamb	Raw	13	218	7.6	200	230
125	Lamb, leg, 83% lean & 17% fat	Raw	10	162	1.4	75[1]	295[1]
126		Roasted	11	208	1.7	70[1]	290[1]
127	loin, 72% lean & 28% fat	Raw	9	145	1.2	75[1]	295[1]
128	66% lean & 34% fat	Broiled	9	172	1.3	70[1]	290[1]
129	rib, 68% lean & 32% fat	Raw	9	132	1.0	75[1]	295[1]
130	62% lean & 38% fat	Broiled	9	156	1.1	70[1]	290[1]
131	shoulder, 74% lean & 26% fat	Raw	9	134	1.0	75[1]	295[1]
132		Roasted	10	172	1.2	70[1]	290[1]
133	Liver, beef	Raw	8	352	6.5	136	281
134		Fried	11	476	8.8	184	380
135	calf	Raw	8	333	8.8	73	281
136		Fried	13	537	14.2	118	453
137	chicken, all classes	Raw	12	236	7.9	70	172
138		Simmered	11	159	8.5	61	151
139	hog	Raw	10	356	19.2	73	261
140		Fried	15	539	29.1	111	395
141	lamb	Raw	10	349	10.9	52	202
142		Broiled	16	572	17.9	85	331
143	turkey, all classes	Raw	....	....	......	63	160
144		Simmered	....	....	......	55	141
145	Liverwurst	Fresh	9	238	5.4	....	....
146		Smoked	10	245	5.9	....	....
147	Lobster, northern	Raw	29	183	0.6	....	....
148		Cooked or canned	65	192	0.8	210	180
149	Lungs, beef	Raw	....	216	......	....	....
150	calf	Raw	....	....	......	....	....
151	lamb	Raw	....	180	......	....	....
152	Mackerel	Smoked	....	....	......	....	....
153	Atlantic	Raw	5	239	1.0	....	....
154		Canned, solids & liquid	185	274	2.1	....	....
155	Pacific	Raw	8	274	2.1	....	....
156		Canned, solids & liquid	260	288	2.2	....	....
157	Milk[6], whole	Pasteurized & raw	117	92	Trace	50	140
158		Dried	909	708	0.5	405	1330
159	skim	Pasteurized & raw	121	95	Trace	52	145
160	nonfat solids, instant	Dried	1293	1005	0.6	526	1725
161	evaporated	Canned	252	205	0.1	118	303
162	Mussels, Pacific	Canned, drained	....	....	......	....	....
163	Atlantic & Pacific	Raw, drained	88	236	3.4	289	315
164	Octopus	Raw	29	173	......	....	....
165	Oysters	Canned, solids & liquid	28	124	5.6	....	70
166		Frozen, solids & liquid	....	....	......	380	210
167	eastern	Raw, drained	94	143	5.5	73	121
168	western	Raw, drained	85	153	7.2	....	....

[1] Imputed, usually from another form of the food or from a similar food. [6] Cow; for information on other milk, *see* Table 1.

continued

2. COMPOSITION OF FOODS, RAW AND PROCESSED: ANIMAL ORIGIN

Part II. Minerals

	Food	Specification	Calcium mg	Phosphorus mg	Iron mg	Sodium mg	Potassium mg
169	Perch, white	Raw	....	192	......	....	....
170	yellow	Raw	....	180	0.6	68	230
171	Pickerel, chain	Raw	....	....	0.7	....	....
172	Pike, blue	Raw	....	....	......	....	....
173	northern	Raw	....	....	......	....	....
174	walleye	Raw	....	214	0.4	51	319
175	Pollock	Raw	....	....	......	48	350
176	Pompano	Raw	....	....	......	47	191
177	Porgy & scup	Raw	54	250	......	63	287
178	Pork, ham	Cured, canned (contents of can)	11	156	2.7	1100 1/	340 1/
179	74% lean & 26% fat	Raw	9	178	2.4	70 1/	285 1/
180		Roasted	10	236	3.0	65 1/	390 1/
181	76% lean & 24% fat	Cured, uncooked	10	162	2.6	....	....
182	84% lean & 16% fat	roasted	9	172	2.6	....	....
183	loin, 80% lean & 20% fat	Raw	10	193	2.6	70 1/	285 1/
184		Roasted	11	256	3.2	65 1/	390 1/
185	Boston butt, 79% lean & 21% fat	Raw	9	173	2.3	70 1/	285 1/
186		Roasted	10	229	2.9	65 1/	390 1/
187	75% lean & 25% fat	Cured, uncooked	10	152	2.6	....	....
188	83% lean & 17% fat	roasted	10	185	3.0	....	....
189	picnic, 74% lean & 26% fat	Raw	9	178	2.4	70 1/	285 1/
190		Simmered	10	139	3.0	65 1/	390 1/
191	70% lean & 30% fat	Cured, uncooked	10	150	2.5	....	....
192	82% lean & 18% fat	roasted	10	182	2.9	....	....
193	spareribs, medium-fat	Raw	8	160	2.2	70 1/	285 1/
194		Braised	9	121	2.6	65 1/	390 1/
195	Quail, flesh & skin	Raw	....	....	......	40	175
196	Rabbit, domesticated, flesh only	Raw	20	352	1.3	43	385
197		Stewed	21	259	1.5	41	368
198	Rockfish, black, canary, yellowtail, rasphead, & bocaccio	Raw	....	....	......	60	388
199	Salami	Dry	14	283	3.6	....	....
200		Cooked	10	200	2.6	....	....
201	Salmon	Broiled or baked	....	414	1.2	116	443
202		Smoked	14	245	......	....	....
203	Atlantic	Raw	79	186	0.9	....	....
204		Canned, solids & liquid	....	....	......	....	....
205	chinook (king)	Raw	....	301	......	45	399
206		Canned, solids & liquid	154 7/	289	0.9	45	366
207	chum	Raw	....	....	......	53	429
208		Canned, solids & liquid	249 7/	352	0.7	53	336
209	coho (silver)	Raw	175	231	......	48	421
210		Canned, solids & liquid	244 7/	288	0.9	48 8/	339
211	humpback (pink)	Raw	....	....	......	64	306
212		Canned, solids & liquid	196 7/	286	0.8	64 9/	361
213	sockeye (red)	Raw	....	....	......	48	391
214		Canned, solids & liquid	259 7/	344	1.2	48 10/	344
215	Sardines, Atlantic	Canned in oil, drained	437 11/	499 12/	2.9	823	590
216	Pacific	Raw	33	215	1.8	....	....
217	Sausage, pork	Raw	5	92	1.4	740	140
218		Cooked	7	162	2.4	958	269
219	Vienna	Canned	8	153	2.1	....	....
220	Scallops, bay & sea	Raw	26	208	1.8	255 13/	396 13/
221		Steamed	115	338	3.0	265	476

1/ Imputed, usually from another form of the food or from a similar food. 7/ If bones are discarded, value will be greatly reduced. 8/ 351 mg with added salt. 9/ 387 mg with added salt. 10/ 522 mg with added salt. 11/ 54 mg without skin and bones. 12/ 319 mg without skin and bones. 13/ Based on frozen scallops, possibly brined.

continued

2. COMPOSITION OF FOODS, RAW AND PROCESSED: ANIMAL ORIGIN

Part II. Minerals

	Food	Specification	Calcium mg	Phosphorus mg	Iron mg	Sodium mg	Potassium mg
222	Shad	Raw	20	260	0.5	54	330
223		Canned, solids & liquid	....	....	0.7	....	....
224	Shrimp	Raw	63	166	1.6	140	220
225		Canned, solids & liquid	59	152	1.8	....	....
226	Smelt, Atlantic, jack, & bay	Raw	....	272	0.4	....	....
227		Canned, solids & liquid	358	370	1.7	....	....
228	Snail	Raw	....	....	3.5	....	....
229	Snapper, red & gray	Raw	16	214	0.8	67	323
230	Squab, flesh only	Raw	....	....	......	....	....
231	Squid	Raw	12	119	0.5	....	....
232	Sturgeon	Raw	....	....	......	....	....
233		Steamed	40	263	2.0	108	235
234		Smoked	....	....	......	....	....
235	Sweetbreads (thymus), beef	Raw	....	393	......	96	360
236		Braised	....	364	......	116	433
237	calf	Raw	....	....	......	....	....
238		Braised	....	....	......	....	....
239	lamb	Raw	....	220	......	....	....
240		Braised	....	204	......	....	....
241	Swordfish	Raw	19	195	0.9	....	....
242		Canned, solids & liquid	....	....	......	....	....
243	Tautog (blackfish)	Raw	....	227	......	....	....
244	Terrapin, diamondback	Raw	....	....	3.2	....	....
245	Tongue, beef, medium-fat	Raw	8	182	2.1	73	197
246		Braised	7	117	2.2	61	164
247	calf	Raw	....	....	......	....	....
248		Braised	....	....	......	....	....
249	hog	Raw	29	186	1.4	....	....
250		Braised	26	119	1.4	....	....
251	lamb	Raw	....	147	......	....	....
252		Braised	....	102	......	....	....
253	Tripe, beef	Commercial	127	86	1.6	72	9
254		Pickled	....	....	......	46	19
255	Trout, brook	Raw	....	266	......	....	....
256	rainbow	Raw	....	....	......	....	....
257		Canned	....	....	......	....	....
258	Tuna	Canned in water, solids & liquid	16	190	1.6	41 [14/]	279 [15/]
259		Canned in oil, drained	8 [1/]	234	1.9	....	....
260	bluefin	Raw	....	....	1.3	....	....
261	yellowfin	Raw	....	....	......	37	....
262	Turkey, flesh only	Canned	10	....	1.4	....	....
263	light meat, all classes	Raw	....	....	1.0	51	320
264		Roasted	....	....	1.2	82	411
265	dark meat, all classes	Raw	....	....	2.0	81	310
266		Roasted	....	....	2.3	99	398
267	Turtle, green	Raw	....	....	......	....	....
268		Canned	....	....	......	....	....
269	Veal, chuck, 86% lean & 14% fat	Raw	11	199	2.9	90 [1/]	320 [1/]
270	85% lean & 15% fat	Braised	12	151	3.5	80 [1/]	500 [1/]
271	flank, 61% lean & 39% fat	Raw	10	155	2.5	90 [1/]	320 [1/]
272	60% lean & 40% fat	Stewed	11	117	3.0	80 [1/]	500 [1/]
273	loin, 85% lean & 15% fat	Raw	11	195	2.9	90 [1/]	320 [1/]
274	77% lean & 23% fat	Broiled	11	225	3.2	80 [1/]	500 [1/]
275	rib, 82% lean & 18% fat	Raw	11	190	2.8	90 [1/]	320 [1/]
276		Roasted	12	248	3.4	80 [1/]	500 [1/]
277	round [16/], 87% lean & 13% fat	Raw	11	200	2.9	90 [1/]	320 [1/]
278	79% lean & 21% fat	Broiled	11	231	3.2	80 [1/]	500 [1/]

[1/] Imputed, usually from another form of the food or from a similar food. [14/] 875 mg with added salt. [15/] 275 mg with added salt. [16/] With rump.

continued

2. COMPOSITION OF FOODS, RAW AND PROCESSED: ANIMAL ORIGIN

Part II. Minerals

	Food	Specification	Calcium mg	Phosphorus mg	Iron mg	Sodium mg	Potassium mg
279	Venison, lean	Raw	10	249	......	....	....
280	Weakfish	Raw	....	....	......	75	317
281		Broiled	....	....	......	560[17]	465
282	Whey	Fluid	51	53	0.1	....	....
283		Dried	646	589	1.4	....	....
284	Whitefish, lake	Raw	....	270	0.4	52	299
285		Smoked	22	274	......	....	....
286	Yoghurt, from whole milk	....	111	87	Trace	47	132
287	from partially skimmed milk	....	120	94	Trace	51	143

17/ With added salt.

Contributor: Watt, Bernice K.

Reference: Watt, B. K., and A. L. Merrill. 1963. U.S. Dept. Agr. Handbook 8.

Part III. Vitamins

	Food	Specification	Thiamine mg	Riboflavin mg	Nicotinic Acid mg	Ascorbic Acid mg	Vitamin A I.U.
1	Abalone	Raw	0.18	0.14	......	......	....
2		Canned	0.12	....	......	......	....
3	Bacon	Uncooked	0.36	0.11	1.8	......	0[1]
4		Broiled or fried, drained	0.51	0.34	5.2	......	0[1]
5	Canadian	Unheated	0.83	0.22	4.7	......	0[1]
6		Broiled or fried, drained	0.92	0.17	5.0	......	0[1]
7	Bass, small- & largemouth	Raw	0.10	0.03	2.1	......	....
8	striped	Raw	....	....	......	......	....
9	Beef, chuck, 82% lean & 18% fat	Raw	0.08	0.17	4.5	......	40
10	81% lean & 19% fat	Braised or pot-roasted	0.05	0.20	4.0	......	40
11	arm, 86% lean & 14% fat	Raw	0.08	0.17	4.7	......	30
12	85% lean & 15% fat	Braised or pot-roasted	0.05	0.21	4.2	......	30
13	flank, 100% lean	Raw	0.09	0.19	5.2	......	10
14		Braised	0.06	0.23	4.6	......	10
15	porterhouse, 63% lean & 37% fat	Raw	0.06	0.13	3.6	......	70
16	57% lean & 43% fat	Broiled	0.06	0.16	4.2	......	70
17	T-bone, 62% lean & 38% fat	Raw	0.06	0.13	3.5	......	70
18	56% lean & 44% fat	Broiled	0.06	0.16	4.1	......	80
19	sirloin, 73% lean & 27% fat	Raw	0.07	0.15	4.1	......	50
20	66% lean & 34% fat	Broiled	0.06	0.18	4.7	......	50
21	rib, 64% lean & 36% fat	Raw	0.06	0.13	3.6	......	70
22		Roasted	0.05	0.15	3.6	......	80
23	round, 89% lean & 11% fat	Raw	0.09	0.18	4.8	......	20
24	81% lean & 19% fat	Broiled	0.08	0.22	5.6	......	30
25	rump, 75% lean & 25% fat	Raw	0.08	0.16	4.2	......	50
26		Roasted	0.06	0.18	4.3	......	50
27	hamburger, lean	Raw	0.09	0.18	5.0	......	20
28		Cooked	0.09	0.23	6.0	......	20
29	regular	Raw	0.08	0.16	4.3	......	40
30		Cooked	0.09	0.21	5.4	......	40
31	chipped	Dried, uncooked	0.07[2]	0.32[2]	3.8[2]	0	....

1/ Or too small to measure. 2/ Imputed, usually from another form of the food or from a similar food.

continued

2. COMPOSITION OF FOODS, RAW AND PROCESSED: ANIMAL ORIGIN

Part III. Vitamins

	Food	Specification	Thiamine mg	Riboflavin mg	Nicotinic Acid mg	Ascorbic Acid mg	Vitamin A I.U.
32	corned, medium-fat	Uncooked	0.03	0.15	1.7	0	....
33		Cooked	0.02	0.18	1.5	0	....
34		Canned	0.02	0.24	3.4	0	....
35	Bluefish	Raw	0.12	0.09	1.9	......	....
36		Broiled or baked[3]	0.11	0.10	1.9	......	50
37	Bologna, all meat	....	....	....	......	......	....
38	Bonito, Atlantic, Pacific, & striped	Raw	....	....	......	......	....
39	Brains, beef, calf, hog, & sheep	Raw	0.23	0.26	4.4	18	0
40	Butter, salted	....	....	....	......	0	3300
41	Butterfish, northern waters	Raw	....	....	......	......	....
42	gulf waters	Raw	....	....	......	......	....
43	Buttermilk	Cultured, from skim milk	0.04	0.18	0.1	1	Trace
44		Dried	0.26	1.72	0.9	......	220
45	Catfish, freshwater	Raw	0.04	0.03	1.7	......	....
46	Caviar, sturgeon	Granular	....	....	......	......	....
47		Pressed	....	....	......	......	....
48	Cheese, American	Pasteurized process	0.02	0.41	Trace	0[1]	1220[2]
49	blue or Roquefort	Natural	0.03	0.61	1.2	0[1]	1240[2]
50	brick	Natural	....	0.45	0.1	0[1]	1240[2]
51	Camembert, domestic	Natural	0.04	0.75	0.8	0[1]	1010[2]
52	cheddar, domestic	Natural	0.03	0.46	0.1	0[1]	1310[2]
53	cottage, creamed	Natural	0.03	0.25	0.1	0[1]	170[2]
54	uncreamed	Natural	0.03	0.28	0.1[2]	0[1]	10[2]
55	cream	Natural	0.02[2]	0.24	0.1	0[1]	1540[2]
56	Limburger	Natural	0.08	0.50	0.2	0[1]	1140[2]
57	Parmesan	Natural	0.02	0.73	0.2	0[1]	1060[2]
58	pimiento	Pasteurized process	....	....	......	......	....
59	Swiss, domestic	Natural	0.01	0.40[2]	0.1[2]	0[1]	1140[2]
60		Pasteurized process	0.01[2]	0.40	0.1	0[1]	1100[2]
61	Chicken, flesh only	Canned	0.04	0.12	4.4	4	230
62	light meat, all classes	Raw	0.05	0.09	10.7	......	60
63		Roasted	0.04	0.10	11.6	......	60
64	dark meat, all classes	Raw	0.08	0.20	5.2	......	150
65		Roasted	0.07	0.23	5.6	......	150
66	Clams	Canned, solids & liquid	0.01	0.11	1.0	......	....
67	soft	Raw, drained	....	....	......	......	....
68	hard	Raw, drained	....	....	......	......	....
69	Cod	Raw	0.06	0.07	2.2	2	0
70		Broiled	0.08	0.11	3.0	......	180
71		Canned	....	0.08	......	......	....
72	Crab	Canned	0.08	0.08	1.9	......	....
73	blue, Dungeness, rock, & king	Steamed	0.16	0.08	2.8	2	2170
74	Crayfish, freshwater, & spiny lobster	Raw	0.01	0.04	1.9	......	....
75	Cream, light	....	0.03	0.15	0.1	1	840
76	heavy whipping	....	0.02	0.11	Trace	1	1540
77	Croaker, Atlantic	Raw	0.12	0.08	5.5	......	60
78		Baked	0.13	0.10	6.5	......	70
79	Duck, domesticated, flesh only	Raw	0.10[2]	0.12[2]	7.7[2]	......	....
80	Eel	Smoked	....	....	......	......	....
81	American	Raw	0.22	0.36	1.4	......	1610
82	Eggs, chicken, whole	Fresh & frozen, raw	0.11	0.30	0.1	0	1180
83		Hard-cooked	0.09	0.28	0.1	0	1180
84		Poached	0.08	0.25	0.1	0	1170
85		Dried	0.33	1.20	0.2	0	4290

1/ Or too small to measure. 2/ Imputed, usually from another form of the food or from a similar food. 3/ Prepared with butter or margarine.

continued

2. COMPOSITION OF FOODS, RAW AND PROCESSED: ANIMAL ORIGIN

Part III. Vitamins

	Food	Specification	Thiamine mg	Riboflavin mg	Nicotinic Acid mg	Ascorbic Acid mg	Vitamin A I.U.
86	whites	Fresh & frozen, raw	Trace	0.27	0.1	0	0
87		Dried (powder)	0.04	1.99	0.7	0	0
88	yolks	Fresh[4/], raw	0.22	0.44	0.1	0	3400
89		Frozen[5/], raw	0.20	0.42	0.1	0	2990
90		Dried	0.41	0.86	0.1	0	5980
91	duck, whole	Raw	0.18	0.30[2/]	0.1	0	1230
92	goose, whole	Raw	....	....	......	......	....
93	turkey, whole	Raw	....	....	Trace	......	....
94	Fish flour, from whole fish	....	0.07	0.62	2.2	......	....
95	Flounder	Baked	0.07	0.08	2.5	2	....
96	Frankfurters, all meat	Raw	....	....	......	......	....
97	Frog legs	Raw	0.14	0.25	1.2	......	0
98	Goose, domesticated, flesh only	Raw	0.10[2/]	0.12[2/]	7.7[2/]	......	....
99		Roasted	0.11[2/]	0.16[2/]	9.3[2/]	......	....
100	Haddock	Raw	0.04	0.07	3.0	......	....
101		Smoked (finnan haddie)	0.06	0.05	2.1	......	....
102	Halibut, Atlantic & Pacific	Raw	0.07	0.07	8.3	......	440
103		Broiled	0.05	0.07	8.3	......	680
104		Smoked	....	....	......	......	....
105	Heart, beef, lean	Raw	0.53	0.88	7.5	2	20
106		Braised	0.25	1.22	7.6	1	30
107	calf	Raw	0.63	1.05	8.1	1	30
108		Braised	0.29	1.44	8.1	Trace	40
109	chicken, all classes	Raw	0.06	0.80	4.6	4	30[2/]
110		Simmered	0.06	0.92	5.3	4	30[2/]
111	hog	Raw	0.43	1.24	6.6	3	30
112		Braised	0.20	1.72	6.7	1	40
113	lamb	Raw	0.45	0.74	6.3	1	70
114		Braised	0.21	1.03	6.4	Trace	100
115	turkey, all classes	Raw	0.23	0.86	5.0	4[2/]	30[2/]
116		Simmered	0.25	0.98	5.7	4[2/]	30[2/]
117	Herring	Canned, solids & liquid	....	0.18	......	......	....
118	Atlantic	Raw	0.02	0.15	3.6	......	110
119	Pacific	Raw	0.02	0.16	3.5	3	100
120	Kidneys, beef	Raw	0.36	2.55	6.4	15[2/]	690
121		Braised	0.51	4.82	10.7	......	1150
122	calf	Raw	....	....	......	6	....
123	hog	Raw	0.58	1.73	9.8	12	130
124	lamb	Raw	0.51	2.42	7.4	15	690
125	Lamb, leg, 83% lean & 17% fat	Raw	0.16	0.22	5.1	......	....
126		Roasted	0.15	0.27	5.5	......	....
127	loin, 72% lean & 28% fat	Raw	0.14	0.20	4.7	......	....
128	66% lean & 34% fat	Broiled	0.12	0.23	5.0	......	....
129	rib, 68% lean & 32% fat	Raw	0.14	0.19	4.4	......	....
130	62% lean & 38% fat	Broiled	0.12	0.21	4.6	......	....
131	shoulder, 74% lean & 26% fat	Raw	0.14	0.19	4.4	......	....
132		Roasted	0.13	0.23	4.7	......	....
133	Liver, beef	Raw	0.25	3.26	13.6	31	43,900
134		Fried	0.26	4.19	16.5	27	53,400
135	calf	Raw	0.20	2.72	11.4	36	22,500
136		Fried	0.24	4.17	16.5	37	32,700
137	chicken, all classes	Raw	0.19	2.49	10.8	17	12,100
138		Simmered	0.17	2.69	11.7	16	12,300
139	hog	Raw	0.30	3.03	16.4	23	10,900
140		Fried	0.34	4.36	22.3	22	14,900

[2/] Imputed, usually from another form of the food or from a similar food. [4/] Small amount of white included. [5/] Considerable amount of white included.

continued

2. COMPOSITION OF FOODS, RAW AND PROCESSED: ANIMAL ORIGIN

Part III. Vitamins

	Food	Specification	Thiamine mg	Riboflavin mg	Nicotinic Acid mg	Ascorbic Acid mg	Vitamin A I.U.
141	lamb	Raw	0.40	3.28	16.9	33	50,500
142		Broiled	0.49	5.11	24.9	36	74,500
143	turkey, all classes	Raw	0.18	1.93	13.2	......	17,700
144		Simmered	0.16	2.09	14.3	......	17,500
145	Liverwurst	Fresh	0.20	1.30	5.7	......	6350
146		Smoked	0.17	1.44	8.2	......	6530
147	Lobster, northern	Raw	0.40	0.05	1.5	......	....
148		Cooked or canned	0.10	0.07	......	......	....
149	Lungs, beef	Raw	....	....	6.2	......	....
150	calf	Raw	....	....	......	......	....
151	lamb	Raw	....	....	......	......	....
152	Mackerel	Smoked	....	....	......	......	....
153	Atlantic	Raw	0.15	0.33	8.2	......	450[2]
154		Canned, solids & liquid	0.06	0.21	5.8	......	430
155	Pacific	Raw	....	....	......	......	120
156		Canned, drained	0.03	0.33	8.8	......	30
157	Milk[6], whole	Pasteurized & raw	0.03	0.17	0.1	1	150
158		Dried	0.29	1.46	0.7	6	1130
159	skim	Pasteurized & raw	0.04	0.18	0.1	1	Trace
160	nonfat solids, instant	Dried	0.35	1.78	0.9	7	30
161	evaporated	Canned	0.04	0.34	0.2	1	320
162	Mussels, Pacific	Canned, drained	....	0.13	......	......	....
163	Atlantic & Pacific	Raw, drained	0.16	0.21	......	......	....
164	Octopus	Raw	0.02	0.06	1.8	......	....
165	Oysters	Canned, solids & liquid	0.02	0.20	0.8	......	....
166		Frozen, solids & liquid	0.14	0.18	2.5	......	310
167	eastern	Raw, drained	0.14	0.18	2.5	......	310
168	western	Raw, drained	0.12	....	1.3	30	....
169	Perch, white	Raw	....	....	......	......	....
170	yellow	Raw	0.06	0.17	1.7	......	....
171	Pickerel, chain	Raw	....	....	......	......	....
172	Pike, blue	Raw	....	....	......	......	....
173	northern	Raw	....	....	......	......	....
174	walleye	Raw	0.25	0.16	2.3	......	....
175	Pollock	Raw	0.05	0.10	1.6	......	....
176	Pompano	Raw	0.41	0.22	......	......	....
177	Porgy & scup	Raw	....	....	......	......	....
178	Pork, ham	Cured, canned (contents of can)	0.53	0.19	3.8	......	0[1]
179	74% lean & 26% fat	Raw	0.77	0.19	4.1	......	0[1]
180		Roasted	0.51	0.23	4.6	......	0[1]
181	76% lean & 24% fat	Cured, uncooked	0.72	0.19	4.1	......	0[1]
182	84% lean & 16% fat	roasted	0.47	0.18	3.6	......	0[1]
183	loin, 80% lean & 20% fat	Raw	0.83	0.20	4.4	......	0[1]
184		Roasted	0.92	0.26	5.6	......	0[1]
185	Boston butt, 79% lean & 21% fat	Raw	0.75	0.18	4.0	......	0[1]
186		Roasted	0.50	0.23	4.4	......	0[1]
187	75% lean & 25% fat	Cured, uncooked	0.71	0.19	4.0	......	0[1]
188	83% lean & 17% fat	roasted	0.53	0.21	4.1	......	0[1]
189	picnic, 74% lean & 26% fat	Raw	0.77	0.19	4.1	......	0[1]
190		Simmered	0.54	0.25	4.8	......	0[1]
191	70% lean & 30% fat	Cured, uncooked	0.69	0.19	3.9	......	0[1]
192	82% lean & 18% fat	roasted	0.52	0.20	4.0	......	0[1]
193	spareribs, medium-fat	Raw	0.70	0.17	3.8	......	0[1]
194		Braised	0.43	0.21	3.4	......	0[1]
195	Quail, flesh & skin	Raw	....	....	......	......	....

[1] Or too small to measure. [2] Imputed, usually from another form of the food or from a similar food. [6] Cow; for information on other milk, *see* Table 1.

continued

2. COMPOSITION OF FOODS, RAW AND PROCESSED: ANIMAL ORIGIN

Part III. Vitamins

	Food	Specification	Thiamine mg	Riboflavin mg	Nicotinic Acid mg	Ascorbic Acid mg	Vitamin A I.U.
196	Rabbit, domesticated, flesh only	Raw	0.08	0.06	12.8	......	....
197		Stewed	0.05	0.07	11.3	......	....
198	Rockfish, black, canary, yellowtail, rasphead, & bocaccio	Raw	0.06	0.12	......	......	....
199	Salami	Dry	0.37	0.25	5.3	......	....
200		Cooked	0.25	0.24	4.1	......	....
201	Salmon	Broiled or baked	0.16	0.06	9.8	......	160
202		Smoked	....	....	......	......	....
203	Atlantic	Raw	....	0.08	7.2	9	....
204		Canned, solids & liquid	....	....	......	......	....
205	chinook (king)	Raw	0.10	0.23	......	......	310
206		Canned, solids & liquid	0.03	0.14	7.3	......	230
207	chum	Raw	0.10	0.06	......	......	....
208		Canned, solids & liquid	0.02	0.16	7.1	......	60
209	coho (silver)	Raw	0.09	0.11	......	1	....
210		Canned, solids & liquid	0.03	0.18	7.4	......	80
211	humpback (pink)	Raw	0.14	0.05	......	......	....
212		Canned, solids & liquid	0.03	0.18	8.0	......	70
213	sockeye (red)	Raw	0.14	0.07	......	......	150
214		Canned, solids & liquid	0.04	0.16	7.3	......	230
215	Sardines, Atlantic	Canned in oil, drained	0.03	0.20	5.4	......	220
216	Pacific	Raw	....	....	......	......	....
217	Sausage, pork	Raw	0.43	0.17	2.3	......	0 1/
218		Cooked	0.79	0.34	3.7	......	0 1/
219	Vienna	Canned	0.08	0.13	2.6	......	....
220	Scallops, bay & sea	Raw	....	0.06	1.3	......	....
221		Steamed	....	....	......	......	....
222	Shad	Raw	0.15	0.24	8.4	......	....
223		Canned, solids & liquid	....	0.16	......	......	....
224	Shrimp	Raw	0.02	0.03	3.2	......	....
225		Canned, solids & liquid	0.01	0.03	1.5	......	50
226	Smelt, Atlantic, jack, & bay	Raw	0.01	0.12	1.4	......	....
227		Canned, solids & liquid	....	....	......	......	....
228	Snail	Raw	....	....	......	......	....
229	Snapper, red & gray	Raw	0.17	0.02	......	......	....
230	Squab, flesh only	Raw	....	....	6.6	......	....
231	Squid	Raw	0.02	0.12	......	......	....
232	Sturgeon	Raw	....	....	......	......	....
233		Steamed	....	....	......	......	....
234		Smoked	....	....	......	......	....
235	Sweetbreads (thymus), beef	Raw	....	....	......	......	....
236		Braised	....	....	......	......	....
237	calf	Raw	0.08	0.17	2.6	......	....
238		Braised	0.06	0.16	2.9	......	....
239	lamb	Raw	....	....	......	......	....
240		Braised	....	....	......	......	....
241	Swordfish	Raw	0.05	0.05	8.0	......	1580
242		Canned, solids & liquid	0.01	0.05	11.4	......	1580
243	Tautog (blackfish)	Raw	....	....	......	......	....
244	Terrapin, diamondback	Raw	....	....	......	......	....
245	Tongue, beef, medium-fat	Raw	0.12	0.29	5.0	......	....
246		Braised	0.05	0.29	3.5	......	....
247	calf	Raw	....	....	......	......	....
248		Braised	....	....	......	......	....
249	hog	Raw	0.17	0.29 2/	5.0 2/	......	....
250		Braised	0.07	0.29 2/	3.5 2/	......	....
251	lamb	Raw	....	....	......	......	....
252		Braised	....	....	......	......	....
253	Tripe, beef	Commercial	....	0.15	1.6	......	....
254		Pickled	....	....	......	......	....

1/ Or too small to measure. 2/ Imputed, usually from another form of the food or from a similar food.

continued

2. COMPOSITION OF FOODS, RAW AND PROCESSED: ANIMAL ORIGIN

Part III. Vitamins

	Food	Specification	Thiamine mg	Riboflavin mg	Nicotinic Acid mg	Ascorbic Acid mg	Vitamin A I.U.
255	Trout, brook	Raw	....	0.07	......	......	....
256	rainbow	Raw	0.08	0.20	8.4	......	....
257		Canned	....	....	......	......	....
258	Tuna	Canned in water, solids & liquid	....	0.10	13.3	......	....
259		Canned in oil, drained	0.05	0.12	11.9	......	80
260	bluefin	Raw	....	....	......	......	....
261	yellowfin	Raw	....	....	......	......	....
262	Turkey, flesh only	Canned	0.02	0.14	4.7	......	130
263	light meat, all classes	Raw	0.06	0.11	11.3	......	....
264		Roasted	0.05	0.14	11.1	......	....
265	dark meat, all classes	Raw	0.09	0.18	4.7	......	....
266		Roasted	0.04	0.23	4.2	......	....
267	Turtle, green	Raw	....	....	......	......	....
268		Canned	....	....	......	......	....
269	Veal, chuck, 86% lean & 14% fat	Raw	0.14	0.26	6.5	......	....
270	85% lean & 15% fat	Braised	0.09	0.29	6.4	......	....
271	flank, 61% lean & 39% fat	Raw	0.12	0.22	5.5	......	....
272	60% lean & 40% fat	Stewed	0.05	0.22	4.2	......	....
273	loin, 85% lean & 15% fat	Raw	0.14	0.26	6.4	......	....
274	77% lean & 23% fat	Broiled	0.07	0.25	5.4	......	....
275	rib, 82% lean & 18% fat	Raw	0.14	0.25	6.3	......	....
276		Roasted	0.13	0.31	7.8	......	....
277	round [7/], 87% lean & 13% fat	Raw	0.14	0.26	6.5	......	....
278	79% lean & 21% fat	Broiled	0.07	0.25	5.4	......	....
279	Venison, lean	Raw	0.23	0.48	6.3	......	....
280	Weakfish	Raw	0.09	0.06	2.7	......	....
281		Broiled	0.10	0.08	3.5	......	....
282	Whey	Fluid	0.03	0.14	0.1	......	10
283		Dried	0.50	2.51	0.8	......	50
284	Whitefish, lake	Raw	0.14	0.12	3.0	......	2260
285		Smoked	....	....	......	......	....
286	Yoghurt, from whole milk	....	0.03	0.16	0.1	1	140
287	from partially skimmed milk	....	0.04	0.18	0.1	1	70

[7/] With rump.

Contributor: Watt, Bernice K.

Reference: Watt, B. K., and A. L. Merrill. 1963. U.S. Dept. Agr. Handbook 8.

3. COMPOSITION OF FOODS, RAW AND PROCESSED: PLANT ORIGIN

Values are for 100 grams edible portion of the more common foods in their simplest form (i.e., without added salt, sugar, fats, fillers, mineral or vitamin enrichment), unless otherwise specified. For information on foods less commonly used or in combined forms, consult the reference. For data on the effect of radiation on foods, *see* Table 7. Dots instead of a value denote lack of reliable data for a constituent believed to be present in measurable amount.

Part I. General Constituents and Energy Values

	Food	Specification	Water %	Ash g	Fat g	Carbohydrates Total g	Carbohydrates Fiber g	Protein g	Food Energy cal
1	Almonds	Dried	4.7	3.0	54.2	19.5	2.6	18.6	598
2	Apples	Fresh-picked, not pared, raw	84.8	0.3	0.6	14.1	1.0	0.2	56
3		pared, raw	85.3	0.3	0.3	13.9	0.6	0.2	53
4		Stored, not pared, raw	83.9	0.4	0.7	14.8	1.0	0.2	60
5		pared, raw	84.8	0.3	0.3	14.4	0.6	0.2	55

continued

3. COMPOSITION OF FOODS, RAW AND PROCESSED: PLANT ORIGIN

Part I. General Constituents and Energy Values

	Food	Specification	Water %	Ash g	Fat g	Carbohydrates Total g	Carbohydrates Fiber g	Protein g	Food Energy cal
6		Dehydrated[1], uncooked	2.5	2.0	2.0	92.1	3.8	1.4	353
7		Dried[1], uncooked	24.0	1.6	1.6	71.8	3.1	1.0	275
8		cooked	78.4	0.5	0.5	20.3	0.9	0.3	78
9	juice	Canned or bottled	87.8	0.2	Trace	11.9	0.1	0.1	47
10	Applesauce	Canned (unsweetened)	88.5	0.3	0.2	10.8	0.6	0.2	41
11	Apricots	Raw	85.3	0.7	0.2	12.8	0.6	1.0	51
12		Canned in water, solids & liquid	89.1	0.5	0.1	9.6	0.4	0.7	38
13		Canned in juice, solids & liquid	84.5	0.7	0.2	13.6	0.4	1.0	54
14		Dehydrated[1], uncooked	3.5	5.3	1.0	84.6	3.8	5.6	332
15		Dried[1], uncooked	25.0	3.0	0.5	66.5	3.0	5.0	260
16		cooked, solids & liquid	75.6	1.0	0.2	21.6	1.0	1.6	85
17	Artichokes, Globe or French	Raw	85.5	0.8	0.2	10.6	2.4	2.9	9[2]
18		Boiled, drained	86.5	0.6	0.2	9.9	2.4	2.8	8[3]
19	Asparagus, spears	Raw	91.7	0.6	0.2	5.0	0.7	2.5	26
20		Boiled, drained	93.6	0.4	0.2	3.6	0.7	2.2	20
21		Frozen, boiled, drained	92.2	0.6	0.2	3.8	0.8	3.2	23
22	green	Canned, drained	92.5	1.3	0.4	3.4	0.8	2.4	21
23	white	Canned, drained	92.3	1.5	0.5	3.6	0.8	2.1	22
24	cuts & tips	Frozen, boiled, drained	92.5	0.6	0.2	3.5	0.8	3.2	22
25	Avocados, California[4]	Raw	73.6	1.2	17.0	6.0	1.5	2.2	171
26	Florida	Raw	78.0	0.9	11.0	8.8	1.5[5]	1.3	128
27	Bamboo shoots	Raw	91.0	0.9	0.3	5.2	0.7	2.6	27
28	Bananas, common	Raw	75.7	0.8	0.2	22.2	0.5	1.1	85
29		Dehydrated or powdered	3	3.2	0.8	88.6	2.0	4.4	340
30	Barley, light	Pearled	11.1	0.9	1.0	78.8	0.5	8.2	349
31	pot or Scotch	Pearled	10.8	1.3	1.1	77.2	0.9	9.6	348
	Beans, common, mature seeds								
32	white	Dried, uncooked	10.9	3.9	1.6	61.3	4.3	22.3	340
33		cooked	69.0	1.4	0.6	21.2	1.5	7.8	118
34	red	Dried, uncooked	10.4	3.7	1.5	61.9	4.2	22.5	343
35		cooked	69.0	1.3	0.5	21.4	1.5	7.8	118
36		canned, solids & liquid	76.0	1.5	0.4	16.4	0.9	5.7	90
37	pinto, calico, & red Mexican	Dried, uncooked	8.3	3.9	1.2	63.7	4.3	22.9	349
38	black, brown, & Bayo	Dried, uncooked	11.2	3.8	1.5	61.2	4.4	22.3	339
39	Beets, common	Raw	87.3	1.1	0.1	9.9	0.8	1.6	43
40		Boiled, drained	90.9	0.7	0.1	7.2	0.8	1.1	32
41		Canned, drained	89.3	0.8	0.1	8.8	0.8	1.0	37
42	greens	Raw	90.9	2.0	0.3	4.6	1.3	2.2	24
43		Boiled, drained	93.6	1.2	0.2	3.3	1.1	1.7	18
44	Blackberries	Raw	84.5	0.5	0.9	12.9	4.1	1.2	58
45		Canned in water, solids & liquid	89.3	0.3	0.6	9.0	2.8	0.8	40
46		Canned in juice, solids & liquid	85.8	0.5	0.8	12.1	2.7	0.8	54
47	Blueberries	Raw	83.2	0.3	0.5	15.3	1.5	0.7	62
48		Canned in water, solids & liquid	89.3	0.2	0.2	9.8	1.0	0.5	39
49		Frozen	85.0	0.2	0.5	13.6	1.5	0.7	55
50	Boysenberries	Canned in water, solids & liquid	89.8	0.3	0.1	9.1	1.9	0.7	36
51		Frozen	86.8	0.3	0.3	11.4	2.7	1.2	48
52	Brazil nuts	....	4.6	3.3	66.9	10.9	3.1	14.3	654
53	Broadbeans, immature seeds	Raw	72.3	1.1	0.4	17.8	2.2	8.4	105
54	mature seeds	Dried, uncooked	11.9	3.1	1.7	58.2	6.7	25.1	338
55	Broccoli spears	Raw	89.1	1.1	0.3	5.9	1.5	3.6	32
56		Boiled, drained	91.3	0.8	0.3	4.5	1.5	3.1	26
57		Frozen, boiled, drained	91.4	0.6	0.2	4.7	1.1	3.1	26

[1] Sulfured. [2] Fresh-picked; 47 cal for stored. [3] Fresh-picked; 44 cal for stored. [4] Mainly Fuerte. [5] Imputed, usually from another form of the food or a similar food.

continued

3. COMPOSITION OF FOODS, RAW AND PROCESSED: PLANT ORIGIN

Part I. General Constituents and Energy Values

	Food	Specification	Water %	Ash g	Fat g	Carbohydrates Total g	Carbohydrates Fiber g	Protein g	Food Energy cal
58	Brussels sprouts	Raw	85.2	1.2	0.4	8.3	1.6	4.9	45
59		Boiled, drained	88.2	0.8	0.4	6.4	1.6	4.2	36
60		Frozen, boiled, drained	89.3	0.8	0.2	6.5	1.2	3.2	33
61	Buckwheat, whole-grain	....	11.0	2.0	2.4	72.9	9.9	11.7	335
62	flour, dark	....	12	1.8	2.5	72.0	1.6	11.7	333
63	light	....	12	0.9	1.2	79.5	0.5	6.4	347
64	Cabbage, common	Raw	92.4	0.7	0.2	5.4	0.8	1.3	24
65		Boiled, drained	93.9	0.5	0.2	4.3	0.8	1.1	20
66	red	Raw	90.2	0.7	0.2	6.9	1.0	2.0	31
67	Cantaloupes, or other netted varieties	Raw	91.2	0.5	0.1	7.5	0.3	0.7	30
68	Carrots	Raw	88.2	0.8	0.2	9.7	1.0	1.1	42
69		Boiled, drained	91.2	0.6	0.2	7.1	1.0	0.9	31
70		Canned, drained	91.2	1.0	0.3	6.7	0.8	0.8	30
71	Cashew nuts	....	5.2	2.6	45.7	29.3	1.4	17.2	561
72	Cauliflower	Raw	91.0	0.9	0.2	5.2	1.0	2.7	27
73		Boiled, drained	92.8	0.6	0.2	4.1	1.0	2.3	22
74		Frozen, boiled, drained	94.0	0.6	0.2	3.3	0.8	1.9	18
75	Celeriac root	Raw	88.4	1.0	0.3	8.5	1.3	1.8	40
76	Celery, green & yellow	Raw	94.1	1.0	0.1	3.9	0.6	0.9	17
77		Boiled, drained	95.3	0.7	0.1	3.1	0.6	0.8	14
78	Cherries, sour, red	Raw	83.7	0.5	0.3	14.3	0.2	1.2	58
79		Canned in water, solids & liquid	88.0	0.3	0.2	10.7	0.1	0.8	43
80		Frozen	84.9	0.3	0.4	13.4	0.3	1.0	55
81	sweet	Raw	80.4	0.6	0.3	17.4	0.4	1.3	70
82		Canned in water, solids & liquid	86.6	0.4	0.2	11.9	0.3	0.9	48
83	Chervil	Raw	80.7	3.5	0.9	11.5	......	3.4	57
84	Chickpeas, mature seeds	Dried, uncooked	10.7	3.0	4.8	61.0	5.0	20.5	360
85	Chicory greens	Raw	92.8	1.3	0.3	3.8	0.8	1.8	20
86	Chinese cabbage	Raw	95.0	0.7	0.1	3.0	0.6	1.2	14
87	Chives	Raw	91.3	0.8	0.3	5.8	1.1	1.8	28
88	Cocoa	High-fat[6/], dry powder	3.0	5.0	23.7	48.3	4.3	16.8	299
89		Low-fat, dry powder	4.4	5.7	7.9	58.0	5.8	20.2	187
90	Coconut, flesh	Raw	50.9	0.9	35.3	9.4	4.0	3.5	346
91		Dried	3.5	1.4	64.9	23.0	3.9	7.2	662
92	liquid	Raw	94.2	0.6	0.2	4.7	Trace	0.3	22
93	Coffee	Dry powder, instant	2.6	9.7	Trace	35[5/]	Trace	Trace	129
94	Collards	Raw	86.9	1.6	0.7	7.2	0.9	3.6	40
95		Boiled, drained	90.8	1.0	0.6	4.9	0.8	2.7	29
96		Frozen, boiled, drained	90.2	0.9	0.4	5.6	1.0	2.9	30
97	Corn, sweet, on cob	Frozen, boiled, drained	73.2	0.7	1.0	21.6	0.7	3.5	94
98	kernels only	Frozen, boiled, drained	77.2	0.5	0.5	18.8	0.5	3.0	79
99	white & yellow, on cob	Raw	72.7	0.7	1.0	22.1	0.7	3.5	96
100		Boiled, drained	74.1	0.6	1.0	21.0	0.7	3.3	91
101	kernels only	Boiled, drained	76.5	0.5	1.0	18.8	0.7	3.2	83
102		Canned, wet pack, drained	75.9	0.9	0.8	19.8	0.8	2.6	84
103	yellow, kernels only	Canned, vacuum pack	75.5	1.0	0.5	20.5	0.8	2.5	83
104	flour	....	12	0.8	2.6	76.8	0.7	7.8	368
105	grits, degermed	Dry	12	0.4	0.8	78.1	0.4	8.7	362
106		Cooked	87.1	0.6	0.1	11.0	0.1	1.2	51
107	meal, white or yellow	Unbolted	12	1.2	3.9	73.7	1.6	9.2	355
108	starch	....	12	0.1	Trace	87.6	0.1	0.3	362
109	Cowpeas[7/], immature seeds	Raw	66.8	1.6	0.8	21.8	1.8	9.0	127
110		Boiled, drained	71.8	1.2	0.8	18.1	1.8	8.1	108
111		Canned, solids & liquid	81.0	1.3	0.3	12.4	0.7	5.0	70
112		Frozen[8/], boiled, drained	66.1	1.1	0.4	23.5	1.5	8.9	130

[5/] Imputed, usually from another form of the food or a similar food. [6/] Breakfast cocoa. [7/] Including blackeye peas. [8/] Blackeye peas only.

continued

3. COMPOSITION OF FOODS, RAW AND PROCESSED: PLANT ORIGIN

Part I. General Constituents and Energy Values

	Food	Specification	Water %	Ash g	Fat g	Carbohydrates Total g	Carbohydrates Fiber g	Protein g	Food Energy cal
113	mature seeds	Dried, uncooked	10.5	3.5	1.5	61.7	4.4	22.8	343
114		cooked	80.0	0.8	0.3	13.8	1.0	5.1	76
115	Crabapples	Raw	81.1	0.4	0.3	17.8	0.6	0.4	68
116	Cranberries	Raw	87.9	0.2	0.7	10.8	1.4	0.4	46
117	Cucumbers	Not pared, raw	95.1	0.5	0.1	3.4	0.6	0.9	15
118		Pared, raw	95.7	0.4	0.1	3.2	0.3	0.6	14
119	Currants, black, European	Raw	84.2	0.9	0.1	13.1	2.4	1.7	54
120	red & white	Raw	85.7	0.6	0.2	12.1	3.4	1.4	50
121	Dandelion greens	Raw	85.6	1.8	0.7	9.2	1.6	2.7	45
122		Boiled, drained	89.8	1.2	0.6	6.4	1.3	2.0	33
123	Dates, domestic	Natural & dry	22.5	1.9	0.5	72.9	2.3	2.2	274
124	Eggplant	Raw	92.4	0.6	0.2	5.6	0.9	1.2	25
125		Boiled, drained	94.3	0.4	0.2	4.1	0.9	1.0	19
126	Endive (curly endive & escarole)	Raw	93.1	1.0	0.1	4.1	0.9	1.7	20
127	Fennel, common	Raw	90.0	1.7	0.4	5.1	0.5	2.8	28
128	Figs	Raw	77.5	0.7	0.3	20.3	1.2	1.2	80
129		Canned in water, solids & liquid	86.6	0.3	0.2	12.4	0.7	0.5	48
130		Dried, uncooked	23.0	2.3	1.3	69.1	5.6	4.3	274
131	Filberts (hazelnuts)	....	5.8	2.5	62.4	16.7	3.0	12.6	634
132	Garlic cloves	Raw	61.3	1.5	0.2	30.8	1.5	6.2	137
133	Ginger root	....	87.0	1.1	1.0	9.5	1.1	1.4	49
134	Gooseberries	Raw	88.9	0.4	0.2	9.7	1.9	0.8	39
135		Canned in water, solids & liquid	92.5	0.3	0.1	6.6	1.3	0.5	26
136	Grapefruit	Canned in water, solids & liquid	91.3	0.4	0.1	7.6	0.2	0.6	30
137	California[9] & Arizona[9]	Raw	87.5	0.4	0.1	11.5	0.2	0.5	44
138	Florida[9]	Raw	89.1	0.4	0.1	9.9	0.2	0.5	38
139	Texas[9]	Raw	87.7	0.4	0.1	11.3	0.2	0.5	43
140	juice	Canned	89.2	0.4	0.1	9.8	Trace	0.5	41
141		Frozen concentrate	62	1.1	0.4	34.6	0.1	1.9	145
142	Grapes, slip skin[10]	Raw	81.6	0.4	1.0	15.7	0.6	1.3	69
143	adherent skin[11]	Raw	81.4	0.4	0.3	17.3	0.5	0.6	67
144	juice	Canned or bottled	82.9	0.3	Trace	16.6	Trace	0.2	66
145	Honeydew melons	Raw	90.6	0.6	0.3	7.7	0.6	0.8	33
146	Horseradish	Raw	74.6	2.2	0.3	19.7	2.4	3.2	87
147	Kale	Raw	87.5	1.5	0.8	6.0	1.3	4.2	38
148		Boiled, drained	91.2	0.9	0.7	4.0	1.1	3.2	28
149		Frozen, boiled, drained	90.5	0.6	0.5	5.4	0.9	3.0	31
150	Kohlrabi	Raw	90.3	1.0	0.1	6.6	1.0	2.0	29
151		Boiled, drained	92.2	0.7	0.1	5.3	1.0	1.7	24
152	Kumquats	Raw	81.3	0.6	0.1	17.1	3.7	0.9	65
153	Lemons	Raw	90.1	0.3	0.3	8.2	0.4	1.1	27
154	juice	Raw	91.0	0.3	0.2	8.0	Trace	0.5	25
155		Canned or bottled	91.6	0.3	0.1	7.6	Trace	0.4	23
156		Frozen, single-strength	92.0	0.2	0.2	7.2	Trace	0.4	22
157		concentrate	58.0	1.4	0.9	37.4	Trace	2.3	116
158	Lentils, mature seeds	Dried, uncooked	11.1	3.0	1.1	60.1	3.9	24.7	340
159		cooked	72.0	0.9	Trace	19.3	1.2	7.8	106
160	Lettuce, butterhead var.[12]	Raw	95.1	1.0	0.2	2.5	0.5	1.2	14
161	cos or romaine[13]	Raw	94.0	0.9	0.3	3.5	0.7	1.3	18
162	crisphead var.[14]	Raw	95.5	0.6	0.1	2.9	0.5	0.9	13
163	looseleaf or bunching var.[15]	Raw	94.0	0.9	0.3	3.5	0.7	1.3	18
164	Lima beans, immature seeds	Raw	67.5	1.5	0.5	22.1	1.8	8.4	123
165		Boiled, drained	71.1	1.0	0.5	19.8	1.8	7.6	111
166		Canned, drained	74.7	1.3	0.3	18.3	1.8	5.4	96

[9] Pink, red, and white. [10] American: Concord, Delaware, Niagara, Catawba, and Scuppernong. [11] European: Malaga, Muscat, Thompson Seedless, Emperor, and Flame Tokay. [12] Boston and Bibb. [13] Dark Green and Paris White. [14] Iceberg, New York, and Great Lakes strains. [15] Grand Rapids, Salad Bowl, and Simpson.

continued

3. COMPOSITION OF FOODS, RAW AND PROCESSED: PLANT ORIGIN

Part I. General Constituents and Energy Values

	Food	Specification	Water %	Ash g	Fat g	Carbohydrates Total g	Carbohydrates Fiber g	Protein g	Food Energy cal
167	Fordhook	Frozen, boiled, drained	73.5	1.3	0.1	19.1	1.6	6.0	99
168	baby	Frozen, boiled, drained	68.8	1.3	0.2	22.3	1.9	7.4	118
169	mature seeds	Dried, uncooked	10.3	3.7	1.6	64.0	4.3	20.4	345
170		cooked	64.1	1.5	0.6	25.6	1.7	8.2	138
171	Limes, acid-type	Raw	89.3	0.3	0.2	9.5	0.5	0.7	28
172	juice	Raw	90.3	0.3	0.1	9.0	Trace	0.3	26
173		Canned or bottled	90.3	0.3	0.1	9.0	Trace	0.3	26
174	Loganberries	Raw	83.0	0.5	0.6	14.9	3.0	1.0	62
175		Canned in water, solids & liquid	89.2	0.3	0.4	9.4	2.0	0.7	40
176		Canned in juice, solids & liquid	85.7	0.4	0.5	12.7	2.1	0.7	54
177	Macadamia nuts	....	3.0	1.7	71.6	15.9	2.5	7.8	691
178	Malt	Dry	5.2	2.4	1.9	77.4	5.7	13.1	368
179	Mangos	Raw	81.7	0.4	0.4	16.8	0.9	0.7	66
180	Molasses, cane, light	....	24	6.3[16]	......	65	......	....	252
181	medium	....	24	8.5[16]	......	60	......	....	232
182	Mung beans, mature seeds	Dried, uncooked	10.7	3.5	1.3	60.3	4.4	24.2	340
183	sprouts	Raw	88.8	0.6	0.2	6.6	0.7	3.8	35
184		Boiled, drained	91.0	0.4	0.2	5.2	0.7	3.2	28
185	Mushrooms[17]	Raw	90.4	0.9	0.3	4.4	0.8	2.7	28
186		Canned, solids & liquid	93.1	1.6	0.1	2.4	0.6	1.9	17
187	Mustard greens	Raw	89.5	1.4	0.5	5.6	1.1	3.0	31
188		Boiled, drained	92.6	0.8	0.4	4.0	0.9	2.2	23
189		Frozen, boiled, drained	93.8	0.5	0.4	3.1	1.0	2.2	20
190	Nectarines	Raw	81.8	0.5	Trace	17.1	0.4	0.6	64
191	Oils, salad or cooking	....	0	0	100	0	0	0	884
192	Okra	Raw	88.9	0.8	0.3	7.6	1.0	2.4	36
193		Boiled, drained	91.1	0.6	0.3	6.0	1.0	2.0	29
194		Frozen, boiled, drained	88.3	0.6	0.1	8.8	1.0	2.2	38
195	Onions, young, green, entire	Raw	89.4	0.7	0.2	8.2	1.2[5]	1.5	36
196	mature	Raw	89.1	0.6	0.1	8.7	0.6	1.5	38
197		Boiled, drained	91.8	0.4	0.1	6.5	0.6	1.2	29
198		Dehydrated flakes	4	3.9	1.3	82.1	4.4	8.7	350
199	Oranges, California, Navels[18]	Raw	85.4	0.5	0.1	12.7	0.5	1.3	51
200	Valencias[19]	Raw	85.6	0.5	0.3	12.4	0.5[5]	1.2	51
201	Florida	Raw	86.4	0.7	0.2[5]	12.0	0.5[5]	0.7	47
202	juice	Raw	88.3	0.4	0.2	10.4	0.1	0.7	45
203		Canned	87.4	0.4	0.2	11.2	0.1	0.8	48
204		Frozen concentrate	58.2	1.3	0.2	38.0	0.2	2.3	158
205	Parsley, common, & curled-leaf var.	Raw	85.1	2.2	0.6	8.5	1.5	3.6	44
206	Parsnips	Raw	79.1	1.2	0.5	17.5	2.0	1.7	76
207		Boiled, drained	82.2	0.9	0.5	14.9	2.0	1.5	66
208	Peaches	Raw	89.1	0.5	0.1	9.7	0.6	0.6	38
209		Canned in water, solids & liquid	91.1	0.3	0.1	8.1	0.4	0.4	31
210		Canned in juice, solids & liquid	87.2	0.5	0.1	11.6	0.4	0.6	45
211		Dehydrated[1], uncooked	3.0	3.3	0.9[5]	88.0	4.0[5]	4.8	340
212		Dried[1], uncooked	25.0	2.9	0.7	68.3	3.1	3.1	262
213		cooked, solids & liquid	76.5	0.9	0.2	21.4	1.0	1.0	82
214	Peanuts, with skins	Raw	5.6	2.3	47.5	18.6	2.4	26.0	564
215		Roasted	1.8	2.7	48.7	20.6	2.7	26.2	582
216	without skins	Raw	5.4	2.3	48.4	17.6	1.9	26.3	568
217	flour	Defatted	7.3	4.1	9.2	31.5	2.7	47.9	371
218	Pears	Not pared, raw	83.2	0.4	0.4	15.3	1.4	0.7	61
219		Canned in water, solids & liquid	91.1	0.2	0.2	8.3	0.7	0.2	32
220		Canned in juice, solids & liquid	87.3	0.3	0.3	11.8	0.8	0.3	46

[1] Sulfured. [5] Imputed, usually from another form of the food or a similar food. [16] Sulfated ash; ash content overestimated by 8-20%. [17] *Agaricus campestris,* cultivated commercially. [18] Winter oranges. [19] Summer oranges.

continued

3. COMPOSITION OF FOODS, RAW AND PROCESSED: PLANT ORIGIN

Part I. General Constituents and Energy Values

	Food	Specification	Water %	Ash g	Fat g	Carbo-hydrates Total g	Carbo-hydrates Fiber g	Protein g	Food Energy cal
221		Dried[1/], uncooked	26.0	1.8	1.8	67.3	6.2	3.1	268
222		cooked, solids & liquid	65.2	0.8	0.8	31.7	2.9	1.5	126
223	Peas, edible pod	Raw	83.3	1.1	0.2	12.0	1.2	3.4	53
224		Boiled, drained	86.6	0.8	0.2	9.5	1.2	2.9	43
225	green, immature seeds	Raw	78.0	0.9	0.4	14.4	2.0	6.3	84
226		Boiled, drained	81.5	0.6	0.4	12.1	2.0	5.4	71
227		Frozen, boiled, drained	82.1	0.7	0.3	11.8	1.9	5.1	68
228	Alaska[20/]	Canned, drained	77.0	1.1	0.4	16.8	2.3	4.7	88
229	sweet[21/]	Canned, drained	79.0	1.0	0.4	15.0	2.2	4.6	80
230	mature seeds, whole	Dried, uncooked	11.7	2.6	1.3	60.3	4.9	24.1	340
231	split[22/]	Dried, uncooked	9.3	2.8	1.0	62.7	1.2	24.2	348
232		cooked	70.0	0.9	0.3	20.8	0.4	8.0	115
233	Pecans	....	3.4	1.6	71.2	14.6	2.3	9.2	687
234	Peppers, hot chili, green	Raw[23/]	88.8	0.6	0.2	9.1	1.8	1.3	37
235		Canned[23/], solids & liquid	92.5	0.4	0.1	6.1	1.2	0.9	25
236	red	Raw[23/]	80.3	1.2	0.4	15.8	2.3	2.3	65
237		Dried[24/]	12.6	7.4	9.1	59.8	26.2	12.9	321
238	sweet, green	Raw	93.4	0.4	0.2	4.8	1.4	1.2	22
239		Boiled, drained	94.7	0.3	0.2	3.8	1.4	1.0	18
240	red	Raw	90.7	0.5	0.3	7.1	1.7	1.4	31
241	Pineapple	Raw	85.3	0.4	0.2	13.7	0.4	0.4	52
242		Canned in water, solids & liquid	89.1	0.3	0.1	10.2	0.3	0.3	39
243		Canned in juice, solids & liquid	84.0	0.4	0.1	15.1	0.3	0.4	58
244	juice	Canned	85.6	0.4	0.1	13.5	0.1	0.4	55
245		Frozen concentrate	53.1	1.2	0.1	44.3	0.3	1.3	179
246	Pistachio nuts	....	5.3	2.7	53.7	19.0	1.9	19.3	594
247	Plums, Damson	Raw	81.1	0.6	Trace	17.8	0.4	0.5	66
248	Greengage	Canned in water, solids & liquid	90.6	0.3	0.1	8.6	0.2	0.4	33
249	Japanese & hybrid	Raw	86.6	0.4	0.2	12.3	0.6	0.5	48
250	prune-type	Raw	78.7	0.6	0.2	19.7	0.4	0.8	75
251	purple	Canned in water, solids & liquid	86.8	0.7	0.2	11.9	0.3	0.4	46
252	Potatoes	Raw	79.8	0.9	0.1	17.1	0.5	2.1	76
253		Not pared, baked	75.1	1.1	0.1	21.1	0.6	2.6	93
254		boiled	79.8	0.9	0.1	17.1	0.5	2.1	76
255		Pared, boiled	82.8	0.7	1.1	14.5	0.5	1.9	65
256		Canned, solids & liquid	88.5	0.4	0.2	9.8	0.2	1.1	44
257		Dehydrated flakes	5.2	3.0	0.6	84.0	1.6[5/]	7.2	364
258	flour	....	7.6	3.7	0.8	79.9	1.6	8.0	351
259	Prunes	Dehydrated, uncooked	2.5	2.4	0.5	91.3	2.2[5/]	3.3	344
260		Dried[25/], uncooked	28.0	1.9	0.6	67.4	1.6	2.1	255
261		cooked, solids & liquid	66.4	0.9	0.3	31.4	0.8	1.0	119
262	juice	Canned or bottled	80	0.5	0.1	19.0	Trace	0.4	77
263	Pumpkin	Raw	91.6	0.8	0.1	6.5	1.1	1.0	26
264		Canned[26/]	90.2	0.6	0.3	7.9	1.3	1.0	33
265	Pumpkin & squash seeds	Dried	4.4	4.9	46.7	15.0	1.9	29.0	553
266	Radishes, common	Raw	94.5	0.8	0.1	3.6	0.7	1.0	17
267	Raisins	Unbleached, uncooked	18.0	1.9	0.2	77.4	0.9	2.5	289
268	Raspberries, black	Raw	80.8	0.6	1.4	15.7	5.1	1.5	73
269		Canned in water, solids & liquid	86.7	0.4	1.1	10.7	3.3	1.1	51
270	red	Raw	84.2	0.5	0.5	13.6	3.0	1.2	57
271		Canned in water, solids & liquid	90.1	0.3	0.1	8.8	2.6	0.7	35
272	Rhubarb	Raw	94.8	0.8	0.1	3.7	0.7	0.6	16
273	Rice, brown	Raw	12.0	1.2	1.9	77.4	0.9	7.5	360
274		Cooked	70.3	1.1	0.6	25.5	0.3	2.5	119

1/ Sulfured. 5/ Imputed, usually from another form of the food or a similar food. 20/ Early or June peas. 21/ Sweet wrinkled peas, sugar peas. 22/ Without seed coat. 23/ Without seeds. 24/ Pods. 25/ Softenized. 26/ May be a mixture of pumpkin and winter squash.

continued

3. COMPOSITION OF FOODS, RAW AND PROCESSED: PLANT ORIGIN

Part I. General Constituents and Energy Values

	Food	Specification	Water %	Ash g	Fat g	Carbohydrates Total g	Carbohydrates Fiber g	Protein g	Food Energy cal
275	white	Raw	12.0	0.5	0.4	80.4	0.3	6.7	363
276		Cooked	72.6	1.1	0.1	24.2	0.1	2.0	109
277	Rutabagas	Raw	87.0	0.8	0.1	11.0	1.1	1.1	46
278		Boiled, drained	90.2	0.6	0.1	8.2	1.1	0.9	35
279	Rye, whole-grain	....	11	1.8	1.7	73.4	2.0	12.1	334
280	flour, light	....	11	0.7	1.0	77.9	0.4	9.4	357
281	medium	....	11	1.1	1.7	74.8	1.0	11.4	350
282	dark	....	11	2.0	2.6	68.1	2.4	16.3	327
283	Safflower seeds	Dried	5.0	4.0	59.5	12.4	......	19.1	615
284	meal	Partially defatted	9.1	6.6	8.2	36.5	7.4	39.6	355
285	Sesame seeds	Dried	5.4	5.3	49.1	21.6	6.3	18.6	563
286	Snap beans, green	Raw	90.1	0.7	0.2	7.1	1.0	1.9	32
287		Boiled, drained	92.4	0.4	0.2	5.4	1.0	1.6	25
288		Canned, drained	91.9	1.3	0.2	5.2	1.0	1.4	24
289	French style	Frozen, boiled, drained	91.9	0.4	0.1	6.0	1.1	1.6	26
290	cut	Frozen, boiled, drained	92.1	0.5	0.1	5.7	1.0	1.6	25
291	yellow	Raw	91.4	0.7	0.2	6.0	1.0	1.7	27
292		Boiled, drained	93.4	0.4	0.2	4.6	1.0	1.4	22
293		Canned, drained	92.2	0.9	0.3	5.2	0.9	1.4	24
294	cut	Frozen, boiled, drained	91.5	0.5	0.1	6.2	1.1	1.7	27
295	Soybeans, immature seeds	Raw	69.2	1.6	5.1	13.2	1.4	10.9	134
296		Boiled, drained	73.8	1.2	5.1	10.1	1.4	9.8	118
297		Canned, drained	76.7	1.9	5.0	7.4	1.4	9.0	103
298	mature seeds	Dried, uncooked	10.0	4.7	17.7	33.5	4.9	34.1	403
299		cooked	71.0	1.5	5.7	10.8	1.6	11.0	130
300	sprouts	Raw	86.3	0.8	1.4	5.3	0.8	6.2	46
301		Boiled, drained	89.0	0.6	1.4	3.7	0.8	5.3	38
302	flour	Full-fat	8.0	4.6	20.3	30.4	2.4	36.7	421
303		Low-fat	8.0	5.3	6.7	36.6	2.5	43.4	356
304		Defatted	8.0	6.0	0.9	38.1	2.3	47.0	326
305	milk	Fluid	92.4	0.5	1.5	2.2	0	3.4	33
306		Powder	4.2	5.7	20.3	28.0	0.2	41.8	429
307	Spinach	Raw	90.7	1.5	0.3	4.3	0.6	3.2	26
308		Boiled, drained	92.0	1.1	0.3	3.6	0.6	3.0	23
309		Canned, drained	91.4	1.7	0.6	3.6	0.9	2.7	24
310	leaf	Frozen, boiled, drained	91.8	1.1	0.3	3.9	0.8	2.9	24
311	chopped	Frozen, boiled, drained	91.9	1.1	0.3	3.7	0.8	3.0	23
	Squash, summer								
312	Crook- & Straightneck	Raw	93.7	0.6	0.2	4.3	0.6	1.2	20
313		Boiled, drained	95.3	0.4	0.2	3.1	0.6	1.0	15
314	scallop var.	Raw	93.3	0.6	0.1	5.1	0.6	0.9	21
315		Boiled, drained	95.0	0.4	0.1	3.8	0.6	0.7	16
316	Zucchini & Cocozelle	Raw	94.6	0.5	0.1	3.6	0.6	1.2	17
317		Boiled, drained	96.0	0.4	0.1	2.5	0.6	1.0	12
	winter								
318	Acorn	Raw	86.3	0.9	0.1	11.2	1.4	1.5	44
319		Baked	82.9	1.1	0.1	14.0	1.8	1.9	55
320	Butternut	Raw	83.7	0.8	0.1	14.0	1.4	1.4	54
321		Baked	79.6	1.0	0.1	17.5	1.8	1.8	68
322	Hubbard	Raw	88.1	0.8	0.3	9.4	1.4	1.4	39
323		Baked	85.1	1.0	0.4	11.7	1.8	1.8	50

continued

3. COMPOSITION OF FOODS, RAW AND PROCESSED: PLANT ORIGIN

Part I. General Constituents and Energy Values

	Food	Specification	Water %	Ash g	Fat g	Carbohydrates Total g	Carbohydrates Fiber g	Protein g	Food Energy cal
324	Strawberries	Raw	89.9	0.5	0.5	8.4	1.3	0.7	37
325		Canned in water, solids & liquid	93.7	0.2	0.1	5.6	0.6	0.4	22
326	Sugar, beet or cane, brown	....	2.1	1.5	0	96.4	0	0	373
327	granulated	....	0.5	Trace	0	99.5	0	0	385
328	Sunflower seeds	Dried	4.8	4.0	47.3	19.9	3.8	24.0	560
329	Sweet potatoes	Not pared, baked	63.7	1.2	0.5	32.5	0.9	2.1	141
330		boiled	70.6	1.0	0.4	26.3	0.7	1.7	114
331		Canned, vacuum pack	71.9	1.0	0.2	24.9	1.0	2.0	108
332	firm-fleshed [27]	Raw	74.0	1.0	0.7	22.5	0.9	1.8	102
333	soft-fleshed [28]	Raw	69.7	1.0	0.3	27.3	0.7	1.7	117
334	Swiss chard	Raw	91.1	1.6	0.3	4.6	0.8	2.4	25
335		Boiled, drained	93.7	1.0	0.2	3.3	0.7	1.8	18
336	Syrup, cane	....	26	1.5	0	68	0	0	263
337	maple	....	33	0.7	......	65	......	....	252
338	sorghum	....	23	2.4	......	68	......	....	257
339	Tangerines, Dancy	Raw	87	0.4	0.2	11.6	0.5	0.8	46
340	juice	Canned	88.8	0.3	0.2	10.2	0.1 [5]	0.5	43
341	Tapioca	Dried	12.6	0.2	0.2	86.4	0.1	0.6	352
342	Tomatoes, green	Raw	93.0	0.5	0.2	5.1	0.5	1.2	24
343	ripe	Raw	93.5	0.5	0.2	4.7	0.5	1.1	22
344		Boiled	92.4	0.6	0.2	5.5	0.6	1.3	26
345		Canned, solids & liquid	93.7	0.8	0.2	4.3	0.4	1.0	21
346	juice	Canned or bottled	93.6	1.1	0.1	4.3	0.2	0.9	19
347	Turnips	Raw	91.5	0.7	0.2	6.6	0.9	1.0	30
348		Boiled, drained	93.6	0.5	0.2	4.9	0.9	0.8	23
349	greens	Raw	90.3	1.4	0.3	5.0	0.8	3.0	28
350		Boiled, drained	93.2	0.8	0.2	3.6	0.7	2.2	20
351		Canned, solids & liquid	93.7	1.3	0.3	3.2	0.7	1.5	18
352		Frozen, boiled, drained	92.7	0.6	0.3	3.9	1.0	2.5	23
353	Walnuts, black	....	3.1	2.3	59.3	14.8	1.7	20.5	628
354	Persian or English	....	3.5	1.9	64.0	15.8	2.1	14.8	651
355	Watermelons	Raw	92.6	0.3	0.2	6.4	0.3	0.5	26
356	Wheat, whole-meal	Dry	10.4	1.8	2.0	72.3	2.2	13.5	338
357		Cooked	87.7	0.8	0.3	9.4	0.3	1.8	45
358	rolled	Dry	10.1	1.8	2.0	76.2	2.2	9.9	340
359		Cooked	79.7	0.8	0.4	16.9	0.5	2.2	75
360	flour, all-purpose	....	12	0.43	1.0	76.1	0.3	10.5	364
361	whole [29]	....	12	1.7	2.0	71.0	2.3	13.3	333
362	germ, crude	....	11.5	4.3	10.9	46.7	2.5	26.6	363
363	Wild rice	Raw	8.5	1.4	0.7	75.3	1.0	14.1	353
364	Yams	Raw	73.5	1.0	0.2	23.2	0.9	2.1	101
365	Yeast, baker's	Dry (active)	5.0	8.3	1.6	38.9	......	36.9 [5]	282
366	brewer's	Debittered	5.0	7.1	1.0	38.4	1.7	38.8 [5]	283

[5] Imputed, usually from another form of the food or a similar food. [27] Refers to flesh of cooked product; Jersey types. [28] Refers to flesh of cooked product; mainly Puerto Rico variety. [29] From hard wheats.

Contributor: Watt, Bernice K.

Reference: Watt, B. K., and A. L. Merrill. 1963. U.S. Dept. Agr. Handbook 8.

continued

3. COMPOSITION OF FOODS, RAW AND PROCESSED: PLANT ORIGIN

Part II. Minerals

	Food	Specification	Calcium mg	Phosphorus mg	Iron mg	Sodium mg	Potassium mg
1	Almonds	Dried	234	504	4.7	4	773
2	Apples	Fresh-picked, not pared, raw	7	10	0.3	1	110
3		pared, raw	6	10	0.3	1	110
4		Stored, not pared, raw	7	10	0.3	1	110
5		pared, raw	6	10	0.3	1	110
6		Dehydrated[1], uncooked	40	66	2.0	7	730
7		Dried[1], uncooked	31	52	1.6	5	569
8		cooked	9	15	0.5	1	162
9	juice	Canned or bottled	6	9	0.6	1	101
10	Applesauce	Canned (unsweetened)	4	5	0.5	2	78
11	Apricots	Raw	17	23	0.5	1	281
12		Canned in water, solids & liquid	12	16	0.3	1	246
13		Canned in juice, solids & liquid	17	23	0.5	1	362
14		Dehydrated[1], uncooked	86	139	5.3	33	1260
15		Dried[1], uncooked	67	108	5.5	26	979
16		cooked, solids & liquid	22	35	1.8	8	318
17	Artichokes, Globe or French	Raw	51	88	1.3	43	430
18		Boiled, drained	51	69	1.1	30	301
19	Asparagus, spears	Raw	22	62	1.0	2	278
20		Boiled, drained	21	50	0.6	1	183
21		Frozen, boiled, drained	22	67	1.1	1	238
22	green	Canned, drained	19	53	1.9	236[2]	166
23	white	Canned, drained	16	41	1.0	236[2]	140
24	cuts & tips	Frozen, boiled, drained	22	64	1.2	1	220
25	Avocados, California[3]	Raw	10	42	0.6	4	604
26	Florida	Raw	10	42	0.6	4	604
27	Bamboo shoots	Raw	13	59	0.5	......	533
28	Bananas, common	Raw	8	26	0.7	1	370
29		Dehydrated or powdered	32	104	2.8	4	1477
30	Barley, light	Pearled	16	189	2.0	3	160
31	pot or Scotch	Pearled	34	290	2.7	......	296
	Beans, common, mature seeds						
32	white	Dried, uncooked	144	425	7.8	19	1196
33		cooked	50	148	2.7	7	416
34	red	Dried, uncooked	110	406	6.9	10	984
35		cooked	38	140	2.4	3	340
36		canned, solids & liquid	29	109	1.8	3	264
37	pinto, calico, & red Mexican	Dried, uncooked	135	457	6.4	10	984
38	black, brown, & Bayo	Dried, uncooked	135	420	7.9	25	1038
39	Beets, common	Raw	16	33	0.7	60	335
40		Boiled, drained	14	23	0.5	43	208
41		Canned, drained	19	18	0.7	236[2]	167
42	greens	Raw	119	40	3.3	130	570
43		Boiled, drained	99	25	1.9	76	332
44	Blackberries	Raw	32	19	0.9	1	170
45		Canned in water, solids & liquid	22	13	0.6	1	115
46		Canned in juice, solids & liquid	25	17	0.9	1	170
47	Blueberries	Raw	15	13	1.0	1	81
48		Canned in water, solids & liquid	10	9	0.7	1	60
49		Frozen	10	13	0.8	1	81
50	Boysenberries	Canned in water, solids & liquid	19[4]	19[4]	1.2[4]	1	85
51		Frozen	25	24	1.6	1	153
52	Brazil nuts	....	186	693	3.4	1	715
53	Broadbeans, immature seeds	Raw	27	157	2.2	4	471
54	mature seeds	Dried, uncooked	102	391	7.1	......	....

[1] Sulfured. [2] Estimated average, based on addition of salt in the amount of 0.6% of the finished product. [3] Mainly Fuerte. [4] Imputed, usually from another form of the food or a similar food.

continued

3. COMPOSITION OF FOODS, RAW AND PROCESSED: PLANT ORIGIN

Part II. Minerals

	Food	Specification	Calcium mg	Phosphorus mg	Iron mg	Sodium mg	Potassium mg
55	Broccoli spears	Raw	103	78	1.1	15	382
56		Boiled, drained	88	62	0.8	10	267
57		Frozen, boiled, drained	41	58	0.7	12	220
58	Brussels sprouts	Raw	36	80	1.5	14	390
59		Boiled, drained	32	72	1.1	10	273
60		Frozen, boiled, drained	21	61	0.8	14	295
61	Buckwheat, whole-grain	....	114	282	3.1	....	448
62	flour, dark	....	33	347	2.8	....	....
63	light	....	11	88	1.0	....	320
64	Cabbage, common	Raw	49	29	0.4	20	233
65		Boiled, drained	44	20	0.3	14	163
66	red	Raw	42	35	0.8	26	268
67	Cantaloupes, or other netted var.	Raw	14	16	0.4	12	251
68	Carrots	Raw	37	36	0.7	47	341
69		Boiled, drained	33	31	0.6	33	222
70		Canned, drained	30	22	0.7	236[2]	120
71	Cashew nuts	....	38	373	3.8	15	464
72	Cauliflower	Raw	25	56	1.1	13	295
73		Boiled, drained	21	42	0.7	9	206
74		Frozen, boiled, drained	17	38	0.5	10	207
75	Celeriac root	Raw	43	115	0.6	100	300
76	Celery, green & yellow	Raw	39	28	0.3	126	341
77		Boiled, drained	31	22	0.2	88	239
78	Cherries, sour, red	Raw	22	19	0.4	2	191
79		Canned in water, solids & liquid	15	13	0.3	2	130
80		Frozen	13	22	0.7	2	188
81	sweet	Raw	22	19	0.4	2	191
82		Canned in water, solids & liquid	15	13	0.3	1	130
83	Chervil	Raw	....	....	....	....	....
84	Chickpeas, mature seeds	Dried, uncooked	150	331	6.9	26	797
85	Chicory greens	Raw	86	40	0.9	....	420
86	Chinese cabbage	Raw	43	40	0.6	23	253
87	Chives	Raw	69	44	1.7	....	250
88	Cocoa	High-fat[5], dry powder	133	648	10.7	6	1522
89		Low-fat, dry powder	153	752	10.7	6	1522
90	Coconut, flesh	Raw	13	95	1.7	23	256
91		Dried	26	187	3.3	....	588
92	liquid	Raw	20	13	0.3	25	147
93	Coffee	Dry powder, instant	179	383	5.6	72	3256
94	Collards	Raw	203	63	1.0	43	401
95		Boiled, drained	152	39	0.6	25	234
96		Frozen, boiled, drained	176	51	1.0	16	236
97	Corn, sweet, on cob	Frozen, boiled, drained	3	96	0.8	1	231
98	kernels only	Frozen, boiled, drained	3	73	0.8	1	184
99	white & yellow, on cob	Raw	3	111	0.7	Trace	280
100		Boiled, drained	3	89	0.6	Trace	196
101	kernels only	Boiled, drained	3	89	0.6	Trace	165
102		Canned, wet pack, drained	5	49	0.5	236[2]	97
103	yellow, kernels only	Canned, vacuum pack	3	73	0.5	236[2]	97[4]
104	flour	....	6	164[4]	1.8	1[4]	....
105	grits, degermed	Dry	4	73	1.0	1	80
106		Cooked	1	10	0.1	....	11
107	meal, white or yellow	Unbolted	20	256	2.4	1[4]	284[4]
108	starch	....	0[6]	0[6]	0[6]	Trace	Trace

[2] Estimated average, based on addition of salt in the amount of 0.6% of the finished product. [4] Imputed, usually from another form of the food or a similar food. [5] Breakfast cocoa. [6] Or too small to measure.

continued

3. COMPOSITION OF FOODS, RAW AND PROCESSED: PLANT ORIGIN

Part II. Minerals

	Food	Specification	Calcium mg	Phosphorus mg	Iron mg	Sodium mg	Potassium mg
109	Cowpeas [7], immature seeds	Raw	27	172	2.3	2	541
110		Boiled, drained	24	146	2.1	1	379
111		Canned, solids & liquid	18	112	1.5	236 [2]	352
112		Frozen [8], boiled, drained	25	168	2.8	39	337
113	mature seeds	Dried, uncooked	74	426	5.8	35	1024
114		cooked	17	95	1.3	8	229
115	Crabapples	Raw	6 [4]	13	0.3 [4]	1 [4]	110 [4]
116	Cranberries	Raw	14	10	0.5	2	82
117	Cucumbers	Not pared, raw	25	27	1.1	6	160
118		Pared, raw	17	18	0.3	6	160
119	Currants, black, European	Raw	60	40	1.1	3	372
120	red & white	Raw	32	23	1.0	2	257
121	Dandelion greens	Raw	187	66	3.1	76	397
122		Boiled, drained	140	42	1.8	44	232
123	Dates, domestic	Natural & dry	59	63	3.0	1	648
124	Eggplant	Raw	12	26	0.7	2	214
125		Boiled, drained	11	21	0.6	1	150
126	Endive (curly endive & escarole)	Raw	81	54	1.7	14	294
127	Fennel, common	Raw	100	51	2.7	....	397
128	Figs	Raw	35	22	0.6	2	194
129		Canned in water, solids & liquid	14	14	0.4	2	155
130		Dried, uncooked	126	77	3.0	34	640
131	Filberts (hazelnuts)	....	209	337	3.4	2	704
132	Garlic cloves	Raw	29	202	1.5	19	529
133	Ginger root	....	23	36	2.1	6	264
134	Gooseberries	Raw	18	15	0.5	1	155
135		Canned in water, solids & liquid	12	10	0.3	1	105
136	Grapefruit	Canned in water, solids & liquid	13	14	0.3	4	144
137	California [9] & Arizona [9]	Raw	32	20	0.4	1	135
138	Florida [9]	Raw	15	15	0.4	1	135
139	Texas [9]	Raw	15	15	0.4	1	135
140	juice	Canned	8	14	0.4	1	162
141		Frozen concentrate	34	60	0.4	4	604
142	Grapes, slip skin [10]	Raw	16	12	0.4	3	158
143	adherent skin [11]	Raw	12	20	0.4	3	173
144	juice	Canned or bottled	11	12	0.3	2	116
145	Honeydew melons	Raw	14	16	0.4	12	251
146	Horseradish	Raw	140	64	1.4	8	564
147	Kale	Raw	179	73	2.2	75	378
148		Boiled, drained	134	46	1.2	43	221
149		Frozen, boiled, drained	121	48	1.0	21	193
150	Kohlrabi	Raw	41	51	0.5	8	372
151		Boiled, drained	33	41	0.3	6	260
152	Kumquats	Raw	63	23	0.4	7	236
153	Lemons	Raw	26	16	0.6	2	138
154	juice	Raw	7	10	0.2	1	141
155		Canned or bottled	7	10	0.2	1	141
156		Frozen, single-strength	7	9	0.3	1	141
157		concentrate	33	47	0.9	5	658
158	Lentils, mature seeds	Dried, uncooked	79	377	6.8	30	790
159		cooked	25	119	2.1	....	249
160	Lettuce, butterhead var. [12]	Raw	35	26	2.0	9	264
161	cos or romaine [13]	Raw	68	25	1.4	9	264

[2] Estimated average, based on addition of salt in the amount of 0.6% of the finished product. [4] Imputed, usually from another form of the food or a similar food. [7] Including blackeye peas. [8] Blackeye peas only. [9] Pink, red, and white. [10] American: Concord, Delaware, Niagara, Catawba, and Scuppernong. [11] European: Malaga, Muscat, Thompson Seedless, Emperor, and Flame Tokay. [12] Boston and Bibb. [13] Dark Green and Paris White.

continued

3. COMPOSITION OF FOODS, RAW AND PROCESSED: PLANT ORIGIN

Part II. Minerals

	Food	Specification	Calcium mg	Phosphorus mg	Iron mg	Sodium mg	Potassium mg
162	crisphead var.[14]	Raw	20	22	0.5	9	175
163	looseleaf or bunching var.[15]	Raw	68	25	1.4	9	264
164	Lima beans, immature seeds	Raw	52	142	2.8	2	650
165		Boiled, drained	47	121	2.5	1	422
166		Canned, drained	28	70	2.4	236[2]	222
167	Fordhook	Frozen, boiled, drained	20	90	1.7	101	426
168	baby	Frozen, boiled, drained	35	126	2.6	129	394
169	mature seeds	Dried, uncooked	72	385	7.8	4	1529
170		cooked	29	154	3.1	2	612
171	Limes, acid-type	Raw	33	18	0.6	2	102
172	juice	Raw	9	11	0.2	1	104
173		Canned or bottled	9	11	0.2	1	104
174	Loganberries	Raw	35	17	1.2	1[4]	170
175		Canned in water, solids & liquid	24	11	0.8	1	115
176		Canned in juice, solids & liquid	27	15	1.2	1	170
177	Macadamia nuts	....	48	161	2.0	......	264
178	Malt	Dry	....	....	4.0	......	....
179	Mangos	Raw	10	13	0.4	7	189
180	Molasses, cane, light	....	165	45	4.3	15	917
181	medium	....	290	69	6.0	37	1063
182	Mung beans, mature seeds	Dried, uncooked	118	340	7.7	6	1028
183	sprouts	Raw	19	64	1.3	5	223
184		Boiled, drained	17	48	0.9	4	156
185	Mushrooms[16]	Raw	6	116	0.8	15	414
186		Canned, solids & liquid	6	68	0.5	400	197
187	Mustard greens	Raw	183	50	3.0	32	377
188		Boiled, drained	138	32	1.8	18	220
189		Frozen, boiled, drained	104	43	1.5	10	157
190	Nectarines	Raw	4	24	0.5	6	294
191	Oils, salad or cooking	....	0	0	0	0	0
192	Okra	Raw	92	51	0.6	3	249
193		Boiled, drained	92	41	0.5	2	174
194		Frozen, boiled, drained	94	43	0.5	2	164
195	Onions, young, green, entire	Raw	51	39	1.0	5	231
196	mature	Raw	27	36	0.5	10	157
197		Boiled, drained	24	29	0.4	7	110
198		Dehydrated flakes	166	273	2.9	88	1383
199	Oranges, California, Navels[17]	Raw	40	22	0.4	1	194
200	Valencias[18]	Raw	40	22	0.8	1	190
201	Florida	Raw	43	17	0.2	1	206[4]
202	juice	Raw	11	17	0.2	1	200
203		Canned	10	18	0.4	1	199
204		Frozen concentrate	33	55	0.4	2	657
205	Parsley, common, & curled-leaf var.	Raw	203	63	6.2	45	727
206	Parsnips	Raw	50	77	0.7	12	541
207		Boiled, drained	45	62	0.6	8	379
208	Peaches	Raw	9	19	0.5	1	202
209		Canned in water, solids & liquid	4	13	0.3	2	137
210		Canned in juice, solids & liquid	6	19	0.5	2	205
211		Dehydrated[1], uncooked	62[4]	151[4]	3.5	21[4]	1229[4]
212		Dried[1], uncooked	48	117	6.0	16	950
213		cooked, solids & liquid	15	37	1.9	5	297
214	Peanuts, with skins	Raw	69	401	2.1	5	674
215		Roasted	72	407	2.2	5	701

1/ Sulfured. 2/ Estimated average, based on addition of salt in the amount of 0.6% of the finished product. 4/ Imputed, usually from another form of the food or a similar food. 14/ Iceberg, New York, and Great Lakes strains. 15/ Grand Rapids, Salad Bowl, and Simpson. 16/ *Agaricus campestris*, cultivated commercially. 17/ Winter oranges. 18/ Summer oranges.

continued

3. COMPOSITION OF FOODS, RAW AND PROCESSED: PLANT ORIGIN

Part II. Minerals

	Food	Specification	Calcium mg	Phosphorus mg	Iron mg	Sodium mg	Potassium mg
216	without skins	Raw	59	409	2.0	5	674
217	flour	Defatted	104	720	3.5	9	1186
218	Pears	Not pared, raw	8	11	0.3	2	130
219		Canned in water, solids & liquid	5	7	0.2	1	88
220		Canned in juice, solids & liquid	8	11	0.3	1	130
221		Dried[1], uncooked	35	48	1.3	7	573
222		cooked, solids & liquid	16	23	0.6	3	269
223	Peas, edible pod	Raw	62	90	0.7	....	170
224		Boiled, drained	56	76	0.5	....	119
225	green, immature seeds	Raw	26	116	1.9	2	316
226		Boiled, drained	23	99	1.8	1	196
227		Frozen, boiled, drained	19	86	1.9	115	135
228	Alaska[19]	Canned, drained	26	76	1.9	236[2]	96
229	sweet[20]	Canned, drained	25	67	1.7	236[2]	96
230	mature seeds, whole	Dried, uncooked	64	340	5.1	35	1005
231	split[21]	Dried, uncooked	33	268	5.1	40	895
232		cooked	11	89	1.7	13	296
233	Pecans	....	73	289	2.4	Trace	603
234	Peppers, hot chili, green	Raw[22]	10	25	0.7	....	....
235		Canned[22], solids & liquid	7	17	0.5	....	....
236	red	Raw[22]	16	49	1.4	25	564
237		Dried[23]	130	240	7.8	373	1201
238	sweet, green	Raw	9	22	0.7	13	213
239		Boiled, drained	9	16	0.5	9	149
240	red	Raw	13	30	0.6	....	....
241	Pineapple	Raw	17	8	0.5	1	146
242		Canned in water, solids & liquid	12	5	0.3	1	99
243		Canned in juice, solids & liquid	16	8	0.4	1	147
244	juice	Canned	15	9	0.3	1	149
245		Frozen concentrate	39	28	0.9	3	472
246	Pistachio nuts	....	131	500	7.3	....	972
247	Plums, Damson	Raw	18	17	0.5	2	299
248	Greengage	Canned in water, solids & liquid	9[4]	13[4]	0.2[4]	1	82
249	Japanese & hybrid	Raw	12	18	0.5	1	170
250	prune-type	Raw	12	18	0.5	1	170
251	purple	Canned in water, solids & liquid	9	10	1.0	2	148
252	Potatoes	Raw	7	53	0.6	3	407
253		Not pared, baked	9	65	0.7	4	503
254		boiled	7	53	0.6	3	407
255		Pared, boiled	6	42	0.5	2	285
256		Canned, solids & liquid	4[4]	30[4]	0.3[4]	1	250
257		Dehydrated flakes	35	173[4]	1.7	89	1600[4]
258	flour	....	33	178	17.2	34	1588
259	Prunes	Dehydrated, uncooked	90	107	4.4	11	940
260		Dried[24], uncooked	51	79	3.9	8	694
261		cooked, solids & liquid	24	37	1.8	4	327
262	juice	Canned or bottled	14	20	4.1	2	235
263	Pumpkin	Raw	21	44	0.8	1	340
264		Canned[25]	25	26	0.4	2	240
265	Pumpkin & squash seeds	Dried	51	1144	11.2	....	....
266	Radishes, common	Raw	30	31	1.0	18	322
267	Raisins	Unbleached, uncooked	62	101	3.5	27	763
268	Raspberries, black	Raw	30	22	0.9	1	199
269		Canned in water, solids & liquid	20	15	0.6	1	135

1/ Sulfured. 2/ Estimated average, based on addition of salt in the amount of 0.6% of the finished product. 4/ Imputed, usually from another form of the food or a similar food. 19/ Early or June peas. 20/ Sweet wrinkled peas, sugar peas. 21/ Without seed coat. 22/ Without seeds. 23/ Pods. 24/ Softenized. 25/ May be a mixture of pumpkin and winter squash.

continued

3. COMPOSITION OF FOODS, RAW AND PROCESSED: PLANT ORIGIN

Part II. Minerals

	Food	Specification	Calcium mg	Phosphorus mg	Iron mg	Sodium mg	Potassium mg
270	red	Raw	22	22	0.9	1	168
271		Canned in water, solids & liquid	15	15	0.6	1	114
272	Rhubarb	Raw	96	18	0.8	2	251
273	Rice, brown	Raw	32	221	1.6	9	214
274		Cooked	12	73	0.5	282	70
275	white	Raw	24	94	0.8	5	92
276		Cooked	10	28	0.2	374	28
277	Rutabagas	Raw	66	39	0.4	5	239
278		Boiled, drained	59	31	0.3	4	167
279	Rye, whole-grain	....	38[4/]	376	3.7	1[4/]	467
280	flour, light	....	22	185	1.1	1[4/]	156
281	medium	....	27[4/]	262	2.6	1[4/]	203
282	dark	....	54	536[4/]	4.5	1	860
283	Safflower seeds	Dried	....	....	....	....	....
284	meal	Partially defatted	75	620	....	....	....
285	Sesame seeds	Dried	1160	616	10.5	60	725
286	Snap beans, green	Raw	56	44	0.8	7	243
287		Boiled, drained	50	37	0.6	4	151
288		Canned, drained	45	25	1.5	236[2/]	95
289	French style	Frozen, boiled, drained	38	30	0.9	2	136
290	cut	Frozen, boiled, drained	40	32	0.7	1	152
291	yellow	Raw	56	43	0.8	7	243
292		Boiled, drained	50	37	0.6	3	151
293		Canned, drained	45	25	1.5	236[2/]	95
294	cut	Frozen, boiled, drained	35	31	0.7	1	164
295	Soybeans, immature seeds	Raw	67	225	2.8	....	....
296		Boiled, drained	60	191	2.5	....	....
297		Canned, drained	67	114	2.8	236[2/]	....
298	mature seeds	Dried, uncooked	226	554	8.4	5	1677
299		cooked	73	179	2.7	2	540
300	sprouts	Raw	48	67	1.0	....	....
301		Boiled, drained	43	50	0.7	....	....
302	flour	Full-fat	199	558	8.4	1	1660
303		Low-fat	263	634	9.1	1	1859
304		Defatted	265	655	11.1	1	1820
305	milk	Fluid	21	48	0.8	....	....
306		Powder	275	....	....	....	....
307	Spinach	Raw	93	51	3.1	71	470
308		Boiled, drained	93	38	2.2	50	324
309		Canned, drained	118	26	2.6	236[2/]	250
310	leaf	Frozen, boiled, drained	105	44	2.5	49	362
311	chopped	Frozen, boiled, drained	113	44	2.1	52	333
	Squash, summer						
312	Crook- & Straightneck	Raw	28	29	0.4	1	202
313		Boiled, drained	25	25	0.4	1	141
314	scallop var.	Raw	28	29	0.4	1	202
315		Boiled, drained	25	25	0.4	1	141
316	Zucchini & Cocozelle	Raw	28	29	0.4	1	202
317		Boiled, drained	25	25	0.4	1	141
	winter						
318	Acorn	Raw	31	23	0.9	1	384
319		Baked	39	29	1.1	1	480

[2/] Estimated average, based on addition of salt in the amount of 0.6% of the finished product. [4/] Imputed, usually from another form of the food or a similar food.

continued

3. COMPOSITION OF FOODS, RAW AND PROCESSED: PLANT ORIGIN

Part II. Minerals

	Food	Specification	Calcium mg	Phosphorus mg	Iron mg	Sodium mg	Potassium mg
320	Butternut	Raw	32	58	0.8	1	487
321		Baked	40	72	1.0	1	609
322	Hubbard	Raw	19	31	0.6	1	217
323		Baked	24	39	0.8	1	271
324	Strawberries	Raw	21	21	1.0	1	164
325		Canned in water, solids & liquid	14	14	0.7	1	111
326	Sugar, beet or cane, brown	....	85	19	3.4	30	344
327	granulated	....	0	0	0.1	1	3
328	Sunflower seeds	Dried	120	837	7.1	30	920
329	Sweet potatoes	Not pared, baked	40	58	0.9	12	300
330		boiled	32	47	0.7	10	243
331		Canned, vacuum pack	25	41	0.8	48	200
332	firm-fleshed[26]	Raw	32	47	0.7	10	243
333	soft-fleshed[27]	Raw	32	47	0.7	10	243
334	Swiss chard	Raw	88	39	3.2	147	550
335		Boiled, drained	73	24	1.8	86	321
336	Syrup, cane	....	60	29	3.6	....	425
337	maple	....	104	8	1.2	10	176
338	sorghum	....	172	25	12.5	....	....
339	Tangerines, Dancy	Raw	40	18	0.4	2	126
340	juice	Canned	18	14	0.2	1	178
341	Tapioca	Dried	10	18	0.4	3	18
342	Tomatoes, green	Raw	13	27	0.5	3	244
343	ripe	Raw	13	27	0.5	3	244
344		Boiled	15	32	0.6	4	287
345		Canned, solids & liquid	6	19	0.5	130	217
346	juice	Canned or bottled	7	18	0.9	200	227
347	Turnips	Raw	39	30	0.5	49	268
348		Boiled, drained	35	24	0.4	34	188
349	greens	Raw	246	58	1.8	....	....
350		Boiled, drained	184	37	1.1	....	....
351		Canned, solids & liquid	100	30	1.6	236[2]	243
352		Frozen, boiled, drained	118	39	1.6	17	149
353	Walnuts, black	....	Trace	570	6.0	3	460
354	Persian or English	....	99	380	3.1	2	450
355	Watermelons	Raw	7	10	0.5	1	100
356	Wheat, whole-meal	Dry	45	398	3.7	2	370
357		Cooked	7	52	0.5	212	48
358	rolled	Dry	36	342	3.2	2	380
359		Cooked	8	76	0.7	Trace	84
360	flour, all-purpose	....	16	87	0.8	2	95
361	whole[28]	....	41	372	3.3	3	370
362	germ, crude	....	72	1118	9.4	3	827
363	Wild rice	Raw	19	339	4.2	7	220
364	Yams	Raw	20	69	0.6	....	600
365	Yeast, baker's	Dry (active)	44[4]	1291[4]	16.1[4]	52[4]	1998[4]
366	brewer's	Debittered	70-760	1753	17.3	121	1894

[2] Estimated average, based on addition of salt in the amount of 0.6% of the finished product. [4] Imputed, usually from another form of the food or a similar food. [26] Refers to flesh of cooked product; Jersey types. [27] Refers to flesh of cooked product; mainly Puerto Rico variety. [28] From hard wheats.

Contributor: Watt, Bernice K.

Reference: Watt, B. K., and A. L. Merrill. 1963. U.S. Dept. Agr. Handbook 8.

continued

3. COMPOSITION OF FOODS, RAW AND PROCESSED: PLANT ORIGIN

Part III. Vitamins

	Food	Specification	Thiamine mg	Riboflavin mg	Nicotinic Acid mg	Ascorbic Acid mg	Vitamin A I.U.
1	Almonds	Dried	0.24	0.92	3.5	Trace	0
2	Apples	Fresh-picked, not pared, raw	0.03	0.02	0.1	7	90
3		pared, raw	0.03	0.02	0.1	4	40
4		Stored, not pared, raw	0.03	0.02	0.1	3	90
5		pared, raw	0.03	0.02	0.1	2	40
6		Dehydrated [1], uncooked	Trace	0.06	0.6	10	....
7		Dried [1], uncooked	0.06	0.12	0.5	10	....
8		cooked	0.01	0.03	0.1	Trace	....
9	juice	Canned or bottled	0.01	0.02	0.1	1	....
10	Applesauce	Canned (unsweetened)	0.02	0.01	Trace	1	40
11	Apricots	Raw	0.03	0.04	0.6	10	2700
12		Canned in water, solids & liquid	0.02	0.02	0.4	4	1830
13		Canned in juice, solids & liquid	0.03	0.03	0.5	6	2700
14		Dehydrated [1], uncooked	Trace	0.08	3.6	15	14,100
15		Dried [1], uncooked	0.01	0.16	3.3	12	10,900
16		cooked, solids & liquid	Trace	0.05	1.0	3	3000
17	Artichokes, Globe or French	Raw	0.08	0.05	1.0	12	160
18		Boiled, drained	0.07	0.04	0.7	8	150
19	Asparagus, spears	Raw	0.18	0.20	1.5	33	900
20		Boiled, drained	0.16	0.18	1.4	26	900
21		Frozen, boiled, drained	0.16	0.14	1.1	26	780
22	green	Canned, drained	0.06	0.10	0.8	15	800
23	white	Canned, drained	0.05	0.06	0.7	15	80
24	cuts & tips	Frozen, boiled, drained	0.14	0.13	1.0	23	850
25	Avocados, California [2]	Raw	0.11	0.20	1.6	14	290
26	Florida	Raw	0.11	0.20	1.6	14	290
27	Bamboo shoots	Raw	0.15	0.07	0.6	4	20
28	Bananas, common	Raw	0.05	0.06	0.7	10	190
29		Dehydrated or powdered	0.18	0.24	2.8	7	760
30	Barley, light	Pearled	0.12	0.05	3.1	0 [3]	0 [3]
31	pot or Scotch	Pearled	0.21	0.07	3.7	0 [3]	0 [3]
	Beans, common, mature seeds						
32	white	Dried, uncooked	0.65	0.22	2.4	....	0
33		cooked	0.14	0.07	0.7	0	0
34	red	Dried, uncooked	0.51	0.20	2.3	....	20
35		cooked	0.11	0.06	0.7	....	Trace
36		canned, solids & liquid	0.05	0.04	0.6	....	Trace
37	pinto, calico, & red Mexican	Dried, uncooked	0.84	0.21	2.2	....	....
38	black, brown, & Bayo	Dried, uncooked	0.55	0.20	2.2	....	30
39	Beets, common	Raw	0.03	0.05	0.4	10	20
40		Boiled, drained	0.03	0.04	0.3	6	20
41		Canned, drained	0.01	0.03	0.1	3	20
42	greens	Raw	0.10	0.22	0.4	30	6100
43		Boiled, drained	0.07	0.15	0.3	15	5100
44	Blackberries	Raw	0.03	0.04	0.4	21	200
45		Canned in water, solids & liquid	0.02	0.02	0.2	7	140
46		Canned in juice, solids & liquid	0.02	0.03	0.3	10	150
47	Blueberries	Raw	0.03 [4]	0.06 [4]	0.5 [4]	14	100
48		Canned in water, solids & liquid	0.01	0.01	0.2	7	40
49		Frozen	0.03	0.06	0.5	7	70
50	Boysenberries	Canned in water, solids & liquid	0.01 [4]	0.10 [4]	0.7 [4]	7	130
51		Frozen	0.02	0.13	1.0	13	170 [4]
52	Brazil nuts	....	0.96	0.12	1.6	....	Trace
53	Broadbeans, immature seeds	Raw	0.28	0.17	1.6	30	220
54	mature seeds	Dried, uncooked	0.50	0.30	2.5	....	70

[1] Sulfured. [2] Mainly Fuerte. [3] Or too small to measure. [4] Imputed, usually from another form of the food or a similar food.

continued

3. COMPOSITION OF FOODS, RAW AND PROCESSED: PLANT ORIGIN

Part III. Vitamins

	Food	Specification	Thiamine mg	Riboflavin mg	Nicotinic Acid mg	Ascorbic Acid mg	Vitamin A I.U.
55	Broccoli spears	Raw	0.10	0.23	0.9	113	2500
56		Boiled, drained	0.09	0.20	0.8	90	2500
57		Frozen, boiled, drained	0.06	0.11	0.5	73	1900
58	Brussels sprouts	Raw	0.10	0.16	0.9	102	550
59		Boiled, drained	0.08	0.14	0.8	87	520
60		Frozen, boiled, drained	0.08	0.10	0.6	81	570
61	Buckwheat, whole-grain	....	0.60	....	4.4	0[3]	0[3]
62	flour, dark	....	0.58	0.15	2.9	0[3]	0[3]
63	light	....	0.08	0.04[4]	0.4[4]	0[3]	0[3]
64	Cabbage, common	Raw	0.05	0 05	0.3	51[5]	130
65		Boiled, drained	0.04	0.04	0.3	33	130
66	red	Raw	0.09	0.06	0.4	61	40
67	Cantaloupes, or other netted var.	Raw	0.04	0.03	0.6	33	3400[6]
68	Carrots	Raw	0.06	0.05	0.6	8	11,000[7]
69		Boiled, drained	0.05	0.05	0.5	6	10,500
70		Canned, drained	0.02	0.03	0.4	2	15,000
71	Cashew nuts	....	0.43	0.25	1.8	....	100
72	Cauliflower	Raw	0.11	0.10	0.7	78	60
73		Boiled, drained	0.09	0.08	0.6	55	60
74		Frozen, boiled, drained	0.04	0.05	0.4	41	30
75	Celeriac root	Raw	0.05	0.06	0.7	8	....
76	Celery, green & yellow	Raw	0.03	0.03	0.3	9	270[8]
77		Boiled, drained	0.02	0.03	0.3	6	230
78	Cherries, sour, red	Raw	0.05	0.06	0.4	10	1000
79		Canned in water, solids & liquid	0.03	0.02	0.2	5	680
80		Frozen	0.04	0.07	0.3	5	1000
81	sweet	Raw	0.05	0.06	0.4	10	110
82		Canned in water, solids & liquid	0.02	0.02	0.2	3	60
83	Chervil	Raw	....	....	.....	9	....
84	Chickpeas, mature seeds	Dried, uncooked	0.31	0.15	2.0	....	50
85	Chicory greens	Raw	0.06	0.10	0.5	22	4000
86	Chinese cabbage	Raw	0.05	0.04	0.6	25	150
87	Chives	Raw	0.08	0.13	0.5	56	5800
88	Cocoa	High-fat[9], dry powder	0.11	0.46	2.4	0	30
89		Low-fat, dry powder	0.11	0.46	2.4	0	10
90	Coconut, flesh	Raw	0.05	0.02	0.5	3	0
91		Dried	0.06	0.04	0.6	0	0
92	liquid	Raw	Trace	Trace	0.1	2	0
93	Coffee	Dry powder, instant	0	0.21	30.6	0	0
94	Collards	Raw	0.20	0.31[4]	1.7[4]	92	6500
95		Boiled, drained	0.14	0.20	1.2	46	5400
96		Frozen, boiled, drained	0.06	0.14	0.6	33	6800
97	Corn, sweet, on cob	Frozen, boiled, drained	0.14	0.08	1.7	7	350[10]
98	kernels only	Frozen, boiled, drained	0.09	0.06	1.5	5	350[10]
99	white & yellow, on cob	Raw	0.15	0.12	1.7	12	400[10]
100		Boiled, drained	0.12	0.10	1.4	9	400[10]
101	kernels only	Boiled, drained	0.11	0.10	1.3	7	400[10]
102		Canned, wet pack, drained	0.03	0.05	0.9	4	350[10]
103	yellow, kernels only	Canned, vacuum pack	0.03[4]	0.06[4]	1.1[4]	5	350
104	flour	....	0.20	0.06	1.4	0[3]	340[10]
105	grits, degermed	Dry	0.13	0.04	1.2	0[3]	440[10]
106		Cooked	0.02	0.01	0.2	0[3]	60[10]
107	meal, white or yellow	Unbolted	0.38	0.11	2.0	0[3]	510[10]
108	starch	....	0[3]	0[3]	0[3]	0[3]	0[3]

[3] Or too small to measure. [4] Imputed, usually from another form of the food or a similar food. [5] Fresh-picked; 42 mg for stored. [6] Orange-fleshed varieties; 280 I.U. for green-fleshed. [7] Average for carrots marketed as fresh-picked. [8] Green varieties; 140 I.U. for yellow. [9] Breakfast cocoa. [10] Yellow varieties; white contain only a trace.

continued

3. COMPOSITION OF FOODS, RAW AND PROCESSED: PLANT ORIGIN

Part III. Vitamins

	Food	Specification	Thiamine mg	Riboflavin mg	Nicotinic Acid mg	Ascorbic Acid mg	Vitamin A I.U.
109	Cowpeas[11], immature seeds	Raw	0.43	0.13	1.6	29	370
110		Boiled, drained	0.30	0.11	1.4	17	350
111		Canned, solids & liquid	0.09	0.05	0.5	3	60
112		Frozen[12], boiled, drained	0.40	0.11	1.4	9	170
113	mature seeds	Dried, uncooked	1.05	0.21	2.2	....	30
114		cooked	0.16	0.04	0.4	....	10
115	Crabapples	Raw	0.03[4]	0.02[4]	0.1[4]	8	40[4]
116	Cranberries	Raw	0.03	0.02	0.1	11	40
117	Cucumbers	Not pared, raw	0.03	0.04	0.2	11	250
118		Pared, raw	0.03	0.04	0.2	11	Trace
119	Currants, black, European	Raw	0.05	0.05	0.3	200	230
120	red & white	Raw	0.4	0.05[4]	0.1	41	120[13]
121	Dandelion greens	Raw	0.19	0.26	......	35	14,000
122		Boiled, drained	0.13	0.16	......	18	11,700
123	Dates, domestic	Natural & dry	0.09	0.10	2.2	0	50
124	Eggplant	Raw	0.05	0.05	0.6	5	10
125		Boiled, drained	0.05	0.04	0.5	3	10
126	Endive (curly endive & escarole)	Raw	0.07	0.14	0.5	10	3300
127	Fennel, common	Raw	....	....	......	31	3500
128	Figs	Raw	0.06	0.05	0.4	2	80
129		Canned in water, solids & liquid	0.03	0.03	0.2	1	30
130		Dried, uncooked	0.10	0.10	0.7	0[3]	80
131	Filberts (hazelnuts)	....	0.46	....	0.9	Trace	....
132	Garlic cloves	Raw	0.25	0.08	0.5	15	Trace
133	Ginger root	Raw	0.02	0.04	0.7	4	10
134	Gooseberries	Raw	....	....	......	33	290
135		Canned in water, solids & liquid	....	....	......	11	200
136	Grapefruit	Canned in water, solids & liquid	0.03	0.02	0.2	30	10
137	California[14] & Arizona[14]	Raw	0.04	0.02	0.2	40	10
138	Florida[14]	Raw	0.04	0.02	0.2	37	80
139	Texas[14]	Raw	0.04	0.02	0.2	38	10[15]
140	juice	Canned	0.03	0.02	0.2	34	10
141		Frozen concentrate	0.14	0.06	0.7	138	30
142	Grapes, slip skin[16]	Raw	0.05[4]	0.03[4]	0.3[4]	4	100
143	adherent skin[17]	Raw	0.05	0.03	0.3	4	100[4]
144	juice	Canned or bottled	0.04	0.02	0.2	Trace	....
145	Honeydew melons	Raw	0.04	0.03	0.6	23	40
146	Horseradish	Raw	0.07	....	......	81	....
147	Kale	Raw	....	....	......	125	8900
148		Boiled, drained	....	....	......	62	7400
149		Frozen, boiled, drained	0.06	0.15	0.7	38	8200
150	Kohlrabi	Raw	0.06	0.04	0.3	66	20
151		Boiled, drained	0.06	0.03	0.2	43	20
152	Kumquats	Raw	0.08	0.10	......	36	600
153	Lemons	Raw	0.04	0.02	0.1	53[18]	20
154	juice	Raw	0.03	0.01	0.1	46	20
155		Canned or bottled	0.03	0.01	0.1	42	20
156		Frozen, single-strength	0.03	0.01	0.1	44	20
157		concentrate	0.14	0.06	0.3	230	80
158	Lentils, mature seeds	Dried, uncooked	0.37	0.22	2.0	....	60
159		cooked	0.07	0.06	0.6	0	20

[3] Or too small to measure. [4] Imputed, usually from another form of the food or a similar food. [11] Including blackeye peas. [12] Blackeye peas only. [13] Red currants only. [14] Pink, red, and white. [15] White-fleshed varieties; 440 I.U. for red-fleshed. [16] American: Concord, Delaware, Niagara, Catawba, and Scuppernong. [17] European: Malaga, Muscat, Thompson Seedless, Emperor, and Flame Tokay. [18] Lemons marketed in summer.

continued

3. COMPOSITION OF FOODS, RAW AND PROCESSED: PLANT ORIGIN

Part III. Vitamins

	Food	Specification	Thia-mine mg	Ribo-flavin mg	Nicotinic Acid mg	Ascorbic Acid mg	Vitamin A I.U.
160	Lettuce, butterhead var.[19/]	Raw	0.06	0.06	0.3	8	970
161	cos or romaine[20/]	Raw	0.05	0.08	0.4	18	1900
162	crisphead var.[21/]	Raw	0.06	0.06	0.3	6	330
163	looseleaf or bunching var.[22/]	Raw	0.05	0.08	0.4	18	1900
164	Lima beans, immature seeds	Raw	0.24	0.12	1.4	29	290
165		Boiled, drained	0.18	0.10	1.3	17	280
166		Canned, drained	0.03	0.05	0.5	6	190
167	Fordhook	Frozen, boiled, drained	0.07	0.05	1.0	17	230
168	baby	Frozen, boiled, drained	0.09	0.05	1.2	12	220
169	mature seeds	Dried, uncooked	0.48	0.17	1.9	....	Trace
170		cooked	0.13	0.06	0.7	....	....
171	Limes, acid-type	Raw	0.03	0.02	0.2	37	10
172	juice	Raw	0.02	0.01	0.1	32	10
173		Canned or bottled	0.02	0.01	0.1	21	10
174	Loganberries	Raw	0.03[4/]	0.04[4/]	0.4[4/]	24	200[4/]
175		Canned in water, solids & liquid	0.01	0.02	0.2	8	140
176		Canned in juice, solids & liquid	0.02	0.03	0.3	12	150
177	Macadamia nuts	....	0.34	0.11	1.3	0	0
178	Malt	Dry	0.49	0.31	9.0	....	....
179	Mangos	Raw	0.05	0.05	1.1	35	4800
180	Molasses, cane, light	....	0.07	0.06	0.2	....	....
181	medium	....	....	0.12	1.2	....	....
182	Mung beans, mature seeds	Dried, uncooked	0.38	0.21	2.6	....	80
183	sprouts	Raw	0.13	0.13	0.8	19	20
184		Boiled, drained	0.09	0.10	0.7	6	20
185	Mushrooms[23/]	Raw	0.10	0.46	4.2	3	Trace
186		Canned, solids & liquid	0.02	0.25	2.0	2	Trace
187	Mustard greens	Raw	0.11	0.22	0.8	97	7000
188		Boiled, drained	0.08	0.14	0.6	48	5800
189		Frozen, boiled, drained	0.03	0.10	0.4	20	6000
190	Nectarines	Raw	....	....	.....	13	1650
191	Oils, salad or cooking	....	0	0	0	0	....
192	Okra	Raw	0.17[4/]	0.21[4/]	1.0[4/]	31	520
193		Boiled, drained	0.13[4/]	0.18[4/]	0.9[4/]	20	490
194		Frozen, boiled, drained	0.14	0.17	1.0	12	480
195	Onions, young, green, entire	Raw	0.05	0.05	0.4	32	2000[4/]
196	mature	Raw	0.03	0.04	0.2	10	40[10/]
197		Boiled, drained	0.03	0.03	0.2	7	40[10/]
198		Dehydrated flakes	0.25	0.18	1.4	35	200[10/]
199	Oranges, California, Navels[24/]	Raw	0.10	0.04	0.4	61[4/]	200[4/]
200	Valencias[25/]	Raw	0.10	0.04	0.4	49[4/]	200[4/]
201	Florida	Raw	0.10	0.04	0.4	45[4/]	200[4/]
202	juice	Raw	0.09	0.03	0.4	50[26/]	200
203		Canned	0.07	0.02	0.3	40	200
204		Frozen concentrate	0.30	0.05	1.2	158	710
205	Parsley, common, & curled-leaf var.	Raw	0.12	0.26	1.2	172	8500
206	Parsnips	Raw	0.08	0.09	0.2	16[27/]	30
207		Boiled, drained	0.07	0.08	0.1	10	30
208	Peaches	Raw	0.02	0.05	1.0	7	1330[28/]
209		Canned in water, solids & liquid	0.01	0.03	0.6	3	450
210		Canned in juice, solids & liquid	0.01	0.04	0.9	4	670

[4/] Imputed, usually from another form of the food or a similar food. [10/] Yellow varieties; white contain only a trace. [19/] Boston and Bibb. [20/] Dark Green and Paris White. [21/] Iceberg, New York, and Great Lakes strains. [22/] Grand Rapids, Salad Bowl, and Simpson. [23/] *Agaricus campestris,* cultivated commercially. [24/] Winter oranges. [25/] Summer oranges. [26/] Value weighted by monthly and total season shipment for marketing as fresh fruit. [27/] Year-round average. Within 3 months of harvest, content is 24 mg; if storage exceeds 6 months, value drops below 12 mg. [28/] Yellow-fleshed varieties; 50 I.U. for white-fleshed.

continued

3. COMPOSITION OF FOODS, RAW AND PROCESSED: PLANT ORIGIN

Part III. Vitamins

	Food	Specification	Thiamine mg	Riboflavin mg	Nicotinic Acid mg	Ascorbic Acid mg	Vitamin A I.U.
211		Dehydrated[1/], uncooked	Trace	0.10	7.8	14	5000[4/]
212		Dried[1/], uncooked	0.01	0.19	5.3	18	3900
213		cooked, solids & liquid	Trace	0.06	1.5	2	1220
214	Peanuts, with skins	Raw	1.14	0.13	17.2	0	....
215		Roasted	0.32	0.13	17.1	0	....
216	without skins	Raw	0.99	0.13	15.8	0	0
217	flour	Defatted	0.75	0.22	27.8	0	....
218	Pears	Not pared, raw	0.02	0.04	0.1	4	20
219		Canned in water, solids & liquid	0.01	0.02	0.1	1	Trace
220		Canned in juice, solids & liquid	0.02	0.03	0.1	2	Trace
221		Dried[1/], uncooked	0.01	0.18	0.6	7	70
222		cooked, solids & liquid	Trace	0.08	0.3	2	30
223	Peas, edible pod	Raw	0.28	0.12	......	21	680[4/]
224		Boiled, drained	0.22	0.11	......	14	610[4/]
225	green, immature seeds	Raw	0.35	0.14	2.9	27	640
226		Boiled, drained	0.28	0.11	2.3	20	540
227		Frozen, boiled, drained	0.27	0.09	1.7	13	600
228	Alaska[29/]	Canned, drained	0.09	0.06	0.8	8	690
229	sweet[30/]	Canned, drained	0.11	0.06	1.0	8	690
230	mature seeds, whole	Dried, uncooked	0.74	0.29	3.0	....	120
231	split[31/]	Dried, uncooked	0.74	0.29	3.0	....	120
232		cooked	0.15	0.09	0.9	....	40
233	Pecans	....	0.86	0.13	0.9	2	130
234	Peppers, hot chili, green	Raw[32/]	0.09	0.06	1.7	235	770
235		Canned[32/], solids & liquid	0.02	0.05	0.8	68	610
236	red	Raw[32/]	0.1	0.2	2.9	369	21,600
237		Dried[33/]	0.23	1.33	10.5	12[34/]	77,000
238	sweet, green	Raw	0.08	0.08	0.5	128	420
239		Boiled, drained	0.06	0.07	0.5	96	420
240	red	Raw	0.08[4/]	0.08[4/]	0.5[4/]	204	4450
241	Pineapple	Raw	0.09	0.03	0.2	17	70
242		Canned in water, solids & liquid	0.08	0.02	0.2	7	50
243		Canned in juice, solids & liquid	0.10	0.03	0.3	10	60
244	juice	Canned	0.05	0.02	0.2	9	50
245		Frozen concentrate	0.23	0.06	0.9	42	50
246	Pistachio nuts	....	0.67	....	1.4	0	230
247	Plums, Damson	Raw	0.08	0.03	0.5	....	300[4/]
248	Greengage	Canned in water, solids & liquid	0.01[4/]	0.02[4/]	0.3[4/]	2	160[4/]
249	Japanese & hybrid	Raw	0.03	0.03	0.5	6	250
250	prune-type	Raw	0.03	0.03	0.5	4	300[35/]
251	purple	Canned in water, solids & liquid	0.02	0.02	0.4	2	1250
252	Potatoes	Raw	0.10	0.04	1.5	20[36/]	Trace
253		Not pared, baked	0.10	0.04	1.7	20	Trace
254		boiled	0.09	0.04	1.5	16	Trace
255		Pared, boiled	0.09	0.03	1.2	16	Trace
256		Canned, solids & liquid	0.04	0.02	0.6	13	Trace
257		Dehydrated flakes	0.23	0.06	5.4	32(10-35)	Trace
258	flour	....	0.42	0.14	3.4	19[4/]	Trace
259	Prunes	Dehydrated, uncooked	0.12	0.22	2.1	4	2170
260		Dried[37/], uncooked	0.09	0.17	1.6	3	1600
261		cooked, solids & liquid	0.03	0.07	0.7	1	750
262	juice	Canned or bottled	0.01	0.01	0.4	2	....

1/ Sulfured. 4/ Imputed, usually from another form of the food or a similar food. 29/ Early or June peas. 30/ Sweet wrinkled peas, sugar peas. 31/ Without seed coat. 32/ Without seeds. 33/ Pods. 34/ Ground powder, stored; 154 mg for fresh-processed. 35/ All prune-type, except Italian and Imperial which average 1340 I.U. 36/ Year-round average. Fresh-picked contain 26 mg; after 3 months' storage, value is half as high, and after 6 months', approximately one-third. 37/ Softenized.

continued

Part III. Vitamins

No.	Food	Specification	Thiamine mg	Riboflavin mg	Nicotinic Acid mg	Ascorbic Acid mg	Vitamin A I.U.
263	Pumpkin	Raw	0.05	0.11	0.6	9	1600
264		Canned [38]	0.03	0.05	0.6	5	6400
265	Pumpkin & squash seeds	Dried	0.24	0.19	2.4	....	70
266	Radishes, common	Raw	0.03	0.03	0.3	26	10
267	Raisins	Unbleached, uncooked	0.11	0.08	0.5	1	20
268	Raspberries, black	Raw	0.03 [4]	0.09 [4]	0.9 [4]	18	Trace
269		Canned in water, solids & liquid	0.01	0.04	0.5	6	Trace
270	red	Raw	0.03	0.09	0.9	25	130
271		Canned in water, solids & liquid	0.01	0.04	0.5	9	90
272	Rhubarb	Raw	0.03 [4]	0.07 [4]	0.3 [4]	9	100
273	Rice, brown	Raw	0.34	0.05	4.7	0 [3]	0 [3]
274		Cooked	0.09	0.02	1.4	0 [3]	0 [3]
275	white	Raw	0.07	0.03	1.6	0 [3]	0 [3]
276		Cooked	0.02	0.01	0.4	0 [3]	0 [3]
277	Rutabagas	Raw	0.07	0.07	1.1	43	580
278		Boiled, drained	0.06	0.06	0.8	26	550
279	Rye, whole-grain	....	0.43	0.22	1.6	0 [3]	0 [3]
280	flour, light	....	0.15	0.07	0.6	0 [3]	0 [3]
281	medium	....	0.30	0.12	2.5	0 [3]	0 [3]
282	dark	....	0.61	0.22	2.7	0 [3]	0 [3]
283	Safflower seeds	Dried	....	....	......	....	....
284	meal	Partially defatted	1.12	0.40	2.2	0	....
285	Sesame seeds	Dried	0.98	0.24	5.4	0	30
286	Snap beans, green	Raw	0.08	0.11	0.5	19	600
287		Boiled, drained	0.07	0.09	0.5	12	540
288		Canned, drained	0.03	0.05	0.3	4	470
289	French style	Frozen, boiled, drained	0.06	0.08	0.3	7	530
290	cut	Frozen, boiled, drained	0.07	0.09	0.4	5	580
291	yellow	Raw	0.08	0.11	0.5	20	250
292		Boiled, drained	0.07	0.09	0.5	13	230
293		Canned, drained	0.03	0.05	0.3	5	100
294	cut	Frozen, boiled, drained	0.07	0.08	0.4	6	100
295	Soybeans, immature seeds	Raw	0.44	0.16	1.4	29	690
296		Boiled, drained	0.31	0.13	1.2	17	660
297		Canned, drained	0.06	....	......	2	340
298	mature seeds	Dried, uncooked	1.10	0.31	2.2	....	80
299		cooked	0.21	0.09	0.6	0	30
300	sprouts	Raw	0.23	0.20	0.8	13	80
301		Boiled, drained	0.16	0.15	0.7	4	80
302	flour	Full-fat	0.85	0.31	2.1	0	110
303		Low-fat	0.83	0.36	2.6	0	80
304		Defatted	1.09	0.34	2.6	0	40
305	milk	Fluid	0.08	0.03	0.2	0	40
306		Powder	....	....	......	....	....
307	Spinach	Raw	0.10	0.20	0.6	51	8100
308		Boiled, drained	0.07	0.14	0.5	28	8100
309		Canned, drained	0.02	0.12	0.3	14	8000
310	leaf	Frozen, boiled, drained	0.08	0.14	0.5	28	8100
311	chopped	Frozen, boiled, drained	0.07	0.15	0.4	19	7900
	Squash, summer						
312	Crook- & Straightneck	Raw	0.05	0.09	1.0	25	460
313		Boiled, drained	0.05	0.08	0.8	11	440
314	scallop var.	Raw	0.05	0.09	1.0	18	190
315		Boiled, drained	0.05	0.08	0.8	8	180

[3] Or too small to measure. [4] Imputed, usually from another form of the food or a similar food. [38] May be a mixture of pumpkin and winter squash.

continued

Part III. Vitamins

	Food	Specification	Thiamine mg	Riboflavin mg	Nicotinic Acid mg	Ascorbic Acid mg	Vitamin A I.U.
316	Zucchini & Cocozelle	Raw	0.05	0.09	1.0	19	320[39]
317		Boiled, drained	0.05	0.08	0.8	9	300[39]
	winter						
318	Acorn	Raw	0.05	0.11	0.6	14	1200[40]
319		Baked	0.05	0.13	0.7	13	1400[40]
320	Butternut	Raw	0.05	0.11	0.6	9	5700[40]
321		Baked	0.05	0.13	0.7	8	6400[40]
322	Hubbard	Raw	0.05	0.11	0.6	11	4300[40]
323		Baked	0.05	0.13	0.7	10	4800[40]
324	Strawberries	Raw	0.03	0.07	0.6	59	60
325		Canned in water, solids & liquid	0.01	0.03	0.4	20	40
326	Sugar, beet or cane, brown	....	0.01	0.03	0.2	0	0
327	granulated	....	0	0	0	0	0
328	Sunflower seeds	Dried	1.96	0.23	5.4	....	50
329	Sweet potatoes	Not pared, baked	0.09	0.07	0.7	22	8100
330		boiled	0.09	0.06	0.6	17	7900
331		Canned, vacuum pack	0.05	0.04	0.6	14	7800
332	firm-fleshed[41]	Raw	0.10	0.06	0.6	23	10,000[42]
333	soft-fleshed[43]	Raw	0.10	0.06	0.6	20	8,000-20,000
334	Swiss chard	Raw	0.06	0.17	0.5	32	6500
335		Boiled, drained	0.04	0.11	0.4	16	5400
336	Syrup, cane	....	0.13	0.06	0.1	0	0
337	maple	....	....	....	.....	0	....
338	sorghum	....	....	0.10	0.1	....	....
339	Tangerines, Dancy	Raw	0.06	0.02	0.1	31	420
340	juice	Canned	0.06[4]	0.02[4]	0.1[4]	22	420
341	Tapioca	Dried	0[3]	0[3]	0[3]	0[3]	0[3]
342	Tomatoes, green	Raw	0.06	0.04	0.5	20	270
343	ripe	Raw	0.06	0.04	0.7	23[44]	900
344		Boiled	0.07	0.05	0.8	24	1000
345		Canned, solids & liquid	0.05	0.03	0.7	17	900
346	juice	Canned or bottled	0.05	0.03	0.8	16	800
347	Turnips	Raw	0.04	0.07	0.6	36	Trace
348		Boiled, drained	0.04	0.05	0.3	22	Trace
349	greens	Raw	0.21[4]	0.39[4]	0.8[4]	139	7600
350		Boiled, drained	0.15	0.24	0.6	69	6300
351		Canned, solids & liquid	0.02	0.09	0.6	19	4700
352		Frozen, boiled, drained	0.05	0.09	0.4	19	6900
353	Walnuts, black	....	0.22	0.11	0.7	....	300
354	Persian or English	....	0.33	0.13	0.9	2	30
355	Watermelons	Raw	0.03	0.03	0.2	7	590
356	Wheat, whole-meal	Dry	0.51	0.13	4.7	0[3]	0[3]
357		Cooked	0.06	0.02	0.6	0[3]	0[3]
358	rolled	Dry	0.36	0.12	4.1	0[3]	0[3]
359		Cooked	0.07	0.03	0.9	0[3]	0[3]
360	flour, all-purpose	....	0.06	0.05	0.9	0[3]	0[3]
361	whole[45]	....	0.55	0.12	4.3	0[3]	0[3]
362	germ, crude	....	2.01	0.68	4.2	0[3]	0[3]
363	Wild rice	Raw	0.45	0.63	6.2	0[3]	0[3]
364	Yams	Raw	0.10	0.04	0.5	9	Trace
365	Yeast, baker's	Dry (active)	2.33	5.41	36.7	Trace	Trace
366	brewer's	Debittered	15.61	4.28	37.9	Trace	Trace

[3] Or too small to measure. [4] Imputed, usually from another form of the food or a similar food. [39] Includes skin; flesh contains no appreciable vitamin A. [40] Fresh-picked; carotenoid content increases during storage. [41] Refers to flesh of cooked product; Jersey types. [42] Varieties with deep-orange flesh; 600 I.U. for light yellow. [43] Refers to flesh of cooked product; mainly Puerto Rico variety. [44] Year-round average. Tomatoes marketed November-May average 10 mg; June-October, 26 mg. [45] From hard wheats.

continued

3. COMPOSITION OF FOODS, RAW AND PROCESSED: PLANT ORIGIN

Part III. Vitamins

Contributor: Watt, Bernice K.

Reference: Watt, B. K., and A. L. Merrill. 1963. U.S. Dept. Agr. Handbook 8.

4. FATTY ACID COMPOSITION OF FOODS AND FEEDS: ANIMAL AND PLANT ORIGIN

Values are percent by weight of the total fatty acids in the lipid extract. Fatty acids present in very small amounts and of no known biological importance have been omitted. All the analyses utilized in this compilation were obtained by gas liquid chromatography. Fatty acid symbols are shown in brackets. For additional information, consult Hilditch, T. P., and P. N. Wilhans, 1964, *The Chemical Constitution of Natural Fats,* 4th ed., J. Wiley, New York; and Goddard, V. R., and L. Goodall, 1959, *Fatty Acids in Animal and Plant Products,* Human Nutrition Research Division, Agricultural Research Service, U.S. Dept. of Agriculture, Washington, D.C. Values are means, ± the standard deviation.

Part I. Saturated Fatty Acids

	Food or Feed	No. of Analyses	Arachidic [20:0]	Lauric [12:0]	Myristic [14:0]	Palmitic [16:0]	Stearic [18:0]	Reference
					Animal Origin			
1	Beef, heart	1	....	....	....	13.0	16.8	25
2	kidney	1	....	....	....	16.8	18.6	25
3	liver	1	....	....	....	12.7	33.9	25
4	rib	3	....	....	3.5 ± 0.1	31.0 ± 0.4	17.6 ± 2.0	9
5	tallow	2	....	....	3.5	28.4	20.4	1,7
6	tongue	1	....	....	3.7	28.0	10.8	25
7	Chicken, breast	1	....	0.2	0.6	19.4	7.5	18
8	heart	2	....	....	0.4	22.1	7.6	17
9	liver	2	....	....	0.2	25.9	14.8	17
10	skin	1	....	....	0.8	16.1	4.6	18
11	thigh	1	....	0.8	0.5	16.2	6.0	18
12	Crab meal	1	....	....	2.7	21.1	3.2	7
13	Eggs, whole	5	....	....	0.1	25.5 ± 0.1	8.9 ± 0.4	8
14	Feather meal	3	1.7 ± 0.6	0.2 ± 0.1	1.9 ± 0.3	29.9 ± 1.0	14.6 ± 0.1	7
15	Fish, freshwater	3	....	....	3.3 ± 1.1	13.9 ± 1.9	3.7 ± 0.3	11
16	saltwater, light meat	12	....	....	4.6 ± 0.5	25.9 ± 0.7	6.0 ± 0.6	24
17	dark meat	12	....	....	4.3 ± 0.5	21.5 ± 2.1	5.2 ± 0.8	11,24
18	solubles, condensed	3	....	....	12.9 ± 1.5	27.8 ± 1.3	3.5 ± 0.5	7
19	Lard	1	....	....	0.9	24.4	10.6	7
20	Meat scraps	3	....	....	2.6	2.8 ± 0.8	16.5 ± 2.5	7
21	Menhaden, meal	3	....	0.1 ± 0.1	12.2 ± 0.9	38.4 ± 0.9	6.1 ± 2.2	7
22	oil	3	....	....	9.4 ± 2.4	18.9 ± 4.2	5.0 ± 0.7	7
23	Milk, skim	3	....	....	3.9 ± 0.4	21.9 ± 2.3	10.4 ± 1.0	7
24	Mutton, adipose fat	4	....	....	2.3	22.9 ± 0.4	26.8 ± 5.8	22
25	meat fat	4	....	....	2.6 ± 0.1	23.4 ± 0.9	13.9 ± 0.5	22
26	Pork, back fat	4	....	0.2 ± 0.1	1.5 ± 0.1	23.2 ± 0.6	10.9 ± 0.1	3
27	bacon	4	....	0.1 ± 0.1	1.5 ± 0.1	24.6 ± 0.4	11.7 ± 0.5	3
28	Boston butt	4	....	0.2 ± 0.1	1.6 ± 0.1	23.1 ± 0.3	9.2 ± 0.1	3
29	chop	4	....	0.2 ± 0.1	1.7 ± 0.1	24.7 ± 0.4	10.5 ± 0.2	3
30	ham	4	....	0.2 ± 0.1	1.5 ± 0.1	23.2 ± 0.6	10.9 ± 0.1	3
31	heart	4	....	0.3 ± 0.1	2.1 ± 0.2	20.4 ± 0.5	13.0 ± 0.7	3
32	kidney	4	....	0.2 ± 0.1	1.8 ± 0.1	2.0 ± 0.1	34.2 ± 2.1	3
33	liver	4	....	0.2 ± 0.1	0.5 ± 0.1	20.9 ± 0.7	20.8 ± 1.2	3
34	picnic shoulder	4	....	0.1 ± 0.1	1.6 ± 0.1	22.9 ± 0.2	8.7 ± 0.2	3

continued

4. FATTY ACID COMPOSITION OF FOODS AND FEEDS: ANIMAL AND PLANT ORIGIN

Part I. Saturated Fatty Acids

	Food or Feed	No. of Analyses	Arachidic [20:0]	Lauric [12:0]	Myristic [14:0]	Palmitic [16:0]	Stearic [18:0]	Reference
35	skin	4	....	0.3 ± 0.1	1.8 ± 0.1	21.8 ± 0.9	6.4 ± 0.2	3
36	tongue	4	....	0.2 ± 0.1	1.5 ± 0.1	23.0 ± 0.3	8.4 ± 0.1	3
37	Poultry, offal oil	3	....	0.2 ± 0.1	1.4 ± 0.1	21.4 ± 0.2	5.9	7
38	products, meal	2	....	....	1.9	21.9	12.3	7
39	Sheep, adipose tissue	6	....	....	3.3 ± 0.3	26.2 ± 0.9	18.2 ± 1.6	26
40	Shellfishes	4	....	....	2.5 ± 0.3	20.9 ± 1.9	5.5 ± 0.7	11
41	Tankage	3	....	....	2.0 ± 0.3	28.3 ± 2.3	19.1 ± 6.6	7
42	Whey, dried	3	....	2.7 ± 0.2	12.8 ± 0.6	37.9 ± 2.1	10.2 ± 2.6	7
				Plant Origin				
43	Alfalfa meal	6	....	1.7 ± 0.5	0.5 ± 0.1	25.8 ± 1.7	3.8 ± 1.3	7
44	Apples, whole	5	6.4 ± 0.8	0.3 ± 0.1	....	15.6 ± 3.1	8.7 ± 0.5	19
45	Barley, whole	3	....	0.5 ± 0.1	....	27.6 ± 2.4	1.5 ± 0.3	7
46	Beet pulp	1	....	....	....	34.6	....	7
47	Bread, white[1/]	9	....	0.8 ± 0.3	2.6 ± 0.8	23.3 ± 1.9	9.2 ± 0.8	10
48	Cake mix, commerical[1/]	9	....	0.2 ± 0.1	1.9 ± 0.1	24.3 ± 0.4	19.3 ± 0.9	21
49	Citrus pulp	2	....	....	....	32.1	1.8	7
50	Coconut oil	2	....	42.4	15.5	10.7	2.7	1,7
51	Corn, whole	6	....	....	....	16.3 ± 1.0	2.6 ± 0.3	7
52	gluten feed	3	....	....	0.1 ± 0.1	20.2 ± 0.2	2.5 ± 1.0	7
53	gluten meal	3	....	....	....	17.2 ± 0.5	0.8 ± 0.1	7
54	oil	8	....	0.1	....	11.4 ± 1.1	2.0 ± 0.1	1,4,7,12
55	Cottonseed, meal	3	....	....	0.5	31.4 ± 0.6	0.6 ± 0.1	7
56	oil	7	....	....	0.8	20.9 ± 0.3	1.9	7,12
57	Distiller's solubles	3	....	....	....	20.0 ± 0.9	1.0 ± 0.3	7
58	Hominy feed	3	....	....	....	14.0 ± 0.3	2.0 ± 0.5	7
59	Lima beans, whole	3	....	....	....	26.0 ± 3.5	3.3 ± 0.1	13
60	Linseed, meal	3	....	....	0.8 ± 0.6	17.7 ± 1.5	2.4 ± 0.5	7
61	oil	4	....	....	....	6.4 ± 0.2	3.3 ± 0.4	4,7
62	Mayonnaise, commercial[1/]	9	....	....	0.2	12.6 ± 0.9	3.4 ± 0.6	6
63	Milo sorghum, whole	2	....	....	....	20.0	1.0	7
64	Oats, whole	3	....	....	0.2 ± 0.1	23.3 ± 0.9	2.0 ± 0.3	7
65	Olive oil	4	....	....	....	13.3 ± 0.3	2.9 ± 0.3	4
66	Palm oil	2	....	....	1.8	42.0	5.4	24
67	Peanut, butter	3	1.0 ± 0.1	....	....	11.7 ± 0.3	5.8 ± 0.6	23
68	meal (55%[2/])	1	....	....	....	20.8	3.1	7
69	oil	5	1.1 ± 0.2	....	....	11.1 ± 0.8	3.0 ± 0.2	3,4,12
70	Pecan oil	1	....	....	....	6.1	0.8	7
71	Pie crust, commercial[1/]	3	....	....	2.0 ± 0.2	23.6 ± 0.9	13.0 ± 0.9	21
72	Rapeseed oil	3	....	....	....	1.7 ± 0.4	0.1 ± 0.1	2
73	Rice, whole	2	0.5	....	1.0	26.0	1.8	14
74	bran oil	1	....	0.5	0.5	17.0	0.5	7
75	Safflower oil	3	0.2 ± 0.1	....	....	7.1 ± 0.4	2.2 ± 0.2	7,12,16
76	Soybeans, whole	2	....	....	0.5	14.3	1.6	7
77	flour	2	....	....	....	14.9	3.9	5
78	meal (44%[2/])	3	....	....	....	23.4 ± 0.6	4.1 ± 0.7	7
79	(50%[2/])	3	....	....	0.3 ± 0.1	23.8 ± 1.3	4.7 ± 0.8	7
80	mill feed	3	....	....	0.2	18.6 ± 5.0	0.9 ± 0.9	7
81	oil	7	....	....	....	9.7 ± 1.7	4.0 ± 0.1	4,15
82	Sunflowers, whole	3	....	....	....	6.8 ± 0.2	3.9 ± 0.1	4
83	Tung oil	1	....	....	....	1.8	1.8	7
84	Wheat, whole	2	....	....	....	21.3	1.0	5,20
85	Yeast, brewer's, dried	1	....	....	1.0	14.5	7.2	7

[1/] Composed of animal as well as plant substances. [2/] Protein.

continued

4. FATTY ACID COMPOSITION OF FOODS AND FEEDS: ANIMAL AND PLANT ORIGIN

Part I. Saturated Fatty Acids

Contributor: Edwards, Hardy M., Jr.

References

[1] Alford, J. A., et al. 1961. J. Food Sci. 26:234.
[2] Beadle, J. B., et al. 1965. J. Am. Oil Chem. Soc. 42:90.
[3] Chung, R. A., and C. C. Lin. 1965. J. Food Sci. 30:860.
[4] Craig, B. M., and N. L. Murtz. 1959. J. Am. Oil Chem. Soc. 36:549.
[5] Daniels, N. W. R., et al. 1966. J. Sci. Food Agr. 17:20.
[6] Eastwood, G., et al. 1963. J. Am. Dietet. Assoc. 42:518.
[7] Edwards, H. M., Jr. 1964. Georgia Agr. Expt. Sta. Tech. Bull. 36.
[8] Edwards, H. M., Jr. 1964. Poultry Sci. 43:751.
[9] Edwards, R. L., et al. 1961. J. Animal Sci. 20:712.
[10] Fleischman, A., G. Eastwood, and M. Davis. 1963. J. Am. Dietet. Assoc. 43:537.
[11] Gruger, E. H., Jr., R. W. Nelson, and M. E. Stansby. 1964. J. Am. Oil Chem. Soc. 41:662.
[12] Hivon, K., S. N. Hagan, and E. B. Wile. 1964. Ibid. 41:362.
[13] Korytnyk, W., and E. A. Metzler. 1963. J. Sci. Food Agr. 14:841.
[14] Lee, T., W. T. Wu, and B. R. Williams. 1965. Cereal Chem. 42:498.
[15] Lugay, J. C., and B. O. Juliano. 1964. J. Am. Oil Chem. Soc. 41:275.
[16] Magidman, P., et al. 1963. Ibid. 40:86.
[17] Marion, J. E., and H. M. Edwards, Jr. 1964. Poultry Sci. 43:911.
[18] Marion, J. E., and J. G. Woodroof. 1963. Ibid. 42:1204.
[19] Meigh, D. F. 1964. J. Sci. Food Agr. 15:436.
[20] Nelson, J. H., R. L. Glass, and W. F. Geddes. 1963. Cereal Chem. 40:343.
[21] Ostwald, R. 1963. J. Am. Dietet. Assoc. 42:32.
[22] Read, W. W. C., and Z. Awdeh. 1963. J. Sci. Food Agr. 14:770.
[23] Roberson, S., J. E. Marion, and J. G. Woodroof. 1966. J. Am. Dietet. Assoc. 49:208.
[24] Roubal, W. T. 1963. J. Am. Oil Chem. Soc. 40:214.
[25] Siedler, A. J., et al. 1964. J. Food Sci. 29:877.
[26] Tove, S. B., and G. Matrone. 1962. J. Nutr. 76:271.

Part II. Monoethenoic, Dienoic, and Trienoic Unsaturated Fatty Acids

	Food or Feed	No. of Analyses	Monoethenoic				Dienoic		Trienoic		Reference
			Eicosenoic [20:1]	Myristoleic [14:1]	Oleic [18:1]	Palmitoleic [16:1]	Eicosadienoic [20:2]	Linoleic [18:2]	Eicosatrienoic [20:3]	Linolenic [18:3]	
	Animal Origin										
1	Beef, heart	1	...	...	17.8	1.0	...	25.3	...	...	25
2	kidney	1	...	...	21.0	1.3	...	18.6	...	...	25
3	liver	1	...	...	14.0	1.0	...	11.2	...	...	25
4	rib	3	...	0.8±0.1	41.1±0.2	4.3±0.5	...	0.7±0.8	...	...	9
5	tallow	2	...	0.6	39.4	3.5	...	3.8	...	0.5	1,7
6	tongue	1	...	...	43.5	3.4	...	3.6	...	...	25
7	Chicken, breast	1	...	2.0	22.1	1.9	...	29.9	0.6	1.0	18
8	heart	2	...	0.2	39.9	5.0	...	21.4	...	...	17
9	liver	2	...	...	37.5	3.0	...	13.5	...	...	17
10	skin	1	...	0.1	28.8	3.1	...	44.0	0.2	1.6	18
11	thigh	1	...	0.9	24.7	2.4	...	38.7	0.2	1.8	18
12	Crab meal	1	...	0.8	23.2	18.4	...	19.4	...	6.5	7
13	Eggs, whole	5	...	...	47.6±0.2	4.8±0.2	...	12.8±0.4	...	...	8
14	Feather meal	3	1.3±0.8	0.3	29.7±1.2	5.8±0.5	...	13.1±0.3	...	...	7
15	Fish, freshwater	3	2.1±0.5	...	21.7±2.8	8.6±1.0	...	4.8±0.4	...	4.1±0.6	11
16	saltwater, light meat	12	3.0±0.5	...	18.2±0.7	5.0±0.4	...	1.1±0.2	...	0.6±0.1	24
17	dark meat	12	4.1±0.8	...	18.1±1.6	5.9±0.7	...	1.3±0.1	...	0.8±0.1	11,24
18	solubles, condensed	3	1.5±0.6	0.7±0.1	16.7±1.3	19.2±2.3	2.1±0.7	3.3±0.5	...	...	7
19	Lard	1	...	...	38.4	6.5	...	19.3	...	...	7
20	Meat scraps	3	...	0.6±0.1	43.5±2.4	5.1±1.3	0.3±0.1	3.6±0.7	...	...	7
21	Menhaden, meal	3	...	0.9±0.1	20.9±1.1	16.8±1.4	...	1.5±0.9	...	0.8±0.5	7
22	oil	3	...	0.3	13.4±1.9	14.5±1.9	...	3.4±1.3	0.2±0.3	1.7±0.4	7

continued

4. FATTY ACID COMPOSITION OF FOODS AND FEEDS: ANIMAL AND PLANT ORIGIN

Part II. Monoethenoic, Dienoic, and Trienoic Unsaturated Fatty Acids

	Food or Feed	No. of Analyses	Monoethenoic				Dienoic		Trienoic		Reference
			Eicosenoic [20:1]	Myristoleic [14:1]	Oleic [18:1]	Palmitoleic [16:1]	Eicosadienoic [20:2]	Linoleic [18:2]	Eicosatrienoic [20:3]	Linolenic [18:3]	
23	Milk, skim	3	....	0.4±0.1	12.2±0.9	3.2±0.5	....	0.1±0.1	1.9±1.6	4.2±1.4	7
24	Mutton, adipose fat	4	....	....	34.0±3.9	1.0±0.1	....	3.0±0.1	....	....	22
25	meat fat	4	....	....	41.9±0.6	1.5±0.1	....	3.3±0.1	....	....	22
26	Pork, back fat	4	1.4±0.3	0.5±0.1	45.3±0.4	2.2±0.3	0.6±0.1	13.2±1.1	....	0.7±0.2	3
27	bacon	4	....	0.1±0.1	44.0±0.2	2.7±0.1	0.4±0.1	12.5±0.5	....	0.4±0.1	3
28	Boston butt	4	0.8±0.1	0.3±0.1	47.1±0.2	3.6±0.1	0.3±0.1	12.2±0.3	0.2±0.1	0.4±0.1	3
29	chop	4	1.2±0.1	0.3±0.1	43.8±0.6	4.1±0.2	0.8±0.1	10.5±0.6	1.1±0.2	0.4±0.1	3
30	ham	4	1.4±0.3	0.5±0.1	45.3±0.4	2.2±0.3	0.6±0.1	13.2±1.1	....	0.7±0.2	3
31	heart	4	0.5±0.1	0.2±0.1	32.4±0.5	2.8±0.2	0.7±0.5	16.5±0.4	0.6±0.2	0.4±0.1	3
32	kidney	4	0.9±0.1	23.3±0.1	14.0±0.3	13.3±0.2	0.8±0.1	0.5±0.1	0.6±0.1	....	3
33	liver	4	0.1±0.1	....	25.8±1.5	1.7±0.1	0.6±0.2	15.8±0.5	0.7±0.2	0.2±0.1	3
34	picnic shoulder	4	1.0±0.2	0.2±0.1	48.1±0.3	3.5±0.1	0.5±0.1	11.4±0.3	0.6±0.1	0.5±0.1	3
35	skin	4	1.0±0.1	0.2±0.1	51.6±1.5	4.2±0.5	0.6±0.1	10.6±0.6	....	0.5±0.1	3
36	tongue	4	1.2±0.1	0.2±0.1	46.6±1.6	3.4±0.1	0.4±0.1	12.7±0.6	0.7±0.2	0.6±0.1	3
37	Poultry, offal oil	3	....	0.2	39.5±0.9	6.8±0.2	....	23.5±0.9	....	1.0±0.3	7
38	products, meal	2	....	0.7	35.9	7.3	....	16.8	....	2.0	7
39	Sheep, adipose tissue	6	....	0.9±0.1	45.9±1.3	4.6±0.6	....	1.5±0.9	....	....	26
40	Shellfishes	4	1.8±0.7	....	10.5±2.6	6.9±2.1	....	1.3±0.3	....	1.2±0.3	11
41	Tankage	3	....	0.1±0.1	41.5±4.9	4.0±0.3	....	3.6±1.4	....	0.9±0.3	7
42	Whey, dried	3	....	1.3±0.6	28.7±1.2	5.4±2.5	....	0.1±0.7	....	0.1±0.4	7
	Plant Origin										
43	Alfalfa meal	6	....	0.1±0.1	5.8±1.0	2.8±0.5	....	18.6±1.1	....	36.1±7.9	7
44	Apples, whole	5	2.4±0.8	....	16.9±0.7	4.5±1.8	....	25.2±1.7	....	7.0±0.6	19
45	Barley, whole	3	....	....	20.5±2.8	0.9±0.9	....	43.3±0.5	....	4.3±0.6	7
46	Beet pulp	1	....	....	12.7	3.8	....	48.8	....	....	7
47	Bread, white [1]	9	....	0.6±0.4	36.7±2.5	1.2±0.5	....	23.1±1.8	....	1.4±0.3	10
48	Cake mix, commercial [1]	9	....	....	41.1±0.8	2.5±0.2	....	9.8±0.4	....	....	21
49	Citrus pulp	2	....	....	23.8	3.9	....	36.7	....	1.8	7
50	Coconut oil	2	....	....	6.8	0.5	....	1.6	....	....	1,7
51	Corn, whole	6	....	....	30.9±2.0	....	....	47.9±1.8	....	2.3±0.1	7
52	gluten feed	3	....	....	24.3±0.5	....	....	46.5±0.9	....	....	7
53	gluten meal	3	....	....	26.7±1.1	0.9±0.3	....	53.0±1.4	....	1.4±0.3	7
54	oil	8	....	....	27.5±0.8	....	....	57.1±0.6	....	1.5±0.1	1,4,7,12
55	Cottonseed, meal	3	....	....	13.5±1.2	....	....	53.1±1.4	....	0.8±0.4	7
56	oil	7	....	....	16.0±0.2	0.6	....	59.6±0.4	....	0.1±0.1	7,12
57	Distiller's solubles	3	....	....	25.0±0.6	0.8±0.3	....	53.0±1.1	....	0.2±0.2	7
58	Hominy feed	3	....	....	28.1±1.3	....	....	54.4±1.6	....	1.4±0.3	7
59	Lima beans, whole	3	....	....	7.5±0.9	....	....	42.4±1.3	....	20.4±1.9	13
60	Linseed, meal	3	....	....	29.9±2.0	2.8±1.7	....	22.9±3.0	....	23.4±5.7	7
61	oil	4	....	....	17.0±1.1	....	....	15.6±0.6	....	57.7±0.7	4,7
62	Mayonnaise, commercial [1]	9	....	....	21.9±0.7	0.6±0.4	....	53.1±2.1	....	8.0±0.5	6
63	Milo sorghum, whole	2	....	....	31.7	5.2	....	40.2	....	....	7
64	Oats, whole	3	....	....	32.5±2.8	....	....	38.2±1.5	....	3.1±0.7	7
65	Olive oil	4	....	....	74.6±1.9	1.1±0.1	....	7.0±0.6	....	1.0±0.2	4
66	Palm oil	2	....	....	39.1	....	....	10.6	....	....	24
67	Peanut, butter	3	....	....	50.1±0.3	....	....	28.1±0.5	....	0.9±0.1	23
68	meal (55% [2])	1	....	....	45.5	1.1	....	19.6	....	....	7
69	oil	5	1.0±0.3	....	52.1±2.5	0.1±0.1	....	27.8±2.2	....	0.5±0.4	3,4,12

[1] Composed of animal as well as plant substances. [2] Protein.

continued

4. FATTY ACID COMPOSITION OF FOODS AND FEEDS: ANIMAL AND PLANT ORIGIN

Part II. Monoethenoic, Dienoic, and Trienoic Unsaturated Fatty Acids

	Food or Feed	No. of Analyses	Monoethenoic				Dienoic		Trienoic		Reference
			Eicosenoic [20:1]	Myristoleic [14:1]	Oleic [18:1]	Palmitoleic [16:1]	Eicosadienoic [20:2]	Linoleic [18:2]	Eicosatrienoic [20:3]	Linolenic [18:3]	
70	Pecan oil	1	...	...	60.6	...	...	32.2	...	0.3	7
71	Pie crust, commercial[1/]	3	...	...	44.5±1.4	2.4±1.3	...	14.0±0.7	...	...	21
72	Rapeseed oil[3/]	3	11.5±1.8	...	14.3±3.4	...	...	13.4±0.6	...	8.9±1.2	2
73	Rice, whole	2	...	...	29.4	0.6	...	36.0	...	1.1	14
74	bran oil	1	...	...	37.5	2.5	...	38.4	...	3.1	7
75	Safflower oil	3	...	...	12.4±0.9	...	...	77.3±1.0	...	0.1±0.4	7,12, 16
76	Soybeans, whole	2	...	...	27.4	0.5	...	45.6	...	10.2	7
77	flour	2	...	...	18.0	...	...	52.1	...	12.2	5
78	meal (44%[2/])	3	...	...	12.2±1.2	...	...	57.2±2.1	...	3.0±0.3	7
79	(50%[2/])	3	...	...	16.2±1.5	1.4±1.4	...	46.6±4.1	...	6.9±0.7	7
80	mill feed	3	...	...	20.9±2.9	...	...	50.7±1.6	...	8.9±0.9	7
81	oil	7	...	...	24.2±0.5	...	...	51.7±0.8	...	7.9±0.6	4,15
82	Sunflowers, whole	3	...	...	15.7±0.2	...	...	73.5±0.5	...	...	4
83	Tung oil[4/]	1	...	...	7.9	0.2	...	8.4	...	...	7
84	Wheat, whole	2	...	...	11.6	...	...	60.9	...	5.4	5,20
85	Yeast, brewer's, dried	1	...	0.8	40.3	30.0	...	5.3	...	...	7

[1/] Composed of animal as well as plant substances. [2/] Protein. [3/] Erucic acid [22:1], 49.5 ± 5.32%. [4/] Elaeostearic acid [18:3] (conjugated double bonds), 80.1%

Contributor: Edwards, Hardy M., Jr.

References

[1] Alford, J. A., et al. 1961. J. Food Sci. 26:234.

[2] Beadle, J. B., et al. 1965. J. Am. Oil Chem. Soc. 42:90.

[3] Chung, R. A., and C. C. Lin. 1965. J. Food Sci. 30:860.

[4] Craig, B. M., and N. L. Murtz. 1959. J. Am. Oil Chem. Soc. 36:549.

[5] Daniels, N. W. R., et al. 1966. J. Sci. Food Agr. 17:20.

[6] Eastwood, G., et al. 1963. J. Am. Dietet. Assoc. 42:518.

[7] Edwards, H. M., Jr. 1964. Georgia Agr. Expt. Sta. Tech. Bull. 36.

[8] Edwards, H. M., Jr. 1964. Poultry Sci. 43:751.

[9] Edwards, R. L., et al. 1961. J. Animal Sci. 20:712.

[10] Fleischman, A., G. Eastwood, and M. Davis. 1963. J. Am. Dietet. Assoc. 43:537.

[11] Gruger, E. H., Jr., R. W. Nelson, and M. E. Stansby. 1964. J. Am. Oil Chem. Soc. 41:662.

[12] Hivon, K., S. N. Hagan, and E. B. Wile. 1964. Ibid. 41:362.

[13] Korytnyk, W., and E. A. Metzler. 1963. J. Sci. Food Agr. 14:841.

[14] Lee, T., W. T. Wu, and B. R. Williams. 1965. Cereal Chem. 42:498.

[15] Lugay, J. C., and B. O. Juliano. 1964. J. Am. Oil Chem. Soc. 41:275.

[16] Magidman, P., et al. 1963. Ibid. 40:86.

[17] Marion, J. E., and H. M. Edwards, Jr. 1964. Poultry Sci. 43:911.

[18] Marion, J. E., and J. G. Woodroof. 1963. Ibid. 42:1204.

[19] Meigh, D. F. 1964. J. Sci. Food Agr. 15:436.

[20] Nelson, J. H., R. L. Glass, and W. F. Geddes. 1963. Cereal Chem. 40:343.

[21] Ostwald, R. 1963. J. Am. Dietet. Assoc. 42:32.

[22] Read, W. W. C., and Z. Awdeh. 1963. J. Sci. Food Agr. 14:770.

[23] Roberson, S., J. E. Marion, and J. G. Woodroof. 1966. J. Am. Dietet. Assoc. 49:208.

[24] Roubal, W. T. 1963. J. Am. Oil Chem. Soc. 40:214.

[25] Siedler, A. J., et al. 1964. J. Food Sci. 29:877.

[26] Tove, S. B., and G. Matrone. 1962. J. Nutr. 76:271.

continued

4. FATTY ACID COMPOSITION OF FOODS AND FEEDS: ANIMAL AND PLANT ORIGIN

Part III. Tetraenoic, Pentaenoic, and Hexaenoic Unsaturated Fatty Acids

	Food or Feed	No. of Analyses	Tetraenoic: Arachidonic [20:4]	Tetraenoic: Docosa-tetraenoic [22:4]	Tetraenoic: Octadeca-tetraenoic [18:4]	Pentaenoic & Hexaenoic: Docosa-pentaenoic [22:5]	Pentaenoic & Hexaenoic: Eicosa-pentaenoic [20:5]	Pentaenoic & Hexaenoic: Docosa-hexaenoic [22:6]	Reference
	Animal Origin								
1	Beef, heart	1	11.1	...	...	...	...	...	8
2	kidney	1	13.8	...	...	...	...	...	8
3	liver	1	7.3	...	...	...	...	...	8
4	tongue	1	2.0	...	...	...	...	...	8
5	Chicken, breast	1	5.6	1.6	0.4	2.2	0.7	0.6	6
6	heart	2	3.4	...	...	...	...	...	5
7	skin	1	0.6	...	0.1	...	...	...	6
8	thigh	1	3.1	1.2	0.3	0.7	0.8	0.7	6
9	Crab meal	1	1.3	...	...	...	3.2	0.2	2
10	Eggs, whole	5	0.3	...	...	...	...	...	3
11	Feather meal	3	1.1 ± 0.7	...	...	...	...	...	2
12	Fish, freshwater	3	3.2 ± 0.5	1.0 ± 0.2	1.4 ± 0.2	3.1 ± 0.2	4.1 ± 1.9	13.7 ± 3.0	4
13	saltwater, light meat [1/]	12	...	1.2 ± 0.1	0.9	1.0	2.2 ± 0.3	18.4 ± 0.7	7
14	dark meat	12	1.9 ± 0.4	0.8 ± 0.3	1.9 ± 0.3	1.5 ± 0.2	8.9 ± 0.8	16.0 ± 2.2	4,7
15	solubles, condensed	3	...	...	...	...	11.7 ± 2.0	0.3 ± 0.1	2
16	Meat scraps	3	...	...	0.1 ± 0.1	...	...	...	2
17	Menhaden, meal	3	...	...	...	...	1.2 ± 0.6	1.2 ± 0.1	2
18	oil [2/]	3	1.0 ± 0.7	...	2.5 ± 0.5	1.5 ± 0.9	18.9 ± 7.5	8.4 ± 1.5	2
19	Milk, skim [3/]	3	...	...	...	5.4 ± 1.9	...	...	2
20	Pork, heart	4	6.6 ± 0.3	...	...	...	...	...	1
21	kidney	4	6.9 ± 0.4	...	...	...	...	...	1
22	liver	4	11.2 ± 0.7	...	...	...	...	...	1
23	Poultry, products, meal	2	...	...	0.8	...	...	...	2
24	Sheep, adipose tissue	6	...	...	...	...	...	...	9
25	Shellfishes	4	3.1 ± 0.7	1.1 ± 0.2	2.4 ± 0.8	1.2 ± 0.2	16.6 ± 2.9	18.0 ± 3.3	4
	Plant Origin								
26	Corn, gluten feed	3	3.2 ± 0.8	...	3.1	...	...	...	2
27	Oats, whole	3	0.6 ± 0.3	...	...	...	...	...	2
28	Soybeans, whole	2	...	...	0.1	...	...	...	2

[1/] Eicosahexaenoic acid [20:6], 7.5 ± 0.9%. [2/] Eicosahexaenoic acid [20:6], 0.4%. [3/] Eicosahexaenoic acid [20:6], 35.7 ± 1.2%.

Contributor: Edwards, Hardy M., Jr.

References

[1] Chung, R. A., and C. C. Lin. 1965. J. Food Sci. 30:860.

[2] Edwards, H. M., Jr. 1964. Georgia Agr. Expt. Sta. Tech. Bull. 36.

[3] Edwards, H. M., Jr. 1964. Poultry Sci. 43:751.

[4] Gruger, E. H., Jr., R. W. Nelson, and M. E. Stansby. 1964. J. Am. Oil Chem. Soc. 41:662.

[5] Marion, J. E., and H. M. Edwards, Jr. 1964. Poultry Sci. 43:911.

[6] Marion, J. E., and J. G. Woodroof. 1963. Ibid. 42:1204.

[7] Roubal, W. T. 1963. J. Am. Oil Chem. Soc. 40:214.

[8] Siedler, A. J., et al. 1964. J. Food Sci. 29:877.

[9] Tove, S. B., and G. Matrone. 1962. J. Nutr. 76:271.

5. AMINO ACID COMPOSITION OF FOODS: ANIMAL AND PLANT ORIGIN

Values are grams of amino acid per 100 grams of nitrogen. Values in parentheses are ranges, estimate "c" (*see* Introduction).

Part I. Essential Amino Acids

	Food	Histidine	Isoleucine	Leucine	Lysine	Methionine	Phenylalanine	Threonine	Tryptophan	Valine
	Animal Origin									
1	Beef[1], raw or canned	21.7(11.2-27.8)	32.7(17.5-37.4)	51.2(41.1-62.2)	54.6(43.6-75.5)	15.5(11.8-19.8)	25.7(21.1-36.6)	27.6(23.0-35.0)	7.3(4.0-11.9)	34.7(30.6-43.6)
2	Brains	16.7(14.4-19.4)	30.3(23.8-35.0)	50.8(26.6-59.4)	45.7(37.4-58.1)	13.2(11.0-16.6)	30.4(23.8-36.4)	29.7(24.4-34.9)	8.3(6.2-10.2)	32.2(10.0-38.8)
3	Buttermilk	18.0(15.3-21.6)	39.9(29.4-47.1)	63.3(51.2-78.4)	53.0(41.9-62.8)	14.9(12.2-17.6)	33.8(25.8-34.7)	30.1(25.2-37.2)	6.9(3.2-9.6)	47.7(42.9-51.0)
4	Casein	19.0(13.1-26.5)	41.2(25.6-51.9)	63.2(51.7-94.2)	50.4(39.3-61.0)	19.4(13.4-25.2)	33.9(25.0-40.0)	26.9(22.5-30.7)	8.4(6.0-13.8)	46.5(34.7-60.1)
5	Cheese, cheddar[2]	20.8(17.1-24.3)	43.0(30.9-70.8)	62.2(45.7-78.4)	46.8(34.3-53.9)	16.6(12.3-21.6)	34.2(22.1-47.8)	23.7(15.2-28.2)	8.7(6.9-11.7)	45.8(36.2-56.0)
6	cottage	20.6(19.2-22.9)	37.1(30.2-44.9)	68.5(59.2-78.0)	53.6(47.2-59.6)	17.6(16.1-19.8)	34.4(32.6-36.2)	29.8(29.4-30.2)	6.7(6.4-7.3)	36.7
7	cream	19.7(16.2-25.7)	36.8(30.5-47.6)	65.4(62.9-68.6)	51.1(47.6-57.1)	16.2(15.2-18.1)	38.8(38.1-39.1)	28.9(26.7-31.4)	5.7(4.8-6.7)	38.1(29.5-45.7)
8	Chicken, flesh only	18.0(13.7-23.3)	33.0(28.8-35.6)	45.2(43.4-46.9)	54.9(46.9-62.2)	16.3(13.4-19.5)	24.6(23.2-25.8)	26.6(23.8-29.3)	7.6(5.8-9.4)	30.7(28.5-33.6)
9	Duck, flesh only	14.2	32.4(32.0-32.7)	48.4(48.3-48.5)	53.8(52.8-54.9)	15.5(15.4-15.6)	24.6(24.4-24.7)	27.3(27.0-27.6)	....	30.0(29.4-30.7)
10	Eggs[3], whole, raw or dried	15.0(8.6-22.8)	41.5(31.9-52.5)	55.0(48.8-60.6)	40.0(31.6-48.8)	19.6(8.8-28.8)	36.1(27.9-50.0)	31.1(23.6-45.6)	10.3(7.1-12.9)	46.4(41.4-54.9)
11	whites, raw or dried	13.5(7.5-17.5)	40.4(28.6-45.6)	55.0(44.4-66.9)	37.5(23.8-50.5)	24.3(16.2-34.2)	39.9(28.1-50.6)	27.6(21.9-32.5)	9.5(6.8-14.2)	48.7(38.1-58.1)
12	yolks, raw or dried	14.1(9.4-18.1)	38.2(25.2-43.1)	52.6(51.9-53.1)	41.2(31.2-54.9)	16.0(12.1-22.6)	27.5(23.3-28.8)	31.7(21.9-38.8)	9.0(6.6-15.9)	43.0(36.6-46.2)
13	Fish, raw or canned	(1.0-44.4)	31.7(15.6-49.6)	47.2(37.4-78.1)	54.8(23.0-123.8)	18.2(5.3-29.2)	23.2(12.5-32.0)	27.1(13.1-50.6)	6.2(1.7-10.6)	33.3(18.1-61.9)
14	flour	10.6(7.6-15.0)	34.8(28.0-46.8)	50.9(39.2-84.6)	60.7(49.3-105.8)	16.6(14.3-19.7)	23.4(8.4-29.2	36.0(18.8-44.9)	6.2(5.4-7.6)	32.2(26.7-39.6)
15	Gelatin	5.0(3.7-6.2)	8.8(3.8-13.6)	19.0(13.8-25.0)	27.4(22.3-38.0)	5.1(2.5-7.9)	13.2(11.2-15.8)	12.4(9.4-16.9)	0.04(0-0.20)	15.7(13.1-21.4)
16	Heart	16.0(10.9-19.1)	31.7(27.4-40.9)	55.8(49.7-69.0)	51.3(43.4-66.5)	14.9(12.8-19.3)	28.3(25.7-31.9)	28.7(24.1-39.6)	8.1(5.8-8.9)	36.0(30.6-44.0)
17	Kidneys	15.7(13.5-18.8)	30.4(27.1-38.8)	54.2(48.3-62.5)	45.3(38.8-52.5)	12.8(10.5-16.8)	29.4(26.9-34.2)	27.7(21.9-30.8)	9.2(6.5-13.0)	36.5(32.5-41.4)
18	Lactalbumin	12.4(9.4-14.4)	40.3(28.2-54.4)	80.1(65.0-116.6)	58.8(41.3-78.7)	14.6(10.1-16.2)	28.3(20.4-35.0)	34.0(28.8-42.5)	14.3(11.2-18.8)	36.9(26.8-42.5)
19	Lamb[1], raw or canned	17.4(14.1-21.4)	32.4(26.5-39.3)	48.4(42.3-53.5)	50.6(41.1-58.6)	15.0(13.8-16.3)	25.4(23.0-30.6)	28.6(24.3-33.0)	8.1(6.4-10.0)	30.8(28.6-34.6)
20	Liver	16.6(11.6-23.8)	32.7(25.0-40.6)	57.7(47.1-73.8)	46.8(34.5-58.8)	14.7(12.1-25.8)	31.5(26.9-37.9)	29.7(20.6-36.9)	9.4(4.6-11.3)	39.3(32.2-44.1)
21	Milk, human	13.8(6.1-17.5)	34.4(24.0-47.5)	56.7(47.5-67.6)	41.3(35.3-51.0)	12.8(5.1-24.9)	27.2(14.2-36.9)	28.4(25.7-40.0)	10.3(5.8-19.4)	39.1(28.3-61.9)
22	cow[4]	16.8(7.7-31.0)	40.7(27.5-53.1)	62.6(51.3-77.9)	49.6(32.5-60.9)	15.6(10.2-24.4)	30.9(23.6-42.3)	29.4(22.5-38.6)	9.0(6.2-11.7)	43.8(28.1-54.1)
23	Pork[1], raw or canned	21.6(13.5-29.4)	32.1(24.7-39.5)	46.0(43.6-54.0)	51.3(46.2-61.6)	15.6(11.2-21.4)	24.6(21.9-27.9)	29.0(21.9-33.6)	8.1(4.6-8.8)	32.5(30.1-36.4)
24	ham[5], uncooked, cooked, or canned	20.1(16.9-23.1)	31.1(26.9-38.1)	48.3(41.9-51.9)	52.5(41.8-70.7)	15.2(11.3-17.5)	23.9(20.6-27.7)	25.6(18.1-30.6)	6.0(4.4-8.2)	32.5(28.7-35.6)
25	Rabbit, flesh only	14.1(13.6-14.4)	32.2(31.8-32.5)	48.7(47.7-49.4)	54.1(52.3-55.1)	16.1(15.6-16.9)	23.6(23.3-23.8)	30.4(30.0-31.2)	....	30.4(30.1-30.6)

1/ Based on data from many cuts. 2/ And other ripened cheeses, such as blue, Limburger, and Swiss; also processed cheese foods. 3/ Chicken. 4/ Nonfat, evaporated, or dried. 5/ And other cured pork products.

continued

5. AMINO ACID COMPOSITION OF FOODS: ANIMAL AND PLANT ORIGIN

Part I. Essential Amino Acids

	Food	Histidine	Isoleucine	Leucine	Lysine	Methionine	Phenylalanine	Threonine	Tryptophan	Valine
26	Sausage, containing liver	18.6(15.5-21.8)	30.6(23.9-38.4)	52.4(46.2-60.7)	48.7(37.5-56.4)	13.0(12.4-13.2)	28.4(27.4-30.0)	27.1(22.5-29.9)	7.0(5.1-8.0)	38.8(34.2-47.0)
27	no liver	16.8(14.0-18.8)	30.3(24.3-34.3)	44.8(40.8-49.8)	50.3(44.3-62.9)	13.2(9.4-16.2)	22.8(16.4-28.3)	25.6(20.4-32.7)	5.3(3.2-6.6)	31.4(22.4-38.6)
28	Shellfish other than shrimp & prawns	9.0(7.5-11.2)	29.6(26.9-30.9)	53.5(44.9-70.6)	40.3(32.8-47.5)	16.3(10.6-27.3)	21.0(16.9-23.6)	18.6(12.0-33.1)	5.4(2.2-10.4)	44.8(18.1-58.5)
29	Shrimp & prawns, raw or canned	22.7(10.0-54.0)	32.4(30.0-36.2)	56.3(48.8-89.4)	45.3(25.3-59.4)	17.7(13.8-23.1)	29.2(23.8-40.0)	25.2(18.3-28.8)	5.6(2.5-6.9)	30.7(25.6-33.1)
30	Tongue, raw or smoked	15.7(12.2-18.0)	30.2(25.6-35.9)	49.0(39.6-56.1)	52.0(44.4-63.4)	13.6(11.7-15.6)	25.2(20.4-28.9)	27.0(20.0-30.4)	7.5(6.5-9.0)	32.0(28.4-35.0)
31	Turkey, flesh only	16.9(13.5-24.1)	32.8(31.1-34.6)	47.8(45.8-50.0)	56.6(52.7-60.3)	17.3(16.8-18.4)	25.0(23.3-27.4)	26.4(21.6-29.4)	....	30.9(29.0-33.1)
32	Veal[1], raw or canned	20.1(14.9-22.6)	33.0(28.1-39.4)	45.8(38.2-50.5)	52.2(46.4-60.1)	14.3(12.4-15.2)	25.4(24.4-27.6)	27.1(23.8-31.9)	8.2(6.5-10.6)	32.3(28.1-35.8)
33	Whey, dried	8.1(7.4-9.8)	37.5(34.6-40.0)	53.3(44.4-58.1)	39.3(29.6-52.3)	9.6(4.0-14.8)	16.5(12.0-20.6)	34.6(29.6-40.6)	7.5(3.7-12.9)	32.7(28.0-40.0)
	Plant Origin									
34	Bananas	....	....	....	28.9(24.1-31.9)	5.5(3.5-7.7)	....	....	9.5(7.6-11.5)	....
35	Barley	10.9(8.5-15.0)	24.8(20.3-30.0)	40.5(34.5-44.4)	19.7(13.8-22.0)	8.4(6.1-13.1)	30.1(24.1-35.6)	19.7(13.8-25.1)	7.3(5.0-9.9)	29.3(23.8-32.6)
36	Beans[6]	17.8(9.4-22.9)	35.5(26.9-42.0)	53.7(45.0-82.5)	46.4(33.1-59.4)	6.3(3.3-11.5)	34.5(20.6-46.2)	27.1(16.2-33.5)	5.8(2.5-10.2)	37.9(30.0-44.5)
37	Breads[7]	12.9(11.2-14.4)	23.7(18.8-28.6)	25.2(7.6-42.7)	14.9(11.2-17.5)	14.8(8.8-18.8)	32.2(30.0-34.4)	18.5(17.5-19.3)	6.1(4.3-9.4)	23.8(18.8-28.8)
38	Broccoli	11.9(10.0-14.3)	23.9(20.8-29.4)	30.8(23.7-39.4)	27.8(15.3-42.4)	9.4(7.0-15.6)	22.6(17.4-27.2)	23.1(19.4-26.8)	7.1(5.4-8.2)	32.2(20.6-39.6)
39	Buckwheat flour	13.7(13.2-14.3)	23.5(21.6-25.2)	36.5(32.7-38.9)	36.7(34.8-38.4)	11.0(9.9-11.6)	23.6(20.9-26.3)	24.6(22.0-26.4)	8.8(6.6-10.5)	32.4(29.5-34.7)
40	Cabbage	11.2(9.4-12.9)	18.0(16.3-19.6)	25.5(23.1-27.9)	29.5(20.5-43.8)	5.8(3.2-8.4)	13.6(10.2-20.0)	17.5(16.3-18.8)	5.0(4.8-5.2)	19.3(15.6-24.8)
41	Carrots	8.6(4.6-11.9)	24.0(17.7-30.0)	33.9(28.8-40.0)	27.0(14.4-35.6)	5.4(1.9-7.9)	21.9(16.3-31.9)	22.3(16.9-28.1)	5.0(2.3-7.4)	29.1(20.8-42.5)
42	Cassava root & flour	9.6(6.1-21.9)	17.4(11.5-33.1)	25.7(18.4-35.0)	25.8(6.5-50.0)	3.9(0-8.9)	17.5(13.3-22.3)	17.2(11.8-23.8)	8.1(0.4-32.9)	19.0(12.6-28.1)
43	Cauliflower	12.6(10.9-13.8)	27.1(25.6-28.8)	42.1(32.7-46.2)	35.0(32.7-37.5)	12.3(3.2-17.5)	19.6(10.7-23.1)	26.5(17.9-31.9)	8.7(5.6-11.2)	37.4(32.7-45.6)
44	Chickpeas, dried	16.8(13.1-21.0)	35.9(31.9-38.8)	46.2(42.1-50.1)	43.1(33.6-57.3)	8.3(4.6-13.3)	30.4(23.4-42.3)	22.2(16.9-29.8)	5.1(2.5-9.4)	30.8(25.0-39.4)
45	Coconut[8]	10.8(9.7-13.1)	28.1(23.2-33.1)	41.9(37.8-49.4)	23.7(16.2-35.4)	11.0(7.8-15.0)	27.1(24.4-37.1)	20.1(18.2-23.6)	5.2(2.7-6.6)	33.1(29.9-38.2)
46	Corn, cornmeal, & grits	12.9(9.0-20.0)	28.9(22.1-40.0)	81.0(58.2-134.4)	18.0(2.8-32.2)	11.6(5.9-24.8)	28.4(20.2-33.3)	24.9(19.4-31.6)	3.8(0.8-7.4)	31.9(26.8-46.7)
47	gluten	12.5(10.6-14.8)	27.7(12.5-32.1)	97.7(68.0-154.4)	11.2(6.9-19.9)	17.6(7.9-31.2)	34.9(25.4-41.7)	21.5(16.9-25.6)	3.7(2.5-5.4)	32.0(28.2-35.6)
48	immature seeds	16.1(15.0-16.9)	23.2(17.2-27.5)	68.7(63.8-74.3)	23.1(19.5-28.2)	12.2(8.8-16.5)	35.0(26.6-46.9)	25.5(23.1-28.8)	3.9(3.1-5.3)	39.0(34.7-45.0)
49	Cottonseed flour & meal	16.6(10.5-22.8)	23.6(20.3-28.1)	36.9(31.1-40.3)	26.8(15.4-35.6)	8.6(3.6-13.1)	32.7(26.0-38.6)	22.1(16.2-27.1)	7.4(2.5-10.2)	30.8(23.2-34.3)
50	Cowpeas, immature seeds	20.6(19.9-21.4)	30.9(28.2-36.3)	43.4(36.9-48.2)	41.0(37.1-43.2)	8.7(7.8-9.2)	34.8(34.0-35.9)	23.5(22.6-25.6)	6.6(5.4-7.7)	34.1(31.0-40.2)
51	dried	18.9(16.2-20.4)	30.3(29.0-32.5)	46.8(43.1-50.1)	40.7(23.2-53.3)	9.6(4.3-20.3)	32.7(31.1-36.4)	24.6(20.3-28.4)	6.0(3.7-9.8)	35.3(32.7-39.6)

[1] Based on data from many cuts. [6] Including kidney, navy, pinto, red, and other beans. [7] Including white bread, hard bread with and without oatmeal, and pumpernickel.

[8] And other palm family nuts and meals, including babassu, cohune, and palm nut.

continued

5. AMINO ACID COMPOSITION OF FOODS: ANIMAL AND PLANT ORIGIN

Part I. Essential Amino Acids

	Food	Histidine	Isoleucine	Leucine	Lysine	Methionine	Phenylalanine	Threonine	Tryptophan	Valine
52	Cucumbers	8.8	19.6	26.5	27.3(25.3-29.4)	5.9(3.3-9.8)	14.7	16.7	4.8(4.0-5.5)	21.6
53	Eggplant	10.7	31.8	38.4(37.4-39.3)	17.1(7.3-34.0)	3.3(1.3-5.3)	27.1	21.4(19.7-23.1)	5.9(5.1-6.7)	36.8
54	Filberts	12.0(11.1-13.6)	35.6(28.2-43.4)	39.2(38.5-40.1)	17.4(15.1-19.6)	5.8(4.4-7.5)	22.4(21.6-23.4)	17.3(16.5-18.5)	8.8(6.8-12.4)	39.0(37.0-41.6)
55	Lentils, dried	13.7(10.6-16.0)	32.9(27.2-40.8)	44.0(33.9-53.2)	38.2(30.6-46.2)	4.5(2.5-9.5)	27.6(23.4-33.2)	22.4(14.9-31.2)	5.4(1.1-12.5)	34.0(30.1-40.3)
56	Lima beans, seeds[9]	20.6(18.9-21.6)	38.3(32.4-41.7)	50.4(47.3-54.1)	39.5(35.8-43.1)	6.7(5.7-8.2)	32.4(28.6-35.1)	28.2(24.7-32.4)	8.1(6.9-9.8)	40.4(38.5-42.1)
57	dried	20.2(18.9-21.4)	36.2(34.9-37.4)	52.0(51.1-52.9)	41.6(35.4-47.4)	10.0(7.8-12.1)	36.9(35.2-38.6)	29.6(29.5-29.8)	5.9(4.4-7.1)	39.2(35.5-48.5)
58	Mung beans, dried	13.9(9.5-16.8)	34.6(29.9-39.2)	56.4(47.8-77.2)	42.7(23.8-57.8)	6.8(3.9-11.7)	29.9(17.2-38.9)	19.6(11.8-25.4)	4.6(2.8-6.6)	37.0(33.0-40.0)
59	Oats, oatmeal, & rolled oats	10.7(7.6-14.8)	30.1(25.9-36.9)	43.7(33.1-55.6)	21.4(11.9-32.0)	8.6(6.5-14.4)	31.1(26.1-45.0)	19.3(13.1-22.5)	7.5(3.7-9.7)	34.7(23.8-43.8)
60	Okra	10.3(6.6-13.0)	24.1(22.0-26.2)	35.1(31.4-38.4)	26.5(15.6-30.8)	7.8(5.4-10.8)	22.6(20.8-24.7)	22.8(22.2-23.9)	6.4(4.4-8.4)	31.5(28.6-36.8)
61	Peanut flour, meal, & butter	15.2(11.2-19.8)	25.7(16.9-31.5)	38.0(28.1-47.5)	22.3(15.6-28.3)	5.5(3.2-10.6)	31.6(26.9-38.8)	16.8(10.0-20.6)	6.9(3.5-12.5)	31.1(23.1-46.9)
62	Peas, seeds[10], raw or canned	10.2(6.1-19.8)	28.7(23.0-36.1)	39.0(29.3-54.6)	29.5(8.9-43.6)	5.0(1.7-9.3)	24.0(15.1-31.8)	22.9(17.3-29.8)	5.2(2.5-7.7)	25.6(19.4-32.8)
63	dried	17.1(13.4-28.8)	35.2(28.8-44.6)	51.7(42.5-63.8)	45.8(39.4-55.4)	7.5(1.9-18.5)	31.5(22.8-40.1)	24.1(17.5-30.6)	6.6(1.6-12.4)	35.0(25.9-48.8)
64	Pecans	15.4(13.1-18.6)	31.2(30.6-31.5)	43.6(38.8-50.9)	24.5(17.3-33.8)	8.6(7.5-10.4)	31.8(29.7-32.9)	21.9(19.3-24.7)	7.8(6.8-8.9)	29.6(22.1-33.6)
65	Peppers	7.1(7.0-7.4)	23.7(22.6-25.5)	23.9(22.5-26.2)	26.6(18.4-39.4)	8.1(2.0-22.5)	28.6(26.2-30.2)	26.1(25.0-27.8)	4.5(3.7-6.2)	17.3(17.0-17.5)
66	Potatoes	9.0(7.5-10.6)	27.4(22.6-33.1)	31.1(26.8-35.2)	33.3(29.2-41.9)	7.8(3.8-10.4)	27.6(19.3-33.8)	24.6(21.5-29.2)	6.7(4.4-11.1)	33.4(29.6-37.8)
67	Rice, brown, converted, & white	10.0(3.7-21.9)	27.9(19.2-42.1)	51.3(36.9-69.2)	23.5(7.6-33.3)	10.7(3.4-23.0)	29.9(23.4-41.9)	23.3(13.8-45.7)	6.4(2.2-9.6)	41.6(29.4-55.8)
68	Sesame seeds & meal	12.1(9.4-14.8)	26.1(22.2-30.0)	46.1(38.2-53.1)	16.0(9.2-25.0)	17.5(11.1-22.5)	40.0(28.0-51.9)	19.4(13.8-22.5)	9.1(6.8-12.5)	24.4(11.2-31.9)
69	Snap beans	11.8(10.8-13.4)	28.2(28.2-28.3)	36.2(33.7-38.6)	32.8(27.9-36.0)	9.0(3.1-14.7)	14.9(7.9-21.9)	23.6(23.3-23.9)	8.6(6.7-12.1)	30.0(29.1-30.8)
70	Sorghum	12.0(8.8-15.8)	34.0(25.6-43.7)	100(57.5-164.4)	17.0(9.4-24.4)	10.8(2.9-19.4)	31.1(24.4-40.1)	22.4(15.8-31.2)	7.0(5.3-8.4)	35.7(27.5-50.4)
71	Soybeans & flour	14.9(7.5-18.8)	33.6(25.0-46.2)	48.2(37.5-55.1)	39.5(23.0-51.2)	8.4(4.2-13.8)	30.9(20.0-34.4)	24.6(16.9-32.6)	8.6(4.4-13.8)	32.8(25.0-40.0)
72	milk	20.3(17.5-23.1)	29.4(27.5-31.2)	51.2(45.6-56.8)	45.2(31.9-61.1)	9.0(7.2-10.8)	32.8(30.0-35.5)	29.6(26.1-33.1)	8.5(7.1-10.9)	31.2(26.9-35.5)
73	Spinach	13.2(6.9-20.0)	29.0(15.2-40.0)	47.8(27.1-59.8)	38.6(19.2-56.0)	10.6(4.1-14.4)	26.9(10.8-37.8)	27.6(14.8-41.4)	10.1(6.8-14.0)	34.3(18.7-51.7)
74	Sunflower seed meal	13.5(10.6-18.5)	29.4(24.4-38.8)	40.0(36.8-48.1)	20.0(16.9-23.8)	10.2(8.1-13.7)	28.1(20.0-35.6)	21.0(16.9-25.0)	7.9(6.1-11.9)	31.2(27.5-35.0)
75	Sweet potatoes	12.4(8.5-16.4)	30.1(22.5-38.8)	35.8(30.3-42.5)	29.5(18.3-37.3)	11.6(5.0-17.0)	34.8(26.8-42.3)	29.4(21.1-36.9)	10.9(5.0-17.1)	46.8(26.3-61.1)
76	Tomatoes & cherry tomatoes	9.4(6.9-11.8)	18.2	25.5	26.0(15.4-31.0)	4.2(1.2-5.8)	17.8(15.4-20.7)	20.7(18.2-23.1)	5.4(2.9-8.4)	17.4(13.8-20.9)
77	Turnip greens	11.0(8.8-15.7)	23.0(15.9-27.8)	44.7(35.1-58.2)	27.8(18.7-47.9)	11.3(1.6-15.9)	31.5(29.1-33.5)	27.0(25.0-29.9)	9.8(8.1-11.6)	32.1(27.0-40.2)
78	Wheat, gluten	13.0(11.9-13.7)	26.2(22.5-29.7)	42.7(35.0-45.6)	10.9(8.8-13.1)	9.9(7.6-12.0)	31.0(27.5-34.6)	15.1(13.1-17.5)	6.1(3.4-8.1)	27.0(21.9-33.4)

[9] Immature; large- and small-seeded varieties. [10] Immature.

continued

5. AMINO ACID COMPOSITION OF FOODS: ANIMAL AND PLANT ORIGIN

Part I. Essential Amino Acids

	Food	Histidine	Isoleucine	Leucine	Lysine	Methionine	Phenylalanine	Threonine	Tryptophan	Valine
79	white flour	11.4(8.1-15.4)	26.2(23.1-29.2)	43.9(41.6-46.9)	13.0(7.7-15.6)	7.5(4.4-10.7)	31.3(28.0-35.0)	16.4(13.1-18.4)	7.0(3.9-8.8)	24.6(18.1-27.9)
80	whole grain & flour	11.9(8.1-16.2)	25.3(18.9-29.8)	39.1(34.6-42.6)	16.0(13.4-21.5)	8.9(4.2-17.5)	28.8(23.2-35.6)	16.8(10.6-20.6)	7.2(5.2-8.5)	27.0(22.4-30.0)
81	Yeast, baker's	16.8(11.9-25.8)	31.2(26.2-35.6)	54.8(41.5-88.8)	43.5(40.0-48.2)	11.8(8.8-18.8)	28.9(24.4-35.3)	31.2(29.6-34.2)	5.8(3.1-7.5)	40.0(31.2-58.5)
82	brewer's, dried	16.9(11.2-25.8)	32.4(19.2-39.4)	43.6(35.9-48.8)	44.6(36.9-56.9)	11.3(6.2-18.8)	25.7(11.8-35.6)	31.8(19.4-40.6)	9.6(5.0-16.9)	36.8(29.4-44.4)
	primary, dried									
83	*S. cerevisiae*[11]	14.9(9.4-20.2)	36.6(20.6-40.4)	44.6(30.0-53.1)	45.1(39.7-50.6)	11.5(5.9-17.5)	24.5(16.5-29.1)	31.8(18.8-37.5)	8.6(7.5-9.9)	34.5(25.0-41.6)
84	*T. utilis*[12]	16.9(16.1-17.7)	44.9(34.4-53.6)	50.1(44.9-54.8)	49.3(42.5-54.5)	9.6(2.9-16.4)	31.9(24.4-39.7)	31.5(26.2-34.0)	8.6(3.5-11.9)	39.2(36.9-41.1)

11/ *Saccharomyces cerevisiae.* 12/ *Torulopsis utilis.*

Contributors: Watt, Bernice K., and Page, Louise

Reference: Orr, M. L., and B. K. Watt. 1957. U.S. Dept. Agr. Home Econ. Res. Rept. 4.

Part II. Nonessential Amino Acids

	Food	Alanine	Arginine	Aspartic Acid	Cystine	Glutamic Acid	Glycine	Proline	Serine	Tyrosine
	Animal Origin									
1	Beef[1], raw or canned	36.1(20.5-40.0)	40.3(33.7-46.9)	58.3(52.5-69.4)	7.9(5.2-11.4)	94.6(76.9-107.0)	38.7(26.3-53.6)	30.8(22.0-40.2)	26.2(23.7-30.0)	21.2(15.6-26.9)
2	Brains	36.0(27.6-41.2)	36.9(31.9-41.2)	68.2(62.5-74.7)	8.7(8.1-10.2)	87.5(73.1-97.7)	25.2(17.8-30.0)	28.7(27.5-30.5)	38.0(27.0-45.4)	26.0(23.8-31.9)
3	Buttermilk	....	30.6(19.4-64.4)	....	5.9	112.9	....	....	24.2	24.9(8.6-33.3)
4	Casein	21.1(15.1-23.8)	25.6(21.6-45.6)	46.5(41.9-52.2)	2.4(1.9-3.4)	145(130-186)	12.5(11.4-13.9)	73.9(67.4-83.5)	41.8(32.7-59.1)	36.6(30.4-43.1)
5	Cheese, cheddar[2]	17.9(17.5-18.1)	23.3(17.2-29.4)	37.2(19.9-51.7)	3.6(1.4-6.6)	175(156-200)	9.8(8.9-11.0)	73.1(67.0-78.7)	38.4(20.1-60.3)	30.5(11.5-38.4)
6	cottage	....	30.1(28.9-31.2)	....	5.5(4.6-6.4)	....	....	....	....	34.4(30.8-39.9)
7	cream	....	22.2(19.1-25.7)	....	6.0(3.8-9.5)	....	....	....	....	28.9(26.7-31.4)
8	Chicken, flesh only	....	39.5(37.0-44.1)	61.4(60.6-62.2)	8.4(7.8-8.9)	100(97.1-103.6)	41.8(40.7-42.9)	....	....	22.0(21.6-22.3)
9	Duck, flesh only	....	38.0(37.8-38.1)	65.8(65.7-65.9)	....	106(105-107)	31.5(29.0-34.0)	....	....	....
10	Eggs[3], whole, raw or dried	....	41.0(35.0-60.6)	43.8(35.6-67.3)	14.6(8.3-18.4)	77.3(74.4-78.8)	22.1(16.2-24.7)	26.5(25.6-28.0)	52.5(46.9-61.8)	26.9(16.3-37.2)
11	whites, raw or dried	47.2(36.1-63.1)	36.7(26.2-41.1)	49.2(35.6-68.7)	15.2(5.6-32.1)	88.0(44.3-112.7)	23.4(20.3-25.0)	23.6(20.5-26.8)	49.1(40.0-67.0)	26.0(18.9-33.5)
12	yolks, raw or dried	....	43.4(41.7-45.0)	34.4(33.8-35.0)	10.5(8.9-19.7)	74.8(73.8-76.2)	21.9(20.6-22.5)	27.7(26.9-28.1)	55.4(53.8-56.6)	29.0(28.1-29.9)
13	Fish, raw or canned	....	35.2(16.2-60.0)	55.1(46.2-63.8)	8.4(3.1-21.5)	79.6(62.1-95.0)	34.5(25.2-46.9)	38.1(35.3-41.1)	19.3(18.8-19.5)	16.9(7.2-29.4)

1/ Based on data from many cuts. 2/ And other ripened cheeses, such as blue, Limburger, and Swiss; also processed cheese foods. 3/ Chicken.

continued

5. AMINO ACID COMPOSITION OF FOODS: ANIMAL AND PLANT ORIGIN

Part II. Nonessential Amino Acids

	Food	Alanine	Arginine	Aspartic Acid	Cystine	Glutamic Acid	Glycine	Proline	Serine	Tyrosine
14	flour	...	42.8(34.5-50.0)	...	...	...	...	...	...	...
15	Gelatin	55.0(43.8-62.4)	51.0(45.0-62.5)	37.2(36.1-38.8)	0.5(0.4-0.6)	61.4(51.2-65.3)	148(120-170)	89.3(82.2-102.3)	21.4(17.3-25.4)	2.6(1.2-5.1)
16	Heart	41.2(39.2-42.5)	39.5(33.3-46.5)	65.9(59.4-70.3)	6.2(5.5-8.4)	93.0(79.9-109.0)	34.4(29.3-46.5)	30.1(28.8-30.9)	28.4(27.7-29.4)	23.2(18.2-27.6)
17	Kidneys	38.0(35.9-39.4)	38.9(36.2-43.3)	64.1(61.2-70.3)	7.6(6.2-8.8)	81.6(76.2-85.9)	37.4(35.9-40.0)	32.3(31.2-34.4)	35.3(33.8-36.2)	23.2(16.4-28.9)
18	Lactalbumin	41.2	22.7(20.0-27.5)	64.3	22.1(16.9-25.2)	104(91.8-117.0)	...	26.8	26.8	24.7(18.1-32.1)
19	Lamb[1], raw or canned	34.9(30.0-38.8)	40.7(37.4-47.4)	57.6(46.3-73.1)	8.2(4.9-19.6)	94.8(80.0-113.0)	36.5(21.2-44.7)	28.9(25.6-32.8)	25.0(22.9-31.2)	21.7(17.9-30.6)
20	Liver	40.0(39.4-40.6)	38.1(21.2-55.4)	64.4(51.1-72.3)	7.7(6.2-12.3)	85.0(62.1-102.7)	38.0(31.4-59.6)	32.1(27.3-36.2)	32.7(29.0-34.4)	23.4(20.5-28.7)
21	Milk, human	22.1(20.0-24.1)	25.3(17.2-42.5)	49.8(34.1-58.3)	12.5(3.9-25.0)	105(79.7-118.4)	13.5(12.3-14.3)	47.3(41.1-50.0)	25.6(17.3-28.6)	32.3(15.0-62.0)
22	cow[4]	22.0(18.4-25.3)	23.3(17.1-31.5)	46.5(37.1-53.5)	5.7(2.5-10.0)	149(134-220)	12.6(10.7-15.0)	70.9(44.8-122.4)	37.6(26.6-54.5)	32.5(25.6-40.0)
23	Pork[1], raw or canned	29.0(18.5-40.0)	38.3(28.1-43.4)	59.2(52.1-69.9)	7.3(4.2-9.8)	95.6(83.1-116.0)	31.0(15.1-40.7)	27.6(25.6-31.6)	25.4(20.1-33.1)	22.3(16.0-27.6)
24	ham[5], uncooked, cooked, or canned	...	39.5(33.8-46.4)	56.1(48.1-63.2)	10.1(9.4-10.8)	88.4(70.6-98.8)	41.2(36.9-47.7)	31.3(30.2-31.8)	25.7(22.7-27.2)	24.1(23.1-25.0)
25	Rabbit, flesh only	...	35.0(34.7-35.2)	63.3(60.0-65.9)	...	108(106-112)	28.5(26.7-29.5)	...	...	...
26	Sausage, containing liver	...	38.7(34.6-47.0)	60.5	7.6(5.1-12.5)	71.5	56.0	39.5	30.5	19.1(12.8-28.5)
27	no liver	...	43.4(38.3-48.8)	58.9(56.0-65.0)	7.8(4.7-10.6)	85.4(76.4-99.6)	52.4(43.0-61.6)	35.6(32.4-41.2)	25.6(24.1-27.1)	20.3(14.9-24.8)
28	Shellfish other than shrimp & prawns	...	38.8(32.9-47.6)	61.8(53.2-70.3)	11.2(9.0-17.2)	76.3(73.7-78.9)	30.5(28.9-32.1)	39.0(36.2-41.9)	20.6(19.5-21.8)	18.3(15.8-20.7)
29	Shrimp & prawns, raw or canned	30.8(26.7-36.0)	55.3(46.9-65.3)	58.1(55.6-60.6)	14.2(4.8-28.7)	96.9(93.8-100.0)	39.8(35.0-44.4)	...	...	24.3(16.0-32.0)
30	Tongue, raw or smoked	39.8(35.7-42.5)	40.6(36.2-45.8)	61.6(55.6-69.9)	7.9(6.6-9.2)	95.5(76.7-110.0)	41.8(34.9-46.9)	35.0(33.8-36.8)	29.1(25.1-32.5)	20.9(19.2-22.8)
31	Turkey, flesh only	...	39.4(36.1-44.2)	63.2(62.9-63.6)	8.6(7.9-9.4)	111(110-112)	33.8(32.8-34.7)	...	...	...
32	Veal[1], raw or canned	37.1(33.8-39.4)	40.7(32.7-47.1)	61.6(56.7-69.4)	7.4(6.0-9.5)	97.5(83.3-107.9)	29.9(25.6-42.6)	25.2(21.8-30.1)	27.5(22.5-30.6)	22.5(18.2-30.4)
33	Whey, dried	...	12.0(8.0-15.6)	...	12.8(9.4-16.2)	69.5(63.0-76.0)	...	...	19.1(16.0-22.2)	6.7(3.7-12.4)
	Plant Origin									
34	Bananas	...	...	...	...	...	...	...	...	16.2
35	Barley	26.8(25.6-28.1)	30.0(17.2-35.6)	32.4(15.6-40.0)	11.7(5.6-15.7)	130(110-144)	26.5(18.1-37.2)	52.6(30.0-63.8)	27.1(17.2-40.0)	21.2(17.5-27.5)
36	Beans[6]	35.6	37.6(29.4-58.8)	41.9	6.2(3.7-12.6)	100	10.6	26.9	32.5	24.1(13.1-36.9)
37	Breads[7]	...	23.6(21.9-25.7)	...	11.6(10.4-13.8)	...	...	...	...	22.6(15.6-30.6)
38	Broccoli	...	36.4(30.5-42.2)	...	...	...	...	...	...	...
39	Buckwheat flour	...	49.7(35.6-59.6)	...	12.2(7.7-16.8)	...	...	...	...	12.8(12.6-12.9)

[1] Based on data from many cuts. [4] Nonfat, evaporated, or dried. [5] And other cured pork products. [6] Including kidney, navy, pinto, red, and other beans. [7] Including white bread, hard bread with and without oatmeal, and pumpernickel.

continued

5. AMINO ACID COMPOSITION OF FOODS: ANIMAL AND PLANT ORIGIN

Part II. Nonessential Amino Acids

	Food	Alanine	Arginine	Aspartic Acid	Cystine	Glutamic Acid	Glycine	Proline	Serine	Tyrosine
40	Cabbage	31.6(18.8-44.4)	47.0(45.5-48.4)	87.5	12.5(10.0-15.0)	118.8	....	....	18.8	13.2
41	Carrots	30.2	21.6(8.8-34.4)	46.7	15.3	113.3	....	....	20.0	10.3(7.3-13.3)
42	Cassava root & flour	31.6(25.2-42.2)	62.3(7.6-135.9)	33.1(24.4-43.3)	6.9(3.3-16.2)	76.3(50.9-117.4)	17.7(13.4-23.2)	13.9(9.3-18.5)	16.4(12.6-21.1)	11.7(8.1-21.6)
43	Cauliflower	50.0	28.6(23.4-31.2)	51.8	....	48.2	42.9	....	....	8.9
44	Chickpeas, dried	21.3	46.6(26.7-56.2)	58.8	8.9(4.1-15.0)	67.6	22.4	36.8	24.6	20.8(12.5-30.6)
45	Coconut[8]	....	75.7(65.6-91.2)	....	9.7(8.1-11.3)	....	....	....	....	15.8(11.8-25.0)
46	Corn, cornmeal, & grits	62.2(58.2-66.1)	22.0(13.1-37.7)	77.6(74.9-80.3)	8.1(5.0-19.0)	110(94.3-140.0)	21.2(18.0-25.9)	52.2(44.3-60.1)	35.3(24.6-53.3)	38.2(13.2-45.9)
47	gluten	....	20.1(18.8-22.0)	12.1	8.8(7.5-9.4)	156(153-161)	25.2(23.4-26.9)	....	....	36.4(23.1-44.4)
48	immature seeds	....	29.4(25.0-38.8)	....	10.4	....	....	....	....	20.9
49	Cottonseed flour & meal	27.0(25.1-28.0)	70.2(46.9-82.5)	64.5(62.0-67.7)	10.2(4.1-16.2)	114(106-125)	29.1(27.6-33.1)	23.4(22.4-25.3)	28.6(27.8-29.3)	17.1(9.4-20.0)
50	Cowpeas, immature seeds	....	40.9(35.8-49.4)	....	....	....	....	....	....	....
51	dried	....	40.2(33.8-47.2)	....	8.1(4.3-11.7)	....	....	....	....	18.5
52	Cucumbers	....	47.1	....	....	....	....	....	....	....
53	Eggplant	....	21.1	....	....	....	....	....	....	....
54	Filberts	....	90.6(85.0-97.3)	44.8(43.8-45.9)	6.9(2.7-15.4)	128(126-131)	59.3(57.4-61.2)	35.1(34.4-35.8)	60.4(57.4-63.4)	18.1
55	Lentils, dried	22.2	47.7(29.4-57.9)	73.0	5.1(1.9-11.1)	92.5	32.5	27.0	28.5	16.6(11.2-22.7)
56	Lima beans, seeds[9]	....	37.8(27.4-43.4)	....	6.9	....	....	....	....	21.6
57	dried	....	39.7(36.8-42.8)	....	9.4(7.3-11.5)	....	....	....	....	16.4
58	Mung beans, dried	18.7	35.1(16.0-64.0)	53.6	3.9(1.8-7.4)	72.0(70.8-73.1)	11.5	27.4(21.9-32.9)	18.8(17.8-19.8)	10.0(8.6-11.5)
59	Oats, oatmeal, & rolled oats	35.6(25.6-44.4)	38.4(25.9-46.9)	24.1(18.8-28.1)	12.7(8.3-18.8)	117(107-128)	26.5(19.4-32.6)	33.2(25.6-40.6)	23.3(14.8-30.6)	21.5(9.4-28.1)
60	Okra	....	32.2(15.8-41.1)	....	5.8(5.1-6.6)	....	....	....	....	27.5
61	Peanut flour, meal, & butter	22.2(18.1-26.2)	66.9(53.7-86.2)	87.8(81.1-94.4)	9.4(5.6-12.0)	120(109-136)	34.7(33.6-35.6)	31.8(31.0-32.5)	41.2	22.4(17.5-28.9)
62	Peas, seeds[10], raw or canned	18.3	55.5(42.6-76.1)	59.6	6.8(3.9-9.6)	44.2	20.2	....	....	15.2(10.0-25.8)
63	dried	25.2(23.5-27.0)	55.2(37.5-67.1)	76.6(54.1-99.0)	8.1(2.9-12.5)	147(94.1-199.0)	36.2(34.5-38.0)	35.2	24.3	25.2(16.6-36.2)
64	Pecans	....	66.8(63.9-71.6)	....	12.2(11.6-12.8)	....	....	....	....	17.8(16.9-18.8)
65	Peppers	....	12.6(12.5-12.7)	....	....	....	....	....	....	....
66	Potatoes	29.2	30.8(27.0-35.9)	....	6.0(3.6-10.6)	62.5	....	20.8	25.0	11.2(9.9-12.5)
67	Rice, brown, converted, & white	....	34.3(14.5-71.4)	28.1(25.9-28.9)	8.1(5.0-15.4)	81.5(64.9-151.0)	40.7(36.2-44.0)	28.8(25.5-31.4)	30.2(27.1-34.5)	27.2(16.5-36.5)

[8] And other palm family nuts and meals, including babassu, cohune, and palm nut. [9] Immature; large- and small-seeded varieties. [10] Immature.

continued

5. AMINO ACID COMPOSITION OF FOODS: ANIMAL AND PLANT ORIGIN

Part II. Nonessential Amino Acids

	Food	Alanine	Arginine	Aspartic Acid	Cystine	Glutamic Acid	Glycine	Proline	Serine	Tyrosine
68	Sesame seeds & meal	21.9	54.7(46.9-62.8)	....	13.6(8.1-21.1)	....	58.1	....	....	26.1(21.9-29.4)
69	Snap beans	25.3	26.3(25.4-27.2)	....	6.3	....	....	....	....	13.1(6.8-19.4)
70	Sorghum	....	23.7(20.0-27.8)	....	10.4(7.7-14.7)	137.0	....	....	31.6	17.2(10.5-26.0)
71	Soybeans & flour	25.7(20.6-30.8)	45.2(33.0-51.9)	75.8(69.4-79.6)	11.1(6.2-14.6)	115(96.5-133.0)	26.1(21.9-28.8)	42.0(37.8-46.2)	40.8(37.9-43.8)	19.9(11.8-26.9)
72	milk	26.2	50.8(49.7-51.9)	71.9	12.0(7.0-14.5)	92.5	28.8	....	40.6	32.5
73	Spinach	19.8(10.0-29.7)	31.6(16.8-44.8)	....	12.4	78.4	....	....	....	19.8(12.7-27.0)
74	Sunflower seed meal	20.0	54.6(36.9-70.6)	....	10.7(10.0-11.5)	....	....	....	....	14.9(13.6-16.2)
75	Sweet potatoes	....	32.6(18.3-57.9)	....	10.0	115.8	....	....	15.8	28.1
76	Tomatoes & cherry tomatoes	31.8(15.4-48.3)	18.2(15.4-20.9)	67.8(58.6-76.9)	....	149(121-177)	20.7	....	20.7	9.0(7.7-10.3)
77	Turnip greens	....	36.0(28.1-48.2)	....	9.6	....	....	....	....	22.6(22.3-23.0)
78	Wheat, gluten	12.8(10.6-16.9)	24.8(11.1-29.6)	20.6(13.7-23.6)	12.3(9.7-16.9)	209(179-241)	20.9(17.5-45.0)	72.6(66.7-88.3)	27.0(25.1-28.5)	18.5(13.4-32.2)
79	white flour	17.2	25.3(19.4-45.9)	24.7(23.8-25.2)	11.4(8.8-14.7)	198(183-211)	20.7(19.6-21.2)	68.1(64.4-70.6)	29.4	19.5(10.8-25.0)
80	whole grain & flour	20.4	27.9(17.3-34.4)	31.8	12.8(5.3-16.9)	182(150-193)	35.6(24.2-47.1)	60.9	26.9	21.8(16.4-30.0)
81	Yeast, baker's	57.2	25.5(15.5-29.6)	76.0	5.7(4.0-10.7)	115.8	37.5	24.7	30.0	27.6(21.7-38.8)
82	brewer's, dried	46.7(31.2-57.2)	30.4(16.2-40.6)	70.7(66.5-76.9)	7.4(0.6-13.8)	85.6(68.8-126.3)	32.8(23.2-38.1)	26.8(23.8-31.9)	35.9(15.0-46.9)	25.7(17.0-40.0)
	primary, dried									
83	*S. cerevisiae* [11]	18.1	26.1(19.1-43.8)	33.8	6.0(5.6-6.9)	77.6(44.4-101.0)	23.0(6.9-27.2)	....	28.8	33.4(15.6-53.1)
84	*T. utilis* [12]	....	45.1(36.6-53.8)	....	5.7(2.5-11.8)	85.9(83.4-90.9)	42.5(29.0-49.2)	....	....	33.3(28.1-38.4)

[11] *Saccharomyces cerevisiae.* [12] *Torulopsis utilis.*

Contributors: Watt, Bernice K., and Page, Louise

Reference: Orr, M. L., and B. K. Watt. 1957. U.S. Dept. Agr. Home Econ. Res. Rept. 4.

6. NUTRITIVE VALUE PER POUND: CLASSES OF FOODS

Nutritive values used in basic computations were for foods as purchased. Except for eggs, nonfat dried milk, fluid whole milk, and enriched white bread, average nutritive values per pound were weighted by estimates--prepared by the Economic and Statistical Analysis Division, Economic Research Service, U.S. Department of Agriculture--of the relative quantities of foods in each group that went into retail channels for civilian consumption during 1965.

	Food	Fat g	Carbohydrate g	Protein g	Food Energy cal	Calcium mg	Iron mg	Thiamine mg	Riboflavin mg	Nicotinic Acid mg	Ascorbic Acid mg	Vitamin A I.U.
1	Meat [1], poultry, & fish	64.5	0.4	67.7	870	55	8.6	0.81	0.94	17.5	2	3100
2	Meat	78.8	0.5	67.9	1000	47	10.1	1.06	0.99	17.6	3	3740
3	Poultry & fish	28.8	0.3	67.1	550	77	4.7	0.18	0.81	17.3	Trace	1510

[1] Excluding bacon and salt pork.

continued

6. NUTRITIVE VALUE PER POUND: CLASSES OF FOODS

	Food	Fat g	Carbohydrate g	Protein g	Food Energy cal	Calcium mg	Iron mg	Thiamine mg	Riboflavin mg	Nicotinic Acid mg	Ascorbic Acid mg	Vitamin A I.U.
4	Bacon & salt pork	328.2	3.4	32.8	3115	44	4.7	1.42	0.43	7.2	0	0
5	Eggs	46.4	3.6	52.1	660	218	9.3	0.42	1.20	0.2	0	4760
6	Dairy products[2,3]	14.6	19.3	15.8	275	509	0.3	0.13	0.70	0.3	4	650
7	Milk, nonfat dried	3.6	237.2	162.8	1645	5933	2.7	1.59	8.16	4.1	32	140
8	fluid whole	15.9	22.2	15.9	295	535	0.2	0.15	0.78	0.3	5	650
9	Cheese, all kinds	92.5	10.7	100.5	1285	2245	3.2	0.11	1.74	0.4	0	3760
10	Fats & oils[4]	425.7	0.6	0.9	3780	29	0	0	0	0	0	4830
11	Butter & margarine	367.0	1.8	2.7	3260	91	0	0	0	0	0	15,000
12	Other	453.7	0	0	4025	0	0	0	0	0	0	0
13	Fruit	1.0	54.0	2.1	215	41	1.7	0.16	0.10	1.2	73	1300
14	Citrus	0.5	36.3	2.4	150	48	0.8	0.26	0.06	1.0	150	570
15	Dried	2.1	319.9	11.5	1210	282	15.5	0.42	0.47	4.9	11	3470
16	Other[5]	1.2	61.6	2.0	245	38	2.1	0.11	0.12	1.3	39	1630
17	Vegetables	1.2	32.1	6.3	150	104	3.2	0.26	0.22	2.6	73	4910
18	Dark-green & deep-yellow vegetables[6]	1.0	27.1	6.8	125	227	4.4	0.26	0.40	2.3	147	24,820
19	Tomatoes	1.5	37.0	6.0	170	59	3.6	0.32	0.20	4.3	93	4900
20	Other	1.2	31.2	6.4	145	99	2.8	0.23	0.20	2.0	52	1450
21	Potatoes & sweet potatoes	0.5	69.0	7.9	305	32	2.5	0.40	0.14	5.4	74	2230
22	Dried beans & peas, nuts, & soybean products	117.9	179.9	108.3	2095	537	24.7	2.34	0.90	32.0	Trace	60
23	Flour & cereal products[7]	5.4	346.9	46.2	1655	81	11.6	1.58	0.83	12.9	0	70
24	Bread, white enriched[8]	14.5	229.1	39.5	1225	381	11.3	1.13	0.95	10.8	Trace	Trace
25	Sugars & other sweeteners	0	435.4	Trace	1685	32	2.9	Trace	Trace	Trace	Trace	0

[2] Excluding butter. [3] Milk equivalent. [4] Including butter. [5] Including fortification of fruit juices and drinks. [6] Excluding sweet potatoes. [7] Including enrichment. [8] 3-4% nonfat dried milk.

Contributor: Friend, Berta

7. NUTRIENT STABILITY

Nutrients are specially sensitive to the reaction (pH) of the solvent, and to exposure to air, light, and heat. **Condition**: cooking refers to ordinary methods of food preparation (nutrient loss is given as percent of the nutrient prior to cooking); Atm = atmospheric. **Reaction**: the stability of the nutrient, in aqueous solution unless otherwise specified, estimated on the basis of the chemical composition or other well-known properties; S = stable (no appreciable breakdown); L = labile (appreciable decomposition).

	Nutrient	Condition	Reaction	Remarks	Reference
	Inorganic Salts				
1	Inorganic salts	pH 7	S	Based on educated judgment[1]	26
2		<pH 7	S		
3		>pH 7	S		
4		Heat	S		
5		Atm O_2	L	Based on educated judgment[1]. Oxidation of some inorganic salts of lower valence states to higher valence states occurs when salts exposed to atmospheric oxygen, e.g., ferrous to ferric iron.	26
6		Light	S	Based on educated judgment[1]	26
7		Cooking	S	Based on educated judgment[1]; very small loss	26

[1] No specific experimental evidence available.

continued

7. NUTRIENT STABILITY

	Nutrient	Condition	Reaction	Remarks	Reference
	Vitamins				
	Water-soluble				
8	Thiamine	<pH 7	L	Unstable at >pH 5.5	61
9		Heat	S	Heat stability a function of pH and nature of the buffer; no destruction in 1% HCl in 7 hr at 100°C; stable in dry form	7,23, 61
10			L	96.4% destroyed at pH 7, 100°C, in 3 hr; 100% destroyed in 15 min at pH 9, 100°C	7,23
11		Atm O_2	L	Unstable in air	36
12		Light	S		36
13		γ-Radiation	L	1.0 megarad causes 100% loss in liquid milk	25
14			L	2.8 megarads cause 60% loss in beef	1,19
15			L	2.8 megarads cause 70-95% loss in foods	73
16		Cooking		25-45% loss	22
17	Riboflavin	pH 7	S	Based on educated judgment[1]; stable in neutral or acid solutions	26
18		<pH 7	S	1.2% decomposed per month at pH 5.0, 27°C	61
19		Heat	S	Based on educated judgment[1]; stable in neutral or acid solutions	26
20		Atm O_2	S	1.2% decomposed per month at pH 5.0, 27°C	61
21		Light	L	Destruction rate in light increases as pH and temp increase; 50% of riboflavin in milk destroyed when exposed to sunlight for 2 hr	51,70, 72
22		γ-Radiation	L	1.0 megarad causes 74% loss in liquid milk	25
23			L	2.8 megarads cause 9% loss in beef	1,18
24		Cooking		0-48% loss	13,22
25	Nicotinic acid[2]	pH 7	S	Autoclaving with water, acid, or alkali used in extracting nicotinic acid from mixture with other food substances	38,59, 62
26		<pH 7	S		
27		>pH 7	S		
28		Heat	S		
29		Atm O_2	S	Based on educated judgment[1]	26
30		Light	S		
31		γ-Radiation		1.0 megarad causes 33.5% loss in liquid milk	25
32			S	2.8 megarads cause no loss in beef	1,18
33		Cooking		0.72% loss	13,22
34	B_6[3]	pH 7	S	Pyridoxine not destroyed by heating with 5 *N* acid or alkali at 100°C, or by autoclaving in acid or alkali; pyridoxal and pyridoxamine stable in hot acid, but pyridoxal partially decomposed by hot alkali	15,33
35		<pH 7	S		
36		>pH 7	S		
37		Heat	S		
38		Atm O_2	S	Oxidized only by such strong agents as hot HNO_3 or H_2O_2	15,33
39		Light	L	Rapidly destroyed by ultraviolet light in neutral or alkaline solution	15,32, 33
40		γ-Radiation	L	50% loss in foods	53
41			L	1.0 megarad causes 89% loss in liquid milk	25
42			L	2.8 megarads cause 24% loss in beef	1,18
43			L	5.6 megarads cause slight loss in vegetables	52
44	Biotin	pH 7	S	Neutral solutions stable several months	61
45		<pH 7	S	Moderately acid solutions stable several months	61
46		>pH 7	L	Alkaline solutions less stable	61
47		Heat	S	50% loss if heated in 20% HCl to 120°C for 6 hr; 40-60% loss if heated in 1 *N* KOH to 120°C for 17 hr	10
48		Atm O_2	S	Stable in air, O_2, and ultraviolet light	13
49		Light	S		
50		γ-Radiation	S	1.0 megarad causes no loss in liquid milk	25
51		Cooking		0-72% loss	13

[1] No specific experimental evidence available. [2] Also known as niacin. Nicotinic acid retains its biological activity, but nicotinamide, which has the same vitamin activity, is partially hydrolyzed by alkali and acid. [3] Information is for B_6 group which includes pyridoxine, pyridoxal, and pyridoxamine.

continued

7. NUTRIENT STABILITY

	Nutrient	Condition	Re-action	Remarks	Refer-ence
52	Panto-thenic acid	pH 7	S	Maximum stability at pH 5.5-7.0; rapidly hydrolyzes under more acidic or alkaline conditions	28
53		<pH 7	L		
54		>pH 7	L		
55		Heat	L		56
56		Atm O_2	S	Based on educated judgment[1]	26
57		Light	S		
58		γ-Radiation	S	1.0 megarad causes no loss in liquid milk	25
59		Cooking		0-44% loss	13
60	Folic acid	Heat	S	Stable to heat at pH 4-12; no destruction at pH 6.8, 100°C for 30 min; 70-100% loss when autoclaved at pH 1.0	17,50
61		Atm O_2	L	Aeration at pH 10 causes partial inactivation. Solutions of reduced folic acid cofactors very susceptible to oxidation unless protected with ascorbate or mercaptoethanol.	17,50, 63
62		Light	L	Rapidly inactivated by light	64
63		Cooking		0-97% loss	13
64	*p*-Amino-benzoic acid	Heat	S	Maximum yields obtained by autoclaving aqueous solutions at pH 7. Only 15% destruction by autoclaving solutions in 6 *N* H_2SO_4 for 60 min; probably stable to autoclaving with 1 *N* NaOH, but long treatment with alkali results in destruction.	39-41, 61, 65
65		Atm O_2	L		39,41, 61
66		Light	S	Based on educated judgment[1]	26
67	Inositol	pH 7	S	Based on educated judgment[1]	26
68		<pH 7	S	Stable to a variety of chemical agents	71
69		>pH 7	S		
70		Heat	S	Stable to refluxing with 10% HCl for 6 hr	71
71		Atm O_2	S		71
72		Light	S		
73		Cooking		0-95% loss	13
74	B_{12}[4]	pH 7	S	Stable for 2 hr at room temp in 0.1 *N* acid or alkali	24
75		<pH 7	S		
76		>pH 7	S		
77		Heat	S	Stable in boiling water at pH 7, for 2 hr. Maximum stability at pH 4.5-5; can be autoclaved in this range at 120°C for 20 min.	24,61
78			L	Deteriorates when heated with either thiamine or nicotinic acid in solution at pH 4-4.5; deteriorates when heated with thiamine in solution at pH 8.[5] Unstable to boiling for 30 min at pH 12.	47,48, 60
79		γ-Radiation	S	1.0 megarad causes 0.4% loss in liquid milk	25
80	Choline	pH 7	S	Based on educated judgment[1]	26
81		>pH 7	S		
82		Heat	S	Stable when autoclaved in 3 *N* HCl for 2 hr	43,55
83		Atm O_2	L		55
84		Light	S		
85	Ascorbic acid	pH 7	L	Decomposes in light (decomposition accelerated by O_2, metal ions)	5,57, 61
86		<pH 7	S		
87		>pH 7	L		
88		Heat	L		
89		Atm O_2	L		
90		Light	L		
91		γ-Radiation	L	1.0 megarad causes 93.9% loss in liquid milk	25
92		Cooking		20-80% loss	22,31

1/ No specific experimental evidence available. 4/ Includes the hydrogenation product (known also as B_{12a} or B_{12b}), which has approximately the same biological activity. 5/ Destruction attributed to attack by breakdown products of thiamine; $FeCl_3$ protects from deterioration. [47,48]

continued

	Nutrient	Condition	Reaction	Remarks	Reference
	Fat-soluble				
93	A[6]	pH 7	S	Stable in inert atmosphere; loses biological activity if heated in presence of O_2 for 5.5 hr	6,57
94		Heat	S		
95		Atm O_2	L		
96		Light	L	Destroyed by ultraviolet light	49,57
97		γ-Radiation	L	1.0 megarad causes 64% loss in liquid milk	25
98		Cooking		10-30% loss	22
99	D_2[7]	pH 7	S	Stable in dry propylene glycol more than 3 yr when stored in amber bottles	61
100		>pH 7	L	Some loss in alkaline feeds	42
101		Heat	L		56
102		Atm O_2	L	Activity lost in mixed feeds, and also under prolonged irradiation in presence of oxygen	8,27
103		Light	L		
104		Cooking		Loss appreciable	27
105	E[8,9]	pH 7	S		61
106		>pH 7	S		
107		Heat	S	In absence of O_2, not affected by H_2SO_4 or HCl at 100°C; stable to heat up to 200°C	20,61
108			L	Dry heat at 150°C for 4 hr leads to measurable destruction	30
109		Atm O_2	S	Vitamin E acetate practically unaffected by air oxidation	61
110			L	Slow oxidation. Only in absence of O_2, stable to heat up to 200°C and not affected by H_2SO_4 and HCl at 100°C.	20,61
111		Light	S	Tocopherols stable in visible light. Vitamin E acetate practically unaffected by visible and ultraviolet light.	20,61
112			L	Tocopherols readily destroyed by ultraviolet light	20
113		γ-Radiation	L	1.0 megarad causes 51% loss in liquid milk	25
114		Cooking		50% loss; deep fat frying and baking result in appreciable destruction	29
115	K[8]	pH 7	S		61
116		<pH 7	S		
117		>pH 7	L	Sensitive to alkali	4
118		Heat	S		3
119		Atm O_2	S		61
120		Light	L		2
121		γ-Radiation	S	Loss was comparatively small	52-54
122				Available vitamin K lowered	35,44
	Essential Unsaturated Fatty Acids				
123	Arachidonic, linoleic, & linolenic acids	pH 7	S	Based on educated judgment[1]	26
124		<pH 7	S		
125		>pH 7	L	Isomerization of double bonds occurs in 7 min in 20% KOH at 178°C; appear to be less labile at lower temperatures. Almost no destruction of multiple unsaturated fatty acids by heat unless in strongly alkaline solution.	12,21, 34
126		Heat	S		
127		Atm O_2	L	Sensitive to light and air oxidation	14
128		Light	L		
129		Cooking		<10% loss; almost no destruction of multiple unsaturated fatty acids by heat unless in strongly alkaline solution	12

[1] No specific experimental evidence available. [6] Insoluble in water or glycerol; soluble in absolute alcohol, methanol, chloroform, ether, fats, and oils. Oil solutions stable to air oxidation; free-alcohol solutions are labile, but esters are more stable. [61] [7] Insoluble in water; soluble in usual organic solvents. [61] [8] Insoluble in water [61]. [9] 47% of the α-tocopherol is lost from flour in 80 days' storage at 37°C [30]. One-third of the α-tocopherol is lost from corn in 12 weeks' storage at room temperature; corn treated with 1% lime, as commonly used in preparation of tortillas, loses 95% of the vitamin in 12 weeks at room temperature. [37]

continued

7. NUTRIENT STABILITY

No.	Nutrient	Condition	Reaction	Remarks	Reference
				Amino Acids	
130	Isoleucine, leucine, & valine	pH 7	S	Based on educated judgment 1/	26
131		<pH 7	S		
132		>pH 7	S	Most amino acids undergo racemization in alkaline solutions, but are otherwise stable	16,68
133		Heat	S	Based on educated judgment 1/	26
134		Atm O_2	S		
135		Light	S		
136		Cooking	S	Based on educated judgment 1/; very small loss	26
137	Lysine	pH 7	S	Based on educated judgment 1/	26
138		<pH 7	S		
139		>pH 7	S	Most amino acids undergo racemization in alkaline solutions, but are otherwise stable	16,68
140		Heat	S	Based on educated judgment 1/	26
141		Atm O_2	S		
142		Light	S		
143		γ-Radiation	S	Lysine in milk, turkey, or beef unaffected	58
144			S	Lysine in corn or wheat protein unaffected	46
145			L	Lysine in legumes markedly destroyed	66
146		Cooking	S	Based on educated judgment 1/; very small loss	26
147	Methionine	pH 7	S	Based on educated judgment 1/	26
148		<pH 7	S		
149		<pH 7	L	In presence of air, acid hydrolysates show some oxidation of methionine to methionine sulfoxides	45
150		>pH 7	S	Most amino acids undergo racemization in alkaline solutions, but are otherwise stable	16,68
151		Heat	S	Based on educated judgment 1/	26
152		Atm O_2	S	Based on educated judgment 1/	26
153			L	In presence of air, acid hydrolysates show some oxidation of methionine to methionine sulfoxides	45
154		Light	S	Based on educated judgment 1/	26
155		Cooking	S	Based on educated judgment 1/; very small loss	26
156	Phenylalanine	pH 7	S	Based on educated judgment 1/	26
157		<pH 7	S		
158		>pH 7	S	Most amino acids undergo racemization in alkaline solutions, but are otherwise stable	16,68
159		Heat	S	Based on educated judgment 1/	26
160		Atm O_2	S		
161		Light	L	Modified by ultraviolet light	11
162		Cooking	S	Based on educated judgment 1/; very small loss	26
163	Threonine	pH 7	S	Based on educated judgment 1/	26
164		>pH 7	L	Most amino acids undergo racemization in alkaline solutions, but are otherwise stable	9,16, 68
165		Heat	S	Based on educated judgment 1/	26
166			S	Undergoes slight destruction by hot 20% HCl in 12 hr; only partial destruction on refluxing with 2.5 N H_2SO_4 for 6 hr	67,69
167		Atm O_2	S	Based on educated judgment 1/	26
168		Light	S		
169		Cooking	S	Based on educated judgment 1/; very small loss	26
170	Tryptophan	pH 7	S	Based on educated judgment 1/	26
171		>pH 7	S	Most amino acids undergo racemization in alkaline solutions, but are otherwise stable	16,68

1/ No specific experimental evidence available.

continued

	Nutrient	Condition	Re-action	Remarks	Reference
172		Heat	S	Based on educated judgment [1]	26
173			L	Completely destroyed by hot 20% HCl in 12 hr; only partial destruction on refluxing with 2.5 N H_2SO_4 for 6 hr	67,69
174		Atm O_2	S	Based on educated judgment [1]	26
175		Light	L	Modified by ultraviolet light	11
176		γ-Radiation	S	Small amount lost	18
177		Cooking	S	Based on educated judgment [1]; very small loss	26

[1] No specific experimental evidence available.

Contributors: (a) Frieden, Earl, (b) Reber, Elwood F., (c) Oace, Susan, (d) Baich, Annette, (e) King, Kendall W.

References

[1] Alexander, H. D., et al. 1956. Federation Proc. 15: 921.

[2] Almquist, H. J. 1937. J. Biol. Chem. 117:517.

[3] Almquist, H. J. 1937. Ibid. 120:635.

[4] Almquist, H. J., and E. L. R. Stokstad. 1937. J. Nutr. 14:435.

[5] Arcus, C. L., and S. S. Zilva. 1940. Biochem. J. 34: 61.

[6] Aykroyd, W. R., and K. V. Krishnan. 1938. Indian J. Med. Res. 25:643.

[7] Beadle, B. W., et al. 1943. J. Biol. Chem. 149:339.

[8] Bills, C. E., et al. 1928. Ibid. 80:557.

[9] Block, H. J., and D. Bolling. 1951. The amino acid composition of proteins and foods. C. C. Thomas, New York.

[10] Brown, G. B., and V. du Vigneaud. 1941. J. Biol. Chem. 141:85.

[11] Buckhman, M. P., and S. E. Manoilov. 1950. Chem. Abstr. 44:1336b.

[12] Chang, I. C. L., and B. M. Watts. 1952. J. Am. Oil Chem. Soc. 29:334.

[13] Cheldelin, V. H., A. M. Woods, and R. J. Williams. 1943. J. Nutr. 26:477.

[14] Coe, M. R., and J. A. LeClerc. 1934. Ind. Eng. Chem. 26:245.

[15] Cunningham, E., and E. E. Snell. 1945. J. Biol. Chem. 158:491.

[16] Dakin, H. D. 1912. Ibid. 13:357.

[17] Daniel, E. P., and O. L. Kline. 1947. Ibid. 170:739.

[18] Day, E. J., et al. 1957. J. Nutr. 62:27.

[19] Day, E. J., et al. 1957. Ibid. 62:107.

[20] Drummond, J. C., et al. 1935. Biochem. J. 129: 456, 2510.

[21] Edisbury, J. R., et al. 1935. Ibid. 29:899.

[22] Elvehjem, C. A., and P. L. Pavcek. 1943. Mod. Hosp. 61:110.

[23] Farrer, K. T. H. 1941. Australian Chem. Inst. J. Proc. 8:113.

[24] Fautes, K. H., et al. 1949. Proc. Roy. Soc. (London), B, 136:592.

[25] Ford, J. E., M. E. Gregory, and S. Y. Thompson. 1962. The effect of gamma irradiation on the vitamins and proteins of liquid milk. National Institute for Research in Dairying, Shinfield, Reading, Berks., England.

[26] Frieden, E. Unpublished. Florida State Univ., Dept. Chemistry, Tallahassee, 1954.

[27] Fritz, J. C., et al. 1942. Poultry Sci. 21:361.

[28] Frost, D. V. 1943. Ind. Eng. Chem., Anal. Ed. 15: 306.

[29] Harris, P. L., et al. 1950. J. Nutr. 40:367.

[30] Harris, R. S. 1962. Vitamins Hormones 20:603.

[31] Heller, C. A., C. M. McCay, and C. B. Lyon. 1943. J. Nutr. 36:377.

[32] Hochberg, M., et al. 1943. J. Biol. Chem. 148:153.

[33] Hochberg, M., et al. 1944. Ibid. 155:129.

[34] Holman, R. T., and G. D. Burr. 1948. Arch. Biochem. 19:474.

[35] Johnson, B. C., et al. 1960. Federation Proc. 19: 1038.

[36] Kinnersly, H. W., et al. 1935. Biochem. J. 29:701.

[37] Kodicke, E., et al. 1959. Brit. J. Nutr. 13:363.

[38] Krehl, W. A., et al. 1944. J. Biol. Chem. 156:1, 13.

[39] Lampen, J. O., and W. H. Peterson. 1944. Ibid. 153: 193.

[40] Landy, M., and D. M. Dicken. 1942. Ibid. 146:109.

[41] Lewis, J. C. 1942. Ibid. 146:441.

[42] Liebscher, L. 1938. Z. Tierernaehr. Futtermittelk. 1:265.

[43] Luecke, R. W., and P. B. Pearson. 1944. J. Biol. Chem. 155:507.

[44] Mameesh, M. S., et al. 1962. J. Nutr. 77:165.

[45] Meister, A. 1965. Biochemistry of the amino acids. Ed. 2. Academic Press, New York. v. 1.

[46] Metta, M. C., and B. C. Johnson. 1959. J. Agr. Food Chem. 7:131.

[47] Mukherjee, S. L., and S. P. Sen. 1957. J. Pharm. Pharmacol. 9:759.

[48] Mukherjee, S. L., and S. P. Sen. 1959. Ibid. 11:26.

[49] Nakamiya, J., et al. 1940. Bull. Inst. Phys. Chem. Res. (Tokyo) 19:1275.

[50] O'Dell, B. L., and A. G. Hogan. 1943. J. Biol. Chem. 149:323.

[51] Peterson, W. J., et al. 1944. J. Am. Chem. Soc. 66: 662.

[52] Richardson, L. R. 1960. Texas Agr. Expt. Sta. Final Rept. DA-49-007-MD-582.

[53] Richardson, L. R., S. Wilkes, and S. J. Ritchey. 1961. J. Nutr. 73:363.

continued

7. NUTRIENT STABILITY

[54] Richardson, L. R., P. Woodworth, and S. Coleman. 1956. Federation Proc. 15:924.

[55] Roman, W. 1930. Biochem. Z. 219:218.

[56] Rosenberg, H. R. 1942. Chemistry and physiology of the vitamins. Interscience, New York.

[57] Rosenberg, H. R. 1945. Ibid. Rev. ed.

[58] Sheffner, A. L., R. Adachi, and H. Spector. 1957. Food Res. 22:455.

[59] Snell, E. E., and L. D. Wright. 1941. J. Biol. Chem. 139:675.

[60] Spray, G. H., and K. B. Taylor. 1958. Nature 182: 1309.

[61] Stecher, P. G., et al., ed. 1960. The Merck index. Ed. 7. Merck, Rahway, N.J.

[62] Steele, H. H. 1945. Cereal Chem. 22:448.

[63] Stokstad, E. L. R., and S. M. Oace. 1965. In A. Albanese, ed. Newer methods of nutritional biochemistry. Academic Press, New York. p. 285.

[64] Stokstad, E. L. R., et al. 1947. J. Biol. Chem. 167: 877.

[65] Thompson, R. C., et al. 1943. Ibid. 148:281.

[66] Tsien, W. S., and B. C. Johnson. 1959. J. Nutr. 68: 419.

[67] Vickery, H. B., and A. White. 1933. J. Biol. Chem. 99:701.

[68] Warner, R. C. 1942. Ibid. 142:741.

[69] White, A., and R. Elman. 1942. Ibid. 143:797.

[70] Williams, R. R., and V. H. Cheldelin. 1942. Science 96:22.

[71] Woolley, D. W. 1941. J. Biol. Chem. 140:453.

[72] Ziegler, W. M. 1944. J. Am. Chem. Soc. 66:1039.

[73] Ziporin, Z. Z., H. F. Kraybill, and H. J. Thach. 1957. J. Nutr. 63:201.

8. COMMON NON-NUTRITIVE COMPONENTS OF FOOD

Direct Food Additive: A substance or mixture of substances, other than a basic foodstuff, that is added intentionally to a food to perform a desired function. **Common Level of Use:** A specified level does not necessarily apply to all of the examples of usage listed for a particular additive. Limits on levels of use of chemicals are in many cases specified by regulations promulgated by the U.S. Food and Drug Administration and the Meat Inspection Division of the U.S. Department of Agriculture. For precise and authoritative information on levels of use permitted in specific applications, the regulations should be consulted. For information on toxicants occurring naturally in foods, consult National Academy of Sciences–National Research Council Publication 1354.

	Direct Food Additive	Function	Important Use In	Common Level of Use
	Preservatives			
	Benzoic acid, sodium benzoate			
1	Methyl *p*-hydroxybenzoate (methylparaben)	Preservative	Canned fruit & vegetable products, margarine, soft drinks	0.1%
2			Beverages, baked goods, candy	0.0004-0.0008%
3			Artificially sweetened preserves, etc.	0.1%
4	Propyl *p*-hydroxybenzoate (propylparaben)	Preservative	Beverages, baked goods, candy	0.001-0.01%
5			Artificially sweetened preserves, etc.	0.1%
6	Propionic acid, calcium propionate, sodium propionate	Mold & rope inhibitor	Bread, etc.	0.125-0.15%
7			Chocolate products, processed cheese	0.24-0.30%
8			Artificially sweetened preserves	0.1%
9	Sodium diacetate	Mold & rope inhibitor	Flour for various breads & other baked goods	3-6 oz/100 lb
10			Cakes	0.06-0.3%
11	Sorbic acid, calcium sorbate, potassium sorbate, sodium sorbate	Fungistat	Beverages, baked goods, soda fountain syrups, salads	Up to 0.1%
12			Cakes, artificially sweetened preserves, etc.	0.1%
13			Cheese	0.2%
	Antioxidants			
14	Ascorbic acid, calcium ascorbate, sodium ascorbate	Antioxidant	Concentrated milk products; cured, comminuted meat products	0.75 oz/100 lb
15			Curing pickle for meats	75 oz/100 gal
16			Frozen fruit flavors, dry milk, juices, etc.	0.01-0.3%
17	Butylated hydroxyanisole (BHA)	Antioxidant	Beverages, ice cream, ices	0.00003%
18			Baked goods, dessert mixes, cereals, processed vegetables, lard & shortening, sausage, etc.	0.01%

continued

8. COMMON NON-NUTRITIVE COMPONENTS OF FOOD

	Direct Food Additive	Function	Important Use In	Common Level of Use
19	Butylated hydroxytoluene (BHT)	Antioxidant	Cereals, fats & shortening, processed potatoes, etc.	0.0033-0.02%
20	Dilauryl thiodipropionate	Antioxidant	General food use	0.02% of fat or oil content
21	Erythorbic acid (isoascorbic acid), sodium erythorbate (sodium isoascorbate)	Antioxidant	Meat products	0.75 oz/100 lb
22			Beverages, baked goods	0.01-0.05%
23	Gum guaiac	Antioxidant	Edible fats	Up to 0.1%
24			Beverages	0.04-0.06%
25	Lecithin	Antioxidant	Prepared cereals, candy, bread, etc.	0.0025-0.25%
26			Margarine	0.5%
27	Nordihydroguaiaretic acid	Antioxidant	General food use	Up to 0.02% of fat content
28			Fats, candy, piecrust, etc.	? 1/
29	Propyl gallate	Antioxidant	Edible fats	0.001-0.01%
30			General food use	Up to 0.02% of fat content
31	Sodium thiosulfate	Antioxidant	Protecting sliced potatoes from browning	0.1%
32	Sulfur dioxide, sodium sulfite, potassium bisulfite, sodium bisulfite, potassium metabisulfite, sodium metabisulfite	Antioxidant, preservative, anti-browning agent	Dried fruits & potatoes, ale, beer, wine, soups, etc.	0.001-0.05% as SO_2
33	Thiodipropionic acid	Antioxidant	General food use	Up to 0.02% of fat content
34	Tocopherols	Antioxidant	Essential oils	0.02-0.1%
35			Rendered animal fats, etc.	Up to 0.03%
			Sequestrants	
36	Calcium salts: acetate, chloride, citrate, diacetate, gluconate, phosphate, phytate, sulfate	Emulsifier	Evaporated milk, frozen desserts	Up to 0.1%
37	Citrate esters: isopropyl, stearyl	Sequestrant, antioxidant	Fats & shortenings, general food uses	0.01-0.02%
38	Citrate salts: calcium, potassium, sodium	Plasticizer, emulsifier	Cheese spreads, cheese foods	Up to 3.0%
39			Other dairy products	0.04-0.37%
40	Citric acid	Sequestrant, antioxidant aid	Lard	Up to 0.01%
41			Prepared cereals & mixes, canned fish cakes, soup bases, margarine, etc.	0.05%
42	Ethylenediaminetetraacetate (EDTA), calcium disodium & disodium dihydrogen salts of EDTA	Sequestrant, metal scavenger	Beverages, cooked crab meat, salad dressings, margarine	0.0025%
43			Vinegar, other foods	0.15%
44	Metaphosphates: calcium, sodium	Emulsifier, sequestrant, texturizer	Beverages, ice cream, cereals, puddings, etc.	0.02-0.5%
45	Phosphates: calcium, potassium, sodium	Emulsifier, texturizer, sequestrant	Evaporated milk	Up to 0.1%
46			Pasteurized processed cheese	Up to 3.0%
47	Pyrophosphate, sodium pyrophosphate	Emulsifier, texturizer	Cheese	Up to 3.0%
48			Cold water pudding mixes	Up to 2.0%
49	Sorbitol	Sequestrant	Confectionery, vegetable oils	0.0025-0.005%
50	Tartaric acid, sodium tartrate	Emulsifier, sequestrant	Processed cheese, cheese spreads, cheese foods	Up to 3.0%

1/ Level of use has not yet been determined.

continued

8. COMMON NON-NUTRITIVE COMPONENTS OF FOOD

No.	Direct Food Additive	Function	Important Use In	Common Level of Use
			Surface Active Agents	
51	Calcium stearyl-2-lactyl-	Emulsifier	Bakery products, dried egg white	Up to 0.5%
52	ate		Liquid & frozen egg white	Up to 0.05%
53	Cholic acid, deoxycholic acid, glycocholic acid	Emulsifier	Dried egg white	Up to 0.1%
54	Dimethyl polysiloxane	Antifoaming agent	Beverages, skim milk, rendered fats, chewing gum base, syrups, etc.	0.00001-0.001%
55	Glycerides: mono- & diglycerides of fatty acids	Emulsifier, defoaming agent	Beverages, ice cream, baked goods other than bread & rolls, confectionery, margarine, etc.	0.0005-0.5%
56			Lard	Up to 16.0%
57			Shortening	Up to 6.4%
58	Glyceryl lacto esters of fatty acids	Emulsifier	Shortening	Up to 1.75%
59	Lecithin	Emulsifier	Chocolate, bakery products, frozen desserts, margarine	Up to 0.5%
60	Polyethylene glycol & mixtures (various molecular weights)	Defoaming agent	Beet sugar & yeast production	0.0001-0.0003%
61	Polyoxyethylene (20) sorbitan mono-oleate	Emulsifier, defoaming agent	Shortenings & edible oils for baking mixes, icings, nonstandardized baked goods, ice cream, etc.	1.0%[2]
62	Polyoxyethylene (20) sorbitan monopalmitate	Emulsifier	Cakes, cake mixes	Up to 0.46%
63	Polyoxyethylene (20) sor-	Emulsifier	Shortenings, edible oils	Up to 1.0%
64	bitan monostearate		Toppings, cakes, cake mixes, confectionery, gelatin desserts, "coffee toners," etc.	0.2-0.46%
65	Polyoxyethylene (20) sorbitan tristearate	Emulsifier	Cakes, mixes, icings, toppings, ice cream, "coffee toners," etc.	0.1-0.4%
66	Sorbitan monostearate	Emulsifier	Cakes, mixes, icings, toppings, "coffee toners," etc.	0.35-0.7%
67			Confectionery coatings	Up to 1.0%
68		Defoaming agent	Beverages, confectionery, etc.	0.0005-0.5%
69	Stearyl-2-lactylic acid	Emulsifier	Nonleavened bakery products, pancake mixes	Up to 0.35%
70			Shortenings for nonleavened bakery products, pancake mixes, icings, fillings	Up to 3.0%
			Stabilizers & Thickeners	
71	Agar-agar	Thickener, stabilizer	Beverages, frozen desserts, icings, etc.	0.006-3.0%
72	Alginates (algins): ammonium, calcium, potassium, sodium	Stabilizer, water retainer	Beverages, frozen desserts, baked goods, icings, meats, cheese spreads, salad dressings, pressure-dispensed whipped cream, etc.	0.005-1.0%
73	Carob bean gum (locust bean gum)	Thickener, stabilizer	Confectionery, syrups, cream cheese, cheese spreads, frozen desserts, salad dressings, etc.	0.5-1.0%
74	Carrageenin (extract of Irish moss)	Stabilizer, emulsifier	Chocolate products, chocolate-flavored drinks, pressure-dispensed whipped cream, syrups, etc.	0.15-0.4%
75			Confectionery	0.0001-1.0%
76			Cheese spreads, salad dressings, frozen desserts	0.5-0.8%
77	Carrageenin salts[3]	Stabilizer	Beverages, baked goods, puddings, jellies[4]	0.02-2.0%
78	Guar gum	Thickener, stabilizer	Beverages	0.0006-0.01%
79			Confectionery, baked goods, cheese spreads, cream cheese, frozen desserts, salad dressings, etc.; meats, as binder	0.2-2.0%
80	Gum acacia	Thickener, stabilizer	Beverages, frozen desserts, candy, baked goods, syrups, puddings, etc.	0.0001-0.75%

[2] If in combination with other polysorbates, combined total is "up to 1.0%." [3] Any mixture of two or more of ammonium, calcium, potassium, or sodium salts. [4] *See also* uses for carrageenin.

continued

8. COMMON NON-NUTRITIVE COMPONENTS OF FOOD

	Direct Food Additive	Function	Important Use In	Common Level of Use
81	Gum karaya (sterculia gum)	Thickener, stabilizer	Syrups, frozen desserts, confectionery[5]	2.0%
82	Gum tragacanth	Thickener, stabilizer	Fruit sherbets, ices, salad dressings, confectionery[5]	2.0%
83	Methylcellulose	Thickener, stabilizer	Canned fruit sweetened with non-nutritive sweetener; binder & thickener in certain foods	1.0%
84			Processed cheese, beverages, confectionery, etc.	0.002-0.3%
85	Sodium carboxymethyl cellulose	Stabilizer	Beverages, frozen desserts, confectionery, baked goods, chocolate milk, syrups, salad dressings, cheeses, cheese spreads, etc.	0.003-3.0%
86	Sodium pectinate	Bonding agent	Artificially sweetened beverages, frozen desserts, etc.	0.5-3.0%
			Bleaching & Maturing Agents	
87	Azodicarbonamide	Bleaching & maturing agent	Flours	Up to 0.0045%
88	Benzoyl peroxide	Bleaching agent	Flours, blue cheese, Gorgonzola cheese	0.001-0.01%
89			Milk used for certain cheeses	0.002%
90	Bromates: calcium, potassium	Maturing agent, dough conditioner	Bromated flours	Up to 0.005%
91			Bromated whole wheat flours	Up to 0.0075%
92	Calcium peroxide	Dough conditioner, oxidizing agent	Bread, rolls, etc.[6]	?[1]
93	Chlorine (gas)	Bleaching, aging, & oxidizing agent	Flours	0.008-0.3%
94	Chlorine dioxide	Bleaching & oxidizing agent	Flours	0.0001-0.0066%
95	Potassium iodate	Dough conditioner, oxidizing agent	Bread, rolls, buns, etc.	0.0075%
			Acids, Alkalies, & Buffers	
96	Acetates: calcium, potassium, sodium	Buffer	Syrups, breakfast cereals, confectionery, beverages, frozen desserts, etc.	0.00001-1.0%
97	Acetic acid	Acid	Many foods	0.005-3.0%
98	Adipic acid	Buffer	Confectionery, as neutralizer	Up to 3.0%
99	Ammonium carbonates	Alkali	Cookies, crackers, confectionery	0.25-0.5%
100	Ammonium phosphates	Buffer	Bakery products	0.25% of flour
101	Calcium carbonate	Alkali	Ice cream, as neutralizer	Up to 2.5%
102			Confectionery	0.25%
103	Calcium gluconate	Buffer	Confectionery	0.25%
104	Calcium lactate	Buffer	Confectionery	0.25%
105	Calcium oxide	Alkali	Ice cream mixes & sour-cream butter, as neutralizer	0.25%
106	Citrates: calcium, potassium, sodium	Buffer	Confectionery, jellies	1.0-2.0%
107	Citric acid	Acid	Many food products, as adjuster of acidity	0.32-4.0%
108	Fumaric acid	Acid	Confectionery	Up to 3.0%
109	Hydrochloric acid	Acid	Conversion of cornstarch to syrup	0.012%
110			Brewing, as adjuster of acidity	0.02%
111	Lactic acid	Acid	Candy, beverages, baked goods, cheeses, other foods	0.05-2.0%
112	Malic acid	Acid	Dairy products, confectionery, bakery products, fruit products, etc.	Up to 4.0%

[1] Level of use has not yet been determined. [5] *See* uses for carob bean gum. [6] *See* bromates.

continued

8. COMMON NON-NUTRITIVE COMPONENTS OF FOOD

No.	Direct Food Additive	Function	Important Use In	Common Level of Use
113	Phosphates: calcium acid, tricalcium, disodium, sodium acid, trisodium, sodium aluminum, sodium acid pyrophosphate	Buffer	Prepared mixes, self-rising flours, canned vegetables, confectionery, evaporated milk, beverages, baking powders	0.1-1.5%
114	Phosphoric acid	Acid	Beverages	Up to 1.0%
115			Brewing, imitation jellies, frozen desserts	0.035-0.25%
116	Potassium acid tartrate	Acid, buffer	Baking powders, confectionery	0.05-0.25%
117	Potassium carbonate, potassium bicarbonate	Alkali	Confectionery	3.0%
118	Potassium sodium tartrate	Buffer	Confectionery, cheeses	0.002%
119	(Rochelle salt)		Fruit jellies	0.002% of sugar
120	Tartaric acid	Acid	Dairy products, jellies, bakery products, beverages, as adjuster of acidity; baking powders, confectionery	Up to 4.0%
			Food Colors	
121	Annatto	Yellow color [7]	Casings for meat products, dairy products, margarine, baked goods, cereals, etc.	0.0002-0.2%
122	Caramel	Brown color	Many foods	?[1]
123	Carbon black	Black color	Confectionery	Up to 0.4%
124	Carmine, carminic acid (aluminum lake of cochineal)	Red color	Applesauce, confectionery, baked goods, meats	0.0002-0.03%
125	Carotenal	Peach to red color	Solid, semisolid, liquid foods	15 mg/lb or pint
126	Carotene	Yellow to orange color	Butter	1.0-4.0 mg/lb
127			Margarine	1.5-3.0 mg/lb
128			Shortening & a number of dairy products	2.5-4.0 mg/lb
129	Cochineal	Red color	Meat products, beverages, confectionery, baked goods	0.0002-0.03%
	Food dyes & colors [8]			
130	Green no. 3 (fast green FCF)	Green color	Mint-flavored jelly	0.00013%
131	Red no. 2 (amaranth)	Red color	Prepared cereals	0.0004%
132			Imitation jellies	0.005-0.008%
133			Beverages	?[1]
134	Red no. 3 (erythrosine)	Red color	Fruit cocktail, fruit salad	0.0056%
135			Cherry pie mix	0.01%
136	Yellow no. 5 (tartrazine)	Yellow color	Prepared cereals	0.004%
137			Imitation strawberry jelly	0.002%
138	Orange B	Orange color	Frankfurter skins	0.015%
139	Saffron	Orange-yellow color	Meat products	?[1]
140	Titanium dioxide	White pigment	Candy	Up to 0.4%
141	Turmeric & curcumin	Yellow color	Meat products	?[1]
			Non-nutritive Sweeteners	
142	Cyclamates (cyclohexylsulfamates): calcium, magnesium, potassium, sodium	Sweetening agent	Artificially sweetened foods	0.2-0.3%
143			Beverages	?[1]
144	Saccharin: ammonium, calcium, sodium	Sweetening agent	Beverages	0.001-0.012%
145			Baked goods, other artificially sweetened foods	0.0012%

[1] Level of use has not yet been determined. [7] Bixin and norbixin are the coloring agents. [8] Others for which a common level of use has not yet been determined: blue no. 1 (brilliant blue), imparts blue color; blue no. 2, imparts blue-indigo color; violet no. 1; and yellow no. 6 (sunset yellow FCF).

continued

8. COMMON NON-NUTRITIVE COMPONENTS OF FOOD

	Direct Food Additive	Function	Important Use In	Common Level of Use
			Flavoring Agents	
146	Acetal	Artificial flavor	Beverages, frozen desserts, candy, baked goods	0.0006-0.012%
147	Acetaldehyde	Artificial flavor	Beverages, frozen desserts, candy, baked goods, chewing gum	0.0004-0.027%
148	Acetanisol	Artificial flavor	Beverages, frozen desserts, candy, baked goods, chewing gum	0.00023-0.084%
149	Acetoin	Artificial flavor	Beverages, frozen desserts, candy, baked goods, margarine, shortening	0.0001-0.005%
150	Allspice oil	Flavor	Beverages, frozen desserts, candy, baked goods, pickles, meats, soups, condiments	0.0015-0.011%
151			Chewing gum	0.17%
152	Allyl cyclohexane acetate	Artificial flavor	Beverages, frozen desserts, candy, baked goods	0.00011-0.0004%
153	Allyl cyclohexane propionate	Artificial flavor	Beverages, frozen desserts, candy, baked goods, gelatin desserts, chewing gum	0.0003-0.003%
154	Allyl hexanoate	Artificial flavor	Beverages, frozen desserts, candy, baked goods, gelatin desserts	0.0007-0.0032%
155			Chewing gum	0.021%
156	Allyl isothiocyanate	Artificial flavor	Beverages, frozen desserts, candy, baked goods, condiments, meats, pickles	0.00005-0.0088%
157	Amyl butyrate	Artificial flavor	Beverages, frozen desserts, candy, baked goods, gelatin desserts	0.0001-0.0076%
158			Chewing gum	0.076%
159	Amyris oil (West Indian	Flavor	Chewing gum	0.0018%
160	sandalwood oil)		Candy	0.0058%
161	Anethole	Artificial flavor	Beverages, frozen desserts, candy, baked goods	0.0011-0.034%
162			Chewing gum, liquors	0.014-0.015%
163	Angelica root oil	Flavor	Beverages, frozen desserts, candy, baked goods, gelatin desserts, liquors	0.0001-0.0015%
164			Chewing gum	0.006%
165	Anise oil	Flavor	Beverages, frozen desserts, candy, baked goods, meats, liquors	0.00075-0.05%
166			Chewing gum	0.32%
167	Anisole	Artificial flavor	Beverages, frozen desserts, candy, baked goods	0.0009-0.0051%
168	Basil oil	Flavor	Beverages, frozen desserts, candy, baked goods, condiments, meats	0.0001-0.0024%
169	Benzaldehyde	Artificial flavor	Beverages, frozen desserts, candy, baked goods, gelatin desserts, chewing gum, cordials	0.0032-0.084%
170	Benzyl acetate	Artificial flavor	Beverages, frozen desserts, candy, baked goods, gelatin desserts	0.0008-0.0034%
171			Chewing gum	0.076%
172	Benzyl alcohol	Artificial flavor	Beverages, frozen desserts, candy, baked goods, gelatin desserts	0.0015-0.022%
173			Chewing gum	0.12%
174	Benzyl butyrate	Artificial flavor	Beverages, frozen desserts, candy, baked goods, gelatin desserts	0.0003-0.001%
175			Chewing gum	0.031%
176	Benzyl cinnamate	Artificial flavor	Beverages, frozen desserts, candy, baked goods, gelatin desserts	0.00014-0.0007%
177			Chewing gum	0.012%
178	Benzyl propionate	Artificial flavor	Beverages, frozen desserts, candy, baked goods, chewing gum	0.0004-0.015%
179	Bitter almond oil	Flavor	Beverages, frozen desserts, candy, baked goods, gelatin desserts, chewing gum	0.0029-0.034%

continued

8. COMMON NON-NUTRITIVE COMPONENTS OF FOOD

	Direct Food Additive	Function	Important Use In	Common Level of Use
180	Bois de rose oil	Flavor	Beverages, frozen desserts, candy, baked goods, chewing gum	0.0001-0.0035%
181	Bornyl acetate	Artificial flavor	Beverages, frozen desserts, candy, baked goods, syrups, gelatin puddings, chewing gum	0.00002-0.007%
182	Butyl acetate	Artificial flavor	Beverages, frozen desserts, candy, baked goods, gelatin desserts	0.0011-0.0032%
183			Chewing gum	0.022%
184	Butyl butyrate	Artificial flavor	Beverages, frozen desserts, candy, baked goods, gelatin desserts	0.0009-0.0024%
185			Chewing gum	0.15%
186	Butyl cinnamate	Artificial flavor	Beverages, frozen desserts, candy, baked goods, liquors	0.000083-0.0015%
187	Butyl phenyl acetate	Artificial flavor	Beverages, frozen desserts, candy, baked goods, gelatin desserts	0.0001-0.0015%
188	Butyric acid	Artificial flavor	Beverages, frozen desserts, candy, baked goods, gelatin desserts, chewing gum, margarine	0.0005-0.027%
189	Caffeine	Flavor	Beverages	0.012%
190	Caraway oil	Flavor	Beverages, frozen desserts, candy, baked goods, meats, condiments, liquors	0.0029-0.015%
191	Cardamom seed oil	Flavor	Beverages, frozen desserts, candy, baked goods, chewing gum, meats, condiments, liquors, pickles	0.00013-0.0057%
192	Carvacrol	Artificial flavor	Beverages, frozen desserts, candy, baked goods, condiments	0.0026-0.012%
193	Carvone	Artificial flavor	Beverages, frozen desserts, candy, baked goods, liquors	0.011-0.085%
194	Cascarilla bark oil	Flavor	Beverages, frozen desserts, candy, baked goods, condiments	0.00023-0.005%
195	Cassia bark oil	Flavor	Beverages, frozen desserts, candy, baked goods, meats, condiments	0.0003-0.029%
196			Chewing gum	0.19%
197	Castor oil	Flavor	Beverages, frozen desserts, candy, baked goods	0.00015-0.054%
198	Celery seed oil	Flavor	Beverages, frozen desserts, candy, baked goods, chewing gum, condiments, meats, pickles	0.0003-0.004%
199	Cinnamaldehyde	Artificial flavor	Beverages, frozen desserts, candy, baked goods, condiments, meats	0.00077-0.07%
200			Chewing gum	0.49%
201	Cinnamon bark oil	Flavor	Beverages, frozen desserts, candy, baked goods, condiments, meats	0.0004-0.011%
202			Chewing gum	0.062%
203	Cinnamon leaf oil	Flavor	Beverages, frozen desserts, candy, baked goods, condiments, pickles	0.00034-0.0054%
204			Chewing gum	0.016%
205	Cinnamyl alcohol	Artificial flavor	Beverages, frozen desserts, candy, baked goods, gelatin desserts, brandy	0.0005-0.0033%
206			Chewing gum	0.072%
207	Cinnamyl anthranilate	Artificial flavor	Beverages, frozen desserts, candy, baked goods, gelatin desserts	0.00017-0.0028%
208			Chewing gum	0.073%
209	Cinnamyl isovalerate	Artificial flavor	Beverages, frozen desserts, candy, baked goods, gelatin desserts, chewing gum	0.00022-0.0019%
210	Cinnamyl propionate	Artificial flavor	Beverages, frozen desserts, candy, baked goods, gelatin desserts, chewing gum	0.0001-0.0053%
211	Citral	Artificial flavor	Beverages, frozen desserts, candy, baked goods	0.0009-0.0043%
212			Chewing gum	0.017%
213	Citric acid	Artificial flavor	Beverages, frozen desserts, candy, baked goods, chewing gum	0.12-0.43%

continued

	Direct Food Additive	Function	Important Use In	Common Level of Use
214	Citronellal	Artificial flavor	Beverages, frozen desserts, candy, baked goods, gelatin desserts, chewing gum	0.00003-0.00047%
215	Citronellol	Artificial flavor	Beverages, frozen desserts, candy, baked goods, gelatin desserts, chewing gum	0.00041-0.0052%
216	Citronellyl acetate	Artificial flavor	Beverages, frozen desserts, candy, baked goods, gelatin desserts	0.00034-0.00097%
217			Chewing gum	0.06%
218	Citronellyl butyrate	Artificial flavor	Beverages, frozen desserts, candy, baked goods, gelatin desserts, chewing gum	0.00023-0.0013%
219	Citronellyl formate	Artificial flavor	Beverages, frozen desserts, candy, baked goods, chewing gum	0.0013-0.01%
220	Citronellyl isobutyrate	Artificial flavor	Beverages, frozen desserts, candy, baked goods, gelatin desserts	0.00017-0.0012%
221	Clove bud oil	Flavor	Beverages, frozen desserts, candy, baked goods, gelatin desserts, condiments, meats, liquors, spiced fruits, jellies	0.0003-0.083%
222			Chewing gum	0.18%
223	Clove leaf oil	Flavor	Beverages, frozen desserts, candy, baked goods, gelatin desserts, condiments, meats, pickles, apple butter	0.0002-0.067%
224	Clove stem oil	Flavor	Beverages, frozen desserts, candy, baked goods, condiments	0.0004-0.0091%
225	Coriander oil	Flavor	Beverages, frozen desserts, candy, baked goods, chewing gum, condiments, meats, liquors	0.00031-0.0047%
226	Cumin oil	Flavor	Beverages, frozen desserts, candy, baked goods, condiments, meats, pickles	0.00005-0.023%
227	Diacetyl	Artificial flavor	Beverages, frozen desserts, candy, baked goods, gelatin desserts, chewing gum, shortening	0.00025-0.0044%
228	Dill oil	Flavor	Beverages, frozen desserts, candy, baked goods, gelatin desserts, chewing gum, meats, condiments, liquors, pickles	0.00016-0.015%
229	3,7-Dimethyl-1-octanol	Artificial flavor	Beverages, frozen desserts, candy, baked goods	0.0004-0.0044%
230	Estragole	Artificial flavor	Beverages, frozen desserts, candy, baked goods, chewing gum	0.001-0.015%
231	Ethyl acetate	Artificial flavor	Beverages, frozen desserts, candy, baked goods, gelatin desserts, liquors	0.005-0.02%
232			Chewing gum	0.14%
233	Ethyl anthranilate	Artificial flavor	Beverages, frozen desserts, candy, baked goods, gelatin desserts, chewing gum	0.0005-0.0079%
234	Ethyl benzoate	Artificial flavor	Beverages, frozen desserts, candy, baked goods, chewing gum	0.00026-0.0059%
235	Ethyl cinnamate	Artificial flavor	Beverages, frozen desserts, candy, baked goods, chewing gum, gelatin desserts	0.00024-0.0012%
236	Ethyl formate	Artificial flavor	Beverages, frozen desserts, candy, baked goods, liquors, gelatin desserts, chewing gum	0.001-0.043%
237	Ethyl heptanoate	Artificial flavor	Beverages, frozen desserts, candy, baked goods, gelatin desserts, chewing gum, liquors	0.00068-0.035%
238	Ethyl hexanoate	Artificial flavor	Beverages, frozen desserts, candy, baked goods, gelatin desserts, chewing gum, jellies	0.00013-0.0032%
239	Ethyl lactate	Artificial flavor	Beverages, frozen desserts, candy, baked goods, gelatin desserts, syrups	0.00054-0.052%
240			Brandy	0.1%
241			Chewing gum	0.31%
242	Ethyl laurate	Artificial flavor	Beverages, frozen desserts, candy, baked goods, chewing gum, gelatin desserts, liqueurs	0.00017-0.0039%

continued

	Direct Food Additive	Function	Important Use In	Common Level of Use
243	Ethyl methyl phenylglycidate	Artificial flavor	Beverages, frozen desserts, candy, baked goods, gelatin desserts	0.00056-0.002%
244			Chewing gum	0.047%
245	Ethyl propionate	Artificial flavor	Beverages, frozen desserts, candy, baked goods, gelatin desserts	0.00077-0.011%
246			Chewing gum	0.11%
247	Ethyl salicylate	Artificial flavor	Beverages, frozen desserts, candy, baked goods, chewing gum	0.00028-0.0016%
248	Ethyl valerate	Artificial flavor	Beverages, frozen desserts, candy, baked goods, gelatin desserts	0.00042-0.0015%
249			Chewing gum	0.026%
250	Ethyl vanillin	Artificial flavor	Beverages, frozen desserts, candy, baked goods, gelatin desserts, chewing gum, chocolate, liquors	0.002-0.025%
251			Imitation vanilla extract	2.8%
252	Eucalyptus oil	Flavor	Beverages, frozen desserts, candy, baked goods, liquors	0.00017-0.013%
253	Eugenol	Artificial flavor	Beverages, frozen desserts, candy, baked goods, gelatin desserts, condiments	0.00006-0.01%
254			Chewing gum	0.05%
255			Meats	0.2%
256	Eugenyl methyl ether	Artificial flavor	Beverages, frozen desserts, candy, baked goods, jellies	0.00048-0.0052%
257	Garlic oil	Flavor	Beverages, frozen desserts, candy, baked goods, chewing gum, condiments	0.000001-0.0016%
258	Geraniol	Artificial flavor	Beverages, frozen desserts, candy, baked goods, gelatin desserts, chewing gum	0.0001-0.0011%
259	Geranyl acetate	Artificial flavor	Beverages, frozen desserts, candy, baked goods, gelatin desserts, chewing gum, syrups	0.0001-0.0017%
260	Geranyl benzoate	Artificial flavor	Beverages, frozen desserts, candy, baked goods	0.00001-0.00005%
261	Geranyl formate	Artificial flavor	Beverages, frozen desserts, candy, baked goods, gelatin desserts	0.00016-0.0075%
262	Geranyl phenyl acetate	Artificial flavor	Beverages, frozen desserts, candy, baked goods, chewing gum	0.00011-0.0011%
263	Ginger oil	Flavor	Beverages, frozen desserts, candy, baked goods, condiments, meats	0.0012-0.0047%
264	Grapefruit oil	Flavor	Beverages, frozen desserts, candy, baked goods, gelatin desserts, toppings	0.016-0.063%
265			Chewing gum	0.15%
266	Heptanal	Artificial flavor	Beverages, candy, baked goods, liqueurs	0.00012-0.00049%
267	Heptyl alcohol	Artificial flavor	Beverages, frozen desserts, candy, baked goods	0.00009-0.0005%
268	α-Hexylcinnamaldehyde	Artificial flavor	Beverages, frozen desserts, candy, baked goods, gelatin desserts	0.000005-0.00065%
269	Hydroxycitronellal dimethylacetal	Artificial flavor	Beverages, frozen desserts, candy, baked goods	0.00005-0.001%
270	α-Ionone	Artificial flavor	Beverages, frozen desserts, candy, baked goods, gelatin desserts, chewing gum, icings	0.00025-0.005%
271	β-Ionone	Artificial flavor	Beverages, frozen desserts, candy, baked goods, gelatin desserts, chewing gum	0.00016-0.0089%
272	Isoamyl butyrate	Artificial flavor	Beverages, frozen desserts, candy, baked goods, gelatin desserts	0.0013-0.006%
273			Chewing gum	0.057%
274	Isoamyl isovalerate	Artificial flavor	Beverages, frozen desserts, candy, baked goods, gelatin desserts, jellies	0.00085-0.006%
275			Chewing gum	0.039%
276	Isoamyl salicylate	Artificial flavor	Beverages, frozen desserts, candy, baked goods	0.00014-0.0003%
277	Isobornyl acetate	Artificial flavor	Beverages, frozen desserts, candy, baked goods, gelatin desserts	0.0004-0.007%

continued

	Direct Food Additive	Function	Important Use In	Common Level of Use
278	Isobutyl acetate	Artificial flavor	Beverages, frozen desserts, candy, baked goods, gelatin desserts	0.0011-0.017%
279			Chewing gum	0.086%
280	Isobutyl butyrate	Artificial flavor	Beverages, frozen desserts, candy, baked goods, gelatin desserts, liquors	0.0002-0.0025%
281	Isobutyl cinnamate	Artificial flavor	Beverages, frozen desserts, candy, baked goods, liquors	0.00013-0.00054%
282	Isobutyl phenyl acetate	Artificial flavor	Beverages, frozen desserts, candy, baked goods, gelatin desserts	0.00028-0.00055%
283	Isoeugenol	Artificial flavor	Beverages, frozen desserts, candy, baked goods, condiments	0.0001-0.0011%
284			Chewing gum	0.1%
285	Isoeugenyl methyl ether	Artificial flavor	Beverages, frozen desserts, candy, baked goods, chewing gum	0.0004-0.011%
286	Isovaleric acid	Artificial flavor	Beverages, frozen desserts, candy, baked goods, cheese	0.00012-0.0012%
287	Juniper oil	Flavor	Beverages, frozen desserts, candy, baked goods, chewing gum, meats, liquors	0.00001-0.0032%
288	Labdanum oil	Flavor	Beverages, frozen desserts, candy, baked goods	0.00004-0.0002%
289	Lactic acid	Artificial flavor	Beverages, frozen desserts, candy, baked goods, gelatin desserts, chewing gum, toppings	0.0014-0.061%
290			Pickles, olives	0.12-2.4%
291	Lauric acid	Artificial flavor	Beverages, frozen desserts, candy, baked goods, gelatin desserts	0.00024-0.0039%
292	Lauryl alcohol	Artificial flavor	Beverages, frozen desserts, candy, baked goods, chewing gum, syrups	0.0001-0.0027%
293	Lavender oil	Flavor	Beverages, frozen desserts, candy, baked goods	0.00029-0.00083%
294			Chewing gum	0.022%
295	Lemon oil	Flavor	Beverages, frozen desserts, baked goods, gelatin desserts, condiments, meats, syrups, icings, cereals	0.001-0.06%
296			Candy, chewing gum	0.11-0.19%
297	Lime oil	Flavor	Beverages, frozen desserts, candy, baked goods, gelatin desserts, condiments	0.002-0.068%
298			Chewing gum	0.31%
299	*d*-Limonene	Artificial flavor	Beverages, frozen desserts, candy, baked goods, gelatin desserts	0.0031-0.04%
300			Chewing gum	0.23%
301	Linaloe wood oil	Flavor	Beverages, frozen desserts, candy, baked goods, liquors	0.0001-0.0016%
302	Linalool	Artificial flavor	Beverages, frozen desserts, candy, baked goods, gelatin desserts, meats, chewing gum	0.00008-0.004%
303	Linalyl acetate	Artificial flavor	Beverages, frozen desserts, candy, baked goods, gelatin desserts, chewing gum	0.00019-0.0013%
304	Linalyl benzoate	Artificial flavor	Beverages, frozen desserts, candy, baked goods, gelatin desserts	0.00003-0.00016%
305	Linalyl butyrate	Artificial flavor	Beverages, frozen desserts, candy, baked goods, gelatin desserts	0.000009-0.0013%
306	Linalyl isobutyrate	Artificial flavor	Beverages, frozen desserts, candy, baked goods	0.00017-0.0013%
307	Linalyl propionate	Artificial flavor	Beverages, frozen desserts, candy, baked goods, gelatin desserts	0.00036-0.0012%
308	Lovage oil	Flavor	Beverages, frozen desserts, baked goods, condiments, meats, candy, syrups, icings	0.00006-0.001%
309	Maltol	Artificial flavor	Beverages, frozen desserts, candy, baked goods, gelatin desserts, chewing gum, jellies	0.0003-0.009%
310	Mandarin oil	Flavor	Beverages, frozen desserts, candy, baked goods, gelatin desserts, chewing gum	0.003-0.035%
311	Marjoram oil	Flavor	Beverages, frozen desserts, candy, baked goods, condiments	0.0001-0.0015%

continued

	Direct Food Additive	Function	Important Use In	Common Level of Use
312	Menthol	Artificial flavor	Beverages, frozen desserts, candy, baked goods	0.0035-0.04%
313			Chewing gum	0.11%
314	4′-Methyl acetophenone	Artificial flavor	Beverages, frozen desserts, candy, baked goods, condiments	0.00011-0.00058%
315			Chewing gum	0.087%
316	*p*-Methylanisole	Artificial flavor	Beverages, frozen desserts, candy, baked goods, gelatin desserts, condiments, syrups	0.00005-0.0008%
317	Methyl anthranilate	Artificial flavor	Beverages, frozen desserts, candy, baked goods, gelatin desserts	0.0016-0.056%
318			Chewing gum	0.22%
319	Methyl benzoate	Artificial flavor	Beverages, frozen desserts, candy, baked goods	0.00022-0.00099%
320	Methylbenzyl acetate	Artificial flavor	Beverages, frozen desserts, candy, baked goods, gelatin desserts, chewing gum	0.0001-0.022%
321	*p*-Methylbenzyl acetone	Artificial flavor	Beverages, frozen desserts, candy, baked goods	0.0001-0.0006%
322	α-Methyl cinnamaldehyde	Artificial flavor	Beverages, frozen desserts, candy, baked goods	0.0001-0.0027%
323			Chewing gum	0.043%
324	6-Methyl-5-hepten-2-one	Artificial flavor	Beverages, frozen desserts, candy, baked goods, gelatin desserts	0.00011-0.00013%
325	Methyl-*N*-methylanthrani-	Artificial flavor	Beverages, frozen desserts, candy, baked goods, jellies	0.0004-0.0018%
326	late		Chewing gum	0.7%
327	Methyl β-naphthyl ketone	Artificial flavor	Beverages, frozen desserts, candy, baked goods, gelatin desserts	0.00005-0.0053%
328			Chewing gum	0.07%
329	Methyl phenyl acetate	Artificial flavor	Beverages, frozen desserts, candy, baked goods, chewing gum, syrups	0.00025-0.0037%
330	Methylundecanal	Artificial flavor	Beverages, frozen desserts, candy, baked goods, gelatin desserts, jellies	0.00003-0.00025%
331	Myristic acid	Artificial flavor	Beverages, frozen desserts, candy, baked goods, gelatin desserts	0.00001-0.0005%
332	Myrrh oil	Flavor	Beverages, frozen desserts, candy, baked goods	0.00013-0.0013%
333	Nerol	Artificial flavor	Beverages, frozen desserts, candy, baked goods, gelatin desserts, chewing gum	0.00008-0.0019%
334	Nerolidol	Artificial flavor	Beverages, frozen desserts, candy, baked goods	0.00009-0.0008%
335	γ-Nonalactone	Artificial flavor	Beverages, frozen desserts, candy, baked goods, gelatin desserts, chewing gum, icings	0.0011-0.0055%
336	Nonanal	Artificial flavor	Beverages, frozen desserts, candy, baked goods, gelatin desserts, chewing gum	0.00013-0.0038%
337	Nonyl acetate	Artificial flavor	Beverages, frozen desserts, candy, baked goods	0.00008-0.00031%
338	Nonyl alcohol	Artificial flavor	Beverages, frozen desserts, candy, baked goods, chewing gum	0.00006-0.0018%
339	Octanal	Artificial flavor	Beverages, frozen desserts, candy, baked goods, gelatin desserts	0.00014-0.0006%
340	1-Octanol	Artificial flavor	Beverages, frozen desserts, candy, baked goods, gelatin desserts, chewing gum	0.00009-0.0057%
341	Octyl acetate	Artificial flavor	Beverages, frozen desserts, candy, baked goods	0.00008-0.0006%
342	Octyl formate	Artificial flavor	Beverages, frozen desserts, candy, baked goods	0.0001-0.0007%
343	Olibanum oil	Flavor	Beverages, frozen desserts, candy, baked goods	0.00006-0.00037%
344	Orange oil	Flavor	Beverages, frozen desserts, candy, baked goods, gelatin desserts, chewing gum	0.013-0.093%
345	Orange peel oil, bitter	Flavor	Beverages, frozen desserts, candy, baked goods, gelatin desserts, chewing gum	0.0067-0.05%
346	sweet	Flavor	Beverages, frozen desserts, baked goods, icings, cereals	0.001-0.043%
347			Candy, gelatin desserts, chewing gum	0.1-0.42%
348	Palma rose oil	Flavor	Beverages, frozen desserts, candy, baked goods	0.00017-0.0013%

continued

	Direct Food Additive	Function	Important Use In	Common Level of Use
349	Parsley oil	Flavor	Beverages, frozen desserts, baked goods, condiments, candy	0.00002-0.00085%
350	Pennyroyal oil	Flavor	Beverages, frozen desserts, candy, baked goods	0.00015-0.0024%
351	Peppermint oil	Flavor	Beverages, frozen desserts, baked goods, gelatin desserts, meats, toppings, liquors	0.0008-0.065%
352			Chewing gum, candy	0.12-0.83%
353	Petitgrain oil	Flavor	Beverages, frozen desserts, candy, baked goods, chewing gum, condiments	0.00014-0.0017%
354	α-Phellandrene	Artificial flavor	Beverages, frozen desserts, candy, baked goods	0.001-0.013%
355	Phenethyl acetate	Artificial flavor	Beverages, frozen desserts, candy, baked goods	0.00014-0.00056%
356	Phenethyl alcohol	Artificial flavor	Beverages, frozen desserts, candy, baked goods, chewing gum	0.00015-0.008%
357	Phenethyl butyrate	Artificial flavor	Beverages, frozen desserts, candy, baked goods	0.00032-0.0013%
358	Phenethyl isobutyrate	Artificial flavor	Beverages, frozen desserts, candy, baked goods	0.00034-0.0013%
359	Phenethyl salicylate	Artificial flavor	Beverages, frozen desserts, candy, baked goods	0.00006-0.0002%
360	Phenoxyethyl isobutyrate	Artificial flavor	Beverages, frozen desserts, candy, baked goods	0.00009-0.003%
361	Phenylacetaldehyde	Artificial flavor	Beverages, frozen desserts, candy, baked goods, chewing gum	0.00006-0.0087%
362	Phenylacetaldehyde dimethylacetal	Artificial flavor	Beverages, frozen desserts, candy, baked goods, chewing gum	0.00004-0.00088%
363	Phenylacetic acid	Artificial flavor	Beverages, frozen desserts, candy, baked goods, gelatin desserts, chewing gum, liquors, syrups	0.00001-0.0027%
364	3-Phenyl-1-propanol	Artificial flavor	Beverages, frozen desserts, candy, baked goods, chewing gum, liqueurs	0.00007-0.0005%
365	2-Phenylpropionaldehyde	Artificial flavor	Beverages, frozen desserts, candy, baked goods	0.0001-0.00055%
366	2-Phenylpropionaldehyde dimethylacetal	Artificial flavor	Beverages, frozen desserts, candy, baked goods, chewing gum, condiments	0.00002-0.0005%
367	3-Phenylpropyl acetate	Artificial flavor	Beverages, frozen desserts, candy, baked goods, chewing gum	0.00032-0.001%
368	Pimenta leaf oil	Flavor	Beverages, frozen desserts, candy, baked goods, chewing gum, condiments, meats	0.00013-0.016%
369	Pine needle oil (dwarf)	Flavor	Beverages, frozen desserts, candy, baked goods	0.00004-0.00019%
370	Pine oil (Scotch)	Flavor	Beverages, candy, baked goods	0.0002-0.0006%
371	Piperonal	Artificial flavor	Beverages, frozen desserts, candy, baked goods, chewing gum, gelatin desserts	0.0006-0.0036%
372	Propenylguaethol	Artificial flavor	Beverages, frozen desserts, candy, baked goods, chocolate	0.00059-0.0025%
373	*p*-Propyl anisole	Artificial flavor	Beverages, frozen desserts, candy, baked goods	0.00043-0.0067%
374	Rhodinyl acetate	Artificial flavor	Beverages, frozen desserts, candy, baked goods	0.00014-0.0018%
375	Rose oil (Bulgarian, True Otto)	Flavor	Beverages, frozen desserts, candy, baked goods, gelatin desserts, chewing gum, jellies	0.000005-0.0015%
376	Rosemary oil	Flavor	Beverages, frozen desserts, candy, baked goods, condiments, meats	0.00005-0.004%
377	Rue oil	Flavor	Beverages, frozen desserts, candy, baked goods, condiments	0.0001-0.0004%
378	Sage oil	Flavor	Beverages, frozen desserts, candy, baked goods, chewing gum, condiments, meats, pickles	0.00024-0.011%
379	Sage oil (Spanish)	Flavor	Beverages, frozen desserts, candy, baked goods, condiments, meats	0.0002-0.005%
380	Sandalwood oil (yellow)	Flavor	Beverages, frozen desserts, candy, baked goods, chewing gum	0.00024-0.0047%
381	Santalol (α & β)	Artificial flavor	Beverages, frozen desserts, candy, baked goods	0.0001-0.001%
382	Santalyl acetate	Artificial flavor	Beverages, frozen desserts, candy, baked goods, chewing gum	0.00005-0.00023%

continued

8. COMMON NON-NUTRITIVE COMPONENTS OF FOOD

	Direct Food Additive	Function	Important Use In	Common Level of Use
383	Savory oil (summer)	Flavor	Candy, baked goods, condiments	0.0004-0.005%
384	Spearmint oil	Flavor	Beverages, frozen desserts, candy, baked goods, fats, oils	0.006-0.18%
385			Icings, condiments	5.0-10.0%
386	Spike lavender oil	Flavor	Beverages, frozen desserts, candy, baked goods	0.001-0.005%
387	Tangerine oil	Flavor	Beverages, frozen desserts, candy, baked goods, chewing gum, gelatin desserts	0.002-0.081%
388	Tarragon oil	Flavor	Beverages, frozen desserts, candy, baked goods, condiments, meats, liquors	0.00005-0.004%
389	α-Terpineol	Artificial flavor	Beverages, frozen desserts, candy, baked goods, gelatin desserts, chewing gum, condiments	0.00054-0.004%
390	Terpinyl acetate	Artificial flavor	Beverages, frozen desserts, candy, chewing gum, condiments, meats, baked goods	0.00017-0.026%
391	Terpinyl propionate	Artificial flavor	Beverages, frozen desserts, candy, baked goods	0.00015-0.001%
392	Thyme oil	Flavor	Beverages, frozen desserts, candy, baked goods, chewing gum, condiments, meats	0.0001-0.01%
393	*o*-Tolyl acetate	Artificial flavor	Beverages, frozen desserts, candy, baked goods, chewing gum, gelatin desserts	0.00003-0.022%
394	*p*-Tolyl acetate	Artificial flavor	Beverages, frozen desserts, candy, baked goods, chewing gum, condiments	0.00003-0.022%
395	*p*-Tolyl isobutyrate	Artificial flavor	Beverages, frozen desserts, candy, baked goods	0.000005-0.0007%
396	Tributyrin	Artificial flavor	Beverages, candy, baked goods, margarine, puddings	0.00001-0.1%
397	γ-Undecalactone	Artificial flavor	Beverages, frozen desserts, candy, baked goods, gelatin desserts, chewing gum	0.0003-0.009%
398	Undecanal	Artificial flavor	Beverages, frozen desserts, candy, baked goods, chewing gum	0.0001-0.0056%
399	Vanilla	Flavor	Beverages, frozen desserts, candy, baked goods, puddings, icings, toppings	0.02-0.063%
400	Vanillin	Artificial flavor	Beverages, frozen desserts, candy, baked goods, gelatin desserts, chewing gum, toppings, chocolate products	0.012-0.097%
401			Syrups	0.033-2.0%
402	Wintergreen oil	Flavor	Beverages, frozen desserts, candy	0.0044-0.026%
403			Baked goods, chewing gum	0.15-0.39%
			Miscellaneous Agents	
404	Aluminum calcium sulfate	Anti-caking agent	Vanilla powder	Up to 2.0%
405	Aluminum sulfate	Firming agent	Pickles	Up to 1.0%
406	Calcium salts: chloride, citrate, gluconate	Firming agent	Canned fruits & vegetables	Up to 0.026-0.051% of calcium content
407	Calcium phosphates: dicalcium orthophosphate, monocalcium orthophosphate	Dough conditioner	Bread, rolls, etc.	0.25% of flour
408	Glycerol	Humectant	Confectionery	Up to 10%
409		Bodying agent, solvent, plasticizer for edible coatings	Many foods	0.001-0.6%
410	Mannitol	Anti-sticking & texturizing agent	Chewing gum	Up to 1.0%
411			Candy	Up to 5.0%
412	Nitrates: potassium, sodium	Color fixative	Cured meats	Up to 0.02%
413			Smoked cured fish	Up to 0.05%

continued

8. COMMON NON-NUTRITIVE COMPONENTS OF FOOD

	Direct Food Additive	Function	Important Use In	Common Level of Use
414	Nitrites: potassium, sodi-	Color fixative	Cured meats	Up to 0.02%
415	um		Smoked cured fish	Up to 0.02%
416	Propylene glycol	Solvent, wetting agent, humectant	Confectionery, flavors, shredded coconut, beverages, meats, baked goods, etc.	0.0007-1.4%
417	Silicates: aluminum cal-	Anti-caking	Salt, vanilla powder	Up to 2.0%
418	cium, calcium, magnesium, sodium alumino-, sodium calcium alumino-, tricalcium	agent	Baking powder	Up to 5.0%
419	Sorbitol	Humectant, texturizing agent	Confectionery	2.2-75%
420			Baked goods	0.025-15%

Contributor: Johnson, Paul E.

General References: **[1]** National Research Council, Food and Nutrition Board. 1965. Natl. Acad. Sci. Natl. Res. Council Publ. 1274. **[2]** National Research Council, Food Protection Committee. 1966. Ibid. 1406.

9. COMPOSITION OF FEEDS: ANIMAL ORIGIN

All values were determined on an "as fed" basis. The absence of a particular feed from one part of a table, despite its presence in another part, indicates that values were unavailable for the constituents under consideration.

Part I. General Constituents and Energy Values

Energy and **TDN** (total digestible nutrient): Unbracketed values are for ruminants; values in brackets are for swine.

	Feed	Specification	Dry Matter %	Ash %	Crude Fiber %	Ether Extract %	Protein % N × 6.25	Protein % Digestible	Energy kcal/kg Digestible	Energy kcal/kg Metabolizable	TDN %
1	Blood [1]	Dehydrated, ground	91.0	5.6	1.0	1.6	79.9	56.7	2640 [2684]	2169 [2206]	60 [61]
2		Spray-dehydrated	91.0	4.8	1.0	1.0	82.2	78.9	3652	3000	83
3	Bone [1]	Dehydrated, ground	95.0	71.8	2.0	3.2	12.1	.....	[660]	[542]	[15]
4	Buttermilk	Dehydrated	93.0	9.6	.....	5.8	32.0	28.8	3652 [3388]	3000 [2784]	83 [77]
5	Carcass residue [1,2]	Dehydrated, ground	92.0	21.4	2.0	8.1	59.8	50.8	....	....	......
6	Casein	Dehydrated	90.0	3.3	.....	0.5	81.8	.....	3828	3146	87
7	Cheese trim	....	75.0	4.0	.....	27.4	31.3	28.2	3652	3000	83
8	Clam shells	Ground	99.0	66.9	.....	.....	1.4	.....	....	....	......
9	Crab process residue	Dehydrated, ground	93.0	40.7	11.0	1.8	31.1	22.7	1188	976	27
10	Fish, herring	Dehydrated, ground (low oil)	92.0	10.8	.....	7.5	70.6	62.8	3344	2740	76
11	menhaden	Dehydrated, ground (low oil)	92.0	19.6	1.0	7.7	61.3	49.6	2552	2091 [3]	58
12	pilchard	Dehydrated, ground (low oil)	92.0	13.7	.....	5.5	65.5	.....	2684	2199	61
13	red-	Dehydrated, ground (low oil)	94.0	25.5	1.0	8.4	57.0	50.2	3256	2667	74
14	salmon	Dehydrated, ground (low oil)	93.0	16.7	.....	9.6	58.0	47.0	3124	2559	71
15	sardine	Dehydrated, ground (low oil)	93.0	15.7	1.0	4.3	65.5	53.7	3124	2559	71
16	shark	Dehydrated, ground (low oil)	91.0	13.4	.....	2.5	72.0	51.1	2420	2057	55
17	tuna	Dehydrated, ground (low oil)	87.0	19.0	1.0	8.9	57.4	41.9	2640	2163	60
18	white-	Dehydrated, ground (low oil)	92.0	21.7	1.0	4.4	63.2	58.8	2728	2236	62

[1] Animal not specified. [2] With blood. [3] For poultry, 2970 kcal/kg.

continued

9. COMPOSITION OF FEEDS: ANIMAL ORIGIN

Part I. General Constituents and Energy Values

	Feed	Specification	Dry Matter %	Ash %	Crude Fiber %	Ether Extract %	Protein % N X 6.25	Protein % Digestible	Energy kcal/kg Digestible	Energy kcal/kg Metabolizable	TDN %
19	solubles[1]	Dehydrated	92.0	15.8	1.0	7.6	62.8	55.9	3476	2847	79
20	viscera[1]	Dehydrated, ground	93.0	5.8	2.0	16.0	65.1	53.4	3960	3244	90
21	Milk[4]	Fresh	12.0	0.8	.....	3.7	3.1	2.9	704	578	16
									[660]	[542]	[15]
22	Oystershells	Ground	100.0	80.8	.....	.....	1.0	.....	....	....	......
23	Pork cracklings	Dry-rendered, dehydrated	93.0	22.8	1.0	10.9	56.9	.....	....	....	......
24	Shrimp process residue	Dehydrated, ground	90.0	26.6	11.0	3.1	47.4	38.4	....	....	......
25	Whale, meat	Heat-rendered, dehydrated, ground	92.0	4.0	1.0	6.8	78.9	67.1	....	....	......
26	solubles	Mechanically extracted, condensed	49.0	2.3	.....	0.2	32.4	28.8	....	....	......
27	Whey	Dehydrated	94.0	9.7	.....	0.8	13.8	11.8	3432[5]	2820[5]	78[5]

[1] Animal not specified. [4] Cow. [5] Also for swine.

Contributors: (a) Sprague, Howard B., (b) Crampton, E. W., (c) Harris, Lorin E.

Reference: National Academy of Sciences–National Research Council, Agricultural Board, U.S.A., and National Advisory Committee on Agricultural Services, Canada. 1964. Natl. Acad. Sci. Natl. Res. Council Publ. 1232.

Part II. Essential Minerals

	Feed	Specification	Major Minerals, % Ca	Fe	Mg	P	K	Na	Minor Minerals, mg/kg Co	Cu	Mn	Zn
1	Blood[1]	Dehydrated, ground	0.28	0.38	0.22	0.22	0.09	0.32	...	9.9	5.3	....
2		Spray-dehydrated	0.45	0.30	0.04	0.37	0.41	0.33	0.1	8.1	6.4	....
3	Bone[1]	Dehydrated, ground	28.98	0.08	0.64	13.59	.....	0.46	0.1	16.3	30.4	424.6
4	Buttermilk	Dehydrated	1.34	.....	0.48	0.94	0.71	0.95	...	....	3.5	....
5	Carcass residue[1,2]	Dehydrated, ground	5.94	.....	0.16	3.17	0.56	1.67	0.2	38.7	19.1	....
6	Casein	Dehydrated	0.61	.....	.....	0.99	.....	.....	...	....	4.4	....
7	Cheese trim	....	0.86	.....	0.02	0.49	0.24	0.71	...	....	....	....
8	Clam shells	Ground	36.39	0.46	0.27	0.03	0.16	0.51	...	....	335.7	....
9	Crab process residue	Dehydrated, ground	15.32	0.44	0.88	1.59	0.45	0.85	...	32.8	133.8	....
10	Fish, herring	Dehydrated, ground (low oil)	2.94	.....	.....	2.20	.....	.....	...	....	9.9	....
11	menhaden	Dehydrated, ground (low oil)	5.49	0.06	.....	2.81	.....	.....	...	8.4	25.7	....
12	pilchard	Dehydrated, ground (low oil)	4.09	0.03	0.31	2.80	0.32	0.17	...	....	9.0	....
13	red-	Dehydrated, ground (low oil)	7.73	.....	.....	3.93	.....	.....	...	....	7.7	....
14	salmon	Dehydrated, ground (low oil)	5.44	0.02	.....	3.26	.....	.....	...	11.9	7.9	....
15	sardine	Dehydrated, ground (low oil)	4.90	0.03	0.10	2.77	0.33	0.18	...	20.2	22.2	....
16	shark	Dehydrated, ground (low oil)	3.48	0.02	0.17	1.83	.....	0.33	...	112.4	90.0	112.4
17	tuna	Dehydrated, ground (low oil)	5.32	.....	.....	3.07	.....	.....	...	....	....	....
18	white-	Dehydrated, ground (low oil)	7.87	.....	.....	3.61	.....	.....	...	....	14.3	....
19	viscera[1]	Dehydrated, ground	0.66	0.05	.....	1.14	.....	.....	0.2	97.0	7.3	....
20	Oystershells	Ground	38.05	0.29	0.30	0.07	0.10	0.21	...	....	133.3	....
21	Pork cracklings	Dry-rendered, dehydrated	7.40	.....	.....	4.13	.....	.....	...	....	14.3	....
22	Shrimp process residue	Dehydrated, ground	7.35	0.01	0.54	1.59	.....	.....	...	....	30.1	....
23	Whale, meat	Heat-rendered, dehydrated, ground	0.25	.....	.....	0.56	.....	.....	...	....	....	....
24	solubles	Mechanically extracted, condensed	0.03	.....	0.02	0.15	0.02	.....	...	....	....	....
25	Whey	Dehydrated	0.87	0.02	0.13	0.79	.....	.....	0.1	43.1	4.6	....

[1] Animal not specified. [2] With blood.

Contributors: (a) Sprague, Howard B., (b) Crampton, E. W., (c) Harris, Lorin E.

continued

Part II. Essential Minerals

Reference: National Academy of Sciences–National Research Council, Agricultural Board, U.S.A., and National Advisory Committee on Agricultural Services, Canada. 1964. Natl. Acad. Sci. Natl. Res. Council Publ. 1232.

Part III. Vitamins

	Feed	Specification	Vitamins, mg/kg							
			Thiamine	Riboflavin	Nicotinic Acid	B_6	Biotin	Pantothenic Acid	Folic Acid	Choline
1	Blood[1]	Dehydrated, ground	...	1.5	31.5	...	...	1.1	...	756.8
2		Spray-dehydrated	0.4	4.2	28.6	...	...	5.3	...	279.4
3	Bone[1]	Dehydrated, ground	0.4	0.9	4.2	...	...	2.4	...	....
4	Buttermilk	Dehydrated	3.5	31.0	8.6	2.4	0.3	30.1	0.4	1808.4
5	Carcass residue[1,2]	Dehydrated, ground	...	2.4	39.2	...	...	2.4	1.5	2169.2
6	Casein	Dehydrated	0.4	1.5	1.3	0.4	...	2.6	0.4	209.0
7	Crab process residue	Dehydrated, ground	...	5.9	....	...	...	6.6	...	....
8	Fish, herring	Dehydrated, ground (low oil)	...	9.0	88.9	...	...	11.4	2.4	4004.0
9	menhaden	Dehydrated, ground (low oil)	0.7	4.8	55.9	...	...	8.8	...	3080.0
10	pilchard	Dehydrated, ground (low oil)	...	9.5	....	...	...	.....	...	2081.2
11	red-	Dehydrated, ground (low oil)	...	7.0	....	...	0.2	8.4	...	3429.8
12	salmon	Dehydrated, ground (low oil)	0.9	5.7	24.9	...	...	6.8	...	2772.0
13	sardine	Dehydrated, ground (low oil)	0.4	5.9	62.0	...	...	9.2	...	2959.0
14	white-	Dehydrated, ground (low oil)	1.8	9.0	69.7	...	...	8.8	...	8916.6
15	solubles[1]	Dehydrated	...	7.7	231.1	...	...	44.9	...	5222.8
16	Milk[3]	Fresh	7.3	1.8	58.3	...	...	8.1	...	875.6
17	Shrimp process residue	Dehydrated, ground	...	4.0	....	...	...	.....	...	5827.8
18	Whale, meat	Heat-rendered, dehydrated, ground	...	8.4	104.7	...	...	2.6	...	....
19	solubles	Mechanically extracted, condensed	...	1.5	22.0	...	...	10.6	0.2	....
20	Whey	Dehydrated	3.7	29.9	11.2	...	0.4	47.7	0.9	19.8

1/ Animal not specified. 2/ With blood. 3/ Cow.

Contributors: (a) Sprague, Howard B., (b) Crampton, E. W., (c) Harris, Lorin E.

Reference: National Academy of Sciences–National Research Council, Agricultural Board, U.S.A., and National Advisory Committee on Agricultural Services, Canada. 1964. Natl. Acad. Sci. Natl. Res. Council Publ. 1232.

Part IV. Amino Acids

	Feed	Specification	Amino Acids, %												
			Arg	CyS	Gly	His	Ile	Leu	Lys	Met	Phe	Thr	Trp	Tyr	Val
1	Blood[1]	Dehydrated, ground	3.50	1.40	.....	4.20	1.00	10.30	6.90	0.90	6.10	3.70	1.10	1.80	6.50
2		Spray-dehydrated	3.30	....	.....	4.80	1.10	10.60	8.20	1.00	5.60	3.60	1.00	2.00	7.20
3	Buttermilk	Dehydrated	1.10	....	.....	0.90	2.70	3.40	2.40	0.70	1.50	1.60	0.50	1.00	2.80
4	Carcass residue[1,2]	Dehydrated, ground	3.60	....	.....	1.90	1.90	5.10	4.00	0.80	2.70	2.40	0.70	.....	4.20
5	Casein	Dehydrated	3.40	0.30	1.50	2.50	5.70	8.60	7.00	2.70	4.60	3.80	1.00	4.70	6.80
6	Crab process residue	Dehydrated, ground	1.70	....	.....	0.50	1.20	1.60	1.40	0.50	1.20	1.00	0.30	1.20	1.50
7	Fish, herring	Dehydrated, ground (low oil)	4.00	1.60	5.00	1.30	3.20	5.10	7.30	2.00	2.60	2.60	0.90	2.10	3.20
8	menhaden	Dehydrated, ground (low oil)	4.00	....	.....	1.60	4.10	5.00	5.30	1.80	2.70	2.90	0.60	1.60	3.60
9	pilchard	Dehydrated, ground (low oil)	.....	1.20[3]	.....	.....	.....	.....	.....	1.90	.....	.....	.....	.....	.....
10	red-	Dehydrated, ground (low oil)	4.00	....	.....	1.30	3.40	4.90	6.50	1.80	2.50	2.60	0.60	1.70	3.30
11	salmon	Dehydrated, ground (low oil)	5.20	0.70	5.20	.....	.....	.....	7.60	1.60	.....	.....	0.50	.....	.....
12	sardine	Dehydrated, ground (low oil)	2.70	0.80	4.50	1.80	3.30	4.70	5.90	2.00	2.60	2.60	0.50	3.00	4.10

1/ Animal not specified. 2/ With blood. 3/ Value for cysteine, not cystine.

continued

9. COMPOSITION OF FEEDS: ANIMAL ORIGIN

Part IV. Amino Acids

	Feed	Specification	Amino Acids, %												
			Arg	CyS	Gly	His	Ile	Leu	Lys	Met	Phe	Thr	Trp	Tyr	Val
13	tuna	Dehydrated, ground (low oil)	6.99	....	.....	.....	.....	....	6.19	1.70	.....	.....	0.90	.....	2.20
14	solubles[1]	Dehydrated	2.40	....	.....	2.60	1.70	2.70	3.00	0.90	1.30	1.20	0.70	0.70	1.90
15	Milk[4]	Fresh	0.10	....	.....	0.10	0.20	0.30	0.30	0.10	0.10	0.10	.....	0.20	0.20
16	Whale, meat	Heat-rendered, dehydrated, ground	.....	....	.....	.....	.....	....	5.70	2.30	.....	.....	.....	.....	.....
17	solubles	Mechanically extracted, condensed	1.60	0.10	.....	0.30	0.50	1.00	.....	0.40	0.60	0.60	0.10	0.40	1.00
18	Whey	Dehydrated	0.40	0.30	.....	0.20	0.90	1.40	1.10	0.20	0.40	0.80	0.20	0.30	0.70

[1] Animal not specified. [4] Cow.

Contributors: (a) Sprague, Howard B., (b) Crampton, E. W., (c) Harris, Lorin E.

Reference: National Academy of Sciences–National Research Council, Agricultural Board, U.S.A., and National Advisory Committee on Agricultural Services, Canada. 1964. Natl. Acad. Sci. Natl. Res. Council Publ. 1232.

10. COMPOSITION OF FEEDS: PLANT ORIGIN

All values were determined on an "as fed" basis. Moisture content may be derived by subtracting percent of dry matter from 100. Values for a feed are usually averages for all stages of maturity of the plant, rather than for any specific stage. The absence of a particular feed from one part of the table, despite its presence in another part, indicates that values were unavailable for the constituents under consideration. **Type**: PR&G = pasture, range plants, and green soiling crops; supp. = supplement.

Part I. General Constituents and Energy Values

Energy and **TDN** (total digestible nutrient): Unbracketed values are for ruminants; values in brackets are for swine; values for poultry appear in the footnotes.

	Feed	Type	Dry Matter %	Ash %	Crude Fiber %	Ether Extract %	Protein, % N X 6.25	Protein, % Digestible	Energy, kcal/kg Digestible	Energy, kcal/kg Metabolizable	TDN %
1	Alfalfa, aerial parts	Fresh PR&G	27.2	2.4	7.4	0.8	5.2	3.5	661	542	15
2		Silage	30.4	2.8	9.2	1.1	5.4	3.1	617	506	14
3	hay	Dry roughage	89.7	8.0	28.2	1.9	15.6	11.0	2205	1806	50
4	Apple pomace[1,2]	Energy feed	91.0	1.9	16.0	4.7	5.4	2.0	2917	2386	66
5	Barley, straw	Dry roughage	88.2	5.8	37.4	1.6	3.6	0.7	1764	1445	40
6	grains	Energy feed	89.0	2.4	5.0	1.9	11.6	.....	3124 [3080]	2566 [2530][3]	71 [70]
7	groats	Energy feed	89.0	1.8	2.0	1.9	12.9	10.2	3520 [3168]	2892 [2603]	80 [72]
8	malt sprouts[1]	Protein supp.	93.0	6.4	14.0	1.4	26.2	.....	2772	2278	63
9	pearl by-products[2]	Energy feed	90.0	3.6	8.0	3.0	12.6	10.2	2596	2133	59
10	Bermuda grass, aerial parts	Fresh PR&G	36.7	3.8	9.5	0.8	4.2	2.0	661	542	15
11	hay	Dry roughage	91.1	6.1	27.0	1.8	8.1	4.1	1940	1590	44
12	Bluestem aerial parts	Fresh PR&G	54.4	4.5	17.8	1.2	3.6	.....	....	....	......
13	Brome, smooth; hay	Dry roughage	89.7	7.9	28.4	2.3	11.0	5.6	2072	1698	47
14	Buckwheat grains	Energy feed	88.0	1.8	9.0	2.5	11.1	8.7	2728	2241	62
15	Buffalo grass aerial parts	Fresh PR&G	47.7	5.9	13.2	0.8	4.4	1.9	926	759	21
16	Canary grass aerial parts	Fresh PR&G	25.8	2.4	6.9	1.0	3.4	.....	....	....	......
17	Carpet grass aerial parts	Fresh PR&G	29.3	3.2	8.1	0.5	2.7	1.2	705	578	16
18	Citrus, seeds[4]	Protein supp.	88.0	6.5	10.0	6.6	35.3	30.0	3300	2712	0.75
19	syrup	Energy feed	65.0	6.1	.....	0.2	7.1	.....	2376	1952	54
20	pomace[1,2]	Energy feed	90.0	6.0	13.0	4.6	6.6	2.9	3300	2712	75

[1] Dehydrated. [2] Ground. [3] For poultry, 2838 kcal/kg. [4] Solvent-extracted, ground.

continued

10. COMPOSITION OF FEEDS: PLANT ORIGIN

Part I. General Constituents and Energy Values

	Feed	Type	Dry Matter %	Ash %	Crude Fiber %	Ether Extract %	Protein, %		Energy, kcal/kg		TDN %
							N × 6.25	Digestible	Digestible	Metabolizable	
21	Clover, alsike; aerial parts	Fresh PR&G	22.6	2.3	5.7	0.7	4.0	3.2	705	578	16
22	hay	Dry roughage	87.9	7.6	25.8	2.5	12.9	8.6	2116	1734	48
23	crimson; aerial parts	Fresh PR&G	17.7	1.6	5.0	0.5	3.0	2.3	485	397	11
24	hay	Dry roughage	87.4	8.3	28.1	2.0	14.8	10.2	2425	1987	55
25	hop; aerial parts	Fresh PR&G	24.5	1.6	5.0	0.9	4.1	2.8	838	686	19
26	ladino; aerial parts	Fresh PR&G	18.7	2.1	2.7	0.9	4.7	.....	....	....	....
27	hay	Dry roughage	91.2	8.6	17.5	3.1	20.9	16.2	2646	2168	60
28	red; aerial parts	Fresh PR&G	23.6	2.1	5.7	0.9	4.3	2.8	750	614	17
29		Silage	27.7	2.6	8.3	1.1	4.2	1.7	....	....	....
30	hay	Dry roughage	87.7	6.9	26.4	2.5	13.1	7.9	2116	1734	48
31	sweet; aerial parts	Fresh PR&G	24.8	2.0	7.3	0.7	4.4	.....	....	....	....
32		Silage	32.0	3.0	10.6	1.2	6.1	4.7	750	614	17
33	hay	Dry roughage	87.2	7.6	28.1	1.9	14.2	.....	1896	1554	43
34	white; aerial parts	Fresh PR&G	18.5	2.2	2.9	0.6	5.1	.....	....	....	....
35	Coconut meat[5]	Protein supp.	93.0	6.9	12.0	6.6	20.4	17.3	3388	2784	77
36	Corn, aerial parts with ears	Fresh PR&G	30.6	1.7	7.7	0.8	2.5	.....	....	....	....
37	& husks	Dry roughage	82.4	5.5	21.3	2.0	7.3	.....	2337	1915	53
38		Silage	25.6	1.5	6.4	0.8	2.1	0.8	....	....	....
39	cobs	Dry roughage	90.4	1.5	32.4	0.5	2.5	.....	2028	1662	46
40	bran[1]	Energy feed	89.0	2.1	10.0	4.4	7.5	4.3	2904	2379	66
41	gluten[1,2]	Protein supp.	91.0	2.4	4.0	2.3	42.9	36.5	3520	2884	80
42	gluten with bran[1,2]	Protein supp.	90.0	6.3	8.0	2.4	25.3	21.8	3300	2704	75
43	germ[6]	Protein supp.	91.0	1.9	11.0	3.7	21.5	.....	3388	2783	77
44	distiller's grains[1]	Protein supp.	92.0	2.6	12.0	9.3	27.1	19.8	3696	3029	84
45	Corn, dent; grains	Energy feed	86.0	1.1	2.0	3.9	9.0	7.2	3520	2884	80
46	Cottonseeds[5]	Protein supp.	93.0	6.1	11.0	5.8	41.4	33.1	....	....	....
47	hulls	Dry roughage	90.3	2.5	42.9	1.4	3.9	.....	1675	1373	38
48	Cowpeas, aerial parts	Silage	26.1	4.0	6.9	1.2	3.7	1.8	573	469	13
49	hay	Dry roughage	90.5	10.4	24.7	2.6	16.6	.....	2249	1842	51
50	Dallis grass, aerial parts	Fresh PR&G	25.0	2.8	7.4	0.6	3.0	2.2	705	578	16
51	hay	Dry roughage	90.9	7.9	30.8	1.9	9.2	.....	....	....	....
52	Emmer grains	Energy feed	91.0	3.4	10.0	1.9	12.9	10.3	3212	2631	73
53	Fescue aerial parts	Fresh PR&G	30.6	2.6	8.7	1.1	4.4	.....	....	....	....
54	Fescue, meadow; hay	Dry roughage	88.5	7.3	27.6	2.6	9.3	4.9	2160	1770	49
55	Flax, straw	Dry roughage	92.9	6.7	43.0	3.1	7.2	5.8	1675	1373	38
56	seeds[5]	Protein supp.	91.0	5.6	9.0	5.2	35.3	30.6	3344	2740	76
									[3388]	[2776]	[77]
57	Grains, brewer's[1]	Protein supp.	92.0	3.6	15.0	6.2	25.9	20.7	2640	2163	60
									[1892]	[1550]	[43]
58	Grama aerial parts	Fresh PR&G	56.9	6.0	17.8	1.0	4.3	.....	....	....	....
59	Johnson grass, aerial parts	Fresh PR&G	29.7	3.1	9.2	0.8	3.4	2.5	705	578	16
60	hay	Dry roughage	90.7	8.0	30.2	1.9	7.0	3.1	2205	1807	50
61	Kentucky bluegrass, aerial parts	Fresh PR&G	31.5	2.5	8.3	1.1	5.0	4.1	926	759	21
62	hay	Dry roughage	88.8	7.3	26.6	2.8	10.7	6.1	2249	1842	51
63	Kudzu hay	Dry roughage	92.3	6.1	31.0	2.3	12.7	8.5	2160	1770	49
64	Lespedeza, aerial parts	Fresh PR&G	31.7	2.7	9.8	0.9	5.1	.....	....	....	....
65	hay	Dry roughage	91.0	5.4	28.2	2.6	13.1	5.6	1984	1625	45
66	Lupine aerial parts	Fresh PR&G	12.9	1.3	3.7	0.4	2.3	.....	....	....	....
67	Millet, proso; grains	Energy feed	90.0	3.2	8.0	4.0	12.0	8.4	3388	2784	77
68	Oats, aerial parts	Fresh PR&G	21.7	2.3	5.7	0.8	3.9	1.2	485	397	11
69		Dry roughage	88.2	6.6	27.3	2.7	8.1	4.9	2513	2059	57
70		Silage	31.7	2.7	10.0	1.3	3.1	1.7	838	686	19
71	straw	Dry roughage	90.1	7.4	36.9	1.9	4.0	0.7	2072	1698	47
72	grains	Energy feed	89.0	3.2	11.0	4.5	11.8	.....	2640	2169	60
									[2860]	[2350] [7]	[65]

[1] Dehydrated. [2] Ground. [5] Mechanically extracted, ground. [6] Dry-milled, mechanically extracted, ground. [7] For poultry, 2618 kcal/kg.

continued

10. COMPOSITION OF FEEDS: PLANT ORIGIN

Part I. General Constituents and Energy Values

	Feed	Type	Dry Matter %	Ash %	Crude Fiber %	Ether Extract %	Protein, % N X 6.25	Protein, % Digestible	Energy, kcal/kg Digestible	Energy, kcal/kg Metabolizable	TDN %
73	rolled groats by-products 2/	Energy feed	91.0	2.2	3.0	5.8	16.9	15.2	4092	3362	93
74	hulls	Dry roughage	93.0	6.0	27.0	2.0	5.6	3.7	1496	1229	34
									[1012]	[832]	[23]
75	Orchard grass, aerial parts	Fresh PR&G	24.9	2.3	6.9	1.1	3.4	.....	705	578	16
76	hay	Dry roughage	88.3	6.7	30.0	3.0	8.6	4.5	2205	1807	50
77	Palm seeds 5/	Protein supp.	93.0	3.9	12.0	7.1	18.5	14.8	3432	2820	78
78	Para grass aerial parts	Fresh PR&G	24.6	2.6	8.0	0.4	1.9	.....	573	469	13
79	Peas, field; aerial parts	Silage	26.7	2.5	7.2	1.1	3.9	3.0	794	651	18
80	Peanuts, kernels 5/	Protein supp.	92.0	5.7	11.0	5.9	45.8	40.8	3344	2747	76
81	shells	Dry roughage	92.3	4.3	60.4	1.1	6.8	1.6	838	668	19
82	Potato process residue 1,2/	Energy feed	90.0	2.8	10.0	0.3	6.7	.....	....	....	......
83	Prairie grass hay	Dry roughage	91.8	7.4	30.6	2.4	5.2	.....	....	....	......
84	Rape aerial parts	Fresh PR&G	16.4	2.2	2.8	0.6	2.6	.....	....	....	......
85	Redtop, aerial parts	Fresh PR&G	27.3	2.3	6.8	1.0	3.6	.....	....	....	......
86	hay	Dry roughage	92.1	6.7	29.2	2.5	7.9	3.6	2160	1770	49
87	Rice, grains	Energy feed	89.0	1.4	2.0	1.2	8.2	.....	....	....	......
88	bran with germ 2/	Energy feed	91.0	10.9	11.0	15.1	13.5	9.2	2420	1987	55
									[3256]	[2675]	[74]
89	Rice, white	Energy feed	89.0	0.5	0.4	0.4	7.3	5.7	3520	2893	80
									[3784]	[3109]	[86]
90	polishings 1/	Energy feed	90.0	8.0	3.0	13.2	11.8	9.0	3432	2820	78
									[3916]	[3218]	[89]
91	Rush hay	Dry roughage	89.7	6.2	27.6	2.1	8.6	.....	....	....	......
92	Rye, aerial parts	Fresh PR&G	20.3	2.2	4.9	0.9	4.7	2.1	705	578	16
93	straw	Dry roughage	88.9	4.3	42.3	1.3	2.7	.....	1764	1445	40
94	grains	Energy feed	89.0	1.7	2.0	1.6	11.9	9.4	3168	2603	72
									[3300]	[2712]	[75]
95	bran 1/	Energy feed	90.0	2.8	3.0	2.0	16.5	.....	2464	2024	56
									[2684]	[2207]	[61]
96	flour by-products 8/	Energy feed	90.0	3.4	6.0	3.1	17.1	13.0	3344	2747	76
									[2948]	[2422]	[67]
97	distiller's grains 1/	Protein supp.	93.0	2.6	14.0	6.4	22.4	13.4	2200	1808	50
98	Ryegrass, aerial parts	Fresh PR&G	24.1	3.2	5.6	0.9	3.9	1.3	661	542	15
99	hay	Dry roughage	87.6	7.4	28.4	2.2	8.4	.....	2205	1807	50
100	Safflower seeds with hulls 5/	Protein supp.	91.0	3.7	31.0	6.0	19.7	15.8	2508	2061	57
101	Sagebrush browse	Fresh PR&G	49.7	3.8	12.5	4.4	5.5	.....	....	....	......
102	Salt grass aerial parts	Fresh PR&G	74.4	5.6	22.5	1.3	4.8	.....	....	....	......
103	Saltbush browse	Fresh PR&G	31.6	5.7	7.6	0.7	3.7	.....	....	....	......
104	Sesame seeds 5/	Protein supp.	93.0	9.3	5.0	5.1	47.9	43.6	3124	2567	71
105	Sorghum, aerial parts with heads	Fresh PR&G	23.3	2.0	6.8	0.6	2.2	.....	....	....	......
106		Dry roughage	85.5	7.3	22.3	2.1	6.8	.....	2160	1770	49
107		Silage	28.9	2.2	7.8	0.8	2.3	.....	....	....	......
108	grains	Energy feed	89.0	1.8	2.0	3.0	11.1	8.6	3520	2893	80
109	Sorghum, kafir; grains	Energy feed	90.0	1.5	2.0	2.9	11.8	9.6	3520	2893	80
									[3520]	[2893]	[80]
110	milo; grains	Energy feed	89.0	1.7	2.0	2.8	11.0	8.6	3696	3037	84
									[3432]	[2820] 9/	[78]
111	Soybeans, aerial parts	Fresh PR&G	23.0	2.4	6.5	0.9	3.8	3.2	661	542	15
112		Silage	28.0	2.8	8.7	0.9	4.1	.....	617	506	14
113	hay	Dry roughage	89.2	7.2	28.6	2.7	14.5	9.7	2028	1662	46
114	seeds 5/	Protein supp.	90.0	5.7	6.0	4.7	43.8	36.8	3388	2784	77
									[3476]	[2856] 10/	[79]
115	flour with germ 4/	Protein supp.	93.0	5.6	2.0	0.8	52.0	43.7	3256	2675	74
116	Spelt grains	Energy feed	90.0	3.5	8.0	2.0	11.9	.....	....	....	......

1/ Dehydrated. 2/ Ground. 4/ Solvent-extracted, ground. 5/ Mechanically extracted, ground. 6/ Dry-milled, mechanically extracted, ground. 7/ For poultry, 2618 kcal/kg. 8/ Maximum fiber = 8.5%. 9/ For poultry, 3256 kcal/kg. 10/ For poultry, 2530 kcal/kg.

continued

10. COMPOSITION OF FEEDS: PLANT ORIGIN

Part I. General Constituents and Energy Values

	Feed	Type	Dry Matter %	Ash %	Crude Fiber %	Ether Extract %	Protein, % N × 6.25	Protein, % Digestible	Energy, kcal/kg Digestible	Energy, kcal/kg Metabolizable	TDN %
117	Sudan grass, aerial parts	Fresh PR&G	21.8	2.1	7.0	0.5	2.4	.....	....	....	....
118		Silage	23.3	2.1	8.0	0.7	2.4	.....	....	....	....
119	hay	Dry roughage	88.9	8.5	25.7	2.0	11.3	5.5	2381	1951	54
120	Sugar beets, pulp[1/]	Energy feed	91.0	3.6	19.0	0.6	9.1	4.3	2728	2241	62
									[2860]	[2350]	[65]
121	molasses	Energy feed	77.0	8.2	.....	0.2	6.7	3.5	2684	2206	61
122	Sugarcane, aerial parts	Fresh PR&G	27.1	1.4	8.0	0.4	1.3	1.4	705	578	16
123	molasses	Energy feed	75.0	8.1	.....	0.1	3.2	.....	3168	2603	72
									[2464]	[2024]	[56]
124	Sunflowers, aerial parts	Silage	22.0	2.3	7.0	0.8	2.1	0.8	485	397	11
125	seeds with hulls[11/]	Protein supp.	93.0	6.8	13.0	7.6	41.0	.....	....	....	....
126	Thistle, Russian; aerial parts	Fresh PR&G	39.4	6.0	12.5	0.7	4.8	2.2	573	469	13
127	Timothy, aerial parts	Fresh PR&G	28.3	2.0	8.0	1.0	3.2	1.4	838	686	19
128		Silage	37.5	2.6	12.7	1.2	3.8	1.9	838	686	19
129	hay	Dry roughage	87.7	4.9	29.6	2.3	6.8	3.1	1984	1625	45
130	Tomato pomace[1,2/]	Energy feed	92.0	4.2	29.0	13.0	21.7	.....	....	....	....
131	Trefoil, bird's-foot; aerial parts	Fresh PR&G	23.3	1.9	5.2	0.6	5.0	.....	....	....	....
132	Vetch, aerial parts	Fresh PR&G	20.5	2.0	5.6	0.6	4.4	.....	....	....	....
133	hay	Dry roughage	88.2	8.0	25.1	2.3	17.6	13.4	2293	1879	52
134	Wheat, aerial parts	Fresh PR&G	24.1	2.9	5.0	0.9	5.5	1.5	750	614	17
135	straw	Dry roughage	90.1	7.3	37.4	1.5	3.2	.....	1896	1554	43
136	grains	Energy feed	89.0	1.6	3.0	1.7	12.7	10.7	3388	2784	77
									[3520]	[2893] [12/]	[80]
137	bran	Energy feed	89.0	6.1	10.0	4.1	16.0	13.0	2772	2278	63
									[2508]	[2061] [13/]	[57]
138	germ	Protein supp.	90.0	4.3	3.0	10.9	26.2	23.0	....	....	....
139	flour by-products[14/]	Energy feed	90.0	4.4	8.0	4.6	17.2	14.5	2728	2241	62
									[2816]	[2314] [15/]	[64]
140	distiller's grains[1/]	Protein supp.	93.0	2.4	12.0	5.8	33.8	24.7	3432	2820	78
141	Wheatgrass, aerial parts	Fresh PR&G	42.3	3.6	13.5	1.2	4.4	.....	....	....	....
142	hay	Dry roughage	90.8	7.5	30.5	2.4	7.9	.....	2205	1807	50
143	Yeast[1/], *Saccharomyces;* brewer's	Protein supp.	93.0	6.4	3.0	1.1	44.6	38.4	3212	2639	73
144	distiller's	Protein supp.	95.0	14.0	7.0	0.6	24.0	20.6	2772	2278	63
145	primary	Protein supp.	93.0	8.0	3.0	1.0	48.0	.....	3300	2712	75
									[2860]	[2350]	[65]
146	*Torula*	Protein supp.	93.0	7.8	2.0	2.5	48.3	41.5	3080	2531	70

[1/] Dehydrated. [2/] Ground. [11/] Mechanically extracted, dehydrated, ground. [12/] For poultry, 3300 kcal/kg. [13/] For poultry, 1144 kcal/kg. [14/] Maximum fiber = 9.5%. [15/] For poultry, 1804 kcal/kg.

Contributors: (a) Sprague, Howard B., (b) Crampton, E. W., (c) Harris, Lorin E.

Reference: National Academy of Sciences–National Research Council, Agricultural Board, U.S.A., and National Advisory Committee on Agricultural Services, Canada. 1964. Natl. Acad. Sci. Natl. Res. Council Publ. 1232.

Part II. Essential Minerals and Carotene

	Feed	Type	Major Minerals, % Ca	Cl	Fe	Mg	P	K	Na	S	Minor Minerals mg/kg Co	Cu	Mn	Zn	Carotene mg/kg
1	Alfalfa, aerial parts	Fresh PR&G	0.47	0.13	0.01	0.07	0.08	0.55	0.05	0.11	0.02	2.7	13.7	4.8	54.1
2		Silage	0.49	0.15	0.01	0.10	0.12	0.73	0.05	0.11	0.05	2.9	15.3	.....	27.3
3	hay	Dry roughage	1.48	0.25	0.02	0.29	0.23	1.59	0.14	0.32	0.12	12.3	46.5	15.2	54.8

continued

10. COMPOSITION OF FEEDS: PLANT ORIGIN

Part II. Essential Minerals and Carotene

	Feed	Type	Major Minerals, %								Minor Minerals mg/kg				Carotene
			Ca	Cl	Fe	Mg	P	K	Na	S	Co	Cu	Mn	Zn	mg/kg
4	Apple pomace[1,2]	Energy feed	0.13	.....	0.03	0.06	0.12	0.45	0.03	.....	.....	.....	7.3	.....	....
5	Barley, straw	Dry roughage	0.30	.....	0.03	0.17	0.08	2.01	0.12	.....	.....	.....	15.2	.....	....
6	grains	Energy feed	0.08	.....	0.01	0.12	0.42	0.56	0.02	.....	0.1	7.6	16.3	15.3	....
7	groats	Energy feed	0.07	.....	.....	0.12	0.36	0.53	.....	.....	.....	.....	....	.....	....
8	malt sprouts[1]	Protein supp.	0.22	.....	.....	0.18	0.73	0.21	.....	.....	.....	.....	31.7	.....	....
9	pearl by-products[2]	Energy feed	0.06	.....	0.01	.....	0.43	.....	.....	.....	.....	.....	30.6	.....	....
10	Bermuda grass, aerial parts	Fresh PR&G	0.19	.....	0.04	0.08	0.08	0.60	0.16	.....	0.02	2.1	36.7	.....	103.2
11	hay	Dry roughage	0.42	.....	0.03	0.15	0.18	1.34	.....	.....	.....	.....	....	.....	59.2
12	Bluestem aerial parts	Fresh PR&G	0.22	.....	0.02	0.10	0.08	0.65	.....	.....	.....	15.0	33.6	.....	64.4
13	Brome, smooth; hay	Dry roughage	0.39	0.40	0.01	0.19	0.25	2.12	0.45	0.18	0.10	10.3	46.9	15.6	....
14	Buckwheat grains	Energy feed	0.11	.....	.....	.....	0.33	0.45	.....	.....	0.06	9.5	33.7	8.7	....
15	Buffalo grass aerial parts	Fresh PR&G	0.25	.....	.....	0.07	0.08	0.34	.....	.....	.....	.....	....	.....	44.7
16	Canary grass aerial parts	Fresh PR&G	0.12	.....	.....	0.07	0.07	0.82	.....	.....	.....	.....	....	.....	....
17	Carpet grass aerial parts	Fresh PR&G	0.13	0.12	0.01	0.06	0.06	0.25	.....	0.03	0.03	.....	141.6	.....	40.9
18	Citrus, seeds[3]	Protein supp.	1.20	.....	0.03	0.60	0.69	1.31	.....	.....	.....	6.6	7.5	7.5	....
19	syrup	Energy feed	1.31	.....	0.03	0.14	0.16	0.09	.....	.....	.....	72.8	26.0	88.9	....
20	pomace[1,2]	Energy feed	1.96	.....	0.02	0.16	0.12	0.62	.....	.....	.....	5.7	6.8	14.5	....
21	Clover, alsike; aerial parts	Fresh PR&G	0.29	0.17	0.01	0.07	0.07	0.61	0.10	0.05	.....	1.4	26.5	13.6	....
22	hay	Dry roughage	1.15	0.69	0.02	0.40	0.22	1.50	0.40	0.18	.....	5.3	60.7	.....	164.4
23	crimson; aerial parts	Fresh PR&G	0.29	0.10	0.01	0.07	0.06	0.43	0.07	0.05	.....	.....	51.4	.....	....
24	hay	Dry roughage	1.24	0.55	0.06	0.24	0.16	1.35	0.34	0.24	.....	.....	149.7	.....	....
25	hop; aerial parts	Fresh PR&G	0.29	.....	0.01	0.05	0.08	0.45	.....	.....	.....	.....	24.3	.....	....
26	ladino; aerial parts	Fresh PR&G	0.25	.....	0.01	0.08	0.07	0.41	0.02	0.02	0.02	2.1	14.3	7.2	59.7
27	hay	Dry roughage	1.26	0.26	0.06	0.46	0.36	1.97	0.12	0.20	0.14	8.0	120.8	15.5	147.0
28	red; aerial parts	Fresh PR&G	0.42	0.17	0.01	0.11	0.07	0.50	0.05	0.08	0.03	2.1	37.6	.....	43.5
29		Silage	0.43	.....	0.01	0.11	0.06	0.48	0.06	.....	.....	.....	....	.....	57.2
30	hay	Dry roughage	1.41	0.23	0.01	0.39	0.19	1.54	0.13	0.11	0.13	9.8	57.6	15.1	32.3
31	sweet; aerial parts	Fresh PR&G	0.33	.....	.....	0.08	0.07	0.41	.....	.....	.....	2.5	31.1	.....	61.3
32		Silage	0.41	.....	.....	0.20	0.05	0.63	.....	.....	.....	.....	7.7	.....	9.1
33	hay	Dry roughage	1.54	.....	0.01	0.54	0.23	1.17	.....	.....	.....	8.8	89.8	.....	108.5
34	white; aerial parts	Fresh PR&G	0.27	.....	0.01	0.06	0.09	0.41	0.07	.....	.....	.....	68.5	.....	....
35	Coconut meat[4]	Protein supp.	0.21	.....	0.19	0.26	0.61	1.12	0.04	.....	2.3	18.7	55.4	.....	....
36	Corn, aerial parts with ears	Fresh PR&G	0.08	0.06	0	0.05	0.07	0.39	0.01	0.05	0.03	1.6	19.8	.....	19.4
37	& husks	Dry roughage	0.41	0.16	0.01	0.24	0.21	0.77	0.02	0.12	.....	4.0	56.1	.....	3.6
38		Silage	0.08	0.05	0.01	0.06	0.06	0.29	0.01	0.03	0.02	2.6	12.5	5.4	11.7
39	cobs	Dry roughage	0.11	.....	0.02	0.06	0.04	0.76	.....	0.42	0.12	6.6	5.6	.....	0.6
40	bran[1]	Energy feed	0.03	.....	.....	0.26	0.19	0.73	.....	.....	.....	.....	16.1	.....	....
41	gluten[1,2]	Protein supp.	0.16	.....	0.04	0.05	0.40	0.03	0.10	.....	0.1	28.2	7.3	.....	....
42	gluten with bran[1,2]	Protein supp.	0.46	.....	0.05	0.29	0.77	0.60	0.95	.....	0.09	47.7	23.8	.....	....
43	germ[5]	Protein supp.	0.09	.....	0.09	0.28	0.56	0.13	.....	.....	.....	11.0	9.0	.....	....
44	distiller's grains[1]	Protein supp.	0.09	.....	0.02	0.06	0.37	0.09	0.90	.....	0.1	44.7	18.9	.....	....
45	Corn, dent; grains	Energy feed	0.03	.....	.....	0.12	0.27	0.28	.....	.....	.....	2.1	5.1	16.9	....
46	Cottonseeds[4]	Protein supp.	0.18	.....	0.01	0.54	1.15	1.20	0.03	.....	0.2	17.6	23.1	.....	....
47	hulls	Dry roughage	0.14	0.02	0.01	0.13	0.09	0.76	0.02	.....	0.02	6.4	48.9	20.0	....
48	Cowpeas, aerial parts	Silage	0.39	.....	0.02	0.07	0.09	0.76	.....	.....	.....	.....	....	.....	....
49	hay	Dry roughage	1.21	0.15	0.08	0.42	0.29	1.80	0.24	0.32	0.06	.....	439.0	.....	....
50	Dallis grass, aerial parts	Fresh PR&G	0.14	.....	.....	0.10	0.07	0.37	.....	.....	0.02	.....	20.0	.....	75.6
51	hay	Dry roughage	0.46	.....	0.01	0.67	0.18	.....	.....	.....	.....	.....	....	.....	....
52	Emmer grains	Energy feed	.....	.....	0.01	.....	0.43	.....	.....	.....	.....	34.5	85.8	.....	....
53	Fescue aerial parts	Fresh PR&G	0.13	.....	0.01	0.06	0.10	0.47	.....	.....	.....	2.1	25.1	.....	....
54	Fescue, meadow; hay	Dry roughage	0.44	.....	.....	0.44	0.32	1.65	.....	.....	.....	.....	21.7	.....	....
55	Flax, straw	Dry roughage	0.67	.....	.....	0.29	0.10	1.62	.....	.....	.....	.....	....	.....	....
56	seeds[4]	Protein supp.	0.44	.....	0.02	0.58	0.89	1.24	0.11	.....	0.4	26.4	39.4	.....	0.2
57	Grains, brewer's[1]	Protein supp.	0.27	.....	0.03	0.14	0.50	0.08	0.26	.....	0.1	21.3	37.6	.....	....
58	Grama aerial parts	Fresh PR&G	0.23	.....	.....	0.07	0.08	0.41	.....	.....	0.10	5.1	29.4	.....	27.6

[1] Dehydrated. [2] Ground. [3] Solvent-extracted, ground. [4] Mechanically extracted, ground. [5] Dry-milled, mechanically extracted, ground.

continued

10. COMPOSITION OF FEEDS: PLANT ORIGIN

Part II. Essential Minerals and Carotene

	Feed	Type	Major Minerals, %								Minor Minerals mg/kg				Carotene
			Ca	Cl	Fe	Mg	P	K	Na	S	Co	Cu	Mn	Zn	mg/kg
59	Johnson grass, aerial parts	Fresh PR&G	0.28	.....	.....	0.07	0.07	0.93	.....	.....	.....	.....	....	.....	58.9
60	hay	Dry roughage	0.73	.....	0.05	0.32	0.28	1.22	.....	.....	.....	.....	....	.....	....
61	Kentucky bluegrass, aerial parts	Fresh PR&G	0.14	0.13	0.01	0.06	0.12	0.65	0.09	0.14	0.03	4.4	7.3	5.4	63.1
62	hay	Dry roughage	0.36	0.41	0.02	0.19	0.23	1.53	0.12	0.20	.....	8.8	82.2	.....	....
63	Kudzu hay	Dry roughage	1.49	.....	.....	0.74	0.43	.....	.....	.....	.....	.....	....	.....	40.7
64	Lespedeza, aerial parts	Fresh PR&G	0.36	.....	0.01	0.09	0.10	0.41	.....	.....	.....	.....	62.9	.....	....
65	hay	Dry roughage	1.00	0.05	0.02	0.25	0.17	0.98	0.06	0.17	0.18	8.0	106.4	26.7	42.8
66	Lupine aerial parts	Fresh PR&G	0.17	.....	.....	0.02	0.04	0.34	.....	.....	.....	.....	....	.....	....
67	Millet, proso; grains	Energy feed	0.05	.....	0.01	0.16	0.28	0.43	0.04	.....	.....	21.6	29.1	13.9	....
68	Oats, aerial parts	Fresh PR&G	0.09	0.17	0.01	0.06	0.08	0.70	0.06	0.08	0.02	.....	69.7	.....	92.8
69		Dry roughage	0.23	0.46	0.04	0.26	0.21	0.85	0.15	.....	0.06	3.9	65.7	.....	88.9
70		Silage	0.12	.....	.....	0.01	0.10	1.08	.....	.....	.....	1.7	12.8	.....	37.8
71	straw	Dry roughage	0.30	0.70	0.02	0.16	0.09	2.20	0.33	0.22	.....	9.1	35.3	.....	....
72	grains	Energy feed	0.10	.....	0.01	0.17	0.35	0.37	0.06	.....	0.06	5.9	38.2	.....	....
73	rolled groats by-products[2]	Energy feed	0.09	.....	0.01	0.19	0.47	0.28	.....	.....	.....	6.4	34.5	.....	....
74	hulls	Dry roughage	0.16	.....	0.01	0.08	0.19	0.59	.....	.....	.....	5.1	18.5	.....	....
75	Orchard grass, aerial parts	Fresh PR&G	0.13	.....	0.01	0.07	0.13	0.86	0.01	0.04	0.02	1.8	35.7	6.1	79.5
76	hay	Dry roughage	0.40	0.36	0.01	0.28	0.33	1.85	.....	0.23	0.02	12.1	220.4	16.0	29.6
77	Palm seeds[4]	Protein supp.	.....	.....	0.02	.....	0.70	.....	.....	.....	.....	67.5	272.1	.....	....
78	Para grass aerial parts	Fresh PR&G	0.15	.....	.....	0.09	0.08	0.38	.....	.....	.....	.....	....	.....	....
79	Peas, field; aerial parts	Silage	0.36	.....	.....	0.10	0.08	0.37	.....	0.07	.....	.....	....	.....	....
80	Peanuts, kernels[4]	Protein supp.	0.17	.....	.....	0.33	0.57	1.15	.....	.....	.....	.....	25.5	.....	....
81	shells	Dry roughage	0.23	.....	0.03	0.15	0.06	0.94	.....	.....	0.10	16.2	62.7	.....	0.8
82	Potato process residue[1,2]	Energy feed	0.15	.....	0.04	0.09	0.12	1.05	0.06	.....	.....	15.4	31.5	.....	....
83	Prairie grass hay	Dry roughage	0.38	0.12	0.01	0.25	0.11	0.68	0.01	.....	0.14	25.9	66.4	.....	29.6
84	Rape aerial parts	Fresh PR&G	0.20	.....	.....	0.01	0.06	0.42	.....	0.08	.....	0.6	3.4	.....	....
85	Redtop, aerial parts	Fresh PR&G	0.17	0.02	0.01	0.07	0.10	0.64	0.01	0.04	.....	7.1	63.6	.....	54.3
86	hay	Dry roughage	0.41	0.06	0.02	0.24	0.21	1.56	0.06	0.21	0.14	10.6	199.4	16.5	....
87	Rice, grains	Energy feed	0.04	.....	.....	0.06	0.23	0.15	0.04	.....	.....	3.3	17.6	1.8	....
88	bran with germ[2]	Energy feed	0.06	.....	0.02	0.95	1.82	1.74	.....	.....	.....	13.0	417.8	29.9	....
89	Rice, white	Energy feed	0.03	.....	.....	0.02	0.12	0.13	.....	.....	.....	2.9	10.9	1.8	....
90	polishings[1]	Energy feed	0.04	.....	.....	0.65	1.42	1.17	0.11	.....	.....	.....	....	.....	....
91	Rush hay	Dry roughage	0.31	.....	0.01	0.26	0.10	0.68	.....	.....	.....	.....	....	.....	....
92	Rye, aerial parts	Fresh PR&G	0.11	.....	.....	0.06	0.09	0.69	.....	.....	.....	.....	....	.....	69.5
93	straw	Dry roughage	0.25	0.21	.....	0.07	0.09	0.86	0.12	0.10	.....	3.6	5.9	.....	....
94	grains	Energy feed	0.06	.....	0.01	0.12	0.34	0.46	0.02	.....	.....	7.8	66.9	30.5	....
95	bran[1]	Energy feed	0.15	.....	.....	.....	1.30	.....	.....	.....	.....	.....	11.9	.....	....
96	flour by-products[6]	Energy feed	0.06	.....	.....	.....	0.63	0.63	.....	.....	.....	.....	44.0	.....	....
97	distiller's grains[1]	Protein supp.	0.13	.....	.....	0.17	0.41	0.11	0.17	.....	.....	.....	18.5	.....	....
98	Ryegrass, aerial parts	Fresh PR&G	0.16	.....	.....	0.08	0.08	0.48	.....	.....	.....	1.1	....	.....	96.7
99	hay	Dry roughage	0.43	.....	0.08	0.30	0.28	1.72	.....	.....	0.11	.....	....	.....	....
100	Safflower seeds with hulls[4]	Protein supp.	0.23	.....	0.05	0.33	0.71	0.72	0.05	.....	.....	9.7	17.8	39.8	....
101	Sagebrush browse	Fresh PR&G	0.38	.....	.....	0.16	0.11	.....	.....	.....	0.10	6.7	15.2	.....	....
102	Salt grass aerial parts	Fresh PR&G	0.16	.....	0.01	0.21	0.07	0.18	.....	.....	.....	.....	115.2	.....	....
103	Saltbush browse	Fresh PR&G	0.66	.....	.....	0.17	0.05	0.26	0.06	.....	0.11	3.2	31.7	.....	....
104	Sesame seeds[4]	Protein supp.	2.03	.....	.....	.....	1.29	.....	.....	.....	.....	.....	48.0	.....	....
105	Sorghum, aerial parts with heads	Fresh PR&G	0.09	.....	.....	0.07	0.04	0.37	.....	.....	.....	.....	30.5	.....	6.2
106		Dry roughage	0.34	.....	.....	0.27	0.15	1.21	.....	.....	.....	7.4	99.0	.....	18.6
107		Silage	0.10	.....	0.01	0.09	0.06	0.40	.....	.....	0.09	.....	....	.....	9.7
108	grains	Energy feed	0.04	.....	.....	0.17	0.31	0.34	0.04	.....	2.8	9.6	14.5	13.7	....
109	Sorghum, kafir; grains	Energy feed	0.04	.....	0.01	.....	0.33	.....	.....	.....	.....	6.3	15.8	.....	....
110	milo; grains	Energy feed	0.04	.....	.....	0.20	0.29	0.35	0.01	.....	0.1	14.1	12.9	.....	....
111	Soybeans, aerial parts	Fresh PR&G	0.30	.....	0.01	0.14	0.12	0.24	.....	.....	.....	2.1	27.5	.....	66.8
112		Silage	0.35	.....	0.01	0.11	0.14	0.26	.....	.....	.....	2.6	31.8	.....	21.7
113	hay	Dry roughage	1.15	0.13	0.03	0.70	0.20	0.86	0.11	0.23	0.08	8.0	82.6	21.4	31.8
114	seeds[4]	Protein supp.	0.27	.....	0.02	0.25	0.63	1.71	0.24	.....	0.2	18.0	32.3	.....	....

[1] Dehydrated. [2] Ground. [4] Mechanically extracted, ground. [6] Maximum fiber = 8.5%.

continued

10. COMPOSITION OF FEEDS: PLANT ORIGIN

Part II. Essential Minerals and Carotene

	Feed	Type	Major Minerals, %								Minor Minerals mg/kg				Carotene mg/kg
			Ca	Cl	Fe	Mg	P	K	Na	S	Co	Cu	Mn	Zn	
115	flour with germ 3/	Protein supp.	0.33	.....	0.02	.....	0.62	.....	0.34	.....	.....	16.1	31.9	20.0	......
116	Sudan grass, aerial parts	Fresh PR&G	0.09	.....	0.01	0.08	0.09	0.47	.....	0.02	0.03	7.8	17.7	.....	39.8
117	Silage	Silage	0.15	.....	.....	0.11	0.05	0.72	.....	.....	.....	8.5	23.0	.....	......
118	hay	Dry roughage	0.50	.....	0.02	0.36	0.28	1.37	0.02	0.05	0.12	32.8	83.0	.....	......
119	Sugar beets, pulp 1/	Energy feed	0.68	.....	0.03	0.27	0.10	0.21	.....	.....	0.1	12.5	35.0	0.7	......
120	molasses	Energy feed	0.16	.....	0.01	0.23	0.03	4.77	1.17	.....	0.4	17.6	4.6	.....	......
121	Sugarcane, aerial parts	Fresh PR&G	0.13	.....	.....	0.17	0.05	.....	.....	.....	.....	.....	......	.....	......
122	molasses	Energy feed	0.89	.....	0.02	0.35	0.08	2.38	.....	.....	.....	59.6	42.2	.....	......
123	Sunflowers, aerial parts	Silage	0.38	.....	.....	0.02	0.05	0.64	0.01	.....	.....	.....	233.9	.....	......
124	seeds with hulls 7/	Protein supp.	0.43	.....	.....	.....	1.04	1.08	.....	.....	.....	.....	22.9	.....	......
125	Thistle, Russian; aerial parts	Fresh PR&G	0.97	.....	.....	0.32	0.07	2.55	.....	0.07	0.07	7.6	13.1	.....	35.1
126	Timothy, aerial parts	Fresh PR&G	0.13	0.14	0.01	0.06	0.10	0.49	0.03	0.04	0.01	2.6	38.1	.....	63.4
127		Silage	0.21	.....	.....	0.06	0.11	0.63	.....	.....	.....	2.1	33.8	.....	29.6
128	hay	Dry roughage	0.32	0.39	0.01	0.15	0.17	1.46	0.12	0.11	0.08	4.5	57.0	14.9	12.0
129	Tomato pomace 1,2/	Energy feed	0.28	.....	.....	.....	0.57	.....	.....	.....	.....	.....	47.3	.....	......
130	Trefoil, bird's-foot; aerial parts	Fresh PR&G	0.41	.....	.....	.....	0.05	0.43	.....	.....	0.05	.....	......	.....	......
131	Vetch, aerial parts	Fresh PR&G	0.27	0.38	0.01	0.05	0.07	0.51	0.10	0.03	0.06	2.0	25.4	.....	......
132	hay	Dry roughage	1.20	.....	0.04	0.24	0.30	1.87	0.46	0.13	0.31	8.7	53.7	.....	......
133	Wheat, aerial parts	Fresh PR&G	0.10	0.16	0.01	0.06	0.08	0.81	0.02	0.06	0.02	.....	10.5	.....	98.2
134	straw	Dry roughage	0.15	0.27	0.01	0.11	0.07	1.00	0.13	0.17	0.04	3.0	36.4	.....	2.0
135	grains	Energy feed	0.5	.....	0.01	0.16	0.36	0.52	0.09	.....	0.08	7.2	48.8	13.7	......
136	bran	Energy feed	0.14	.....	0.02	0.55	1.17	1.24	0.06	.....	0.1	12.3	115.7	.....	......
137	germ	Protein supp.	0.07	.....	0.01	.....	1.04	.....	.....	.....	.....	8.8	134.9	.....	......
138	flour by-products 8/	Energy feed	0.15	.....	0.01	0.37	0.91	0.98	0.22	.....	0.1	22.0	118.4	.....	......
139	distiller's grains 1/	Protein supp.	0.10	.....	.....	.....	0.50	.....	.....	.....	.....	.....	......	.....	......
140	Wheatgrass, aerial parts	Fresh PR&G	0.19	.....	0.01	0.06	0.09	1.12	0.22	0.06	0.04	3.0	13.5	.....	86.8
141	hay	Dry roughage	0.30	.....	0.01	0.20	0.18	2.4	.....	.....	.....	.....	10.2	.....	......
142	Yeast 1/, *Saccharomyces;* brewer's	Protein supp.	0.13	.....	0.01	0.23	1.43	1.72	0.07	.....	0.2	33.0	5.7	38.7	......
143	primary	Protein supp.	0.36	.....	0.03	0.36	1.72	.....	.....	.....	.....	.....	3.7	.....	......
144	*Torula*	Protein supp.	0.57	.....	0.01	0.13	1.68	1.88	0.01	.....	.....	13.4	12.8	99.2	......

1/ Dehydrated. 2/ Ground. 3/ Solvent-extracted, ground. 7/ Mechanically extracted, dehydrated, ground. 8/ Maximum fiber = 9.5%.

Contributors: (a) Sprague, Howard B., (b) Crampton, E. W., (c) Harris, Lorin E.

Reference: National Academy of Sciences–National Research Council, Agricultural Board, U.S.A., and National Advisory Committee on Agricultural Services, Canada. 1964. Natl. Acad. Sci. Natl. Res. Council Publ. 1232.

Part III. Vitamins

	Feed	Type	Vitamins, mg/kg								
			Thiamine	Riboflavin	Nicotinic Acid	B_6	Biotin	Pantothenic Acid	Folic Acid	Choline	α-Tocopherol
1	Barley, grains	Energy feed	5.1	2.0	57.4	2.9	0.2	6.5	0.5	1029.9	6.1
2	malt sprouts 1/	Protein supp.	0.7	1.5	43.3	.....	.....	8.6	0.2	1584.0	....
3	pearl by-products 2/	Energy feed	5.9	2.2	63.6	.....	.....	7.7	0.8	1201.2	....
4	Buckwheat grains	Energy feed	3.3	10.6	17.8	.....	.....	....	.....	....	....
5	Citrus, syrup	Energy feed	.....	6.2	26.6	.....	.....	12.5	.....	....	....
6	pomace 1,2/	Energy feed	1.5	2.4	21.6	.....	.....	13.0	.....	844.8	....
7	Coconut meat 3/	Protein supp.	0.7	3.1	24.9	.....	.....	6.6	1.3	919.6	....
8	Corn, bran 1/	Energy feed	4.4	1.5	42.0	.....	0.1	5.3	.....	....	....

1/ Dehydrated. 2/ Ground. 3/ Mechanically extracted, ground.

continued

10. COMPOSITION OF FEEDS: PLANT ORIGIN

Part III. Vitamins

	Feed	Type	Vitamins, mg/kg								
			Thiamine	Riboflavin	Nicotinic Acid	B_6	Biotin	Pantothenic Acid	Folic Acid	Choline	α-Tocopherol
9	gluten 1,2/	Protein supp.	0.2	1.5	49.9	.....	.....	10.3	0.2	330.0	....
10	gluten with bran 1,2/	Protein supp.	2.0	2.4	71.9	.....	0.3	17.2	0.2	1515.8	....
11	germ 4/	Protein supp.	7.0	5.5	53.0	.....	3.4	3.5	0.7	1942.6	....
12	distiller's grains 1/	Protein supp.	1.8	3.1	42.2	.....	0.4	5.9	.....	1859.0	....
13	Corn, dent; grains	Energy feed	4.0	1.3	21.4	7.2	0.1	5.3	0.2	537.3	....
14	Cottonseeds 3/	Protein supp.	5.3	5.3	33.9	.....	.....	10.3	3.7	2776.4	....
15	Flax seeds 3/	Protein supp.	5.1	3.5	35.6	.....	.....	17.8	2.9	1863.4	....
16	Oats, grains	Energy feed	6.2	1.6	15.8	1.2	0.3	12.9	0.4	1073.0	5.9
17	rolled groats by-products 2/	Energy feed	7.0	2.0	10.8	1.3	.....	14.7	0.4	1265.0	....
18	Peanut kernels 3/	Protein supp.	7.3	5.3	169.0	.....	.....	48.2	.....	1683.0	....
19	Rice, grains	Energy feed	2.8	0.6	35.6	6.2	0.1	6.2	0.2	906.6	7.0
20	bran with germ 2/	Energy feed	22.4	2.6	303.2	.....	4.2	23.5	.....	1254.0	....
21	Rice, white	Energy feed	0.6	0.6	14.1	0.4	.....	3.3	.....	906.6	3.6
22	polishings 1/	Energy feed	19.7	1.8	531.7	.....	0.6	58.3	.....	1306.8	....
23	Rye, grains	Energy feed	3.9	1.6	1.2	.....	0.06	6.9	0.6	....	15
24	bran 1/	Energy feed	3.1	0.2	27.9	.....	.....	16.9	.....	....	....
25	flour by-products 5/	Energy feed	3.3	2.4	16.9	.....	.....	23.1	.....	....	....
26	distiller's grains 1/	Protein supp.	1.3	.....	16.9	.....	.....	....	.....	....	....
27	Safflower seeds with hulls 3/	Protein supp.	.....	18.0	85.8	.....	1.4	4.0	22.0	0.4	....
28	Sesame seeds 3/	Protein supp.	2.9	3.7	....	.....	.....	6.4	.....	1533.4	....
29	Sorghum grains	Energy feed	4.1	1.3	43.1	5.3	2.6	11.1	0.2	677.5	....
30	Sorghum, kafir; grains	Energy feed	3.8	1.4	36.6	6.8	.....	12.2	.....	....	....
31	milo; grains	Energy feed	3.9	1.2	42.7	4.1	.....	11.4	.....	677.5	....
32	Soybeans, seeds 3/	Protein supp.	4.0	.....	30.4	.....	0.3	....	6.6	2673.0	....
33	flour with germ 6/	Protein supp.	1.5	.....	59.8	.....	0.7	....	.....	2246.2	....
34	Sugar beets, pulp 1/	Energy feed	0.4	0.7	16.3	.....	.....	1.5	.....	129.4	....
35	molasses	Energy feed	.....	2.4	42.2	.....	.....	4.6	.....	....	....
36	Sugarcane molasses	Energy feed	0.9	3.3	34.3	.....	.....	38.3	.....	875.6	....
37	Tomato pomace 1,2/	Energy feed	11.9	6.2	....	.....	.....	....	.....	....	....
38	Wheat, grains	Energy feed	4.9	1.2	56.6	.....	0.1	12.1	0.4	830.2	15.5
39	bran	Energy feed	7.9	3.1	209.2	.....	.....	29.0	1.8	10.8	987.8
40	germ	Protein supp.	27.9	5.1	47.3	.....	.....	11.2	2.0	3009.6	132.7
41	flour by-products 7/	Energy feed	12.8	2.0	98.6	.....	.....	19.8	0.9	1073.6	....
42	distiller's grains 1/	Protein supp.	2.0	3.7	55.9	.....	.....	8.1	.....	....	....
43	Yeast 1/, *Saccharomyces;* brewer's	Protein supp.	91.7	35.0	447.5	43.3	.....	109.8	9.7	3885.2	....
44	distiller's	Protein supp.	76.6	27.1	255.2	.....	.....	36.1	11.2	....	....
45	primary	Protein supp.	6.4	38.7	300.1	.....	1.6	311.3	31.0	....	....
46	*Torula*	Protein supp.	6.2	44.4	500.3	29.5	1.1	82.9	23.3	2910.6	....

1/ Dehydrated. 2/ Ground. 3/ Mechanically extracted, ground. 4/ Dry-milled, mechanically extracted, ground. 5/ Maximum fiber = 8.5%. 6/ Solvent-extracted, ground. 7/ Maximum fiber = 9.5%.

Contributors: (a) Sprague, Howard B., (b) Crampton, E. W., (c) Harris, Lorin E.

Reference: National Academy of Sciences–National Research Council, Agricultural Board, U.S.A., and National Advisory Committee on Agricultural Services, Canada. 1964. Natl. Acad. Sci. Natl. Res. Council Publ. 1232.

Part IV. Amino Acids

	Feed	Type	Amino Acids, %												
			Arg	CyS	Gly	His	Ile	Leu	Lys	Met	Phe	Thr	Trp	Tyr	Val
1	Barley grains	Energy feed	0.53	0.18	0.36	0.27	0.53	0.80	0.53	0.18	0.62	0.36	0.18	0.36	0.62
2	Buckwheat grains	Energy feed	0.97	.....	.....	0.26	0.35	0.53	0.62	0.18	0.44	0.44	0.18	.....	0.53
3	Corn, germ 1/	Protein supp.	.....	.....	.....	.....	.....	1.70	0.90	0.30	0.80	0.90	0.30	1.50	1.30
4	gluten 2,3/	Protein supp.	1.40	0.60	1.50	1.00	2.30	7.60	0.80	1.00	2.90	1.40	0.20	1.00	2.20
5	gluten with bran 2,3/	Protein supp.	0.80	.....	.....	0.60	1.20	2.60	0.80	0.30	0.90	0.80	0.20	0.90	1.30
6	distiller's grains 2/	Protein supp.	1.00	.....	.....	0.60	1.00	3.60	0.90	0.40	0.60	0.30	0.20	0.90	1.20

1/ Dry-milled, mechanically extracted, ground. 2/ Dehydrated. 3/ Ground.

continued

10. COMPOSITION OF FEEDS: PLANT ORIGIN

Part IV. Amino Acids

	Feed	Type	Amino Acids, %												
			Arg	CyS	Gly	His	Ile	Leu	Lys	Met	Phe	Thr	Trp	Tyr	Val
7	Cottonseeds 4/	Protein supp.	4.30	.....	.....	1.10	1.60	2.60	1.60	0.60	2.20	1.40	0.70	.....	2.00
8	Grains, brewer's 2/	Protein supp.	1.30	.....	.....	0.50	1.50	2.30	0.90	0.40	1.30	0.90	0.40	1.20	1.60
9	Oats, grains	Energy feed	0.71	0.18	.....	0.18	0.53	0.89	0.36	0.18	0.62	0.36	0.18	0.53	0.62
10	rolled groats by-products 3/	Energy feed	1.00	0.20	0.20	0.30	0.60	1.00	0.50	0.20	0.60	0.50	0.20	0.60	0.70
11	Peanut kernels 4/	Protein supp.	4.69	.....	.....	1.00	2.00	3.10	1.30	0.60	2.30	1.40	0.50	.....	2.20
12	Rice, grains	Energy feed	0.45	0.09	.....	0.09	0.36	0.53	0.27	0.18	0.36	0.27	0.09	0.62	0.45
13	bran with germ 3/	Energy feed	0.50	0.10	.....	0.20	0.40	0.60	0.50	.....	0.40	0.40	0.10	.....	0.60
14	Rice, white	Energy feed	0.36	0.09	0.71	0.18	0.45	0.71	0.27	0.27	0.53	0.36	0.09	0.62	0.53
15	polishings 2/	Energy feed	0.50	0.10	.....	0.10	0.30	0.50	0.50	.....	0.30	0.30	0.10	.....	.....
16	Rye grains	Energy feed	0.53	0.18	.....	0.27	0.53	0.71	0.45	0.18	0.62	0.36	0.09	0.27	0.62
17	Safflower seeds with hulls 4/	Protein supp.	1.20	0.80	.....	.....	.....	.....	0.70	0.40	.....	.....	0.30	.....	.....
18	Sorghum grains	Energy feed	0.36	0.18	.....	0.27	0.53	1.42	0.27	0.09	0.45	0.27	0.09	0.36	0.53
19	Sorghum, kafir; grains	Energy feed	0.36	.....	.....	0.27	0.54	1.62	0.27	0.18	0.63	0.45	0.18	.....	0.63
20	milo; grains	Energy feed	0.36	0.18	.....	0.27	0.53	1.42	0.27	0.09	0.45	0.27	0.09	0.36	0.53
21	Soybeans, seeds 4/	Protein supp.	2.60	0.60	2.50	1.10	2.80	3.60	2.70	0.80	2.10	1.70	0.60	1.40	2.20
22	flour with germ 5/	Protein supp.	3.10	0.60	.....	0.70	.....	.....	4.20	0.90	1.80	.....	1.00	.....	0.30
23	Spelt grains	Energy feed	0.50	.....	.....	0.20	0.40	0.70	0.30	0.20	0.50	0.40	0.10	.....	0.50
24	Sugar beet pulp 2/	Energy feed	0.30	.....	.....	0.20	0.30	0.60	0.60	.....	0.30	0.40	0.10	0.40	0.40
25	Sunflower seeds with hulls 6/	Protein supp.	.....	.....	.....	.....	.....	.....	2.00	1.60	.....	.....	.....	.....	.....
26	Tomato pomace 2,3/	Energy feed	1.20	.....	.....	0.40	0.70	1.70	1.60	0.10	0.90	0.70	0.20	.....	1.00
27	Wheat, grains	Energy feed	0.71	0.18	0.89	0.27	0.53	0.89	0.45	0.18	0.62	0.36	0.18	0.45	0.53
28	bran	Energy feed	1.00	0.30	0.90	0.30	0.60	0.90	0.60	0.10	0.50	0.40	0.30	0.40	0.70
29	germ	Protein supp.	1.60	0.50	.....	0.50	1.20	1.10	1.60	0.30	0.80	0.80	0.30	.....	1.10
30	flour by-products 7/	Energy feed	0.90	0.20	0.40	0.40	0.80	1.20	0.70	0.20	0.70	0.60	0.20	0.40	0.80
31	distiller's grains 2/	Protein supp.	1.10	.....	.....	0.80	2.00	1.70	0.70	.....	1.70	0.90	.....	0.50	1.70
32	Yeast 2/, *Saccharomyces;* brewer's	Protein supp.	2.20	0.50	1.70	1.10	2.10	3.20	3.00	0.70	1.80	2.10	0.50	1.50	2.30
33	distiller's	Protein supp.	1.10	.....	.....	0.60	1.40	1.70	0.70	0.40	0.60	1.00	0.20	.....	1.30
34	primary	Protein supp.	2.60	0.50	.....	5.60	3.60	3.72	3.80	1.00	2.50	2.50	0.40	.....	3.20
35	*Torula*	Protein supp.	2.60	0.60	2.70	1.40	2.90	3.50	3.80	0.80	3.00	2.60	0.50	2.10	2.90

2/ Dehydrated. 3/ Ground. 4/ Mechanically extracted, ground. 5/ Solvent-extracted, ground. 6/ Mechanically extracted, dehydrated, ground. 7/ Maximum fiber = 9.5%.

Contributors: (a) Sprague, Howard B., (b) Crampton, E. W., (c) Harris, Lorin E.

Reference: National Academy of Sciences–National Research Council, Agricultural Board, U.S.A., and National Advisory Committee on Agricultural Services, Canada. 1964. Natl. Acad. Sci. Natl. Res. Council Publ. 1232.

11. DRINKING WATER

Part I. Comparison of Standards

Unless otherwise indicated, the International Standard for drinking water gives the recommended quality limits. AWWA: American Water Works Association report of Task Group 2225M. *Abbreviations:* No req. = no requirement; Unobj. = unobjectionable; Inoff. = inoffensive.

	Water Quality Criteria	Drinking-Water Standards: International	Public Health Service	AWWA 1/
	Biological			
1	Coliform organisms/ 100 ml	10 2/; 1.0 3/	1.0	0.1
2	Coliform organisms, total count	No limit	No req.	No req.
3	Microscopic organisms	No req.	No req.	0
4	Viruses	No req.	No req.	No req.
	Physical			
5	Color, cobalt scale units	5	15	3
6	Odor	Unobj.	Inoff. 4/	No req.
7	Taste	Unobj.	Inoff.	None
8	Turbidity, silica scale units	5	5	0.1

1/ Criteria are tentative. 2/ In 90% of the samples of untreated water examined in any one year. 3/ In treated water. 4/ Maximum threshold number, 3.

continued

11. DRINKING WATER

Part I. Comparison of Standards

	Water Quality Criteria	Drinking-Water Standards: International	Public Health Service	AWWA[1/]
	Chemical[5/]			
9	Alkyl benzene sulfonate	0.5	0.5[6/]	0.2
10	Aluminum	No req.	No req.	0.05
11	Arsenic	0.05	0.01[6/]; 0.05[7/]	0.01
12	Barium	1.0[8/]	1.0[7/]	0.5
13	Cadmium	0.01[8/]	0.01[7/]	0.01
14	Calcium	75	No req.	No req.
15	Calcium carbonate[9/]	No req.	No req.	80
16	Carbon alcohol extract	No req.	No req.	0.1
17	Carbon chloroform extract	0.2	0.2[6/]	0.04
18	Chloride	200	250[6/]	No req.
19	Chromium, hexavalent	0.05[8/]	0.05[7/]	0.01
20	Copper	1.0	1.0[7/]	0.2
21	Cyanide	0.2[8/]	0.01[6/]; 0.2[7/]	0.01
22	Fluoride	1.0-1.5	0.8-1.7[6/]; 1.4-2.4[7/]	0.7-1.2
23	Hydrogen ion (pH)	7.0-8.5	No req.	No req.
24	Iron	0.3	0.3[6/]	0.05
25	Lead	0.05[8/]	0.05[7/]	0.05
26	Magnesium	50	No req.	No req.
27	Magnesium + sodium sulfate	500	No req.	No req.
28	Manganese	0.1	0.05[6/]	0.01
29	Nitrate	45	45	23
30	Phenol	0.001	0.001[6/]	0.0005
31	Selenium	0.01[8/]	0.01[7/]	0.1
32	Silver	No req.	0.05[7/]	0.02
33	Sulfate	200	250[6/]	No req.
34	Zinc	5.0	5.0[6/]	1.0
35	Total dissolved solids	500	500[6/]	No req.
	Radiochemical[10/]			
36	Strontium-90	30	10[11/]	5
37	Radium-226	10	3[11/]	3
38	Gross beta	1000	1000[11/]	100
	Reference	[3]	[2]	[1]

[1/] Criteria are tentative. [5/] Values are ppm, except the value for pH. [6/] Recommended. [7/] Mandatory limit. [8/] Tolerance limit, comparable to the mandatory limit of the Public Health Service standards. [9/] Criterion for hardness. [10/] Values are μμc/liter. [11/] For full interpretation, consult 1962 Public Health Service Drinking-Water Standards.

Contributor: Taylor, Floyd B.

References

[1] American Water Works Association. 1967. Willing Water 11(6).

[2] U.S. Public Health Service. 1962. U.S. Public Health Serv. Publ. 956.

[3] World Health Organization. 1963. International standards for drinking water. Columbia Univ. Press, New York.

Part II. Chemicals in Interstate Carrier Water Supplies

Analyses were made by the Water Quality Section Laboratory, Basic Data Branch, Division of Water Supply and Pollution Control, Department of Health, Education, and Welfare. **Limit:** Values are from the 1962 Public Health Service Drinking-Water Standards. Values in parentheses are ranges, estimate "c" (*see* Introduction).

	Substance	Limit mg/liter[1/]	Occurrence in Water Supplies mg/liter[1/]	Effects
1	Alkyl benzene sulfonate	0.5	0.054(0-0.640)	Not highly toxic. Rats fed 0.5% in subacute and 2-yr tests show no effects.
2	Arsenic	0.01[2/]	0.01[3/](0-0.03)	Serious systemic poison, cumulative and causing chronic effects. Severe poisoning usually from 100 mg.
3	Carbon chloroform extract	0.2	65(7-267) ppm	Not a health hazard at limit given

[1/] Unless otherwise indicated. [2/] Concentration of arsenic higher than 0.05 mg/liter constitutes grounds for rejection of the water supply. [3/] True average is less, due to significant numbers of "less than" values in the original results.

continued

Part II. Chemicals in Interstate Carrier Water Supplies

	Substance	Limit mg/liter [1]	Occurrence in Water Supplies mg/liter [1]	Effects
4	Chloride	250	39.9(0.7-490)	Limit set by taste
5	Copper	1	0.032(0-0.600)	Not a health hazard except when large amounts are ingested. Adults require approx 1 mg/day.
6	Cyanide	0.01	....	Rapid, fatal poison. Toxic effects do not occur from doses of 10 mg or less.
7	Fluoride	0.7-1.2 [4]	0.62(0-2.5)	Small amounts beneficial; dosage above 2250 mg can cause death
8	Nitrate	45	1.5(0-19.0)	Excess amounts can cause methemoglobinemia in infants
9	Sulfate	250	59.4(0-320)	Dosage above 750 mg/liter usually has laxative effects
10	Zinc	5	1.33 [3](<0.06-7.0)	0.3 mg/kg/day required by children; 675-2280 mg/liter may be emetic
	Minor minerals			
11	Antimony	....	<0.025(<0.0001-<0.1)	Effects similar to arsenic, but less acute. Recommended limits: not greater than 0.1 mg/liter; routinely, <0.05 mg/liter; over long periods of time, <0.01 mg/liter.
12	Barium	1.0 [5]	0.049(0.0007-0.9)	Stimulant to heart and other muscle; 550-600 mg $BaCl_2$ is fatal
13	Beryllium	....	<0.00013(0.00001-0.0007)	Some beryllium salts poisonous in occupational exposure
14	Bismuth	....	<0.013(0.00007-<0.07)	Water supplies containing bismuth should be avoided
15	Boron	....	0.1(0-1.0)	Little known about toxic properties
16	Cadmium	0.01 [5]	0.008 [3](<0.0004-0.06)	Food containing 13-15 ppm has caused illness
17	Chromium	0.05 [5]	0.003 [3](<0.0003-0.04)	Carcinogenic when inhaled. Significant accumulation in tissues of rats after ingesting more than 5 mg/liter for 1 yr.
18	Cobalt	....	<0.0056(<0.0003-0.03) [6]	Beneficial in small amounts, such as 7 μg/day
19	Lead	0.05	0.017 [3](0.001-0.40)	Cumulative body poison; serious effects
20	Molybdenum	....	<0.0096(<0.0004-0.2)	Necessary for plants and poultry. Excessive intake may be toxic to higher animals; chronic or acute effects not well known.
21	Nickel	....	<0.0117(<0.0004-0.04)	May cause dermatitis in sensitive people. Doses of 30-73 mg $NiSO_4 \cdot 6H_2O$ have produced toxic effects.
22	Selenium	0.01 [5]	0.008 [3](0-0.1)	Essential in low concentrations; toxic to man and other animals in high concentrations
23	Silver	0.05 [5]	0.13 [3](0-2) μg/liter	Produces irreversible, adverse cosmetic changes
24	Tin	....	<0.006(<0.0003-0.03)	Used in food containers without known harmful effects
25	Vanadium	....	<0.006(<0.0004-0.07)	May be beneficial in prevention of heart disease
	Radiochemicals			
26	Radium-226	3 μμc/liter [7]	1.21 [3](<0.5-28.8) μμc/liter	An internal alpha emitter which can destroy bone marrow
27	Strontium-90	10 μμc/liter [7]	1.0(0.1-3.3) μμc/liter	An internal beta emitter which affects bone

[1] Unless otherwise indicated. [3] True average is less, due to significant numbers of "less than" values in the original results. [4] Concentration of fluoride higher than 1.4-2.4 mg/liter constitutes grounds for rejection of the water supply. [5] A higher concentration of the mineral constitutes grounds for rejection of the water supply. [6] Upper limit of range is not for an interstate carrier water supply. [7] For full interpretation, consult 1962 Public Health Service Drinking-Water Standards.

Contributor: Taylor, Floyd B.

General References

[1] Taylor, F. B. Unpublished. U.S. Public Health Service, Region 1, John F. Kennedy Federal Building, Boston, Mass., 1967.

[2] U.S. Public Health Service. 1960-61. U.S. Public Health Serv. Publ. 1049.

[3] U.S. Public Health Service. 1962. Ibid. 956.

[4] U.S. Public Health Service. 1962-63. Ibid. 1049-A.

12. COMPOSITION OF NATURAL WATERS

Values in parentheses are ranges, estimate "c" (*see* Introduction).

Part I. Amount of Dissolved Solids

Values are mg/liter of dissolved solids. Total content of dissolved solids in certain surface, ground, enclosed basin, spring, mine, brackish, and other categories of natural waters, except seawater, may differ by an order of magnitude or more from the mean; also, relative proportions of various dissolved substances may deviate considerably from the mean.

	Substance	Swiss Alpine Lakes	World River Waters	Carbonate Ground Waters	Chloride Ground Waters	Siliceous Ground Waters	Sulfate Ground Waters	Seawater
1	Boron, as H_3BO_3	....	....	3	....	....	....	28
2	Bromine	....	<0.1	....	10	....	....	66
3	Calcium	38.5	15.0	233	300	24	232	406
4	Carbon, as CO_3 or HCO_3	51.4	58.4	1664	187	119	138	140
5	Chlorine	5.3	7.8	129	2296	229	43	19,260
6	Iron	0.4	<0.1	106	2	3	51	<1
7	Magnesium	2.5	4.1	160	62	4	158	1292
8	Potassium	2.4	2.3	31	35	27	10	385
9	Silicon, as SiO_2	7.3	13.1	142	9	413	30	<1
10	Sodium	4.5	6.3	835	1160	260	279	10,710
11	Strontium	....	....	....	1	....	....	8
12	Sulfur, as SO_4	25.9	11.2	101	111	111	2327	2688
13	Other	1.8	1.8	32	27	16	32	17
14	Total solids	140.0(<10->500)	120.0(<10->1000)	3436(<500-8000)	4200(<100-293,000)	1220(<500-2800)	3300(<100-178,000)	35,000(20,000-40,000)

Contributor: ZoBell, Claude E.

General References

[1] Clarke, F. W. 1924. U.S. Geol. Surv. Bull. 770:881.

[2] Conway, E. J. 1942. Proc. Roy. Irish Acad., B, 48: 119.

[3] Erikson, E. 1952. Tellus 4:215, 280.

[4] Goldberg, E. D. 1963. In M. N. Hill, ed. The sea. Interscience, New York. v. 2, pp. 3-25.

[5] Gorham, E. 1958. Phil. Trans. Roy. Soc. London, B, 679:147.

[6] Hutchinson, G. E. 1957. A treatise on limnology. J. Wiley, New York. v. 1.

[7] Livingstone, D. A. 1963. U.S. Geol. Surv. Profess. Papers 440-G.

[8] Rankama, K., and T. G. Sahama. 1950. Geochemistry. Univ. Chicago Press, Chicago.

[9] Sverdrup, H. U., M. W. Johnson, and R. H. Fleming. 1942. The oceans. Prentice-Hall, New York.

Part II. Percent of Total Solids

Values are percent of total solids, unless otherwise indicated. Seawater is fairly constant in composition and salinity, whereas rain, river, lake, ground, spring, mineral, and other natural waters vary greatly depending on season, rainfall, geographic location, and many other factors.

	Substance	Rainwater 1/	World River Waters	Chloride Ground Waters	Sulfate Ground Waters	Seawater	Great Salt Lake	Dead Sea
1	Boron, as H_3BO_3	....	0.05	....	....	0.08	....	....
2	Bromine	....	0.02	0.23	....	0.19	....	1.72
3	Calcium	12.2	12.43	7.15	7.02	1.16	0.16	4.37
4	Carbon, as CO_3 or HCO_3	....	48.66	4.45	4.18	0.40	0.09	....
5	Chlorine	12.2	6.31	54.67	1.29	55.03	55.48	67.26

1/ The amount of rainfall and its chemical composition--which varies greatly--have a pronounced effect on other kinds of surface or enclosed basin waters.

continued

12. COMPOSITION OF NATURAL WATERS

Part II. Percent of Total Solids

	Substance	Rainwater 1/	World River Waters	Chloride Ground Waters	Sulfate Ground Waters	Seawater	Great Salt Lake	Dead Sea
6	Iron	....	0.45	0.05	1.59	<0.01	....	....
7	Magnesium	2.4	3.41	1.48	4.79	3.68	2.76	13.62
8	Potassium	7.3	1.96	0.84	0.32	1.10	1.66	1.68
9	Silicon, as SiO_2	....	10.92	0.22	0.90	<0.01	....	....
10	Sodium	9.7	5.28	27.58	8.46	30.60	33.07	11.14
11	Strontium	....	....	0.03	....	0.02	....	....
12	Sulfur, as SO_4	48.7	9.30	2.65	70.52	7.68	6.68	0.08
13	Other	7.5	1.21	0.65	0.96	0.05	0.10	0.13
14	Salinity 2/	ca. 0.001 (0->0.05)	ca. 0.012 (<0.001->0.1)	ca. 0.42 (<0.01-29.31)	ca. 0.33 (<0.01-17.78)	ca. 3.5 (2.0-4.0)	ca. 20.5 (14.1-27.2)	ca. 23.1 (16.0-26.0)

1/ The amount of rainfall and its chemical composition--which varies greatly--have a pronounced effect on other kinds of surface or enclosed basin waters. 2/ Values are approximations of percent salinity.

Contributor: ZoBell, Claude E.

General References: *See* Part I.

II. ANIMAL NUTRITION

13. NUTRITIONAL STANDARDS: MAN

Part I. United States: Children and Adults

Allowances are those recommended by the Food and Nutrition Board, National Research Council (1963 revision) for the maintenance of good nutrition in essentially healthy, normally active persons in the temperate climates of the USA, under current conditions of living. These daily allowances afford a margin of sufficiency above average physiological requirements, and can be obtained from a variety of common foods that also provide other nutrients for which human requirements are less well defined. For a detailed discussion of allowances, and for information on nutrients not tabulated, consult the reference.

	Subjects				Calories[2]	Protein g	Calcium[3] g	Iron mg	Thiamine mg	Riboflavin mg	Nicotinic Acid Equiv.[4] mg	Ascorbic Acid mg	Vitamin A I.U.	Vitamin D I.U.
	Sex	Age[1] yr	Wt kg	Ht cm										
1	♂♀	0-1	8	....	kg × 115 ±15[5]	kg × 2.5 ±0.5[5]	0.7[6]	kg × 1.0	0.4[6]	0.6[6]	6[6]	30	1500	400
2		1-3	13	87	1300	32	0.8	8	0.5	0.8	9	40	2000	400
3		3-6	18	107	1600	40	0.8	10	0.6	1.0	11	50	2500	400
4		6-9	24	124	2100	52	0.8	12	0.8	1.3	14	60	3500	400
5	♂	9-12	33	140	2400	60	1.1	15	1.0	1.4	16	70	4500	400
6		12-15	45	156	3000	75	1.4	15	1.2	1.8	20	80	5000[7]	400
7		15-18	61	172	3400	85	1.4	15	1.4	2.0	22	80	5000[7]	400
8		18-35[8]	70	175	2900	70	0.8	10	1.2	1.7	19	70	5000[7]	....
9		35-55	70	175	2600	70	0.8	10	1.0	1.6	17	70	5000[7]	....
10		55-75	70	175	2200	70	0.8	10	0.9	1.3	15	70	5000[7]	....
11	♀	9-12	33	140	2200	55	1.1	15	0.9	1.3	15	80	4500	400
12		12-15	47	158	2500	62	1.3	15	1.0	1.5	17	80	5000[7]	400
13		15-18	53	163	2300	58	1.3	15	0.9	1.3	15	70	5000[7]	400
14		18-35[8]	58	163	2100	58	0.8	15	0.8	1.3	14	70	5000[7]	....
15		35-55	58	163	1900	58	0.8	15	0.8	1.2	13	70	5000[7]	....
16		55-75	58	163	1600	58	0.8	10	0.8	1.2	13	70	5000[7]	....
17	Pregnant[9,10]				+200	+20	+0.5	+5	+0.2	+0.3	+3	+30	+1000	400
18	Lactating[10]				+1000	+40	+0.5	+5	+0.4	+0.6	+7	+30	+3000	400

[1] Values are for midpoint of range unless otherwise indicated. [2] The following formulas were used (where W = weight in kilograms, and resulting values were rounded to nearest 50 cal) to adjust calorie allowances for adults of various body weight and age at a mean environmental temperature of 20°C, assuming average physical activity: ♂, 25 yr, 725 + 31 W; 45 yr, 650 + 28 W; 65 yr, 550 + 23.5 W; ♀, 25 yr, 525 + 27 W; 45 yr, 475 + 24.5 W; 65 yr, 400 + 20.5 W. During pregnancy, observations of body weight will indicate recommendations for changes in calorie requirements; during lactation, the basic diet of the individual woman should be supplemented by approx 120 cal/100 ml milk produced. [3] Phosphorus intake from birth to 18 years, and during latter part of pregnancy or during lactation, should be at least equal to the calcium intake; phosphorus intake by adults will usually be 1½ times as great. Intake of 100-150 μg iodine/day is also recommended for adults. [4] Nicotinic acid equivalents include dietary sources of the preformed vitamin and the precursor tryptophan; 60 mg tryptophan is equivalent to 1 mg nicotinic acid. [5] Allowances/kg decrease progressively from birth. [6] Allowances increase proportionately with calories to maximum values shown. [7] 1000 I.U. from preformed vitamin A, and 4000 I.U. from β-carotene. [8] Values are for 25-year-olds. [9] 2nd and 3rd trimesters. [10] Except for vitamin D, allowances are in addition to those shown for the nonpregnant and nonlactating woman of similar age.

Contributors: (a) Voris, LeRoy, (b) Leitch, Isabella

Reference: National Academy of Sciences–National Research Council, Food and Nutrition Board. 1964. Natl. Acad. Sci. Natl. Res. Council Publ. 1146:vii.

continued

13. NUTRITIONAL STANDARDS: MAN

Part II. Canada and United Kingdom: Children and Adults

The dietary standard for Canada recommends daily intake of nutrients adequate for the maintenance of health among the majority of Canadians; allowances are in excess of known minimal requirements. The dietary standard for the United Kingdom recommends daily levels of nutrients believed to be sufficient to establish and maintain a good nutritional state. All allowances must be adjusted to the needs of the individual, particularly with respect to age, body weight, degree of activity, and physiological adaptation. The calorie allowances quoted for the 25-29 age groups in Canada are for the lightest work category (regarded as typical); those for the United Kingdom adults are for the moderately active.

	Subjects			Calories	Protein g	Calcium[1] g	Iron mg	Thiamine mg	Riboflavin mg	Nicotinic Acid mg	Ascorbic Acid mg	Vitamin A[2] I.U.	Vitamin D I.U.
	Sex	Age yr	Wt kg										
				Canada[3] [2]									
1	♂♀	0-1	3.2-9.1	360-900	12-24	0.5	5	0.3	0.5	3	20	1000	400
2		1-2	9.1-11.8	900-1200	25-30	0.7	5	0.4	0.6	4	20	1000	400
3		2-3	14.1	1400	30	0.7	5	0.4	0.7	4	20	1000	400
4		4-6	18.1	1700	30	0.7	5	0.5	0.9	5	20	1000	400
5		7-9	25.9	2100	40	1.0	5	0.7	1.1	7	30	1500	400
6		10-12	34.9	2500	50	1.2	12	0.8	1.3	8	30	2000	400
7	♂	13-15	49.0	3100	75	1.2	12	0.9	1.6	9	30	2700	400
8		16-17	61.7	3700	55	1.2	12	1.1	1.9	11	30	3200	400
9		18-19	65.3	3800	60	0.9	6	1.1	1.9	11	30	3200	400
10		25-29	71.7	2850	50	0.5	6	0.9	1.4	9	30	3700	....
11	♀	13-15	49.0	2600	75	1.2	12	0.8	1.3	8	30	2700	400
12		16-17	54.4	2400	50	1.2	12	0.7	1.2	7	30	3200	400
13		18-19	56.2	2450	50	0.9	10	0.7	1.2	7	30	3200	400
14		25-29	56.2	2400	39	0.5	10	0.7	1.2	7	30	3700	....
15	Pregnant[4]			Up to 2900	49	1.2	13	0.85	1.45	8.5	40	4200	400
16	Lactating			2900-3400	49-59	1.2	13	1.0	1.7	10	50	5200	400
				United Kingdom[5] [1,3]									
17	♂♀	<1	8	800	28	1	6	0.3	0.5	3	10	1500	800
18		1-3	12	1300	46	1	7	0.5	0.8	5	15	1500	400
19		4-6	18	1600	56	1	8	0.6	1	6	15	1500	400
20		7-9	27	1950	68	1	10	0.8	1.2	8	20	1500	400
21	♂	10-12	35	2450	86	1.2	12	1	1.5	10	25	1500	400
22		13-15	49	3150	110	1.4	15	1.3	1.9	13	30	1500	400
23		16-20	63	3400	119	1.4	15	1.4	2.1	14	30	2500	400
24		>20	65	3000	87[6]	0.8	12	1.2	1.8	12	20	5000	....
25	♀	10-12	35	2450	86	1.2	12	1	1.5	10	25	1500	400
26		13-15	49	2750	96	1.3	15	1.1	1.6	11	30	1500	400
27		16-20	54	2500	88	1.0	15	1.0	1.5	10	30	2500	400
28		>20	56	2500	73[6]	0.8	12	1.0	1.5	10	20	5000	....
29	Pregnant			2750	96	1.5	15	1.1	1.6	11	40	6000	400-600
30	Lactating			3000	111	2.0	15	1.4	2.1	...	50	8000	800

1/ For Canadians, phosphorus intake should be equal to calcium intake. 2/ Canadian values are based on a mixed diet supplying both vitamin A and carotene; as preformed vitamin A, the suggested intake would be approximately two-thirds of the indicated allowance. United Kingdom values are based on a mixed diet containing one-third vitamin A and two-thirds carotene. 3/ Iodine in table salt in proportions of 1:10,000, as prevails in Canada, meets requirements. 4/ 3rd trimester. 5/ 0.15 mg iodine from birth to 20 years and during pregnancy and lactation; 0.1 mg after age 20. 6/ Protein allowance is increased with calories on the basis that protein in diet should provide not less than 11% of the energy for adults not engaged in hard work.

continued

13. NUTRITIONAL STANDARDS: MAN

Part II. Canada and United Kingdom: Children and Adults

Contributors: (a) Monagle, J. E., (b) Leitch, Isabella

References

[1] British Medical Association, Committee on Nutrition. 1950. Report. British Medical Association, London.

[2] Canadian Council on Nutrition. 1964. Can. Bull. Nutr. 6(1).

[3] Great Britain National Food Survey Committee. 1954. Gt. Brit. Natl. Food Surv. Comm. Ann. Rept. 1951-52.

Part III. Other Countries and FAO: Adults

Because of the differences in objective and in the "reference" individual, there is no uniform agreement among countries as to the nutrient allowances considered desirable as a national guide. Allowances, in general, are for individuals engaged in light or moderate work.

	Country	Subjects			Calories	Protein g	Calcium g	Iron mg	Thiamine mg	Riboflavin mg	Nicotinic Acid Equiv.[1/] mg	Ascorbic Acid mg	Vitamin A I.U.
		Sex	Age yr	Wt kg									
1	Australia	♂	25	65	2700	65	0.7	10	1.1	1.6	18[2/]	30	2500[3/]
2		♀	25	55	2300	55	0.6	12	0.9	1.4	15[2/]	30	2000[3/]
3	Central America	♂	25	55	2700	55	0.7	10	1.4	1.4	14	50	4333[4/]
4	& Panama	♀	25	50	2000	50	0.7	10	1.0	1.2	10	45	4333[4/]
5	India	♂	25.4	55	2800	55	....	...	...	....	.....	...	....
6		♀	21.5	45	2300	45	....	...	...	....	.....	...	....
7	Japan	♂	.....	56	3000	70	0.6	10	1.5	1.5	15	65	2000[5/]
8		♀	.....	48.5	2400	60	0.6	10	1.2	1.2	12	60	2000[5/]
9	Netherlands	♂	20-29	70	3000	70	1.0	10	1.2	1.8	12	50	5500[6/]
10		♀	20-29	60	2400	60	1.0	12	1.0	1.5	10	50	5500[6/]
11	Norway	♂	25	70	3400	70	0.8	12	1.7	1.8	17	30	2500
12		♀	25	60	2500	60	0.8	12	1.3	1.5	13	30	2500
13	Philippines	♂	.....	53	2600	55	0.7	6	1.6	1.4[7/]	16	75	4000[8/]
14		♀	.....	45	2300	45	0.7	10	1.4	1.1[7/]	14	70	4000[8/]
15	South Africa	♂	.....	73	3000	65	0.7	9	1.0	1.6	15	40	4000[8/]
16		♀	.....	60	2300	55	0.6	12	0.8	1.4	12	40	4000[8/]
17	USSR	♂♀	.....	...	.....	...	....	...	2.0[9/]	2.5	15	70[9/]	5000[10/]
18	FAO[11/]	♂	25	65	3200	43	0.4-0.5	...	...	....	....	...	....
19		♀	25	55	2300	36	0.4-0.5	...	...	....	....	...	....

[1/] Nicotinic acid equivalents include dietary sources of the preformed vitamin and the precursor, tryptophan; 60 mg tryptophan is equivalent to 1 mg nicotinic acid. [2/] Preformed nicotinic acid plus (grams protein × 0.16). [3/] 3 I.U. carotene = 1 I.U. vitamin A activity. [4/] 0.0003 mg vitamin A alcohol = 1 I.U. vitamin A activity. [5/] Or 6000 I.U. carotene. [6/] 1500 I.U. as preformed vitamin A + 4000 I.U. activity as carotene. [7/] Grams protein × 0.025. [8/] Assumes two-thirds contributed by carotene. [9/] To be increased up to 50% in far north. [10/] I.U. = 0.3 μg of natural vitamin. [11/] Food and Agriculture Organization of the United Nations.

Contributor: Voris, LeRoy

Reference: Maynard, L. A. 1964. Natl. Acad. Sci. Natl. Res. Council Publ. 1146:58.

14. NUTRIENT REQUIREMENTS: DOMESTIC ANIMALS

Values are the daily ration for a single animal, unless otherwise indicated.

Part I. General Requirements

DE = apparent digestible energy. **TDN** = total digestible nutrient. Calculations for beef cattle, dairy cattle, horse, sheep, and swine are based on 4.4 kcal DE per g TDN.

	Animal	Specification	Body Weight kg	Avg Daily Gain g	Daily Feed g	Protein		DE kcal	TDN kg	Reference
						Total g	Digestible g			
	Cat									2
1	Young	Growth	....	....	....	>30/100 g of diet	....	250/kg body wt[1]	....	
2	Adult	Maintenance	....	....	....	21/100 g of diet	....	60-90/kg body wt	....	
	Cattle, beef[2]									3
3	Calf, weanling	Wintering	181	454	4763	499	318	10,500	2.40	
4			227	454	5715	590	363	12,600	2.86	
5			272	454	6487	590	363	14,300	3.27	
6	Short yearling	Finishing	181	1043	5353	590	454	15,600	3.54	
7			272	1089	7439	817	590	21,700	4.94	
8			363	998	8800	862	680	25,700	5.85	
9			454	998	10,433	1043	771	30,500	6.94	
10	Yearling	Wintering	272	454	6487	544	318	14,300	3.27	
11			363	318	7167	544	318	15,800	3.58	
12			408	227	7167	544	318	15,800	3.58	
13		Finishing	272	1179	7938	817	590	22,800	5.17	
14			363	1225	10,115	998	771	29,000	6.58	
15			454	1179	11,703	1179	862	33,600	7.62	
16			499	1043	11,703	1179	862	33,500	7.62	
17	2-yr-old	Finishing	363	1270	10,569	1043	771	29,700	6.76	
18			454	1315	12,792	1270	953	35,900	8.17	
19			544	1225	14,062	1406	1043	39,500	8.98	
20	Heifer & steer	Growth	181	726	5534	635	408	12,800	2.90	
21			272	635	7439	680	408	16,400	3.72	
22			363	544	8664	680	408	19,100	4.36	
23			454	454	9571	726	454	21,100	4.81	
24	Heifer	Pregnancy, wintering	318	680	9072	680	408	20,000	4.54	
25			408	363	8165	635	363	18,000	4.08	
26			454	227	8165	635	363	18,000	4.08	
27	Cow	Pregnancy, wintering	363	680	9979	771	454	22,000	4.99	
28			454	181	8165	635	363	18,000	4.08	
29			544	0	8165	635	363	18,000	4.08	
30			544	−227	7983	590	363	15,000	3.40	
31		Lactation, first 3-4 mo postpartum	408-499	0	12,701	1043	635	33,600	7.62	
32	Bull, moderately active	Growth & maintenance	272	1043	7348	907	544	20,200	4.58	
33			454	726	9072	1089	635	24,000	5.44	
34			635	454	11,204	1089	635	28,400	6.44	
35			816	0	11,567	1089	680	28,000	6.35	
	Cattle, dairy[2]									8
36	Calf	Slaughter	35	500	700	155	140	3500	0.80	
37			50	700	1200	270	240	6200	1.40	
38			75	900	2000	400	360	10,100	2.30	
39			100	1100	2800	600	450	13,200	3.00	
40			150	1200	3200	640	480	14,100	3.20	

[1] But decreased rapidly to approximately 134 kcal/kg body wt at 30 weeks of age. [2] Requirements based on air-dry feed containing 90% dry matter.

continued

14. NUTRIENT REQUIREMENTS: DOMESTIC ANIMALS

Part I. General Requirements

	Animal	Specification	Body Weight kg	Avg Daily Gain g	Daily Feed g	Protein Total g	Protein Digestible g	DE kcal	TDN kg	Reference
41	Heifer[3/]	Herd replacement	25	300	400	90	80	2200	0.50	
42			35	450	700	155	140	3300	0.75	
43			50	500	1000	200	180	4400	1.00	
44			75	550	2000	340	240	6600	1.50	
45			100	650	2800	430	280	8400	1.90	
46			150	700	4000	480	320	11,200	2.55	
47			200	700	5200	520	380	13,900	3.15	
48			250	650	6200	630	400	15,600	3.55	
49			300	600	7200	660	410	18,000	4.10	
50			350	600	8000	675	415	19,800	4.50	
51			400	600	8800	700	420	20,200	4.60	
52			450	500	9200	725	435	20,700	4.70	
53			500	400	9600	750	450	21,100	4.80	
54			550	300	9800	765	460	21,600	4.90	
55			600	200	10,000	780	470	22,000	5.00	
56	Cow[3/]	Maintenance	350	0	5200	375	225	12,300	2.80	
57			400	0	5800	417	250	13,000	2.95	
58			450	0	6200	450	270	14,100	3.20	
59			500	0	7000	500	300	15,200	3.45	
60			550	0	7800	533	330	16,700	3.80	
61			600	0	8000	567	340	17,400	3.95	
62			650	0	8600	608	365	18,500	4.20	
63			700	0	9200	650	390	19,400	4.40	
64			750	0	9800	692	415	20,500	4.65	
65			800	0	10,400	733	440	21,600	4.90	
66		Pregnancy, last 2-3 mo	400	....	9800	817	490	23,600	5.35	
67			550	....	12,800	993	605	29,900	6.80	
68			700	....	15,200	1200	720	35,200	8.00	
69	Bull	Growth	25-150[4/]	300-700	400-4000	90-480	80-320	2200-11,200	0.50-2.55	
70			200	1000	5800	610	425	15,400	3.5	
71			250	1000	6700	620	435	17,600	4.0	
72			300	1000	8000	685	480	21,100	4.8	
73			400	900	9600	800	555	25,500	5.8	
74			500	800	10,400	890	580	27,200	6.2	
75			600	700	11,200	950	615	28,600	6.5	
76			700	600	12,000	1050	650	30,800	7.0	
77			800	500	13,300	1100	690	33,000	7.5	
78			900	0	13,600	1150	710	35,200	8.0	
79			1000	0	14,500	1200	740	37,400	8.5	
80	Mature	Maintenance & breeding	500	0	7800	675	450	19,400	4.4	
81			600	0	8800	735	490	22,000	5.0	
82			700	0	10,000	810	540	25,100	5.7	
83			800	0	11,000	885	590	28,200	6.4	
84			900	0	12,200	960	640	30,800	7.0	
85			1000	0	13,500	1035	690	34,300	7.8	
86			1100	0	14,500	1110	740	37,000	8.4	
87			1200	0	15,500	1200	800	39,600	9.0	

[3/] Additional nutrients required per kilogram of milk produced, depending on volume and fat content of milk.

[4/] Requirements are the same as for growing heifers of equal weight (*see* lines 41-46).

continued

Part I. General Requirements

	Animal	Specification	Body Weight kg	Avg Daily Gain g	Daily Feed g	Protein: Total g	Protein: Digestible g	DE kcal	TDN kg	Reference
	Dog									1
88	Young	Growth	2.3	....	181.4[5]	min. 20	....	500	....	
89			4.5	....	299.4[5]	min. 40	....	840	....	
90			6.8	....	381.0[5]	min. 60	....	1050	....	
91			13.6	....	680.4[5]	min. 120	....	1920	....	
92			>22.7	....	1179.4[5]	min. 200	....	3100	....	
93	Adult	Maintenance	2.3	0	90.7[5]	min. 10	....	250	....	
94			4.5	0	149.7[5]	min. 20	....	420	....	
95			6.8	0	190.5[5]	min. 30	....	525	....	
96			13.6	0	340.2[5]	min. 60	....	960	....	
97			>22.7	0	567.0[5]	min. 100	....	1550	....	
98	Guinea pig	Growth	....	....	8/100 g body wt	2/100 g body wt	....	....	....	2
	Hamster									2
99	Young	Growth	0.030	0-3	....	....	....	....	....	
100			0.060	0.786	6.0	....	....	....	....	
101			0.100	0.357	5.8	....	....	....	....	
102	Adult	Maintenance	0.060-0.100	0	....	....	....	24	....	
	Horse[2,6]									9
103	270 kg at maturity	Growth	90	410	2770	360	240	7600	1.72	
104			185	180	2680	270	200	7400	1.68	
105			270	0	3400	270	190	9400	2.13	
106	365 kg at maturity	Growth	90	640	3040	500	340	8400	1.91	
107			185	410	4260	410	280	11,800	2.68	
108			270	230	4720	360	270	13,000	2.95	
109			365	0	4220	320	230	11,600	2.63	
110	455 kg at maturity	Growth	90	730	3040	540	380	8400	1.91	
111			185	540	4490	500	340	12,400	2.81	
112			270	360	5170	450	300	14,200	3.22	
113			365	230	5580	410	290	15,400	3.49	
114			455	0	4940	410	270	13,600	3.08	
115	545 kg at maturity	Growth	90	1000	3400	820	500	9400	2.13	
116			185	820	5080	640	450	14,000	3.18	
117			270	590	5940	540	390	16,400	3.72	
118			365	360	6080	500	340	16,800	3.81	
119			455	180	6080	450	320	18,800	3.81	
120			545	0	5670	450	310	15,600	3.54	
121	635 kg at maturity	Growth	90	1220	3630	860	600	10,000	2.27	
122			185	1000	5310	770	540	14,600	3.31	
123			270	820	6530	680	490	18,000	4.08	
124			365	590	6990	640	430	19,200	4.35	
125			455	360	6990	540	380	19,200	4.35	
126			545	180	6800	500	360	18,800	4.26	
127			635	0	6350	500	350	17,600	3.99	
128	Mature	Light work	185	0	3760	200	140	10,400	2.36	
129			270	0	5080	260	190	14,000	3.18	

2/ Requirements based on air-dry feed containing 90% dry matter. 5/ Dry foods contain 6-12% moisture. Calculation of amounts of dry food required are based on energy supplied by food containing 91% dry matter, 76% protein plus carbohydrate, 5% fat, and 10% ash, fiber, and other inert material. 6/ Little specific information on nutrient requirements of horses; data shown were derived in many instances from experimental results obtained with cattle.

continued

14. NUTRIENT REQUIREMENTS: DOMESTIC ANIMALS

Part I. General Requirements

	Animal	Specification	Body Weight kg	Avg Daily Gain g	Daily Feed g	Protein: Total g	Protein: Digestible g	DE kcal	TDN kg	Reference
130			365	0	6260	330	230	17,200	3.90	
131			455	0	7390	390	270	20,400	4.63	
132			545	0	8480	450	310	23,400	5.31	
133			635	0	9530	500	350	26,200	5.94	
134		Medium work	185	0	4350	200	140	12,000	2.72	
135			270	0	5900	260	190	16,200	3.67	
136			365	0	7350	330	230	20,200	4.58	
137			455	0	8620	390	270	23,800	5.40	
138			545	0	9930	450	310	27,400	6.21	
139			635	0	11,110	500	350	30,600	6.94	
140	♀	Pregnancy, last quarter	185	....	2630	260	180	7200	1.63	
141			270	....	3630	360	250	10,000	2.27	
142			365	....	4450	440	300	12,200	2.77	
143			455	....	5310	510	360	14,600	3.31	
144			545	....	6080	590	420	16,800	3.81	
145			635	....	6800	670	470	18,800	4.26	
146		Lactation, peak	185	....	6990	790	550	19,200	4.35	
147			270	....	7980	890	630	22,000	4.99	
148			365	....	9430	1060	740	26,000	5.90	
149			455	....	10,430	1160	810	28,800	6.53	
150			545	....	11,520	1300	910	31,800	7.21	
151			635	....	13,150	1410	980	36,200	8.21	
152	Monkey, rhesus	Growth	<0.5[7]	500/6 mo[8]	....	2/kg body wt	....	40/kg body wt	....	2
153	Mouse weanling, ♂	....	....	....	3.5[9]	0.56[9]	....	14.5[9]	....	2
154	21 day	....	0.009-0.012	5-13[9]	....	....	....	....	....	
155	CF No. 1	....	....	13-14[9]	3.9-4.0/g gain[9]	....	....	....	....	
	Rabbit[10]									6
156	♂♀, avg wt, 3.0 kg	Growth	1.81-4.08	....	145.152	22.680	13.608	....	0.086184	
157		Growth & fattening	1.81	31.75	113.400	18.144	13.608	....	0.072576	
158			2.27	31.75	136.080	22.680	18.144	....	0.086184	
159			2.72	31.75	154.224	22.680	18.144	....	0.099792	
160			3.18	31.75	172.368	27.216	22.6800	....	0.113400	
161		Maintenance	2.27	0	90.720	13.608	9.072	....	0.049896	
162			4.54	0	149.688	18.144	13.608	....	0.081648	
163			6.80	0	204.120	22.680	18.144	....	0.113400	
164	♀	Pregnancy	2.27	....	113.400	18.144	13.608	....	0.068040	
165			4.54	....	185.976	27.216	22.6800	....	0.108864	
166			6.80	....	254.016	36.288	27.216	....	0.149688	
	Rat, laboratory									2
167	♂, 23 days[11]	Growth	0.055	5.0[12]	9	1.8[13]	1.1[14]	36[15]	....	
168	33 days[16]	Growth	0.110	5.4[12]	15	3.0[13]	1.8[14]	60[15]	....	
169	42 days[17]	Growth	0.165	5.7[12]	18	3.6[13]	2.2[14]	72[15]	....	
170	53 days[18]	Growth	0.220	5.5[12]	21	4.2[13]	2.5[14]	84[15]	....	
171	108 days[19]	Growth	0.385	3.9[12]	20	4.0[13]	2.4[14]	80[15]	....	
172	350 days, adult	Maintenance	0.550	....	19	1.33[13]	0.76[14]	76[15]	....	

7/ Average birth weight. 8/ Up to age 3½ years. 9/ Based on average daily feed requirements during 2-week period following weaning. 10/ Values based on air-dry weights. 11/ 10% of mature weight. 12/ Expected daily gain from 21 days to age specified. 13/ Dietary N X 6.25. 14/ Dietary N X 6.25, with a true digestibility and biological value of 100%. 15/ Gross energy. 16/ 20% of mature weight. 17/ 30% of mature weight. 18/ 40% of mature weight. 19/ 70% of mature weight.

continued

Part I. General Requirements

	Animal	Specification	Body Weight kg	Avg Daily Gain g	Daily Feed g	Protein: Total g	Protein: Digestible g	DE kcal	TDN kg	Reference
173	♀, 26 days[16]	Growth	0.065	4.2[12]	10	2.0[13]	1.2[14]	40[15]	....	
174	35 days[17]	Growth	0.098	3.9[12]	14	2.8[13]	1.7[14]	56[15]	....	
175	44 days[18]	Growth	0.130	3.7[12]	15	3.0[13]	1.8[14]	60[15]	....	
176	96 days[19]	Growth	0.228	2.5[12]	16	3.2[13]	1.9[14]	64[15]	....	
177	350 days, adult	Maintenance	0.325	....	13	0.91[13]	0.52[14]	52[15]	....	
178	adult	Pregnancy	....	4	19[20]	3.8[13]	2.3[14]	76[15,20]	....	
179		Lactation	....	0	33[21]	6.6[13]	4.0[14]	131[15,21]	....	
	Sheep[2]									5
180	Lamb	Fattening	27.2	158.8	1224.7	145.2	81.7	3000	0.68040	
181			31.8	181.4	1406.2	154.2	86.2	3600	0.81648	
182			36.3	204.1	1542.2	163.3	90.7	4200	0.95256	
183			40.8	204.1	1678.3	163.3	90.7	4600	1.04328	
184			45.4	181.4	1769.0	163.3	90.7	4800	1.08864	
185	Lamb & yearling, ♂	....	36.3	181.4	1451.5	145.2	81.7	4000	0.90720	
186			45.4	136.1	1678.3	145.2	81.7	4200	0.95256	
187			54.4	90.7	1905.1	145.2	81.7	4200	0.95256	
188			63.5	45.4	2086.6	145.2	81.7	4600	1.04328	
189			72.6	45.4	2177.3	145.2	81.7	4800	1.08864	
190	♀	Replacement	27.2	136.1	1224.7	136.1	72.6	3000	0.68040	
191			36.3	90.7	1451.5	127.0	68.0	3200	0.72576	
192			45.4	63.5	1542.2	117.9	63.5	3400	0.77112	
193			54.4	31.8	1542.2	108.9	59.0	3400	0.77112	
194	♀	Pregnancy, first 15 wk	45.4	31.8	1179.4	95.3	54.4	2600	0.58968	
195			54.4	31.8	1360.8	108.9	59.0	3000	0.68040	
196			63.5	31.8	1542.2	122.5	68.0	3400	0.77112	
197			72.6	31.8	1723.7	136.1	72.6	3800	0.86184	
198		Pregnancy, last 6 wk	45.4	167.8	1723.7	145.2	81.7	4000	0.90720	
199			54.4	167.8	1905.1	154.2	86.2	4400	0.99792	
200			63.5	167.8	2086.6	163.3	90.7	4800	1.08864	
201			72.6	167.8	2177.3	167.8	90.7	5000	1.13400	
202		Lactation, first 8-10 wk	45.4	−36.3	2086.6	181.4	99.8	5400	1.22472	
203			54.4	−36.3	2268.0	190.5	104.3	5800	1.31544	
204			63.5	−36.3	2494.8	199.6	108.9	6200	1.40616	
205			72.6	−36.3	2585.5	208.7	113.4	6200	1.40616	
206		Lactation, last 12-14 wk	45.4	31.8	1723.7	145.2	81.7	4000	0.90720	
207			54.4	31.8	1905.1	154.2	86.2	4400	0.99792	
208			63.5	31.8	2086.6	163.3	90.7	4800	1.08864	
209			72.6	31.8	2177.3	167.8	90.7	5000	1.13400	
	Swine									4
210	Meat-type	Finishing, full-fed	56.7-79.4	771.1	3039.1	394.6	....	10,000	2.26800	
211			79.4-102.1	861.8	3538.1	426.4	....	11,600	2.63088	
212	Bacon-type[22]	Finishing, full-fed	34.0-56.7	680.4	2358.7	376.5	....	7200	1.63296	
213			56.7-79.4	771.1	3039.1	426.4	....	9400	2.13192	
214			79.4-102.1	816.5	3538.1	494.4	....	11,000	2.49480	
215		Growth	4.5-11.3	272.2	544.32	117.9	....	1920	0.435456	
216			11.3-22.7	453.6	1134.0	204.1	....	4000	0.90720	
217			22.7-34.0	589.7	1678.3	267.6	....	5400	1.22472	
218			34.0-56.7	725.8	2358.7	331.1	....	7800	1.76904	

[2] Requirements based on air-dry feed containing 90% dry matter. [12] Expected daily gain from 21 days to age specified. [13] Dietary N X 6.25. [14] Dietary N X 6.25, with a true digestibility and biological value of 100%. [15] Gross energy. [16] 20% of mature weight. [17] 30% of mature weight. [18] 40% of mature weight. [19] 70% of mature weight. [20] Female carrying litter of 8 or 9 pups. [21] Female and litter of 6 pups. [22] Two more weeks are usually required to produce a 90.72-kg, bacon-type hog than a 90.72-kg, meat-type hog.

continued

14. NUTRIENT REQUIREMENTS: DOMESTIC ANIMALS

Part I. General Requirements

	Animal	Specification	Body Weight kg	Avg Daily Gain g	Daily Feed g	Protein: Total g	Protein: Digestible g	DE kcal	TDN kg	Reference
219	♂, young	Breeding	136.1	453.6	2721.6	408.2	....	8400	1.90512	
220	adult	Breeding	226.8	....	3402.0	444.5	....	10,400	2.35872	
221	Gilt	Pregnancy	136.1	453.6	2494.8	399.1	....	8200	1.85976	
222		Lactation	158.8	....	4989.6	748.4	....	16,400	3.71952	
223	Sow	Pregnancy	226.8	317.5	2938.4	412.8	....	9800	2.22264	
224		Lactation	204.1	....	5670.0	734.8	....	18,800	4.26384	
	Chicken									7
225	Single-comb	Growth	0.250	....	27	5.4	....	....	....	
226	White Leg-		0.500	....	45	9	....	....	....	
227	horns or simi-		0.750	....	57	10.1	....	....	....	
228	lar breeds		1.000	....	65	10.4	....	....	....	
229			1.250	....	79	12.6	....	....	....	
230			1.500	....	84	13.4	....	....	....	
231	Adult	60% egg production	1.800	....	110	16.5	....	....	....	
232		Breeding	1.800	....	110	16.5	....	....	....	
233	Heavy breeds	Growth	0.250	....	35	7	....	....	....	
234			0.500	....	57	11	....	....	....	
235			0.750	....	73	15	....	....	....	
236			1.000	....	84	17	....	....	....	
237			1.500	....	100	20	....	....	....	
238	Adult	60% egg production	2.500	....	125	18.7	....	....	....	
239		Breeding	2.500	....	125	18.7	....	....	....	

Contributors: (a) Sprague, H. G., (b) Beeson, W. M.

References

[1] National Research Council, Committee on Animal Nutrition. 1962. Natl. Acad. Sci. Natl. Res. Council Publ. 989.

[2] Ibid. 990.

[3] National Research Council, Committee on Animal Nutrition. 1963. Natl. Acad. Sci. Natl. Res. Council Publ. 1137.

[4] National Research Council, Committee on Animal Nutrition. 1964. Ibid. 1192.

[5] Ibid. 1193.

[6] National Research Council, Committee on Animal Nutrition. 1966. Natl. Acad. Sci. Natl. Res. Council Publ. 1194.

[7] Ibid. 1345.

[8] Ibid. 1349.

[9] Ibid. 1401.

Part II. Minerals

	Animal	Specification	Body Weight kg	Calcium g	Iodine mg	Magnesium mg	Phosphorus g	Sodium + Chlorine g	Reference
1	Cat	Growth	....	Required	Required	....	....	....	2
	Cattle, beef[1/]								3
2	Calf, weanling	Wintering	181	13	Required	Required	10	10	
3			227	13	Required	Required	10	10	
4			272	13	Required	Required	10	10	
5	Short yearling	Finishing	181	20	Required	Required	15	....	
6			272	20	Required	Required	17	....	
7			363	20	Required	Required	18	....	
8			454	21	Required	Required	21	....	

1/ Also required: cobalt, copper, iron, manganese, molybdenum, potassium, selenium, sulfur, and zinc. In excess, copper, fluorine, molybdenum, selenium, and salt are toxic.

continued

14. NUTRIENT REQUIREMENTS: DOMESTIC ANIMALS

Part II. Minerals

	Animal	Specification	Body Weight kg	Calcium g	Iodine mg	Magnesium mg	Phosphorus g	Sodium + Chlorine g	Reference
9	Yearling	Wintering	272	13	Required	Required	11	10	
10			363	13	Required	Required	12	10	
11			408	13	Required	Required	12	10	
12		Finishing	272	20	Required	Required	17	....	
13			363	20	Required	Required	20	....	
14			454	23	Required	Required	23	....	
15			499	23	Required	Required	23	....	
16	2-yr-old	Finishing	363	22	Required	Required	22	....	
17			454	26	Required	Required	26	....	
18			544	28	Required	Required	28	....	
19	Heifer & steer	Growth	181	16	Required	Required	11	10	
20			272	16	Required	Required	12	10	
21			363	16	Required	Required	13	10	
22			454	14	Required	Required	14	10	
23	Heifer	Pregnancy, wintering	318	15	Required	Required	14	....	
24			408	13	Required	Required	12	....	
25			454	13	Required	Required	12	....	
26	Cow	Pregnancy, wintering	363	16	Required	Required	15	....	
27			454	13	Required	Required	12	....	
28			544	13	Required	Required	12	....	
29			544	13	Required	Required	12	....	
30		Lactation, first 3-4 mo postpartum	408-499	30	Required	Required	23	26	
31	Bull, moderately active	Growth & maintenance	272	21	Required	Required	15	....	
32			454	19	Required	Required	15	....	
33			635	17	Required	Required	16	....	
34			816	18	Required	Required	18	....	
	Cattle, dairy[2]								8
35	Calf	Slaughter	35	2.8	Required	Required	2.1	Required	
36			50	4.8	Required	Required	3.6	Required	
37			75	8.0	Required	Required	6.0	Required	
38			100	9.5	Required	Required	8.4	Required	
39			150	12.0	Required	Required	11.4	Required	
40	Heifer	Herd replacement	25	2.0	Required	Required	1.5	Required	
41			35	2.8	Required	Required	2.1	Required	
42			50	4.0	Required	Required	3.0	Required	
43			75	8.0	Required	Required	6.0	Required	
44			100	9.6	Required	Required	8.4	Required	
45			150	12	Required	Required	11	Required	
46			200	13	Required	Required	12	Required	
47			250	14	Required	Required	13	Required	
48			300	15	Required	Required	14	Required	
49			350	16	Required	Required	15	Required	
50			400	16	Required	Required	15	Required	
51			450	16	Required	Required	15	Required	
52			500	16	Required	Required	15	Required	
53			550	16	Required	Required	15	Required	
54			600	16	Required	Required	15	Required	
55	Cow	Maintenance	350	10	Required	Required	10	20-25[3]	
56			400	11	Required	Required	11	20-25[3]	

[2]/ Also required: cobalt, copper, iron, manganese, potassium, selenium, sulfur, and zinc. In excess, fluorine and molybdenum are toxic. [3]/ Additional 18 g salt/10 kg milk produced are required.

continued

Part II. Minerals

	Animal	Specification	Body Weight kg	Calcium g	Iodine mg	Magnesium mg	Phosphorus g	Sodium + Chlorine g	Reference
57			450	12	Required	Required	12	20-25[3]	
58			500	14	Required	Required	14	20-25[3]	
59			550	15	Required	Required	15	20-25[3]	
60			600	16	Required	Required	16	20-25[3]	
61			650	17	Required	Required	17	20-25[3]	
62			700	18	Required	Required	18	20-25[3]	
63			750	20	Required	Required	20	20-25[3]	
64			800	22	Required	Required	22	20-25[3]	
65		Pregnancy, last	400	21	Required	Required	19	Required	
66		2-3 mo	550	28	Required	Required	26	Required	
67			700	34	Required	Required	32	Required	
68	Bull	Growth	25-150	2.0-12[4]	Required	Required	1.5-11[4]	Required	
69			200	14	Required	Required	13	Required	
70			250	15	Required	Required	14	Required	
71			300	17	Required	Required	15	Required	
72			400	17	Required	Required	16	Required	
73			500	18	Required	Required	17	Required	
74			600	18	Required	Required	17	Required	
75			700	19	Required	Required	18	Required	
76			800	21	Required	Required	20	Required	
77			900	22	Required	Required	20	Required	
78			1000	23	Required	Required	22	Required	
79	Mature	Maintenance &	500	11	Required	Required	11	Required	
80		breeding	600	12	Required	Required	12	Required	
81			700	15	Required	Required	15	Required	
82			800	17	Required	Required	17	Required	
83			900	20	Required	Required	20	Required	
84			1000	22	Required	Required	22	Required	
85			1100	24	Required	Required	24	Required	
86			1200	25	Required	Required	25	Required	
	Dog[5]								1
87	Young	Growth	2.3	1.2	0.150	50	1.0	1.20	
88			4.5	2.4	0.300	100	2.0	2.40	
89			6.8	3.6	0.450	150	3.0	3.60	
90			13.6	7.2	0.900	300	6.0	7.20	
91			>22.7	12.0	1.500	500	10.0	12.00	
92	Adult	Maintenance	2.3	0.6	0.075	25	0.5	0.85	
93			4.5	1.2	0.150	50	1.0	1.70	
94			6.8	1.8	0.225	75	1.5	2.55	
95			13.6	3.6	0.450	150	3.0	5.10	
96			>22.7	6.0	0.750	250	5.0	8.50	
97	Guinea pig[6]	Growth	....	0.1/100 g body wt	Required	28/100 g body wt	0.05/100 g body wt	Required	2
98	Hamster	Growth	....	0.6/100 g of diet	....	....	0.35/100 g of diet	....	2
	Horse[7]								9
99	270 kg at maturity	Growth	90	11	0.10	Required	10	Required	
100			185	11	0.10	Required	11	Required	
101			270	6	0.10	Required	6	50-60	

[3] Additional 18 g salt/10 kg milk produced are required. [4] Requirements are the same as for growing heifers of equal weight (*see* lines 40-45). [5] Also required: copper, iron, manganese, potassium, zinc, and probably cobalt. In excess, iodine is toxic. [6] Also required: cobalt, copper, iron, manganese, potassium, and zinc. [7] Also required: cobalt, copper, fluorine, iron, and potassium. In excess, fluorine is toxic. Not demonstrated to be essential: molybdenum, selenium, and sulfur.

continued

Part II. Minerals

	Animal	Specification	Body Weight kg	Calcium g	Iodine mg	Magnesium mg	Phosphorus g	Sodium + Chlorine g	Reference
102	365 kg at maturity	Growth	90	14	0.10	Required	11	Required	
103			185	17	0.10	Required	13	Required	
104			270	13	0.10	Required	13	Required	
105			365	9	0.10	Required	9	50-60	
106	455 kg at maturity	Growth	90	16	0.10	Required	11	Required	
107			185	15	0.10	Required	12	Required	
108			270	14	0.10	Required	12	Required	
109			365	13	0.10	Required	12	Required	
110			455	11	0.10	Required	11	50-60	
111	545 kg at maturity	Growth	90	19	0.10	Required	16	Required	
112			185	18	0.10	Required	17	Required	
113			270	18	0.10	Required	17	Required	
114			365	18	0.10	Required	17	Required	
115			455	12	0.10	Required	12	Required	
116			545	12	0.10	Required	12	50-60	
117	635 kg at maturity	Growth	90	24	0.10	Required	17	Required	
118			185	21	0.10	Required	17	Required	
119			270	19	0.10	Required	17	Required	
120			365	18	0.10	Required	17	Required	
121			455	14	0.10	Required	14	Required	
122			545	13	0.10	Required	13	Required	
123			635	13	0.10	Required	13	50-60	
124	Mature	Light work	185	6	0.10	Required	6	50-60	
125			270	9	0.10	Required	9	50-60	
126			365	10	0.10	Required	10	50-60	
127			455	12	0.10	Required	12	50-60	
128			545	14	0.10	Required	14	50-60	
129			635	16	0.10	Required	16	50-60	
130		Medium work	185	8	0.10	Required	8	50-60	
131			270	10	0.10	Required	10	50-60	
132			365	12	0.10	Required	12	50-60	
133			455	14	0.10	Required	14	50-60	
134			545	16	0.10	Required	16	50-60	
135			635	18	0.10	Required	18	50-60	
136	♀	Pregnancy, last quarter	185	9	0.10[8]	Required	8	Required	
137			270	12	0.10[8]	Required	11	Required	
138			365	14	0.10[8]	Required	13	Required	
139			455	16	0.10[8]	Required	15	Required	
140			545	18	0.10[8]	Required	17	Required	
141			635	20	0.10[8]	Required	19	Required	
142		Lactation, peak	185	18	0.10	Required	13	Required	
143			270	23	0.10	Required	18	Required	
144			365	27	0.10	Required	22	Required	
145			455	30	0.10	Required	24	Required	
146			545	34	0.10	Required	27	Required	
147			635	37	0.10	Required	30	Required	
148	Monkey, rhesus[9]	Growth & maintenance	....	0.155/kg body wt	0.0006/kg body wt	0.01/kg body wt	0.17/kg body wt	0.36/kg body wt	2

[8] Supplemental iodine is required in the goiter belt. [9] Presumably values are extrapolations from requirements of other laboratory animals and of man; also presumably required: copper, fluorine, iron, manganese, potassium, sulfur, and zinc.

continued

14. NUTRIENT REQUIREMENTS: DOMESTIC ANIMALS

Part II. Minerals

	Animal	Specification	Body Weight kg	Calcium g	Iodine mg	Magnesium mg	Phosphorus g	Sodium + Chlorine g	Reference
149	Mouse, laboratory[10]	Growth	....	0.021[11]	....	....	0.018[11]	0.018[11]	2
150	Rabbit[12]	....	....	....	....	Required	Required	....	6
151	Rat, laboratory[13]	Growth	....	0.060[14,15]	0.0015	4[15]	0.050[15]	0.010[15]	2
152		Pregnancy	....	0.120[14,15]	0.003	10[15]	0.100[15]	0.105[15]	
153		Lactation	....	0.180[14,15]	0.0045	15[15]	0.150[15]	0.095[15]	
	Sheep[16]								5
154	Lamb	Fattening	27.2	2.9	Required	1520	2.6	8	
155			31.8	2.9	Required	1520	2.6	8	
156			36.3	3.0	Required	1520	2.7	9	
157			40.8	3.0	Required	1520	2.7	9	
158			45.4	3.1	Required	1520	2.8	10	
159	Lamb & yearling, ♂	....	36.3	3.0	Required	1520	2.7	9	
160			45.4	3.1	Required	1520	2.8	10	
161			54.4	3.2	Required	1520	2.9	11	
162			63.5	3.3	Required	1520	3.0	11	
163			72.6	3.4	Required	1520	3.1	12	
164	♀	Replacement	27.2	2.9	Required	1520	2.6	8	
165			36.3	3.0	Required	1520	2.7	9	
166			45.4	3.1	Required	1520	2.8	10	
167			54.4	3.2	Required	1520	2.9	11	
168	♀	Pregnancy, first 15 wk	45.4	3.2	Required	1520	2.5	9	
169			54.4	3.3	Required	1520	2.6	10	
170			63.5	3.4	Required	1520	2.7	11	
171			72.6	3.5	Required	1520	2.8	12	
172		Pregnancy, last 6 wk	45.4	4.2	Required	1520	3.1	10	
173			54.4	4.4	Required	1520	3.3	11	
174			63.5	4.6	Required	1520	3.5	12	
175			72.6	4.8	Required	1520	3.7	13	
176		Lactation, first 8-10 wk	45.4	6.2	Required	1520	4.6	11	
177			54.4	6.5	Required	1520	4.8	12	
178			63.5	6.8	Required	1520	5.0	13	
179			72.6	7.1	Required	1520	5.2	14	
180		Lactation, last 12-14 wk	45.4	4.6	Required	1520	3.4	10	
181			54.4	4.8	Required	1520	3.6	11	
182			63.5	5.0	Required	1520	3.8	12	
183			72.6	5.2	Required	1520	4.0	13	
	Swine[17]								4
184	Meat-type	Finishing, full-fed	56.7-79.4	15.2	....	Required	12.2	15.2	
185			79.4-102.1	17.7	....	Required	14.2	17.7	
186	Bacon-type	Finishing, full-fed	34.0-56.7	11.8	....	Required	9.4	11.8	
187			56.7-79.4	15.2	....	Required	12.2	15.2	
188			79.4-102.1	17.7	....	Required	14.2	17.7	

[10] Also required: iron, manganese, potassium, and zinc. [11] Based on average daily feed requirements during 2-week period following weaning. [12] Also required: cobalt, copper, iron, manganese, and potassium. [13] Also required: manganese, potassium, and sulfur. For growth, copper, iron, selenium, and zinc are required, although the need for these during gestation and lactation are in question. Not required: fluorine, and apparently cobalt except as a constituent of vitamin B_{12}. [14] For maintenance, 10-15 mg/day are required after a period of 40-50 mg/day. [15] Calculated from values obtained experimentally, assuming a daily feed intake of 10 g for growth, 20 g for gestation, and 30 g for lactation. [16] Also required: cobalt, copper, fluorine, selenium, sulfur, and zinc. The need for molybdenum is doubtful; it is toxic in excess, as are cobalt, fluorine, iodine, and selenium. [17] Also required: copper, iron, manganese, potassium, selenium, zinc, and, for growth, copper and iron. In excess, copper, iron, manganese, selenium, and zinc are toxic. Requirement unknown: cobalt.

continued

14. NUTRIENT REQUIREMENTS: DOMESTIC ANIMALS

Part II. Minerals

	Animal	Specification	Body Weight kg	Calcium g	Iodine mg	Magnesium mg	Phosphorus g	Sodium + Chlorine g	Reference
189		Growth	4.5-11.3	4.4	<0.2/100 lb body wt	Required	3.3	2.7	
190			11.3-22.7	7.4	<0.2/100 lb body wt	Required	5.7	5.7	
191			22.7-34.0	10.9	<0.2/100 lb body wt	Required	8.4	8.1	
192			34.0-56.7	11.8	<0.2/100 lb body wt	Required	9.4	11.8	
193	♂, young	Breeding	136.1	16.3	<0.2/100 lb body wt	Required	10.9	13.6	
194	adult	Breeding	226.8	20.4	0.20/kg feed	400/kg feed	13.6	17.0	
195	Gilt	Pregnancy	136.1	15.0	0.20/kg feed	400/kg feed	10.0	12.5	
196		Lactation	158.8	29.9	0.20/kg feed	400/kg feed	20.0	25.5	
197	Sow	Pregnancy	226.8	17.7	0.2/100 lb body wt	400/kg feed	11.8	14.7	
198		Lactation	204.1	34.0	0.20/kg feed	400/kg feed	22.7	28.4	
	Chicken[18]								7
199	Single-comb White	Growth	0.250	0.27	0.009	13	0.19	0.040[19]	
200	Leghorns or simi-		0.500	0.45	0.015	22	0.31	0.067[19]	
201	lar breeds		0.750	0.57	0.020	28	0.40	0.085[19]	
202			1.000	0.65	0.023	....	0.39	0.097[19]	
203			1.250	0.79	0.028	....	0.47	0.119[19]	
204			1.500	0.84	0.029	....	0.50	0.126[19]	
205	Adult	60% egg production	1.800	3	0.033	....	0.66	0.165[19]	
206		Breeding	1.800	3	0.033	....	0.66	0.165[19]	
207	Heavy breeds	Growth	0.250	0.35	0.011	17	0.24	0.052[19]	
208			0.500	0.57	0.020	28	0.40	0.085[19]	
209			0.750	0.73	0.025	36	0.51	0.10[19]	
210			1.000	0.84	0.029	42	0.59	0.12[19]	
211			1.500	1	0.035	50	0.70	0.15[19]	
212	Adult	60% egg production	2.500	3.44	0.037	....	0.75	0.19[19]	
213		Breeding	2.500	3.44	0.037	....	0.75	0.19[19]	

[18] Also required: manganese, potassium, and zinc. [19] Sodium only.

Contributors: (a) Sprague, H. G., (b) Beeson, W. M.

References

[1] National Research Council, Committee on Animal Nutrition. 1962. Natl. Acad. Sci. Natl. Res. Council Publ. 989.

[2] Ibid. 990

[3] National Research Council, Committee on Animal Nutrition. 1963. Natl. Acad. Sci. Natl. Res. Council Publ. 1137.

[4] National Research Council, Committee on Animal Nutrition. 1964. Ibid. 1192.

[5] Ibid. 1193.

[6] National Research Council, Committee on Animal Nutrition. 1966. Natl. Acad. Sci. Natl. Res. Council Publ. 1194.

[7] Ibid. 1345.

[8] Ibid. 1349.

[9] Ibid. 1401.

continued

14. NUTRIENT REQUIREMENTS: DOMESTIC ANIMALS

Part III. Vitamins

	Animal	Specification	Body Weight kg	Riboflavin mg	Nicotinic Acid mg	Vitamin B_6 mg	Pantothenic Acid mg	Vitamin B_{12} mg	Vitamin A I.U.	Vitamin D I.U.	Reference
1	Cat[1]	Growth	....	0.4/100 g of diet	4/100 g of diet	0.2/100 g of diet	0.5/100 g of diet	....	2500/100 g of diet	100/100 g of diet	2
	Cattle, beef[2]										3
2	Calf, weanling	Wintering	181	Required	Required	Required	Required	Required	7900	1200	
3			227	Required	Required	Required	Required	Required	9500	1500	
4			272	Required	Required	Required	Required	Required	10,700	1800	
5	Short yearling	Finishing	181	Required	Required	Required	Required	Required	8850	1200	
6			272	Required	Required	Required	Required	Required	12,300	1800	
7			363	Required	Required	Required	Required	Required	14,600	2400	
8			454	Required	Required	Required	Required	Required	17,300	3000	
9	Yearling	Wintering	272	Required	Required	Required	Required	Required	10,700	1800	
10			363	Required	Required	Required	Required	Required	11,900	2400	
11			408	Required	Required	Required	Required	Required	11,900	2700	
12		Finishing	272	Required	Required	Required	Required	Required	13,100	1800	
13			363	Required	Required	Required	Required	Required	16,700	2400	
14			454	Required	Required	Required	Required	Required	19,400	3000	
15			499	Required	Required	Required	Required	Required	19,400	3300	
16	2-yr-old	Finishing	363	Required	Required	Required	Required	Required	17,500	2400	
17			454	Required	Required	Required	Required	Required	21,200	3000	
18			544	Required	Required	Required	Required	Required	23,300	3600	
19	Heifer & steer	Growth	181	Required	Required	Required	Required	Required	9200	1200	
20			272	Required	Required	Required	Required	Required	12,300	1800	
21			363	Required	Required	Required	Required	Required	14,300	2400	
22			454	Required	Required	Required	Required	Required	15,800	3000	
23	Heifer	Pregnancy,	318	Required	Required	Required	Required	Required	20,000	2100	
24		wintering	408	Required	Required	Required	Required	Required	18,000	2700	
25			454	Required	Required	Required	Required	Required	18,000	3000	
26	Cow	Pregnancy,	363	Required	Required	Required	Required	Required	22,000	2400	
27		wintering	454	Required	Required	Required	Required	Required	18,000	3000	
28			544	Required	Required	Required	Required	Required	18,000	3600	
29			544	Required	Required	Required	Required	Required	17,600	3600	
30		Lactation, first 3-4 mo postpartum	408-499	Required	Required	Required	Required	Required	42,000	2700-3300	
31	Bull, moderately	Growth &	272	Required	Required	Required	Required	Required	24,300	1800	
32	active	mainten-	454	Required	Required	Required	Required	Required	30,000	3000	
33		ance	635	Required	Required	Required	Required	Required	37,100	4200	
34			816	Required	Required	Required	Required	Required	38,300	5400	
	Cattle, dairy[3]										8
35	Calf	Slaughter	35	Required	Required	Required	Required	Required	1500	230	
36			50	Required	Required	Required	Required	Required	2100	330	
37			75	Required	Required	Required	Required	Required	3200	500	
38			100	Required	Required	Required	Required	Required	4200	660	
39			150	Required	Required	Required	Required	Required	6400	1000	

1/ Also required: choline, thiamine, and vitamin E. Not required: folic acid and ascorbic acid. Requirement unknown: biotin, inositol, and vitamin K. 2/ Also required: thiamine, biotin, vitamin E, and vitamin K. Nutrient requirements of rumen microorganisms supplied simultaneously. 3/ Dietary supplements of thiamine, riboflavin, nicotinic acid, vitamin B_6, biotin, pantothenic acid, vitamin B_{12}, and choline are required before development of a functional rumen. In older animals, rumen synthesization and natural feeds supply adequate amounts of the B vitamins, folic acid, and vitamin K. Also required: choline and vitamin E. Excess vitamin D leads to calcification. Antibiotics used as additives.

continued

Part III. Vitamins

	Animal	Specification	Body Weight kg	Riboflavin mg	Nicotinic Acid mg	Vitamin B_6 mg	Pantothenic Acid mg	Vitamin B_{12} mg	Vitamin A I.U.	Vitamin D I.U.	Reference
40	Heifer	Herd replacement	25	Required	Required	Required	Required	Required	1000	165	
41			35	Required	Required	Required	Required	Required	1500	230	
42			50	Required	Required	Required	Required	Required	2100	330	
43			75	Required	Required	Required	Required	Required	3200	500	
44			100	Required	Required	Required	Required	Required	4200	660	
45			150	Required	Required	Required	Required	Required	6400	1000	
46			200	Required	Required	Required	Required	Required	8500	1300	
47			250	Required	Required	Required	Required	Required	10,600	....	
48			300	Required	Required	Required	Required	Required	12,700	....	
49			350	Required	Required	Required	Required	Required	14,800	....	
50			400	Required	Required	Required	Required	Required	17,000	....	
51			450	Required	Required	Required	Required	Required	19,100	....	
52			500	Required	Required	Required	Required	Required	21,200	....	
53			550	Required	Required	Required	Required	Required	23,200	....	
54			600	Required	Required	Required	Required	Required	25,400	....	
55	Cow	Maintenance	350	Required	Required	Required	Required	Required	14,800	....	
56			400	Required	Required	Required	Required	Required	16,800	....	
57			450	Required	Required	Required	Required	Required	19,200	....	
58			500	Required	Required	Required	Required	Required	21,200	....	
59			550	Required	Required	Required	Required	Required	23,200	....	
60			600	Required	Required	Required	Required	Required	25,600	....	
61			650	Required	Required	Required	Required	Required	27,600	....	
62			700	Required	Required	Required	Required	Required	29,600	....	
63			750	Required	Required	Required	Required	Required	32,000	....	
64			800	Required	Required	Required	Required	Required	34,000	....	
65		Pregnancy, last 2-3 mo	400	Required	Required	Required	Required	Required	25,600	....	
66			550	Required	Required	Required	Required	Required	35,200	....	
67			700	Required	Required	Required	Required	Required	44,800	....	
68	Bull	Growth	25-150	Required	Required	Required	Required	Required	1000-6400[4/]	165-1000[4/]	
69			200	Required	Required	Required	Required	Required	8500	....	
70			250	Required	Required	Required	Required	Required	10,600	....	
71			300	Required	Required	Required	Required	Required	12,700	....	
72			400	Required	Required	Required	Required	Required	17,000	....	
73			500	Required	Required	Required	Required	Required	21,200	....	
74			600	Required	Required	Required	Required	Required	25,200	....	
75			700	Required	Required	Required	Required	Required	29,600	....	
76			800	Required	Required	Required	Required	Required	34,000	....	
77			900	Required	Required	Required	Required	Required	38,000	....	
78			1000	Required	Required	Required	Required	Required	42,400	....	
79	Mature	Maintenance & breeding	500	Required	Required	Required	Required	Required	21,200	....	
80			600	Required	Required	Required	Required	Required	25,600	....	
81			700	Required	Required	Required	Required	Required	29,600	....	
82			800	Required	Required	Required	Required	Required	34,000	....	
83			900	Required	Required	Required	Required	Required	38,000	....	
84			1000	Required	Required	Required	Required	Required	42,400	....	
85			1100	Required	Required	Required	Required	Required	46,800	....	
86			1200	Required	Required	Required	Required	Required	50,800	....	

[4/] Requirements are the same as for growing heifers of equal weight (*see* lines 40-45).

continued

14. NUTRIENT REQUIREMENTS: DOMESTIC ANIMALS

Part III. Vitamins

	Animal	Specification	Body Weight kg	Riboflavin mg	Nicotinic Acid mg	Vitamin B_6 mg	Pantothenic Acid mg	Vitamin B_{12} mg	Vitamin A I.U.	Vitamin D I.U.	Reference
	Dog[5]										1
87	Young	Growth	2.3	0.200	0.900	0.100	0.225	0.0030	450	45	
88			4.5	0.400	1.800	0.200	0.450	0.0060	900	90	
89			6.8	0.600	2.700	0.300	0.675	0.0090	1350	135	
90			13.6	1.200	5.400	0.600	1.350	0.0180	2700	270	
91			>22.7	2.000	9.000	1.000	2.250	0.0300	4500	450	
92	Adult	Maintenance	2.3	0.100	0.550	0.050	0.115	0.0015	225	15	
93			4.5	0.200	1.100	0.100	0.230	0.0030	450	30	
94			6.8	0.300	1.650	0.150	0.345	0.0045	675	45	
95			13.6	0.600	3.300	0.300	0.690	0.0090	1350	90	
96			>22.7	1.000	5.500	0.500	1.150	0.0150	2250	150	
97	Guinea pig[6]	Growth	....	0.13/100 g body wt	0.4/100 g body wt	0.13/100 g body wt	0.16/100 g body wt	....	0.96[7]/100 g body wt	Not required	2
98	Hamster[8]	Growth	....	0.6/100 g of diet	....	0.6/100 g of diet	4/100 g of diet	Not required	1300/100 g of diet	Not required	2
	Horse[9]										9
99	270 kg at maturity	Growth	90	....	Required	....	....	....	1700	Required	
100			185	....	Required	....	....	....	3300	Required	
101			270	....	Required	....	....	....	5000	Required	
102	365 kg at maturity	Growth	90	....	Required	....	....	....	1700	Required	
103			185	....	Required	....	....	....	3300	Required	
104			270	....	Required	....	....	....	5000	Required	
105			365	....	Required	....	....	....	6700	Required	
106	455 kg at maturity	Growth	90	....	Required	....	....	....	1700	Required	
107			185	....	Required	....	....	....	3300	Required	
108			270	....	Required	....	....	....	5000	Required	
109			365	....	Required	....	....	....	6700	Required	
110			455	....	Required	....	....	....	8300	Required	
111	545 kg at maturity	Growth	90	....	Required	....	....	....	1700	Required	
112			185	....	Required	....	....	....	3300	Required	
113			270	....	Required	....	....	....	5000	Required	
114			365	....	Required	....	....	....	6700	Required	
115			455	....	Required	....	....	....	8300	Required	
116			545	....	Required	....	....	....	10,000	Required	
117	635 kg at maturity	Growth	90	....	Required	....	....	....	1700	Required	
118			185	....	Required	....	....	....	3300	Required	
119			270	....	Required	....	....	....	5000	Required	
120			365	....	Required	....	....	....	6700	Required	
121			455	....	Required	....	....	....	8300	Required	
122			545	....	Required	....	....	....	10,000	Required	
123			635	....	Required	....	....	....	11,700	Required	
124	Mature	Light work	185	....	Required	....	....	....	3300	Required	
125			270	....	Required	....	....	....	5000	Required	
126			365	....	Required	....	....	....	6700	Required	
127			455	....	Required	....	....	....	8300	Required	
128			545	....	Required	....	....	....	10,000	Required	

5/ Also required: choline, thiamine, and vitamin E. 6/ Also required: choline, thiamine, folic acid, ascorbic acid, and α-tocopherol. Vitamin K is not required for growing animal, but is required for reproduction. 7/ Milligrams β-carotene. 8/ Also required: thiamine and α-tocopherol. Requirement unknown: nicotinic acid, inositol, choline, and vitamin K. Not required: biotin, folic acid, and ascorbic acid. 9/ Also required: thiamine. Requirement unknown: ascorbic acid and vitamin E.

continued

Part III. Vitamins

	Animal	Specification	Body Weight kg	Riboflavin mg	Nicotinic Acid mg	Vitamin B_6 mg	Pantothenic Acid mg	Vitamin B_{12} mg	Vitamin A I.U.	Vitamin D I.U.	Reference
129			635	....	Required	....	....	....	11,700	Required	
130		Medium work	185	....	Required	....	....	....	3300	Required	
131			270	....	Required	....	....	....	5000	Required	
132			365	....	Required	....	....	....	6700	Required	
133			455	....	Required	....	....	....	8300	Required	
134			545	....	Required	....	....	....	10,000	Required	
135			635	....	Required	....	....	....	11,700	Required	
136	♀	Pregnancy, last quarter	185	....	Required	....	....	....	9300	Required	
137			270	....	Required	....	....	....	14,000	Required	
138			365	....	Required	....	....	....	18,700	Required	
139			455	....	Required	....	....	....	23,300	Required	
140			545	....	Required	....	....	....	28,000	Required	
141			635	....	Required	....	....	....	32,700	Required	
142		Lactation, peak	185	....	Required	....	....	....	9300	Required	
143			270	....	Required	....	....	....	14,000	Required	
144			365	....	Required	....	....	....	18,700	Required	
145			455	....	Required	....	....	....	23,300	Required	
146			545	....	Required	....	....	....	28,000	Required	
147			635	....	Required	....	....	....	32,700	Required	
148	Monkey, rhesus[10]	Growth	....	0.075/100 g of diet	3.8/100 g of diet	0.127/100 g of diet	Required	0.0025/100 g of diet	Required	Required	2
149	Mouse, laboratory[11]	Growth	....	0.014[12]	0.1[12]	0.0035[12]	0.03[12]	0.00002[12]	2[12]	0.5[12]	2
150	Rabbit[13]		....	Required	<11/kg body wt	0.039	Required	Required	Required	Required	6
151	Rat, laboratory[14]	Growth	....	0.025	0.15[15,16]	0.012	0.08[15,17]	0.00005[15]	200/kg body wt	....	2
152		Pregnancy	....	0.08	....	0.012	0.16[15,17]	0.0001[15]	240[15]	....	
153		Lactation	....	0.12	....	0.012	0.3[15,17]	0.00015[15]	360[15]	....	
	Sheep[18]										5
154	Lamb	Fattening	27.2	....	....	....	....	....	550	150	
155			31.8	....	....	....	....	....	660	175	
156			36.3	....	....	....	....	....	770	200	
157			40.8	....	....	....	....	....	825	225	
158			45.4	....	....	....	....	....	935	250	
159	Lamb & yearling, ♂	....	36.3	....	....	....	....	....	1035	200	
160			45.4	....	....	....	....	....	1260	250	
161			54.4	....	....	....	....	....	1530	300	
162			63.5	....	....	....	....	....	1800	350	
163			72.6	....	....	....	....	....	2025	400	

[10] Also required: thiamine, biotin, folic acid, ascorbic acid, and α-tocopherol. Requirement unknown: inositol, choline, and vitamin K. [11] Also required: choline, thiamine, biotin, folic acid, α-tocopherol, and vitamin K. Requirement unknown: inositol. [12] Based on average daily feed requirements during 2-week period following weaning. [13] Also required: biotin, choline, folic acid, α-tocopherol, and, for reproduction, vitamin K. Not required: ascorbic acid. [14] Also required: choline, thiamine, α-tocopherol, and vitamin K. [15] Calculated from values obtained experimentally, assuming a daily feed intake of 10 g for growth, 20 g for pregnancy, and 30 g for lactation. [16] Assuming there is no more than 0.15% tryptophan in the diet. [17] As calcium pantothenate, 0.8 mg calcium pantothenate/100 g diet was sufficient to permit tissue acetylation reactions in the adult animal. [18] Also required: vitamin E. Young lambs with undeveloped rumen require thiamine, riboflavin, folic acid, and possibly other B vitamins. Adults with functioning rumen do not require a dietary supplement of B vitamins, ascorbic acid, or vitamins K_1 and K_2.

continued

Part III. Vitamins

	Animal	Specification	Body Weight kg	Riboflavin mg	Nicotinic Acid mg	Vitamin B_6 mg	Pantothenic Acid mg	Vitamin B_{12} mg	Vitamin A I.U.	Vitamin D I.U.	Reference
164	♀	Replacement	27.2	....	....	....	....	....	765	150	
165			36.3	....	....	....	....	....	1035	200	
166			45.4	....	....	....	....	....	1260	250	
167			54.4	....	....	....	....	....	1530	300	
168	♀	Pregnancy, first 15 wk	45.4	....	....	....	....	....	935	250	
169			54.4	....	....	....	....	....	1100	300	
170			63.5	....	....	....	....	....	1320	350	
171			72.6	....	....	....	....	....	1485	400	
172		Pregnancy, last 6 wk	45.4	....	....	....	....	....	2320	250	
173			54.4	....	....	....	....	....	2720	300	
174			63.5	....	....	....	....	....	3160	350	
175			72.6	....	....	....	....	....	3640	400	
176		Lactation, first 8-10 wk	45.4	....	....	....	....	....	2320	250	
177			54.4	....	....	....	....	....	2720	300	
178			63.5	....	....	....	....	....	3160	350	
179			72.6	....	....	....	....	....	3640	400	
180		Lactation, last 12-14 wk	45.4	....	....	....	....	....	2320	250	
181			54.4	....	....	....	....	....	2720	300	
182			63.5	....	....	....	....	....	3160	350	
183			72.6	....	....	....	....	....	3640	400	
	Swine[19]										4
184	Meat-type	Finishing, full-fed	56.7-79.4	6.7	33.5[20]	....	33.5	0.0335	4000[21]	402	
185			79.4-102.1	7.8	39.0[20]	....	39.0	0.0390	4700[21]	468	
186	Bacon-type	Finishing, full-fed	34.0-56.7	5.2	26.0[20]	....	26.0	0.0260	3100[21]	312	
187			56.7-79.4	6.7	33.5[20]	....	33.5	0.0335	4000[21]	402	
188			79.4-102.1	7.8	39.0[20]	....	39.0	0.0390	4700[21]	468	
189		Growth	4.5-11.3	1.8	12.0[20]	0.6	7.2	0.012	1200[21]	120	
190			11.3-22.7	3.5	20.0[20]	1.2	12.5	0.0175	2000[21]	225	
191			22.7-34.0	4.4	22.2[20]	1.8	18.5	0.0185	2200[21]	333	
192			34.0-56.7	5.2	26.0[20]	....	26.0	0.0260	3100[21]	312	
193	♂, young	Breeding	136.1	9.0	48.0[20]	....	36.0	0.030	9000[21]	600	
194	adult	Breeding	226.8	11.2	60[20]	....	45.0	0.0375	11,250[21]	750	
195	Gilt	Pregnancy	136.1	8.2	44.0[20]	....	33.0	0.0275	8250[21]	550	
196		Lactation	158.8	16.5	88.0[20]	....	66.0	0.0550	16,500[21]	1100	
197	Sow	Pregnancy	226.8	9.8	52.0[20]	....	39.0	0.0325	9750[21]	650	
198		Lactation	204.1	18.8	100.0[20]	....	75.0	0.0625	18,750[21]	1250	

[19] Also required: biotin, folic acid, *p*-aminobenzoic acid, ascorbic acid, vitamin K, and, for early growth, choline. Requirement unknown: inositol and vitamin E. [20] Assuming all of the nicotinic acid in cereal grains and their by-products is in a bound form, and is therefore unavailable to the animal. [21] Based on conversion of β-carotene in the intestinal walls to biologically active vitamin A: 1 mg β-carotene = 500 I.U.

continued

14. NUTRIENT REQUIREMENTS: DOMESTIC ANIMALS

Part III. Vitamins

	Animal	Specification	Body Weight kg	Ribo-flavin mg	Nicotin-ic Acid mg	Vitamin B_6 mg	Pantho-thenic Acid mg	Vitamin B_{12} mg	Vitamin A I.U.	Vitamin D I.U.	Ref-er-ence
	Chicken[22]										7
199	Single-comb	Growth	0.250	0.096	0.73	0.081	0.27	0.00024	54	5.4	
200	White Leg-		0.500	0.162	1.21	0.13	0.45	0.00040	90	9	
201	horns or		0.750	0.206	1.54	0.17	0.57	0.00051	114	11.4	
202	similar		1.000	0.117	0.71	....	0.65	....	130	13	
203	breeds		1.250	0.142	0.87	....	0.79	....	158	15.8	
204			1.500	0.151	0.92	....	0.84	....	168	16.8	
205	Adult	60% egg production	1.800	0.242	....	0.33	0.242	....	440	55	
206		Breeding	1.800	0.420	....	0.49	1.10	0.00033	440	55	
207	Heavy breeds	Growth	0.250	0.12	0.95	0.10	0.35	0.00032	70	7	
208			0.500	0.20	1.53	0.17	0.57	0.00051	114	11.4	
209			0.750	0.26	1.97	0.22	0.73	0.00066	146	14.6	
210			1.000	0.30	2.3	0.25	0.84	0.00076	168	16.8	
211			1.500	0.36	2.7	0.30	1	0.00090	200	20	
212	Adult	60% egg production	2.500	0.27	....	0.37	0.27	....	500	62	
213		Breeding	2.500	0.48	....	0.56	1.25	0.00037	500	62	

[22] Also required: thiamine, biotin, folic acid, vitamin E, vitamin K, and, for growth, choline.

Contributors: (a) Sprague, H. G., (b) Beeson, W. M.

References

[1] National Research Council, Committee on Animal Nutrition. 1962. Natl. Acad. Sci. Natl. Res. Council Publ. 989.

[2] Ibid. 990.

[3] National Research Council, Committee on Animal Nutrition. 1963. Natl. Acad. Sci. Natl. Res. Council Publ. 1137.

[4] National Research Council, Committee on Animal Nutrition. 1964. Ibid. 1192.

[5] Ibid. 1193.

[6] National Research Council, Committee on Animal Nutrition. 1966. Natl. Acad. Sci. Natl. Res. Council Publ. 1194.

[7] Ibid. 1345.

[8] Ibid. 1349.

[9] Ibid. 1401.

15. AMINO ACID REQUIREMENTS: VERTEBRATES

Essential amino acids are not synthesized by the body, and therefore must be supplied by the diet in proper proportions and amounts to meet the requirements for maintenance of nitrogen balance in the adult and for normal growth in the young. Nonessential amino acids, if not supplied in the diet, can be synthesized in adequate amounts from other nitrogen sources, and can be utilized by man and probably by most other vertebrates. Values are adequate for the specified requirement; twice the values should give an acceptable margin of safety.

	Animal	Require-ment for	Amino Acid	Value	Unit of Measure-ment	Ref-er-ence
	Man					
1	Infant,	Growth	L-His	32	mg/kg body wt/day	4
2	<1 yr		L-Ile	90		
3			L-Leu	150		
4			L-Lys	105		
5			L-Met	65[1]		
6			L-Phe	90		
7			L-Thr	60		
8			L-Trp	22		
9			L-Val	93		

[1] Plus 50 mg cystine/kg body wt/day.

continued

	Animal	Requirement for	Amino Acid	Value	Unit of Measurement	Reference
10	Adult,	Nitrogen	L-Ile	700	mg/day	4,10,
11	♂[2]	balance[3]	L-Leu	1100		11
12			L-Lys	800		
13			L-Met	1100[4]		
14			L-Phe	1100[5]		
15			L-Thr	500		
16			L-Trp	250		
17			L-Val	800		
18	♀[2]	Nitrogen	L-Ile	450	mg/day	4
19		balance[3]	L-Leu	620		
20			L-Lys	500		
21			L-Met	350[6]		
22			L-Phe	220[7]		
23			L-Thr	305		
24			L-Trp	157		
25			L-Val	650		
	Dog, cocker spaniel[8]					
26	Young,	Growth	L-Arg	270	mg/kg	2
27	1.5		L-His	60	body	
28	kg[9]		L-Ile	330	wt/day	
29			L-Leu	370		
30			L-Lys	220		
31			L-Met	210		
32			L-Phe	190		
33			L-Thr	140		
34			L-Trp	60		
35			L-Val	300		
36	Adult,	Nitrogen	L-Arg	70	mg/kg	3
37	7 kg[10]	balance[11]	L-His	25	body	
38			L-Ile	80	wt/day	
39			L-Leu	110		
40			L-Lys	60		
41			L-Met	70		
42			L-Phe	65		
43			L-Thr	55		
44			L-Trp	15		
45			L-Val	85		
	Rat, white[12]					
46	Young	Growth	L-Arg	0.20	% of	7
47			L-His	0.30	diet	
48			L-Ile	0.50		
49			L-Leu	0.80		
50			L-Lys	0.90		
51			L-Met	0.60[13]		
52			L-Phe	0.90[14]		
53			L-Thr	0.50		
54			L-Trp	0.15		
55			L-Val	0.70		
56			Non-essential	6.45		
57	Adult	Maintenance	L-His	0.07	% of	7
58			L-Ile	0.43	diet	
59			L-Leu	0.25		
60			L-Lys	0.14		
61			L-Met	0.23[15]		
62			L-Phe	0.19[16]		
63			L-Thr	0.17		
64			L-Trp	0.07		
65			L-Val	0.31		
66			Non-essential	2.14		
67	0.15	Maintenance[17]	L-His	35	mg/kg	1,12
68	kg		L-Ile	180	body	
69			L-Leu	110	wt/day	
70			L-Lys	60		
71			L-Met	90		
72			L-Phe	50		
73			L-Thr	85		
74			L-Trp	30		
75			L-Val	120		
76		Repletion[18,19]	L-His	120	mg/kg	1,12
77			L-Ile	345	body	
78			L-Leu	415	wt/day	
79			L-Lys	330		
80			L-Met	220		
81			L-Phe	255		
82			L-Thr	245		
83			L-Trp	80		
84			L-Val	290		
85	Swine,	Growth[20]	L-Arg	0.20	% of	8
86	young,		L-His	0.20	diet	
87	11.25-		L-Ile	0.55		
88	33.75 kg		L-Leu	0.60		
89			L-Lys	0.75		

[2] Values are minimum requirements as determined for normal, young, healthy adults; twice these values is a safe allowance, but probably should be increased more than twice for growth, rehabilitation from disease, and during pregnancy and lactation. [3] Nonessential amino acids utilized: L-Ala, L-Arg, L-Asp, L-Cit, L-CyS, L-Glu, Gly, L-His, L-Hyp, L-Pro, L-Ser, L-Tyr. [4] Or 200 mg methionine + 810 mg cystine. [5] Or 300 mg phenylalanine + 1100 mg tyrosine. [6] Plus 200 mg cystine/day. [7] Plus 900 mg tyrosine/day. [8] Data do not make clear whether all amino acids listed are indispensable. [9] Amino acids supplied from egg proteins. [10] Amino acids supplied by egg albumin; values for egg protein maintenance for several breeds are similar [5]. [11] Values are minimum intake for maintenance of nitrogen balance. [12] Amino acid requirements of mouse, relative to protein intakes, may be similar to those of growing rat [6]. [13] One-third to one-half may be supplied by cystine. [14] One-third may be supplied by tyrosine. [15] In presence of ample tyrosine. [16] Probably one-third to one-half may come from cystine. [17] Nonessential amino acids utilized: L-Ala, L-Arg, L-Asp, L-CyS, L-Glu, Gly, L-Tyr. [18] Values are allowances for rapid weight recovery and protein repletion in adult, protein-depleted rats. [19] Nonessential amino acids utilized: L-Ala, L-Arg, L-Asp, L-CyS, L-Glu, Gly, L-Hyp, L-Tyr. [20] Values are adequate, but minimum requirements are not yet established.

continued

15. AMINO ACID REQUIREMENTS: VERTEBRATES

	Animal	Requirement for	Amino Acid	Value	Unit of Measurement	Reference
90			L-Met	0.55[21]		
91			L-Phe	0.50[14]		
92			L-Thr	0.45		
93			L-Trp	0.13		
94			L-Val	0.50		
95	Chicken,	Growth	L-Arg	1.2	% of	9
96	young		Gly	1.0	diet	
97			L-His	0.4		
98			L-Ile	0.75		
99			L-Leu	1.4		
100			L-Lys	1.1		
101			L-Met	0.75[22]		
102			L-Phe	1.3[23]		
103			L-Thr	0.7		
104			L-Trp	0.2		
105			L-Val	0.85		
106	Turkey,	Growth	L-Arg	1.6	% of	9
107	young		Gly	1.0	diet	
108			L-Ile	0.84		
109			L-Lys	1.5		
110			L-Met	0.87[24]		
111			L-Trp	0.26		

14/ One-third may be supplied by tyrosine. 21/ One-half may be supplied by cystine. 22/ Or 0.4% methionine + 0.35% cystine. 23/ Or 0.7% phenylalanine + 0.6% tyrosine. 24/ Or 0.52% methionine + 0.35% cystine.

Contributors: (a) Rose, William C., (b) Almquist, H. J., (c) Morgan, Agnes Fay, (d) Frost, Douglas V., (e) Beeson, W. M., (f) Harper, A. E.

References

[1] Frost, D. V., and H. R. Sandy. 1951. J. Biol. Chem. 189:249.
[2] Mabee, D. M., and A. F. Morgan. 1951. J. Nutr. 43:261.
[3] Morgan, A. F., et al. 1951. Ibid. 43:63.
[4] National Research Council, Committee on Amino Acids. 1959. Natl. Acad. Sci. Natl. Res. Council Publ. 711:10.
[5] National Research Council, Committee on Animal Nutrition. 1962. Natl. Acad. Sci. Natl. Res. Council Publ. 989:9.
[6] Ibid. 990:40.
[7] Ibid. 990:54.
[8] National Research Council, Committee on Animal Nutrition. 1964. Ibid. 1192:16.
[9] National Research Council, Committee on Animal Nutrition. 1966. Ibid. 1345:6.
[10] Rose, W. C. 1947. Proc. Am. Phil. Soc. 91:112.
[11] Rose, W. C. 1949. Federation Proc. 8:546.
[12] Steffee, C. H., et al. 1950. J. Nutr. 40:483.

16. FACTORS AFFECTING NUTRIENT REQUIREMENTS AND AVAILABILITY: MAN

Part I. Factors Influencing Requirements

The daily requirement of a nutrient may be increased or decreased by a change in the daily intake of some other nutrient, or by changes in other existing conditions of health or disease. The minimum requirement of many of the nutrients is as yet undetermined for man. **Requirement**: + = increased; − = decreased.

	Nutrient	Influencing Factors	Requirement	Reference
		General Constituents & Energy Values		
1	Fat	Malabsorption syndromes (*see* Part II, line 3), hyperinsulinism	+	10
2	Protein	Growth, pregnancy and lactation	+	1,15
3		Large body size	+	15
4		Hypermetabolic states (*see* line 11)	+	4,6,12
5		Kwashiorkor, protein-calorie malnutrition, starvation, simple protein depletion[1] (*see* Part II, lines 12-18)	+	2,4,5,12
6		Small body size	−	12,15
7		Hypometabolic states (*see* line 14)	−	4,6,12

1/ Primary or secondary.

continued

16. FACTORS AFFECTING NUTRIENT REQUIREMENTS AND AVAILABILITY: MAN

Part I. Factors Influencing Requirements

	Nutrient	Influencing Factors	Requirement	Reference
8	Total calories	Growth	+	15
9	(energy)	Pregnancy and lactation, large body size, physical activity, cold climate, exposure to cold	+	1,15
10		Hard work in hot climate	+	15
11		Fever, hyperthyroidism, leukemia, acromegaly, hyperadrenalism, certain drugs	+	1,4,6, 12,14, 16
12		Aging after maturity	−	15
13		Small body size, physical inactivity, at rest in tropical climate	−	1,15
14		Hypothyroidism, panhypopituitarism, hypoadrenalism	−	6
		Minerals		
15	Calcium	Growth & dentition	+	1,6
16		Pregnancy & lactation	+	1,15
17		Rickets, osteomalacia, calcium deficiency with or without tetany	+	1,4
18	Chlorine	Hypochloremic alkalosis	+	6,16
19	Fluorine	Dental caries[2]	+	1,4
20	Iodine	Iodine deficiency, endemic goiter	+	1,15
21	Iron	Growth, pregnancy & lactation	+	11
22		Blood loss: physiological (menstruation), pathological	+	11
23		Menopause	−	11
24	Magnesium	Magnesium deficiency	+	16
25	Phosphorus	Growth, pregnancy & lactation	+	6
26		Phosphorus deficiency due to rickets	+	4,6
27	Potassium	Potassium deficiency	+	4
28	Sodium	Sodium deficiency	+	3,16
		Vitamins		
29	Thiamine	Hypermetabolic states (*see* line 11)	+	1,4,10
30		Increased proportion of calories derived from carbohydrate sources, increased caloric requirement	+	4,10
31		Beriberi (heart disease, neuropathy), polyneuritis (chronic alcoholism, pernicious vomiting of pregnancy), Wernicke's encephalopathy, Korsakoff's psychosis, delirium tremens	+	1,4, 10,16
32		Decreased caloric requirement	−	3,4
33		Hypometabolic states (*see* line 14), increased proportion of calories derived from noncarbohydrate sources	−	1,4
34	Riboflavin	Growth	+	4,12
35		Pregnancy & lactation, increased caloric requirement	+	1,12
36		Hypermetabolic states (*see* line 11)	+	1,16
37		Riboflavin deficiency	+	1,4
38		Decreased caloric requirement	−	1,12
39		Hypometabolic states (*see* line 14)	−	1,16
40	Nicotinic acid	Large body size, increased caloric requirement	+	3,9
41		Hypermetabolic states (*see* line 11)	+	8,10
42		Pellagra	+	1,4,10
43		Low protein and tryptophan intake	+	3,10
44		Small body size, decreased caloric requirement	−	9,10
45		Hypometabolic states (*see* line 14)	−	6
46		High tryptophan intake	−	1,3,4
47	Vitamin B_6	High protein intake, certain inborn errors of metabolism	+	10
48		Vitamin B_6 deficiency[1], pregnancy	+	4

[1] Primary or secondary. [2] Fluorine has not been demonstrated to be an essential nutrient, but in amounts of 1 ppm it is useful in prevention of dental caries.

continued

16. FACTORS AFFECTING NUTRIENT REQUIREMENTS AND AVAILABILITY: MAN

Part I. Factors Influencing Requirements

	Nutrient	Influencing Factors	Requirement	Reference
49		Low protein intake	−	10
50	Pantothenic acid	Stress situations (?)	+	10
51	Folic acid	Pregnancy & lactation	+	13
52		Alcohol ingestion (?)	+	10
53		Sprue, nutritional megaloblastic anemia, megaloblastic anemia of infancy, megaloblastic anemia of pregnancy, intestinal malabsorption syndromes (*see* Part II, lines 3 & 52), megaloblastic anemia of chronic liver disease, administration of folic acid antagonists, deficiencies in some hemoglobinopathies	+	1,4,10
54	Vitamin B_{12}	Nutritional megaloblastic anemia, pernicious anemia & postgastrectomy, intestinal malabsorption syndromes (e.g., sprue, gluten-induced enteropathy, diseases of intestine such as regional ileitis, diverticulosis, strictures, anastomoses, resection of ileum), certain nutritional neuropathies, fish tapeworm anemia, megaloblastic anemia of liver disease[3]	+	4,10, 16
55	Choline	"Methyl group" deficiency	+	1,4,7
56		Methionine or methyl precursors in diet	−	4,7
57	Ascorbic acid	Pregnancy & lactation	+	1,6,15
58		Growth	+	3
59		Metabolic stress due to infectious disease, hypermetabolic states, trauma, burns, surgery, toxic reactions from certain drugs	+ [4]	4,16
60		Tissue repair, high intake of tyrosine & phenylalanine in premature infants	+	4,10
61		Scurvy	+	1,4,12
62	Vitamin A & precursors	Growth (e.g., bones, teeth)	+ [4]	1
63		Night blindness, xerophthalmia & keratomalacia, follicular hyperkeratosis[5]	+	1,4,12
64	Vitamin D	Inadequate exposure to ultraviolet radiation, growth & dentition, hypoparathyroidism	+	1,16
65		Pregnancy & lactation	+	1,4,15
66		Rickets, osteomalacia	+	1,4,10
67		Renal tubular dysfunction associated with rickets & osteomalacia	+	10
68		Exposure to ultraviolet radiation	−	1,16
69		High dietary calcium & phosphorus	−	4
70		Citrate administration	−	10
71	Vitamin E	Malabsorption syndromes (*see* Part II, line 3), diets high in polyunsaturated fat	+	10
72		Diets high in saturated fat	−	10
73	Vitamin K	Pregnancy	+	1,4
74		Hemorrhagic disease of newborn, obstructive jaundice, hypoprothrombinemia due to oral antibiotics, hypoprothrombinemia due to administration of certain anticoagulants	+	1,4,10

[3] Occasionally. [4] Evidence suggests increased requirement, but definite proof is lacking. [5] Relationship to vitamin A deficiency questionable.

Contributors: Goldsmith, Grace A., and Unglaub, Walter G.

References

[1] American Medical Association, Council on Foods and Nutrition. 1951. Handbook of nutrition. Ed. 2. Blakiston, Philadelphia.

[2] Autret, M., and M. Beliar. 1954. Sindrome policarencial infantil (kwashiorkor) and its prevention in Central America. United Nations Food and Agriculture Organization, Rome.

[3] Beaton, G. H., and E. W. McHenry, ed. 1964. Nutrition. A comprehensive treatise. Academic Press, New York. v. 1-3.

[4] Bourne, G. H., and G. W. Kidder, ed. 1953. Biochemistry and physiology of nutrition. Academic Press, New York. v. 2.

[5] Brock, J. F., and M. Autret. 1952. Kwashiorkor in Africa. World Health Organization, Geneva.

[6] Duncan, G. G., ed. 1964. Diseases of metabolism. Ed. 5. W. B. Saunders, Philadelphia.

[7] Gabuzda, G. J. 1956. J. Am. Med. Assoc. 160:969.

[8] Goldsmith, G. A. 1946. Southern Med. J. 39:485.

[9] Goldsmith, G. A. 1956. J. Am. Dietet. Assoc. 32(4): 312.

[10] Goldsmith, G. A. 1964. In G. G. Duncan, ed. Diseases of metabolism. Ed. 5. W. B. Saunders, Philadelphia. pp. 567-663.

[11] Gubler, C. J. 1956. Science 123:87.

continued

16. FACTORS AFFECTING NUTRIENT REQUIREMENTS AND AVAILABILITY: MAN

Part I. Factors Influencing Requirements

[12] Jolliffe, N., F. F. Tisdall, and P. R. Cannon, ed. 1962. Clinical nutrition. Ed. 2. P. B. Hoeber, New York.

[13] Jukes, T. H. 1952. B-vitamins for blood formation. C. C. Thomas, Springfield, Ill.

[14] McLester, J. S., and W. J. Darby. 1952. Nutrition and diet in health and disease. Ed. 6. W. B. Saunders, Philadelphia.

[15] National Academy of Sciences—National Research Council, Food and Nutrition Board. 1964. Natl. Acad. Sci. Natl. Res. Council Publ. 1146.

[16] Wohl, M. G., and R. S. Goodhart, ed. 1964. Modern nutrition in health and disease. Lea and Febiger, Philadelphia.

Part II. Factors Influencing Biological Availability

Availability: + = increased; – = decreased.

	Nutrient	Influencing Factors	Availability	Reference
		General Constituents & Energy Values		
1	Essential fatty acids	Poor absorption (*see* line 3)	–	1,2,4
2	Fat	Increased absorption due to emulsifying agents	+	5
3		Poor absorption due to deficiency of fat-splitting enzymes, pancreatic diseases, deficiency of bile salts, sprue, gluten-induced enteropathy, gastric & intestinal resection, diseases of intestine (e.g., tumors, infection, Whipple's disease)	–	1,4,10
4		Loss from body due to chyluria, chylous transudates	–	13,16
5	Carbohydrate	Increased gluconeogenesis	+	6
6		Decreased absorption due to gastrointestinal diseases, sprue, hypoadrenalism, hypothyroidism, panhypopituitarism, deficiency of intestinal enzymes	–	4,10, 13
7		Increased loss; glycosuria	–	6,13
8		Impaired gluconeogenesis; diabetes mellitus	–	6
9	Protein	Adequate energy production from carbohydrate & fat	+	1
10		Proper amino acid balance in ingested protein	+	2,4,13
11		Anabolic hormones, growth hormones, estrogens, androgens	+	6,13
12		Inadequate energy production from carbohydrate & fat due to low intake, diabetes mellitus	–	13
13		Amino acid deficiency or imbalance in ingested protein	–	1,4,13
14		Catabolic hormones, adrenocortical hormones	–	6
15		Excessive heat or chemical treatment of protein	–	1
16		Defective absorption due to deficiency of digestive enzymes, diarrhea, intestinal parasites, diseases of the gastrointestinal tract, gastrectomy or intestinal resection, sprue, gluten-induced enteropathy	–	1,4,10, 13
17		Loss in urine, exudates, transudates, hemorrhage, protein-losing enteropathy	–	4,6,13
18		Loss of nitrogen from tissues due to caloric deficiency, burns, trauma, surgery	–	4,13
19	Total calories (energy)	Decreased absorption, increased loss from the body, or defective utilization of protein, carbohydrate, or fat (*see also* lines 3, 4, 6-8, 12-18)	–	2,6,13
		Minerals		
20	Calcium	Increased absorption due to high dietary acidity, L-arginine & L-lysine in diet, lactose in diet, citrates in diet, vitamin D, parathyroid hormone	+	1,2,4, 6
21		Decreased absorption due to low gastric acidity, low dietary acidity, acids (phytic, oxalic, or benzoic) in diet, phosphorus in diet, impaired fat absorption[1/]	–	1,6
22		Increased loss due to bed rest, immobilization, antianabolic hormones, primary & secondary hyperparathyroidism, renal rickets	–	1,6
23		Decreased ionized calcium due to phosphorus retention, alkalosis	–	6,13

[1/] Due to deficiency of bile salts, pancreatic disease, sprue syndrome, gluten-induced enteropathy, and steatorrhea in disease of the gastrointestinal tract.

continued

Part II. Factors Influencing Biological Availability

	Nutrient	Influencing Factors	Availability	Reference
24	Chlorine	Loss due to vomiting, diarrhea, diuresis, salt-losing nephropathy, excessive sweating	–	6,13
25	Iron	Absorption increase due to ascorbic acid, iron deficiency, hemochromatosis, erythropoetin	+	6,11,13
26		Absorption decrease due to low gastric acidity, phytate in diet, phosphate in diet	–	11
27		Utilization decreased by infections[2]	–	14
28		Increased urinary excretion in nephrosis	–	11
29	Magnesium	Loss in gastrointestinal secretions, diarrhea, chronic alcoholism & hepatic cirrhosis, after parathyroidectomy	–	6,13
30	Phosphorus	Vitamin D	+	1,2
31		Decreased absorption due to phytate in diet, excess calcium in diet, administration of aluminum hydroxide	–	1,6
32		Increased excretion due to alkalosis, bone injury, hyperparathyroidism, immobilization	–	1,4,6
33	Potassium	Retention due to anuria, adrenal insufficiency	+	4,6
34		Loss due to metabolic alkalosis & acidosis, administration of ACTH & adrenal cortical hormones, negative nitrogen balance, diarrhea, chronic renal insufficiency, treatment with diuretic agents, primary aldosteronism	–	4,6
35	Sodium	Retention due to administration of ACTH & adrenal cortical hormones, hyperadrenalism, hyperpituitarism	+	6
36		Excessive loss in sweat due to high environmental temperature, fever	–	2,13
37		Excessive loss in urine due to adrenal insufficiency, diuresis, certain injuries & infections of the central nervous system, salt-losing nephropathy	–	6,13
38		Excessive loss from gastrointestinal tract in diarrhea & vomiting	–	6,13
		Vitamins		
39	Thiamine	Decreased absorption due to thiaminase in raw fish, administration of live yeast or alkali, low gastric acidity, gastrointestinal diseases	–	1,10, 13
40		Loss due to diuresis	–	10,17
41	Riboflavin	Decreased absorption due to disease of the gastrointestinal tract	–	1,16
42		Increased excretion in association with protein breakdown	–	1,15
43	Nicotinic acid	Treatment of cereals with alkali to release bound nicotinic acid	+	9,10
44		Oral antibiotics	–	8
45		Decreased absorption due to disease of the gastrointestinal tract	–	7
46		Decreased formation from tryptophan in vitamin B_6 deficiency	–	1,4
47	Vitamin B_6	Administration of isonicotinic acid hydrazide[3]	–	3
48	Biotin	Raw egg white in diet	–	1,4
49		Oral antibiotics	–	8
50	Pantothenic acid	Synthesis by intestinal microorganisms (?)	+	10
51	Folic acid	Synthesis by intestinal microorganisms	+	10
52		Decreased absorption due to gastrointestinal disease, sprue, gluten-induced enteropathy, intestinal infections, strictures, tumors, diverticuli, anastomoses, blind loops, resections	–	10
53	Vitamin B_{12}	Increased absorption due to administration of sorbitol	+	10
54		Poor absorption due to lack of intrinsic factor in gastric juice (pernicious anemia, gastric resection), intestinal malabsorption syndromes (e.g., sprue, gluten-induced enteropathy), diseases of intestine (e.g., regional ileitis, diverticulosis, strictures, anastomoses, resection of ileum), fish tapeworm infestation	–	4,10
55	Choline	Oral antibiotics	+	12
56	Ascorbic acid	Administration of alkali	–	4,10
57		Destruction during preparation or storage of food[4], gastric achlorhydria	–	4,13
58		Increased loss in urine due to certain drugs	–	10,16
59	Vitamin A & precursors	Increased absorption due to ready release of food carotene, emulsifying agents	+	1
60		Decreased absorption due to food carotene not readily released, defective absorption of fat (*see* line 3), ingestion of mineral oil, destruction of vitamin A in gastrointestinal tract by oxidizing agents (e.g., rancid fat, ferric iron), low dietary fat	–	1,4,13

2/ Poor utilization cannot be corrected by iron administration. 3/ Vitamin B_6 antagonist. 4/ Effected by high temperature, presence of alkali, copper, iron.

continued

16. FACTORS AFFECTING NUTRIENT REQUIREMENTS AND AVAILABILITY: MAN

Part II. Factors Influencing Biological Availability

	Nutrient	Influencing Factors	Availability	Reference
61		Defective storage in liver disease	−	4
62		Defective conversion of carotene to vitamin A due to diabetes, hypothyroidism	−	4,13
63		Defective transport due to protein deficiency	−	10
64	Vitamin D	Decreased absorption due to defective absorption of fat (*see* line 3), low dietary fat	−	1,4,13
65	Vitamin E	Malabsorption due to low fat diet, poor absorption of fat (*see* line 3)	−	1,4,10, 13
66	Vitamin K	Synthesis by intestinal microorganisms	+	1
67		Oral antibiotics, inadequate intestinal flora in newborn infants	−	1
68		Defective absorption due to defective absorption of fat (*see* line 3), low dietary fat	−	1,4,13
69		Defective utilization in advanced liver disease	−	4,16

Contributors: Goldsmith, Grace A., and Unglaub, Walter G.

References

[1] American Medical Association, Council on Foods and Nutrition. 1951. Handbook of nutrition. Ed. 2. Blakiston, Philadelphia.

[2] Beaton, G. H., and E. W. McHenry, ed. 1964. Nutrition. A comprehensive treatise. Academic Press, New York. v. 1-3.

[3] Biehl, J. P., and R. W. Vilter. 1954. Proc. Soc. Exptl. Biol. Med. 85:389.

[4] Bourne, G. H., and G. W. Kidder, ed. 1953. Biochemistry and physiology of nutrition. Academic Press, New York. v. 2.

[5] Brien, F. S., et al. 1952. Gastroenterology 20:294.

[6] Duncan, G. G., ed. 1964. Diseases of metabolism. Ed. 5. W. B. Saunders, Philadelphia.

[7] Goldsmith, G. A. 1946. Southern Med. J. 39:485.

[8] Goldsmith, G. A. 1956. New Engl. J. Med. 254:165.

[9] Goldsmith, G. A. 1964. In G. H. Beaton and E. W. McHenry, ed. Nutrition. Academic Press, New York. v. 2, pp. 505-582.

[10] Goldsmith, G. A. 1964. In G. G. Duncan, ed. Diseases of metabolism. Ed. 5. W. B. Saunders, Philadelphia. pp. 567-663.

[11] Gubler, C. J. 1956. Science 123:87.

[12] Hoffbauer, F. W., ed. 1951. Josiah Macy, Jr., Found. Conf. Liver Injury, 10th, Trans.

[13] Jolliffe, N., F. F. Tisdall, and P. R. Cannon, ed. 1962. Clinical nutrition. Ed. 2. P. B. Hoeber, New York.

[14] Kuhns, W. J., et al. 1950. J. Clin. Invest. 29:1505.

[15] Pollack, H., and J. J. Bookman. 1951. J. Lab. Clin. Med. 38:561.

[16] Wohl, M. G., and R. S. Goodhart, ed. 1964. Modern nutrition in health and disease. Lea and Febiger, Philadelphia.

[17] Wohl, M. G., et al. 1953. Circulation 8:744.

17. SPECIAL FOOD MIXTURES: MAN

Part I. United States

	Description [Amount]	Ingredients	Concentration
	Infant Formulas [1]		
1	Formula near-	Water	87.5%
2	ly identical	Protein	1.5%
3	to mother's	Fat	3.7%
4	milk in nu-	Carbohydrate	7%
5	tritional	Minerals (ash)	0.34%
6	breadth and	Calcium	0.065%
7	balance	Copper	0.4 mg
8	[1 quart,	Iodine	65 µg
9	normal	Iron	1.4 mg (0.00015%)
10	dilution]	Phosphorus	0.05%
		Vitamins	
11		Thiamine	0.4 mg
12		Riboflavin	1 mg
13		Nicotinamide	4 mg
14		B_6	0.3 mg
15		Pantothenic acid	2 mg
16		B_{12}	1 µg
17		Choline	85 mg
18		Ascorbic acid	50 mg
19		A	1500 U.S.P. units
20		D	400 U.S.P. units
21		E	5 I.U.

continued

17. SPECIAL FOOD MIXTURES: MAN

Part I. United States

	Description [Amount]	Ingredients	Concentration
22	Milk-free	Water	85.5%
23	soya formu-	Crude fiber	0.2%
24	la for infants	Energy	20 cal/fluid oz
25	and children	Protein	3.2%
26	allergic to	Fat	2.6%
27	milk or sus-	Carbohydrate	7.7%
28	pected of	Minerals (ash)	0.7%
29	having milk	Calcium	1 g (0.1%)
30	sensitivity	Copper	0.4 mg
31	[1 quart,	Iodine	65 µg
32	containing 1	Iron	8 mg (0.00085%)
33	pint of con-	Phosphorus	0.5 g (0.05%)
	centrated	Vitamins	
34	formula	Thiamine	0.5 mg
35	liquid]	Riboflavin	1 mg
36		Nicotinamide	7 mg
37		B_6	0.4 mg
38		Calcium pantothenate	2.5 mg
39		B_{12}	2 µg
40		Choline	85 mg
41		Ascorbic acid	50 mg
42		A	1500 U.S.P. units
43		D	400 U.S.P. units
44		E	5 I.U.
45	Hypoallergen-	Water	86%
46	ic formula,	Energy	20 cal/fluid oz
47	supplying	Protein (equivalent)	2.2%
48	milk protein	Fat	2.6%
49	nutrients in	Carbohydrate	8.5%
50	enzymatical-	Minerals (ash)	0.6%
51	ly hydro-	Calcium	0.9 g (0.1%)
52	lyzed form,	Copper	0.4 mg
53	for infants	Iodine (as iodide)	65.0 µg
54	and children	Iron	12 mg (0.001%)
55	sensitive to	Magnesium	50 mg
56	intact pro-	Phosphorus	0.65 g (0.07%)
57	teins of milk	Potassium	0.9 g
58	and other	Zinc	3.0 mg
	foods [1	Vitamins	
59	quart, con-	Thiamine	0.46 mg
60	taining 4.8	Riboflavin	1.8 mg
61	ounces con-	Nicotinamide	4 mg
62	centrated	B_6	0.5 mg
63	formula	Biotin	0.03 mg
64	powder]	Calcium pantothenate	3.2 mg
65		Folic acid	50 µg
66		B_{12}	4.5 µg
67		Choline chloride	150 mg
68		Ascorbic acid	50 mg
69		A	1500 U.S.P. units
70		D	400 U.S.P. units
71		E	5 I.U.
72	High protein	Water	85.9%
73	formula,	Protein	3.9% 1/
74	containing	Fat	2%
75	protein	Carbohydrate	7.3%
76	milk, enzy-	Lactic acid	0.3%
77	matic ca-	Minerals (ash)	0.6%
78	sein hy-	Calcium	0.1%
79	drolysate,	Iron	0.0003%
80	and banana	Phosphorus	0.09%
	powder,	Vitamins	
81	for dietary	Thiamine	0.2 mg
82	manage-	Ascorbic acid	2 mg
83	ment of	A	5000 U.S.P. units
84	celiac con-	D	1000 U.S.P. units
85	ditions and	E	10 I.U.
	diarrhea [1 quart, containing 5.2 ounces concentrated formula powder]		
86	Low phenyl-	Water	86%
87	alanine	Energy	20 cal/fluid oz
88	formula	Protein (equivalent)	Approx 15%
89	for use as	Phenylalanine	$<$0.06-$>$0.1% 2/
90	basic food	Fat	2.7%
91	of infants	Carbohydrate	8.5%
92	and chil-	Minerals (ash)	0.75%
93	dren with	Calcium	0.1%
94	phenyl-	Copper	0.4 mg
95	ketonuria	Iodine	65.0 µg
96	[1 quart,	Iron	0.0015%
97	normal	Phosphorus	0.07%
98	dilution]	Zinc	3.0 mg
		Vitamins	
99		Thiamine	0.46 mg
100		Riboflavin	1.8 mg
101		Nicotinamide	4.0 mg
102		B_6	0.5 mg
103		Biotin	0.03 mg
104		Calcium pantothenate	3.2 mg
105		Folic acid	0.05 mg
106		B_{12}	4.5 µg
107		Choline chloride	150 mg
	Weight Control Dietaries [1]		
108	Milkshake-	Energy	900 cal
109	flavored	Protein	70 g (7.4%)
110	liquid	Fat	20 g (2.1%)
111	[32 fluid	Carbohydrate	110 g (11.6%)
	ounces]	Minerals	
112		Calcium	2.1 g
113		Copper	1.5 mg
114		Iron	10 mg
115		Manganese	2 mg

1/ Including the protein equivalent of the casein hydrolysate. 2/ Of powder used in one quart dilution.

continued

17. SPECIAL FOOD MIXTURES: MAN

Part I. United States

	Description [Amount]	Ingredients	Concentration
116		Phosphorus	1.7 g
117		Potassium	2.6 g
118		Sodium	1.2 g
		Vitamins	
119		Thiamine	2 mg
120		Riboflavin	3 mg
121		Nicotinamide	15 mg
122		B_6	2 mg
123		Calcium pantothenate	10 mg
124		B_{12}	2 μg
125		Ascorbic acid	100 mg
126		A	5000 U.S.P. units
127		D	400 U.S.P. units
128		E	10 I.U.
129	Vegetable	Energy	225 cal
130	and beef	Protein	17.5 g (6.9%)
131	diet din-	Fat	6.8 g (2.7%)
132	ner [9	Carbohydrate	23.5 g (9.2%)
	ounces]	Minerals	
133		Calcium	0.37 g
134		Copper	0.37 mg
135		Iodine	37.5 μg
136		Iron	2.5 mg
137		Manganese	0.5 mg
138		Phosphorus	0.31 g
139		Potassium	0.52 g
140		Sodium	0.84 g
		Vitamins	
141		Thiamine	0.5 mg
142		Riboflavin	0.75 mg
143		Nicotinamide	3.75 mg
144		B_6	0.5 mg
145		Calcium pantothenate	2.5 mg
146		B_{12}	0.5 μg
147		Ascorbic acid	25 mg
148		A	1250 U.S.P. units
149		E	2.5 I.U.
150	Rice and	Energy	225 cal
151	chicken	Protein	17.5 g (6.9%)
152	diet din-	Fat	6.8 g (2.7%)
153	ner [9	Carbohydrate	23.5 g (9.2%)
	ounces]	Minerals	
154		Calcium	0.41 g
155		Copper	0.37 mg
156		Iodine	37.5 μg
157		Iron	2.5 mg
158		Manganese	0.5 mg
159		Phosphorus	0.33 g
160		Potassium	0.68 g
161		Sodium	0.90 g
		Vitamins	
162		Thiamine	0.5 mg
163		Riboflavin	0.75 mg
164		Nicotinamide	3.75 mg
165		B_6	0.5 mg
166		Calcium pantothenate	2.5 mg
167		B_{12}	0.5 μg
168		Ascorbic acid	25 mg
169		A	1250 U.S.P. units
170		E	2.5 I.U.
171	Tuna and	Energy	225 cal
172	noodles	Protein	17.5 g (6.9%)
173	diet din-	Fat	6.8 g (2.7%)
174	ner [9	Carbohydrate	23.5 g (9.2%)
	ounces]	Minerals	
175		Calcium	0.39 g
176		Copper	0.37 mg
177		Iodine	37.5 μg
178		Iron	2.5 mg
179		Manganese	0.5 mg
180		Phosphorus	0.38 g
181		Potassium	0.6 g
182		Sodium	0.85 g
		Vitamins	
183		Thiamine	0.5 mg
184		Riboflavin	0.75 mg
185		Nicotinamide	3.75 mg
186		B_6	0.5 mg
187		Calcium pantothenate	2.5 mg
188		B_{12}	0.5 μg
189		Ascorbic acid	25 mg
190		A	1250 U.S.P. units
191		E	2.5 I.U.
192	Diet cookies	Energy	225 cal
193	[9 cookies]	Protein	17.5 g (30.8%)
194		Fat	5 g (8.8%)
195		Carbohydrate	27.5 g (48.5%)
		Minerals	
196		Calcium	0.4 g
197		Copper	375 μg
198		Iodine	37.5 μg
199		Iron	2.5 mg
200		Magnesium	75 mg
201		Manganese	0.5 mg
202		Phosphorus	0.33 g
203		Potassium	275 mg
204		Sodium	200 mg
		Vitamins	
205		Thiamine	0.5 mg
206		Riboflavin	0.75 mg
207		Nicotinamide	3.75 mg
208		B_6	0.5 mg
209		Calcium pantothenate	2.5 mg
210		B_{12}	0.5 μg
211		Ascorbic acid	25 mg
212		A	1250 U.S.P. units

continued

17. SPECIAL FOOD MIXTURES: MAN

Part I. United States

	Description [Amount]	Ingredients	Concentration
213		D	100 U.S.P. units
214		E	2.5 I.U.
		Army Survival Rations [2]	
215	Cheese and	Water	0.7 g
216	potato	Energy	134 cal
217	food bar	Protein	2.4 g
218	[32 g]	Fat	4.4 g
219		Carbohydrate	23.6 g
220		Minerals (ash)	0.9 g
221		Calcium	84 mg
222		Iron	1.6 mg
		Vitamins	
223		Thiamine	0.03 mg
224		Riboflavin	0.04 mg
225		Nicotinic acid	0.5 mg
226	Chicken-	Water	0.5 g
227	flavored	Energy	106 cal
228	food bar	Protein	1.7 g
229	[24 g]	Fat	3.0 g
230		Carbohydrate	18.0 g
231		Minerals (ash)	0.8 g
232		Calcium	2 mg
233		Iron	1.8 mg
		Vitamins	
234		Thiamine	0.15 mg
235		Riboflavin	0.08 mg
236		Nicotinic acid	0.1 mg
237	Cornflake	Water	3.6 g
238	food bar	Energy	253 cal
239	[56.70 g]	Protein	5.2 g
240		Fat	8.8 g
241		Carbohydrate	37.9 g
242		Minerals (ash)	1.2 g
243		Calcium	4 mg
244		Iron	0.2 mg
		Vitamins	
245		Thiamine	0.15 mg
246		Riboflavin	0.11 mg
247		Nicotinic acid	0.9 mg
248	Rice-corn-	Water	2.6 g
249	flake food	Energy	266 cal
250	bar [56.70	Protein	5.4 g
251	g]	Fat	10.1 g
252		Carbohydrate	37.6 g
253		Minerals (ash)	1.1 g
254		Calcium	4 mg
255		Iron	0.7 mg
		Vitamins	
256		Thiamine	0.35 mg
257		Riboflavin	0.12 mg
258		Nicotinic acid	1.39 mg
259	Fruitcake	Water	4.4 g
260	food bar	Energy	193 cal
261	[48.20 g]	Protein	4.7 g
262		Fat	5.6 g
263		Carbohydrate	33.1 g
264		Minerals (ash)	0.4 g
265		Calcium	18 mg
266		Iron	1.0 mg
		Vitamins	
267		Thiamine	0.01 mg
268		Riboflavin	0.04 mg
269		Nicotinic acid	0.1 mg
270		A	200 I.U.
271	Chocolate	Water	4.4 g
272	fudge food	Energy	221 cal
273	bar [56.70	Protein	4.6 g
274	g]	Fat	6.0 g
275		Carbohydrate	40.3 g
276		Minerals (ash)	1.4 g
277		Calcium	151 mg
278		Iron	0.5 mg
		Vitamins	
279		Thiamine	0.04 mg
280		Riboflavin	0.22 mg
281		Nicotinic acid	0.17 mg
282	General pur-	Water	10.8 g
283	pose sur-	Energy	784 cal
284	vival food	Protein	16.0 g
285	packet	Fat	25.2 g
286	MIL-F-	Carbohydrate	127.2 g
287	43231, con-	Minerals (ash)	4.0 g
288	sisting of	Calcium	176 mg
289	4 food bars	Iron	3.88 mg
	[182.84 g	Vitamins	
290	average	Thiamine	0.48 mg
291	weight] [3]	Riboflavin	0.40 mg
292		Nicotinic acid	2.72 mg
293		A	30 I.U.

[3] In addition, the packet contains 2.5 g instant coffee, 6 g sugar, and 7.09 g chicken soup base.

Contributors: (a) Shanton, John Lynn, (b) Calhoun, William K.

References

[1] Mead Johnson Laboratories. 1967. Food products. Mead Johnson Research Center, Evansville, Indiana.

[2] U.S. Army Natick Laboratories. 1964. MIL-F-43231. Department of the Army, Natick, Mass.

continued

17. SPECIAL FOOD MIXTURES: MAN

Part II. Latin America, Africa, Asia, and Worldwide

	Name of Mixture	Ingredients	Concentration	Reference
		Latin America		
1	Incaparina	Corn, whole, ground, cooked	29 g/100 g	1,2,7
2	Formula 9	Sorghum flour, cooked	29 g/100 g	
3		Cottonseed flour	38 g/100 g	
4		*Torula* yeast	3 g/100 g	
5		L-Lysine hydrochloride[1]	0.2 g/100 g	
6		Calcium carbonate	1 g/100 g	
7		Vitamin A	4500 I.U./100 g	
8	Incaparina	Corn, whole, ground, cooked	58 g/100 g	3,7
9	Formula 14	Soybean flour	38 g/100 g	
10		*Torula* yeast	3 g/100 g	
11		DL-Methionine[1]	0.2 g/100 g	
12		Calcium phosphate	1 g/100 g	
13		Vitamin A	4500 I.U./100 g	
14	Incaparina	Corn, whole, ground, cooked	58 g/100 g	1,4,7
15	Formula 15	Cottonseed flour	19 g/100 g	
16		Soybean flour	19 g/100 g	
17		*Torula* yeast	3 g/100 g	
18		L-Lysine hydrochloride[1]	0.1 g/100 g	
19		DL-Methionine[1]	0.2 g/100 g	
20		Calcium carbonate	1 g/100 g	
21		Vitamin A	4500 I.U./100 g	
		Africa		
22	Biscuit Meal	Peanuts, whole, ground	41 g/100 g	5
23	(Uganda)	Cornmeal	26 g/100 g	
24		Milk, skim, dried	15 g/100 g	
25		Sucrose	12 g/100 g	
26		Cottonseed oil	6 g/100 g	
27	Pro Nutro	Cornmeal, whole-grain, white	19.3 g/100 g	6
28		yellow	19.3 g/100 g	
29		Soybeans, dehulled[2]	17.7 g/100 g	
30		Peanuts, dehulled, shredded	14 g/100 g	
31		Milk, skim, dried	10 g/100 g	
32		Whey powder	6 g/100 g	
33		Sugar	4.1 g/100 g	
34		Malt-extract solids	2.3 g/100 g	
35		Wheat germ	2 g/100 g	
36		Fish protein concentrate	2 g/100 g	
37		*Torula* yeast	1.5 g/100 g	
38		Salt	1 g/100 g	
39		Bone phosphate	0.8 g/100 g	
		Asia		
40	Multipurpose	Peanut flour, ground	75 g/100 g	8,10
41	Food (India)	Bengal gram flour	25 g/100 g	
	Formula 2	Vitamin & mineral premix		
42		Calcium phosphate	6.1 g/lb[3]	
43		Thiamine	1.48 mg/lb[3]	
44		Riboflavin	4.9 mg/lb[3]	

[1] Commercial amino acid fortification, recommended by the Institute of Nutrition for Central America and Panama (INCAP), to begin in 1967. [2] Dehulled soybeans and dried skim milk are maintained at the specified levels; other ingredients may vary, depending on availability. [3] Of final product.

continued

17. SPECIAL FOOD MIXTURES: MAN

Part II. Latin America, Africa, Asia, and Worldwide

	Name of Mixture	Ingredients	Concentration	Reference
45		Vitamin A	14,800 I.U./lb[3/]	
46		Vitamin D	1340 I.U./lb[3/]	
47	Bal Ahar	Wheat flour, whole-grain	65 g/100 g	9
48	Formula 2A	Cottonseed flour	25 g/100 g	
49		Bengal or red gram flour	10 g/100 g	
		Vitamins & minerals		
50		Calcium phosphate	≮400 mg/100 g	
51		Iron salt	≮10 mg/100 g	
52		Thiamine	≮0.4 mg/100 g	
53		Riboflavin	≮0.3 mg/100 g	
54		Nicotinic acid	≮0.5 mg/100 g	
55		Vitamin A palmitate	≮1300 I.U./100 g	
		Worldwide		
56	Blended Food	Cornmeal, gelatinized	68.05 g/100 g	11
57	Product,	Soybean flour, defatted	25 g/100 g	
58	Child Food	Milk, skim, dried	5 g/100 g	
59	Supplement	Calcium phosphate, dibasic	0.55 g/100 g	
60	Formula 2-	Mineral premix	1.3 g/100 g	
61	CSM	Calcium carbonate, precipitated, FCC grade	2724 g/1000 lb[3/]	
62		Ferrous sulfate, purified food grade	109 g/1000 lb[3/]	
63		Iodized salt (0.007% I_2), food grade	3051 g/1000 lb[3/]	
64		Zinc sulfate, hydrated FCC	18.2 g/1000 lb[3/]	
65		Vitamin-antioxidant premix	0.1 g/100 g	
66		Thiamine mononitrate	1.25 g/1000 lb[3/]	
67		Riboflavin	1.75 g/1000 lb[3/]	
68		Nicotinic acid	22.50 g/1000 lb[3/]	
69		Vitamin B_6	0.25 g/1000 lb[3/]	
70		Calcium D-pantothenate	12.50 g/1000 lb[3/]	
71		Folic acid	0.15 g/1000 lb[3/]	
72		Vitamin B_{12}	0.000015 g/1000 lb[3/]	
73		Vitamin A (stabilized retinyl palmitate)	30,000,000 U.S.P. units/1000 lb[3/]	
74		Vitamin D stabilized	900,000 U.S.P. units/1000 lb[3/]	
75		Butylated hydroxyanisole	10 g/1000 lb[3/]	
76		Butylated hydroxytoluene	10 g/1000 lb[3/]	

3/ Of final product.

Contributors: Rosenfield, Daniel, and Altschul, Aaron M.

References

[1] Behar, M., and R. Bressani. 1966. Natl. Acad. Sci. Natl. Res. Council Publ. 1282:213.

[2] Bressani, R., and L. G. Elias. 1962. Arch. Venezolanos Nutr. 12:245.

[3] Bressani, R., and L. G. Elias. 1966. J. Food Sci. 31:626.

[4] Bressani, R., et al. 1967. Arch. Latinoam. Nutr. 17(3):177.

[5] Dean, R. F. A. 1961. Natl. Acad. Sci. Natl. Res. Council Publ. 843:77.

[6] Hind Brothers and Co., Ltd., Durban, Natal, Republic of South Africa.

[7] Institute of Nutrition for Central America and Panama, Apartado Postal No. 1188, Guatemala City, Guatemala.

[8] Meals for Millions Foundation, 1800 Olympic, Santa Monica, Calif., 90404.

[9] Scrimshaw, N. S., and G. K. Parman. 1966. Rept. U.S. Dept. State Agency Intern. Develop. (Wash., D.C.).

[10] Subrahmanyan, V., et al. 1957. Food Sci. (Mysore) 6:76.

[11] U.S. Department of Agriculture. 1966. Agr. Stab. Conserv. Serv. Announ. PS-GR-16(& Suppl.).

	Type of Diet [Reference]	Ingredient	Concentration
	Cat 1/		
	Stock diet, da Silva's [10]		
1	Diet A	Butter, lard, or vegetable oil	5%
2		Casein, crude	10%
3		Liver, beef, raw	35%
4		Milk, whole, dried	20%
5		Oats, compressed, slightly cooked	30%
6	Diet B	Beef, lean muscle, raw	20%
7		Bone meal	2%
8		Butter, lard, or vegetable oil	10%
9		Casein, crude	10%
10		Cod liver oil	3%
11		Oats, compressed, slightly cooked	20%
12		Potatoes, cooked, mashed	15%
13		Sardines, deboned & eviscerated	20%
14	Diet C	Beef, lean muscle, raw	33.3%
15		Potatoes, cooked, mashed	33.3%
16		Sardines, deboned & eviscerated	33.3%
17	Purified diet, Gershoff's [10]	Casein, purified	32.1%
18		Choline chloride	0.3%
19		Cod liver oil	1.0%
20		Corn oil	12.5%
21		Fat, hydrogenated	12.5%
22		Sucrose	37.6%
23		Salt mix, Hegsted's IV	4.0%
24		$CaCO_3$	600 2/
25		$CaHPO_4 \cdot 2H_2O$	150 2/
26		$CuSO_4 \cdot 5H_2O$	0.6 2/
27		$MgSO_4 \cdot 7H_2O$	204 2/
28		$MnSO_4 \cdot 4H_2O$	10 2/
29		KI	1.6 2/
30		K_2HPO_4	645 2/
31		NaCl	335 2/
32		$ZnCl_2$	0.5 2/
33		Ferric citrate	55 2/
		Vitamin mix, Gershoff's	
34		Thiamine	0.4 mg %
35		Riboflavin	0.8 mg %
36		Nicotinic acid	4 mg %
37		B_6	0.4 mg %
38		Biotin	0.02 mg %
39		Calcium pantothenate	2 mg %
40		Folic acid	0.1 mg %
41		Choline	300 mg %
42		Menadione	0.1 mg %
	Dog		
	Meal-type diet (91% dry matter) [9]		
43	Ration 1	Bone meal, steamed	2%
44		Cereal grains	51.23%
45		Fat, edible	2%
46		Fermentation solubles, dried	1%
47		Fish meal (60% protein)	5%
48		Meat & bone meal (55% protein)	8%
49		Milk, skim, dried	4%
50		Soybean meal	12%
51		Wheat bran	4%
52		Wheat germ meal	8%
53		Yeast, brewer's, dried	2%
54		Iron oxide	0.02%
55		Salt, iodized	0.50%
56		Vitamins A & D feeding oil 3/	0.25%
57	Ration 2	Cornflakes	26.75%
58		Fish meal (60% protein)	3%
59		Meat & bone meal (55% protein)	15%
60		Milk, skim, dried	2.5%
61		Soybean grits	19%
62		Wheat flakes	26.7%
63		Wheat germ meal	5%
64		Yeast, brewer's, dried	0.5%
65		Salt, iodized	0.25%
66		Vitamins A & D feeding oil 3/	0.5%
67		Riboflavin supplement, BY-500	0.8%
	Guinea Pig 4/		
68	National Institutes of Health diet [10]	Alfalfa leaf meal, U.S. No. 1 5/	40%
69		Oat groats, pure	15%
70		Soybean meal (44% protein)	13%
71		Wheat, whole, No. 1, pulverized	30.5%
72		Wheat germ oil, cold pressed	0.25%
73		Yeast, irradiated	2.5%
74		Calcium carbonate	1%
75		Salt, iodized	2.5%
	Purified diet [10]		
76	Reid & Briggs	Casein	30 g 6/
77		Cellophane	15 g 6/

1/ Growing animal. 2/ Parts by weight. 3/ 2250 I.U. vitamin A/g and 400 I.U. vitamin D/g diet. 4/ Daily consumption per animal approximately equal to one-twelfth of body weight. Commercial pelleted diets formulated for guinea pigs support normal growth and reproduction when sufficient stable ascorbic acid is present in feed; otherwise a fresh vegetable such as kale or cabbage should supplement the diet. 5/ Carotene content not less than 100 μg/g. 6/ Per 100 g diet.

continued

	Type of Diet [Reference]	Ingredient	Concentration
78		Corn oil	7.3 g[6]
79		Cornstarch	20 g[6]
80		Glucose	7.8 g[6]
81		Sucrose	10.3 g[6]
82		Magnesium oxide	0.5 g[6]
83		Potassium acetate	2.5 g[6]
84		Salt mix, Briggs, et al	6 g[6]
		Vitamins	
85		Thiamine	1.6 mg[6]
86		Riboflavin	1.6 mg[6]
87		Nicotinic acid	20 mg[6]
88		B_6	1.6 mg[6]
89		Biotin	0.06 mg[6]
90		Calcium or sodium pantothenate	4 mg[6]
91		Folic acid	1 mg[6]
92		Inositol	0.2 g[6]
93		B_{12}	0.004 mg[6]
94		Choline chloride	0.2 g[6]
95		Ascorbic acid	200 mg[6]
96		A acetate	0.6 mg[6]
97		D_2	0.004 mg[6]
98		α-Tocopherol acetate	2 mg[6]
99		Menadione	0.2 mg[6]
100	Roine, et al	Casein	30 g[6]
101		Gum arabic	15 g[6]
102		Soybean oil	4 g[6]
103		Sucrose	43.5 g[6]
104		Magnesium oxide	0.5 g[6]
105		Potassium acetate	2.5 g[6]
106		Salt mix, Hegsted's IV	4 g[6]
107		$CaCO_3$	600[2]
108		$CaHPO_4 \cdot 2H_2O$	150[2]
109		$CuSO_4 \cdot 5H_2O$	0.6[2]
110		$MgSO_4 \cdot 7H_2O$	204[2]
111		$MnSO_4 \cdot 4H_2O$	10[2]
112		KI	1.6[2]
113		K_2HPO_4	645[2]
114		NaCl	335[2]
115		$ZnCl_2$	0.5[2]
116		Ferric citrate	55[2]
		Vitamins	
117		Thiamine	1 mg[6]
118		Riboflavin	1.4 mg[6]
119		Nicotinic acid	10 mg[6]
120		B_6	1 mg[6]
121		Biotin	0.04 mg[6]
122		Calcium or sodium pantothenate	3 mg[6]
123		Folic acid	0.3 mg[6]
124		*p*-Aminobenzoic acid	10 mg[6]
125		Inositol	0.2 g[6]
126		Choline chloride	0.3 g[6]
127		Ascorbic acid (fed separately)	12.5 mg[7]
128		β-Carotene	1.2 mg[6]
129		D_2	0.008 mg[6]
130		α-Tocopherol	12 mg[6]
131		Menadione	0.2 mg[6]
		Hamster	
132	Purified diet [10]	Casein, purified	24%
133		Cellulose	3%
134		Cod liver oil[8]	0.3%
135		Corn oil	5%
136		Cystine	0.3%
137		Liver extract	1%
138		Sucrose	62.4%
139		Salt mix, Hegsted's IV	4%
140		$CaCO_3$	600[2]
141		$CaHPO_4 \cdot 2H_2O$	150[2]
142		$CuSO_4 \cdot 5H_2O$	0.6[2]
143		$MgSO_4 \cdot 7H_2O$	204[2]
144		$MnSO_4 \cdot 4H_2O$	10[2]
145		KI	1.6[2]
146		K_2HPO_4	645[2]
147		NaCl	335[2]
148		$ZnCl_2$	0.5[2]
149		Ferric citrate	55[2]
		Vitamins	
150		Thiamine	0.6 mg[6]
151		Riboflavin	0.6 mg[6]
152		Nicotinic acid	2 mg[6]
153		B_6	0.6 mg[6]
154		Biotin	0.01 mg[6]
155		Calcium pantothenate	4 mg[6]
156		Folic acid	0.2 mg[6]
157		*p*-Aminobenzoic acid	30 mg[6]
158		Inositol	100 mg[6]
159		B_{12}	0.005 mg[6]
160		Choline chloride	100 mg[6]
161		α-Tocopherol	2.5 mg[6]
162		Menadione	0.6 mg[6]
		Horse	
163	Purified diet [15]	Casein	2 lb
164		Corn oil	0.5 lb
165		Cornstarch	4 lb
166		Solka-floc	5 lb
167		Cerelose	1 lb
168		Dicalcium phosphate	0.15 lb
169		Trace-mineralized salt	0.05 lb
		Vitamins	
170		Thiamine	100 mg[9]
171		Riboflavin	1 mg[9]
172		Nicotinic acid	0.1 mg[9]

[2] Parts by weight. [6] Per 100 g diet. [7] Per day. [8] 6000 I.U. vitamin A/g and 850 I.U. vitamin D/g diet. [9] Per lb feed.

continued

	Type of Diet [Reference]	Ingredient	Concentration
173		B_6	1.5 mg[9]
174		Pantothenate	100 μg[9]
175		A	200 I.U.[9]
176		Carotene	5 mg[9]
177		D	400 I.U.[9]
178		α-Tocopherol	30 mg[9]
179		K	3 mg[9]
	Monkey		
180	Colony	Basal mix	2 kg
181	diet[10],	Alfalfa meal	2%
182	Schmidt	Bone meal	0.75%
183	[10]	Milk, powdered	4.5%
184		Soybean meal	12.5%
185		Sucrose	0.75%
186		Wheat, ground	76.25%
187		Yeast, brewer's	1.25%
188		Calcium carbonate	1.5%
189		Salt	0.5%
190		Thiamine	0.01%
191		Riboflavin	0.01%
192		Nicotinic acid	0.02%
193		B_6	0.01%
194		Calcium pantothenate	0.02%
195		Folic acid, 3%	0.12%
196		Eggs, fresh	3
197		Rice, brown	200 g
198		Water	2.5 pints
199		Salt, iodized	10 g
200		Ascorbic acid	3 g
201		Vitamin D, water-soluble	7500 I.U.
	Mouse		
	Stock diet [10]		
202	Bell	Alfalfa leaf meal	5%
203		Barley, fine	12.475%
204		Lard, emulsified, stabilized	2.5%
205		Limestone, ground	1%
206		Linseed meal	7.5%
207		Meat meal	15%
208		Molasses	5%
209		Oat groats, fine	20%
210		Wheat, finely ground	15%
211		Wheat bran	15%
212		Yeast, brewer's, dried	1%
213		Manganese sulfate	0.025%
214		Salt, iodized	0.5%
215		Vitamin A	1000 I.U.
216		Vitamin D_2	14.5 I.U.
217	Maynard	Barley, malted, ground	10%
218	& Loosli	Bone meal, steamed	1%

	Type of Diet [Reference]	Ingredient	Concentration
219		Cornmeal, yellow	20%
220		Limestone, ground	1%
221		Linseed meal	15%
222		Milk, skim, dried	15%
223		Oat flour	15%
224		Wheat red dog flour	22%
225		Sodium chloride	1%
	Semi-purified diet [10]		
226	Bell	Casein, vitamin-free	22.3 g[6]
227		Cellulose	11.2 g[6]
228		Corn oil	5 g[6]
229		Cornstarch	44.3 g[6]
230		Sucrose	11.2 g[6]
231		Salt mix	6 g[6]
232		$CaCO_3$	42.1%
233		$CaHPO_4 \cdot 2H_2O$	25.1%
234		$CuSO_4 \cdot 5H_2O$	0.05%
235		$FeSO_4 \cdot 7H_2O$	1.8%
236		$MgSO_4 \cdot 7H_2O$	1.8%
237		$MnSO_4 \cdot 5H_2O$	0.05%
238		KCl	6.69%
239		NaCl	22.4%
240		$KI\text{-}Ca(C_{18}H_{35}O_2)_2$	0.01%
		Vitamins	
241		Thiamine	0.3 mg[6]
242		Riboflavin	0.4 mg[6]
243		Nicotinic acid	0.3 mg[6]
244		B_6	0.1 mg[6]
245		Biotin	0.01 mg[6]
246		Pantothenic acid	0.9 mg[6]
247		Folic acid	2.5 mg[6]
248		*p*-Aminobenzoic acid	1.2 mg[6]
249		Inositol	0.1 mg[6]
250		B_{12}	0.5 μg[6]
251		Choline	135 mg[6]
252		A, stabilized	50 I.U.[6]
253		D	20 I.U.[6]
254	Fenton,	Casein, vitamin-free	30 g[6]
255	et al	Cellulose	2 g[6]
256		Cod liver oil concentrate	0.2 g[6]
257		Corn oil	10 g[6]
258		Sucrose	53 g[6]
259		Salt mix, Sure's No. 2	5 g[6]
260		$CaCO_3$	600[2]
261		$CaHPO_4 \cdot 2H_2O$	190[2]
262		$CoCl_2$	0.5[2]
263		$CuSO_4$	0.4[2]
264		$MgSO_4$	99[2]
265		$MnSO_4$	8[2]
266		KI	1.6[2]
267		$K_2Al_2(SO_4)_4$	0.4[2]

2/ Parts by weight. 6/ Per 100 g diet. 9/ Per lb feed. 10/ At each feeding, rice, salt, and water are autoclaved for not less than 15 minutes at 15 lb pressure, then mixed with fresh eggs and with an appropriate amount of basal mixture; additional water, containing dissolved ascorbic acid and vitamin D, is added slowly while mixing. Ration is 32 g/kg body wt/feeding, twice daily; diet makes enough to feed 100 kg of monkeys.

continued

	Type of Diet [Reference]	Ingredient	Concentration
268		K_2HPO_4	645[2]
269		$Na_2B_4O_7$	0.5[2]
270		NaCl	335[2]
271		NaF	0.5[2]
272		$ZnCl_2$	0.5[2]
273		Ferric citrate	55[2]
		Vitamins	
274		Thiamine	0.5 mg[6]
275		Riboflavin	1 mg[6]
276		Nicotinic acid	1 mg[6]
277		B_6	0.5 mg[6]
278		Biotin	0.02 mg[6]
279		Pantothenic acid	6 mg[6]
280		Folic acid	0.05 mg[6]
281		Choline	150 mg[6]
282		α-Tocopherol	6 mg[6]
283		Menadione	1 mg[6]
		Rabbit	
	Stock diet[11] [12]		
284	Growth, normal[12]	Alfalfa hay	60%
285		Barley, grains	15%
286		Corn, grains	22%
287		Soybean meal	3%
288	Growth, normal, & fattening[13,14]	Alfalfa hay	40%
289		Barley, grains	32%
290		Oats, grains	18%
291		Soybean meal	5%
292		Wheat bran	5%
293	Maintenance[15]	Alfalfa hay	70%
294		Oats, grains	20%
295		Wheat, grains	10%
296	Pregnancy[15]	Clover hay	50%
297		Oats, grains	44%
298		Soybean meal	6%
299	Lactation[15,16]	Alfalfa hay	40%
300		Sorghum, grains	25%
301		Soybean meal	10%
302		Wheat, grains	25%
		Rat	
303	Basal ration[17] [8]	Butterfat	9%
304		Casein	35%
305		Cornstarch	37%
306		Lard	15%
307		Salt mix, Osborne & Mendel's No. 4	4%
308		$CaCO_3$	134.8 g
309		HCl	53.4 g

	Type of Diet [Reference]	Ingredient	Concentration
310		$MgCO_3$	24.2 g
311		$MnSO_4$	0.079 g
312		H_3PO_4	103.2 g
313		$K_2Al_2(SO_4)_4$	0.0245 g
314		K_2CO_3	141.3 g
315		KI	0.02 g
316		Na_2CO_3	34.2 g
317		NaF	0.248 g
318		H_2SO_4	9.2 g
319		Citric acid · H_2O	111.1 g
320		Ferric citrate · H_2O	6.34 g
321	Purified diet[18] [13]	Casein, vitamin-free	18.0%
322		Lard or vegetable oil	5.0%
323		DL-Methionine	0.23%
324		Sucrose	70-73%
325		Salt mix, Jones-Foster's	4.0%
326		$CaCO_3$	1.5266 g
327		$CoCl_2 \cdot 6H_2O$	80.0 μg
328		$CuSO_4 \cdot 5H_2O$	1.92 mg
329		$FeSO_4 \cdot 7H_2O$	0.1080 g
330		$MgSO_4$	0.2292 g
331		$MnSO_4 \cdot 2H_2O$	17.8 mg
332		KI	3.16 mg
333		KH_2PO_4	1.5560 g
334		NaCl	0.5572 g
335		$ZnCl_2$	1.04 mg
336		Vitamins	2.77%
337		Thiamine HCl	2.2 mg[6]
338		Riboflavin	2.2 mg[6]
339		Nicotinic acid	9.9 mg[6]
340		B_6 HCl	2.2 mg[6]
341		Biotin	44.0 μg[6]
342		Calcium pantothenate	6.60 mg[6]
343		Folic acid	198 μg[6]
344		*p*-Aminobenzoic acid	11 mg[6]
345		Inositol	11 mg[6]
346		B_{12}	3.0 μg[6]
347		Choline chloride	165 mg[6]
348		A	1982 I.U.[6]
349		D	220 I.U.[6]
350		E	11 I.U.[6]
351		Menadione	4.95 mg[6]
		Sheep	
	Creep ration [11]		
352	Farm use[19]	Alfalfa hay	Free choice
353		Bone meal or dicalcium phosphate	1 lb
354		Corn, shelled	60 lb

[2] Parts by weight. [6] Per 100 g diet. [11] To each diet, add 0.5% salt, iodized if region is iodine-deficient. [12] Weight, 4-9 lb. [13] Initial weight, 4 lb; final weight, 8 lb. [14] May also appropriate during pregnancy and lactation. [15] Average weight, 10 lb. [16] Litter of 7. [17] For rapid growth, 0.2-0.6 g yeast and 20-30 g lettuce were added daily; for slow growth, 0.05-0.2 g yeast and a small amount of lettuce.

[18] Permits maximum growth; excessive in most nutrients, and contains nutrients not shown to be required by the rat. However, performance on this diet exceeds performance on diets based on the requirements recommended in reference 10. [19] Ration ground at first, fed whole later; hay and grain should be fed twice daily.

continued

	Type of Diet [Reference]	Ingredient	Concentration
355		Linseed or soybean meal	10 lb
356		Oats	20 lb
357		Wheat bran	10 lb
358		Trace-mineralized salt	0.5 lb
359	Farm	Alfalfa, leafy, ground	65 lb
360	use[20]	Bone meal	1 lb
361		Chlortetracycline	7.5 mg[21]
362		Corn, shelled yellow	12 lb
363		Molasses	3 lb
364		Oats, native white	9 lb
365		Soybean meal (44% chemically pure)	10 lb
366		Vitamin A	555 I.U.
367		Vitamin D	55 I.U.
368	Farm	Alfalfa, leafy	30 lb
369	use[20]	Corn, ear	55 lb
370		Molasses	5 lb
371		Oxytetracycline	7.5 mg[21]
372		Soybean meal	10 lb
373	Farm	Corn, ground or shelled	85 lb
374	use[22]	Soybean meal or pellets	15 lb
375	Range	Alfalfa hay	Free choice
376	use	Barley, steam-rolled	70 lb
377		Dried beet pulp & molasses	30 lb
		Swine	
	Natural ration [2, 3, 7]		
378	Weaning	Corn, yellow, ground	49.0%
379	to 40	Fat, stabilized	2.5%
380	lb[23]	Milk, skim, dried	10.0%
381		Soybean meal (50% protein)	25.0%
382		Sugar, beet or cane	10.0%
383		Calcium carbonate (38% Ca)	0.5%
384		Dicalcium phosphate (26% Ca, 18% P)	1.5%
385		Trace-mineralized salt	0.5%
386		Copper	10 ppm
387		Iodine	1 ppm
388		Iron	10 ppm
389		Manganese	10 ppm
390		Zinc	100 ppm
391		Vitamin premix	1.0%
392		Riboflavin	3 mg[9]
393		Nicotinic acid	15 mg[9]
394		Pantothenic acid	9 mg[9]
395		B_{12}	20 μg[9]
396		Choline	150 mg[9]
397		A	3000 I.U.
398		D	450 I.U.
399	40-200 lb[24]	Alfalfa meal, dehydrated (17% protein)	10.0%
400		Corn, yellow, ground	63.0%
401		Fish meal	2.0%
402		Oats	10.0%
403		Soybean meal	12.0%
404		Dicalcium phosphate (26% Ca, 18% P)	1.5%
405		Trace-mineralized salt	0.5%
406		Copper	10 ppm
407		Iodine	1 ppm
408		Iron	10 ppm
409		Manganese	10 ppm
410		Zinc	100 ppm
411		Vitamin premix	1.0%
412		Riboflavin	2 mg[9]
413		Nicotinic acid	10 mg[9]
414		Pantothenic acid	6 mg[9]
415		B_{12}	14 μg[9]
416		Choline	100 mg[9]
417		A	2000 I.U.
418		D	300 I.U.
419	Pregnancy &	Alfalfa meal, dehydrated (17% protein)	10.0%
420	lacta-	Corn, yellow, ground	50.5%
421	tion[25]	Oats	20.0%
422		Soybean meal (50% protein)	11.0%
423		Wheat middlings	5.0%
424		Calcium carbonate (38% Ca)	1.0%
425		Dicalcium phosphate (26% Ca, 18% P)	1.0%
426		Trace-mineralized salt	0.5%
427		Copper	10 ppm
428		Iodine	1 ppm
429		Iron	10 ppm
430		Manganese	10 ppm
431		Zinc	100 ppm
432		Vitamin premix	1.0%
433		Riboflavin	3 mg[9]
434		Nicotinic acid	15 mg[9]
435		Pantothenic acid	9 mg[9]
436		B_{12}	10 μg[9]
437		Choline	400 mg[9]
438		A	2500 I.U.[9]
439		D	400 I.U.[9]
	Purified ration		
440	Weaning	Casein	26.1%
441	to 200	Lard or stabilized fat	11.0%
442	lb [2,	Sucrose	57.7%
443	3, 7]	Salt mix	5.2%
444		$CaCO_3$	16.9%
445		$CaHPO_4 \cdot 2H_2O$	46.3%

[9] Per lb feed. [20] Ration is ground, pelleted, and self-fed. [21] Per lb ration. [22] Ground ration can be hand-fed; whole-grain ration may be self-fed. [23] Diet includes 0.84% calcium, 0.6% phosphorus, and 20.0% protein. [24] Diet includes 0.7% calcium, 0.6% phosphorus, and 16% protein. [25] Diet includes 0.8% calcium, 0.6% phosphorus, and 15% protein.

continued

	Type of Diet [Reference]	Ingredient	Concentration
446		$CoCO_3$	0.016%
447		$CuSO_4$	0.02%
448		$Fe_4(P_2O_7)_3 \cdot 9H_2O$	2.1%
449		$MgCO_3$	8.5%
450		$MnCl_2$	0.02%
451		KCl	6.7%
452		KI, stabilized	0.228%
453		K_2HPO_4	5.7%
454		NaCl	13.5%
455		ZnO	0.016%
		Vitamins	
456		Thiamine	4.0 mg[9/]
457		Riboflavin	3.0 mg[9/]
458		Nicotinic acid	10.0 mg[9/]
459		B_6	2.0 mg[9/]
460		Calcium pantothenate	7.0 mg[9/]
461		B_{12}	15.0 μg[9/]
462		Choline	500.0 mg[9/]
463		A	3000 I.U.[9/]
464		D	450 I.U.[9/]
465		E	10 I.U.[9/]
466		K	150 μg[9/]
467	Pregnancy & lactation [2,5]	Casein	26.1%
468		Lard or stabilized fat	11.0%
469		Sucrose	57.7%
470		Salt mix	5.2%
471		$CaCO_3$	16.9%
472		$CaHPO_4 \cdot 2H_2O$	46.3%
473		$CoCO_3$	0.016%
474		$Fe_4(P_2O_7)_3 \cdot 9H_2O$	2.1%
475		$MgCO_3$	8.5%
476		$MnCl_2$	0.02%
477		KCl	6.7%
478		KI, stabilized	0.228%
479		K_2HPO_4	5.7%
480		NaCl	13.5%
481		ZnO	0.016%
		Vitamins	
482		Thiamine	4.0 mg[9/]
483		Riboflavin	4.0 mg[9/]
484		Nicotinic acid	15.0 mg[9/]
485		B_6	3.0 mg[9/]
486		Calcium pantothenate	8.0 mg[9/]
487		B_{12}	20.0 μg[9/]
488		Choline	750.0 mg[9/]
489		A	5000 I.U.[9/]
490		D	500 I.U.[9/]
491		E	40.0 mg[9/]
492		K	2.0 mg[9/]
	Chicken		
493	Stock diet [1,6]	Corn (8.5% protein)	58.22%
494		Soybean meal (48% protein)	30.78%
495		Soybean oil	5.0%
496		Dicalcium phosphate	2.10%
497		Limestone	1.50%
498		Salt	0.45%
499		Premix	1.95%
500		Manganese	137 mg[26/]
501		Zinc	48 mg[26/]
502		Butylated hydroxytoluene	125 mg[26/]
503		Penicillin	4.36 mg[26/]
504		Sulfur amino acids	0.8%[27/]
505		Riboflavin	8.8 mg[26/]
506		Nicotinic acid	40 mg[26/]
507		Pantothenic acid	17.6 mg[26/]
508		Vitamin B_{12}	6.5 μg[26/]
509		Choline	2 g[26/]
510		Vitamin A	5000 I.U.[26/]
511		Vitamin D_3	2250 I.U.[26/]
512		Vitamin E	8.8 I.U.[26/]
513		Menadione sodium bisulfite	1.23 mg[26/]
514	Purified diet [14]	Butylated hydroxytoluene, 25%	0.05%
515		Cellulose	3.0%
516		Choline chloride, 70%	0.20%
517		Glycine	0.30%
518		DL-Methionine	0.50%
519		Soybean oil	5.0%
520		Soybean protein, isolated	30.0%
521		Glucose monohydrate	53.87%
522		Salt premix	6.08%
523		$CaCO_3$	19.10 g[26/]
524		$Ca(H_2PO_4)_2 \cdot H_2O$	21.15 g[26/]
525		$CuSO_4 \cdot 5H_2O$	0.015 g[26/]
526		$FeSO_4$	0.2 g[26/]
527		$MnSO_4 \cdot H_2O$	0.51 g[26/]
528		KI	0.04 g[26/]
529		K_2HPO_4	11.20 g[26/]
530		NaCl	8.4 g[26/]
531		$Na_2MoO_4 \cdot 2H_2O$	0.0025 g[26/]
532		$ZnCO_3$	0.18 g[26/]
533		Vitamin premix	1.0%
534		Thiamine HCl	6 mg[26/]
535		Riboflavin	9 mg[26/]
536		Nicotinic acid	50 mg[26/]
537		B_6-HCl	8 mg[26/]
538		Biotin	0.3 mg[26/]
539		Calcium D-pantothenate	20 mg[26/]
540		Folic acid	2 mg[26/]
541		Inositol	1000 mg[26/]
542		B_{12}	20 μg[26/]
543		A	25,000 U.S.P. units[26/]
544		D_3	1200 I.C.U.[26/]

[9/] Per lb feed. [26/] Per kg diet. [27/] Of total diet; total sulfur amino acids were raised to this level by the addition of DL-methionine [1].

continued

	Type of Diet [Reference]	Ingredient	Concentration
545		E	17.6 I.U.[26]
546		Menadione sodium bisulfite	2 mg[26]
		Salmonids[28]	
547	Test	Casein, vitamin-free	38 parts
548	diet[29]	Corn oil	9 parts
549	[16]	Gelatin	12 parts
550		Dextrin, white	28 parts
551		Water	200 parts
552		Salt mix	4 parts
553		U.S.P. XII No. 2, plus the following:	
554		$AlCl_3$	15 mg[30]
555		$CoCl_2$	100 mg[30]
556		CuCl	10 mg[30]
557		$MnSO_4$	80 mg[30]
558		KI	15 mg[30]
559		$ZnSO_4$	300 mg[30]
560		α-Cellulose mix	9 parts
561		α-Cellulose[31]	8 parts
562		Vitamins	1 part
563		Thiamine HCl	5 mg[32]
564		Riboflavin	20 mg[32]
565		Nicotinic acid	75 mg[32]
566		B_6-HCl	5 mg[32]
567		Biotin	0.5 mg[32]
568		Calcium pantothenate	50 mg[32]
569		Folic acid	1.5 mg[32]
570		Inositol	200 mg[32]
571		B_{12}[33]	10 μg[32]
572		Choline chloride	500 mg[32]
573		Ascorbic acid	100 mg[32]
574		β-Carotene[34]	2 mg[32]
575		D_3[34]	5 μg[32]
576		α-Tocopherol acetate[34,35]	40 mg[32]
577		Menadione[34]	4 mg[32]
		Trout	
578	Stock	Corn gluten meal	18%
579	diet,	Feeding oil	4%
580	normal	Fish meal	35%
581	growth	Fish solubles, condensed	4%
582	[17]	Soybean meal	10%
583		Wheat middlings	16%
584		Whey	4%
585		Yeast, brewer's	4%
586		Salt	2%
587		Vitamin premix	4%
588		Thiamine	6.6 mg[6]
589		Riboflavin	11 mg[6]
590		Nicotinic acid	55 mg[6]
591		B_6	4.6 mg[6]
592		Biotin	0.04 mg[6]
593		Calcium pantothenate	5.3 mg[6]
594		Folic acid	0.87 mg[6]
595		B_{12}	0.002 mg[6]
596		Choline chloride	109 mg[6]
597		Ascorbic acid	26 mg[6]
598		A	350 I.U.[6]
599		D_3	70 I.U.[6]
600		E	24 I.U.[6]
601		Menadione sodium bisulfite	1 mg[6]
		Channel Catfish	
602	Purified	Agar	0.2%
603	diet[36],	Casein	23.5%
604	mainte-	Cellulose flour	5.0%
605	nance &	Corn oil	4.2%
606	growth	Dextrin, white	3.6%
607	[4]	Water	57.8%
608		U.S.P. XIV (1950) salt mix	3.7%
609		$CaCO_3$	68.6 g[37]
610		$Ca_3(C_6H_5O_7)_2 \cdot 4H_2O$	308.3[37]
611		$CaHPO_4 \cdot 2H_2O$	112.8 g[37]
612		$CuSO_4 \cdot 5H_2O$	78 mg[37]
613		$MgCO_3$	35.2 g[37]
614		$MgSO_4$	38.3 g[37]
615		$MnSO_4$	200 mg[37]
616		KCl	124.7 g[37]
617		KI	41 mg[37]
618		K_2HPO_4	218.8 g[37]
619		NaCl	77.1 g[37]
620		NaF	507 mg[37]
621		Ferric ammonium citrate	15.3 g[37]
622		Ferric ammonium sulfate	92 mg[37]

[6] Per 100 g diet. [26] Per kg diet. [28] Also bass, bluegill sunfish, and channel catfish, and in Japan, carp, eel, and yellowtail. [29] Dissolve gelatin in cold water; heat, with stirring, on water bath to 80°C. Remove from heat and add, with stirring, casein, dextrin, oils, salts, and vitamins as temperature decreases. Mix well to 40°C, and pour into containers. Move to refrigerator to harden, then remove from trays and store in sealed containers in refrigerator until used. Consistency of diet is adjusted by the amount of water in the final mix, and by the length and strength of beating. For a complete vitamin test diet, delete β-carotene, D_3, and 2 parts corn oil, and add 2 parts cod liver oil. [30] Per 100 mg mix. [31] Delete 2 parts α-cellulose and add 2 parts sodium carboxymethyl cellulose for preliminary feeding. [32] Per 100 g solids. [33] Add in water during final mixing. [34] Added in corn oil for fat-soluble vitamin test diet. [35] Dissolve in oil mixture. [36] Diet was tested for periods up to 9 months in troughs and aquariums. Feed conversions (weight gain/weight of feed offered on a dry-weight basis) averaged 0.9 for test fingerlings. Vitamin-deficient diets were prepared by replacing a vitamin with an equal amount of cellulose flour. [37] Per kg mix.

continued

	Type of Diet [Reference]	Ingredient	Concentration
623		Vitamin mix, in dextrose	2.0%[38]
624		Thiamine HCl	1.0 mg [39]
625		Riboflavin	1.0 mg[39]
626		Nicotinic acid	4.5 mg[39]
627		B_6-HCl	1.0 mg[39]
628		Biotin	0.02 mg[39]
629		Calcium pantothenate	3.0 mg[39]
630		Folic acid	0.09 mg[39]
631		*p*-Aminobenzoic acid	5.0 mg[39]
632		Inositol	5.0 mg[39]
633		B_{12}	0.00135 mg[39]
634		Choline chloride	75.0 mg[39]
635		Ascorbic acid	45.0 mg[39]
636		A, 200,000 units/g	4.5 mg[39]
637		D, 400,000 units/g	0.25 mg[39]
638		α-Tocopherol	5.0 mg[39]
639		Menadione	2.25 mg[39]

[38] Dextrose was 1%, and vitamin mix, 1%. [39] Per g mix.

Contributors: (a) Sprague, H. G., (b) Cunha, T. J., (c) Mertz, Edwin T., (d) Warner, R. G., (e) Moment, Gairdner B., (f) Halver, John E., (g) Dupree, Harry K., (h) Willoughby, Harvey, (i) Tyznik, W. J.

References

[1] Cromwell, G. L., et al. 1967. Poultry Sci. 46:705.
[2] Cunha, T. J. Unpublished. Univ. Florida, Gainesville, 1967.
[3] Cunha, T. J., D. C. Lindley, and M. E. Ensminger. 1946. J. Animal Sci. 5:219.
[4] Dupree, H. K., and K. E. Sneed. 1966. U.S. Bur. Sport Fisheries Wildlife Tech. Paper 9.
[5] Ensminger, M. E., J. P. Bowland, and T. J. Cunha. 1947. J. Animal Sci. 6:409.
[6] Featherston, W. R. Unpublished. Purdue Univ., Lafayette, Ind., 1967.
[7] Heinemann, W. W., et al. 1946. J. Nutr. 31:107.
[8] Moment, G. B. 1933. J. Exptl. Zool. 65:359.
[9] National Research Council, Committee on Animal Nutrition. 1962. Natl. Acad. Sci. Natl. Res. Council Publ. 989.
[10] Ibid. Publ. 990.
[11] National Research Council, Committee on Animal Nutrition. 1964. Ibid. 1193.
[12] National Research Council, Committee on Animal Nutrition. 1966. Ibid. 1194.
[13] Santos, A. C., and R. G. Warner. Unpublished. Cornell Univ., Ithaca, N.Y., 1966.
[14] Scholz, T. E., and W. R. Featherston. 1967. J. Nutr. 91:223.
[15] Tyznik, W. J. Unpublished. Ohio State Univ., Dept. Animal Science, Columbus, 1967.
[16] Western Fish Nutrition Laboratory. Unpublished. U.S. Dept. of Interior, Bureau of Sport Fisheries and Wildlife, Cook, Wash., 1967.
[17] Willoughby, H., C. L. Sowards, and W. E. Shanks. Unpublished. U.S. Dept. of Interior, Bureau of Sport Fisheries and Wildlife, Washington, D.C., 1967.

19. ZOO DIETS: WILD ANIMALS

Abbreviations: TDN = total digestible nutrient; BHA = butylated hydroxyanisole; BHT = butylated hydroxytoluene.

Part I. New York Zoological Park

	Order & Species	Sex	Wt kg	Feed/ Wk kg	Feed/ Day/Kg Body Wt g	Basic Diet
	Mammalia					
	Artiodactyla					
1	*Alcelaphus buselaphus jacksoni*	♂	158	27	24	59% alfalfa, 41% GLF[1]
2	*Ammotragus lervia*	♀	58	14.5	35	70% hay, 30% GLF[1]

[1] Theoretical analysis: 73% TDN, 16% protein, 4% fat, 8% fiber. Ingredients: 25.4% hominy feed, 15% wheat middlings, 12% corn gluten feed, 10% ground oats, 10% wheat bran, 5% dehydrated alfalfa meal, 5% corn distiller's dried grains, 5% linseed oil, 3% wheat germ meal, 2% dehulled soybean meal, 1% salt, 0.75% dicalcium phosphate, 0.75% ground limestone, 0.05% Z-4 mineral mix (calcium iodate, cobalt carbonate, copper oxide, iron carbonate, manganolis oxide, zinc oxide), 5% molasses, 0.05% vitamin premix. Ingredients of vitamin premix: 2,000,000 units A, 4,000,000 units D, 2000 units E.

continued

19. ZOO DIETS: WILD ANIMALS

Part I. New York Zoological Park

	Order & Species	Sex	Wt kg	Feed/ Wk kg	Feed/ Day/Kg Body Wt g	Basic Diet
3	*Anoa depressicornis*	...	105	10.9	14	40% alfalfa, 20% GLF[1], 15% monkey pellets[2], 10% bread, 10% yam, 5% carrot
4	*Axis axis*	♂	80	29	51	55% alfalfa, 45% GLF[1]
5	*Bison bison bison*	♂	841	159	27	70% brome hay, 30% GLF[1]
6	*B. bonasus bonasus*	♂	682	127	26	63% brome hay, 37% GLF[1]
7	*Budorcas taxicolor taxicolor*	♀	323	53	23	47% alfalfa, 22% GLF[1], 9% oats, 6% cabbage, 6% white potato, 3% apple, 3% bread, 2% carrot, 2% yam
8	*Camelus dromedarius*	♀	455	150	47	85% alfalfa hay, 15% GLF[1]
9	*Capra ibex sibirica*	♀	53	15.3	41	70% hay, 30% GLF[1]
10	*Cervus canadensis roosevelti*	♂	364	175	69	57% alfalfa hay, 43% GLF[1]
11	*C. elaphus*	♂	427	54	19	59% alfalfa hay, 41% GLF[1]
12	*C. nippon hurtulorum*	♂	91	32	50	50% alfalfa hay, 50% GLF[1]
13	*C. nippon nippon*	♀	57	22	53	71% alfalfa hay, 29% GLF[1]
14	*C. nippon taiouanus*	♂	91	35	55	55% alfalfa, 45% GLF[1]
15	*Choeropsis liberiensis*	♀	218	59	38	55% alfalfa, 22% GLF[1], 11% bread, 11% potato, 1% carrot
16	*Connochaetes gnou*	♂	136	35	37	82% alfalfa hay, 18% GLF[1]
17	*Damaliscus dorcas phillipsi*	♂	132	24	25	71% alfalfa, 29% GLF[1]
18	*Elaphurus davidianus*	♂	272	95	50	67% alfalfa hay, 33% GLF[1]
19	*Gazella thomsoni*	♂	26	9	46	55% alfalfa, 45% GLF[1]
20	*Giraffa camelopardalis rothschildi*	♀	491	104	30	46% alfalfa, 21% GLF[1], 12% oats, 6% banana, 6% cabbage, 2% apple, 2% carrot, 2% white potato, 2% yam, 1% bread
21	*Hemitragus jemlahicus*	♀	60	16.2	38	70% hay, 30% GLF[1]
22	*Hippopotamus amphibius*	♀	2273	267	17	71% alfalfa hay, 17% GLF[1], 8% cabbage, 2% bread, 1% apple, 1% carrot
23	*Lama glama*	♂	159	41	38	69% alfalfa, 31% GLF[1]
24	*L. guanicoe*[3]	♂	130	32	35	60% alfalfa hay, 40% GLF[1]
25	*Okapia johnstoni*	♀	229	69	42	42% alfalfa, 29% GLF[1], 9% banana, 9% cabbage, 3% carrot, 3% white potato, 2% bread, 2% yam, 1% apple
26	*Oryx gazella gazella*	♂	158	34	30	50% alfalfa, 50% GLF[1]
27	*Ovis musimon*	♀	42	10.7	36	70% hay, 30% GLF[1]
28	*Pecari tajacu*	...	28	7	35	20% banana, 20% cabbage, 20% carrot, 20% peanuts, 10% apple, 10% GLF[1]
29	*Poephagus grunniens*	♂	545	80	21	60% brome hay, 40% GLF[1]
30	*Rangifer tarandus*	♂	102	48	68	67% alfalfa hay, 33% GLF[1]
31	*Sylvicapra grimmia*	♂	19	8	60	56% alfalfa, 44% GLF[1]
32	*Syncerus caffer nanus*	♂	364	175	69	57% alfalfa hay, 43% GLF[1]
33	*Tragelaphus angasi*	♂	138	24	24	57% alfalfa, 43% GLF[1]
34	*Tragulus napu*	♂	2.5	1.603	91	30% apple, 20% banana, 10% bread, 10% carrot, 10% GLF[1], 10% lettuce, 10% yam
	Perissodactyla					
35	*Ceratotherium simum simum*	♂	2272	339	21	84% brome/alfalfa hay, 13% GLF[1], 2% bread, 1% carrot
36	*Diceros bicornis*	♂	1364	229	23	80% alfalfa, 10% GLF[1], 7% potato, 1.5% bread, 1.5% carrot

[1] Theoretical analysis: 73% TDN, 16% protein, 4% fat, 8% fiber. Ingredients: 25.4% hominy feed, 15% wheat middlings, 12% corn gluten feed, 10% ground oats, 10% wheat bran, 5% dehydrated alfalfa meal, 5% corn distiller's dried grains, 5% linseed oil, 3% wheat germ meal, 2% dehulled soybean meal, 1% salt, 0.75% dicalcium phosphate, 0.75% ground limestone, 0.05% Z-4 mineral mix (calcium iodate, cobalt carbonate, copper oxide, iron carbonate, manganolis oxide, zinc oxide), 5% molasses, 0.05% vitamin premix. Ingredients of vitamin premix: 2,000,000 units A, 4,000,000 units D, 2000 units E. [2] Guaranteed analysis: ≮25% crude protein, ≮5% crude fat, ≯4.5% crude fiber, ≯3% added minerals. Ingredients: animal fat preserved with BHA, brewer's dried yeast, dehydrated alfalfa meal, dried skim milk, fish meal, ground yellow corn, soybean meal, steamed bone meal, calcium carbonate, cobalt carbonate, copper oxide, defluorinated phosphate, iodized salt, iron oxide, iron sulfate, manganese sulfate, manganous oxide, zinc oxide, thiamine, riboflavin supplement, nicotinic acid, vitamin B_6 HCl, calcium pantothenate, folic acid, vitamin B_{12} supplement, ascorbic acid, vitamin A supplement, vitamin D activated animal sterol (source of vitamin D_3), vitamin E supplement. [3] Synonym: *L. huanacus*.

continued

19. ZOO DIETS: WILD ANIMALS

Part I. New York Zoological Park

	Order & Species	Sex	Wt kg	Feed/ Wk kg	Feed/ Day/Kg Body Wt g	Basic Diet
37	*Equus grevyi*	♂	341	48	21	69% brome hay, 27% GLF[1/], 4% carrot
	Hyracoidea					
38	*Procavia capensis*	♂	3.5	1.120	45	30% monkey pellets[2/], 15% lettuce, 10% apple, 10% banana, 10% GLF[1/], 10% orange, 10% yam, 5% nuts
	Proboscidea					
39	*Elephas maximus indicus*	♀	3222	968	42	90% brome/alfalfa hay, 5% GLF[1/], 1.6% bread, 1.6% potato, 1.4% cabbage, 0.4% carrot
40	*Loxodonta africana cxyotis*	♀	1137	327	41	88% brome/alfalfa hay, 6% GLF[1/], 2% cabbage, 2% potato, 1% bread, 1% carrot
	Tubulidentata					
41	*Orycteropus afer ruvanensis*	♂	70	28.4	57	55% chopped meat, 35% evaporated milk, 10% raw egg yolk, water to soupy texture
	Pinnipedia					
42	*Eumetopias jubata*	♂	625	93	21	100% mackerel
43	*Halichoerus grypus*	♀	145	52.5	51	100% mackerel
44	*Phoca vitulina concolor*	♂	50	11.2	32	100% mackerel
	Carnivora					
45	*Acinonyx jubatus*	♂	50	12	34	80% whole horsemeat, 20% Diet M[4/]. Liver, heart, kidney 1 day/wk.
46	*Ailurus fulgens fulgens*	♂	4	7.2	257	30% banana, 20% apple, 15% yam, 8% chopped meat, 8% whole meat, 5% Diet M[4/], 5% lettuce, 5% orange, 4% grapes
47	*Arctictis binturong*	♂	12	8.1	96	50% banana, 20% horsemeat, 20% orange, 5% apple, 5% yam
48	*Canis dingo*	♂	2.0	7	50	60% dog mixture[5/], 20% chopped meat, 20% whole meat
49	*C. lupus nubilus*	♂	33.3	8.7	37	65% horsemeat, 35% dog meal[6/]
50	*Cerdocyon thous*	♀	3.2	2.68	120	80% Diet M[4/], 20% whole meat
51	*Crocuta crocuta germinans*	♂	83	15.0	26	65% whole meat, 35% chopped horsemeat. Liver, heart, kidney 1 day/wk.
52	*Crossarchus obscurus*	♀	1.2	2.03	241	60% Diet M[4/], 15% chopped meat, 10% apple, 10% banana, 5% kale
53	*Felis bengalensis*	♂	2	3.4	243	60% horsemeat, 30% liver, 10% fish. 1 tsp calcium lactate & 0.6 ml Vipenta[7/] per day
54	*F. chaus*	♂	5.8	3.0	73	60% horsemeat, 30% liver, 10% fish. 1 tsp calcium lactate & 0.6 ml Vipenta[7/] per day.
55	*F. concolor missoulensis*	♀	41.6	10	34	75% whole meat, 25% chopped horsemeat. Liver, heart, 1 day/wk.
56	*F. jagouaroundi fossata*	♀	6.6	4.2	90	60% whole meat, 15% sliced meat, 10% fish, 8% liver, 7% chopped meat. 1 tsp calcium lactate & 0.6 ml Vipenta[7/] per day.

[1/] Theoretical analysis: 73% TDN, 16% protein, 4% fat, 8% fiber. Ingredients: 25.4% hominy feed, 15% wheat middlings, 12% corn gluten feed, 10% ground oats, 10% wheat bran, 5% dehydrated alfalfa meal, 5% corn distiller's dried grains, 5% linseed oil, 3% wheat germ meal, 2% dehulled soybean meal, 1% salt, 0.75% dicalcium phosphate, 0.75% ground limestone, 0.05% Z-4 mineral mix (calcium iodate, cobalt carbonate, copper oxide, iron carbonate, manganolis oxide, zinc oxide), 5% molasses, 0.05% vitamin premix. Ingredients of vitamin premix: 2,000,000 units A, 4,000,000 units D, 2000 units E. [2/] Guaranteed analysis: ≮25% crude protein, ≮5% crude fat, ≯4.5% crude fiber, ≯3% added minerals. Ingredients: animal fat preserved with BHA, brewer's dried yeast, dehydrated alfalfa meal, dried skim milk, fish meal, ground yellow corn, soybean meal, steamed bone meal, calcium carbonate, cobalt carbonate, copper oxide, defluorinated phosphate, iodized salt, iron oxide, iron sulfate, manganese sulfate, manganous oxide, zinc oxide, thiamine, riboflavin supplement, nicotinic acid, vitamin B_6 HCl, calcium pantothenate, folic acid, vitamin B_{12} supplement, ascorbic acid, vitamin A supplement, vitamin D activated animal sterol (source of vitamin D_3), vitamin E supplement. [4/] 30 lb chopped meat, 20 cups meal, ½ cup ground limestone. ½ cup Paltone. [5/] 9 lb chopped meat, 6 cups soaked dog pellets, 2 tbsp cod liver oil, 2 tsp bone meal. [6/] Guaranteed analysis: ≮27% crude protein, ≮9% crude fat, ≯4.5% crude fiber, ≯10% ash. [7/] Per 0.6 ml: 1 mg thiamine, 1 mg riboflavin, 10 mg nicotinamide, 1 mg vitamin B_6, 30 μg *d*-biotin, 10 mg D-Panthenol, 50 mg ascorbic acid, 5000 U.S.P. units vitamin A, 400 U.S.P. units vitamin D_2, 2 I.U. vitamin E.

continued

Part I. New York Zoological Park

	Order & Species	Sex	Wt kg	Feed/ Wk kg	Feed/ Day/Kg Body Wt g	Basic Diet
57	*F. libyca*	♀	4	2.0	71	60% cat chow[8/], 40% chopped meat
58	*F. manul*	♀	2.9	2.87	141	30% whole meat, 25% fish, 25% liver, 20% chopped meat. 1 tsp calcium lactate & 0.6 ml Vipenta[7/] per day.
59	*F. nigripes*	♂	1.2	2.039	242	60% horsemeat, 30% liver, 10% fish
60	*Fennecus zerda*	♂	1.5	1.8	171	60% dog mixture[5/], 20% chopped meat, 20% whole meat
61	*Grison furox*	♀	2	4.4	314	60% whole meat, 20% Diet M[4/], 20% fish
62	*Herpestes edwardsi*	♀	1.1	1.96	254	50% Diet M[4/], 15% apple, 15% banana, 15% chopped meat, 5% kale
63	*Lutragale perspicillata perspicillata*	♀	10	7.2	102	100% Diet M[4/]
64	*Lynx rufus baileyi*	♂	10	3.5	50	90% Diet M[4/], 10% whole meat
65	*Martes americana actuosa*	♀	1.2	1.57	186	80% Diet M[4/], 20% chopped meat
66	*M. penanti*	♂	6.2	2.1	47	100% Diet M[4/]
67	*Mellivora capensis leuconota*	♂	14.5	7.0	68	40% dog food[9/], 25% banana, 20% horsemeat, 15% raw egg
68	*Mungos mungo*	♂	3.18	3.81	171	60% Diet M[4/], 15% chopped meat, 10% apple, 10% banana, 5% kale
69	*Nandinia binotata*	♂	3.0	5.25	250	30% banana, 20% apple, 20% Diet M[4/], 20% orange, 10% meat
70	*Otocyon megalotis*	♂	4	0.96	34	60% dog mixture[5/], 20% chopped meat, 20% whole meat
71	*Panthera leo*	♂	162.5	32.5	28	75% whole meat, 25% chopped horsemeat[10/]. Liver, heart, kidney 1 day/wk.
72	*P. nebulosa*	♂	25	7.5	43	100% whole horsemeat, 2 tsp calcium lactate, 5 drops cod liver oil. Liver, heart, kidney 1 day/wk.
73	*P. onca*	♀	62	15.0	34	65% whole meat, 35% chopped horsemeat[10/]. Liver, heart, kidney 1 day/wk.
74	*P. pardus*	♂	83.3	17.5	30	70% whole meat, 30% chopped horsemeat[10/]. Liver, heart, kidney 1 day/wk.
75	*P. tigris longipilis*	♂	185	36.6	28	100% chopped beef, 4 tbsp cod liver oil, 4 tbsp limestone
76	*P. tigris tigris*	♀	125	72	82	80% whole meat, 20% chopped horsemeat[10/]. Liver, heart, kidney 1 day/wk.
77	*P. uncia*	♀	37.5	12.5	47	80% whole meat, 20% chopped meat. Liver, heart, kidney 1 day/wk.
78	*Potos flavus*	♂	2.5	8.4	480	25% apple, 25% banana, 25% orange, 10% carrot, 10% Diet M[4/], 5% yam
79	*Procyon cancrivorus*	♀	6	4.2	100	30% Diet M[4/], 20% fish, 20% whole meat, 10% apple, 10% banana, 10% orange
80	*P. lotor*	♀	7	5.1	104	70% Diet M[4/], 10% monkey pellets[2/], 10% whole meat, 5% banana, 5% fish

2/ Guaranteed analysis: ≮25% crude protein, ≮5% crude fat, ≯4.5% crude fiber, ≯3% added minerals. Ingredients: animal fat preserved with BHA, brewer's dried yeast, dehydrated alfalfa meal, dried skim milk, fish meal, ground yellow corn, soybean meal, steamed bone meal, calcium carbonate, cobalt carbonate, copper oxide, defluorinated phosphate, iodized salt, iron oxide, iron sulfate, manganese sulfate, manganous oxide, zinc oxide, thiamine, riboflavin supplement, nicotinic acid, vitamin B_6 HCl, calcium pantothenate, folic acid, vitamin B_{12} supplement, ascorbic acid, vitamin A supplement, vitamin D activated animal sterol (source of vitamin D_3), vitamin E supplement. 4/ 30 lb chopped meat, 20 cups meal, ½ cup ground limestone, ½ cup Paltone. 5/ 9 lb chopped meat, 6 cups soaked dog pellets, 2 tbsp cod liver oil, 2 tsp bone meal. 7/ Per 0.6 ml: 1 mg thiamine, 1 mg riboflavin, 10 mg nicotinamide, 1 mg vitamin B_6, 30 μg *d*-biotin, 10 mg D-Panthenol, 50 mg ascorbic acid, 5000 U.S.P. units vitamin A, 400 U.S.P. units vitamin D_2, 2 I.U. vitamin E. 8/ Guaranteed analysis: ≮27% crude protein, ≮7% crude fat, ≯3% crude fiber, ≯10.6% ash. 9/ Guaranteed analysis: ≯13% crude protein, ≮5% crude fat, ≯1% crude fiber, ≯1% ash, ≯74% moisture. 10/ 20 lb chopped horsemeat, 1 lb ground limestone, 4 oz cod liver oil.

continued

19. ZOO DIETS: WILD ANIMALS

Part I. New York Zoological Park

	Order & Species	Sex	Wt kg	Feed/ Wk kg	Feed/ Day/Kg Body Wt g	Basic Diet
81	*Pteronura brasiliensis brasiliensis*	♀	21.2	15.8	106	38% fish, 37% meat, 25% Diet M[4]
82	*Suricata suricatta*	♀	1	0.4	57	60% Diet M[4], 20% whole meat, 10% apple, 10% banana
83	*Tayra barbara*	♂	5.5	6.3	163	60% Diet M[4], 10% banana, 10% chopped meat, 10% whole meat, 5% apple, 5% grapes
84	*Thalarctos maritimus*	♂	80	33.5	59	45% horsemeat, 25% dog meal[6], 15% apple, 15% mackerel, 3 tsp limestone, 3 tsp Paltone[11] per day
85	*Tremarctos ornatus*	♂	100	23.3	33	37% bread, 25% apple, 14% horsemeat, 12% grapes, 12% milk
86	*Vulpes fulva fulva*	♀	1.8	0.45	35.7	60% dog meal[6], 30% meat, 10% egg
87	*V. macrotis neomexicana*	♀	3	2.27	108	90% Diet M[4], 10% whole meat
88	*V. pallidus*	♀	3.0	0.96	46	60% dog mixture[5], 20% chopped meat, 20% whole meat
	Rodentia					
89	*Atherurus centralis centralis*	♀	3.5	5.25	214	15% apple, 15% banana, 15% carrot, 15% yam, 10% GLF[1], 10% mixed nuts, 10% monkey pellets[2], 10% orange
90	*Coendou prehensilis*	♀	1.8	4.3	341	20% apple, 20% banana, 20% cabbage, 20% carrot, 20% yam
91	*Dasyprocta paraguayensis*	♂	2	2.1	150	30% apple, 30% carrot, 20% monkey pellets[2], 15% GLF[1], 5% cabbage
92	*Hydrochoerus hydrochaeris*	♂	50	15.26	43	25% carrot, 20% apple, 20% monkey pellets[2], 20% yam, 10% GLF[1], 5% cabbage
93	*Hystrix indica*	...	17	6.6	55	20% apple, 10% banana, 10% bread, 10% carrot, 10% monkey pellets[2], 10% large nuts, 10% peanuts, 10% potato, 5% GLF[1], 5% sunflower seeds
94	*Malacothrix typica*	♀	0.033	0.035	151	20% carrot, 20% GLF[1], 20% monkey pellets[2], 20% lettuce, 10% bird seed, 10% sunflower seeds
95	*Pedetes cafer*	♂	4	5.6	200	25% carrot, 20% banana, 15% apple, 10% bread, 10% GLF[1], 10% monkey pellets[2], 10% yam
96	*Perognathus penicillatus penicillatus*	...	0.025	0.049	280	20% GLF[1], 15% carrot, 15% kale, 10% bird seed, 10% lettuce, 10% monkey pellets[2], 10% sunflower seeds, 10% yam
97	*Phloeomys cumingi*	♂	3.11	0.980	45	20% GLF[1], 20% yam, 15% apple, 15% carrot, 15% lettuce, 10% monkey pellets[2], 5% sunflower seeds
98	*Proechimys* sp.	♂	0.845	0.797	134	20% banana, 20% monkey pellets[2], 20% orange, 15% apple, 15% yam, 5% GLF[1], 5% sunflower seeds
99	*Rhabdomys pumilio*	♀	0.072	0.056	111	15% apple, 15% GLF[1], 15% monkey pellets[2], 15% orange, 10% bird seed, 10% lettuce, 10% peanuts, 10% sunflower seeds
100	*Sciurus granatensis*	♂	0.4	0.490	175	20% mixed nuts, 10% apple, 10% GLF[1], 10% grapes, 10% kale, 10% lettuce, 10% monkey pellets[2], 10% orange, 5% banana, 5% sunflower seeds

[1] Theoretical analysis: 73% TDN, 16% protein, 4% fat, 8% fiber. Ingredients: 25.4% hominy feed, 15% wheat middlings, 12% corn gluten feed, 10% ground oats, 10% wheat bran, 5% dehydrated alfalfa meal, 5% corn distiller's dried grains, 5% linseed oil, 3% wheat germ meal, 2% dehulled soybean meal, 1% salt, 0.75% dicalcium phosphate, 0.75% ground limestone, 0.05% Z-4 mineral mix (calcium iodate, cobalt carbonate, copper oxide, iron carbonate, manganolis oxide, zinc oxide), 5% molasses, 0.05% vitamin premix. Ingredients of vitamin premix: 2,000,000 units A, 4,000,000 units D, 2000 units E. [2] Guaranteed analysis: ≮25% crude protein, ≮5% crude fat, ≯4.5% crude fiber, ≯3% added minerals. Ingredients: animal fat preserved with BHA, brewer's dried yeast, dehydrated alfalfa meal, dried skim milk, fish meal, ground yellow corn, soybean meal, steamed bone meal, calcium carbonate, cobalt carbonate, copper oxide, defluorinated phosphate, iodized salt, iron oxide, iron sulfate, manganese sulfate, manganous oxide, zinc oxide, thiamine, riboflavin supplement, nicotinic acid, vitamin B_6 HCl, calcium pantothenate, folic acid, vitamin B_{12} supplement, ascorbic acid, vitamin A supplement, vitamin D activated animal sterol (source of vitamin D_3), vitamin E supplement. [4] 30 lb chopped meat, 20 cups meal, ½ cup ground limestone, ½ cup Paltone. [5] 9 lb chopped meat, 6 cups soaked dog pellets, 2 tbsp cod liver oil, 2 tsp bone meal. [6] Guaranteed analysis: ≮27% crude protein, ≮9% crude fat, ≯4.5% crude fiber, ≯10% ash. [11] Per oz: bone meal, corn oil, defatted milk solids, meat, 7.8 g *Torula* yeast, 800 mg lecithin & cephalin (soybean), 15 mg casein lacto albuminate, 15 mg calcium gluconate, 15 mg calcium phosphate, 1.5 mg cobalt sulfate, 1.5 mg copper sulfate, 1.5 mg zinc sulfate, 8 mg thiamine mononitrate, 8 mg riboflavin, 62 mg nicotinamide, 10 mg calcium *dl*-pantothenate, 80 μg folic acid, 1.6 μg vitamin B_{12} activity, 15 mg choline chloride, 16,250 units vitamin A, 16,250 units vitamin D_3.

continued

19. ZOO DIETS: WILD ANIMALS

Part I. New York Zoological Park

	Order & Species	Sex	Wt kg	Feed/ Wk kg	Feed/ Day/Kg Body Wt g	Basic Diet
101	*S. variegatoides dorsalis*	♀	0.4	0.525	187	20% mixed nuts, 10% apple, 10% GLF[1/], 10% grapes, 10% kale, 10% lettuce, 10% monkey pellets[2/], 10% orange, 5% banana, 5% sunflower seeds
	Lagomorpha					
102	*Lepus townsendii townsendii*	♂	3.5	3.3	134	20% carrot, 20% yam, 10% apple, 10% lettuce, 10% monkey pellets[2/], 10% peanuts, 5% GLF[1/], 5% sunflower seeds
	Edentata					
103	*Chaetophractus villosus*	♀	7.5	2.5	47	100% anteater diet[12/]
104	*Choloepus hoffmanni*	♂	7.8	2.8	57	20% banana, 20% bread, 15% apple, 15% orange, 10% Diet M[4/], 10% grapes, 10% lettuce
105	*Dasypus novemcinctus*	♀	5	2.9	82	100% anteater diet[12/]
106	*Myrmecophaga tridactyla*	♂	20	11.6	83	35% chopped meat, 30% evaporated milk, 30% mixed baby cereal, 5% raw egg yolk, 1 tbsp cod liver oil, 2 tsp bone meal
	Primates					
107	*Alouatta seniculus*	♂	4	6	215	28% banana, 12% Diet A[13/], 11% kale, 10% apple, 10% orange, 6% boiled egg, 6% grapes, 6% yam, 5% lettuce, 3% carrot, 3% monkey chow[2/]
108	*Aotus trivirgatus* spp.	♂	0.75	2	380	20% apple, 20% banana, 20% orange, 10% kale, 10% yam, 5% grapes, 4% carrot, 4% Diet A[13/], 4% monkey chow[2/], 3% boiled egg
109	*Cacajao calvus*	♀	2	4	285	22% banana, 15% Diet A[13/], 11% kale, 8% lettuce, 7% apple, 7% carrot, 7% orange, 7% yam, 6% monkey chow[2/], 5% boiled egg, 5% grapes
110	*Callithrix geoffroyi*	♂	0.75	1	189	23% banana, 16% orange, 12% yam, 8% apple, 8% carrot, 8% grapes, 8% kale, 8% Diet A[13/], 5% boiled egg, 4% monkey chow[2/]
111	*Cebus albifrons*	♀	2	4	285	22% banana, 15% Diet A[13/], 11% kale, 8% lettuce, 7% apple, 7% carrot, 7% orange, 7% yam, 6% monkey chow[2/], 5% boiled egg, 5% grapes
112	*Cercopithecus diana*	♂	8	8	142	18% Diet A[13/], 15% banana, 15% orange, 10% apple, 10% yam, 8% kale, 5% boiled egg, 5% carrot, 5% lettuce, 5% monkey chow[2/], 4% grapes
113	*C. mona mona*	♂	3	6	286	25% Diet A[13/], 18% banana, 12% apple, 12% orange, 9% yam, 6% kale, 6% lettuce, 5% boiled egg, 3% grapes, 2% carrot, 2% monkey chow[2/]
114	*C. neglectus*	♂	8	6	108	18% banana, 13% apple, 13% orange, 12% Diet A[13/], 9% yam, 7% kale, 6% boiled egg, 6% carrot, 6% lettuce, 6% grapes, 4% monkey chow[2/]

[1/] Theoretical analysis: 73% TDN, 16% protein, 4% fat, 8% fiber. Ingredients: 25.4% hominy feed, 15% wheat middlings, 12% corn gluten feed, 10% ground oats, 10% wheat bran, 5% dehydrated alfalfa meal, 5% corn distiller's dried grains, 5% linseed oil, 3% wheat germ meal, 2% dehulled soybean meal, 1% salt, 0.75% dicalcium phosphate, 0.75% ground limestone, 0.05% Z-4 mineral mix (calcium iodate, cobalt carbonate, copper oxide, iron carbonate, manganolis oxide, zinc oxide), 5% molasses, 0.05% vitamin premix. Ingredients of vitamin premix: 2,000,000 units A, 4,000,000 units D, 2000 units E. [2/] Guaranteed analysis: ≮25% crude protein, ≮5% crude fat, ≯4.5% crude fiber, ≯3% added minerals. Ingredients: animal fat preserved with BHA, brewer's dried yeast, dehydrated alfalfa meal, dried skim milk, fish meal, ground yellow corn, soybean meal, steamed bone meal, calcium carbonate, cobalt carbonate, copper oxide, defluorinated phosphate, iodized salt, iron oxide, iron sulfate, manganese sulfate, manganous oxide, zinc oxide, thiamine, riboflavin supplement, nicotinic acid, vitamin B_6 HCl, calcium pantothenate, folic acid, vitamin B_{12} supplement, ascorbic acid, vitamin A supplement, vitamin D activated animal sterol (source of vitamin D_3), vitamin E supplement. [4/] 30 lb chopped meat, 20 cups meal, ½ cup ground limestone, ½ cup Paltone. [12/] 35% chopped meat, 30% evaporated milk, 30% mixed baby cereal, 5% raw egg yolks, 1 tbsp cod liver oil, 2 tsp bone meal. [13/] 20% ground corn, 20% ground wheat, 20% soybean meal, 10% brewer's yeast, 10% dried skim milk, 10% feeding oats, 5% alfalfa meal, 2% oystershell, 1% salt, 1% vitamin-mineral mixture, 1% vitamins A & D.

continued

19. ZOO DIETS: WILD ANIMALS

Part I. New York Zoological Park

	Order & Species	Sex	Wt kg	Feed/ Wk kg	Feed/ Day/Kg Body Wt g	Basic Diet
115	*C. talapoin*	♂	1	3	428	14% banana, 13% apple, 13% Diet A[13], 13% orange, 10% yam, 8% kale, 6% boiled egg, 6% carrot, 6% grapes, 6% lettuce, 5% monkey chow[2]
116	*Galago senegalensis* spp.	♂	0.23	0.410	254	20% apple, 20% banana, 20% orange, 20% yam, 10% Diet M[4], 10% meat
117	*Gorilla gorilla beringei*	♂	193	51	37	19% kale, 16% apple, 12% banana, 12% orange, 11% carrot, 6% celery, 6% grapes, 6% meat & broth, 6% yam, 4% crushed pineapple, 3% monkey chow[2], 2% boiled egg
118	*G. gorilla gorilla*	♂	190	48	35	19% kale, 16% apple, 12% banana, 12% orange, 11% carrot, 6% celery, 6% grapes, 6% meat & broth, 6% yam, 4% crushed pineapple, 3% monkey chow[2], 2% boiled egg
119	*Lagothrix lagotricha*	♂	5	9	256	28% orange, 15% Diet A[13], 14% banana, 8% apple, 8% yam, 7% kale, 5% boiled egg, 5% lettuce, 4% grapes, 4% monkey chow[2], 2% carrot
120	*Lemur cattus*	♂	2	3	214	19% banana, 14% kale, 12% Diet A[13], 12% yam, 7% apple, 7% lettuce, 7% orange, 6% boiled egg, 6% grapes, 5% carrot, 5% monkey chow[2]
121	*Macaca fuscata yakui*	♂	5	7	200	22% banana, 12% apple, 12% carrot, 12% kale, 12% orange, 5% boiled egg, 5% celery, 5% Diet A[13], 5% grapes, 5% monkey chow[2], 5% yam
122	*M. maurus ochreatus*	♂	4	8	285	19% banana, 19% Diet A[13], 19% orange, 10% apple, 7% kale, 7% yam, 5% boiled egg, 5% carrot, 5% monkey chow[2], 4% grapes
123	*M. silenus*	♂	4	8	285	20% Diet A[13], 15% banana, 15% orange, 10% apple, 8% monkey chow[2], 8% yam, 6% kale, 5% boiled egg, 5% carrot, 5% grapes, 3% lettuce
124	*M. sylvana*	♂	11	10	129	22% banana, 17% kale, 16% Diet A[13], 10% orange, 9% carrot, 5% apple, 5% celery, 4% boiled egg, 4% grapes, 4% lettuce, 4% monkey chow[2]
125	*Mandrillus sphinx*	♂	45	27	84	18% banana, 12% apple, 12% orange, 11% carrot, 11% lettuce, 9% Diet A[13], 9% kale, 6% yam, 3% boiled egg, 3% celery, 3% grapes, 3% monkey chow[2]
126	*Nasalis larvatus*	♂	6	9	213	30% banana, 20% lettuce, 7% kale, 5% carrot, 5% celery, 5% grapes, 5% orange, 4% apple, 4% Diet A[13], 4% monkey chow[2], 4% yam, 3% boiled egg
127	*Perodicticus potto edwardsi*	♀	1.14	0.427	53	25% banana, 20% apple, 20% orange, 20% yam, 10% Diet M[4], 5% meat
128	*Pongo pygmaeus*	♂	59	20	47	25% orange, 21% carrot, 21% kale, 13% apple, 8% monkey chow[2], 5% crushed pineapple, 4% boiled egg, 4% grapes, 4% meat & broth
129	*Saguinus oedipus*	♂	0.5	0.78	222	24% banana, 15% orange, 12% apple, 12% Diet A[13], 10% carrot, 10% kale, 6% boiled egg, 6% monkey chow[2], 5% yam
130	*Saimiri sciurea*	♂	0.5	2	570	20% apple, 20% banana, 20% orange, 10% kale, 10% yam, 5% grapes, 4% carrot, 4% Diet A[13], 4% monkey chow[2], 3% boiled egg

[2] Guaranteed analysis: ≮25% crude protein, ≮5% crude fat, ≯4.5% crude fiber, ≯3% added minerals. Ingredients: animal fat preserved with BHA, brewer's dried yeast, dehydrated alfalfa meal, dried skim milk, fish meal, ground yellow corn, soybean meal, steamed bone meal, calcium carbonate, cobalt carbonate, copper oxide, defluorinated phosphate, iodized salt, iron oxide, iron sulfate, manganese sulfate, manganous oxide, zinc oxide, thiamine, riboflavin supplement, nicotinic acid, vitamin B_6 HCl, calcium pantothenate, folic acid, vitamin B_{12} supplement, ascorbic acid, vitamin A supplement, vitamin D activated animal sterol (source of vitamin D_3), vitamin E supplement. [4] 30 lb chopped meat, 20 cups meal, ½ cup ground limestone, ½ cup Paltone. [13] 20% ground corn, 20% ground wheat, 20% soybean meal, 10% brewer's yeast, 10% dried skim milk, 10% feeding oats, 5% alfalfa meal, 2% oystershell, 1% salt, 1% vitamin-mineral mixture, 1% vitamins A & D.

continued

Part I. New York Zoological Park

	Order & Species	Sex	Wt kg	Feed/Wk kg	Feed/Day/Kg Body Wt g	Basic Diet
131	*Symphalangus syndactylus*	♂	7	11	227	29% banana, 14% kale, 9% Diet A[13], 7% apple, 7% carrot, 7% orange, 7% yam, 5% lettuce, 4% boiled egg, 4% celery, 4% grapes, 3% monkey chow[2]
132	*Theropithecus gelada*	♂	18	14	111	24% banana, 15% carrot, 12% apple, 12% Diet A[13], 12% kale, 8% orange, 4% yam, 3% boiled egg, 3% celery, 3% grapes, 3% monkey chow[2], 1% string beans
	Chiroptera					
133	*Artibeus lituratus*	♀	0.09	0.8	126.9	90% banana, 10% chopped meat. 1 tsp Mellins Food[14] per day.
134	*Carollia perspicillata*	♂	0.04	0.455	162	50% banana, 30% grapes, 10% chopped meat, 10% Diet M[4]. 1½ tsp Mellins Food[14] per day.
135	*Noctilio labialis*	♂	0.025	0.010	57	100% mealworms. 0.1 ml Vipenta[7] per day.
136	*N. leporinus*	♂	0.07	0.210	428	90% mackerel, 10% chopped meat. 0.2 ml Vipenta[7] per day.
137	*Phyllostomus hastatus hastatus*	♂	0.05	0.441	126	50% banana, 30% grapes, 10% chopped meat, 10% Diet M[4]. 1 tsp Mellins Food[14] per day.
138	*Pteropus giganteus*	♀	0.63	1.29	292	35% banana, 30% grapes, 15% Diet M[4], 10% apple, 10% orange
139	*Rousettus aegyptiacus*	♂	0.2	0.26	185	60% banana, 20% Diet M[4], 10% apple, 10% grapes
	Insectivora					
140	*Echinops telfairi*	♂	0.13	0.028	30	40% Diet M[4], 30% chopped meat, 15% apple, 15% banana
141	*Erinaceus europaeus*	♂	1	0.36	51	60% dog meal[6], 30% horsemeat, 10% egg
142	*Paraechinus hypomelas*	♀	0.4	0.54	192	60% dog meal[6], 30% horsemeat, 10% egg
143	*Tenrec ecaudatus*	...	1	1.22	174	60% Diet M[4], 15% banana, 15% chopped meat, 5% apple, 5% orange
	Marsupialia					
144	*Caluromys* sp.	♂	0.5	0.903	258	25% banana, 20% apple, 15% Diet M[4], 15% grapes, 15% orange, 10% chopped meat
145	*Caluromysiops irrupta*	♀	0.6	1	238	20% Diet M[4], 20% chopped meat, 15% apple, 15% banana, 15% grapes, 15% orange
146	*Dactylopsila trivirgata melampus*	♂	0.43	0.5	178	25% apple, 25% banana, 25% orange, 10% Diet M[4], 10% chopped meat, 5% grapes
147	*Lutreolina crassicaudata*	♂	1.4	0.917	93	60% Diet M[4], 20% fish, 20% liver
148	*Macropus robustus robustus*	♂	33.3	7.2	31	20% apple, 20% carrot, 20% monkey pellets[2], 15% banana, 15% GLF[1], 10% bread

[1] Theoretical analysis: 73% TDN, 16% protein, 4% fat, 8% fiber. Ingredients: 25.4% hominy feed, 15% wheat middlings, 12% corn gluten feed, 10% ground oats, 10% wheat bran, 5% dehydrated alfalfa meal, 5% corn distiller's dried grains, 5% linseed oil, 3% wheat germ meal, 2% dehulled soybean meal, 1% salt, 0.75% dicalcium phosphate, 0.75% ground limestone, 0.05% Z-4 mineral mix (calcium iodate, cobalt carbonate, copper oxide, iron carbonate, manganolis oxide, zinc oxide), 5% molasses, 0.05% vitamin premix. Ingredients of vitamin premix: 2,000,000 units A, 4,000,000 units D, 2000 units E. [2] Guaranteed analysis: ≮25% crude protein, ≮5% crude fat, ≯4.5% crude fiber, ≯3% added minerals. Ingredients: animal fat preserved with BHA, brewer's dried yeast, dehydrated alfalfa meal, dried skim milk, fish meal, ground yellow corn, soybean meal, steamed bone meal, calcium carbonate, cobalt carbonate, copper oxide, defluorinated phosphate, iodized salt, iron oxide, iron sulfate, manganese sulfate, manganous oxide, zinc oxide, thiamine, riboflavin supplement, nicotinic acid, vitamin B_6 HCl, calcium pantothenate, folic acid, vitamin B_{12} supplement, ascorbic acid, vitamin A supplement, vitamin D activated animal sterol (source of vitamin D_3), vitamin E supplement. [4] 30 lb chopped meat, 20 cups meal, ½ cup ground limestone, ½ cup Paltone. [6] Guaranteed analysis: ≮27% crude protein, ≮9% crude fat, ≯4.5% crude fiber, ≯10% ash. [7] Per 0.6 ml: 1 mg thiamine, 1 mg riboflavin, 10 mg nicotinamide, 1 mg vitamin B_6, 30 μg *d*-biotin, 10 mg D-Panthenol, 50 mg ascorbic acid, 5000 U.S.P. units vitamin A, 400 U.S.P. units vitamin D_2, 2 I.U. vitamin E. [13] 20% ground corn, 20% ground wheat, 20% soybean meal, 10% brewer's yeast, 10% dried skim milk, 10% feeding oats, 5% alfalfa meal, 2% oystershell, 1% salt, 1% vitamin-mineral mixture, 1% vitamins A & D. [14] 79.6% available carbohydrates (58.9% maltose, 20.7% dextrins), 10.3% protein N × 6.25, 5.6% moisture, 0.2% fat, 0.2% crude fiber, 3.9% ash, 17.5 mg iron/100 g, 1 mg thiamine/100 g.

continued

19. ZOO DIETS: WILD ANIMALS

Part I. New York Zoological Park

	Order & Species	Sex	Wt kg	Feed/ Wk kg	Feed/ Day /Kg Body Wt g	Basic Diet
149	*Marmosa* sp.	♀	0.05	0.07	200	20% banana, 20% chopped meat, 15% apple, 15% Diet M[4], 15% grapes, 15% orange
150	*Petaurus breviceps*	♂	0.06	0.147	350	30% Diet M[4], 30% chopped meat, 15% banana, 10% apple, 10% orange, 5% sunflower seeds
151	*Protemnodon agilis*	♂	14.5	4.3	42	20% apple, 20% banana, 20% carrot, 20% GLF[1], 20% monkey pellets[2]
				Aves		
	Strigiformes					
152	*Nyctea scandiaca*	...	2	1	29	50% horsemeat, 50% rats
	Charadriiformes					
153	*Larus marinus*	...	2	2	143	50% chopped butterfish, 50% horsemeat
	Falconiformes					
154	*Haliaeetus leucocephalus alascanus*	...	4	1.7	48	66% rats, 34% butterfish
155	*Vultur gryphus*	...	11	2.7	77	50% horsemeat, 50% rats
	Ciconiiformes					
156	*Leptoptilos crumeniferus*	...	9	2.6	41	100% sliced butterfish
	Pelecaniformes					
157	*Pelecanus occidentalis*	...	4	4	170	100% whole butterfish
158	*P. onocrotalus*	...	9	5.4	100	100% whole butterfish
	Casuariiformes					
159	*Casuarius casuarius aruensis*	...	35	35	100	30% bread, 25% banana, 13% horsemeat, 10% boiled egg, 8% apple, 7% orange, 5% white mice, 2% kale
160	*Dromiceius novaehollandiae*	...	26	21	115	30% turkey pellets, 20% chopped kale, 15% chopped butterfish, 15% chopped meat, 10% apple, 10% scratch
	Struthioniformes					
161	*Struthio camelus massaicus*	...	127	49	55	35% turkey pellets, 25% chopped kale, 25% chopped cooked meat, 14% game bird food, trace of crushed limestone, Vitamycin & caradee
	Sphenisciformes					
162	*Aptenodytes patagonica patagonica*	...	14	10.5	100	100% mackerel
163	*Eudyptes crestatus*	...	4	7	250	100% smelt

[1] Theoretical analysis: 73% TDN, 16% protein, 4% fat, 8% fiber. Ingredients: 25.4% hominy feed, 15% wheat middlings, 12% corn gluten feed, 10% ground oats, 10% wheat bran, 5% dehydrated alfalfa meal, 5% corn distiller's dried grains, 5% linseed oil, 3% wheat germ meal, 2% dehulled soybean meal, 1% salt, 0.75% dicalcium phosphate, 0.75% ground limestone, 0.05% Z-4 mineral mix (calcium iodate, cobalt carbonate, copper oxide, iron carbonate, manganolis oxide, zinc oxide), 5% molasses, 0.05% vitamin premix. Ingredients of vitamin premix: 2,000,000 units A, 4,000,000 units D, 2000 units E. [2] Guaranteed analysis: ≮25% crude protein, ≮5% crude fat, ≯4.5% crude fiber, ≯3% added minerals. Ingredients: animal fat preserved with BHA, brewer's dried yeast, dehydrated alfalfa meal, dried skim milk, fish meal, ground yellow corn, soybean meal, steamed bone meal, calcium carbonate, cobalt carbonate, copper oxide, defluorinated phosphate, iodized salt, iron oxide, iron sulfate, manganese sulfate, manganous oxide, zinc oxide, thiamine, riboflavin supplement, nicotinic acid, vitamin B_6-HCl, calcium pantothenate, folic acid, vitamin B_{12} supplement, ascorbic acid, vitamin A supplement, vitamin D activated animal sterol (source of vitamin D_3), vitamin E supplement. [4] 30 lb chopped meat, 20 cups meal, ½ cup ground limestone, ½ cup Paltone.

Contributor: House, H. B.

continued

19. ZOO DIETS: WILD ANIMALS

Part II. San Diego Zoological Garden

	Order & Species (Synonym)	Sex	Wt kg	Feed/ Wk kg	Feed/ Day/Kg Body Wt g	Basic Diet
	Mammalia					
	Artiodactyla[1/]					
1	*Alces alces andersoni*	♀	296	74	36	32% wafers[2/], 26% apple, 26% carrot, 16% beet pulp
2	*Ammotragus lervia*[3/]	♀	50	7	19	100% wafers[2/]
3	*Anoa depressicornis*	♀	160	18	16	100% wafers[2/]
4	*Antilocapra americana*	♀	32	1.2	5	100% wafers[2,4/]
5	*Antilope cervicapra*	♂	32	11	49	100% wafers[2/]
6	*Axis axis (A. maculatus)*	♀	23	4	26	100% wafers[2/]
7	*Bison bison bison*	♂	450	43	14	93% wafers[2/], 7% alfalfa hay
8	*Boselaphus tragocamelus*	♂	190	34	26	100% wafers[2/]
9	*Camelus bactrianus*	♀	600	57	12	100% wafers[2/]
10	*Cervus canadensis canadensis*	♀	194	100	75	52% carrot pulp, 38% wafers[2/], 10% rolled barley
11	*C. unicolor equinus*	♀	22	16	10	80% alfalfa hay, 13% lettuce, 7% carrot
12	*Choeropsis liberiensis*	♂	193	22	16	57% carrot, 43% alfalfa hay
13	*Connochaetes taurinus albojubatus (Gorgon taurinus albojubatus)*	♂	194	32	23	100% wafers[2/]
14	*Giraffa camelopardalis rothschildi*	♂	910	115	18	28% alfalfa hay, 19% wafers[2/], 10% apple, 8% carrot, 8% celery, 8% white oats, 7% lettuce, 5% sweet potato, 3% bread, 3% onion, 1% acacia bark & leaves
15	*Hemitragus jemlahicus jemlahicus*	♀	55	19	58	100% wafers[2/]
16	*Hippotragus niger roosevelti*	♂	170	32	27	100% wafers[2/]
17	*Lama glama*	♀	136	14	14	100% wafers[2/]
18	*L. guanicoe (L. huanacho)*	♀	91	11	17	100% wafers[2/]
19	*L. pacos*	♂	82	15	27	100% wafers[2/]
20	*Muntiacus reevesi*	♂	18	3	25	60% rolled barley, 14% carrot, 12% apple, 8% bread, 6% lettuce
21	*Ovis canadensis canadensis*	♀	55	19	49	100% wafers[2/]
22	*Syncerus caffer*	♂	280	32	16	100% wafers[2/]
23	*Vicugna vicugna mensalis*	♀	64	12	27	100% wafers[2/]
	Perissodactyla					
24	*Tapirus terrestris*	♂	200	49	35	84% wafers[2/], 6% apple, 4% sweet potato, 3% banana, 3% lettuce
	Carnivora					
25	*Acinonyx jubatus*	♂	32	16	85	100% raw horsemeat, 2 tsp bone meal, 1 tsp Vitamycin
26	*Ailurus fulgens fulgens*	♀	7	4	82	38% banana, 32% apple, 16% peeled sweet potato, 9% grapes, 4% hard-boiled egg yolk, 1% bamboo leaves & twigs
27	*Canis dingo*	♂	20	5	31	62% raw horsemeat with bones, 38% dog chow[5/]. ½ tsp bone meal/day.
28	*C. lupus nubilus*	♂	27	7	35	52% raw horsemeat with bones, 48% dog chow[5/]
29	*Crocuta crocuta*	♀	27	8	40	100% raw horsemeat with bones

[1/] Trace-mineralized salt blocks are available. [2/] Guaranteed analysis: ≮52% TDN, ≮13.5% crude protein, ≮2.1% fat, ≯23.5% crude fiber, ≮1.0% calcium, ≮0.3% phosphorus, ≮10,000,000 units vitamin A activity per ton. Formula: 1200 lb alfalfa hay, 400 lb milo stover or coarse Sudan hay, 400 lb protein (18%) concentrate. Formula for 18% protein concentrate: 45 lb rolled barley, 25 lb soybean meal (expeller type), 15 lb wheat standard middlings, 10 lb beet pulp, 1.5 lb dicalcium phosphate, 1.5 lb salt, 2 lb Vit-Trace mineral premix. Ingredients of Vit-Trace mineral premix, per lb: 75 mg cobalt, 1.50 g copper, 0.25 g iodine, 2.50 g iron, 2.50 g manganese, 2.50 g zinc, 1,250,000 units vitamin A, 50,000 units vitamin D, 10,000 units vitamin E. [3/] Fed heavily by public. [4/] A large amount of grass grows in animal enclosure and is available for grazing. [5/] Guaranteed analysis: ≮23% crude protein, ≮8% crude fat, ≯4.5% crude fiber, ≯10% ash. Ingredients: animal fat preserved with BHA, artificial coloring, brewer's dried yeast, cereal food fines, dried whey, ground grain sorghums, ground oat groats, ground yellow corn, ground wheat, meat & bone meal, soybean meal, wheat germ meal, wheat middlings, cobalt carbonate, copper oxide, iron oxide, manganese sulfate, manganous oxide, zinc oxide, iodized salt, thiamine, riboflavin supplement, nicotinic acid, vitamin B_6 HCl, vitamin B_{12} supplement, vitamin A supplement, vitamin D activated plant sterol, vitamin E supplement.

continued

Part II. San Diego Zoological Garden

	Order & Species (Synonym)	Sex	Wt kg	Feed/ Wk kg	Feed/ Day/Kg Body Wt g	Basic Diet
30	*Felis canadensis*	♂	9	4	58	60% ground raw horsemeat, 39% cat chow 6/, 1% raw egg. ½ tsp bone meal/day.
31	*F. chaus fulvidina*	♂	8	2.5	46	60% ground raw horsemeat, 39% cat chow 6/, 1% raw egg. ⅓ tsp bone meal/day.
32	*Helarctos malayanus* 7/	♀	77	4	8	100% dog chow 5/
33	*Panthera onca*	♂	55	16	42	100% raw horsemeat with bones. 1 tsp bone meal/day. Fasted 1 day/wk.
34	*Thalarctos maritimus* 7/	♀	340	15	6	60% raw horsemeat, 40% dog chow 5/
35	*Ursus arctos arctos* 7/	♂	270	10	5	35% dog chow 5/, 25% lettuce, 18% apple, 14% orange, 8% mixed dried fruit
36	*U. horribilis horribilis* 7/	♂	270	12	4	50% mixed dried fruit, 25% apple, 20% lettuce, 5% hard-boiled egg. Fasted 1 day/wk.
	Primates					
37	*Cercopithecus albogularis erythrarchus (C. mitis erythrarchus)*	♀	2	1	72	29% monkey chow 8/, 22% apple, 16% banana, 14% celery, 6% lettuce, 5% grapes, 5% orange, 3% eugenia browse
38	*Colobus guereza kikuyuensis (C. polykomos kikuyuensis)*	♂	8	3	54	25% monkey chow 8/, 23% apple, 22% banana, 8% celery, 7% lettuce, 6% grapes, 4% eugenia browse, 4% orange, 1% hard-boiled egg
39	*Cynopithecus niger (Macaca niger)* 3/	♂	12	2	22	54% monkey chow 8/, 16% lettuce, 9% banana, 6% apple, 5% celery, 4% grapes, 4% orange, 2% hard-boiled egg
40	*Gorilla gorilla*	♂	136	28	29	19% monkey chow 8/, 16% apple, 16% carrot, 14% banana, 12% celery, 7% lettuce, 5% hard-boiled egg, 4% browse (bamboo, acacia, or banana), 3% bread, 2% grapes, 2% reconstituted condensed milk
41	*Hylobates lar*	♀	4	4	132	26% apple, 19% monkey chow 8/, 18% banana, 16% celery, 8% lettuce, 7% grapes, 4% orange, 2% hard-boiled egg
42	*Macaca cyclopis* 3/	♂	12	0.8	10	50% lettuce, 50% monkey chow 8/
43	*M. nemestrina leonina (M. nemestrina andamensis)* 3/	♂	6	1.2	28	35% monkey chow 8/, 22% lettuce, 15% apple, 12% banana, 8% celery, 4% grapes, 4% orange
44	*Pan troglodytes schweinfurthii*	♀	25	8	46	25% monkey chow 8/, 18% banana, 15% apple, 13% celery, 10% orange, 8% grapes, 8% lettuce, 3% hard-boiled egg
45	*Pongo pygmaeus*	♀	25	5	29	20% apple, 20% monkey chow 8/, 17% banana, 15% carrot, 14% celery, 8% grapes, 6% hard-boiled egg

3/ Fed heavily by public. 5/ Guaranteed analysis: ≮23% crude protein, ≮8% crude fat, ≯4.5% crude fiber, ≯10% ash. Ingredients: animal fat preserved with BHA, artificial coloring, brewer's dried yeast, cereal food fines, dried whey, ground grain sorghums, ground oat groats, ground yellow corn, ground wheat, meat & bone meal, soybean meal, wheat germ meal, wheat middlings, cobalt carbonate, copper oxide, iron oxide, manganese sulfate, manganous oxide, zinc oxide, iodized salt, thiamine, riboflavin supplement, nicotinic acid, vitamin B_6 HCl, vitamin B_{12} supplement, vitamin A supplement, vitamin D activated plant sterol, vitamin E supplement. 6/ Guaranteed analysis: ≮30% crude protein, ≮7% crude fat, ≯4.5% crude fiber, ≯11.5% ash. Ingredients: animal fat preserved with BHA, artificial coloring, brewer's dried yeast, condensed fish solubles, dried skim milk, dried whey, fish meal, ground grain sorghums, ground oat groats, ground wheat, ground yellow corn, meat & bone meal, poultry by-product meal, soybean meal, wheat germ meal, cobalt carbonate, copper oxide, iron oxide, manganese sulfate, manganous oxide, defluorinated phosphate, iodized salt, thiamine, riboflavin supplement, nicotinic acid, *p*-aminobenzoic acid, vitamin B_{12} supplement, choline chloride, vitamin A supplement, vitamin D activated plant sterol, vitamin E supplement, menadione sodium bisulfite. 7/ Fed heavily by the public (primarily bread). 8/ Guaranteed analysis: ≮15% crude protein, ≮5% crude fat, ≯3% crude fiber, ≯3% added minerals. Ingredients: animal fat preserved with BHA, brewer's dried yeast, dehydrated alfalfa meal, dried skim milk, ground wheat, ground yellow corn, soybean meal, steamed bone meal, sucrose, calcium carbonate, cobalt carbonate, copper oxide, iron oxide, manganese sulfate, manganous oxide, zinc oxide, defluorinated phosphate, iodized salt, thiamine, riboflavin supplement, nicotinic acid, vitamin B_6 HCl, calcium pantothenate, folic acid, vitamin B_{12} supplement, ascorbic acid, vitamin A supplement, vitamin D activated animal sterol, vitamin E supplement.

continued

Part II. San Diego Zoological Garden

	Order & Species (Synonym)	Sex	Wt kg	Feed/ Wk kg	Feed/ Day/Kg Body Wt g	Basic Diet
	Aves					
	Strigiformes					
46	*Nyctea scandiaca*	♂	1	1	143	100% fresh-killed rats
	Falconiformes					
47	*Haliaeetus leucocephalus*	♂	7	4	84	80% mackerel, 20% horsemeat
48	*Vultur gryphus*	♂	18	4	32	50% horse heart, 50% horsemeat; rats or mice when available
	Ciconiiformes					
49	*Leptoptilos dubius*	♂	6	2	48	50% anchovies, 50% raw horsemeat
	Pelecaniformes					
50	*Pelecanus onocrotalus*	♂	7	1.2	25	100% chopped mackerel
	Casuariiformes					
51	*Dromiceius novaehollandie*	♂	18	7	53	35% dog chow[5], 35% turkey pellets[9], 30% lettuce
	Struthioniformes					
52	*Struthio camelus camelus*	♂	40	15	53	35% dog chow[5], 35% turkey pellets[9], 30% lettuce

[5] Guaranteed analysis: ≮23% crude protein, ≮8% crude fat, ≯4.5% crude fiber, ≯10% ash. Ingredients: animal fat preserved with BHA, artificial coloring, brewer's dried yeast, cereal food fines, dried whey, ground grain sorghums, ground oat groats, ground yellow corn, ground wheat, meat & bone meal, soybean meal, wheat germ meal, wheat middlings, cobalt carbonate, copper oxide, iron oxide, manganese sulfate, manganous oxide, zinc oxide, iodized salt, thiamine, riboflavin supplement, nicotinic acid, vitamin B_6 HCl, vitamin B_{12} supplement, vitamin A supplement, vitamin D activated plant sterol, vitamin E supplement. [9] Guaranteed analysis: ≮20% crude protein, ≮2.5% crude fat, ≯7% crude fiber, ≯9% ash, ≯5% added minerals. Ingredients: animal fat preserved with BHA, cottonseed meal, dehulled pressed safflower seed, dehydrated alfalfa meal preserved with ethoxyquin, fish meal, ground grain sorghums, ground yellow corn, hydrolyzed poultry feathers, meat & bone meal, methionine hydroxy analogue calcium, soybean meal, wheat mill run, BHT (preservative), zinc bacitracin, calcium carbonate, copper sulfate, manganese sulfate, manganous oxide, zinc oxide, iodized salt, low-fluorine rock phosphate, riboflavin supplement, nicotinic acid, vitamin B_6 HCl, calcium pantothenate, vitamin B_{12} supplement, vitamin A supplement, vitamin D activated animal sterol, vitamin E supplement, menadione sodium bisulfite.

Contributors: Kuehn, Gary, and Nelson, Lester S.

Part III. Philadelphia Zoological Garden

These diets have been developed and used by the Philadelphia Zoological Garden for captive wild animals. Although completely adequate for the majority of animals within the groups listed, the diets may not be suitable for certain untested rare species. Diets are for adult animals, unless otherwise specified.

	Animal: Type	Animal: Group	Feed/ Day/Kg Body Wt, g	Basic Diet	Feed Supplement
	Mammalia				
1	Herbivores	Artiodactyla (except swine), Perissodactyla, Proboscidea, & Macropodidae	10-40	**Diet H**[1]: 15% ground yellow corn, 10% ground whole wheat, 10% ground rolled oats, 10% soybean meal, 5.2% brewer's yeast, 26% alfalfa leaf meal, 2.5% oystershell flour, 1% iodized salt, 0.3% A-D feeding oil, 10% linseed meal, 10% brewer's grains[3]	Hay[2], green leaves, or fresh-cut grass (5-10 g/kg body wt); equal quantities of apples, carrots, green lettuce, or cabbage (10-50 g/kg body wt)

[1] Deteriorates after 2 weeks under refrigeration. [2] Free choice. [3] Mix dry beet pulp (45% of total dry weight of feed needed) with equal amount of water; let stand 1-2 hours, then add to **Diet H** ingredients (also 45% of total dry weight) and 10% chopped cabbage and carrots.

continued

19. ZOO DIETS: WILD ANIMALS

Part III. Philadelphia Zoological Garden

	Animal: Type	Animal: Group	Feed/Day/Kg Body Wt, g	Basic Diet	Feed Supplement
2	Omnivores	Tayassuidae, Suidae, Hyracoidea, Rodentia, & Primates	5-50[4]	**Diet O**[1]: 15% ground yellow corn, 15% ground whole wheat, 10% ground whole barley, 10% ground rolled oats, 10% cottonseed meal, 10% soybean meal, 10% brewer's yeast, 10% dried skimmed milk, 5% alfalfa leaf meal, 2% oystershell flour, 1% iodized salt, 2% A-D feeding oil[5]	Citrus fruits, green vegetables, & carrots (for bulk, increase these items)
3		Ursidae	5-50[4]	Half **Diet O**, half raw meat or fish	
4	Carnivores	Felidae, immature	25-75	90% ground raw meat, 2% oystershell flour, 2% A-D feeding oil, whole milk twice daily	
5		mature	20-100	Raw horsemeat, whale meat, or beef	Raw liver twice weekly (10-50 g/kg body wt)
6		Viverridae, Canidae, & Didelphidae	25-75	**Diet C**[6]: 55% ground raw horsemeat, 31% **Diet O**, 10% raw carrots, 2% oystershell flour, 2% A-D feeding oil	
7		Mustelidae & Procyonidae	25-75	**Diet C** (*see* line 6)	Apples & carrots
				Aves	
8	Omnivores	Psittaciformes[7], Columbidae, Rallidae, Psophiidae, Gruidae, Phasianoidea, Anatidae, Phoenicopteridae[8], & Casuariiformes	5-50[4]	**Diet O** (*see* line 2)	Citrus fruits, green vegetables, & carrots (for bulk, increase these items)
9		Cariamidae, Eurypygidae, & Threskiornithidae	5-50[4]	Half **Diet O**, half **Diet C** (*see* lines 2 & 6)	
10		Rheiformes & Struthioniformes	5-50[4]	Half **Diet H**, half **Diet O** (*see* lines 1 & 2)	
11	Carnivores	Corvidae, Strigiformes, Laridae, Falconiformes, Cochleariidae, & Ardeidae	25-75	**Diet C** (*see* line 6)	
12	Cage birds	Passeriformes, Ramphastidae, Capitonidae, Bucerotidae[9], Coraciidae, Momotidae, Trogoniformes, & Musophagidae	25-75	**Diet B**[6,10]: 20% ground raw carrots, 20% ground cooked meat, 50% **Diet O**, 7% ground hard-cooked eggs & shells, 3% A-D feeding oil	Diced oranges, apples, grapes, cherries, & green lettuce
				Reptilia	
13	Carnivores	Heloderma, Ophisaurus, Eumeces, Iguanidae, Testudinidae	25-75	**Diet C** (*see* line 6)	

[1] Deteriorates after 2 weeks under refrigeration. [4] Depending on weight and activity. [5] Mix 9 parts of **Diet O** ingredients with one part ground cooked meat and enough broth to make a stiff mash; press and refrigerate 24-28 hours before using. [6] Deteriorates after 48 hours under refrigeration. [7] Small lories and parakeets need whole seed also. [8] To start on diet, form a mash with water. [9] One or two mice per bird added to diet. [10] May be combined with **Diet C** in varying proportions.

Contributor: Ratcliffe, Herbert L.

continued

19. ZOO DIETS: WILD ANIMALS

Part IV. Lincoln Park Zoological Gardens of Chicago

Amounts of feed are the daily ration for a single adult animal, unless otherwise specified.

	Animal Group	Specific Animal	Specific Diet	Basic Group Diet
			Mammalia	
1	Elephantidae	Elephant	2 bales timothy hay, 1 pail Purina D&A chow, 1 bushel fruit & vegetable mix, approx 55 gal water (free choice)	
2	Bovidae	Antelope	Purina dry & freshening chow (free choice), hay (alfalfa mainly), mineralized salt block (free choice), vitamin-mineral supplement added to grain daily, water (free choice)	
3	Tayassuidae	Peccary	For 4 animals: 15-18 lb of basic diet + fruits & vegetables	50% horsemeat, 15% standard brand kibbled dog food, 20% water, 10% beef kidney, 3% beef suet, vitamin-mineral supplement added to grain daily, water (free choice)
4	Ursidae	Black, brown, & sloth bears; also polar bear cub	6 lb of basic diet	
5		Grizzly bear	7 lb of basic diet + 2 herring	
6		Polar bear	9 lb of basic diet + 6 herring	
7	Canidae	Cape hunting dog	1½-2 lb of basic diet	
8		Coyote & wolf	2 lb of basic diet	
9		Dingo	1½ lb of basic diet	
10		Fox	½-1 lb of basic diet	
11	Felidae	Jaguar	6 lb of basic diet	Horsemeat plus vitamin-mineral supplement 3 days/wk, chicken with viscera 2 days/wk, horse liver 1 day/wk, then 1 day/wk without food
12		Leopard	4 lb of basic diet	
13		Lion	12-15 lb of basic diet	
14		Tiger	14-17 lb of basic diet	
15	Primates	Chimpanzee, gorilla, & orangutan	Basic diet + reconstituted FMS milk powder with vitamins added	Monkey chow biscuits, fruit & vegetable plate, raw horsemeat (very small piece), water (free choice)
16	Small mammalian species	Rodents	Basic diet	50% ground horsemeat, 50% moistened mink mixture by volume. Added: cod-liver oil, hard-boiled egg, honey, molasses, peanut oil, Vigran multiple vitamin tablets, mineral mixture with vitamins A & D.
17		Omnivores	Basic diet + mixed fruits & vegetables	
18		Anteaters	Basic diet + banana (homogenized)	
			Aves	
19	Passeriformes		Basic diet + standard finch mix & Provam powder with honey & evaporated milk added	Currants (soaked), grapes, ground apple, ground boiled horsemeat, ground carrot, ground horsemeat, Mexican dried flies, sliced banana, vitamin supplements
20	Psittaciformes		Basic diet + raw Spanish peanuts & sunflower seeds	
21		Lorikeets	Basic diet + raw Spanish peanuts, sunflower seeds, & Provam powder with honey & evaporated milk added	
22	Small seedeaters		Basic diet + standard finch mix	
23	Galliformes & Columbidae	Gallinaceous birds, hoatzin, & fruit pigeon	Whole corn; mealworms weekly	
24	Fish-eating birds		Smelt and/or herring, depending on bird size	
25	Birds of prey		Basic diet	Raw horsemeat 6 days/wk, chicken heads twice weekly, fresh rabbits & chickens when available
26	Struthioniformes & Rheiformes	Ostrich & rhea	Basic diet + 6 heads escarole, horse chow, alfalfa hay, fresh fruits & vegetables	
27	Anatidae	Duck, goose & swan	Whole corn, duck chow, escarole; fish twice weekly	

Contributor: Fisher, Lester E.

20. NUTRIENT REQUIREMENTS AND UTILIZATION: INSECTS

Stage: A = adult; L = Larva; N = nymph.

Part I. Minerals

All species of insects require carbon, hydrogen, oxygen, and nitrogen in various molecular combinations. These elements, as universal components of living tissues, are present in the structure of the insect body and in its food. A number of different minerals, some only as traces, also are consumed and are present in the tissues of the insect. The mineral composition of the insect may influence considerably the chemical reactions taking place in the tissues, but it is difficult to determine whether some of the trace elements are utilized specifically. The data were taken mainly from studies in which the insect was noticeably affected by the presence or absence of a mineral element in its rearing medium or food. *Abbreviations:* U = utilized; U̸ = not utilized.

	Species (Synonym)	Stage	Minerals											Reference
			Ca	Cl	Cu	Fe	Mg	Mn	P	K	Na	Zn	Other	
1	*Acyrthosiphon pisum*	L	......	U	...	...	U	....	U	U	....	...	....	1
2	*Aedes aegypti*	L	U	U̸	...	...	U̸	....	...	U̸	U̸	...	....	29
3	*A. australis (A. concolor)*	L	U 1/	...	...	...	...	....	...	...	U 1/	...	....	32
4	*Alabama argillacea*	L	......	...	U	...	...	....	...	...	....	U	....	6
5	*Anthonomus grandis*	L	U̸	...	U̸	U̸	U	U̸	...	...	U̸	U̸	U̸ 2/	30
6	*Blattella germanica*	N	......	...	U	...	U	U	...	...	....	U	U̸ 3/	4,15
7	*Bombyx mori*	L	......	...	...	...	...	....	...	...	U̸	...	....	28
8		A 4/	......	...	U	U	...	....	...	U 5/	U	...	U̸ 6/	5
9	*Culex pipiens*	L	......	U	...	...	...	....	...	...	....	...	U̸ 7/	2,31
10	*Culiseta incidens (Theobaldia incidens)*	L	U	...	...	U̸	U	....	...	U	U	...	....	14
11	*Drosophila melanogaster*	L	U̸ 8/	...	...	U̸ 8/	U	U̸ 8/	U	U	U	...	....	25
12		A	......	...	...	...	U	....	...	U	....	...	....	26
13	*Hyalophora cecropia (Platysamia cecropia)*	L	......	...	...	U	...	....	...	...	....	...	....	24
14	*Locusta migratoria*	N 9/	U	U	...	...	U	....	U	U	U	...	U 10/	7
15	*Melanoplus differentialis*	Egg	......	...	U	...	...	....	...	...	....	...	....	3
16	*Musca domestica*	A	U	...	...	U	U	U 11/	U	...	....	...	....	21,22
17	*Myzus persicae*	L & A	......	...	U	U	U	U	U 12/	U	....	U	U 10/	8-10
18	*Nosopsyllus fasciatus*	L	......	...	...	U	...	....	...	...	....	...	....	27
19	*Periplaneta americana*	A	U	...	...	U	...	....	...	U	....	...	....	20,23
20	*Phaenicia sericata (Lucilia sericata)*	L	......	...	...	...	...	....	U	...	....	...	....	16
21	*Pleolophus basizonus (Aptesis basizonus)*	A	......	...	...	...	...	U	...	...	....	...	....	12
22	*Pseudosarcophaga* sp. *(P. affinis)*	L	U̸ 13/	U̸ 14/	...	U̸	U̸	....	U	U	U̸	...	U̸ 15/	17
23	*Sarcophaga argyrostoma (S. falculata)*	L	......	...	U	...	...	....	...	...	....	...	....	11
24	*Schistocerca gregaria*	N 9/	U	U	...	...	U	....	U	U	U	...	U 10/	7
25	*Tenebrio molitor*	L	......	...	...	...	...	....	...	U	....	U	....	13
26	*Tribolium confusum*	L	U̸ 8,16/	...	U	U	U	U	...	U	U̸ 8,16/	U	....	18,19

1/ In balanced solution only. 2/ Cobalt, iodine, and molybdenum. 3/ Fluorine and lead; also cadmium, selenium, and strontium, which are toxic for this organism. 4/ Utilization was judged by effect of element on fecundity. 5/ Utilized as KOH, but not as KCl. 6/ Cobalt and mercury, which are toxic for this organism. 7/ Mercury, which is toxic for this organism. 8/ Omission or addition in dietary salt mixture had no effect. 9/ Utilization of elements was assumed, since growth was good on a simplified salt mixture consisting only of the elements' salt components. 10/ Sulfur. 11/ Replaceable by magnesium. 12/ Utilized as phosphate. 13/ Only present in chemically defined medium as calcium pantothenate. 14/ Only present in chemically defined medium as hydrochlorides of amino acids or vitamins. 15/ Sulfur; only present in chemically defined medium as sulfur-containing amino acids. 16/ References cite conflicting data.

Contributors: (a) House, H. L., (b) Mittler, Thomas E., (c) Gordon, H. T.

References

[1] Auclair, J. L. 1965. Ann. Entomol. Soc. Am. 58:855.

[2] Bodine, J. H. 1923. Biol. Bull. 45:149.

[3] Bodine, J. H., and T. N. Tahmisian. 1943. Ibid. 85: 157.

[4] Brooks, M. A. 1960. Proc. Helminthol. Soc. Wash. D.C. 27:212.

[5] Cavazza, F. 1917. Redia 12:69.

[6] Creighton, J. T. 1938. J. Econ. Entomol. 31:735.

[7] Dadd, R. H. 1961. J. Insect Physiol. 6:126.

[8] Dadd, R. H. 1967. Ibid. 13:763.

[9] Dadd, R. H., and T. E. Mittler. 1965. Ibid. 11:717.

[10] Dadd, R. H., and T. E. Mittler. 1966. Experientia 22:832.

[11] Dennell, R. 1947. Proc. Roy. Soc. (London), B, 134:79.

continued

Part I. Minerals

[12] Finlayson, T. 1961. Can. Entomologist 93:626.
[13] Fraenkel, G. 1958. J. Nutr. 65:361.
[14] Frost, F. M., W. B. Herms, and W. M. Hoskins. 1961. J. Exptl. Zool. 73:461.
[15] Gordon, H. T. 1959. Ann. N.Y. Acad. Sci. 77:290.
[16] Hobson, R. P. 1935. Biochem. J. 29:1286.
[17] House, H. L. Unpublished. Canada Dept. of Agriculture, Entomology Laboratory, Belleville, Ontario, 1967.
[18] Huot, L., R. Bernard, and A. Lemonde. 1957. Can. J. Zool. 35:513.
[19] Medici, J. C., and M. W. Taylor. 1966. J. Nutr. 88:181.
[20] Roeder, K. D. 1948. J. Cellular Comp. Physiol. 31:327.
[21] Sacktor, B. 1952. J. Gen. Physiol. 35:397.
[22] Sacktor, B. 1953. Ibid. 36:371.
[23] Sacktor, B., and D. Bodenstein. 1952. J. Cellular Comp. Physiol. 40:157.
[24] Sanborn, R. C., and C. M. Williams. 1950. J. Gen. Physiol. 33:579.
[25] Sang, J. H. 1956. J. Exptl. Biol. 33:45.
[26] Sang, J. H., and R. C. King. 1961. Ibid. 38:793.
[27] Sharif, M. 1937. Parasitology 29:225.
[28] Tobias, J. M. 1948. J. Cellular Comp. Physiol. 31:143.
[29] Trager, W. 1936. Biol. Bull. 71:343.
[30] Vanderzant, E. S. 1965. J. Insect Physiol. 11:659.
[31] Wigglesworth, V. B. 1938. J. Exptl. Biol. 15:235.
[32] Woodhill, A. R. 1936. Bull. Entomol. Res. 27:633.

Part II. Vitamins

No insects are known to require vitamins D or K, or the provitamins of D or K. Vitamins and other essential organic compounds reported to be beneficial but not essential are listed as "required." An entry followed by a question mark indicates conflicting data, with the preponderance of evidence favoring the information given. *Abbreviations:* R = required; ℞ = not required.

	Species (Synonym)	Stage	Vitamins												Reference
			Thiamine	Riboflavin	Nicotinic Acid	B_6	Biotin	Pantothenic Acid	Folic Acid	*p*-Aminobenzoic Acid	Inositol	B_{12}	Choline	Other	
1	*Acheta domesticus*	N	R	R	R	R	R	R	R	℞	R	...	R	R[1]	51,58
2	*Aedes aegypti*	L	R	R	R	R	R	R	R	R[2]	℞	R[3]	R	...	1,64
3		A	℞	℞	℞	℞	℞	℞	℞	℞	℞	℞	℞	...	64
4	*Anthonomus grandis*	L	R	R	R	R	℞	R	R	...	R	...	R	R[4]	68,69
5	*Attagenus* sp.	L	R	R	R	R	R	R	R	℞	℞	...	R	...	50,52,53
6	*Blattella germanica*	N	...	℞	...	℞	R[5]	...	R[5]	...	R	R[5]	R[6]	...	32
7	*Bombyx mori*	L	R	℞	R	R	℞	R	℞	...	...	...	R[7]	R[4]	36,37,43
8	*Calliphora vicina*	L	R	R	R	R	R	...	R	...	℞	℞	R	...	63
9	*Chilo suppressalis*	L	R	R	R	R	R	R	R	℞	℞	...	℞	...	42
10	*Dacus dorsalis*	A	R	...	R	...	...	...	R	...	...	...	R	...	34
11	*Dermestes maculatus*	L	R	R	R	R	R	R	R	℞	℞	...	R	...	15,18,19,21,28,31
12	*Drosophila melanogaster*	L	R	R	R	R	R	R	R	℞	℞	R?	R	...	35,61
13		A	R	R	R	R	℞	R	R	...	...	℞	℞	...	62
14	*Exeristes comstockii*	A[8]	R	℞	℞	℞	...	R	R	℞	℞	℞	℞	℞[1]	4
15	*Hylemya antiqua*	L	R	R	R	R	R	R	R	...	...	R[2]	R	...	29
16	*Lasioderma serricorne*	L	℞	℞	℞	℞?	R?	℞?	℞	℞?	℞	...	R?	...	3,20-23,57
17		A[9]	R	R	R	R	R	R	R	℞	℞	...	R	...	3,20,22,23,57
18	*Musca domestica*	L	R	R	R	R	R	R	℞?	℞	℞	℞	R?	...	5,41
19	*M. domestica vicina*	L	R	R	R	R	R	R	R	...	...	...	R	...	46
20	*Myzus persicae*	L & A	R	R	R	R	R	R[10]	R	...	R	...	R	R[4]	14

[1] Vitamin E. [2] Slightly beneficial. [3] May promote pupation slightly. [4] Ascorbic acid. [5] Has little or no effect on growth of first generation; various effects appear later. [6] May be replaced by betaine. [7] Cannot be replaced by carnitine. [8] Reproduction and egg viability affected by vitamins listed. [9] Subjects were deprived of normally present intracellular symbiotes. [10] Pantothenate.

continued

Part II. Vitamins

	Species (Synonym)	Stage	Vitamins												Reference
			Thiamine	Riboflavin	Nicotinic Acid	B_6	Biotin	Pantothenic Acid	Folic Acid	*p*-Aminobenzoic Acid	Inositol	B_{12}	Choline	Other	
21	*Oryzaephilus surinamensis*	....	℞	R	R	℞	℞	R	...	℞	℞	...	℞	...	3,20-23,57
22	*Ostrinia nubilalis*	L	...	...	...	...	...	...	...	...	...	...	...	R[4/]	7
23	*Palorus ratzeburgi*	L	R	R	R	R	R?	R	R?	℞	℞	...	R	...	9
24	*Pectinophora gossypiella*	L	R	R	R	R	R	R	R	...	R	℞	...	℞[1/]	55,66,67
25	*Phormia regina*	L	R	R	R	R	R	R	R	℞	℞	...	R[11/]	...	6,49
26	*Pseudosarcophaga* sp. *(P. affinis)*	L	R	R	R	R	R	R	℞	℞	℞	R[2/]	R	R[12/]	2,38-40
27	*Ptinus tectus*	L	R	R	R	R	R	R	...	℞?	℞?	...	R	...	20-23
28	*Schistocerca gregaria*	N	R	R	R	R	R	R	R	℞	R	℞	R	R[13/]	10-13
29	*Stegobium paniceum*	L[9/]	R	R	R	R	R	R	R	℞	℞?	...	R?	...	3,20,21,23,57
30		A	R	℞	℞	℞	R?	℞	℞?	℞	℞	...	℞?	...	3,20,22,23,57
31	*Tenebrio molitor*	L	R	R	R	R	R	R	R	℞	℞	...	℞?	...	16,17,19,24-27,44,45,48
32	*Tribolium castaneum*	L	R	R	R	R	R	R	R	...	...	...	...	...	25
33	*T. confusum*	L	R	R	R	R	R	R	R	℞	℞	...	R	...	19-25,30,33,47,54,59,60,65
34	*Trichoplusia ni*	L	...	...	...	...	...	...	...	...	...	...	...	R[4/]	8
35	*Trogoderma granarium*	L	R	R	R	℞	℞	R	℞	℞	℞	...	R	...	56

[1/] Vitamin E. [2/] Slightly beneficial. [4/] Ascorbic acid. [9/] Subjects were deprived of normally present intracellular symbiotes. [11/] May be replaced by carnitine, but not by betaine. [12/] Vitamins A and E; however, ascorbic acid is not required. [13/] Carotene, which is required for pigmentation, and ascorbic acid; however, vitamin E is not required.

Contributor: House, H. L.

References

[1] Akov, S. 1962. J. Insect Physiol. 8:319.

[2] Barlow, J. S. 1963. Nature 197:311.

[3] Blewett, M., and G. Fraenkel. 1944. Proc. Roy. Soc. (London), B, 132:212.

[4] Bracken, G. K. 1966. Can. Entomologist 98:913.

[5] Brookes, V. J., and G. Fraenkel. 1958. Physiol. Zool. 31:208.

[6] Brust, M., and G. Fraenkel. 1955. Ibid. 28:186.

[7] Chippendale, G. M., and S. D. Beck. 1964. Entomol. Exptl. Appl. 7:241.

[8] Chippendale, G. M., S. D. Beck, and F. M. Strong. 1965. J. Insect Physiol. 11:211.

[9] Cooper, M. I., and G. Fraenkel. 1952. Physiol. Zool. 25:120.

[10] Dadd, R. H. 1957. Nature 179:427.

[11] Dadd, R. H. 1960. J. Insect Physiol. 4:319.

[12] Dadd, R. H. 1960. Proc. Roy. Soc. (London), B, 153:128.

[13] Dadd, R. H. 1961. J. Insect Physiol. 6:1.

[14] Dadd, R. H., D. L. Krieger, and T. E. Mittler. 1967. Ibid. 13:249.

[15] Fraenkel, G. 1943. Sci. J. Roy. Coll. Sci. 13:59.

[16] Fraenkel, G. 1948. Biochem. J. 42:xvi.

[17] Fraenkel, G. 1952. Arch. Biochem. Biophys. 38:405.

[18] Fraenkel, G. Unpublished. Univ. Illinois, Dept. Entomology, Urbana, 1952.

[19] Fraenkel, G., and M. Blewett. 1942. Nature 150:177.

[20] Fraenkel, G., and M. Blewett. 1943. Biochem. J. 37:686.

[21] Fraenkel, G., and M. Blewett. 1943. Ibid. 37:692.

[22] Fraenkel, G., and M. Blewett. 1943. Nature 151:703.

[23] Fraenkel, G., and M. Blewett. 1943. Ibid. 152:506.

[24] Fraenkel, G., and M. Blewett. 1946. Ibid. 157:697.

[25] Fraenkel, G., and M. Blewett. 1947. Biochem. J. 41:469.

[26] Fraenkel, G., M. Blewett, and M. Coles. 1948. Nature 161:981.

[27] Fraenkel, G., M. Blewett, and M. Coles. 1950. Physiol. Zool. 23:92.

[28] Fraenkel, G., J. A. Reid, and M. Blewett. 1941. Biochem. J. 25:712.

[29] Friend, W. G., and R. L. Patton. 1956. Can. J. Zool. 34:152.

[30] Frobrich, G. 1940. Z. Vergleich. Physiol. 27:335.

[31] Gay, F. J. 1938. J. Exptl. Zool. 79:93.

[32] Gordon, H. T. 1959. Ann. N.Y. Acad. Sci. 77:290.

[33] Grob, C. A., T. Reichstein, and H. Rosenthal. 1945. Experientia 1:275.

[34] Hagen, K. S. 1958. Proc. Intern. Congr. Entomol., 10th, Montreal, 1956, 3:25.

[35] Hinton, T., D. T. Noyes, and J. Ellis. 1951. Physiol. Zool. 24:335.

[36] Horie, Y., and T. Ito. 1963. Nature 197:98.

[37] Horie, Y., and T. Ito. 1965. J. Insect Physiol. 11:1585.

[38] House, H. L. 1954. Can. J. Zool. 32:342.

[39] House, H. L. 1966. J. Insect Physiol. 12:409.

continued

Part II. Vitamins

[40] House, H. L. Unpublished. Canada Dept. of Agriculture, Entomology Laboratory, Belleville, Ontario, 1967.

[41] House, H. L., and J. S. Barlow. 1958. Ann. Entomol. Soc. Am. 51:299.

[42] Ishii, S., and H. Urushibara. 1954. Nogyo Gijutsu Kenkyusho Hokoku, C, 4:109.

[43] Ito, T., and N. Arai. 1965. Sanshi Shikensho Hokoku 20:1.

[44] Leclercq, J. 1948. Biochim. Biophys. Acta 2:329.

[45] Leclercq, J. 1949. Arch. Intern. Physiol. 57:67.

[46] Levinson, Z. H., and E. D. Bergmann. 1959. J. Insect Physiol. 3:293.

[47] Lund, H. P., and R. J. Bushnell. 1939. J. Econ. Entomol. 32:640.

[48] Martin, H. E., and L. Hare. 1942. Biol. Bull. 83:428.

[49] McGinnis, A. J., R. W. Newburgh, and V. H. Cheldelin. 1956. J. Nutr. 58:309.

[50] McKennis, H., Jr. 1947. J. Biol. Chem. 167:645.

[51] Meikle, J. E. S., and J. E. McFarlane. 1965. Can. J. Zool. 43:87.

[52] Moore, W. 1943. Ann. Entomol. Soc. Am. 36:483.

[53] Moore, W. 1946. Ibid. 39:513.

[54] Offhaus, K. 1940. Z. Vergleich. Physiol. 27:384.

[55] Ouye, M. T., and E. S. Vanderzant. 1964. J. Econ. Entomol. 57:427.

[56] Pant, N. C. 1956. Indian J. Entomol. 18:259.

[57] Pant, N. C., and G. Fraenkel. 1950. Science 112:498.

[58] Ritchot, C., and J. E. McFarlane. 1961. Can. J. Zool. 39:11.

[59] Roeder, K. D., ed. 1953. Insect physiology. J. Wiley. New York.

[60] Rosenthal, H., and T. Reichstein. 1942. Nature 150:546.

[61] Sang, J. H. 1956. J. Exptl. Biol. 33:45.

[62] Sang, J. H., and R. C. King. 1961. Ibid. 38:793.

[63] Sedee, D. J. 1958. Entomol. Exptl. Appl. 1:38.

[64] Singh, K. R. P., and A. W. A. Brown. 1957. J. Insect Physiol. 1:199.

[65] Street, H. R., and L. S. Palmer. 1935. Proc. Soc. Exptl. Biol. Med. 32:1500.

[66] Vanderzant, E. S. 1957. J. Econ. Entomol. 50:219.

[67] Vanderzant, E. S. 1959. Ibid. 52:1018.

[68] Vanderzant, E. S. 1963. Ibid. 56:357.

[69] Vanderzant, E. S., M. C. Pool, and C. D. Richardson. 1962. J. Insect Physiol. 8:287.

Part III. Sugars

An entry followed by a question mark indicates conflicting data, with the preponderance of evidence favoring the information given. *Abbreviations:* U = utilized; U̸ = not utilized; u = poorly utilized; R̸ = not required.

	Species[1] (Synonym)	Stage	Sugars																	Reference
			Arabinose	Cellobiose	Fructose	Galactose	Glucose	Lactose	Maltose	Mannose	Melezitose	Melibiose	Raffinose	Rhamnose	Ribose	Sorbose	Sucrose	Trehalose	Xylose	
1	*Aedes aegypti*	L	U̸	U̸?	U?	U?	U?	U?	U?	U?	....	...	U̸	U̸	...	U̸	U	u?	u?	27,53,56
2		A	U̸	U̸	U	u	U	U̸	U	U̸	U	u	u	U̸	U̸	U̸	u	u	U̸	26
3	*Aglais urtica*	L	...	...	...	...	U	....	...	...	....	...	...	...	...	...	U	...	...	16
4	*Anagasta kuehniella* (*Ephestia kuehniella*)	L[2]	...	...	U	U̸	U	U̸	U	...	....	...	U̸	...	...	U̸	U̸	...	U̸	21,24
5	*Anastrepha ludens*	A	U̸	U̸	U	U	U	U̸	U	U	U	...	U	U̸	...	...	U	U	U̸	1
6	*Anthonomus grandis*	L	...	U	U	u	U	U	U	u	....	u	...	...	u	...	U	...	...	54
7	*Apis mellifera*	L	...	...	u	U̸	U?	U̸	U	...	U	...	...	...	...	...	U	U	...	5
8		A[3]	u	u	U	u	U	R̸	U	U̸[4]	U	R̸	U?	u	...	U̸	U	U	U?	35,36,44,49, 51,55
9	*Automeris io*	L	...	...	...	...	U[5]	....	...	...	....	...	...	...	...	...	...	...	...	8
10	*Blattella germanica*	N[6]	u[7]	U̸	U	U	U[8]	U	U	U	U	U	U	U̸	U̸[7]	U̸	U	U	U̸[7]	28
11	*Bombyx mori*	L	U̸	U	U	u	U	U	U	U	U	U	U	U̸	u	U̸[9]	U	U	U	39
12	*Cadra cautella* (*Ephestia cautella*) & *E. elutella*	L[10]	...	...	U[11]	...	U	....	...	...	....	...	...	...	...	...	...	...	...	24

[1] *Attagenus* sp. does not require carbohydrates [45]. [2] Requires approximately 80% carbohydrate for optimum diet. [3] Does not utilize fucose. [4] Toxic. [5] Reducing sugars. [6] Nonaseptic roach; requires approximately 30% carbohydrate for optimum diet. [7] D-form is slightly toxic. [8] May be partly replaced by adonitol and arabinose. [9] Toxic or inhibitory. [10] Requires approximately 50% carbohydrate for optimum diet. [11] Has a retarding effect on growth.

continued

Part III. Sugars

	Species (Synonym)	Stage	Sugars: Arabinose	Cellobiose	Fructose	Galactose	Glucose	Lactose	Maltose	Mannose	Melezitose	Melibiose	Raffinose	Rhamnose	Ribose	Sorbose	Sucrose	Trehalose	Xylose	Reference
13	*Calliphora vicina*	A[12]	Ʉ	Ʉ	U	U	U	u	U	U	U	U	U	Ʉ	...	Ʉ	U	U	u	18,19,31,33, 51
14	*Callosobruchus maculatus*	L	...	...	...	....	...	....	...	...	....	...	...	...	...	...	U[13]	...	...	41
15	*Chilo suppressalis*	L	Ʉ	Ʉ	U	Ʉ	U	Ʉ	U	Ʉ	Ʉ	Ʉ	u	Ʉ	Ʉ	Ʉ	U	u	Ʉ	37
16	*Dacus dorsalis*	A	...	...	U	....	U	....	...	...	....	...	...	...	...	...	U	...	...	30
17	*Drosophila melanogaster*	L[14]	...	...	U	....	U	U	Ʉ	...	....	...	...	...	...	...	U	...	...	52
18		A[15]	u	Ʉ	U	U[16]	U	Ʉ[16]	U	U	U	U	U	Ʉ	u	u	U	U	u	29,32,33,46, 51
19	*Galleria mellonella*	L	...	...	...	....	U	....	...	...	....	...	...	...	...	Ʉ[9]	....	...	...	13
20	*Gasterophilus intestinalis*	L	...	...	U	....	...	....	...	...	....	...	...	...	...	...	....	...	...	43
21	*Lasioderma serricorne*[17]	L	...	...	...	....	U	....	...	...	....	...	...	...	...	...	u?	...	...	22
22	*Locusta migratoria*	N[18]	Ʉ	U	U	Ʉ	U	u	U	U	U	U	U	Ʉ	Ʉ	Ʉ[9]	U	U	Ʉ	12
23	*Lyctus* sp.	L	...	...	...	....	U	....	...	...	....	...	...	...	...	...	U	...	...	48
24	*Macrocentrus ancylivorus*	A[19]	...	...	U	u	U	Ʉ	U	...	....	...	...	...	...	...	U	...	...	50
25	*Malacosoma neustria*	L	...	...	...	....	U?	....	...	...	....	...	...	...	...	...	U?	...	...	16
26	*Melanoplus bivittatus*	A	...	...	...	U	U	....	...	...	....	...	...	...	...	...	....	...	...	7
27	*Merodon equestris* (*Lampetia equestris*)	A	...	...	U	....	U	.....	U	...	....	...	...	...	...	...	U	...	U	15
28	*Musca domestica*	A	Ʉ	Ʉ	U	U	U	U	U	U	U	U	U	Ʉ	Ʉ	Ʉ	U	U	Ʉ	26
29	*Myzus persicae*	L & A	...	u	u	U	U	Ʉ	U	Ʉ	U	U	U	Ʉ	Ʉ	u	U[20]	U	Ʉ	14
30	*Oryzaephilus surinamensis*	L	Ʉ	...	U	Ʉ	U	U	U	u	....	...	Ʉ	...	...	Ʉ	Ʉ	...	Ʉ	21,22
31	*Ostrinia nubilalis* (*Pyrausta nubilalis*)	L[21]	...	...	U	....	U	Ʉ	Ʉ	...	....	...	...	...	...	...	U	...	...	2,3,6
32	*Phalera bucephala*	L[22]	...	...	...	....	U	....	...	...	....	...	...	...	...	...	U	...	...	16
33	*Phormia regina*	A[23]	u	u	U	U	U	u	U	U	U	u	U	u	u	u	U	U	u	34
34	*Pieris brassicae*	L	...	...	...	....	U	....	...	...	....	...	...	...	...	...	U	...	...	16
35	*Plodia interpunctella*[10]	....	...	...	U[11]	....	U	....	...	...	....	...	...	...	...	...	....	...	...	24
36	*Prodenia eridania*	L	...	...	...	....	U	....	...	...	....	...	...	...	...	...	U?	...	...	11
37	*Pseudosarcophaga* sp. (*P. affinis*)	L	...	...	...	....	U	....	...	...	....	...	...	...	...	...	....	...	...	38
38	*Ptinus tectus*	L[24]	...	...	...	....	U	....	...	...	....	...	...	...	...	...	....	...	...	22
39	*Sarcophaga bullata*	A	Ʉ	Ʉ	U	U	U	Ʉ	U	U	U	u	U	Ʉ	Ʉ	Ʉ	U	U	Ʉ	26
40	*Schistocerca gregaria*	N[18]	...	U[25]	U	u	U	U	U	u	U[25]	U	U	...	...	Ʉ	U	U	...	12
41	*Stegobium paniceum*	L[10]	Ʉ	...	Ʉ	Ʉ	U	Ʉ	U	Ʉ	....	...	U	...	...	Ʉ	Ʉ	...	Ʉ	21,22

9/ Toxic or inhibitory. 10/ Requires approximately 50% carbohydrate for optimum diet. 11/ Has a retarding effect on growth. 12/ Does not utilize fucose or lyxose. 13/ A sugar, probably sucrose, is utilized. 14/ Response to sugar depends partly on the composition of the rest of the diet. 15/ Utilizes fucose poorly; male probably requires only sugars, but female needs additional nutrients. 16/ Affects female more than male. 17/ Does not require carbohydrates. 18/ Requires approximately 26% carbohydrate for optimum diet; however, effects of specific carbohydrate vary with the carbohydrate level of the diet. 19/ Requires approximately 5% carbohydrate for optimum diet. 20/ 10-20% required for optimum diet. 21/ Requires approximately 25% carbohydrate for optimum diet. 22/ Requires approximately 50-80% carbohydrate for optimum diet. 23/ Utilizes lyxose poorly; does not utilize fucose. 24/ Grows well in absence of carbohydrates. 25/ Gives good growth, but produces no adults.

continued

Part III. Sugars

	Species (Synonym)	Stage	Sugars																	Reference
			Arabinose	Cellobiose	Fructose	Galactose	Glucose	Lactose	Maltose	Mannose	Melezitose	Melibiose	Raffinose	Rhamnose	Ribose	Sorbose	Sucrose	Trehalose	Xylose	
42	*Tenebrio molitor*	L[26/]	Ʉ	u	U	Ʉ	U	u	U	Ʉ	....	...	U	...	Ʉ	Ʉ	U	...	u	17,20,25,40, 42,51
43	*Tineola bisselliella*[17/]	L	...	...	...	...	U	...	...	...	....	...	...	...	...	...	...	...	...	23
44	*Tribolium confusum*	L[24/]	Ʉ	U?	Ʉ	Ʉ	U	Ʉ	U	Ʉ	....	U?	U	U?	...	Ʉ	Ʉ	...	Ʉ	4,9,21,22
45	*Trogoderma granarium*	L	Ʉ	U	u	u	U	u	U	u	U	U	U	Ʉ	...	Ʉ	U	Ʉ	Ʉ	47
46	*Zootermopsis angusticollis*	A[27/]	...	...	U	U	U	U	U	...	....	...	...	...	...	...	U	...	...	10

[17/] Does not require carbohydrates. [24/] Grows well in absence of carbohydrates. [26/] Requires approximately 80-85% carbohydrate for optimum diet. [27/] Defaunated.

Contributors: (a) House, H. L., (b) Mittler, Thomas E., (c) Gordon, H. T.

References

[1] Baker, A. C., et al. 1944. U.S. Dept. Agr. Misc. Publ. 531.
[2] Beck, S. D. 1950. Physiol. Zool. 23:353.
[3] Beck, S. D., J. H. Lilly, and J. F. Stauffer. 1949. Ann. Entomol. Soc. Am. 42:483.
[4] Bernard, R., and A. Lemonde. 1949. Rev. Can. Biol. 8:498.
[5] Bertholf, L. M. 1927. J. Agr. Res. 35:429.
[6] Bottger, G. T. 1942. Ibid. 65:493.
[7] Brown, A. W. A. 1937. Bull. Entomol. Res. 28:333.
[8] Brown, F. M. 1930. Ann. N.Y. Acad. Sci. 32:221.
[9] Chiu, S. F., and C. M. McCay. 1939. Ann. Entomol. Soc. Am. 32:164.
[10] Cook, S. F. 1943. Physiol. Zool. 16:123.
[11] Crowell, H. H. 1941. Ann. Entomol. Soc. Am. 34: 503.
[12] Dadd, R. H. 1960. J. Insect Physiol. 5:301.
[13] Dadd, R. H. 1964. Ibid. 10:161.
[14] Daniels, S. C., Jr., R. H. Dadd, and T. E. Mittler. Unpublished. Univ. of California, Berkeley, 1968.
[15] Doucette, C. F., and P. M. Eide. 1955. Ann. Entomol. Soc. Am. 48:343.
[16] Evans, A. C. 1939. Trans. Roy. Entomol. Soc. London 89:13.
[17] Evans, A. C., and E. R. Goodliffe. 1939. Proc. Roy. Entomol. Soc. London, A, 14:57.
[18] Fraenkel, G. 1936. Nature 137:237.
[19] Fraenkel, G. 1940. J. Exptl. Biol. 17:18.
[20] Fraenkel, G. 1955. J. Cellular Comp. Physiol. 45: 393.
[21] Fraenkel, G. Unpublished. Univ. Illinois, Dept. Entomology, Urbana, 1952.
[22] Fraenkel, G., and M. Blewett. 1943. J. Exptl. Biol. 20:28.
[23] Fraenkel, G., and M. Blewett. 1946. Ibid. 22:156.
[24] Fraenkel, G., and M. Blewett. 1946. Ibid. 22:162.
[25] Fraenkel, G., M. Blewett, and M. Coles. 1950. Physiol. Zool. 23:92.
[26] Galan, R., and G. Fraenkel. 1957. J. Cellular Comp. Physiol. 50:1.
[27] Golberg, L., and B. DeMeillon. 1948. Biochem. J. 43:372.
[28] Gordon, H. T. 1959. Ann. N.Y. Acad. Sci. 77:290.
[29] Guyenot, E. 1917. Bull. Biol. France Belg. 51:1.
[30] Hagen, K. S. 1958. Proc. Intern. Congr. Entomol., 10th, Montreal, 1956, 3:25.
[31] Haslinger, F. 1936. Z. Vergleich. Physiol. 22:614.
[32] Hassett, C. C. 1948. Biol. Bull. 95:114.
[33] Hassett, C. C. Unpublished. Medical Division, Army Chemical Center, Md., 1953.
[34] Hassett, C. C., V. G. Dethier, and J. Gans. 1950. Biol. Bull. 99:446.
[35] Haydak, M. H. 1935. J. Econ. Entomol. 28:657.
[36] Haydak, M. H. 1937. Ann. Entomol. Soc. Am. 30: 258.
[37] Hirano, C., and S. Ishii. 1957. Nogyo Gijutsu Kenkyusho Hokoku, C, 7:89.
[38] House, H. L. Unpublished. Dept. of Agriculture, Entomology Laboratory, Belleville, Ontario, Canada, 1952.
[39] Ito, T. 1960. Nature 187:527.
[40] Lafon, M., and G. Teissier. 1939. Compt. Rend. Soc. Biol. 131:75.
[41] Larson, A. W., and C. K. Fischer. 1925. J. Agr. Res. 29:297.
[42] Leclercq, J. 1948. Arch. Intern. Physiol. 56:130.
[43] Levenbook, L. 1947. Nature 160:465.
[44] Melampy, R. M., and S. E. McGregor. 1939. J. Econ. Entomol. 32:721.
[45] Moore, W. 1946. Ann. Entomol. Soc. Am. 39:513.
[46] Ohsawa, W., and H. Tsukuda. 1956. J. Inst. Polytech. Osaka City Univ., D, 7:163.
[47] Pant, N. C., and N. K. Uberoi. 1958. Experientia 14:1.
[48] Parkin, E. A. 1936. Ann. Appl. Biol. 23:369.
[49] Phillips, E. F. 1927. J. Agr. Res. 35:385.
[50] Pielou, D. P., and R. F. Glasser. 1953. Can. J. Zool. 31:121.
[51] Roeder, K. D., ed. 1953. Insect physiology. J. Wiley, New York.
[52] Sang, J. H. 1956. J. Exptl. Biol. 33:45.
[53] Trager, W. 1948. J. Biol. Chem. 176:1211.
[54] Vanderzant, E. S. 1965. J. Insect Physiol. 11:659.
[55] Vogel, B. 1931. Z. Vergleich. Physiol. 14:273.
[56] Wigglesworth, V. B. 1942. J. Exptl. Biol. 19:56.

continued

Part IV. Carbohydrates Other Than Sugars

An entry followed by a question mark indicates conflicting data, with the preponderance of evidence favoring the information given. *Abbreviations:* U = utilized; U̸ = not utilized; u = poorly utilized; R̸ = not required.

	Species[1/] (Synonym)	Stage	Carbohydrates														Reference
			Cellulose	Dextrin	Dulcitol	Glycerol	Glycogen	Inositol	Inulin	Mannitol	α-Methyl-glucoside	D-Methyl-glucoside	α-Methyl Mannoside	Sorbitol	Starch	Other	
1	*Aedes aegypti*	L	...	...	U?	...	...	...	...	U?	U?	...	...	U?	U	u[2/]	51
2		A	...	u	U̸	U̸	U̸	U̸	U̸	U̸	...	U̸	U̸	u	U̸	...	27
3	*Aglais urtica*	L	...	...	...	...	...	...	...	...	...	...	...	...	U̸	...	17
4	*Anagasta kuehniella (Ephestia kuehniella)*	L[3/]	...	U	...	...	...	...	U̸	U̸	U̸	...	...	U	U	...	22,25
5	*Anastrepha ludens*	A	...	U	...	...	...	...	...	U	...	...	...	...	...	U̸[4/]	1
6	*Anthonomus grandis*	L	U̸	...	...	...	...	...	...	...	...	...	...	...	U	...	49
7	*Apis mellifera*	L	...	U?	...	...	U̸	...	...	...	...	...	...	...	U̸	...	6
8		A	...	R̸	R̸	U	...	R̸?	U̸	U	U	...	...	U	u	U̸[5/]	33,35,36,41,46,47,50
9	*Automeris io*	L	...	...	...	...	...	...	...	...	...	...	...	...	R̸	...	9
10	*Blattella germanica*	N[6/]	...	...	U̸	U	...	U̸	...	U	U	...	...	U	U	u[7/]	28
11	*Bombyx mori*	L	...	U	U̸	...	...	u	...	U	...	U̸	U̸	U	u	...	38
12	*Cadra cautella (Ephestia cautella) & Ephestia elutella*	L[8/]	...	...	...	...	...	...	...	...	...	...	...	...	U̸	...	25
13	*Calliphora vicina*	A	...	u	...	u	u	U̸	U̸?	U	U	...	U̸	U[9/]	u	U̸[10/]	19,20,31,47
14	*Chilo suppressalis*	L	...	...	...	...	U	...	u	...	...	...	...	...	u	...	37
15	*Dacus dorsalis*	A	...	u	...	...	...	...	...	...	...	...	...	...	...	...	30
16	*Drosophila melanogaster*	L	...	...	...	...	...	...	...	...	...	...	...	...	U	...	48
17		A	...	u	U̸	U	u	u	U̸	u	u	...	...	u	u?	...	29,32,43,47
18	*Galleria mellonella*	L	...	U	...	...	...	...	U̸	...	...	...	...	...	...	...	14
19	*Lasioderma serricorne*[11/]	L	...	...	...	...	...	...	...	...	...	...	...	...	U	...	23
20	*Locusta migratoria*	N[12/]	...	U	...	U̸	...	u	...	u	...	...	U̸	u	U	...	13
21	*Lyctus* sp.	L	R̸	...	...	...	...	...	...	...	...	...	...	...	U	R̸[13/]	3,45
22	*Malacosoma neustria*	L	...	...	...	...	...	...	...	...	...	...	...	...	u?	...	17
23	*Melanoplus bivittatus*	A	...	u	...	...	u	...	u	...	...	...	...	...	u	u[14/]	8
24	*Musca domestica*	A	...	U	U̸	u	u	u	U̸	U̸	...	u	U̸	U	U	...	27
25	*Myzus persicae*	L & A	...	...	...	...	...	...	...	...	...	...	...	U	...	...	15
26	*Oryzaephilus surinamensis*	L	U̸	U	...	...	...	...	U̸	U	U̸	...	...	U	U	...	22,23
27	*Ostrinia nubilalis (Pyrausta nubilalis)*	L[15/]	U̸	...	...	...	...	...	...	...	...	...	...	...	U̸	...	3,4,7
28	*Phalera bucephala*	L[16/]	U̸	...	...	...	...	...	...	...	...	...	...	...	U̸	...	16,17
29	*Phormia regina*	A	...	...	u	u	...	u	...	...	u	...	...	U	...	u[4/]	34
30	*Pieris brassicae*	L	...	...	...	...	...	...	...	...	...	...	...	...	U̸	...	17
31	*Plodia interpunctella*	L[8/]	...	...	...	...	...	...	...	...	...	...	...	...	U̸	...	25
32	*Prodenia eridania*	L	...	...	...	...	...	...	...	...	...	...	...	...	U̸	...	12
33	*Ptinus tectus*	L[17/]	...	...	...	...	...	...	...	...	...	...	...	...	U	...	23
34	*Sarcophaga bullata*	A	...	U	U̸	u	u	u	U̸	U	...	u	U̸	U	u	...	27
35	*Schistocerca gregaria*	N[12/]	...	u	...	U̸	...	U	...	U	...	...	u	U[18/]	U	...	13
36	*Stegobium paniceum*	L[8/]	U̸	...	...	...	...	...	U̸	U	U̸?	...	...	U̸	U	...	22,23

[1/] *Attagenus* sp. does not require carbohydrates [42]. [2/] α-Methyl galactoside. [3/] Requires approximately 80% carbohydrate for optimum diet. [4/] Erythritol. [5/] Hemicellulose; however, other polysaccharides are utilized. Erythritol is not required. [6/] Nonaseptic roach; requires approximately 30% carbohydrate for optimum diet. [7/] Adonitol and arabitol; adonitol partly replaces glucose. [8/] Requires approximately 50% carbohydrate for optimum diet. [9/] Utilized better than other carbohydrates. [10/] Erythritol, β-methyl fructopyranoside, β-methyl galactoside, and β-methyl glucoside; however, α-methyl galactoside is utilized. [11/] Does not require carbohydrates. [12/] Requires approximately 26% carbohydrate for optimum diet; however, effects of specific carbohydrate vary with the carbohydrate level of the diet. [13/] Hemicellulose. [14/] Other polysaccharides. [15/] Requires approximately 25% carbohydrate for optimum diet. [16/] Requires approximately 50-80% carbohydrate for optimum diet. [17/] Grows well in absence of carbohydrates. [18/] Gives good growth, but produces no adults.

continued

Part IV. Carbohydrates Other Than Sugars

	Species (Synonym)	Stage	Carbohydrates														Reference
			Cellulose	Dextrin	Dulcitol	Glycerol	Glycogen	Inositol	Inulin	Mannitol	α-Methyl-glucoside	D-Methyl-glucoside	α-Methyl Mannoside	Sorbitol	Starch	Other	
37	*Tenebrio molitor*	L[19]	...	U	Ʉ	...	U	...	Ʉ	U	Ʉ	...	...	U	U	u[20]	18,21,26,39,40,47
38	*Tineola bisselliella*[11]	L	...	...	...	...	...	Ʉ	...	...	...	...	...	...	U[21]	...	24
39	*Tribolium confusum*	L[17]	...	U?	...	...	...	...	U?	U	Ʉ	...	...	U	U	...	5,10,22,23
40	*Trogoderma granarium*	L	...	...	Ʉ	...	...	...	...	Ʉ	...	...	...	Ʉ	u	...	44
41	*Zootermopsis angusticollis*	A[22]	Ʉ	...	...	...	...	...	...	...	...	...	...	...	U	Ꞧ[14]	2,11

11/ Does not require carbohydrates. 14/ Other polysaccharides. 17/ Grows well in absence of carbohydrates. 19/ Requires approximately 80-85% carbohydrate for optimum diet. 20/ Hemicellulose; however, β-methyl glucoside is not utilized. 21/ Has a retarding effect on growth. 22/ Defaunated.

Contributors: (a) House, H. L., (b) Mittler, Thomas E.

References

[1] Baker, A. C., et al. 1944. U.S. Dept. Agr. Misc. Publ. 531.
[2] Ball, G. H., and E. W. Clark. Unpublished. Univ. California, Dept. Zoology, Los Angeles, 1952.
[3] Beck, S. D. 1950. Physiol. Zool. 23:353.
[4] Beck, S. D., J. H. Lilly, and J. F. Stauffer. 1949. Ann. Entomol. Soc. Am. 42:483.
[5] Bernard, R., and A. Lemonde. 1949. Rev. Can. Biol. 8:498.
[6] Bertholf, L. M. 1927. J. Agr. Res. 35:429.
[7] Bottger, G. T. 1942. Ibid. 65:493.
[8] Brown, A. W. A. 1937. Bull. Entomol. Res. 28:333.
[9] Brown, F. M. 1930. Ann. N.Y. Acad. Sci. 32:221.
[10] Chiu, S. F., and C. M. McCay. 1939. Ann. Entomol. Soc. Am. 32:164.
[11] Cook, S. F. 1943. Physiol. Zool. 16:123.
[12] Crowell, H. H. 1941. Ann. Entomol. Soc. Am. 34: 503.
[13] Dadd, R. H. 1960. J. Insect Physiol. 5:301.
[14] Dadd, R. H. 1964. Ibid. 10:161.
[15] Daniels, S. C., Jr., R. H. Dadd, and T. E. Mittler. Unpublished. Univ. of California, Berkeley, 1968.
[16] Evans, A. C. 1939. Proc. Roy. Entomol. Soc. London, A, 14:25.
[17] Evans, A. C. 1939. Trans. Roy. Entomol. Soc. London 89:13.
[18] Evans, A. C., and E. R. Goodliffe. 1939. Proc. Roy. Entomol. Soc. London, A, 14:57.
[19] Fraenkel, G. 1936. Nature 137:237.
[20] Fraenkel, G. 1940. J. Exptl. Biol. 17:18.
[21] Fraenkel, G. 1955. J. Cellular Comp. Physiol. 45: 393.
[22] Fraenkel, G. Unpublished. Univ. Illinois, Dept. Entomology, Urbana, 1952.
[23] Fraenkel, G., and M. Blewett. 1943. J. Exptl. Biol. 20:28.
[24] Fraenkel, G., and M. Blewett. 1946. Ibid. 22:156.
[25] Fraenkel, G., and M. Blewett. 1946. Ibid. 22:162.
[26] Fraenkel, G., M. Blewett, and M. Coles. 1950. Physiol. Zool. 23:92.
[27] Galan, R., and G. Fraenkel. 1957. J. Cellular Comp. Physiol. 50:1.
[28] Gordon, H. T. 1959. Ann. N.Y. Acad. Sci. 77:290.
[29] Guyenot, E. 1917. Bull. Biol. France Belg. 51:1.
[30] Hagen, K. S. 1958. Proc. Intern. Congr. Entomol., 10th, Montreal, 1956, 3:25.
[31] Haslinger, F. 1936. Z. Vergleich. Physiol. 22:614.
[32] Hassett, C. C. 1948. Biol. Bull. 95:114.
[33] Hassett, C. C. Unpublished. Medical Division, Army Chemical Center, Md., 1953.
[34] Hassett, C. C., V. G. Dethier, and J. Gans. 1950. Biol. Bull. 99:446.
[35] Haydak, M. H. 1935. J. Econ. Entomol. 28:657.
[36] Haydak, M. H. 1937. Ann. Entomol. Soc. Am. 30: 258.
[37] Hirano, C., and S. Ishii. 1957. Nogyo Gijutsu Kenkyusho Hokoku, C, 7:89.
[38] Ito, T. 1960. Nature 187:527.
[39] Lafon, M., and G. Teissier. 1939. Compt. Rend. Soc. Biol. 131:75.
[40] Leclercq, J. 1948. Arch. Intern. Physiol. 56:130.
[41] Melampy, R. M., and S. E. McGregor. 1939. J. Econ. Entomol. 32:721.
[42] Moore, W. 1946. Ann. Entomol. Soc. Am. 39:513.
[43] Ohsawa, W., and H. Tsukuda. 1956. J. Inst. Polytech. Osaka City Univ., D, 7:163.
[44] Pant, N. C., and N. K. Uberoi. 1958. Experientia 14:1.
[45] Parkin, E. A. 1936. Ann. Appl. Biol. 23:369.
[46] Phillips, E. F. 1927. J. Agr. Res. 35:385.
[47] Roeder, K. D., ed. 1953. Insect Physiology. J. Wiley, New York.
[48] Sang, J. H. 1956. J. Exptl. Biol. 33:45.
[49] Vanderzant, E. S. 1965. J. Insect Physiol. 11:659.
[50] Vogel, B. 1931. Z. Vergleich. Physiol. 14:273.
[51] Wigglesworth, V. B. 1942. J. Exptl. Biol. 19:56.

continued

20. NUTRIENT REQUIREMENTS AND UTILIZATION: INSECTS

Part V. Proteins

All stages of insects are larval, unless otherwise specified. *Abbreviations:* S = good support of growth and development; $ = little or no support; s = poor support.

	Species (Synonym)	Total Protein[1] %	Proteins: Brain Protein	Casein	Cottonseed Protein	Fibrin	Gelatin	Glycinin	Lactalbumin	Liver Protein	Peanut Protein	Soybean Protein	Wheat Gluten	Zein	Other	Reference
1	*Aedes aegypti*	......	...	S	...	...	...	...	...	...	...	...	...	...	...	34
2	*Anagasta kuehniella (Ephestia kuehniella)*	45	...	S	...	...	...	...	...	...	...	...	...	...	...	11,12,15,18
3	*Argyrotaenia velutinana*	3[2]	...	s	...	...	...	...	...	...	...	S	...	...	S[3]	31
4	*Attagenus* sp.	6-12	...	S	...	...	...	...	...	...	...	...	...	...	...	28
5	*Blattella germanica*[4]	15-30	...	S	...	S	s	...	s	...	...	...	s	$	s[5]	26,27,29
6	*Dermestes maculatus*	......	S[6]	S	s[7]	S	...	s	S	S	S	S[7]	...	$	...	10,21,22,30
7	*Drosophila melanogaster*	2-3	...	S	...	...	$	...	...	...	...	...	...	...	...	2,23,24,32
8	*Ephestia elutella*	20	...	S	...	...	...	...	...	...	...	...	...	...	...	8,15
9	*Lasioderma serricorne*	45	...	S	...	...	...	...	S	...	...	...	...	...	...	9,11
10	*Oryzaephilus surinamensis*	45	...	S	...	...	...	...	...	...	...	...	...	...	...	9,11
11	*Ostrinia nubilalis (Pyrausta nubilalis)*	20-30	...	S	...	$	$	...	$	...	...	...	$	$	...	1,3
12	*Periplaneta americana*	25	...	S	...	...	...	...	...	...	...	...	s	...	...	33
13	*Ptinus tectus*	45	...	S	...	...	...	...	...	...	...	...	...	...	...	9,11
14	*Stegobium paniceum*	45	...	S	...	...	...	...	...	...	...	...	...	...	...	9,11
15	*Tenebrio molitor*	15-45	S[6]	S	s	s	$	s	S	S	S	s	S	$	s[8]	7,16,17,19,20,25,30
16	*Tineola bisselliella*	20-80	...	S	...	...	...	...	...	...	...	...	...	...	...	6,8,14
17	*Tribolium confusum*	15-45	S[6]	S	S	S	$	S	S	S	S	S	S	s	s[9]	4,5,10-13,30

1/ Amount present in a diet that maintains growth and development. 2/ Diet was a dilute aqueous suspension or gel. 3/ Egg albumin. 4/ Nymph. 5/ Hemoglobin. 6/ Wilson B protein. 7/ Only when heated. 8/ Edestin; however, gliadin gives little or no support of growth and development. 9/ Edestin and gliadin.

Contributors: (a) Beck, Stanley D., (b) Fraenkel, Gottfried S., (c) Gordon, H. T.

References

[1] Beck, S. D., J. H. Lilly, and J. F. Stauffer. 1949. Ann. Entomol. Soc. Am. 42:483.
[2] Begg, M., and F. W. Robertson. 1950. J. Exptl. Biol. 26:380.
[3] Bottger, G. T. 1942. J. Agr. Res. 65:493.
[4] Chapman, R. N. 1924. J. Gen. Physiol. 6:565.
[5] Chiu, S. F., and C. M. McCay. 1939. Ann. Entomol. Soc. Am. 32:164.
[6] Crowell, M. F., and C. M. McCay. 1937. Physiol. Zool. 10:368.
[7] Fraenkel, G. 1948. Biochem. J. 42:1.
[8] Fraenkel, G. Unpublished. Univ. Illinois, Dept. Entomology, Urbana, 1953.
[9] Fraenkel, G., and M. Blewett. 1943. Biochem. J. 37: 686.
[10] Fraenkel, G., and M. Blewett. 1943. Ibid. 37:692.
[11] Fraenkel, G., and M. Blewett. 1943. J. Exptl. Biol. 20:28.
[12] Fraenkel, G., and M. Blewett. 1943. Nature 151:703.
[13] Fraenkel, G., and M. Blewett. 1943. Trans. Entomol. Soc. London 93:457.
[14] Fraenkel, G., and M. Blewett. 1946. J. Exptl. Biol. 22:156.
[15] Fraenkel, G., and M. Blewett. 1946. Ibid. 22:162.
[16] Fraenkel, G., and M. Blewett. 1946. Nature 157:697.
[17] Fraenkel, G., and M. Blewett. 1947. Biochem. J. 41:469.
[18] Fraenkel, G., and M. Blewett. 1947. Ibid. 41:475.
[19] Fraenkel, G., M. Blewett, and M. Coles. 1948. Nature 161:981.
[20] Fraenkel, G., M. Blewett, and M. Coles. 1950. Physiol. Zool. 23:92.
[21] Fraenkel, G., J. A. Reid, and M. Blewett. 1941. Biochem. J. 25:712.
[22] Gay, F. J. 1938. J. Exptl. Zool. 79:93.
[23] Hinton, T., D. T. Noyes, and J. Ellis. 1951. Physiol. Zool. 24:335.
[24] Lafon, M. 1939. Ann. Physiol. Physicochim. Biol. 15:215.
[25] Lafon, M., and G. Teissier. 1939. Compt. Rend. Soc. Biol. 131:75.
[26] McCay, C. M. 1933. J. Biol. Chem. 100:67.
[27] Melampy, R. M., and L. A. Maynard. 1937. Physiol. Zool. 10:36.
[28] Moore, W. 1946. Ann. Entomol. Soc. Am. 39:513.
[29] Noland, J. L., and C. A. Baumann. 1951. Ibid. 44: 184.
[30] Printy, G. E., and G. Fraenkel. Unpublished. Univ. Illinois, Dept. Entomology, Urbana, 1952.
[31] Rock, G. C., and K. W. King. 1967. J. Insect Physiol. 13:175.
[32] Shultz, J., P. St. Lawrence, and D. Newmeyer. 1946. Anat. Record 96:540.
[33] Sieburth, J. F., M. G. Bonsall, and B. A. McLaren. 1951. Ann. Entomol. Soc. Am. 44:463.
[34] Trager, W. 1948. J. Biol. Chem. 176:1211.

continued

Part VI. Amino Acids

An entry followed by a question mark indicates conflicting data, with the preponderance of evidence favoring the information given. *Abbreviations:* R = required; ℟ = not required.

	Species (Synonym)	Stage	Amino Acids																				Reference
			Alanine	Arginine	Aspartic Acid	Cysteine	Cystine	Glutamic Acid	Glycine	Histidine	Hydroxyproline	Isoleucine	Leucine	Lysine	Methionine	Phenylalanine	Proline	Serine	Threonine	Tryptophan	Tyrosine	Valine	
1	*Aedes aegypti*	L	℟	R	℟	R	R	℟	℟	R	R	R	R	R	R	R	R	R	R	R	℟	R	36
2		A[1]	R	R	...	R	R	...	...	R	...	R	R	R	R	R	...	...	R	R	...	R	8,36
3	*Agrotis orthogonia*	L[2,3]	℟	℟	℟	R	R	℟	℟	R	...	R	R	R	R?	R	℟	℟	...	...	℟	R	22
4	*Anthonomus grandis*	L	℟	R	℟	℟	℟	℟	℟	R	...	R	R	R	R	R	℟	℟	R	R	℟	R	40
5		A	℟	R	℟	℟	℟	℟	℟	R	...	R	R	R	R	R	℟	℟	R	R	℟	R	39
6	*Apis mellifera*	L	℟	R	℟	℟	℟	℟	℟	R	℟	R	R	R	...	R	...	℟	R	R	℟	R	7
7	*Argyrotaenia velutinana*	......	℟	R	℟	℟	...	℟	℟	R	...	R	R	R	R	R	℟	℟	R	R	℟	R	31
8	*Attagenus* sp.	L[4]	℟	R	℟	...	℟	℟	℟	R	℟	R	R	R	R	R	℟	℟	R	R	℟	R	28
9	*Blattella germanica*	N[5]	R?	R	℟	...	R?	℟	℟	R	℟	R	R	R	R?	℟	R?	R?	R?	R?	℟	R	12,13,17,29,32
10	*Bombyx mori*	L[3]	℟	R	R	℟	℟	℟	℟	R	℟	R	R	R	R	R	R	℟	R	R	℟	R	1,10
11	*Calliphora vicina*	L[6]	℟	R	℟	℟	℟	℟	R?	R	℟	R	R	R	R	R	...	℟	R	R	℟	R	35
12	*Chilo suppressalis*	L[3]	℟	R	℟	℟	℟	℟	℟	R	℟	R	R	R	R	R	℟	℟	R	R	℟	R	19,20
13	*Dermestes maculatus*	L	...	...	...	...	R	...	...	...	...	...	...	...	...	...	...	...	...	...	...	...	11
14	*Drosophila melanogaster*	L[7]	℟	R	℟	...	℟	℟	R	R	℟	R	R	R	R	R	℟	℟	R	R	℟	R	14,16,23,33
15		A	℟	R	℟	℟	℟	℟	℟	R	...	R	R	R	R	R	℟	℟	R	R	℟	R	34
16	*Hylemya antiqua*	L	℟	R	℟	℟	℟	℟	℟	R	℟	R	R	R	R	R	℟	℟	R	R	℟	R	9
17	*Myzus persicae*	L&A[8]	℟	℟	℟	℟	...	℟	...	R	...	R	...	℟	R	℟	℟	℟	℟	℟	℟	℟	2,27
18	*Oryzaephilus surinamensis*	L[9]	R	R	...	R	R	...	R	R	...	R	R	R	R	...	R	...	...	R	...	R	3-6,37
19	*Pectinophora gossypiella*	L	℟	R	℟	℟	℟	℟	℟	R	...	R	R	R	R	R	℟	℟	R	R	℟	R	38
20	*Phaenicia sericata*	L	...	...	...	...	R	...	...	...	...	...	...	...	...	...	...	...	...	...	...	...	26
21	*Phormia regina*	L[10]	℟	R	℟	℟	℟	℟	℟	R	℟	R	R	R	℟	R	R	...	R	R	℟	R	15,25
22		L[11]	℟	R	℟	R	R	...	℟	R	...	R	R	R	R	R	℟	℟	R	...	℟?	R	21
23	*Pseudosarcophaga* sp. *(P. affinis)*	L	℟	R	℟	...	℟	℟	R	R	℟	R	R	R	R	R	℟	℟	R	R	℟	R	18
24	*Tenebrio molitor*	L	...	...	...	...	...	...	...	...	...	...	...	R	...	...	...	...	...	R	...	...	24
25	*Tribolium castaneum*	L	...	R	...	...	...	...	...	R	...	R	R	...	...	...	...	...	...	...	...	...	37
26	*T. confusum*	L	...	R	...	...	...	...	...	R	...	R	R	R	R	R	...	...	R	R	...	R	37
27	*Trogoderma granarium*	L[12]	℟	R	℟	℟	℟	℟	℟	R	℟	R	R	R	R	R	℟	℟	R	R	℟	R	30

1/ Amino acids listed are required for oviposition; omission of cysteine, cystine, histidine, and methionine reduced ovarian growth. 2/ Experiment utilized glucose-U-^{14}C, an indirect method based on radioactivity of the amino acid formed. 3/ Subject can convert phenylalanine to tyrosine. 4/ Does not require norleucine. 5/ May require methionine in nonsterile cultures; only males may require proline and serine. 6/ Glycine is stimulatory. 7/ Can substitute citrulline partially for arginine; requires glycine for maximum growth; D-serine is extremely toxic, and L-serine is slightly toxic. 8/ Both require methionine as a feeding stimulant; also require asparagine and glutamine. 9/ May need alanine, cystine, and proline to correct an imbalance; arginine, cysteine, cystine, and proline are slightly inhibitory at levels tested, and the racemic form of alanine is slightly toxic or inhibitory. 10/ Shows a dietary requirement either for methionine or cystine, and either for glutamic acid or aspartic acid, when groups of 2 or more amino acids are omitted. 11/ Experiment utilized glutamic acid-U-^{14}C, an indirect method based on radioactivity of the amino acid formed. 12/ Growth was better when all 20 amino acids were present, rather than just the 10 required.

Contributors: (a) House, H. L., (b) Gordon, H. T., (c) Mittler, Thomas E.

References

[1] Arai, N., and T. Ito. 1964. Nippon Sanshigaku Zasshi 33:107.

[2] Dadd, R. H., and D. L. Krieger. 1968. J. Insect Physiol. 14:741.

[3] Davis, G. R. F. 1956. Can. J. Zool. 34:82.

[4] Davis, G. R. F. 1959. Ann. Entomol. Soc. Am. 52:164.

[5] Davis, G. R. F. 1961. J. Insect Physiol. 6:122.

[6] Davis, G. R. F. 1961. J. Nutr. 75:275.

continued

Part VI. Amino Acids

[7] DeGroot, A. P. 1952. Experientia 8:192.
[8] Dimond, J. B., et al. 1956. Can. Entomologist 88:57.
[9] Friend, W. G., R. H. Backs, and L. M. Case. 1957. Can. J. Zool. 35:535.
[10] Fukuda, T. 1956. Nature 177:429.
[11] Gay, F. J. 1938. J. Exptl. Zool. 79:93.
[12] Henry, S. M. 1962. Trans. N.Y. Acad. Sci. 24:676.
[13] Hilchey, J. D. 1953. Contrib. Boyce Thompson Inst. 17:203.
[14] Hinton, T., D. T. Noyes, and J. Ellis. 1951. Physiol. Zool. 24:335.
[15] Hodgson, E., V. H. Cheldelin, and R. W. Newburgh. 1956. Can. J. Zool. 34:527.
[16] Hoog, E. G. van 't. 1935. Z. Vitaminforsch. 4:300.
[17] House, H. L. 1949. Can. Entomologist 81:133.
[18] House, H. L. Unpublished. Canada Dept. of Agriculture, Entomology Laboratory, Belleville, Ontario, 1952.
[19] Ishii, S., and C. Hirano. 1955. Nogyo Gijutsu Kenkyusho Hokoku, C, 5:35.
[20] Ishii, S., and C. Hirano. 1958. Proc. Intern. Congr. Entomol., 10th, Montreal, 1956. 2:295.
[21] Kasting, R., and A. J. McGinnis. 1960. Can. J. Biochem. Physiol. 38:1229.
[22] Kasting, R., and A. J. McGinnis. 1962. J. Insect Physiol. 8:97.
[23] Lafon, M. 1939. Ann. Physiol. Physicochim. Biol. 15:215.
[24] Leclercq, J. 1948. Experientia 4:436.
[25] McGinnis, A. J., R. W. Newburgh, and V. H. Cheldelin. 1956. J. Nutr. 58:309.
[26] Michelbacher, A. E., W. M. Hoskins, and W. B. Herms. 1932. J. Exptl. Zool. 64:109.
[27] Mittler, T. E. 1967. Nature 214:386.
[28] Moore, W. 1946. Ann. Entomol. Soc. Am. 39:513.
[29] Noland, J. L., and C. A. Baumann. 1951. Ibid. 44:184.
[30] Pant, N. C., J. K. Nayar, and P. Gupta. 1958. Experientia 14:176.
[31] Rock, G. C., and K. W. King. 1967. J. Insect Physiol. 13:59.
[32] Roeder, K. D., ed. 1953. Insect physiology. J. Wiley, New York.
[34] Rudkin, G. T., and J. Shultz. 1947. Anat. Record 99:613.
[34] Sang, J. H., and R. C. King. 1961. J. Exptl. Biol. 38:793.
[35] Sedee, D. J. W. 1954. Acta Physiol. Pharmacol. Neerl. 3:262.
[36] Singh, K. R. P., and A. W. A. Brown. 1957. J. Insect Physiol. 1:199.
[37] Taylor, M. W., and J. C. Medici. 1966. J. Nutr. 88:176.
[38] Vanderzant, E. S. 1958. J. Econ. Entomol. 51:309.
[39] Vanderzant, E. S. 1963. J. Insect Physiol. 9:683.
[40] Vanderzant, E. S. 1965. Ibid. 11:659.

Part VII. Fatty Acids and Sterols

All insects tested were unable to synthesize sterols and therefore required a dietary sterol for growth [11]. The sterols have both a metabolic role as precursors of ecdysones (steroid moulting hormones), and a structural role in membranous subcellular components [53]. Earlier studies have reported utilization of sterols (e.g., zymosterol, 7-dehydrocholesterol) now known to be difficult to obtain in a pure state. Recent investigations show that a trace of utilizable sterol (e.g., cholesterol) present with a larger amount of nonutilizable sterol may make the mixture capable of supporting growth [9,11]. Therefore where serious doubt exists as to the significance of the experimental findings, a question mark has been inserted after the entry. The following steroid derivatives tested in different species have consistently failed to support growth: steroid hydrocarbons; steroids of the androstane, pregnane, estrane, and cholane series; compounds of the calciferol group; certain derivatives, the molecules of which contain an oxygen function in addition to the 3β-hydroxyl group; certain derivatives in which the 3β-hydroxyl group is replaced by other functional groups (e.g., Cl, Br, NH_2, sulfhydryl, oxymethyl). 3α-Hydroxyl and 5β (copro-) steroids are generally reported inactive; however, consult references 44 and 45 for conflicting evidence. A fatty acid has been listed as "required" if its absence results in suboptimal performance in growth, development, and reproduction, and if no other substance at the same level of definition can fulfill its nutritional function. Essential fatty acids are those without which growth eventually ceases entirely. *Abbreviations:* R = required; R̸ = Not required; E = essential; S = good support of growth and maturation; s = moderate support; S̸ = ineffective.

continued

Part VII. Fatty Acids and Sterols

	Species (Synonym)	Stage	Fatty Acids							Sterols 1/								Reference
			Requirement	Arachidonic Acid	Linoleic Acid	Linolenic Acid	Oleic Acid	Stearic Acid	Other	Cholestanol	Cholesterol	7-Dehydrocholesterol	Ergosterol	Sitosterol	Stigmasterol	Zymosterol	Other	
1	*Acheta domesticus*	N	R?2/	....	....	S?	....	....	....	......	S	...	S	S	s	...	....	7,57,58,61,67
2	*Aedes aegypti*	L3/	Ꞧ4/	....	Ꞩ	Ꞩ	Ꞩ5/	Ꞩ	Ꞩ6/	s	S	Ꞩ	s	S	S	s	....	1,34,35,71,72
3	*Anagasta kuehniella* *(Ephestia kuehniella)*	L	E	s7/	S	S	Ꞩ	....	Ꞩ8/	s	S	S	s	S	..	Ꞩ	....	22-24,26,27, 29,31
4	*Anthonomus grandis*	L&A	R	....	S	S	s7/	....	....	......	S9/	...	...	S	S	...	....	20,73,74
5	*Argyrotaenia velutinana*	.....	R	Ꞩ10/	S	S	s7/	Ꞩ	Ꞩ11/	......	....	...	...	..	..	...	....	68
6	*Attagenus* sp.	L	Ꞧ	....	....	...	....	....	....	Ꞩ	S	s?	Ꞩ	..	..	...	....	59,60,63
7	*Blattella germanica*	N&A	R	Ꞩ10/	S	S	s? 7/	....	....	Ꞩ	S	Ꞩ?	s?	S	S	...	....	10,11,36,65
8	*Bombyx mori*	L	R	....	S12/	S12/	s13/	s13/	s11,13/	Ꞩ	s	Ꞩ	Ꞩ	S	S	...	....	47-51
9	*Cadra cautella (Ephestia cautella)*	L	E	....	S	...	....	....	....	......	S	...	...	..	..	...	....	26,27
10	*Callosobruchus chinensis*	L	......	....	....	...	....	....	....	S	S	...	...	S	S	...	s?14/	43-45
11	*Chilo suppressalis*	L	Ꞧ	....	Ꞩ	Ꞩ5/	Ꞩ	....	....	......	S	...	...	..	..	...	....	38,46
12	*Cochliomyia hominivorax*	.....	Ꞧ	....	....	...	....	....	....	Ꞩ	S	...	Ꞩ	Ꞩ	..	...	....	33
13	*Dermestes maculatus*	L	......	....	....	...	....	....	....	Ꞩ	S	...	Ꞩ	Ꞩ	Ꞩ	...	Ꞩ15/	9,12,22,31,32
14	*Drosophila melanogaster*	L	Ꞧ	....	....	...	....	....	....	s	S	...	S	s	s	...	....	4,40,69
15	*D. pachea*	.....	......	....	....	...	....	....	....	......	Ꞩ?16/	S	Ꞩ	Ꞩ	Ꞩ	...	S17/	37
16	*Ephestia elutella*	L	E	....	S	S	Ꞩ	....	....	......	S	...	...	..	..	...	....	26,27
17	*Galleria mellonella*	L	R	Ꞩ	S	S	Ꞩ	Ꞩ	Ꞩ18/	......	S	...	...	..	..	...	....	16,17
18	*Lasioderma serricorne*	L3/	Ꞧ	....	....	...	....	....	....	s	S	S	S	S	..	s?	....	22
19	*Locusta migratoria*	N	E	s? 7/	S	S	Ꞩ	Ꞩ	Ꞩ18/	S	S	Ꞩ	Ꞩ	S	Ꞩ	...	Ꞩ19/	14,15
20	*Melanoplus bivittatus*	N	R	....	S20/	...	....	....	....	......	....	...	...	..	..	...	....	64
21	*Musca domestica*	L	Ꞧ	....	....	...	Ꞩ	Ꞩ21/	Ꞩ18,21/	......	S	...	...	..	..	...	....	5

1/ Simple aliphatic esters of utilizable sterols are also utilized, but some nonhydrolyzable esters (e.g., trimethyl acetate, *p*-tosylate) are not [11]. 2/ Most growth and sex-maturation effects previously attributed to lipids are now ascribed to vitamin E; linoleic and linolenic acids and esters may have a behavioral, pherohormone-like effect on growth [57,61]. 3/ Reduced growth and limited metamorphosis can occur in the absence of lipids. 4/ Recent studies indicate no requirement for lipids other than a sterol [1]. It is possible that early growth-promoting effects ascribed to lecithin and cephalin were largely caused by either sterol impurities, or by changes in the feeding rate due to physical alterations in the media brought about by these phospholipids. 5/ Toxic. 6/ Lauric and myristic acids, which are toxic; also palmitic acid, triolein, tripalmitin, and tristearin. 7/ Has some beneficial effect on growth, usually without effecting wing symptoms. However, it is possible that the test fatty acids contained traces of linoleic acid; the requirement for linoleic and linolenic acids is often accompanied by specific wing symptoms. 8/ Docosahexanoic acid. 9/ Essential for egg hatchability. 10/ Methyl arachidonate. 11/ Palmitic acid. 12/ Requirement is often indicated by wing malformation and failure of pupal eclosion. 13/ Fatty acid requirement is usually satisfied by linoleic and linolenic acids; fatty acids giving good or moderate support of growth and maturation caused comparatively small retardation in growth rate, and may be examples of the optimal balance type of requirement. 14/ Epicholestanol. 15/ Various cholestenols, ergostenols, and stigmastenols. 16/ Only case reported thus far which cannot utilize cholesterol (Δ^5-sterol), but requires a Δ^7-sterol instead [37]; compounds in the cactus habitat of this species may be related to this requirement. Cholesterol has been found less effective than some plant sterols for *Bombyx* and *Ostrinia*. 17/ Δ^7-Cholestenol and Δ^7-stigmastenol; however, 7-dehydrostigmasterol gives moderate support, and Δ^7-ergostenol and 4α-methyl-Δ^7-cholestenol are ineffective. 18/ Myristic and palmitic acids. 19/ Stigmasteryl acetate. 20/ Affects molting and wing formation. 21/ May be slightly toxic.

continued

20. NUTRIENT REQUIREMENTS AND UTILIZATION: INSECTS

Part VII. Fatty Acids and Sterols

	Species (Synonym)	Stage	Fatty Acids: Requirement	Arachidonic Acid	Linoleic Acid	Linolenic Acid	Oleic Acid	Stearic Acid	Other	Sterols1/: Cholestanol	Cholesterol	7-Dehydrocholesterol	Ergosterol	Sitosterol	Stigmasterol	Zymosterol	Other	Reference
22	*M. domestica vicina*	L	℞	....	$	$	....	....	....	$22/	S	s	...	S	s	...	$23/	55,70
23	*Myzus persicae*	L&A	℞24/	....	...	...	....	....	....	......	....	...	...	...	..	...	....	18
24	*Oryzaephilus surinamensis*	L3/	R25/	....	s	...	S13/	....	S11,13/	s	S	S	s	S	..	s?	....	19,22,23
25	*Ostrinia nubilalis (Pyrausta nubilalis)*	L	R	....	S	...	....	....	....	......	s	...	S	S	s	...	....	2,3,76
26	*Pectinophora gossypiella*	L	E	....	S	S	$	....	....	......	S	...	S	S	S	...	....	75,76
27	*Phaenicia sericata*	L	℞	....	...	...	....	....	....	......	S	...	s	S	..	...	....	39,62
28	*Phormia regina*	L	℞	....	...	...	....	....	....	......	S	...	s	S	..	$	....	6
29	*Plodia interpunctella*	L	℞	....	...	...	....	....	....	......	S	...	...	...	..	...	....	26,27
30	*Pseudosarcophaga* sp. *(P. affinis)*	L	R26/	$	$	$	S13/	s13/	s13,27/	S	S	S	...	S	S	...	....	41,42
31	*Ptinus tectus*	L	℞	....	...	...	....	....	....	s	S	S	S	s	..	s?	....	22
32	*Schistocerca gregaria*	N	R	....	S28/	...	$	$	$18/	S	S	$	$	S	..	...	$29/	13-15
33	*Stegobium paniceum*	L	℞	....	...	...	....	....	....	s	S	S	S	S	..	$	....	22,23
34	*Tenebrio molitor*	L	℞	....	...	...	....	....	....	......	S	...	S	S	S	...	S30/	28,30,52,54,56
35	*Tineola bisselliella*	L	℞	....	...	...	....	....	....	......	S	...	...	..	..	...	....	25
36	*Tribolium confusum*	L3/	℞	....	...	...	....	....	....	s	S	S	S	S	..	$	....	21-23,66
37	*Trichoplusia ni*	L	R	$	S	S31/	$	....	....	......	....	...	...	..	..	...	....	8

1/ Simple aliphatic esters of utilizable sterols are also utilized, but some nonhydrolyzable esters (e.g., trimethyl acetate, *p*-tosylate) are not **[11]**. 3/ Reduced growth and limited metamorphosis can occur in the absence of lipids. 11/ Palmitic acid. 13/ Fatty acid requirement is usually satisfied by linoleic and linolenic acids; fatty acids giving good or moderate support of growth and maturation caused comparatively small retardation in growth rate, and may be examples of the optimal balance type of requirement. 18/ Myristic and palmitic acids. 22/ Cholestanol acetate. 23/ Epicholestanol acetate. 24/ Sterols and other lipids also not required. 25/ References cite conflicting data regarding fatty acid requirement. 26/ Mixture of fatty acids required. 27/ Palmitic acid; however, palmitoleic acid is ineffective. 28/ Crude form. 29/ Vitamin D_2, cholestenone, 7-hydroxycholesteryl dibenzoate, and stigmasteryl acetate; however, cholesteryl acetate gives good support of growth and maturation. 30/ Stigmastanol. 31/ For wing development.

Contributors: (a) Dadd, R. H., (b) Clayton, Raymond B., (c) House, H. L.

References

[1] Akov, S. 1962. J. Insect Physiol. 8:319.

[2] Beck, S. D. 1950. Physiol. Zool. 23:353.

[3] Beck, S. D., J. H. Lilly, and J. F. Stauffer. 1949. Ann. Entomol. Soc. Am. 42:483.

[4] Begg, M., and F. W. Robertson. 1950. J. Exptl. Biol. 26:380.

[5] Brookes, V. J., and G. Fraenkel. 1958. Physiol. Zool. 31:208.

[6] Brust, M., and G. Fraenkel. 1955. Ibid. 28:186.

[7] Chauvin, R. 1949. Compt. Rend. 229:902.

[8] Chippendale, G. M., S. D. Beck, and F. M. Strong. 1964. Nature 204:710.

[9] Clark, A. J., and K. Bloch. 1959. J. Biol. Chem. 234:2583.

[10] Clark, A. J., and K. Bloch. 1959. Ibid. 234:2589.

[11] Clayton, R. B. 1964. J. Lipid Res. 5:3.

[12] Clayton, R. B., and K. Bloch. 1963. J. Biol. Chem. 238:586.

[13] Dadd, R. H. 1960. J. Insect Physiol. 4:319.

[14] Dadd, R. H. 1960. Ibid. 5:161.

[15] Dadd, R. H. 1961. Ibid. 6:126.

[16] Dadd, R. H. 1964. Ibid. 10:161.

[17] Dadd, R. H. 1966. Ibid. 12:1479.

continued

Part VII. Fatty Acids and Sterols

[18] Dadd, R. H., and T. E. Mittler. 1966. Experientia 22:832.
[19] Davis, G. R. F. 1967. Rev. Can. Biol. 26:119.
[20] Earle, N. W., B. Slatten, and M. L. Burks. 1967. J. Insect Physiol. 13:187.
[21] Fraenkel, G. Unpublished. Univ. Illinois, Dept. Entomology, Urbana, 1952.
[22] Fraenkel, G., and M. Blewett. 1943. Biochem. J. 37:692.
[23] Fraenkel, G., and M. Blewett. 1943. J. Exptl. Biol. 20:28.
[24] Fraenkel, G., and M. Blewett. 1945. Nature 155: 392.
[25] Fraenkel, G., and M. Blewett. 1946. J. Exptl. Biol. 22:156.
[26] Fraenkel, G., and M. Blewett. 1946. Ibid. 22:162.
[27] Fraenkel, G., and M. Blewett, 1946. Ibid. 22:172.
[28] Fraenkel, G., and M. Blewett. 1946. Nature 157:697.
[29] Fraenkel, G., and M. Blewett. 1947. Biochem. J. 41:475.
[30] Fraenkel, G., M. Blewett, and M. Coles. 1950. Physiol. Zool. 23:92.
[31] Fraenkel, G., J. A. Reid, and M. Blewett. 1941. Biochem. J. 35:712.
[32] Gay, F. J. 1938. J. Exptl. Zool. 79:93.
[33] Gingrich, R. E. 1964. Ann. Entomol. Soc. Am. 57: 351.
[34] Golberg, L., and B. DeMeillon. 1948. Biochem. J. 43:372.
[35] Golberg, L., B. DeMeillon, and M. Laviopierre. 1944. Nature 154:608.
[36] Gordon, H. T. 1959. Ann. N.Y. Acad. Sci. 77:290.
[37] Heed, W. B., and H. W. Kircher. 1965. Science 149: 758.
[38] Hirano, C. 1963. Nippon Oyo Dobutsu Konchu Gaku Zasshi 7:59.
[39] Hobson, R. P. 1935. Biochem. J. 29:2023.
[40] Hoog, E. G. van 't. 1936. Z. Vitaminforsch. 5:118.
[41] House, H. L. Unpublished. Canada Dept. of Agriculture, Entomology Laboratory, Belleville, Ontario, 1967.
[42] House, H. L., and J. S. Barlow. 1960. J. Nutr. 72: 409.
[43] Ishii, S. 1951. Botyu Kagaku 16:83.
[44] Ishii, S. 1952. Nogyo Gijutsu Kenkyusho Hokoku, C, 1:185.
[45] Ishii, S. 1955. Ibid., C, 5:29.
[46] Ishii, S., and H. Urushibara. 1954. Ibid., C, 4:109.
[47] Ito, T. 1961. Nature 191:882.
[48] Ito, T. 1961. Sanshi Shikensho Hokoku 17:91.
[49] Ito, T., and Y. Horie. 1966. Annotationes Zool. Japon. 39:1.
[50] Ito, T., and S. Nakasone. 1966. Sanshi Shikensho Hokoku 20:375.
[51] Ito, T., and S. Nakasone. 1967. J. Insect Physiol. 13:281.
[52] Lafon, M., and G. Teissier. 1939. Compt. Rend. Soc. Biol. 131:75.
[53] Lasser, N. L., and R. B. Clayton. 1966. J. Lipid Res. 7:413.
[54] Leclercq, J. 1948. Biochim. Biophys. Acta 2:614.
[55] Levinson, Z. H., and E. D. Bergmann. 1957. Biochem. J. 65:254.
[56] Martin, H. E., and L. Hare. 1942. Biol. Bull. 83:428.
[57] McFarlane, J. E. 1966. J. Insect Physiol. 12:179.
[58] McFarlane, J. E., B. Neilson, and A. S. K. Ghouri. 1959. Can. J. Zool. 37:913.
[59] McKennis, H., Jr. 1947. J. Biol. Chem. 167:645.
[60] McKennis, H., Jr. 1954. Proc. Soc. Exptl. Biol. Med. 87:289.
[61] Meikle, J. E. S., and J. E. McFarlane. 1965. Can. J. Zool. 43:87.
[62] Michelbacher, A. E., W. M. Hoskins, and W. B. Herms. 1932. J. Exptl. Zool. 64:109.
[63] Moore, W. 1946. Ann. Entomol. Soc. Am. 39:513.
[64] Nayar, J. K. 1964. Can. J. Zool. 42:11.
[65] Noland, J. L. 1954. Arch. Biochem. Biophys. 48: 370.
[66] Offhaus, K. 1940. Z. Vergleich. Physiol. 27:384.
[67] Ritchot, C., and J. E. McFarlane. 1962. Can. J. Zool. 40:371.
[68] Rock, G. C., R. L. Patton, and E. H. Glass. 1965. J. Insect Physiol. 11:91.
[69] Shultz, J., P. St. Lawrence, and D. Newmeyer. 1946. Anat. Record 96:540.
[70] Silverman, P. H., and Z. H. Levinson. 1954. Biochem. J. 58:291.
[71] Singh, K. R. P., and A. W. A. Brown. 1957. J. Insect Physiol. 1:199.
[72] Trager, W. 1948. J. Biol. Chem. 176:1211.
[73] Vanderzant, E. S. 1963. J. Econ. Entomol. 56:357.
[74] Vanderzant, E. S. 1964. J. Insect Physiol. 10:267.
[75] Vanderzant, E. S., D. Kerur, and R. Reiser. 1957. J. Econ. Entomol. 50:606.
[76] Vanderzant, E. S., and R. Reiser. 1956. Ibid. 49: 454.

continued

Part VIII. Miscellaneous Organic Compounds

Compounds reported to be beneficial but not essential are listed as "required"; compounds listed as "utilized" are not necessarily required or beneficial. An entry followed by a question mark indicates conflicting data, with the preponderance of evidence favoring the information given. *Abbreviations:* R = required; R̸ = not required; U = utilized; U̸ = not utilized; u = poorly utilized.

	Species (Synonym)	Stage	Compounds																	Reference
			Adenine	Betaine	Butterfat	Carnitine	Cod Liver Oil	Corn Oil	Cytosine	Deoxyribonucleic Acid	Glutathione	Guanine	Lecithin	Ribonucleic Acid	Thymine	Uracil	Wheat Germ Oil	Yeast Oil	Other	
1	*Acheta domesticus*	N	...	...	...	...	...	...	...	...	...	...	...	R̸[1]	...	...	U	...	...	23,26
2	*Aedes aegypti*	L	R̸	...	...	R?	...	...	R̸	R̸	R?	...	u[2]	R	R̸	R̸	...	U	u[3]	1,16,30
3		A	...	...	...	R̸	...	...	...	...	...	...	...	...	...	...	...	...	...	30
4	*Anagasta kuehniella (Ephestia kuehniella)*	L	...	...	u	...	U	...	...	...	...	...	...	...	...	...	U	U̸	...	14
5	*Anthonomus grandis*	L	...	R̸	...	R̸	...	...	...	...	...	...	...	...	...	...	...	...	...	31
6		A	...	...	...	...	...	U	...	...	...	...	...	...	...	...	...	...	...	32
7	*Blattella germanica*	N[4]	R̸	R̸[5]	...	...	...	...	...	...	...	...	...	...	...	R̸[6]	...	...	...	17
8		N&A	...	...	...	...	...	U[7]	...	...	...	...	...	...	...	...	...	...	...	17
9	*Bombyx mori*	L	...	...	...	R̸[5]	...	...	...	...	...	...	...	...	...	...	...	...	...	19
10	*Cadra cautella (Ephestia cautella)*	L	...	...	u	...	U	...	...	...	...	...	...	...	...	...	U	U	...	14
11	*Calliphora vicina*	L	...	...	...	R̸	...	...	...	...	...	...	...	R	...	...	...	...	R[8]	29
12	*Drosophila melanogaster*	L	R	...	...	R̸	...	...	R̸	R̸	...	R̸	...	R	R̸	R̸	...	...	R[9]	18,27,34
13		A	...	...	...	...	...	...	...	...	...	...	...	R̸	...	...	...	...	...	28
14	*Ephestia elutella*	L	...	...	u	...	U	...	...	...	...	...	...	...	...	...	U[10]	U	...	14
15	*Exeristes comstockii*	A	...	...	...	...	...	...	...	...	...	...	...	R̸[11]	...	...	...	...	...	3
16	*Galleria mellonella*	L	...	...	...	...	...	...	...	...	...	...	...	R̸	...	...	U	...	...	11
17	*Hylemya antiqua*	L	...	...	...	...	...	...	...	...	...	...	...	...	...	...	...	...	R[12]	15
18	*Locusta migratoria*	N	...	...	...	...	...	...	...	...	...	...	...	...	...	...	U	...	...	8,10
19	*Melanoplus bivittatus*	N	...	...	...	...	...	...	...	...	...	...	R̸[13]	...	...	...	...	...	...	25
20	*Musca domestica*	L	R	...	U̸[14]	R̸	U̸[14]	...	...	...	...	R	R̸	R	...	...	u	...	R̸[15]	4
21	*Palorus ratzeburgi*	L	...	...	...	R	...	...	...	...	...	...	...	...	...	...	...	...	...	2
22	*Pectinophora gossypiella*	L	...	...	...	...	...	U	...	...	...	...	...	...	...	...	...	...	...	33
23	*Phaenicia sericata*	L	...	...	U	...	...	...	...	...	...	...	...	...	...	...	...	...	...	24
24	*Phormia regina*	L	R̸	R̸[16]	...	R̸[5]	...	...	...	R̸[17]	...	R̸	...	R̸	...	R̸	...	...	...	5,6
25	*Plodia interpunctella*	L	...	...	u	...	...	...	...	...	...	...	...	...	...	...	U	...	...	14
26	*Pseudosarcophaga* sp. *(P. affinis)*	L	R̸	...	...	R̸	...	...	R̸	R	R[18]	R̸	...	R	R̸	R̸	...	...	R̸[19]	20-22
27	*Schistocerca gregaria*	N	...	...	...	R̸	...	...	...	...	R̸	...	...	R̸	...	...	U	...	R̸[20]	7,9,10
28	*Tenebrio molitor*	L	...	...	...	R	...	...	...	...	...	...	...	...	...	...	...	...	...	2
29	*Tineola bisselliella*	L	...	...	...	...	...	...	...	...	...	...	...	...	...	...	U	...	...	13
30	*Tribolium confusum*	L	...	...	...	...	...	...	...	...	...	...	...	...	...	...	U	...	...	12

[1] Nucleic acids probably are not needed in a satisfactory diet. [2] Can partially replace biotin. [3] Kerasin and sphingomyelin; however, cephalin is not utilized. [4] Reared nonaseptically. [5] Can replace choline. [6] Growth was not affected by omission of uracil from diet, but effect was apparent in the second generation as paralysis and abortion of eggs. [7] Growth was good without corn oil in the diet, but no eggs hatched. [8] Strepogenin. [9] Adenosine, adenylic acid, cytidylic acid, guanosine (?), guanylic acid, hypoxanthine (?), uridylic acid (?), and xanthine (?); however, cytidine, orotic acid, thioctic acid, and uridine are not required. Cytidylic or uridylic acid is effective only when combined with adenylic acid; orotic acid may be substituted for cytidylic acid. [10] Reduced growth and limited metamorphosis can occur in the absence of wheat germ oil. [11] Affects reproduction and egg viability. [12] Coenzyme A and thioctic acid, which are slightly beneficial. [13] This species apparently can synthesize all the lipids it requires. [14] May be slightly toxic. [15] Lipoic acid. [16] Cannot replace choline. [17] May slightly promote pupation. [18] Slightly beneficial. [19] Adenosine, cytidine, guanosine, hypoxanthine, orotic acid, uridine, and xanthine; however, adenylic acid, cytidylic acid, guanylic acid, and uridylic acid are required. [20] Chlorophyll.

continued

20. NUTRIENT REQUIREMENTS AND UTILIZATION: INSECTS

Part VIII. Miscellaneous Organic Compounds

Contributor: House, H. L.

References

[1] Akov, S. 1962. J. Insect Physiol. 8:319.
[2] Beck, S. D. Unpublished. Univ. Wisconsin, Dept. Entomology, Madison, 1951.
[3] Bracken, G. K. 1965. Can. Entomologist 97:1037.
[4] Brookes, V. J., and G. Fraenkel. 1958. Physiol. Zool. 31:208.
[5] Brust, M., and G. Fraenkel. 1955. Ibid. 28:186.
[6] Cheldelin, V. H., and R. W. Newburgh. 1959. Ann. N.Y. Acad. Sci. 77:373.
[7] Dadd, R. H. 1960. J. Insect Physiol. 4:319.
[8] Dadd, R. H. 1960. Ibid. 5:161.
[9] Dadd, R. H. 1960. Proc. Roy. Soc. (London), B, 153:128.
[10] Dadd, R. H. 1961. J. Insect Physiol. 6:126.
[11] Dadd, R. H. 1964. Ibid. 10:161.
[12] Fraenkel, G., and M. Blewett. 1943. Biochem. J. 37:692.
[13] Fraenkel, G., and M. Blewett. 1946. J. Exptl. Biol. 22:156.
[14] Fraenkel, G., and M. Blewett. 1946. Ibid. 22:172.
[15] Friend, W. G., and R. L. Patton. 1956. Can. J. Zool. 34:152.
[16] Golberg, L., and B. DeMeillon. 1948. Biochem. J. 43:372.
[17] Gordon, H. T. 1959. Ann. N.Y. Acad. Sci. 77:290.
[18] Hinton, T. 1956. Physiol. Zool. 29:20.
[19] Horie, Y., and T. Ito. 1965. J. Insect Physiol. 11:1585.
[20] House, H. L. 1954. Can. J. Zool. 32:358.
[21] House, H. L. 1964. Ibid. 42:801.
[22] House, H. L. Unpublished. Canada Dept. of Agriculture, Entomology Laboratory, Belleville, Ontario, 1967.
[23] McFarlane, J. E., B. Neilson, and A. S. K. Ghouri. 1959. Can. J. Zool. 37:913.
[24] Michelbacher, A. E., W. M. Hoskins, and W. B. Herms. 1932. J. Exptl. Zool. 64:109.
[25] Nayar, J. K. 1964. Can. J. Zool. 42:23.
[26] Ritchot, C., and J. E. McFarlane. 1962. Ibid. 40:371.
[27] Sang, J. H. 1957. Proc. Roy. Soc. Edinburgh, B, 66:339.
[28] Sang, J. H., and R. C. King. 1961. J. Exptl. Biol. 38:793.
[29] Sedee, D. J. 1958. Entomol. Exptl. Appl. 1:38.
[30] Singh, K. R. P., and A. W. A. Brown. 1957. J. Insect Physiol. 1:199.
[31] Vanderzant, E. S. 1963. J. Econ. Entomol. 56:357.
[32] Vanderzant, E. S. 1964. J. Insect Physiol. 10:267.
[33] Vanderzant, E. S., D. Kerur, and R. Reiser. 1957. J. Econ. Entomol. 50:606.
[34] Villee, C. A., and H. B. Bissell. 1948. J. Biol. Chem. 172:59.

21. SYNTHETIC DIETS: INSECTS

Data are for insects that have been extensively studied in nutritional research. A diet for a single species may be suitable for other species with similar dietary habits.

	Insect [Type of Medium]	Ingredient	Value	Reference
		Diptera		
1	*Aedes ae-*	Water	To 100 ml	1,26
2	*gypti*	$CaCl_2$	1.2 mg/100 ml	
3	[Liq-	$FeSO_4 \cdot 7H_2O$	1.2 mg/100 ml	
4	uid 8/,	$MgSO_4 \cdot 7H_2O$	20.0 mg/100 ml	
5	sterile]	$MnSO_4 \cdot 4H_2O$	1.2 mg/100 ml	
6		K_2HPO_4	60.0 mg/100 ml	
7		KH_2PO_4	60.0 mg/100 ml	
8		NaCl	1.2 mg/100 ml	
9		Thiamine HCl	0.2 mg/100 ml	
10		Riboflavin	0.2 mg/100 ml	
11		Nicotinamide	1.0 mg/100 ml	
12		Vitamin B_6 HCl	0.4 mg/100 ml	
13		Biotin	0.01 mg/100 ml	
14		Calcium pantothenate	1.0 mg/100 ml	
15		Folic acid	0.1 mg/100 ml	
16		Choline chloride	10.0 mg/100 ml	
17		Cholesterol	0.6 mg/100 ml	
18		Casein, vitamin-free	1.0 g/100 ml	
19		Ribonucleic acid	100.0 mg/100 ml	
20		pH = 6.5		
21	*Drosophi-*	Water	To 100 ml	8,24
22	*la mela-*	$MgSO_4 \cdot 7H_2O$	62.0 mg/100 ml	
23	*nogaster*	KH_2PO_4	183.0 mg/100 ml	
24	[Agar	$NaHCO_3$	150.0 mg/100 ml	
25	base 2/,	Na_2HPO_4	189.0 mg/100 ml	
26	sterile]	Thiamine HCl	0.2 mg/100 ml	
27		Riboflavin	0.1 mg/100 ml	
28		Nicotinic acid	1.2 mg/100 ml	
29		Vitamin B_6 HCl	0.3 mg/100 ml	
30		Biotin	0.016 mg/100 ml	

1/ Supports slow growth (as compared to growth with adequate crude and natural diets). 2/ Supports good growth (as compared to growth with adequate crude and natural diets).

continued

	Insect [Type of Medium]	Ingredient	Value	Reference
31		Calcium pantothenate	1.6 mg/100 ml	
32		Folic acid	0.3 mg/100 ml	
33		Lecithin	0.4 g/100 ml	
34		Cholesterol	30 mg/100 ml	
35		Agar	3.0 g/100 ml	
36		Sucrose	0.75 g/100 ml	
37		Casein, vitamin-free	5.5 g/100 ml	
38		Ribonucleic acid	400.0 mg/100 ml	
39	*Hylemya*	Water	100 ml	13
40	*antiqua*	U.S.P. XII No. 2[4/]	0.2 g/100 ml	
41	[Agar	Thiamine HCl	0.2 mg/100 ml	
42	base[3/],	Riboflavin	0.2 mg/100 ml	
43	sterile]	Nicotinic acid	1.0 mg/100 ml	
44		Vitamin B_6 HCl	3.0 mg/100 ml	
45		Biotin	0.002 mg/100 ml	
46		Calcium pantothenate	0.6 mg/100 ml	
47		Folic acid	0.6 mg/100 ml	
48		Vitamin B_{12}	0.004 mg/100 ml	
49		Choline chloride	2.0 mg/100 ml	
50		Coenzyme A	0.15 mg/100 ml	
51		DL-6-Thioctic acid	0.05 mg/100 ml	
52		Cholesterol	10 mg/100 ml	
53		Agar	2.0 g/100 ml	
54		Glucose	1.5 g/100 ml	
55		L-Amino acid mix[5/]	2.4 g/100 ml	
56		Ribonucleic acid	100.0 mg/100 ml	
57		Inosine	3.0 mg/100 ml	
58		Thymine	0.4 mg/100 ml	
59		pH = 6.1		
60	*Musca do-*	Water	68.5 ml	4
61	*mestica* [Agar	McCollum's mix 185 No. 2[6/]	0.3 g/100 g	
62	base[1/],	Thiamine HCl	1.7 mg/100 g	
63	sterile]	Riboflavin	0.8 mg/100 g	
64		Nicotinic acid	3.3 mg/100 g	
65		Vitamin B_6 HCl	0.8 mg/100 g	
66		Biotin	0.067 mg/100 g	
67		Calcium pantothenate	1.7 mg/100 g	
68		Folic acid	0.2 mg/100 g	
69		Inositol	16.7 mg/100 g	
70		Choline chloride	33.3 mg/100 g	
71		Lecithin	0.9 g/100 g	
72		Cholesterol	267 mg/100 g	
73		Agar	2.0 g/100 g	
74		Casein, vitamin-free	26.7 g/100 g	
75		Ribonucleic acid	667.0 mg/100 g	
76		Adenine	16.0 mg/100 g	
77		Guanine	16.0 mg/100 g	
78		Uracil	16.0 mg/100 g	

[1/] Supports slow growth (as compared to growth with adequate crude and natural diets). [2/] Supports good growth (as compared to growth with adequate crude and natural diets). [3/] Supports better growth than do natural diets.

	Insect [Type of Medium]	Ingredient	Value	Reference
79		Methyl *p*-hydroxybenzoate	0.6 g/100 g	
80		pH = 5.5		
81	*Phormia*	Water	To 100 ml	15,22
82	*regina*	$CaCl_2$	1.3 mg/100 ml	
83	[Agar	KCl	1.3 mg/100 ml	
84	base[2/],	K_2HPO_4	30.0 mg/100 ml	
85	sterile]	$NaHCO_3$	1.3 mg/100 ml	
86		NaCl	60.0 mg/100 ml	
87		$NaH_2PO_4 \cdot H_2O$	35.0 mg/100 ml	
88		Thiamine HCl	0.5 mg/100 ml	
89		Riboflavin	1.5 mg/100 ml	
90		Nicotinic acid	1.5 mg/100 ml	
91		Vitamin B_6 HCl	1.5 mg/100 ml	
92		Biotin	0.0005 mg/100 ml	
93		Calcium pantothenate	1.5 mg/100 ml	
94		Folic acid	0.5 mg/100 ml	
95		Inositol	10.0 mg/100 ml	
96		Choline chloride	10.0 mg/100 ml	
97		Cholesterol	80 mg/100 ml	
98		Agar	2.0 g/100 ml	
99		Casein, vitamin-free	0.4 g/100 ml	
100		L-Amino acid mix[5,7/]	3.0 g/100 ml	
101		Ribonucleic acid	160.0 mg/100 ml	
102		pH = 5.6		
103	*Pseudo-*	Water	To 100 ml	17,18
104	*sar-*	U.S.P. XII No. 2[4/]	0.066 g/100 ml	
105	*copha-*	Thiamine HCl	0.1 mg/100 ml	
106	*ga* sp.[8/]	Riboflavin	0.2 mg/100 ml	
107	[Agar	Nicotinic acid	0.3 mg/100 ml	
108	base[2/],	Vitamin B_6 HCl	0.9 mg/100 ml	
109	sterile]	Biotin	0.00009 mg/100 ml	
110		Calcium pantothenate	0.4 mg/100 ml	
111		Folic acid	0.3 mg/100 ml	
112		*p*-Aminobenzoic acid	0.9 mg/100 ml	
113		Inositol	6.0 mg/100 ml	
114		Choline chloride	2.0 mg/100 ml	
115		Vitamin A	3.0 mg/100 ml	
116		α-Tocopherol	1.0 mg/100 ml	
117		Linoleic acid	60 mg/100 ml	
118		Linolenic acid	20 mg/100 ml	
119		Oleic acid	192 mg/100 ml	
120		Palmitic acid	88 mg/100 ml	
121		Stearic acid	40 mg/100 ml	
122		Polysorbate 80	270 mg/100 ml	
123		Cholesterol	100 mg/100 ml	
124		Agar	0.75 g/100 ml	
125		Glucose	0.5 g/100 ml	
126		L-Amino acid mix[5/]	2.0 g/100 ml	
127		Ribonucleic acid	75.0 mg/100 ml	
128		pH = 5.8		

[4/] Consult reference 27. [5/] Usually 18 amino acids. [6/] Consult reference 21. [7/] Both D- and L-amino acids. [8/] Synonym: *Agria affinis.*

continued

	Insect [Type of Medium]	Ingredient	Value	Reference
		Lepidoptera		
129	*Bombyx*	Water	60 ml	16,19
130	*mori*	Wesson's mix [10]	1.6 g/100 g	
131	[Sol-	Thiamine HCl	0.8 mg/100 g	
132	id [9],	Riboflavin	0.8 mg/100 g	
133	sterile]	Nicotinic acid	4.0 mg/100 g	
134		Vitamin B_6 HCl	1.2 mg/100 g	
135		Biotin	0.08 mg/100 g	
136		Calcium pantothenate	6.0 mg/100 g	
137		Folic acid	0.1 mg/100 g	
138		Inositol	8.0 mg/100 g	
139		Choline chloride	60.0 mg/100 g	
140		L-Ascorbic acid	800.0 mg/100 g	
141		Soybean oil	1.2 g/100 g	
142		β-Sitosterol	120 mg/100 g	
143		Cellulose	14.3 g/100 g	
144		Glucose	7.2 g/100 g	
145		Starch	7.2 g/100 g	
146		Soybean meal	7.2 g/100 g	
147		Morin [11]	0.1 g/100 g	
148		Mulberry leaf extract [11]	0.2 g/100 g	
149	*Ephestia* sp. [Sol-	McCollum's mix 185 No. 2 [6]	1.9 g/100 g	10,11
150	id [2],	Thiamine HCl	2.5 mg/100 g	
151	dry,	Riboflavin	1.2 mg/100 g	
152	not	Nicotinic acid	2.5 mg/100 g	
153	sterile]	Vitamin B_6 HCl	1.2 mg/100 g	
154		Calcium pantothenate	2.5 mg/100 g	
155		Inositol	25.0 mg/100 g	
156		Choline chloride	50.0 mg/100 g	
157		Wheat germ oil	0.9 g/100 g	
158		Cholesterol	900 mg/100 g	
159		Glucose	75.2 g/100 g	
160		Casein, vitamin-free	18.8 g/100 g	
161		Yeast [12]	2.4 g/100 g	
162	*Ostrinia*	Water	81.4 ml	3,6
163	*nubi-*	Wesson's mix [10]	1.0 g/100 g	
164	*lalis*	Thiamine HCl	0.3 mg/100 g	
165	[Agar	Riboflavin	0.5 mg/100 g	
166	base [2],	Nicotinic acid	1.0 mg/100 g	
167	sterile]	Vitamin B_6 HCl	0.3 mg/100 g	
168		Biotin	0.02 mg/100 g	
169		Calcium pantothenate	1.0 mg/100 g	
170		Folic acid	0.3 mg/100 g	
171		Inositol	20.0 mg/100 g	
172		Vitamin B_{12}	0.002 mg/100 g	
173		Choline chloride	100.0 mg/100 g	
174		L-Ascorbic acid	480.0 mg/100 g	
175		α-Tocopherol	2.2 mg/100 g	
176		Corn oil	0.2 g/100 g	
177		Cholesterol	300 mg/100 g	
178		Agar	2.4 g/100 g	
179		Cellulose	5.1 g/100 g	
180		Glucose	3.4 g/100 g	
181		Sodium alginate	0.5 g/100 g	
182		Casein, vitamin-free	5.1 g/100 g	
183		Sorbic acid	0.1 g/100 g	
184	*Pecti-*	Water	To 100 ml	29,30
185	*nophora*	Wesson's mix [10]	1.2 g/100 g	
186	*gossyp-*	Thiamine HCl	0.5 mg/100 g	
187	*iella*	Riboflavin	1.0 mg/100 g	
188	[Agar	Nicotinic acid	4.0 mg/100 g	
189	base [2],	Vitamin B_6 HCl	0.5 mg/100 g	
190	sterile]	Biotin	0.02 mg/100 g	
191		Calcium pantothenate	2.0 mg/100 g	
192		Folic acid	0.5 mg/100 g	
193		Vitamin B_{12}	0.002 mg/100 g	
194		Choline chloride	100.0 mg/100 g	
195		α-Tocopherol	10.0 mg/100 g	
196		Corn oil	0.25 g/100 g	
197		Cholesterol	50 mg/100 g	
198		Agar	3.0 g/100 g	
199		Cellulose	4.0 g/100 g	
200		Sucrose	5.0 g/100 g	
201		Sodium alginate	0.5 g/100 g	
202		Casein, vitamin-free	5.0 g/100 g	
203		L-Cystine	0.1 g/100 g	
204		Glycine	0.15 g/100 g	
205		pH = 6.5		
		Coleoptera		
206	*Anthon-*	Water	To 100 ml	28
207	*omus*	$CaCO_3$	120.0 mg/100 ml	
208	*grandis*	$CoCl_2 \cdot 6H_2O$	0.25 mg/100 ml	
209	[Agar	$CuSO_4 \cdot 5H_2O$	0.5 mg/100 ml	
210	base [1],	$FeSO_4 \cdot 7H_2O$	10.0 mg/100 ml	
211	sterile]	$MgSO_4 \cdot 7H_2O$	50.0 mg/100 ml	
212		$MnSO_4 \cdot H_2O$	2.5 mg/100 ml	
213		KI	0.5 mg/100 ml	
214		K_2HPO_4	160.0 mg/100 ml	
215		NaCl	20.0 mg/100 ml	
216		$Na_2MoO_4 \cdot 2H_2O$	0.25 mg/100 ml	
217		$NaH_2PO_4 \cdot H_2O$	80.0 mg/100 ml	
218		$Zn(C_2H_3O_2)_2 \cdot 2H_2O$	0.5 mg/100 ml	
219		Thiamine HCl	0.3 mg/100 ml	
220		Riboflavin	0.5 mg/100 ml	

1/ Supports slow growth (as compared to growth with adequate crude and natural diets). 2/ Supports good growth (as compared to growth with adequate crude and natural diets). 6/ Consult reference 21. 9/ Supports poor growth (as compared to growth with natural diet). 10/ Consult reference 31. 11/ Consult reference 19. 12/ Water-insoluble residue.

continued

	Insects [Type of Medium]	Ingredient	Value	Reference
221		Nicotinamide	1.0 mg/100 ml	
222		Vitamin B_6 HCl	0.3 mg/100 ml	
223		Biotin	0.02 mg/100 ml	
224		Calcium pantothenate	1.0 mg/100 ml	
225		Folic acid	0.3 mg/100 ml	
226		Inositol	20.0 mg/100 ml	
227		Vitamin B_{12}	0.002 mg/100 ml	
228		Choline chloride	50.0 mg/100 ml	
229		Linolenic acid	20 mg/100 ml	
230		Cholesterol	50 mg/100 ml	
231		Agar	3.0 g/100 ml	
232		Sucrose	3.5 g/100 ml	
233		L-Amino acid mix[5]	2.1 g/100 ml	
234		pH = 6.2		
235	*Tene- brio*	McCollum's mix 185 No. 2[6]	1.9 g/100 g	9,12, 20
236	*molitor*	$ZnCl_2$	4.0 mg/100 g	
237	[Sol-	Thiamine HCl	2.5 mg/100 g	
238	id[2],	Riboflavin	1.3 mg/100 g	
239	dry,	Nicotinic acid	5.0 mg/100 g	
240	not	Vitamin B_6 HCl	1.3 mg/100 g	
241	sterile]	Biotin	0.025 mg/100 g	
242		Calcium pantothenate	2.5 mg/100 g	
243		Folic acid	0.25 mg/100 g	
244		Inositol	25.0 mg/100 g	
245		Choline chloride	50.0 mg/100 g	
246		Carnitine	0.3 mg/100 g	
247		Cholesterol	970 mg/100 g	
248		Glucose	77.6 g/100 g	
249		Casein, vitamin-free	19.4 g/100 g	
250	*Triboli-*	$Ca(H_2PO_4)_2 \cdot H_2O$	160.0 mg/100 g	23,25
251	*um con-*	$CuSO_4 \cdot 5H_2O$	5.0 mg/100 g	
252	*fusum*	$FeSO_4 \cdot 7H_2O$	40.0 mg/100 g	
253	[Sol-	$MgSO_4$[13]	320.0 mg/100 g	
254	id[2],	$MnSO_4 \cdot H_2O$	10.0 mg/100 g	
255	dry,	KH_2PO_4	1360.0 mg/100 g	
256	not	NaCl	100.0 mg/100 g	
257	sterile]	$ZnCl_2$	10.0 mg/100 g	
258		Thiamine HCl	1.2 mg/100 g	
259		Riboflavin	1.8 mg/100 g	
260		Nicotinic acid	10.0 mg/100 g	
261		Vitamin B_6 HCl	1.6 mg/100 g	
262		Biotin	0.06 mg/100 g	
263		Calcium pantothenate	4.0 mg/100 g	
264		Folic acid	0.5 mg/100 g	
265		*p*-Aminobenzoic acid	50.0 mg/100 g	
266		Inositol	200.0 mg/100 g	
267		Vitamin B_{12}	0.05 mg/100 g	
268		Choline chloride	400.0 mg/100 g	
269		L-Ascorbic acid	1.0 mg/100 g	
270		Menadione	0.1 mg/100 g	
271		Carnitine	1.0 mg/100 g	
272		Corn oil	3.0 g/100 g	
273		Cholesterol	370 mg/100 g	
274		Starch	74.0 g/100 g	
275		L-Amino acid mix[5]	20.0 g/100 g	
		Homoptera		
276	*Acyrtho-*	Water	To 100 ml	2
277	*siphon*	U.S.P. XII No. 2[4]	0.005 g/100 ml	
278	*pisum*	$MgCl_2 \cdot 6H_2O$	200.0 mg/100 ml	
279	[Liq-	K_3PO_4	500.0 mg/100 ml	
280	uid[2],	Thiamine HCl	2.5 mg/100 ml	
281	sterile]	Riboflavin	5.0 mg/100 ml	
282		Nicotinic acid	10.0 mg/100 ml	
283		Vitamin B_6 HCl	2.5 mg/100 ml	
284		Biotin	0.1 mg/100 ml	
285		Calcium pantothenate	5.0 mg/100 ml	
286		Folic acid	1.0 mg/100 ml	
287		*p*-Aminobenzoic acid	10.0 mg/100 ml	
288		Inositol	50.0 mg/100 ml	
289		Choline chloride	50.0 mg/100 ml	
290		L-Ascorbic acid	10.0 mg/100 ml	
291		Cholesterol	2.5 mg/100 ml	
292		Sucrose	35.0 g/100 ml	
293		L-Amino acid mix[5]	4.3 g/100 ml	
294		pH = 7.6		
		Orthoptera		
295	*Blattella*	$CaCO_3$	200.0 mg/100 g	14
296	*germa-*	$Cu(C_2H_3O_2)_2 \cdot H_2O$	10.0 mg/100 g	
297	*nica*	$Fe(C_3H_5O_3)_2 \cdot 3H_2O$	46.7 mg/100 g	
298	[Sol-	$MgSO_4$[13]	480.0 mg/100 g	
299	id[2],	$Mn(C_2H_3O_2)_2 \cdot 4H_2O$	36.8 mg/100 g	
300	dry,	KH_2PO_4	1360.0 mg/100 g	
301	not	K_2SO_4	440.0 mg/100 g	
302	sterile]	NaCl	120.0 mg/100 g	
303		$Zn(C_2H_3O_2)_2 \cdot 2H_2O$	22.0 mg/100 g	
304		Thiamine HCl	12.0 mg/100 g	
305		Riboflavin	13.5 mg/100 g	
306		Nicotinic acid	18.0 mg/100 g	
307		Vitamin B_6 HCl	7.4 mg/100 g	
308		Biotin	1.0 mg/100 g	
309		Calcium pantothenate	8.6 mg/100 g	
310		Folic acid	8.0 mg/100 g	
311		Inositol	721.0 mg/100 g	
312		Vitamin B_{12}	0.36 mg/100 g	
313		Choline chloride	280.0 mg/100 g	
314		Corn oil	3.0 g/100 g	
315		Cholesterol	1000 mg/100 g	
316		Cellulose	26.4 g/100 g	
317		Glucose	36.0 g/100 g	
318		Casein, vitamin-free	30.0 g/100 g	

[2] Supports good growth (as compared to growth with adequate crude and natural diets). [4] Consult reference 27. [5] Usually 18 amino acids. [6] Consult reference 21. [13] Anhydrous salt.

continued

21. SYNTHETIC DIETS: INSECTS

	Insect [Type of Medium]	Ingredient	Value	Reference
319	*Schisto-*	Galaxos salt DL6[14]	4.1 g/100 g	5,7
320	*cerca*	Thiamine HCl	2.5 mg/100 g	
321	*grega-*	Riboflavin	2.5 mg/100 g	
322	*ria*	Nicotinic acid	10.0 mg/100 g	
323	[Sol-	Vitamin B_6 HCl	2.5 mg/100 g	
324	id[1],	Biotin	0.1 mg/100 g	
325	dry,	Calcium pantothenate	5.0 mg/100 g	
326	not	Folic acid	2.5 mg/100 g	
327	sterile]	*p*-Aminobenzoic acid	2.5 mg/100 g	
328		Inositol	25.0 mg/100 g	
329		Choline chloride	125.0 mg/100 g	
330		L-Ascorbic acid	270.0 mg/100 g	
331		β-Carotene	67.5 mg/100 g	
332		α-Tocopherol	33.8 mg/100 g	
333		Linoleic acid	540 mg/100 g	
334		Cholesterol	540 mg/100 g	
335		Cellulose	40.5 g/100 g	
336		Dextrin	13.5 g/100 g	
337		Sucrose	13.5 g/100 g	
338		Casein, vitamin-free	16.2 g/100 g	
339		Egg albumin	5.4 g/100 g	
340		Peptone	5.4 g/100 g	

1/ Supports slow growth (as compared to growth with adequate crude and natural diets). 14/ Consult reference 7.

Contributor: Vanderzant, Erma S.

References

[1] Akov, S. 1962. J. Insect Physiol. 8:319.
[2] Auclair, J. L. 1965. Ann. Entomol. Soc. Am. 58:855.
[3] Veck, S. D., and J. F. Stauffer. 1950. J. Econ. Entomol. 43:4.
[4] Brooks, V. J., and G. Fraenkel. 1958. Physiol. Zool. 31:208.
[5] Cavanagh, G. G. 1963. J. Insect Physiol. 9:759.
[6] Chippendale, G. M., and S. D. Beck. 1964. Entomol. Exptl. Appl. 7:241.
[7] Dadd, R. H. 1960. J. Insect Physiol. 4:319.
[8] Erk, F. C., and J. H. Sang. 1966. Ibid. 12:43.
[9] Fraenkel, G. 1958. J. Nutr. 65:361.
[10] Fraenkel, G., and M. Blewett. 1946. J. Exptl. Biol. 22:172.
[11] Fraenkel, G., and M. Blewett. 1947. Biochem. J. 41:669.
[12] Fraenkel, G., and J. LeClercq. 1956. Arch. Intern. Physiol. Biochim. 64:601.
[13] Friend, W. G., E. H. Salkeld, and I. L. Stevenson. 1959. Ann. N.Y. Acad. Sci. 77:384.
[14] Gordon, H. T. 1959. Ibid. 77:290.
[15] Hodgson, E., V. H. Cheldelin, and R. W. Newburgh. 1960. Arch. Biochem. Biophys. 87:48.
[16] Horie, Y., and T. Ito. 1965. J. Insect Physiol. 11:1585.
[17] House, H. L. 1966. Ibid. 12:409.
[18] House, H. L., and J. S. Barlow. 1960. J. Nutr. 72:409.
[19] Ito, T., and Y. Horie. 1962. J. Insect Physiol. 8:569.
[20] LeClercq, J., and L. Lopez-Francos. 1964. Arch. Intern. Physiol. Biochim. 72:95.
[21] McCollum, E. V., and N. J. Simmonds. 1918. J. Biol. Chem. 33:55.
[22] McGinnis, A. J., R. W. Newburgh, and V. H. Cheldelin. 1956. J. Nutr. 58:309.
[23] Medici, J. C., and M. W. Taylor. 1966. Ibid. 88:181.
[24] Sang, J. H. 1956. J. Exptl. Biol. 33:45.
[25] Taylor, M. W., and J. C. Medici. 1966. J. Nutr. 88:176.
[26] Trager, W. 1948. J. Biol. Chem. 176:1211.
[27] U.S. Pharmacopoeial Convention. 1942. Pharmacopoeia of the U.S. Rev. 12. Mack, Easton, Penna. p. 637.
[28] Vanderzant, E. S. 1965. J. Insect Physiol. 11:659.
[29] Vanderzant, E. S., D. Kerur, and R. Reiser. 1957. J. Econ. Entomol. 50:606.
[30] Vanderzant, E. S., and R. Reiser. 1956. Ibid. 49:454.
[31] Wesson, L. G. 1932. Science 75:339.

22. CULTURE MEDIA: PROTOZOA

Part I. Parasitic Amoebae

	Medium	Species Showing Growth
	Bacteria Cultures[1]	
	Diphasic	
1	**Slant**: coagulated whole egg in Locke's, Ringer's, or saline solution. **Overlay**: Locke's, Ringer's, or saline solution, alone or with one or more of the following: serum, egg white, rice (starch, flour, or powder).	*Dientamoeba fragilis* [45] 2/, [25] 3/; *Endolimax nana* [16, 45] 2/; *Entamoeba aulastomi* [19] 2/; *E. coli* [26] 2/, [41] 4/; *E. gingivalis* [18] 2/; *E. histolytica* [7,16] 2/, [8, 42] 3/; *E. invadens* [27] 2/; *Iodamoeba buetschlii* [45] 2/

1/ Growth occurs in presence of one or more types of metabolizing cell: bacteria, protozoa, or metazoa. 2/ Xenic growth (unknown number of associates present in culture). 3/ Monoxenic growth (one identified associate present). 4/ Dixenic growth (two identified associates present).

continued

22. CULTURE MEDIA: PROTOZOA

Part I. Parasitic Amoebae

	Medium	Species Showing Growth
2	**Slant**: coagulated serum. **Overlay**: Ringer's or saline solution, serum, egg white, rice.	*Endolimax nana, Entamoeba coli, E. gingivalis, E. histolytica* [16]2/; *E. invadens* [28]3/; *E. muris* [39]2/
3	**Slant**: liver infusion, salts, agar. **Overlay**: saline, serum, rice.	*Entamoeba histolytica* [9]2/, [10]3/; *E. invadens* [40]2/
4	**Slant**: alcoholic extract of tissue or egg yolk, salts, agar. **Overlay**: buffered saline.	*Dientamoeba fragilis, Endolimax nana, Entamoeba coli, E. histolytica, Iodamoeba buetschlii* [35]2/
	Liquid	
5	Locke's, Ringer's, or normal saline solution, serum, rice	*Endamoeba thomsoni* [48]2/; *Entamoeba barreti* [5]2/; *E. histolytica* [11,12]2/; *E. invadens* [40]2/; *E. ranarum* [6]2/
6	Egg-yolk infusion, rice, with or without liver extract	*Dientamoeba fragilis* [3]2/; *Entamoeba coli* [3]2/; *E. histolytica* [1]2/; *E. invadens* [27,32]2/; *E. terrapinae* [32]2/
7	Fluid thioglycollate broth, serum5/	*Entamoeba coli, E. histolytica* [46]3/
8	Trypticase, tryptose, or lactalbumin hydrolysate, yeast extract, glucose, cysteine, salts, serum5/	*Entamoeba histolytica* [30]3/
9	Trypticase, glucose, cysteine, thiomalate, salts, serum5/	*Entamoeba histolytica* [43]3/
10	Gastric mucin extract, egg-yolk infusion, salts, rice	*Entamoeba histolytica* [17]2/
11	Balanced salt solution, 1.4% sodium bicarbonate, serum, rice6/	*Dientamoeba fragilis, Endolimax nana, Entamoeba coli, E. histolytica, E. invadens* [36]2/
12	12 amino acids, 10 vitamins, trace minerals, salts, nucleic acid, cholesterol, rice	*Entamoeba histolytica* [23]3/
13	20 amino acids, 10 vitamins, trace minerals, salts, nucleic acid, nitrogenous bases, glucose, glycogen, cholesterol, rice	*Entamoeba histolytica* [22]2,3/
	Protozoa Cultures1/	
14	Trypticase-dextrose broth with serum7/	*Entamoeba histolytica* [38]3/; *E. invadens, E. terrapinae* [13]3/
15	Trypticase, egg-yolk infusion, tissue-culture medium, salts, hemolyzed red blood cells, serum7/	*Entamoeba histolytica* [37]3/
16	Tryptose, trypticase, yeast extract, glucose, salts, cysteine, ascorbic acid, hemolyzed red blood cells, serum	*Entamoeba histolytica* [15]3/
	Tissue Cultures1/	
17	Saline, tissue slice	*Entamoeba invadens* [34]
18	Balanced salt solution, chick embryo (minced or sliced), serum	*Entamoeba histolytica* [47]
	Axenic Cultures8/	
	Diphasic	
19	**Slant**: tryptose, trypticase, yeast extract, glucose, salts, cysteine, ascorbic acid, serum, agar. **Overlay**: cell-free chick embryo extract, 16 vitamins; all ingredients in slant except serum.	*Entamoeba histolytica* [14]
	Liquid	
20	**Heat-stable portion**: liver-infusion broth, gastric mucin, trypticase, salts. **Heat-labile portion**: raw-liver extract.	*Entamoeba invadens* [50]
21	**Heat-stable portion**: liver-infusion broth, gastric mucin, trypticase, salts, 0.1% agar. **Heat-labile portion**: chick embryo or raw-liver extract, serum, tissue culture medium.	*Entamoeba histolytica* [24]

1/ Growth occurs in presence of one or more types of metabolizing cell: bacteria, protozoa, or metazoa. 2/ Xenic growth (unknown number of associates present in culture). 3/ Monoxenic growth (one identified associate present). 5/ Preconditioned with a bacterium. 6/ Incubated in carbon dioxide atmosphere. 7/ Preconditioned with a trypanosomatid. 8/ Growth occurs in absence of any other metabolizing cell. 9/ Incubated in pure nitrogen atmosphere.

continued

22. CULTURE MEDIA: PROTOZOA

Part I. Parasitic Amoebae

	Medium	Species Showing Growth
22	Trypticase, ox-liver digest, glucose, salts	*Entamoeba invadens* [29]
23	Trypticase, ox-liver digest, glucose, salts, cysteine, ascorbic acid, serum, 16 vitamins	*Entamoeba histolytica, E. invadens, E. terrapinae* [15]
	Special Purpose Media	
	Diphasic	
24	**Slant**: liver concentrate, salts, agar. **Overlay**: egg-yolk infusion, serum, rice. (Encystment medium)	*Entamoeba histolytica* [2][2,3/]; *E. invadens* [4][3/]
	Liquid	
25	Egg-yolk infusion, trypticase, glucose, salts, sodium thioglycollate. (Isolation & shipping medium)	*Entamoeba histolytica* [21][2/]
26	Trypticase, glucose, cysteine, thiomalic acid, salts, serum.[9/] (Mass cultivation in petri dish)	*Entamoeba histolytica* [44][3/]
	Slant	
27	Yeast autolysate, proteose-peptone, cholesterol, serum, salts, agar, rice. (Migration studies)	*Entamoeba histolytica* [49][2/]
	Slide culture	
28	**Slide well**: horse serum, rice, bacteria. **Cover slip**: layer of non-nutrient agar. (Cell-division studies)	*Entamoeba histolytica, E. invadens* [20][2/]
	Chick embryo	
29	Inoculated via chorioallantoic membrane blood vessel	*Entamoeba invadens* [31]
30	Intestinal explant	*Entamoeba invadens* [33]

[2/] Xenic growth (unknown number of associates present in culture). [3/] Monoxenic growth (one identified associate present). [9/] Incubated in pure nitrogen atmosphere.

Contributors: Diamond, Louis S., and Bartgis, I. Louise.

References

[1] Balamuth, W. 1946. Am. J. Clin. Pathol. 16:380.
[2] Balamuth, W. 1951. J. Infect. Diseases 88:230.
[3] Balamuth, W. 1953. Am. J. Trop. Med. Hyg. 2:191.
[4] Balamuth, W. 1962. J. Parasitol. 48:101.
[5] Barret, H. P., and N. M. Smith. 1924. Am. J. Hyg. 4:155.
[6] Barret, H. P., and N. M. Smith. 1926. Ann. Trop. Med. Parasitol. 20:85.
[7] Boeck, W. C., and J. Drbohlav. 1925. Am. J. Hyg. 5:371.
[8] Chinn, B. D., et al. 1942. Am. J. Trop. Med. 22:137.
[9] Cleveland, L. R., and J. Collier. 1930. Am. J. Hyg. 12:606.
[10] Cleveland, L. R., and E. P. Sanders. 1930. Science 72:149.
[11] Craig, C. F. 1926. Am. J. Trop. Med. 6:333.
[12] Craig, C. F. 1926. Ibid. 6:461.
[13] Diamond, L. S. 1960. J. Parasitol. 46:484.
[14] Diamond, L. S. 1961. Science 134:336.
[15] Diamond, L. S. 1968. J. Parasitol., v. 54.
[16] Dobell, C., and P. P. Laidlaw. 1926. Parasitology 18:283.
[17] Dolkart, R. E., and B. Halpern. 1958. Am. J. Trop. Med. Hyg. 7:595.
[18] Drbohlav, J. 1925. Ann. Parasitol. Humaine Comparee 3:361.
[19] Drbohlav, J. 1925. Ibid. 3:367.
[20] Dubey, J. P., and S. R. Das. 1966. Nature 211:992.
[21] Gleason, N. N., M. Goldman, and R. K. Carver. 1960. Am. J. Trop. Med. Hyg. 9:46.
[22] Hallman, F. A., J. B. Michaelson, and J. N. DeLamater. 1950. Am. J. Trop. Med. 30:363.
[23] Hansen, E. L., and H. H. Anderson. 1948. Parasitology 39:69.
[24] Jackson, G. J., and N. R. Stoll. 1964. Am. J. Trop. Med. Hyg. 13:520.
[25] Jacobs, L. 1953. Ann. N.Y. Acad. Sci. 56:1057.
[26] Mayfield, M. F. 1944. Proc. Soc. Exptl. Biol. Med. 55:20.
[27] McConnachie, E. W. 1955. Parasitology 45:452.
[28] McConnachie, E. W. 1956. Ibid. 46:117.
[29] McConnachie, E. W. 1962. Nature 194:603.
[30] McDade, J. J., and J. G. Shaffer. 1959. Am. J. Trop. Med. Hyg. 8:540.
[31] Meerovitch, E. 1956. Can. J. Microbiol. 2:1.
[32] Meerovitch, E. 1958. Can. J. Zool. 36:513.
[33] Meerovitch, E. 1961. Can. J. Microbiol. 7:685.
[34] Miller, M. J. 1953. Nature 172:1192.
[35] Nelson, C. E. 1947. Am. J. Trop. Med. 27:545.
[36] Nelson, C. E., and M. M. Jones. 1964. Am. J. Trop. Med. Hyg. 13:667.
[37] Pan, C.-T. 1960. J. Infect. Diseases 106:284.
[38] Phillips, B. P. 1951. Am. J. Trop. Med. 31:290.
[39] Pruss, J. 1959. Z. Tropenmed. Parasitol. 10:30.

continued

Part I. Parasitic Amoebae

[40] Ratcliffe, H. L., and Q. M. Geiman. 1934. Science 79:324.
[41] Reardon, L. V., E. Verder, and C. W. Rees. 1952. Am. J. Trop. Med. Hyg. 1:155.
[42] Rees, C. W., et al. 1941. Am. J. Trop. Med. 21:567.
[43] Reeves, R. E., H. E. Meleney, and W. W. Frye. 1957. Am. J. Hyg. 66:56.
[44] Reeves, R. E., and A. B. Ward. 1965. J. Parasitol. 51:321.
[45] St. John, J. H. 1926. Am. J. Trop. Med. 6:319.
[46] Shaffer, J. G., F. W. Ryden, and W. W. Frye. 1949. Am. J. Hyg. 49:127.
[47] Shaffer, J. G., H. S. Sienkiewicz, and J. E. Washington. 1953. Ibid. 57:336.
[48] Smith, N. M., and H. P. Barret. 1928. J. Parasitol. 14:272.
[49] Snyder, T. L., and H. E. Meleney. 1946. Ibid. 32:354.
[50] Stoll, N. R. 1957. Science 126:1236.

Part II. Ciliata

For additional information on laboratory strains of free-living and parasitic protozoa (with sources from which they may be obtained and directions for their maintenance), consult reference 30.

	Medium	Species Showing Growth
	Agnotobiotic Freshwater Ciliate Cultures	
1	Wheat infusion [17]: Boil wheat grains in small amount of water. Add 20-70 boiled grains/liter springwater. 1/ Let stand one day or more before inoculating.	Many species [18,30]
2	Hay infusion [18]: 1-6 g timothy or other hay/liter water. Autoclave or boil.	Many species [18,30]
3	Cerophyl infusion [2]: Heat 10 ml Cerophyl solution 2/ (5% extract) to simmering; boil 10 minutes, filter. Restore to volume; add 15 ml Osterhout solution (0.01% NaCl, 0.00085% $MgCl_2$, 0.00023% KCl, 0.0004% $MgSO_4$, 0.0001% $CaCl_2$), 3 ml 0.05 *M* KH_2PO_4, 7 ml 0.05 *M* Na_2HPO_4, & 965 ml distilled water to bring to one liter.	Many species [12,18,30]
4	*Didinium* medium [4]: 0.01% Knop solution, NaOH-KH_2PO_4; buffer to pH 6.8. Concentrate paramecia by centrifuging and add to medium. *Didinium* encysts when food is exhausted.	*Didinium nasutum* [4]
5	Hay-pea infusion: 5 g timothy hay, 10 halves of split peas, 10 grains wheat/liter water. Bring to boiling point; inoculate next day.	*Euplotes patella* [36]
6	Lettuce infusion [37]: Dry lettuce leaves in oven until they are crisp or brown, not burned; powder dried leaves and boil 1.5 g in one liter distilled water for 5 minutes; filter and autoclave. For use, dilute 1:3 with distilled water.	*Frontonia vesiculosa* [40], *Paramecium* spp. [37]
7	*Spirostomum* medium (enriched hay-wheat infusion): Boil 1% timothy hay & 1% wheat grains in springwater. Cool, then add 1 tablespoon fresh cow manure/liter. Inoculate after 2-3 days.	*Spirostomum* spp. [33]
8	1 part Knop solution, 2 parts soil extract. Consult reference 41 for method of preparation.	*Stentor coeruleus* [41]
9	Hard-boiled egg-yolk medium: Use 66 g hard-boiled egg yolk/liter water. Let stand 2 days; inoculate with *Chilomonas*, then *Stentor*.	*Stentor* spp. [18]
10	Inorganic medium: Peters' solution, plus *Colpidium campylum* grown in Cerophyl medium	*Stentor coeruleus* [9]
11	Rice infusion: Boil 1 part rice stalks in 4 parts pond water.	*Stylonychia* spp. [5]
12	Tela broth: 0.02% proteose-peptone, 0.2% Cerophyl solution 2/, 0.3% wheat kernel broth	*Telotrochidium henneguyi* [11]
13	Alfalfa-wheat infusion: 20 g alfalfa hay, 30 g wheat grains/liter water. Boil 5 minutes, filter, and autoclave. Before using, dilute 50% with sterile springwater.	*Vorticella* spp. [10]
	Agnotobiotic Sewage Ciliate Cultures	
14	Glaxo "complan" extract: 0.05% in distilled water	*Pyxidiella curvicaula* [8]

1/ For *Paramecium,* 60-70 grains/liter; for *Stentor* and *Vorticella,* 20 grains/liter; for hypotrichs, 40 grains/liter. 2/ A dried grass preparation.

continued

Part II. Ciliata

	Medium	Species Showing Growth
	Agnotobiotic Parasitic & Symbiotic Ciliate Cultures	
15	Egg-yolk infusion: Boil 2-4 eggs 15 minutes. Crumble yolks in 125 ml 0.8% NaCl; boil 10 minutes, then filter. Restore volume to 125 ml. Autoclave filter precipitate. Add 125 ml *M*/15 phosphate buffer, pH 7.5. Loopful of rice starch may be added before inoculation.	General intestinal ciliates [3]
	Balantidium media	
16	1 part horse serum, 16 parts Ringer's solution. Sterilize by filtration.	*Balantidium coli* [18]
17	Mix cecal contents of swine with 9 parts Ringer's solution. Strain mixture through sieve. Adjust pH to 8.0. Add powdered rice starch periodically.	*Balantidium coli* [24]
18	*Nyctotherus* medium: 5% rabbit or human serum in 0.5% NaCl	*Nyctotherus ovalis* [25]
	Opalinid media	
19	0.8% NaCl, 30% K-Na tartrate, drop of egg albumin	Opalinids [19]
20	0.4% NaCl, 0.001% $MgSO_4$, 0.1% K_2HPO_4, 1% purified gum arabic. Adjust to pH 7.1 with NaOH solution. Add frog liver extract, yeast extract, beef extract, peptone, & either cysteine HCl or ascorbic acid.	*Cepedea dimidiata* [21]
	Ruminant media	
21	30 ml mineral solution, 1.0 ml starch suspension, 1.0 ml antibiotic solution, 3.0 ml rumen liquor, 1.0 ml 0.5% Na_2S solution, 15.0 mg grass powder. Consult references 26 & 27 for method of preparation.	*Entodinium*, other rumen protozoa [26,27]
22	Place in cylinder inorganic solution of 0.6% NaCl, 0.1% $NaHCO_3$, 0.1% K_2HPO_4, 0.01% $MgSO_4$, 0.01% $CaCl_2$. Bubble 95% N_2 & 5% CO_2 through it for 15 minutes. In 50-ml Erlenmeyer flask, mix 20 ml inorganic solution, 20 ml inoculum, 16 mg powdered cellulose, 16 ml powdered grass. Bubble N-CO_2 mixture during incubation.	*Eudiplodinium neglectum* [16]
23	0.3% NaCl, 0.01% $MgSO_4$, 0.01% $CaCl_2$, 0.1% KH_2PO_4. Add 0.5% $NaHCO_3$ to keep solution buffered at pH 6.7. Incubate in 100% CO_2 atmosphere. 0.001% resazurin used as oxidation-reduction indicator. Add powdered wheat, dried bluegrass as substrate.	*Ophryoscolex purkinjei* [22]
24	Thioglycollate medium: 7 parts fluid thioglycollate (wt/vol, 2.98%), 2 parts beef heart infusion broth (wt/vol, 50%), 3 parts distilled water. Control contaminating microflora with 0.2 parts 0.1 g/ml streptomycin sulfate solution & 0.2 parts 20 μ/ml penicillin G solution.	*Colpoda maupasi* [29]
	Agnotobiotic Marine Ciliate Cultures	
25	Erdschreiber medium: 5 ml soil extract, 0.01% KNO_3, $Na_2HPO_4 \cdot 12H_2O$, 95 ml 0.02% seawater	General marine ciliates [1]
26	Cerophyl infusion: 0.8% Cerophyl solution2/ in seawater	*Euplotes cristatus* [38]
27	Sea-lettuce infusion: boiled seawater & *Ulva*	*Glauconema trihymene* [35]
	Axenic Cultures3/	
28	1.5% proteose-peptone, 0.5% bacto casitone, 0.1% Basamin-Busch yeast extract, 0.1% Na_2HPO_4, 0.2% NaCl, 0.005% $MgCl_2 \cdot 6H_2O$	*Colpidium, Glaucoma,* 4 species of *Tetrahymena* [20]
29	Chemically defined medium containing 16 amino acids, 4 nucleotides, acetate glucose, stigmasterol, 10 vitamins, trace metals	*Colpidium campylum, Tetrahymena paravorax, T. pyriformis* [34]
30	Chemically defined medium containing 12 essential amino acids, 7 B-complex vitamins, a purine, a pyrimidine, inorganic salts	*Glaucoma chattoni* [14]
31	0.1% proteose-peptone, 0.05% trypticase, 0.01% yeast nucleic acid, 0.001% triethylenemelamine 4T, 0.0005% stigmasterol, 0.005% $MgSO_4 \cdot 7H_2O$, vitamins	*Paramecium aurelia* [31]
32	Partially chemically defined medium similar to some chemically defined media for *Tetrahymena*	*Paramecium aurelia* [32]
33	T-2 & T-3 media: partially chemically defined media. The most complex T-3 contains liver hydrolysate, yeast nucleic acid, 47 other components including inorganic salts, amino acids, nucleotides, vitamins, coenzymes; also traces of unknown components.	*Telotrochidium henneguyi* [11]

2/ A dried grass preparation. 3/ Used in nutritional, biochemical, and biophysical studies.

continued

Part II. Ciliata

	Medium	Species Showing Growth
34	TP medium: 0.25% tryptone, 0.25% proteose-peptone, 0.1% $NaC_2H_3O_2 \cdot 3H_2O$, 0.1% glucose, 0.01% yeast extract, 0.01% $MgSO_4 \cdot 7H_2O$, 0.0002% thiamine HCl, 0.1% K_2HPO_4. Adjust pH to 7.3-7.4.	*Tetrahymena* spp. [2]
35	Chemically defined medium containing 12 essential amino acids, 6 B-complex vitamins, a purine, a pyrimidine, inorganic salts	*Tetrahymena paravorax* [13]
36	Defined basal medium A: complex, chemically defined medium with 38 components, including 17 amino acids or their derivatives, 8 vitamins, trace metals, inorganic salts	*Tetrahymena pyriformis* [28]
37	2.0% proteose-peptone, 0.1% yeast extract, 0.2% sodium acetate, mixture of bivalent cations, 0.5-1% glucose added in some experiments	*Tetrahymena pyriformis* [6]
38	1.2% proteose-peptone, 0.8% glucose; pH 7.2	*Tetrahymena pyriformis* [7]
39	2% proteose-peptone, 0.2% bacto yeast extract	*Tetrahymena pyriformis* [39]
40	1% bacto tryptone, 0.05% bacto yeast extract	*Tetrahymena pyriformis* [23]
41	Chemically defined medium	*Tetrahymena setifera* [15]

Contributor: Lee, John J.

References

[1] Arnold, Z. 1954. J. Paleontol. 28:404.
[2] Balamuth, W. 1967. Syllabus of laboratory exercises for a National Science Foundation summer institute in protozoology. Univ. California, Berkeley.
[3] Balamuth, W., and J. G. Sandza. 1944. Proc. Soc. Exptl. Biol. Med. 57:161.
[4] Beers, C. D. 1937. In P. S. Galtsoff, ed. Culture methods for invertebrate animals. Dover Press, New York. p. 100.
[5] Chen, Y. 1944. J. Morphol. 75:335.
[6] Conner, R. L., and S. G. Cline. 1967. J. Protozool. 14:22.
[7] Culbertson, J. R. 1966. Ibid. 13:397.
[8] Curds, C. R. 1964. Ibid. 11:552.
[9] De Terra, N. 1966. Ibid. 13:491.
[10] Finley, H. 1936. Trans. Am. Microscop. Soc. 55:323.
[11] Finley, H., and D. McLaughlin. 1965. J. Protozool. 12:41.
[12] Hirshfield, H. I., I. R. Isquith, and A. V. Bhandary. 1965. Ibid. 12:136.
[13] Holz, G. G., J. A. Erwin, and B. Wagner. 1961. Ibid. 8:297.
[14] Holz, G. G., et al. 1961. Ibid. 8:192.
[15] Holz, G. G., et al. 1962. Ibid. 9:359.
[16] Hungate, R. E. 1942. Biol. Bull. 83:303.
[17] Hyman, L. H. 1931. Trans. Am. Microscop. Soc. 50:50.
[18] Kirby, H. 1950. Materials and methods in the study of protozoa. Univ. California Press, Berkeley.
[19] Konsuloff, S. 1922. Arch. Protistenk. 44:285.
[20] Loefer, J. B., and O. H. Scherbaum. 1963. J. Protozool. 10:275.
[21] Lwoff, A., and S. Valentini. 1948. Ann. Inst. Pasteur 75:1.
[22] Mah, R. A. 1964. J. Protozool. 11:546.
[23] Mueller, M., P. Rohlich, and I. Toro. 1965. Ibid. 12:27.
[24] Nelson, E. C. 1940. Am. J. Trop. Med. 20:731.
[25] Nelson, E. C. 1943. Am. J. Hyg. 38:185.
[26] Quinn, L. Y., W. Burroughs, and W. C. Christiansen, 1962. Appl. Microbiol. 10:583.
[27] Rahman, S. A., D. B. Purser, and W. J. Tyznik. 1964. J. Protozool. 11:51.
[28] Rosenbaum, N., et al. 1966. Ibid. 13:533.
[29] Rudzinska, M. A., G. J. Jackson, and M. Tuffrau. 1966. Ibid. 13:440.
[30] Society of Protozoologists, Committee on Cultures. 1958. Ibid. 5:1.
[31] Soldo, A. T., G. A. Godoy, and W. J. Van Wagtendonk. 1966. Ibid. 13:492.
[32] Soldo, A. T., and W. J. Van Wagtendonk. 1961. Ibid. 8:41.
[33] Sprecht, H. 1935. Arch. Protistenk. 85:150.
[34] Stillwell, R. H. 1967. J. Protozool. 14:19.
[35] Thompson, J. C. 1966. Ibid. 13:393.
[36] Turner, J. P. 1930. Univ. Calif. (Berkeley) Publ. Zool. 33:193.
[37] Wichterman, R. 1940. Proc. Penna. Acad. Sci. 23: 151.
[38] Wichterman, R. 1967. J. Protozool. 14:49.
[39] Winicur, S., and J. S. Roth. 1965. Ibid. 12:166.
[40] Yusa, A. 1965. Ibid. 12:51.
[41] Zech, L. 1966. Ibid. 13:532.

continued

Part III. Trichomonadidae

	Medium	Species Showing Growth[1]
	Agnotobiotic Cultures[2]	
1	Egg-yolk infusion: with or without liver extract, with rice starch, 1-10% serum enrichment. For preparation, consult reference 4.	Most species can be isolated and maintained in the presence of balanced contaminants.[3]
2	Amaro's medium [1]: 0.5% NaCl, 0.04% KCl, 0.014% $CaCl_2$, 0.01% $MgSO_4 \cdot 7H_2O$, 0.1% $MgCl_2 \cdot 6H_2O$, 0.11% $Na_2HPO_4 \cdot 2H_2O$, 0.03% KH_2PO_4, 0.04% $NaHCO_3$, 0.5% liver extract, 0.1% yeast extract, 0.3% horse serum, 100 units/ml K-penicillin G, 100 µg/ml dihydrostreptomycin. Adjust to pH 6.0-8.0 with KOH before autoclaving; add sterile $NaHCO_3$, horse serum, & antibiotics aseptically after medium has cooled.	Most species can be isolated and maintained in the presence of balanced contaminants.[3]
	Axenic Cultures[4]	
3	Diamond's medium [7]: 2% trypticase, 1% yeast extract, 0.5% maltose, 0.1% L-cysteine HCl, 0.02% L-ascorbic acid, 0.08% KH_2PO_4, 0.08% K_2HPO_4, 0.05-0.10% agar, 10% inactivated sterile horse or sheep serum. Adjust to pH 6.0-8.0 with KOH, NaOH, or HCl (base or acid depends on species). Use with antibiotics for axenic isolation or retardation of bacterial growth. Autoclave 9 ml of medium 15 minutes at 15-lb pressure; add serum & antibiotics aseptically after medium has cooled. Use as soon as possible. Shelf life, 30 days at 4°C.	*Hypotrichomonas acosta, Monocercomonas* sp. (NS-1:PRR), *M. colubrorum, Trichomitis batrachorum, Tritrichomonas augusta* [27]; *Pentatrichomonas hominis, Tetratrichomonas gallinarum, Trichomonas gallinae, T. vaginalis; Tritrichomonas eberthi* [7]; *Tetratrichomonas buttreyi* [7,11,17]; *Trichomonas rotunda* [17]; *Tritrichomonas enteris* [2]; *T. foetus* [11]; *T. suis* [7,17]
4	CPLM medium [24]: 3.0% bacto peptone, 0.1% agar, 0.2% cysteine HCl, 0.16% maltose, 20 ml liver infusion/100 ml medium, 65 ml Ringer's solution/100 ml medium, 10% sterile serum. Prepare as above. 0.002% methylene blue may be added as an indicator. 0.1% Wilson's gastric mucin 1701X stimulatory for *Trichomitis batrachorum* & *Tetratrichomonas prowazeki.*	*Hypotrichomonas acosta, Tritrichomonas augusta* [26]; *Pentatrichomonas hominis* [5,45]; *Tetratrichomonas buttreyi, Trichomonas rotunda, Tritrichomonas suis* [17]; *Tetratrichomonas prowazeki* [19]; *Trichomitis batrachorum* [19]; *Trichomonas gallinae* [20]; *T. vaginalis* [24,51]; *Tritrichomonas enteris* [2]; *T. foetus* [12]
5	Fluid thioglycollate medium[5], with 5-10% sterile serum	*Hypotrichomonas acosta* [26]; *Pentatrichomonas hominis, Trichomonas vaginalis* [6]; *Tetratrichomonas prowazeki* [19]; *Trichomonas gallinae* [20]
6	STS medium [25]: 2% trypticase, 0.15% cysteine HCl, 0.1% maltose, 0.1% agar, 5% sterile serum	*Trichomonas vaginalis* [25]; *Tritrichomonas augusta* [38]
7	BMH medium [27]: 0.5% glucose, 1.0% trypticase, 0.25% yeast extract, 0.01% KH_2PO_4, 0.25% Na_2 glycerophosphate$\cdot 5H_2O$, 0.004% Ca pantothenate, 0.005% cholesterol, 0.0001% triethylenemelamine 4T, 0.1% agar, 0.04% ascorbic acid, 0.05% thiomalic acid, 0.004% trace-minerals mixture No. 50, 1.0 ml/100 vitamin mixture No. 12. Grow newly inoculated cultures for 2 days at 25°C, then place at 15°C for 1-2 months.	*Hypotrichomonas acosta, Monocercomonas* sp. (NS-1:PRR), *M. colubrorum, Trichomitis batrachorum, Tritrichomonas augusta.* [27]

[1] Species isolated from homoiotherms: *Pentatrichomonas hominis, Tetratrichomonas buttreyi, T. gallinarum, Trichomonas gallinae, T. tenax, T. vaginalis, Tritrichomonas eberthi, T. enteris, T. foetus, T. suis.* Species isolated from poikilotherms: *Hypotrichomonas acosta, Monocercomonas* sp. (NS-1:PRR), *M. colubrorum, Tetratrichomonas prowazeki, Trichomitis batrachorum, Tritrichomonas augusta.* [2] Many media for parasitic amoeba also support agnotobiotic trichomonad cultures [48,49] (*see* Part I). [3] In addition to species listed in footnote 1, the following have been cultured agnotobiotically (in the presence of unknown other organisms): *Metatrichomonas termopsidis, Monocercomonas verrens, Tetratrichomonas limacis, T. microti, T. ovis, Trichomitis marmotae.* [4] Because media for axenic culture support high bacterial populations, antibiotics are necessary to retard bacterial overgrowth or for axenic isolation. The following antibiotic combinations have been successful for axenic isolation: 10,000 units/ml Na- or K-penicillin, 1000 µg/ml streptomycin [7]; 2000 µg/ml dehydrostreptomycin, 250 µg/ml chloramphenicol, 60 µg/ml polymyxin B [26, 27]. For molds and yeasts: 300 µg/ml nystatin [18]. *See* also references 19 and 42. [5] Or without indicator, Brewer-modified.

continued

22. CULTURE MEDIA: PROTOZOA

Part III. Trichomonadidae

	Medium	Species Showing Growth[1/]
	Special Purpose Media	
8	Complex, chemically better-defined media [43]: mixtures of salts, amino acids, nucleotides, lipids, trace metals, vitamins, & one or more poorly defined complex natural organic substances	*Hypotrichomonas acosta* [26]; *Monocercomonas* sp. (NS-1:PRR), *M. colubrorum, Tritrichomonas augusta* [27]; *Trichomonas gallinae* [44]; *T. vaginalis* [46]
9	Complex medium for axenic *Trichomonas tenax*	*Trichomonas tenax* [8]
10	Media & techniques for freezing cultures	*Pentatrichomonas hominis* [9,35]; *Trichomonas gallinae* [9,21,22,35]; *T. vaginalis* [9,10,21,22,36]; *Tritrichomonas foetus* [15,16,28-33,35,37]
11	Solid media for cloning & drug testing	*Pentatrichomonas hominis, Tetratrichomonas gallinarum, Tritrichomonas augusta, T. suis* [39]; *Trichomonas gallinae* [3,39]; *T. vaginalis* [14,23,39,41]; *Tritrichomonas foetus* [39,50]
12	Tissue culture	*Trichomonas gallinae, T. vaginalis.* [20]
13	Bulk growth or continuous flow culture	*Pentatrichomonas hominis, Trichomonas vaginalis* [13,34,40]; *Tritrichomonas augusta* [40,47]

1/ Species isolated from homoiotherms: *Pentatrichomonas hominis, Tetratrichomonas buttreyi, T. gallinarum, Trichomonas gallinae, T. tenax, T. vaginalis, Tritrichomonas eberthi, T. enteris, T. foetus, T. suis.* Species isolated from poikilotherms: *Hypotrichomonas acosta, Monocercomonas* sp. (NS-1:PRR), *M. colubrorum, Tetratrichomonas prowazeki, Trichomitis batrachorum, Tritrichomonas augusta.*

Contributor: Lee, John J.

References

[1] Amaro, A. 1965. Intern. Conf. Protozool., 2nd, Proc. 1:225.
[2] Anderson, F. L., and N. D. Levine. 1962. J. Protozool. 9(Suppl.):18.
[3] Asami, K., Y. Nodake, and T. Ueno. 1955. Exptl. Parasitol. 4:34.
[4] Balamuth, W., and J. G. Sandza. 1944. Proc. Soc. Exptl. Biol. Med. 57:161.
[5] De Carneri, I. 1955. Nature 176:605.
[6] De Carneri, I. 1956. Riv. Parassitol. 17:247.
[7] Diamond, L. S. 1957. J. Parasitol. 43:488.
[8] Diamond, L. S. 1960. Ibid. 46:43.
[9] Diamond, L. S. 1962. J. Protozool. 9:442.
[10] Diamond, L. S., et al. 1965. Cryobiology 1:295.
[11] Doran, D. J. 1957. J. Protozool. 4:182.
[12] Doran, D. J. 1958. Ibid. 5:89.
[13] Feinberg, F. G. 1953. Nature 171:1165.
[14] Filadoro, F., and N. Orsi. 1958. Antibiot. Chemotherapy 8:561.
[15] Fitzgerald, P. R., and N. D. Levine. 1957. J. Protozool. 4(Suppl.):5.
[16] Fitzgerald, P. R., and N. D. Levine. 1961. Ibid. 8:21.
[17] Hibler, C. P., et al. 1960. Ibid. 7:159.
[18] Honigberg, B. M. 1957. J. Parasitol. 43:43.
[19] Honigberg, B. M. 1958. J. Protozool. 5(Suppl.):15.
[20] Honigberg, B. M. 1961. Intern. Conf. Protozool., 1st, Prague, Abstr., p. 62.
[21] Honigberg, B. M., and V. M. King. 1962. J. Protozool. 9(Suppl.):18.
[22] Honigberg, B. M., et al. 1965. Intern. Conf. Protozool., 2nd, Proc. 1:236.
[23] Ivey, M. H. 1961. J. Parasitol. 47:539.
[24] Johnson, G., and M. Trussell. 1943. Proc. Soc. Exptl. Biol. Med. 54:245.
[25] Kupferberg, A. B., et al. 1953. Ann. N.Y. Acad. Sci. 56:1006.
[26] Lee, J. J., and S. Pierce. 1960. J. Protozool. 7:402.
[27] Lee, J. J., et al. 1962. Ibid. 9:445.
[28] Levine, N. D., and F. L. Anderson. 1966. Ibid. 13:199.
[29] Levine, N. D., W. E. McCaul, and M. Mizell. 1957. Ibid. 4(Suppl.):5.
[30] Levine, N. D., and W. C. Marquart. 1954. Ibid. 1(Suppl.):4.
[31] Levine, N. D., and W. C. Marquart. 1955. Ibid. 2:100.
[32] Levine, N. D., M. Mizell, and D. A. Houlahan. 1958. Exptl. Parasitol. 7:236.
[33] Levine, N. D., et al. 1962. J. Protozool. 9:347.
[34] McEntegart, M. G. 1952. J. Clin. Pathol. 5:275.
[35] McEntegart, M. G. 1954. J. Hyg. 52:545.
[36] McEntegart, M. G. 1959. Nature 183:270.
[37] McWade, D. M., and J. A. Williams. 1954. Mich. State Univ. Agr. Expt. Sta. Quart. Bull. 37:248.
[38] Samuels, R. 1958. J. Protozool. 5(Suppl.):9.
[39] Samuels, R. 1962. Ibid. 9:103.
[40] Samuels, R., and E. A. Beil. 1963. Ibid. 9(Suppl.):19.
[41] Samuels, R., and D. J. Stouder. 1960. Ibid. 7:5.
[42] Seneca, H., and D. Ides. 1953. Am. J. Trop. Med. Hyg. 6:1045.
[43] Shorb, M. S. 1964. In S. H. Hutner, ed. Biochemistry and physiology of protozoa. Academic Press, New York, v. 3, p. 384.
[44] Shorb, M. S., and P. G. Lund. 1959. J. Protozool. 6:122.

continued

Part III. Trichomonadidae

[45] Solomon, J. M. 1957. J. Parasitol. 43(Suppl.):39.
[46] Sprince, H., and A. B. Kupferberg. 1947. J. Bacteriol. 53:435.
[47] Twohy, D. W., and P. A. Tucker. 1961. J. Protozool. 8(Suppl.):5.
[48] Wenrich, D. H. 1945. J. Parasitol. 31:375.
[49] Wenrich, D. H. 1946. Ibid. 32:40.
[50] West, R. A., et al. 1962. J. Protozool. 9:65.
[51] Wirtschafter, S. K. 1954. J. Parasitol. 40:100.

Part IV. Trypanosomatidae

	Medium	Species Showing Growth
	Blood Agar 1-4/	
1	**Solid phase:** 14 g agar, 6 g NaCl, 900 ml distilled H_2O, 450 ml defibrinated rabbit blood. For variations, consult references.	*Leishmania donovani, L. tropica* [34]; *L. enrietti* [6]; *L. tarentolae* [52]; *Trypanosoma ambystomae* [22]; *T. avium* [3]; *T. brucei, T. lewisi* [25]; *T. cruzi, T. duttoni, T. melophagium, T. rotatorium, T. theileri* [37]; *T. striati* [39]
2	**Solid phase:** 10-15 g agar, 10 g glucose, 1000 ml horsemeat broth, 1000 ml defibrinated horse blood	*Crithidia melophagia, Leptomonas ctenocephali, L. fasciculata, Trypanosoma cruzi, T. rotatorium, T. syrnii, T. theileri* [35]; *Leishmania brasiliensis, L. donovani, L. tropica* [40]; *Trypanosoma conorrhini* [9]
3	**Solid phase:** 50 g bacto beef, 20 g neopeptone, 5 g NaCl, 20 g bacto agar, 100-150 ml defibrinated human or rabbit blood. Variation: Locke's solution overlay [20,49] 5/.	*Crithidia fasciculata, Leishmania brasilensis, L. donovani, L. tropica, Trypanosoma lewisi, T. pipistrelli, T. ranarum* [49]; *Leishmania enrietti* [15]; *Trypanosoma conorrhini* [20]; *T. cruzi* [44,49]; *T. rangeli* [48]
4	**Solid phase:** 20 g agar, 20 g neopeptone, 6.0 g NaCl, 250 ml defibrinated rabbit blood. **Liquid phase:** neopeptone broth.	*Crithidia luciliae, Herpetomonas muscarum* [58]; *Trypanosoma cruzi, T. lewisi,* avian & frog trypanosomes [12]
5	**Solid phase:** 31 g nutrient agar, 5 g plain agar, 167 ml inactivated human plasma, 167 ml washed human red blood cells	*Trypanosoma gambiense, T. rhodesiense* [59]
6	**Solid phase:** 3 g bacto beef, 5 g bacto peptone, 8 g NaCl, 15 g bacto agar, 333 ml citrated human or rabbit blood. **Liquid phase:** Locke's solution.	*Trypanosoma congolense* [47]; *T. gambiense, T. rhodesiense* [51]
	Semisolid Media 2,3,6/	
7	1 part 3% agar, 8 parts Locke's solution with 0.2% glucose, 1 part rabbit serum	*Crithidia oncopelti* 7/, *Herpetomonas muscarum* 8/, *Leishmania agamae, L. ceramodactyli, L. donovani, L. tarentolae, L. tropica, Trypanosoma cruzi, T. ptyodactyli, T. rabinowitschi* [1]
8	Mixture of 21 amino acids, 3 salts, 10 vitamins, glucose, guanosine, adenine SO_4, uracil, uric acid, urea, creatine, creatinine, nucleic acid, 0.2% agar, heat-coagulated red blood cells	*Trypanosoma cruzi* [23]
	Liquid Media 2,3,6/	
9	0.5 ml human or monkey blood, 0.5 ml 2% sodium citrate in 0.85% NaCl solution, 1 ml Ringer's solution (with 0.6% NaCl). For variation, consult reference 5.	*Trypanosoma brucei* [5]; *T. congolense, T. gambiense* [5,41]; *T. cruzi* [41]
10	Overlay from entry 3 for trypanosomes of the *lewisi* group & from entry 6 for the African trypanosomes	*Trypanosoma congolense* [56]; *T. cruzi* [55]; *T. gambiense, T. rhodesiense* [51]

1/ Test-tube cultures usually contain 5 ml base; flask or plate cultures contain varying amounts of base, depending on size of container. 2/ Cultures usually maintained at 22-25°C. 3/ Ingredients are given in amounts to be added to one liter of distilled water, unless otherwise specified. 4/ Diphasic test-tube cultures receive 2-3 ml overlay; flask cultures, approximately 15 ml for each 25 ml base. 5/ 30% blood for all isolations and newly isolated cultures; 10% for most established cultures. 6/ Varying amounts of media are used, depending on size of container. 7/ Synonym: *Strigomonas oncopelti.* 8/ Synonym: *H. muscidarum.* 9/ Cultures usually maintained at 25-35°C.

continued

Part IV. Trypanosomatidae

	Medium	Species Showing Growth
11	10 ml 5% lactalbumin hydrolysate in Earle's saline, 5 ml filtered & unheated calf serum, 5 ml red cell lysate, 100 ml 0.1% glucose in Earle's saline	*Trypanosoma gambiense* [32]
12	Neopeptone broth (*see* entry 4), plus 5% defibrinated rabbit blood	*Trypanosoma ranarum* [57]
	Dialysate Medium[2,6]	
13	Cellophane loop filled with Locke's solution suspended in tubes of diphasic blood agar. Variations: loop suspended in blood-coagulum-peptone medium [13]; loop suspended in heart-brain infusion & hemoglobin solution [26].	*Trypanosoma cruzi* [13,26,50]
	Defined & Partially Defined Media[2,3,6]	
14	Mixture of amino acids, salts (including trace metals), carbohydrate, purines, pyrimidines, vitamins, growth factors, hemin. Variations: only methionine as amino acid & no hemin [31]; addition of glycine, alone or plus choline [17].	*Blastocrithidia culicis, Crithidia* spp. [16]; *C. oncopelti*[7] [31]; *Herpetomonas culicidarum* [7]; *Leishmania tarentolae* [52]; *Leptomonas* spp. [17]; *Trypanosoma ranarum, T. mega* [18]
15	Entry 8 without agar	*Trypanosoma cruzi* [23]
16	15 g bacto tryptose, 2 g glucose, 1 mg thiamine, 3 mg folic acid, 20 mg hemin, 25 mg sodium stearate, 4 g NaCl, 5 g $Na_3PO_4 \cdot 12H_2O$, 0.4 g KCl, 1000 ml twice-distilled H_2O	*Crithidia fasciculata* [49]; *Trypanosoma cruzi* [4]
	Avian Embryo Cultures[9]	
17	Chorioallantoic membrane	*Leishmania donovani, Trypanosoma gambiense* [43]; *Leishmania tropica* [36]; *Trypanosoma brucei, T. evansi* [24, 43]; *T. cruzi* [14,38]; *T. equiperdum, T. rhodesiense* [24]
18	Intra-yolk sac	*Leishmania brasiliensis, L. donovani, L. tropica* [21]; *Trypanosoma brucei, T. equiperdum, T. evansi* [28]; *T. cruzi* [27]
	Tissue Cultures[10,11]	
19	Mammalian tissues in nutrient fluid	*Leishmania donovani* [19]; *Trypanosoma cruzi* [30,38]; *T. gambiense, T. rhodesiense* [10]
20	Avian tissues in nutrient fluid	*Trypanosoma cruzi* [29,30]
21	Insect tissues in nutrient fluid	*Trypanosoma brucei, T. congolense* [53]; *T. rhodesiense* [33]
	Transformation Media[12]	
22	NNN (*see* entry 1) at 37°C	*Trypanosoma conorrhini* [11]
23	Weinman's blood agar (*see* entry 5), with or without salivary gland substances, at 25°C	*Brucei*-group trypanosomes [2]
24	Blood lysate & glucose solution with whole blood, at 36-37.5°C	*Trypanosoma theileri* [42]
25	Hanks' saline solution, lactalbumin & calf serum with or without mammalian tissues, at 37°C	*Trypanosoma conorrhini* [9]
26	Tumor cells ("L") in nutrient fluid at 37°C	*Trypanosoma cruzi* [54]
27	Insect tissues in nutrient fluid at 38°C	*Trypanosoma vivax* [53]
28	Nutrient medium with normal or immune rat serum at 37°C	*Trypanosoma lewisi* [8]
29	Nutrient medium with calf serum or urea at 26°C	*Trypanosoma mega* [45,46]

[2] Cultures usually maintained at 22-25°C. [3] Ingredients are given in amounts to be added to one liter of distilled water, unless otherwise specified. [6] Varying amounts of media are used, depending on size of container. [7] Synonym: *Strigomonas oncopelti.* [9] Cultures usually maintained at 25-35°C. [10] Cultures usually maintained at 25-38°C. [11] *See also* Transformation Media. [12] Supporting change to the bloodstream form or invertebrate infective form which normally have not developed in vitro.

continued

22. CULTURE MEDIA: PROTOZOA

Part IV. Trypanosomatidae

Contributor: Tobie, Eleanor Johnson

References

[1] Adler, S. 1934. Trans. Roy. Soc. Trop. Med. Hyg. 28:201.
[2] Amrein, Y. U., R. Geigy, and M. Kauffmann. 1965. Acta Trop. 22:193.
[3] Baker, J. R. 1956. Parasitology 46:308.
[4] Bone, G. J., and G. Parent. 1963. J. Gen. Microbiol. 31:261.
[5] Brutsaert, P., and C. Henrard. 1938. Compt. Rend. Soc. Biol. 127:1469.
[6] Coutinho, J. O. 1955. Folia Clin. Biol. (Sao Paulo) 23:91.
[7] Cowperthwaite, J., et al. 1953. Ann. N.Y. Acad. Sci. 56:972.
[8] D'Alesandro, P. A. 1962. J. Protozool. 9:351.
[9] Deane, M. P., and L. M. Deane. 1961. Rev. Inst. Med. Trop. Sao Paulo 3:149.
[10] Demarchi, J., and J. Nicoli. 1960. Ann. Inst. Pasteur 99:120
[11] Desowitz, R. S. 1963. J. Protozool. 10:390.
[12] Diamond, L. S., and C. M. Herman. 1954. J. Parasitol. 40:195.
[13] Fife, E. H., and J. F. Kent. 1960. Am. J. Trop. Med. Hyg. 9:512.
[14] Ganapati, P. N. 1948. Nature 162:963.
[15] Greenblatt, C. L., and P. Glaser. 1965. Exptl. Parasitol. 16:36.
[16] Guttman, H. N. 1963. Ibid. 14:129.
[17] Guttman, H. N. 1966. J. Protozool. 13:390.
[18] Guttman, H. N. Unpublished. New York Univ., Bronx, 1967.
[19] Hawking, F. 1948. Trans. Roy. Soc. Trop. Med. Hyg. 41:545.
[20] Johnson, E. M. 1947. J. Parasitol. 33:85.
[21] Jones, H., G. Rake, and D. Hamre. 1944. Am. J. Trop. Med. 24:381.
[22] Lehmann, D. L. 1955. J. Protozool. 2:28.
[23] Little, P. A., and J. J. Oleson. 1951. J. Bacteriol. 61:709.
[24] Longley, J., N. M. Clausen, and A. L. Tatum. 1939. Proc. Soc. Exptl. Biol. Med. 41:365.
[25] MacNeal, W. J. 1904. J. Infect. Diseases 1:517.
[26] Maekelt, G. A. 1964. Rev. Venezolana Sanidad Asistencia Social 29:1.
[27] Manso Soto, A. E., C. A. Loretti, and J. A. Rispoli. 1950. Mision Estud. Patol. Reg. Arg. 21:23.
[28] Merchant, D. J. 1947. Proc. Soc. Exptl. Biol. Med. 64:391.
[29] Meyer, H., and M. X. de Oliveira. 1948. Parasitology 39:91.
[30] Neva, F. A., M. F. Malone, and B. R. Myers. 1961. Am. J. Trop. Med. Hyg. 10:140.
[31] Newton, B. A. 1956. Nature 177:279.
[32] Nicoli, J. 1961. Bull. Soc. Pathol. Exotique 54:77.
[33] Nicoli, J., and G. Vattier. 1964. Ibid. 57:213.
[34] Nicolle, C. 1908. Compt. Rend. 146:842.
[35] Nöller, W. 1917. Arch. Schiffs. Tropenhyg. 21:53.
[36] Oberling, C., and N. Ansari. 1951. Bull. Soc. Pathol. Exotique 44:542.
[37] Packchanian, A. 1934. Science 80:407.
[38] Pipkin, A. C. 1960. Exptl. Parasitol. 9:167.
[39] Qadri, S. S. 1962. Parasitology 52:229.
[40] Ray, J. C. 1932. Indian J. Med. Res. 20:355.
[41] Reichenow, E. 1934. Arch. Schiffs. Tropenhyg. 38:292.
[42] Ristic, M., and W. Trager. 1958. J. Protozool. 5:146.
[43] Rodhain, J., and L. van den Berghe. 1943. Ann. Soc. Belge Med. Trop. 23:141.
[44] Senekjie, H. A. 1943. Am. J. Trop. Med. 23:523.
[45] Steinert, M. 1958. Exptl. Cell. Res. 15:531.
[46] Steinert, M. 1958. Ibid. 15:560.
[47] Tobie, E. J. 1958. J. Parasitol. 44:241.
[48] Tobie, E. J. 1961. Exptl. Parasitol. 11:1.
[49] Tobie, E. J. Unpublished. Natl. Institutes of Health, Bethesda, Md., 1967.
[50] Tobie, E. J., and C. W. Rees. 1948. J. Parasitol. 34:162.
[51] Tobie, E. J., T. von Brand, and B. Mehlman. 1950. Ibid. 36:48.
[52] Trager, W. 1957. J. Protozool. 4:269.
[53] Trager, W. 1959. Ann. Trop. Med. Parasitol. 53:473.
[54] Trejos, A., et al. 1963. Exptl. Parasitol. 13:211.
[55] von Brand, T., E. M. Johnson, and C. W. Rees. 1946. J. Gen. Physiol. 30:163.
[56] von Brand, T., and E. J. Tobie. 1959. J. Parasitol. 45:204.
[57] Wallace, F. G. 1956. J. Protozool. 3:47.
[58] Wallace, F. G., and T. B. Clark. 1959. Ibid. 6:58.
[59] Weinman, D. 1960. Trans. Roy. Soc. Trop. Med. Hyg. 54:180.

Part V. Phytomastigina

	Constituents of Medium	Concentration mg/liter
	Marine Flagellates[1] [9]	
1	Ca, as Cl	400
2	$MgCl_2 \cdot 6H_2O$	4000
3	$MgSO_4 \cdot 7H_2O$	7000
4	KCl	700
5	K_3PO_4	10
6	NaCl	28,000

[1] Chrysomonads, cryptomonads, dinoflagellates, and also diatoms.

continued

Part V. Phytomastigina

	Constituents of Medium	Concentration mg/liter[2]
7	$NaNO_3$	100
8	P II metals[3]	10 ml
9	S II metals[4]	10 ml
10	Sodium glycerophosphate	10
11	Sodium metasilicate·$9H_2O$	150
12	Nitrilotriacetic acid	100
13	Tris[5]	1000
14	Thiamine HCl	100 μg
15	Biotin	1 μg
16	Vitamin B_{12}	0.2 μg
17	pH = 7.8-8.0	
	Chilomonas paramecium [4]	
18	NH_4Cl	200
19	H_3BO_3	115
20	$CaCl_2$	55
21	$CoSO_4 \cdot 7H_2O$	19
22	$CuSO_4 \cdot 5H_2O$	15.7
23	$FeSO_4 \cdot 7H_2O$	40
24	$MgSO_4 \cdot 7H_2O$	800
25	$MnSO_4 \cdot 4H_2O$	81
26	K_2HPO_4	200
27	$Na_2MoO_4 \cdot 2H_2O$	15
28	$ZnSO_4 \cdot 7H_2O$	220
29	EDTA[6]	500
30	Thiamine HCl	10 μg
31	pH = 3.5-7.5	
	Chlamydomonas moewusii [6]	
32	B	20
33	Ca	50
34	Co	0.5
35	Cu	2
36	Fe	10
37	$MgSO_4 \cdot 7H_2O$	500
38	Mn	4
39	Mo	4
40	K_2HPO_4	250
41	Zn	20
42	Ammonium acetate	1000
43	EDTA[6]	200
44	Glycine	2000
45	pH = 7.5	
	Chlorogonium spp.[7] [7]	
46	NH_4NO_3	500
47	$FeCl_3 \cdot 6H_2O$	2.5
48	$MgSO_4 \cdot 7H_2O$	100
49	$MnCl_2 \cdot 4H_2O$	0.1
50	KH_2PO_4	500
51	NaCl	100
52	pH = 7.0	
	Euglena gracilis [5]	
53	B, as H_3BO_3	0.1
54	$CaCO_3$	80
55	Co, as SO_4	0.1
56	Cu, as SO_4	0.08
57	Fe, as SO_4	2
58	$MgSO_4 \cdot 7H_2O$	400
59	Mn, as SO_4	0.5
60	Mo, as $(NH_4)_6Mo_7O_{24} \cdot 4H_2O$	0.35
61	KH_2PO_4	300
62	V, as $Na_3VO_4 \cdot 16H_2O$	0.01
63	Zn, as SO_4	1
64	Ammonium succinate	600
65	Sucrose	15,000
66	DL-Malic acid	1000
67	DL-Aspartic acid	2000
68	L-Glutamic acid	3000
69	Glycine	2500
70	Thiamine HCl	0.6
71	Vitamin B_{12}	0.0002
72	pH = 3-6	
	Haematococcus sp. [3]	
73	$CaSO_4 \cdot 2H_2O$	10
74	Co, as SO_4	0.5 μg
75	Cu, as SO_4	0.005
76	Fe, as SO_4	0.5
77	$MgCl_2 \cdot 6H_2O$	40
78	Mn, as SO_4	0.05
79	Mo, as Na	0.5 μg
80	KCl	8
81	KNO_3	100
82	K_2HPO_4	10
83	NaCl	300
84	Zn, as SO_4	0.005
85	Citric acid	40
86	Thiamine	100 μg
87	Vitamin B_{12}	0.1 μg
88	Glycine	250
89	Glycylglycine	500
90	pH = 8.0	

[2] Unless otherwise specified. [3] 1 ml of P II metals contains 0.2 mg B (as H_3BO_3), 0.001 mg Co (as Cl), 0.01 mg Fe (as Cl), 0.04 mg Mn (as Cl), 0.005 mg Zn (as Cl), 1 mg ethylenediamine tetraacetic acid. [4] 1 ml of S II metals contains 1.0 mg Br (as Na), 0.001 mg I (as K), 0.02 mg Li (as Cl), 0.05 mg Mo (as Na), 0.02 mg Rb (as Cl), 0.2 mg Sr (as Cl). [5] Tris(hydroxymethyl)aminomethane. [6] Ethylenediamine tetraacetate. [7] *C. elongatum* and *C. euchlorum.*

continued

Part V. Phytomastigina

	Constituents of Medium	Concentration mg/liter[2]
	Ochromonas spp.[8] [1]	
91	NH_4Cl	500[9]; 400[10]
92	B, as H_3BO_3	0.1
93	$CaCO_3$	50[9]; 150[10]
94	Co, as SO_4	0.1
95	Cu, as SO_4	0.08
96	Fe, as SO_4	2
97	$MgCO_3$ (basic)	400[9]; 500[10]
98	$MgSO_4 \cdot 7H_2O$	1000[9]
99	Mn, as SO_4	0.5
100	Mo, as $(NH_4)_6Mo_7O_{24} \cdot H_2O$	0.35
101	KH_2PO_4	300
102	V, as $Na_3VO_4 \cdot 16H_2O$	0.01
103	Zn, as SO_4	1
104	Ammonium citrate	1200[10]
105	Nitrilotriacetic acid	200[9]; 300[10]
106	Thiamine HCl	1[9]; 2[10]
107	Biotin	10 µg[9]; 4 µg[10]
108	Vitamin B_{12}	1 µg[10]
109	Glucose	10,000
110	L-Arginine HCl	400[9]; 500[10]
111	L-Glutamic acid	10,000[9]; 3000[10]
112	Glycine	100[9]
113	L-Histidine HCl	400[9]; 500[10]
114	DL-Methionine	600[10]
115	pH = 5.0	
	Polytoma uvella[11] [2]	
116	NH_4Cl	500
117	H_3BO_3	120
118	$CaCl_2$	60
119	$CoSO_4 \cdot 7H_2O$	20
120	$CuSO_4 \cdot 5H_2O$	13
121	$FeSO_4 \cdot 7H_2O$	40
122	$MgSO_4 \cdot 7H_2O$	160
123	$MnSO_4 \cdot 4H_2O$	50
124	K_2HPO_4	40
125	$Na_2MoO_4 \cdot 7H_2O$	15
126	$ZnSO_4 \cdot 7H_2O$	220
127	Sodium acetate $\cdot 3H_2O$	2720
128	EDTA[6]	100
129	Tris[5]	1210
130	pH = 8.0	
	Polytomella caeca[12] [8]	
131	$MgSO_4 \cdot 7H_2O$	100
132	KH_2PO_4	500
133	NaCl	100
134	Ammonium acetate[13]	2000
135	Thiamine	0.3-1.0
136	pH = 6.5	
	Synura spp.[14] [10]	
137	$(NH_4)_2SO_4$	60
138	Ca, as Cl	4
139	Fe, as Cl	0.5
140	Mg, as Cl	0.5
141	Mn, as Cl	0.01
142	K, as Cl	2
143	Sodium citrate $\cdot H_2O$	20
144	Sodium glycerophosphate $\cdot 5H_2O$	50
145	Sodium metasilicate $\cdot 9H_2O$	30
146	Vitamin B_{12}	0.4 µg
147	L-Histidine, free base	200
148	pH = 6.0	
	Volvox spp.[15] [10]	
149	Ca, as NO_3	20
150	$MgSO_4 \cdot 7H_2O$	40
151	KCl	50
152	P IV metals[16]	3.0-40 ml/liter
153	Sodium glycerophosphate $\cdot 5H_2O$	50
154	Biotin	0.1 µg
155	Vitamin B_{12}	0.1 µg
156	Glycylglycine[17]	500 mg
157	pH = 7.2-7.8	

[2] Unless otherwise specified. [5] Tris(hydroxymethyl)aminomethane. [6] Ethylenediamine tetraacetate. [8] *O. danica* and *O. malhamensis.* [9] *O. danica.* [10] *O. malhamensis.* [11] Other *Polytoma* species might grow in the same medium if thiamine HCl were added at 100 µg/liter. [12] Sterilize medium, than add sufficient $CaCl_2$ and $FeC_6H_5O_7 \cdot 3H_2O$ to give a final concentration of 10 mg of each per liter. [13] May be substituted with NH_4Cl and *n*-butanol (1 ml/liter). [14] *S. caroliniana* and *S. petersenii.* [15] *V. globator, V. tertius,* and other Volvocales. [16] 1 ml of P IV metals contains 0.001 mg Co (as Cl), 0.04 mg Fe (as Cl), 0.01 mg Mn (as Cl), 0.005 mg Mo (as Na), 0.005 mg Zn (as Cl), 1 mg hydroxyethyl ethylenediamine tetraacetate. [17] To buffer at pH 6.0-6.5, substitute 200 mg histidine per liter.

Contributor: Provasoli, Luigi

References

[1] Aaronson, S., and H. Baker. 1959. J. Protozool. 6: 282.

[2] Cirillo, V. P. 1955. Proc. Soc. Exptl. Biol. Med. 88: 352.

continued

22. CULTURE MEDIA: PROTOZOA

Part V. Phytomastigina

[3] Droop, M. R. 1961. Rev. Algol. 5:247.
[4] Holz, G. G. 1954. J. Protozool. 1:114.
[5] Hutner, S. H., and M. K. Bach. 1955. Ibid. 3:101.
[6] Hutner, S. H., et al. 1950. Proc. Am. Phil. Soc. 94: 152.
[7] Loefer, J. B. 1934. Biol. Bull. 66:1.
[8] Lwoff, A. 1941. Ann. Inst. Pasteur 66:407.
[9] Provasoli, L. 1964. Proc. Intern. Seaweed Symp., 4th, Biarritz, France, 1961, p. 9.
[10] Provasoli, L., and I. J. Pintner. 1960. Ecol. Algae Symp. Ecol. Pymatuning Lab. Univ. Pittsburgh Spec. Publ. 2:84.

23. CULTURE MEDIA: ANIMAL TISSUES

Part I. Balanced Salt Solutions

In general, these diluents are used only in combination with naturally occurring body substances (e.g., blood serum, tissue extracts), and/or with more complex, chemically defined, feeding solutions. pH of the final medium must be regulated.

	Constituent	Concentration mg/liter
	Ringer (Mammalian) [9]	
1	$CaCl_2$	250
2	KCl	420
3	NaCl	9000
	Ringer (Amphibian) [8]	
4	$CaCl_2$	120
5	KCl	140
6	$NaHCO_3$	200
7	NaCl	6500
	Locke[1/] [6]	
8	$CaCl_2$	240
9	KCl	420
10	$NaHCO_3$	300
11	NaCl	9000
12	Glucose	1000
	Locke[1/] [6]	
13	$CaCl_2$	200
14	KCl	200
15	$NaHCO_3$	200
16	NaCl	9500
17	Glucose	1000
	Tyrode [10]	
18	$CaCl_2$	200
19	$MgCl_2 \cdot 6H_2O$	100[2/]
20	KCl	200
21	$NaHCO_3$	1000
22	NaCl	8000
23	$NaH_2PO_4 \cdot H_2O$	50
24	Glucose	1000
	Gey (For Tubes) [3]	
25	$CaCl_2$	170
26	$MgCl_2 \cdot 6H_2O$	210
27	$MgSO_4 \cdot 7H_2O$	70
28	KCl	370
29	KH_2PO_4	30
30	$NaHCO_3$	2270
31	NaCl	7000
32	$Na_2HPO_4 \cdot 2H_2O$	150
33	Glucose	1000
	Gey (For Slides) [3]	
34	$CaCl_2$	170
35	$MgCl_2 \cdot 6H_2O$	210
36	$MgSO_4 \cdot 7H_2O$	70
37	KCl	370
38	KH_2PO_4	30
39	$NaHCO_3$	227
40	NaCl	8000
41	$Na_2HPO_4 \cdot 2H_2O$	150
42	Glucose	1000
	Earle [2]	
43	$CaCl_2$	200
44	$MgSO_4$	100
45	KCl	400
46	$NaHCO_3$	2200
47	NaCl	6800
48	$NaH_2PO_4 \cdot H_2O$	140
49	Glucose	1000
	Hanks[3/] [4]	
50	$CaCl_2$	200
51	$MgSO_4 \cdot 7H_2O$	200
52	KCl	400
53	KH_2PO_4	100
54	$NaHCO_3$	1273
55	NaCl	8000
56	$Na_2HPO_4 \cdot 2H_2O$	100
57	Glucose	2000
	Hanks[3/] [5]	
58	$CaCl_2$	140
59	$MgSO_4 \cdot 7H_2O$	200
60	KCl	400
61	KH_2PO_4	60
62	$NaHCO_3$	350
63	NaCl	8000
64	$Na_2HPO_4 \cdot 2H_2O$	60
65	Glucose	1000
	Puck (Saline F) [7]	
66	$CaCl_2 \cdot 2H_2O$	16
67	$MgSO_4 \cdot 7H_2O$	154
68	KCl	285
69	KH_2PO_4	83
70	$NaHCO_3$	1200
71	NaCl	7400
72	$Na_2HPO_4 \cdot 7H_2O$	290
73	Glucose	1100
	Puck (Saline G) [7]	
74	$CaCl_2 \cdot 2H_2O$	16
75	$MgSO_4 \cdot 7H_2O$	154
76	KCl	400
77	KH_2PO_4	150
78	$NaHCO_3$	0
79	NaCl	8000
80	$Na_2HPO_4 \cdot 7H_2O$	290
81	Glucose	1100
	Dulbecco [1]	
82	$CaCl_2$	100
83	$MgCl_2 \cdot 6H_2O$	100
84	KCl	200
85	KH_2PO_4	200
86	NaCl	8000
87	Na_2HPO_4	1150

[1/] One of several solutions described by Locke. [2/] Or may be 214 mg/liter; degree of hydration not reported. [3/] One of two solutions described by Hanks.

Contributors: (a) Waymouth, Charity, (b) Ambrose, Charles Tesch

continued

23. CULTURE MEDIA: ANIMAL TISSUES

Part I. Balanced Salt Solutions

References

[1] Dulbecco, R., and M. Vogt. 1954. J. Exptl. Med. 99:167.

[2] Earle, W. R. 1943. J. Natl. Cancer Inst. 4:165.

[3] Gey, G. O., and M. K. Gey. 1936. Am. J. Cancer 27:55.

[4] Hanks, J. H. 1948. J. Cellular Comp. Physiol. 31:235.

[5] Hanks, J. H., and R. E. Wallace. 1949. Proc. Soc. Exptl. Biol. Med. 71:196.

[6] Locke, F. S. 1901. Centr. Physiol. 14:670.

[7] Puck, T. T., S. J. Cieciura, and A. Robinson. 1958. J. Exptl. Med. 108:945.

[8] Ringer, S. 1883. J. Physiol. (London) 4:222.

[9] Ringer, S. 1886. Ibid. 7:291.

[10] Tyrode, M. V. 1910. Arch. Intern. Pharmacodyn. 20:205.

Part II. Constituents of Synthetic Media

	Constituent	Concentration mg/liter
	Eagle's Basal [1]	
1	$CaCl_2$	111
2	$MgCl_2 \cdot 6H_2O$	102
3	KCl	373
4	$NaHCO_3$	1680
5	NaCl	5845
6	$NaH_2PO_4 \cdot H_2O$	138
7	Thiamine HCl	0.34
8	Riboflavin	0.04
9	Nicotinamide	0.12
10	Pyridoxal HCl	0.2
11	Biotin	0.24
12	Pantothenic acid	0.2
13	Folic acid	0.44
14	Choline	0.12
15	Glucose	900
16	L-Arginine	17.5
17	L-Cystine	12.0
18	L-Glutamine	292.0
19	L-Histidine	7.75
20	L-Isoleucine	26.0
21	L-Leucine	26.0
22	L-Lysine	29.0
23	L-Methionine	7.5
24	L-Phenylalanine	16.5
25	L-Threonine	24.0
26	L-Tryptophan	4.0
27	L-Tyrosine	18.0
28	L-Valine	23.0
29	Penicillin	50.0
30	Streptomycin	50.0
31	Phenol red	5.0
	Eagle's Minimum Essential [2]	
32	$CaCl_2$	200
33	$MgCl_2 \cdot 6H_2O$	200
34	KCl	400
35	$NaHCO_3$	2000
36	NaCl	6800
37	$NaH_2PO_4 \cdot 2H_2O$	150
38	Thiamine	1.0
39	Riboflavin	0.1
40	Nicotinamide	1.0
41	Pyridoxal	1.0
42	Pantothenate	1.0
43	Folic acid	1.0
44	*m*-Inositol	2.0
45	Choline	1.0
46	Glucose	1000
47	L-Arginine	105.0
48	L-Cystine	24.0
49	L-Glutamine	292.0
50	L-Histidine	31.0
51	L-Isoleucine	52.0
52	L-Leucine	52.0
53	L-Lysine	58.0
54	L-Methionine	15.0
55	L-Phenylalanine	32.0
56	L-Threonine	48.0
57	L-Tryptophan	10.0
58	L-Tyrosine	36.0
59	L-Valine	46.0
	Earle's NCTC-117 [3]	
60	$CaCl_2$	200
61	$MgSO_4$	100
62	KCl	400
63	$NaHCO_3$	2200
64	NaCl	6800
65	$NaH_2PO_4 \cdot H_2O$	140
66	Sodium glucuronate $\cdot H_2O$	1.8
67	Thiamine HCl	0.025
68	Riboflavin	0.025
69	Nicotinic acid	0.0625
70	Nicotinamide	0.0625
71	Pyridoxal HCl	0.0625
72	Pyridoxine HCl	0.0625
73	Biotin	0.025
74	Calcium pantothenate	0.025
75	Folic acid	0.025
76	*p*-Aminobenzoic acid	0.125
77	*m*-Inositol	0.125
78	Vitamin B_{12}	10.0
79	Choline chloride	1.25
80	Ascorbic acid	50.0
81	Vitamin A alcohol	0.25
82	Vitamin D_2	0.25
83	α-Tocopherol phosphate, disodium	0.025
84	Menadione	0.025
85	Polysorbate 80	12.5
86	Glucose	1000
87	D-Glucosamine HCl	3.85
88	D-Glucuronolactone	1.8
89	L-Alanine	31.48
90	L-α-Amino-*n*-butyric acid	5.51
91	L-Arginine HCl	31.16
92	L-Asparagine $\cdot H_2O$	9.19
93	L-Aspartic acid	9.91
94	L-Cysteine HCl	260.0
95	L-Cystine	10.49
96	L-Glutamic acid	8.26
97	L-Glutamine	135.73
98	Glycine	13.51
99	L-Histidine HCl $\cdot H_2O$	26.65
100	Hydroxy-L-proline	4.09
101	L-Isoleucine	18.04
102	L-Leucine	20.44
103	L-Lysine HCl	38.43
104	L-Methionine	4.44
105	L-Ornithine HCl	9.41

continued

Part II. Constituents of Synthetic Media

	Constituent	Concentration mg/liter
106	L-Phenylalanine	16.53
107	L-Proline	6.13
108	L-Serine	10.75
109	L-Taurine	4.18
110	L-Threonine	18.93
111	L-Tryptophan	17.50
112	L-Tyrosine	16.44
113	L-Valine	25.00
114	Glutathione, sodium	10.0
115	Deoxycytidine HCl	10.0
116	Thymidine	10.0
117	Ethanol	40.0
118	Phenol red, sodium	20.0

Evans' NCTC-133 [4]

	Constituent	Concentration mg/liter
119	$CaCl_2$	200
120	$MgSO_4$	100
121	KCl	400
122	$NaC_2H_3O_2 \cdot 3H_2O$	50.0
123	$NaHCO_3$	2200
124	NaCl	6800
125	$NaH_2PO_4 \cdot H_2O$	140
126	Thiamine HCl	0.025
127	Riboflavin	0.025
128	Nicotinamide	0.0625
129	Pyridoxal HCl	0.0625
130	D-Biotin	0.025
131	Calcium pantothenate	0.025
132	Folic acid	0.025
133	*m*-Inositol	0.125
134	Vitamin B_{12}	10.0
135	Choline chloride	1.25
136	D-Glucose	1000
137	D-Glucosamine HCl	3.85
138	D-Glucuronolactone	1.8
139	L-Alanine	31.48
140	L-α-Amino-*n*-butyric acid	5.51
141	L-Arginine HCl	31.16
142	L-Asparagine $\cdot H_2O$	9.19
143	L-Aspartic acid	9.91
144	L-Cystine	10.49
145	L-Glutamic acid	8.26
146	L-Glutamine	135.73
147	Glycine	13.51
148	L-Histidine $HCl \cdot H_2O$	26.65
149	Hydroxy-L-proline	4.09
150	L-Isoleucine	18.04
151	L-Leucine	20.44
152	L-Lysine HCl	38.43
153	L-Methionine	4.44
154	L-Ornithine HCl	9.41
155	L-Phenylalanine	16.53
156	L-Proline	6.13
157	L-Serine	10.75
158	L-Taurine	4.18
159	L-Threonine	18.93
160	L-Tryptophan	17.50
161	L-Tyrosine	16.44
162	L-Valine	25.00
163	Deoxycytidine HCl	10.0
164	Thymidine	10.0
165	Phenol red, sodium	20.0

Evans' NCTC-135 [4]

	Constituent	Concentration mg/liter
166	$CaCl_2$	200
167	$MgSO_4$	100
168	KCl	400
169	$NaC_2H_3O_2 \cdot 3H_2O$	50.0
170	$NaHCO_3$	2200
171	NaCl	6800
172	$NaH_2PO_4 \cdot H_2O$	140
173	Sodium glucuronate $\cdot H_2O$	1.8
174	Thiamine HCl	0.025
175	Riboflavin	0.025
176	Nicotinic acid	0.0625
177	Nicotinamide	0.0625
178	Pyridoxal HCl	0.0625
179	Pyridoxine HCl	0.0625
180	D-Biotin	0.025
181	Calcium pantothenate	0.025
182	Folic acid	0.025
183	*p*-Aminobenzoic acid	0.125
184	*m*-Inositol	0.125
185	Vitamin B_{12}	10.0
186	Choline chloride	1.25
187	Ascorbic acid	50.0
188	Vitamin A alcohol	0.25
189	Vitamin D_2	0.25
190	α-Tocopherol phosphate, disodium	0.025
191	Menadione	0.025
192	Polysorbate 80	12.5
193	Glucose	1000
194	D-Glucosamine HCl	3.85
195	D-Glucuronolactone	1.8
196	L-Alanine	31.48
197	L-α-Amino-*n*-butyric acid	5.51
198	L-Arginine HCl	31.16
199	L-Asparagine $\cdot H_2O$	9.19
200	L-Aspartic acid	9.91
201	L-Cystine	10.49
202	L-Glutamic acid	8.26
203	L-Glutamine	135.73
204	Glycine	13.51
205	L-Histidine $HCl \cdot H_2O$	26.65
206	Hydroxy-L-proline	4.09
207	L-Isoleucine	18.04
208	L-Leucine	20.44
209	L-Lysine HCl	38.43
210	L-Methionine	4.44
211	L-Ornithine HCl	9.41
212	L-Phenylalanine	16.53
213	L-Proline	6.13
214	L-Serine	10.75
215	L-Taurine	4.18
216	L-Threonine	18.93
217	L-Tryptophan	17.50
218	L-Tyrosine	16.44
219	L-Valine	25.00
220	Glutathione, sodium	10.0
221	Deoxyadenosine	10.0
222	Deoxycytidine HCl	10.0
223	Deoxyguanosine	10.0
224	Thymidine	10.0
225	Diphosphopyridine nucleotide	7.0
226	Flavin adenine dinucleotide	1.0
227	Triphosphopyridine nucleotide	1.0
228	Uridine triphosphate, sodium	1.0
229	5-Methylcytosine	0.1
230	Cocarboxylase	1.0
231	Coenzyme A	2.5
232	Ethanol	40.0
233	Phenol red	20.0

Ham's F-12 [6]

	Constituent	Concentration mg/liter
234	$CaCl_2 \cdot 2H_2O$	44.11
235	$CuSO_4 \cdot 5H_2O$	0.002
236	$FeSO_4 \cdot 7H_2O$	0.834
237	$MgCl_2 \cdot 6H_2O$	122.0
238	KCl	223.5
239	$NaHCO_3$	1176
240	NaCl	7600
241	$Na_2HPO_4 \cdot 7H_2O$	268.1
242	$ZnSO_4 \cdot 7H_2O$	0.862
243	Sodium pyruvate	110.1
244	Thiamine HCl	0.337
245	Riboflavin	0.038
246	Nicotinamide	0.037
247	Pyridoxine HCl	0.062
248	Biotin	0.007

continued

Part II. Constituents of Synthetic Media

	Constituent	Concentration mg/liter
249	Calcium pantothenate	0.476
250	Folic acid	1.32
251	*m*-Inositol	18.0
252	Vitamin B_{12}	1.36
253	Choline chloride	13.96
254	Linoleic acid	0.084
255	Lipoic acid	0.206
256	Glucose	1802
257	L-Alanine	8.91
258	L-Arginine HCl	210.7
259	L-Asparagine	13.21
260	L-Aspartic acid	13.31
261	L-Cysteine HCl	31.52
262	L-Glutamic acid	14.71
263	L-Glutamine	146.1
264	Glycine	7.51
265	L-Histidine HCl	20.96
266	L-Isoleucine	3.94
267	L-Leucine	13.12
268	L-Lysine HCl	36.54
269	L-Methionine	4.48
270	L-Phenylalanine	4.96
271	L-Proline	34.53
272	L-Serine	10.51
273	L-Threonine	11.91
274	L-Tryptophan	2.04
275	L-Tyrosine	5.44
276	L-Valine	11.7
277	Hypoxanthine	4.08
278	Thymidine	0.73
279	Putrescine·2HCl	0.161
280	Phenol red	1.17
	Healy and Parker's CMRL-1066 [12]	
281	$CaCl_2$	200
282	$MgSO_4 \cdot 7H_2O$	200
283	KCl	400
284	$NaC_2H_3O_2 \cdot 3H_2O$	83.0
285	$NaHCO_3$	2200
286	NaCl	6800
287	$NaH_2PO_4 \cdot H_2O$	140
288	Sodium glucuronate·H_2O	4.2
289	Thiamine HCl	0.01
290	Riboflavin	0.01
291	Nicotinic acid	0.025
292	Nicotinamide	0.025
293	Pyridoxal HCl	0.025
294	Pyridoxine HCl	0.025
295	Biotin	0.01
296	Calcium pantothenate	0.01
297	Folic acid	0.01
298	*p*-Aminobenzoic acid	0.05
299	*m*-Inositol	0.05
300	Choline HCl	0.50
301	Ascorbic acid	50.0
302	Cholesterol	0.2
303	Polysorbate 80	5.0
304	Glucose	1000
305	L-Alanine	25.0
306	L-Arginine HCl	70.0
307	L-Aspartic acid	30.0
308	L-Cysteine HCl·H_2O	260.0
309	L-Cystine	20.0
310	L-Glutamic acid	75.0
311	L-Glutamine	100.0
312	Glycine	50.0
313	L-Histidine HCl·H_2O	20.0
314	Hydroxy-L-proline	10.0
315	L-Isoleucine	20.0
316	L-Leucine	60.0
317	L-Lysine HCl	70.0
318	L-Methionine	15.0
319	L-Phenylalanine	25.0
320	L-Proline	40.0
321	L-Serine	25.0
322	L-Threonine	30.0
323	L-Tryptophan	10.0
324	L-Tyrosine	40.0
325	L-Valine	25.0
326	Glutathione	10.0
327	Deoxyadenosine	10.0
328	Deoxycytidine	10.0
329	Deoxyguanosine	10.0
330	5-Methyldeoxycytidine	0.1
331	Thymidine	10.0
332	Diphosphopyridine nucleotide	7.0
333	Flavin adenine dinucleotide	1.0
334	Triphosphopyridine nucleotide	1.0
335	Uridine triphosphate	1.0
336	Cocarboxylase	1.0
337	Coenzyme A	2.5
338	Ethanol	16.0
	Healy and Parker's CMRL-1415 [7]	
339	$CaCl_2$	140
340	$MgSO_4 \cdot 7H_2O$	240
341	KCl	400
342	$NaHCO_3$	1000
343	NaCl	6800
344	Na_2HPO_4	200
345	$NaH_2PO_4 \cdot H_2O$	50
346	Sodium pyruvate	225
347	*d*-Biotin (U.S.P.)	1.0
348	Calcium pantothenate	0.5
349	Folic acid (USP)	1.0
350	*m*-Inositol (NF)	2.0
351	Choline chloride	1.0
352	Ascorbic acid	50.0
353	D-Galactose	500
354	D-Glucose	500
355	L-Alanine	30.0
356	L-Arginine (free base)	500.0
357	L-Aspartic acid	10.0
358	L-Cysteine (free base)	179.0
359	L-Cystine	24.0
360	L-Glutamic acid	10.0
361	L-Glutamine	292.0
362	Glycine	17.0
363	L-Histidine (free base)	31.0
364	Hydroxy-L-proline	10.0
365	L-Isoleucine	52.0
366	L-Leucine	52.0
367	L-Lysine (free base)	47.0
368	L-Methionine	15.0
369	L-Phenylalanine	32.0
370	L-Proline	30.0
371	L-Serine	12.0
372	L-Threonine	48.0
373	L-Tryptophan	10.0
374	L-Tyrosine	36.0
375	L-Valine	46.0
376	Glutathione	10.0
377	Deoxyadenosine	10.0
378	Deoxycytidine	10.0
379	Deoxyguanosine	10.0
380	5-Methyldeoxycytidine	0.1
381	Thymidine	10.0
382	Diphosphopyridine nucleotide	7.0
383	Flavin adenine dinucleotide	1.0
384	Triphosphopyridine nucleotide	1.0
385	Uridine triphosphate	1.0
386	Cocarboxylase	1.0
387	Codecarboxylase	1.0
388	Phenol red	20.0
	Leibovitz' L-15 [9]	
389	$CaCl_2$	140
390	$MgCl_2 \cdot 6H_2O$	200

continued

Part II. Constituents of Synthetic Media

	Constituent	Concentration mg/liter
391	$MgSO_4 \cdot 7H_2O$	200
392	KCl	400
393	KH_2PO_4	60
394	NaCl	8000
395	Na_2HPO_4	190
396	Sodium pyruvate	550
397	Thiamine monophosphate	1.0
398	Riboflavin-5-phosphate, sodium	0.1
399	Nicotinamide	1.0
400	Pyridoxine HCl	1.0
401	DL-Calcium pantothenate	1.0
402	Folic acid	1.0
403	Inositol	2.0
404	Choline	1.0
405	D(+)Galactose	900
406	DL-α-Alanine	450
407	L-Arginine (free base)	500
408	L-Asparagine	250
409	L-Cysteine (free base)	120
410	L-Glutamine	300
411	Glycine	200
412	L-Histidine (free base)	250
413	DL-Isoleucine	250
414	L-Leucine	125
415	L-Lysine	75
416	DL-Methionine	150
417	DL-Phenylalanine	250
418	L-Serine	200
419	DL-Threonine	600
420	L-Tryptophan	20
421	L-Tyrosine	300
422	DL-Valine	200
423	Amphotericin B	3 μg/ml
424	Penicillin	300 units/ml
425	Streptomycin	300 μg/ml
426	Phenol red	10.0
	Moore's RPMI-1640 [10]	
427	$Ca(NO_3)_2 \cdot 4H_2O$	100
428	$MgSO_4 \cdot 7H_2O$	100
429	KCl	400
430	$NaHCO_3$	2000
431	NaCl	6000
432	$Na_2HPO_4 \cdot 7H_2O$	1512
433	Thiamine HCl	1.0
434	Riboflavin	0.2
435	Nicotinamide	1.0
436	Pyridoxine HCl	1.0
437	Biotin	0.2
438	Calcium pantothenate	0.25
439	Folic acid	1.0
440	*p*-Aminobenzoic acid	1.0
441	Inositol	35.0
442	Vitamin B_{12}	0.005
443	Choline chloride	3.0
444	Glucose	2000
445	L-Arginine	200.0
446	L-Asparagine	50.0
447	L-Aspartic acid	20.0
448	L-Cystine	50.0
449	L-Glutamic acid	20.0
450	L-Glutamine	300.0
451	Glycine	10.0
452	L-Histidine	15.0
453	Hydroxy-L-proline	20.0
454	L-Isoleucine	50.0
455	L-Leucine	50.0
456	L-Lysine HCl	40.0
457	L-Methionine	15.0
458	L-Phenylalanine	15.0
459	L-Proline	20.0
460	L-Serine	30.0
461	L-Threonine	20.0
462	L-Tryptophan	5.0
463	L-Tyrosine	20.0
464	L-Valine	20.0
465	L-Glutathione (reduced)	1.0
466	Phenol red	5.0
	Parker's Medium 199 [11]	
467	$CaCl_2$	200
468	$Fe(NO_3)_3 \cdot 9H_2O$	0.1
469	$MgSO_4 \cdot 7H_2O$	200
470	KCl	400
471	$NaC_2H_3O_2$	50
472	$NaHCO_3$	2200
473	NaCl	6800
474	$NaH_2PO_4 \cdot H_2O$	140
475	Thiamine HCl	0.01
476	Riboflavin	0.01
477	Nicotinic acid	0.025
478	Nicotinamide	0.025
479	Pyridoxal HCl	0.025
480	Pyridoxine HCl	0.025
481	Biotin	0.01
482	Calcium pantothenate	0.01
483	Folic acid	0.01
484	*p*-Aminobenzoic acid	0.05
485	*m*-Inositol	0.05
486	Choline HCl	0.50
487	Ascorbic acid	0.05
488	Vitamin A	0.1
489	Vitamin D_2	0.1
490	α-Tocopherol phosphate	0.01
491	Menadione	0.01
492	Cholesterol	0.2
493	Polysorbate 80	20.0
494	Glucose	1000
495	2-Deoxy-D-ribose	0.5
496	D-Ribose	0.5
497	DL-Alanine	50.0
498	L-Arginine HCl	70.0
499	DL-Aspartic acid	60.0
500	L-Cysteine HCl	0.1
501	L-Cystine	20.0
502	DL-Glutamic acid	150.0
503	L-Glutamine	100.0
504	Glycine	50.0
505	L-Histidine HCl	20.0
506	Hydroxy-L-proline	10.0
507	DL-Isoleucine	40.0
508	DL-Leucine	120.0
509	L-Lysine HCl	70.0
510	DL-Methionine	30.0
511	DL-Phenylalanine	50.0
512	L-Proline	40.0
513	DL-Serine	50.0
514	DL-Threonine	60.0
515	DL-Tryptophan	20.0
516	L-Tyrosine	40.0
517	DL-Valine	50.0
518	Glutathione	0.05
519	Adenylic acid	0.2
520	Adenosine triphosphate	10.0
521	Adenine	10.0
522	Guanine HCl	0.3
523	Hypoxanthine	0.3
524	Xanthine	0.3
525	Thymine	0.3
526	Uracil	0.3
	Trowell's T-8 [13]	
527	$CaCl_2$	220
528	$MgSO_4 \cdot 7H_2O$	250
529	KCl	450
530	$NaHCO_3$	2820
531	NaCl	6100
532	$NaH_2PO_4 \cdot 2H_2O$	450
533	Thiamine HCl	17.0
534	*p*-Aminobenzoic acid	35.0
535	Glucose	4000
536	L-Arginine HCl	21.0

continued

Part II. Constituents of Synthetic Media

	Constituent	Concentration mg/liter
537	L-Cysteine HCl	47.0
538	L-Histidine HCl	10.0
539	L-Isoleucine	26.0
540	L-Leucine	26.0
541	L-Lysine HCl	36.0
542	DL-Methionine	15.0
543	DL-Phenylalanine	33.0
544	DL-Threonine	48.0
545	L-Tryptophan	4.0
546	L-Tyrosine	18.0
547	L-Valine	23.0
548	Insulin	50.0
549	Chloramphenicol	30.0
550	Phenol red	10.0
	Waymouth's MAB-87/3 [5]	
551	$CaCl_2 \cdot 2H_2O$	120
552	$CoCl_2 \cdot 6H_2O$	0.022
553	$CuSO_4 \cdot 5H_2O$	0.05
554	$FeSO_4$	0.45
555	$MgCl_2 \cdot 6H_2O$	240
556	$MgSO_4 \cdot 7H_2O$	100
557	$MnSO_4 \cdot H_2O$	0.016
558	KCl	150
559	KH_2PO_4	208
560	$NaHCO_3$	2240
561	NaCl	6000
562	Na_2HPO_4	300
563	$ZnSO_4 \cdot 7H_2O$	0.03
564	Ammonium paramolybdate	0.025
565	Thiamine HCl	10.0
566	Riboflavin	1.0
567	Nicotinamide	1.0
568	Pyridoxine HCl	1.0
569	Biotin	0.02
570	Calcium pantothenate	1.0
571	Folic acid	0.5
572	*m*-Inositol·$2H_2O$	1.0
573	Vitamin B_{12}	0.2
574	Choline chloride	250.0
575	Ascorbic acid	17.5
576	Glucose	5000
577	L-Alanine	11.2
578	L-Arginine HCl	75.0
579	L-Asparagine	24.0
580	L-Aspartic acid	60.0
581	L-Cysteine HCl	90.0
582	L-Cystine	15.0
583	L-Glutamic acid	150.0
584	L-Glutamine	350.0
585	Glycine	50.0
586	L-Histidine HCl	150.0
587	L-Isoleucine	25.0
588	L-Leucine	50.0
589	L-Lysine HCl	240.0
590	L-Methionine	50.0
591	L-Phenylalanine	50.0
592	L-Proline	50.0
593	L-Serine	12.8
594	L-Threonine	75.0
595	L-Tryptophan	40.0
596	L-Tyrosine	40.0
597	L-Valine	65.0
598	Glutathione	15.0
599	Hypoxanthine	25.0
600	Thymidine	25.0
601	Insulin	8.0
602	Phenol red	10.0
	Waymouth's MD-705/1 [8]	
603	$CaCl_2 \cdot 2H_2O$	120
604	$CoCl_2 \cdot 6H_2O$	0.11
605	$CuSO_4 \cdot 5H_2O$	0.25
606	$FeSO_4$	0.26
607	$MgCl_2 \cdot 6H_2O$	240
608	$MgSO_4 \cdot 7H_2O$	100
609	$MnSO_4 \cdot H_2O$	0.08
610	KCl	150
611	KH_2PO_4	80
612	$NaHCO_3$	2240
613	NaCl	6000
614	Na_2HPO_4	300
615	$ZnSO_4 \cdot 7H_2O$	0.15
616	Ammonium paramolybdate	0.12
617	Thiamine HCl	10.0
618	Riboflavin	1.0
619	Nicotinamide	1.0
620	Pyridoxine HCl	1.0
621	Biotin	0.02
622	Calcium pantothenate	1.0
623	Folic acid	0.5
624	*m*-Inositol	1.0
625	Vitamin B_{12}	0.2
626	Choline HCl	250.0
627	Ascorbic acid	17.5
628	Glucose	5000
629	L-Arginine HCl	75.0
630	L-Aspartic acid	60.0
631	L-Cysteine HCl	90.0
632	L-Cystine	15.0
633	L-Glutamic acid	150.0
634	L-Glutamine	350.0
635	Glycine	50.0
636	L-Histidine HCl	150.0
637	L-Isoleucine	25.0
638	L-Leucine	50.0
639	L-Lysine HCl	240.0
640	L-Methionine	50.0
641	L-Phenylalanine	50.0
642	L-Proline	50.0
643	L-Threonine	75.0
644	L-Tryptophan	40.0
645	L-Tyrosine	40.0
646	L-Valine	65.0
647	Glutathione	15.0
648	Hypoxanthine	25.0
649	Phenol red	10.0

Contributor: Waymouth, Charity

References

[1] Eagle, H. 1955. Science 122:501.

[2] Eagle, H. 1959. Ibid. 130:432.

[3] Earle, W. R. 1962. In J. W. Castor, ed. New developments in tissue culture. Rutgers Univ. Press, New Brunswick, N.J. pp. 1-22.

[4] Evans, V. J., et al. 1964. Exptl. Cell. Res. 36:439.

[5] Gorham, L. W., and C. Waymouth. 1965. Proc. Soc. Exptl. Biol. Med. 119:287.

[6] Ham, R. G. 1965. Proc. Natl. Acad. Sci. U.S. 53:288.

[7] Healy, G. M., and R. C. Parker. 1966. J. Cell Biol. 30:531, 539.

[8] Kitos, P. A., R. Sinclair, and C. Waymouth. 1962. Exptl. Cell Res. 27:307.

[9] Leibovitz, A. 1963. Am. J. Hyg. 78:173.

[10] Moore, G. E., R. E. Gerner, and H. A. Franklin. 1967. J. Am. Med. Assoc. 199:519.

[11] Morgan, J. F., H. J. Morton, and R. C. Parker. 1950. Proc. Soc. Exptl. Biol. Med. 73:1.

[12] Parker, R. C. 1961. Methods of tissue culture. Ed. 3. Harper, New York. p. 77.

[13] Trowell, O. A. 1959. Exptl. Cell Res. 16:118.

continued

Part III. Original Use of Synthetic Media

Only the cells or tissues for which the media were first designed are listed, but most of the media now are used for cells and tissues of different organs and different animal species. For information on osmotic properties of living cells, consult reference 2; for information on Ringer solutions, consult reference 22.

	Designer of Medium	Code Name of Medium	Original Use	Reference
1	Biggers & Lucy	BL-1 (modified No. 858[1])	Chick bone tissue	1
2	Dupree, Sanford, Westfall, & Covalesky	NCTC-118	Mouse cell lines, established	3
3	Eagle	Basal medium, supplemented with serum protein	Human & mouse cells, established	4
4	Eagle	Minimal essential medium, supplemented with serum protein	Mammalian cells	5
5	Earle	NCTC-117	Mouse cell lines, established	6
6	Evans, Bryant, Fioramonti, McQuilkin, Sanford, & Earle	NCTC-107	Mouse L cells, established	7
7	Evans, Bryant, Kerr, & Schilling	Modifications of NCTC-107 & 109	Human, hamster, monkey, & mouse cells, established	9
8	Evans, Fioramonti, Sanford, Earle, & Westfall	Modifications of NCTC-109	Mouse cell lines, established	8
9	Fischer & Sartorelli	Defined medium, supplemented with serum	Mouse leukemic cells	10
10	Garvey	Defined medium	Rat liver reticuloendothelial cells	11
11	Gorham & Waymouth	MAB-87/3	Mouse embryo limb buds & other freshly explanted fetal tissues	12
12	Ham	F-10, supplemented with serum or protein	Human & hamster diploid cell lines	13
13	Ham	F-12	Hamster & mouse cells, established	14
14	Hanss & Moore	RMPI-213 & RMPI-1311 ± serum supplement	Human tumor cells (monolayer or suspension), established	15
15	Healy, Fisher, & Parker	No. 858	Mouse L cells, established	16
16	Healy & Parker	CMRL-1415 (& CMRL-1415-ATM) ± $NaHCO_3$, protein, & other supplements	Mouse embryo cells, freshly explanted	17
17	Jacobs	S-BME, supplemented with serum	Human diploid cells	18
18	Kelley, Vail, Adamson, & Palmer	SRI-14, supplemented with serum	Human HEp-2 cells, established	19
19	Kitos, Sinclair, & Waymouth	MD-705/1	Mouse cells & tissues	20
20	Leibovitz	L-15, without $NaHCO_3$, supplemented with serum	Human & mouse cells, established	21
21	McCoy, Maxwell, & Kruse	No. 5a, supplemented with dialyzed serum	Rat tumor cells	23
22	McCoy, Maxwell, & Neuman	No. 3, supplemented with dialyzed serum	Rat tumor cells	24
23	McQuilkin, Evans, & Earle	NCTC-109	Mouse cell lines, established	25
24	Melnick, Hsiung, Rappaport, Howes, & Reissig	SM-2	Monkey kidney cells, freshly explanted	26
25	Michl	Defined medium, supplemented with serum fractions	Human, mouse, rabbit, & rat cells, established	27
26	Moore, Gerner, & Franklin	RPMI-1640	Human normal & leukemic cells; hamster tumor cell lines, initiating	28
27	Moore, Sandberg, & Ulrich	RPMI-906, 1595, & 1630, supplemented with serum	Mouse L-1210 cells, established	29
28	Morgan, Campbell, & Morton	M-150	Chick tissues, freshly explanted	30
29	Morgan, Morton, & Parker	No. 199	Chick embryo tissues, freshly explanted	31
30	Nagle, Tribble, Anderson, & Gary	Defined medium	Cells in suspension, established	32
31	Neuman & McCoy	Basal medium, supplemented with dialyzed serum	Rat tumor cells	33
32	Neuman & McCoy	No. 2, supplemented with dialyzed serum	Rat tumor cells	34
33	Parker	CMRL-1066	Mouse L cells, established	35
34	Price, Kerr, Andresen, Bryant, & Evans	NCTC-131, 132, 133, 135, 138, 139, & 140, modifications of NCTC-109	Human, hamster, monkey, & mouse cells, established	36

[1] *See* entry 15.

continued

23. CULTURE MEDIA: ANIMAL TISSUES

Part III. Original Use of Synthetic Media

	Designer of Medium	Code Name of Medium	Original Use	Reference
35	Puck, Cieciura, & Robinson	N-15 & N-16, supplemented with serum	Mammalian cells	37
36	Rappaport, Poole, & Rappaport	SM-3	Human HeLa cells, established	38
37	Sanford, Dupree, & Covalesky	Modifications of NCTC-109	Mouse cells, established	39
38	Tritsch & Moore	Medium-213, supplemented with serum	Human tumor cells (RPMI line No. 191)	40
39	Trowell	T-8	Mouse & rat organs	41
40	Waymouth	MB-752/1	Mouse cells & tissues	42
41	Waymouth	R-252/1 & 2	Mouse & rat retina organ cultures	43

Contributor: Waymouth, Charity

References

[1] Biggers, J. D., and J. A. Lucy. 1960. J. Exptl. Zool. 144:253.
[2] Dick, D. A. T. 1959. Intern. Rev. Cytol. 8:387.
[3] Dupree, L. T., et al. 1962. Exptl. Cell Res. 28:381.
[4] Eagle, H. 1955. Science 122:501.
[5] Eagle, H. 1959. Ibid. 130:432.
[6] Earle, W. R. 1962. In J. W. Castor, ed. New developments in tissue culture. Rutgers Univ. Press, New Brunswick, N.J. pp. 1-22.
[7] Evans, V. J., et al. 1956. Cancer Res. 16:77.
[8] Evans, V. J., et al. 1958. Am. J. Hyg. 66:66.
[9] Evans, V. J., et al. 1964. Exptl. Cell Res. 36:439.
[10] Fischer, G. A., and A. S. Sartorelli. 1964. Methods Med. Res. 10:247.
[11] Garvey, J. S. 1961. Nature 191:972.
[12] Gorham, L. W., and C. Waymouth. 1965. Proc. Soc. Exptl. Biol. Med. 119:287.
[13] Ham, R. G. 1963. Exptl. Cell Res. 29:515.
[14] Ham, R. G. 1965. Proc. Natl. Acad. Sci. U.S. 53:288.
[15] Hanss, J., and G. E. Moore. 1964. Exptl. Cell Res. 34:243.
[16] Healy, G. M., D. C. Fisher, and R. C. Parker. 1955. Proc. Soc. Exptl. Biol. Med. 89:71.
[17] Healy, G. M., and R. C. Parker. 1966. J. Cell Biol. 30:531, 539.
[18] Jacobs, J. P. 1966. Nature 210:100.
[19] Kelley, G. G., et al. 1961. Am. J. Hyg. 73:231.
[20] Kitos, P. A., R. Sinclair, and C. Waymouth. 1962. Exptl. Cell Res. 27:307.
[21] Leibovitz, A. 1963. Am. J. Hyg. 78:173.
[22] Lockwood, A. P. M. 1961. Comp. Biochem. Physiol. 2:241.
[23] McCoy, T. A., M. Maxwell, and P. F. Kruse. 1959. Proc. Soc. Exptl. Biol. Med. 100:115.
[24] McCoy, T. A., M. Maxwell, and R. E. Neuman. 1956. Cancer Res. 16:979.
[25] McQuilkin, W. T., V. J. Evans, and W. R. Earle. 1957. J. Natl. Cancer Inst. 19:885.
[26] Melnick, J. L., et al. 1957. Texas Rept. Biol. Med. 15:496.
[27] Michl, J. 1962. Exptl. Cell Res. 26:129.
[28] Moore, G. E., R. E. Gerner, and H. A. Franklin. 1967. J. Am. Med. Assoc. 199:519.
[29] Moore, G. E., A. A. Sandberg, and K. Ulrich. 1966. J. Natl. Cancer Inst. 36:405.
[30] Morgan, J. F., E. M. Campbell, and H. J. Morton. 1955. Ibid. 16:557.
[31] Morgan, J. F., H. J. Morton, and R. C. Parker. 1950. Proc. Soc. Exptl. Biol. Med. 73:1.
[32] Nagle, S. C., et al. 1963. Proc. Soc. Exptl. Biol. Med. 112:340.
[33] Neuman, R. E , and T. A. McCoy. 1956. Science 124:124.
[34] Neuman, R. E., and T. A. McCoy. 1958. Proc. Soc. Exptl. Biol. Med. 98:303.
[35] Parker, R. C. 1961. Methods of tissue culture. Ed. 3. Harper, New York. p. 77.
[36] Price, F. M., et al. 1966. J. Natl. Cancer Inst. 37:601.
[37] Puck, T. T., S. J. Cieciura, and A. Robinson. 1958. J. Exptl. Med. 108:945.
[38] Rappaport, C., J. P. Poole, and H. P. Rappaport. 1960. Exptl. Cell Res. 20:465.
[39] Sanford, K. K., L. T. Dupree, and A. B. Covalesky. 1963. Ibid. 31:345.
[40] Tritsch, G. L., and G. E. Moore. 1962. Ibid. 28:360.
[41] Trowell, O. A. 1959. Ibid. 16:118.
[42] Waymouth, C. 1959. J. Natl. Cancer Inst. 22:1003.
[43] Waymouth, C. 1965. Develop. Biol. 12:115.

III. PLANT NUTRITION

24. NUTRIENT REQUIREMENTS: BACTERIA

Part I. Vitamins and Other Essential Organic Compounds

There are no specific requirements for most strains of the following species: *Aerobacter aerogenes* [28,34]; *Erwinia* spp., soft-rot group [61]; *Escherichia coli* [12,18,34]; *Pasteurella pestis,* anaerobic strains [21]; *P. pseudotuberculosis* [2]; *Salmonella choleraesuis* [37]; *S. enteritidis* [37]; *S. schottmuelleri* [37]; *S. typhosa* [22]; *Serratia marcescens* [34,63]; and *Shigella alkalescens* [13]. *Abbreviations:* R = required; R̸ = not required; r = occasionally required; S = stimulatory for growth.

	Species (Synonym)	Vitamins											Other Organic Compounds	Reference
		Thiamine	Riboflavin	Nicotinic Acid	B_6	Biotin	Pantothenic Acid	Folic Acid	p-Aminobenzoic Acid	Inositol	B_{12}	K		
	Acetobacter spp.													
1	Glycophilic	r	...	R	...	...	R	...	R[1/]	...	...	...	...	6,20,53
2	Lactophilic[2/]	R̸	R̸	R̸	R̸	R̸	R̸	R̸	R̸	R̸	R̸	R̸	...	6
3	*A. suboxydans*	...	...	R	...	...	R[3/]	...	R	...	...	...	...	48,65
4	*Bacillus alvei*	R	...	R̸	...	R̸	...	...	...	...	...	...	...	27
5	*B. anthracis*	R	R̸	R̸	R̸	R̸	R̸	...	R̸	R̸	...	...	...	3,5,17
6	*B. brevis*	R̸	...	R̸	...	R̸	...	...	...	...	...	...	...	27
7	*B. cereus*	R̸	...	R̸	...	R̸	...	...	...	...	...	...	...	27
8	*B. cereus mycoides*	R̸	...	R̸	...	R̸	...	...	...	...	...	...	...	27
9	*B. circulans*	R	...	R̸	...	R	...	...	...	...	...	...	...	27
10	*B. coagulans*	R	...	R̸[4/]	...	R	...	...	...	...	...	...	...	27
11	*B. licheniformis*	R̸	...	R̸	...	R̸	...	...	...	...	...	...	...	27
12	*B. macerans*	R	...	R̸	...	R	...	...	...	...	...	...	...	27
13	*B. megaterium*	R̸	...	R̸	...	R̸	...	...	...	...	...	...	...	27
14	*B. pasteuri*	R	...	R[5/]	R[5/]	...	...	...	...	...	...	...	...	27
15	*B. polymyxa*	R̸	...	R̸	...	R	...	...	...	...	...	...	...	27
16	*B. pumilis*	R̸	...	R̸	...	R	...	...	...	...	...	...	...	27
17	*B. sphaericus*	R	...	R̸	...	R[5/]	...	...	...	...	...	...	...	27
18	*B. subtilis*	R̸	...	R̸	...	R̸	...	...	...	...	...	...	...	27
19	*B. subtilis niger*	R̸	...	R̸	...	R̸	...	...	...	...	...	...	...	27
20	*Bacteroides melaninogenicus*	...	...	...	...	...	...	...	...	...	...	R[6,7/]	R[8/]	56
21	*B. succinogenes*	...	...	...	...	R	...	...	S	...	...		R[9/]	7-9
22	*Brucella abortus*	R	...	R	...	R[10/]	R[10/]	...	...	...	...	...	...	35,44,57
23	*B. melitensis*	R	...	R	...	R[10/]	R[10/]	...	...	...	...	...	...	35,44,57
24	*B. suis*	R	...	R	...	R[10/]	R[10/]	...	...	...	...	...	...	35,44,57
25	*Clostridium parabotulinum,* types A & B	R	...	R[6/]	R[6/]	R	...	...	R[11/]	...	...	...	...	24,42
26	*C. perfringens*	...	R[6/]	...	R[12/]	R	R	...	...	...	...	...	S[13,14/]	4
27	*C. tetani*	R[15/]	R	R	R	R	R	R	...	...	...	...	R[13,14,16/]	14,23,47
28	*Corynebacterium diphtheriae*	...	...	R	...	R[17/]	R[18/]	...	...	...	...	...	R[15,16/]	11,46
29	*Erwinia amylovora*	...	...	R	...	...	...	...	...	...	...	...	...	61
30	*E. tracheiphila*	R[6/]	R̸	R[6/]	R̸	R̸	R̸	R̸	R̸	R̸	R̸	R̸	R̸	3,61
31	*Haemophilus influenzae*	...	...	...	...	...	...	...	...	...	...	...	R[19,20/]	38-40

1/ By some species; stimulatory to other species. 2/ Ammonia utilized as sole source of nitrogen. 3/ Coenzyme A gives faster growth response than pantothenic acid; pantoic acid or pantoyl lactone moiety of pantothenic acid also active. 4/ Except one strain which requires nicotinic acid [10]. 5/ Requirement variable. 6/ By some strains. 7/ Other vitamin needs unknown. 8/ Heme required. 9/ Both branched- and straight-chain volatile fatty acids. 10/ For some strains, stimulatory but not required. 11/ Folic acid may be substituted. 12/ Pyridoxal. 13/ Adenine. 14/ Uracil. 15/ Or stimulatory. 16/ Oleic acid. 17/ Pimelic acid may be substituted. 18/ β-Alanine may be substituted. 19/ Diphosphopyridine nucleotide. 20/ Hemin.

continued

24. NUTRIENT REQUIREMENTS: BACTERIA

Part I. Vitamins and Other Essential Organic Compounds

	Species (Synonym)	Vitamins											Other Organic Compounds	Reference
		Thiamine	Riboflavin	Nicotinic Acid	B_6	Biotin	Pantothenic Acid	Folic Acid	*p*-Aminobenzoic Acid	Inositol	B_{12}	K		
32	*H. parainfluenzae*	.....	....	......	....	......	......	......	......	...	....	......	R[19,21]	38
	Lactobacillus spp.													
33	Heterofermentative	R	℞	R	r[22,23]	R	R	r[22]	r[22]	...	R[6]	......	R[24]	25,31,58-60
34	Homofermentative	℞	R	R	r[22,23]	R	R	r[22]	r[22]	...	R[6]	......	R[24]	25,31,58-60
35	*Leuconostoc citrovorum*	r[13]	r[13]	R[6]	r[13]	R	R	R[25]	......	...	....	......	....	16,32,33,43,55
36	*L. dextranicum*	r[13]	r[13]	R[6]	r[13]	R	R	R	......	...	....	......	....	16,32,33,43,55
37	*L. mesenteroides*	r[13]	r[13]	R[6]	r[13]	R	R	R	......	...	....	......	....	16,32,33,43,55
38	*Pasteurella multocida*	.....	....	R[26]	....	R[6]	R	......	℞	℞	....	......	....	2,3,29
39	*P. pestis,* aerobic strains	.....	....	......	....	......	......	......	......	...	....	......	R[20]	21
40	*P. tularensis*	R[27]	℞	℞	℞	......	℞	......	......	...	....	......	R[28]	2,3,49,64
41	*Proteus morganii*	℞	℞	℞	℞	......	R	......	......	℞	....	......	....	3,52
42	*P. vulgaris*	.....	....	R	....	......	......	......	......	...	....	......	....	15,41,50
43	*P. vulgaris,* X_{19}[29]	.....	....	R	....	......	......	......	......	...	....	......	....	45
44	*Rhizobium* spp.	R[30]	....	......	R[30]	R[30]	......	......	......	...	....	......	....	1,19
45	*Salmonella gallinarum*	R	....	......	....	......	......	......	......	...	....	......	....	22
46	*S. gallinarum (S. pullorum)*	.....	....	R[31]	....	......	......	......	......	...	....	......	....	22
47	*Shigella paradysenteriae*	℞	℞	R	....	......	R[31]	......	......	...	....	℞	....	3,13,30,66
48	*S. sonnei*	℞	℞	R	....	......	R[31]	......	......	...	....	℞	....	3,13,30,66
	Staphylococcus albus													
49	Coagulase + strains	R	....	R	....	......	......	......	......	...	....	......	....	26,51
50	Coagulase − strains	R	....	R	r	R	r	......	......	...	....	......	....	26,51
51	*S. aureus*	.....	....	......	....	......	......	......	R[6]	...	....	......	....	36
52	Coagulase + strains	R	....	R	....	......	......	......	......	...	....	......	....	26,51
53	Coagulase − strains	R	....	R	r	R	r	......	......	...	....	......	....	26,51
54	*Treponema* sp., Reiter strain	S	S	R	....	R	R	......	......	...	....	......	R[32,33]	62
55	*Veillonella alcalescens*	R[34]	....	......	R[12]	......	......	......	......	...	....	......	R[35]	54
56	*V. parvula*	R	....	......	R[12]	......	......	......	......	...	....	......	℞[35]	54

[6] By some strains. [12] Pyridoxal. [13] Adenine. [19] Diphosphopyridine nucleotide. [20] Hemin. [21] Putrescine required by one strain. [22] As a growth stimulant. [23] Pyridoxal phosphate required for some strains. [24] Pantethine required by some strains. [25] Folinic acid is also required for strain 8081. [26] Nicotinamide. [27] Thiamine diphosphate. [28] Adenosine triphosphate. [29] Occasionally strains have no known requirement. [30] Singly or in different combinations by some strains; no vitamins required by other strains. [31] By a few strains; no specific requirements for other strains. [32] Uracil or cytosine. [33] Albumin plus oleic acid or polysorbate 80. [34] Usually. [35] Putrescine or cadaverine.

Contributors: (a) Koser, Stewart A., (b) Smith, Nathan R.

References

[1] Allen, E. K., and O. N. Allen. 1950. Bacteriol. Rev. 14:273.

[2] Berkman, S. 1942. J. Infect. Diseases 71:201.

[3] Berkman, S. Unpublished. Bio-Science Laboratories, Los Angeles, Calif., 1967.

[4] Boyd, M. J., M. A. Logan, and A. A. Tytell. 1948. J. Biol. Chem. 174:1013.

[5] Brewer, C. R., et al. 1946. Arch. Biochem. 10:65.

[6] Brown, G. D., and C. Rainbow. 1956. J. Gen. Microbiol. 15:61.

[7] Bryant, M. P., and R. N. Doetsch. 1954. J. Dairy Sci. 37:1176.

[8] Bryant, M. P., and R. N. Doetsch. 1954. Science 120:944.

[9] Bryant, M. P., and R. N. Doetsch. 1955. J. Dairy Sci. 38:340.

[10] Cleverdon, R. C., M. J. Pelczar, Jr., and R. N. Doetsch. 1949. J. Bacteriol. 58:113.

[11] Cohen, S., J. C. Snyder, and J. H. Mueller. 1941. Ibid. 41:581.

[12] Dolt, M. L. 1908. J. Infect. Diseases 5:616.

[13] Dorfman, A., et al. 1939. Ibid. 65:163.

[14] Feeney, R. E., J. H. Mueller, and P. A. Miller. 1943. J. Bacteriol. 46:559.

[15] Fildes, P. 1938. Brit. J. Exptl. Pathol. 19:239.

[16] Gaines, S., and G. L. Stahly. 1943. J. Bacteriol. 46:441.

[17] Gladstone, G. P. 1939. Brit. J. Exptl. Pathol. 20:189.

[18] Gordon, M. H. 1917. J. Roy. Army Med. Corps 28:371.

[19] Graham, P. H. 1963. J. Gen. Microbiol. 30:245.

continued

Part I. Vitamins and Other Essential Organic Compounds

[20] Hall, A. N., et al. 1953. Arch. Biochem. Biophys. 46:485.
[21] Herbert, D. 1949. Brit. J. Exptl. Pathol. 30:509.
[22] Johnson, E. A., and L. F. Rettger. 1943. J. Bacteriol. 45:127.
[23] Kaufman, L., and J. C. Humphries. 1958. Appl. Microbiol. 6:311.
[24] Kindler, S. H., J. Mager, and N. Grossowicz. 1956. J. Gen. Microbiol. 15:386.
[25] Kitay, E., W. S. McNutt, and E. E. Snell. 1950. J. Bacteriol. 59:727.
[26] Knight, B. C. J. G. 1937. Biochem. J. 31:731.
[27] Knight, B. C. J. G., and H. Proom. 1950. J. Gen. Microbiol. 4:508.
[28] Koser, S. A. 1923. J. Bacteriol. 8:493.
[29] Koser, S. A., S. Berkman, and A. Dorfman. 1941. Proc. Soc. Exptl. Biol. Med. 47:504.
[30] Koser, S. A., A. Dorfman, and F. Saunders. 1938. Ibid. 38:311.
[31] Koser, S. A., and B. J. Fisher. 1950. J. Dental Res. 29:760.
[32] Koser, S. A., and G. J. Kasai. 1948. J. Infect. Diseases 83:271.
[33] Koser, S. A., and G. J. Kasai. 1950. Ibid. 86:95.
[34] Koser, S. A., and L. F. Rettger. 1919. Ibid. 24:301.
[35] Koser, S. A., and M. H. Wright. 1942. Ibid. 71:86.
[36] Lampen, J. O. Unpublished. Squibb Institute for Medical Research, New Brunswick, N.J., 1967.
[37] Lederberg, J. 1947. Arch. Biochem. 13:287.
[38] Lwoff, A., and M. Lwoff. 1936. Compt. Rend. 203:520.
[39] Lwoff, A., and M. Lwoff. 1937. Ann. Inst. Pasteur 59:129.
[40] Lwoff, A., and M. Lwoff. 1937. Compt. Rend. 204:1510.
[41] Lwoff, A., and A. Querido. 1939. Compt. Rend. Soc. Biol. 130:1569.
[42] Mager, J., S. H. Kindler, and N. Grossowicz. 1954. J. Gen. Microbiol. 10:130.
[43] McCleskey, C. S., and R. O. Barnett. 1949. Proc. Louisiana Acad. Sci. 12:38.
[44] McCullough, N. B., and L. A. Dick. 1942. J. Infect. Diseases 71:193,198.
[45] Morel, M. 1941. Ann. Inst. Pasteur 67:285.
[46] Mueller, J. H. 1940. Bacteriol. Rev. 4:97.
[47] Mueller, J. H., and P. A. Miller. 1942. J. Bacteriol. 43:763.
[48] Novelli, G. D., R. M. Flynn, and F. Lipmann. 1949. J. Biol. Chem. 177:493.
[49] O'Kane, D. J. 1946. J. Bacteriol. 51:559.
[50] Pelczar, M. J., Jr., and J. R. Porter. 1940. Ibid. 39:429.
[51] Pelczar, M. J., Jr., and J. R. Porter. 1942. Ibid. 41:137.
[52] Pelczar, M. J., Jr., and J. R. Porter. 1943. Arch. Biochem. 2:323.
[53] Rao, M. R. R., and J. L. Stokes. 1953. J. Bacteriol. 65:405.
[54] Rogosa, M., and F. S. Bishop. 1964. Ibid. 87:574.
[55] Sauberlich, H. E., and C. A. Baumann. 1948. J. Biol. Chem. 176:165.
[56] Sawyer, S. J., J. B. Macdonald, and R. J. Gibbons. 1962. Arch. Oral Biol. 7:685.
[57] Schuhardt, V. T., and G. A. Beal. 1943. J. Bacteriol. 46:219.
[58] Shankman, S., et al. 1947. J. Biol. Chem. 168:23.
[59] Skeggs, H. R. 1951. J. Cellular Comp. Physiol. 38:227.
[60] Snell, E. E. 1945. J. Bacteriol. 50:373.
[61] Starr, M. P., and M. Mandell. 1950. Ibid. 60:669.
[62] Steinman, H. G., V. I. Oyama, and H. O. Schulze. 1954. Ibid. 67:597.
[63] Sullivan, M. X. 1905. J. Med. Res. 14:109.
[64] Tamura, J. T., and D. E. Fleming. 1949. Bacteriol. Proc. 49:37.
[65] Underkofler, L. A., A. C. Bantz, and W. H. Peterson. 1943. J. Bacteriol. 45:183.
[66] Weil, A. J., and J. Black. 1944. Proc. Soc. Exptl. Biol. Med. 55:24.

Part II. Amino Acids

There are no specific requirements for most strains of the following species: *Aerobacter aerogenes* [15,17]; *Erwinia* spp., soft-rot group [23]; *E. amylovora* [23]; *E. tracheiphila* [23]; *Escherichia coli* [4,11,17]; and *Serratia marcescens* [17,26]. Amino acids have no effect on the growth of *Bacillus licheniformis, B. macerans, B. megaterium, B. polymyxa, B. pumilis, B. subtilis,* and *B. subtilis niger,* but ammonia is essential for their growth [14]. *Abbreviations:* R = required; R̸ = not required; r = occasionally required; S = stimulatory for growth.

	Species (Synonym)	Arginine	Asparagine	Aspartic Acid	Citrulline	Cystine	Glutamic Acid	Histidine	Hydroxyproline	Isoleucine	Leucine	Lysine	Methionine	Phenylalanine	Serine	Threonine	Tryptophan	Tyrosine	Valine	Unspecified	Reference
1	*Acetobacter suboxydans*	...	......	...	...	R 1,2/	...	R 1/	...	R 1/	...	.....	...	...	...	...	......	...	R 1/	R 3/	25
2	*Bacillus alvei*	...	......	...	...	......	...	.....	...	.....	...	.....	...	...	...	...	......	...	.....	R 4/	14
3	*B. anthracis*	...	......	...	...	......	...	.....	...	.....	...	.....	...	...	...	...	......	...	.....	R 4/	3,10
4	*B. brevis*	...	......	...	...	......	...	.....	...	.....	...	.....	...	...	...	...	......	...	.....	R 4/	14
5	*B. cereus*	...	......	...	...	......	...	.....	...	.....	...	.....	...	...	...	...	......	...	.....	R 4/	14

1/ For satisfactory growth. 2/ Or methionine. 3/ Alanine and proline also required for satisfactory growth. 4/ For growth.

continued

24. NUTRIENT REQUIREMENTS: BACTERIA

Part II. Amino Acids

	Species (Synonym)	Arginine	Asparagine	Aspartic Acid	Citrulline	Cystine	Glutamic Acid	Histidine	Hydroxyproline	Isoleucine	Leucine	Lysine	Methionine	Phenylalanine	Serine	Threonine	Tryptophan	Tyrosine	Valine	Unspecified	Reference
6	*B. cereus mycoides*	...	...	...	...	...	...	...	...	...	...	...	...	...	...	...	...	...	...	R[4]	14
7	*B. circulans*	...	...	...	...	...	...	...	...	...	...	...	...	...	...	...	...	...	...	R[4]	14
8	*B. coagulans*	...	...	...	...	...	...	...	...	...	...	...	...	...	...	...	...	...	...	R[4]	14
9	*B. pasteuri*[5]	...	...	...	...	...	...	...	...	...	...	...	...	...	...	...	...	...	...	R[4]	14
10	*B. sphaericus*	...	...	...	...	...	...	...	...	...	...	...	...	...	...	...	...	...	...	R[4]	14
11	*Brucella abortus*	...	...	...	...	...	...	...	...	...	...	...	...	...	...	...	...	...	...	R[4]	9,19
12	*B. melitensis*	...	...	...	...	...	...	...	...	...	...	...	...	...	...	...	...	...	...	R[4]	9,19
13	*B. suis*	...	...	...	...	...	...	...	...	...	...	...	...	...	...	...	...	...	...	R[6]	9,19
14	*Clostridium parabotulinum,* type A	R	...	...	...	...	...	...	...	R	R	...	R	R	...	R	R	R	R	R[7]	13,18
15	*C. perfringens,* strain BP6K	R	...	...	...	R	R	...	R	R	R	...	R	R	R	...	R	R	R	...	2
16	*C. tetani*	R	...	S	...	...	...	R	...	R	R	S	S	S	S	S	R	R	R	...	7,20
17		R	...	R	...	...	R	R	...	R	S	R	R	R	S	R	R	R	R	S[8]	1
18	*Lactobacillus* spp., heterofermentative	...	...	...	...	...	...	...	...	...	...	...	...	...	...	...	...	...	...	R[9]	16
19	*L. arabinosus,* 17-5	R	...	R̸	R̸	R	R	R̸	R̸	R	R	R ?	R	...	R̸	R	R	R	R	R̸[10]	23
20	*Leuconostoc citrovorum*	...	...	...	...	...	...	...	...	...	...	...	...	...	...	...	R	...	...	R	5,6
21	*L. dextranicum*	...	...	...	...	...	...	...	...	...	...	...	...	...	...	...	R	...	...	R	5,6
22	*L. mesenteroides,* P-60	R	...	R	R̸	R	R	R	R̸	R	R	R	R	...	R	R	R	R	R	R[10]	23
23	*Pasteurella multocida*	...	...	...	...	...	...	...	...	...	...	...	...	...	...	...	...	...	...	R[9]	16
24	*P. pestis*	...	...	...	...	...	...	...	...	...	...	...	...	...	...	...	...	...	...	R[11]	22
25	*P. tularensis*	...	...	...	...	R	...	...	...	...	...	...	...	...	...	...	...	...	...	R	27
26	*Proteus morganii*	...	...	...	...	R	...	...	...	...	...	...	...	...	...	...	...	...	...	...	21
27	*Salmonella choleraesuis*	...	R[12]	...	...	...	...	...	...	...	...	...	...	...	...	...	...	r	...	r	12
28	*S. enteritidis*	...	R[12]	...	...	...	...	...	...	...	...	...	...	...	...	...	...	r	...	r	12
29	*S. gallinarum (S. pullorum)*	...	R[12]	...	...	...	...	...	...	...	...	...	...	...	...	...	...	r	...	r	12
30	*S. schottmuelleri*	...	R[12]	...	...	...	...	...	...	...	...	...	...	...	...	...	...	r	...	r	12
31	*S. typhosa*	...	...	...	...	...	...	...	...	...	...	...	...	...	...	...	R[13]	...	...	...	8
32	*Shigella paradysenteriae*	...	...	...	...	...	...	...	...	...	...	...	...	...	...	...	...	...	...	R[14]	16
33	*S. sonnei*	...	...	...	...	...	...	...	...	...	...	...	...	...	...	...	...	...	...	R[15]	9
34	*Staphylococcus albus*	...	...	...	...	...	...	...	...	...	...	...	...	...	...	...	...	...	...	R[14,15]	16
35	*S. aureus*	...	...	...	...	...	...	...	...	...	...	...	...	...	...	...	...	...	...	R[14,15]	16
36	*Treponema* sp., Reiter strain[16]	R	...	R	...	R	R	R	...	R	R	R	R	R	...	R	R	...	R	...	24

[4] For growth. [5] Ammonia has a variable effect on growth. [6] For some strains; no specific requirement for most strains. [7] Growth is better with 19 amino acids. [8] Glycine. [9] Many different amino acids. [10] Alanine, glycine, and proline. [11] Ten or more amino acids. [12] Usually sufficient; ammonium sulfate may be substituted for asparagine. [13] By some strains. [14] Usually several amino acids. [15] Varied amino acids. [16] Requires ammonium ion, for which amino acids cannot be substituted.

Contributors: (a) Koser, Stewart A., (b) Smith, Nathan R., (c) Snell, Esmond E.

References

[1] Beheler, W. M., and J. C. Humphries. 1962. Bacteriol. Proc. 62:52.

[2] Boyd, M. J., M. A. Logan, and A. A. Tytell. 1948. J. Biol. Chem. 174:1013.

[3] Brewer, C. R., et al. 1946. Arch. Biochem. 10:65.

[4] Dolt, M. L. 1908. J. Infect. Diseases 5:616.

[5] Dunn, M. S., et al. 1944. J. Biol. Chem. 156:703.

[6] Dunn, M. S., et al. 1947. Ibid. 168:1.

[7] Feeney, R. E., J. H. Mueller, and P. A. Miller. 1943. J. Bacteriol. 46:559, 563.

[8] Fildes, P., G. P. Gladstone, and B. C. J. G. Knight, 1933. Brit. J. Exptl. Pathol. 14:189.

[9] Gerhardt, P., and J. B. Wilson. 1948. J. Bacteriol. 56:17.

[10] Gladstone, G. P. 1939. Brit. J. Exptl. Pathol. 20:189.

[11] Gordon, M. H. 1917. J. Roy. Army Med. Corps 28:371.

[12] Hajna, A. J. 1935. J. Bacteriol. 29:253.

[13] Kindler, S. H., J. Mager, and N. Grossowicz. 1956. J. Gen. Microbiol. 15:394.

continued

24. NUTRIENT REQUIREMENTS: BACTERIA

Part II. Amino Acids

[14] Knight, B. C. J. G., and H. Proom. 1950. Ibid. 4:508.
[15] Koser, S. A. 1923. J. Bacteriol. 8:493.
[16] Koser, S. A. Unpublished. Univ. Chicago, Dept. Microbiology, Chicago, 1967.
[17] Koser, S. A., and L. F. Rettger. 1919. J. Infect. Diseases 24:301.
[18] Mager, J., S. H. Kindler, and N. Grossowicz. 1954. J. Gen. Microbiol. 10:130.
[19] McCullough, N. B., and L. A. Dick. 1943. Proc. Soc. Exptl. Biol. Med. 52:310.
[20] Mueller, J. H., and P. A. Miller. 1942. J. Bacteriol. 43:763.
[21] Pelczar, M. J., Jr., and J. R. Porter. 1943. Arch. Biochem. 2:323.
[22] Rao, M. S. 1939. Indian J. Med. Res. 27:75.
[23] Snell, E. E. 1945. Advan. Protein Chem. 2:85.
[24] Steinman, H. G., H. Eagle, and V. I. Oyama. 1953. J. Biol. Chem. 200:775.
[25] Stokes, J. L., and A. Larsen. 1945. J. Bacteriol. 49:495.
[26] Sullivan, M. X. 1905-6. J. Med. Res. 14:109.
[27] Tamura, J. T., and I. W. Gibby. 1943. J. Bacteriol. 45:361.

25. NUTRIENT REQUIREMENTS AND UTILIZATION: FUNGI

Part I. Vitamins

Different isolates of the same species may have different vitamin requirements. *Abbreviations:* R = required (organism must have vitamins supplied to it in the substrate); ℞ = not required (organism synthesizes vitamins needed for metabolism).

	Species (Synonym)	Thiamine	Biotin	Other	Reference
	Phycomycetes				
1	*Absidia coerulea*	℞	℞	℞	106,107
2	*A. glauca*	℞	℞	℞	89
3	*A. orchidis*	℞	℞	℞	106,107
4	*A. ramosa*	R[1/]	℞	℞	108
5	*A. repens*	℞	℞	℞	106,107
6	*A. spinosa*	℞	℞	℞	11
7	*Achlya conspicua*	℞	℞	℞	47
8	*Allomyces arbuscula*	R[2/]	℞	℞	84
9	*Aphanomyces camptostylus*	℞	℞	℞	47
10	*A. phycophilus*	R	℞	℞	123
11	*Basidiobolus ranarum*	℞	℞	℞	116
12	*Blakeslea trispora*	R[1/]	℞	℞	42,47,91
13	*Blastocladia pringsheimii*	R	R	R[3/]	17
14	*Chaetocladium brefeldii*	R	℞	℞	11,47,91
15	*C. macrosporum*	R	℞	℞	11,47,91
16	*Chaetostylum fresenii*	℞	℞	℞	11
17	*Choanephora cucurbitarum*	R	℞	℞	52,106,107
18	*Circinella aspera*	℞	℞	℞	46,89,91
19	*C. spinosa*	℞	℞	℞	46,89,91
20	*Coemansia interrupta*	R	R	℞	52
21	*Cunninghamella bertholletiae*	℞	℞	℞	46
22	*C. echinulata*	℞	℞	℞	106,107
23	*C. elegans*	℞	℞	℞	91,106,107
24	*Dicranophora fulva*	R	℞	℞	91,106,107
25	*Haplosporangium parvum*	℞	℞	℞	20
26	*Isoachlya monilifera*	℞	℞	℞	47
27	*Mortierella candelabrum*	℞	℞	℞	89,91
28	*M. isabellina*	℞	℞	℞	91,106,107
29	*M. puisilla*	℞	℞	℞	91,106,107
30	*Mucor circinelloides*	℞	℞	℞	89
31	*M. genevensis*	℞	℞	℞	130
32	*M. griseolilacinus*	℞	℞	℞	89
33	*M. hiemalis*	℞	℞	℞	34
34	*M. mucedo*	R	℞	℞	106,107
35	*M. mucilagineus*	℞	℞	℞	11
36	*M. ramannianus*	R[4/]	℞	℞	91,106,107
37	*M. stolonifer*	℞	℞	℞	73
38	*M. tenuis*	℞	℞	℞	11
39	*Parasitella simplex*	R	℞	℞	91,106,107
40	*Phycomyces blakesleeanus*	R[5/]	℞	℞	43,88,105, 106
41	*P. nitens*	R	℞	℞	47,91
42	*Phytophthora arecae*	R	℞	℞	100
43	*P. boehmeriae*	R	℞	℞	100
44	*P. cactorum*	R	℞	℞	100
45	*P. cambivora*	R	℞	℞	100
46	*P. capsici*	R	℞	℞	100
47	*P. cinnamoni*	R	℞	℞	100
48	*P. citricola*	R	℞	℞	100
49	*P. citrophthora*	R	℞	℞	100
50	*P. cryptogea*	R	℞	℞	100
51	*P. drechsleri*	R	℞	℞	100
52	*P. erythroseptica*	R	℞	℞	100
53	*P. heveae*	R	℞	℞	100
54	*P. hibernalis*	R	℞	℞	100

[1/] Pyrimidine portion. [2/] Plus an unknown "cofactor" which is not nicotinic acid or biotin. [3/] Nicotinic acid. [4/] Thiazole portion. [5/] Or pyrimidine plus thiazole.

continued

Part I. Vitamins

	Species (Synonym)	Thiamine	Biotin	Other	Reference
55	*P. himalayensis*	R	℞	℞	100
56	*P. ilicis*	R	℞	℞	100
57	*P. infestans*	R	℞	℞	100
58	*P. lateralis*	R	℞	℞	100
59	*P. megasperma*	R	℞	℞	100
60	*P. oryzae (Pythiomorpha oryzae)*	R	℞	℞	11
61	*Phytophthora palmivora*	R	℞	℞	100
62	*P. parasitica*	R	℞	℞	100
63	*P. parasitica nicotianae*	R	℞	℞	100
64	*P. phaseoli*	R	℞	℞	100
65	*P. quininea*	R	℞	℞	100
66	*P. sojae*	R	℞	℞	100
67	*P. syringae*	R	℞	℞	100
68	*Pilaira anomala*	R	℞	℞	47,91,109
69	*P. moreaui*	R	℞	℞	47,91,109
70	*Piptocephalis freseniana*	℞	℞	℞	91,106
71	*Pythium* spp.[6]	℞	℞	℞	87
72	*P. acanthicum*	R[1]	℞	℞	87
73	*P. acanthophoron*	℞	℞	℞	87
74	*P. afertile*	℞	℞	℞	87
75	*P. anandrum*	R[1]	℞	℞	87
76	*P. aphanidermatum*	℞	℞	℞	87
77	*P. arrhenomanes*	℞	℞	℞	87
78	*P. ascophallon*	R	℞	℞	48,91
79	*P. butleri*	R[1]	℞	℞	91,106,107
80	*P. carolinianum*	R[1]	℞	℞	87
81	*P. catenulatum*	℞	℞	℞	87
82	*P. chamaihyphon*	R[1]	℞	℞	87
83	*P. debaryanum*	℞	℞	℞	87
84	*P. deliense*	℞	℞	℞	87
85	*P. dissotocum*	℞	℞	℞	87
86	*P. graminicolum*	℞	℞	℞	87
87	*P. helicandrum*	R[1]	℞	℞	87
88	*P. helicoides*	R[1]	℞	℞	87
89	*P. hyphalosticton*	℞	℞	℞	102
90	*P. intermedium*	℞	℞	℞	87
91	*P. irregulare*	℞	℞	℞	87
92	*P. mamillatum*	℞	℞	℞	87
93	*P. multisporum*	℞	℞	℞	87
94	*P. myriotylum*	℞	℞	℞	87
95	*P. oedochilum*	R[1]	℞	℞	87
96	*P. oligandrum*	R[1]	℞	℞	87
97	*P. paroecandrum*	℞	℞	℞	87
98	*P. periplocum*	R[1]	℞	℞	87
99	*P. plerosporon*	R[1]	℞	℞	87
100	*P. polycladon*	R[1]	℞	℞	48,91
101	*P. polymastum*	R	℞	℞	89,91
102	*P. polytylum*	R[1]	℞	℞	87
103	*P. proliferum*	R[1]	℞	℞	87
104	*P. rostratum*	℞	℞	℞	87
105	*P. salpingophorum*	℞	℞	℞	87
106	*P. scleroteichum*	℞	℞	℞	87
107	*P. spinosum*	℞	℞	℞	87
108	*P. splendens*	℞	℞	℞	87
109	*P. torulosum*	℞	℞	℞	87
110	*P. ultimum*	℞	℞	℞	87
111	*P. undulatum*	R[1]	℞	℞	87
112	*P. vexans (P. ascophallon)*	R	℞	℞	87
113	*Rhizopus bovinus (R. arrhizus)*	℞	℞	℞	91,106,107
114	*R. chinensis*	℞	℞	℞	91,106,107
115	*R. japonicus*	℞	℞	℞	91,106,107
116	*R. maydis (R. arrhizus)*	℞	℞	℞	91,106,107
117	*R. nigricans*	℞	℞	℞	91,106,107
118	*R. nodosus (R. arrhizus)*	℞	℞	℞	91,106,107
119	*R. oryzae*	℞	℞	℞	91,106,107
120	*R. suinus*	℞	℞	℞	91,106,107
121	*R. tonkinensis*	℞	℞	℞	91,106,107
122	*R. tritici*	℞	℞	℞	91,106,107
123	*Saprolegnia delica*	℞	℞	℞	91
124	*S. mixta*	℞	℞	℞	45
125	*Syncephalastrum cinereum*	℞	℞	℞	91,106,107
126	*Thamnidium elegans*	℞	℞	℞	91,106,107
127	*Thraustotheca clavata*	℞	R	℞	48,91
128	*Trachysphaera fructigena*	℞	R	℞	48
129	*Zygorhynchus dangeardi*	℞	℞	℞	91,106,107
130	*Z. exponens*	℞	℞	℞	11,91
131	*Z. heterogamus*	℞	℞	℞	46,91
132	*Z. moelleri*	℞	℞	℞	89,91
	Ascomycetes				
133	*Allescheria boydii*	℞	R	℞	20,120
134	*Ascobolus denudatus*	℞	℞	℞	34
135	*A. furfuraceus*	℞	℞	℞	68,69
136	*A. leveillei*	℞	℞	℞	34
137	*Ascoidea rubescens*	R	℞	R[7]	28
138	*Ashbya gossypii*	R	R	R[8]	110
139	*Bombardia lutea*	℞	℞	℞	128
140	*Botryotinia convoluta*	R[9]	℞	℞	51
141	*Bulgaria inquinans*	R	℞	℞	30
142	*Ceratocystis fimbriata (Ceratostomella fimbriata)*	R[10]	R[9]	R[7,9]	52,93,94
143	*Ceratocystis minor (Ceratostomella pini)*	R	R[9]	R[7,9]	93,94
144	*Ceratocystis pilifera (Ceratostomella pilifera)*	R[9]	℞	R[7,9]	93,94
145	*Ceratocystis pluriannulata (Ceratostomella pluriannulata)*	R[9]	℞	R[7,9]	93,94

[1] Pyrimidine portion. [6] 19 unidentified isolates. [7] Vitamin B_6. [8] Inositol. [9] Partial requirement. [10] Reported to be the only vitamin required for 2 isolates.

continued

Part I. Vitamins

	Species (Synonym)	Thiamine	Biotin	Other	Reference
146	*Ceratostomella adiposum*	℞	℞	R[8]	93,94
147	*C. ips*	R	R[9]	R[7,9]	93,94
148	*C. leptographioides*	℞	R[9]	℞	95
149	*C. microspora*	R	R[9]	R[7,9]	93,94
150	*C. montium*	R	R[9]	R[7,9]	93,94
151	*C. multiannulata*	R[9]	℞	R[7,9]	93,94
152	*C. obscura*	R	R	℞	94,95
153	*C. penicillata*	R	R[9]	R[7,9]	94
154	*C. piceaperda*	R	R[9]	R[7,9]	93,94
155	*C. pseudotsugae*	R[9]	℞	R[7,9]	93,94
156	*C. radicicola*	R	R	℞	94,95
157	*C. rostrocylindrica*	℞	℞	℞	94
158	*C. stenoceras*	R	℞	℞	94
159	*C. ulmi*	R[9]	℞	R[7,9]	93,94
160	*Chaetomium bostrychodes*	℞	℞	℞	91,113
161	*C. cochliodes*	℞	℞	℞	34,91
162	*C. convolutum*	R	R	℞	50,52
163	*C. elatum*	℞	℞	℞	91,113
164	*C. globosum*	℞	℞	℞	52
165	*Ciboria acerina*	R[11]	R[11]	℞	51
166	*C. pseudotuberosa*	R[9]	℞	℞	51
167	*Ciborinia erythronii*	℞	℞	℞	51
168	*Cordyceps militaris*	℞	℞	℞	52
169	*Coryne sarcoides*	R	R	℞	13
170	*Cudonia circinans*	R	℞	℞	30
171	*Daldinia concentrica*	℞	℞	℞	52
172	*Dasyobolus immersus*	R	℞	℞	46
173	*Debaryomyces fabryi*	℞	R	℞	14
174	*D. guilliermondii*	℞	R	℞	14
175	*D. hudeloi*	℞	R	℞	20
176	*D. matruchoti subglobosus*	℞	R	℞	14
177	*D. membranaefaciens*	R	R	℞	12,14
178	*Dermea balsamea (Dermatea balsamea)*	R	℞	℞	48,91
179	*Diaporthe strumella*	℞	℞	℞	46
180	*Dipodascus uninucleatus*	R	R	℞	48,91
181	*Dothidella quercus*	℞	℞	℞	91,128
182	*Endothia parasitica*	R	R	℞	52
183	*Epichloe typhina*	R	℞	R[8,9]	51,52
184	*Eremascus fertilis*	℞	℞	℞	91,113
185	*Eremothecium ashbyii*	R	R	R[8]	23,110
186	*Glomerella cingulata*	℞	℞	℞	52,91,101
187	*Grosmannia serpens*	℞	R	℞	94
188	*Gymnoascus setosus*	℞	℞	℞	34,91
189	*Hansenula anomala*	℞	℞	℞	42
190	*H. suaveolens*	℞	R	℞	14
191	*H. subpelliculosa*	R	℞	℞	14
192	*Helvella infula*	R	℞	℞	43
193	*Histoplasma capsulatum*	℞	R[11]	℞	20,103
194	*Hypoxylon pruinatum*	R	R	℞	27,91
195	*Lachnum pygmaeum*	R	R	℞	30
196	*Lambertella corni-maris*	R	R[9]	℞	34,51
197	*L. hicoriae*	R	R[9]	℞	51
198	*L. pruni*	R	R[9]	℞	51,52
199	*L. viburni*	R	R[9]	℞	51
200	*Lophodermium pinastri*	R	R	R[8,9]	47
201	*Martinia panamaensis*	R[9]	℞	℞	51
202	*Melanospora destruens*	R	R	℞	35,91
203	*Monascus purpureus*	℞	℞	℞	113
204	*Monilia albicans*	℞	R	℞	13
205	*M. metalondinensis*	℞	R	℞	13
206	*Monilinia fructicola*	℞[9]	℞	℞	52,122
207	*M. laxa*	R	℞	℞	43
208	*Mycosphaerella confusa*	℞	℞	℞	46
209	*M. grossulariae*	℞	℞	℞	46
210	*M. sentina*	R	℞	℞	91,113
211	*Nectria coccinea*	R[9]	℞	℞	43,52
212	*Nematospora coryli*	℞	℞	℞	25
213	*N. gossypii*	R	R	R[8]	43,110
214	*Neocosmospora vasinfecta*	℞	℞	℞	52
215	*Neurospora crassa*	℞	R	℞	16,52,91
216	*N. sitophila*	℞	R	℞	16,52,91
217	*N. tetrasperma*	℞	R	℞	16,52,91
218	*Ophiobolus graminis*	R	R	℞	52,124
219	*O. miyabeanus*	℞	℞	℞	91,104
220	*O. oryzinus*	℞	R	℞	48,91
221	*Ophiostoma catonianum*	R	R	R[7]	48,52,94
222	*O. coeruleum*	R	℞	℞	28
223	*O. fagi*	℞	R[9]	R[7]	28
224	*Phacidium infestans*	R[9]	℞	℞	79
225	*Physalospora vaccinii (Acanthorhynchus vaccinii)*	R[12]	R[12]	℞	48
226	*Pichia alcoholophila*	℞	R	℞	13
227	*P. belgica*	R	R	R[7,8]	14
228	*P. dombrowskii*	R	℞	℞	14
229	*P. kluyveri*	R	R	℞	14
230	*Piedraia hortai*	R	℞	℞	20
231	*Pleurage curvicolla*	R	R	℞	52,91
232	*Podospora curvula*	R	R	℞	52
233	*Pseudopeziza ribis*	℞	R	℞	48
234	*Pyronema confluens*	R	℞	℞	41
235	*P. domesticum*	℞	℞	℞	34,91
236	*Rosellinia arcuata*	℞	R	℞	48,91
237	*R. necatrix*	℞	℞	℞	34,113
238	*R. thelena*	℞	℞	℞	34,113
239	*Saccharomyces carlsbergensis*	℞	R	R[13]	12,115
240	*S. carlsbergensis mandshuricus*	℞	R	R[7,13]	12,115

[7] Vitamin B_6. [8] Inositol [9] Partial requirement. [11] Requirement varies from "R" to "℞," depending on the isolate. [12] Either thiamine or biotin. [13] Pantothenic acid.

continued

25. NUTRIENT REQUIREMENTS AND UTILIZATION: FUNGI

Part I. Vitamins

	Species (Synonym)	Thiamine	Biotin	Other	Reference
241	*S. cerevisiae ellipsoideus*	R	R	R[8,13]	12,115
242	*S. chodati*	℞	R	R[7,13]	12,115
243	*S. fragilis*	R	R	R[7,13]	12,115
244	*S. globosus*	R	R	R[3]	12,115
245	*S. logos*	R	℞	R[13]	14
246	*S. macedoniensis*	R	R	R[3,13]	12
247	*S. oviformis*	℞	R	R[7,13]	12
248	*S. tubiformis*	℞	R	R[13]	12
249	*S. uvarum*	℞	R	R[8,13]	12
250	*Saccharomycodes ludwigii*	R	R	R[14]	12
251	*Saccobolus depauperatus*	℞	R	℞	48,91
252	*Schizosaccharomyces pombe*	℞	R	R[15]	14
253	*Schwanniomyces occidentalis*	℞	R	℞	14
254	*Sclerotinia camelliae*	R	R	R[8,9]	52
255	*S. minor*	R[9]	R[9]	℞	51,52
256	*S. sclerotiorum*	℞	℞	℞	52
257	*S. smilacinae (Stromatinia smilacinae)*	R[9]	℞	℞	51
258	*Sordaria fimicola*	℞[16]	R	℞	48,52,91
259	*Spathularia flavida*	R	R	R[7]	30
260	*Spermophthora gossypii*	℞	℞	℞	25
261	*Sphaeropsis malorum*	℞	℞	℞	52,91
262	*Sphaerulina trifolii*	R	℞	℞	91
263	*Sporormia intermedia*	℞	R	℞	48,91
264	*Torulaspora delbrueckii*	℞	R	℞	14
265	*T. fermentati*	℞	R	℞	14
266	*Ustulina vulgaris*	℞	℞	℞	131
267	*Valsa ceratophora*	R[9]	℞	℞	27,91
268	*V. pini*	R	R	R[8]	91
269	*Venturia inaequalis*	℞	℞	℞	127
270	*Xylaria arbuscula*	℞	℞	℞	10,91
271	*X. hypoxylon*	R	℞	℞	10,91
272	*X. polymorpha*	℞	℞	℞	10,91
273	*Zygosaccharomyces barkeri*	R	R	R[13]	12
274	*Z. bisporus*	R	R	℞	14,99
275	*Z. japonicus*	R	R	R[8,13]	14,99
276	*Z. lactis*	℞	R	R[3]	14,99
277	*Z. mandshuricus*	R	R	℞	12,99
278	*Z. marxianus*	℞	R	R[3]	12,99
279	*Z. nadsonii*	℞	R	R[13]	12
280	*Z. pastori*	℞	R	R[13]	12
281	*Z. pini*	℞	R	℞	14
282	*Z. priorianus*	℞	R	R[8,13]	14
	Basidiomycetes				
283	*Agaricus bisporus (Psalliota bispora)*	R[12]	R[12]	℞	119
284	*A. campestris (Psalliota campestris)*	℞	℞	℞	89,91,106, 107
285	*Amanita pantherina*	R[5]	℞	℞	65
286	*Armillaria mellea*	℞	℞	℞	34
287	*Boletus elegans*	R	℞	℞	63,91
288	*B. granulatus*	R[5,9]	℞	℞	65,66,91
289	*B. luteus*	R[5]	℞	℞	65,66,91
290	*B. piperatus*	R[5,9]	R[9]	℞	65,66,91
291	*B. variegatus*	R[5]	℞	℞	65,66,91
292	*B. viscidus*	R	℞	℞	66
293	*Calocera viscosa*	R	℞	℞	30
294	*Clavaria ligula*	R	℞	℞	56
295	*Clitocybe alexandri*	R	℞	℞	56
296	*C. aurantiaca*	R	℞	℞	56
297	*C. clavipes*	R	℞	℞	56
298	*C. cyathiformis*	R	℞	℞	56
299	*C. geotropa*	R[9]	℞	℞	56
300	*C. infundibuliformis*	R	℞	℞	56
301	*C. nebularis*	R	℞	℞	56
302	*C. odora*	R	℞	℞	56
303	*C. pithyophila*	R	℞	℞	56
304	*Clitopilus prunulus*	R[5]	℞	℞	63,65,66
305	*Collybia ambusta*	R	℞	℞	56
306	*C. butyracea*	R	℞	℞	56
307	*C. dryophila*	R	R	℞	57
308	*C. tuberosa*	R[1]	℞	℞	30,47
309	*C. velutipes*	R[17]	R[9]	℞	56,59
310	*Coprinus atramentarius*	R[1]	℞	℞	26
311	*C. comatus*	R[1]	℞	℞	26
312	*C. cordisporus*	R[5]	℞	℞	26
313	*C. ephemeroides*	R[5]	℞	℞	26
314	*C. ephemerus*	R[1]	℞	℞	26
315	*C. fimetarius*	R[1]	℞	℞	26
316	*C. lagopus*	R[1]	℞	℞	26
317	*C. micaceus*	R[1]	℞	℞	26
318	*C. niveus*	R[5]	℞	℞	26
319	*C. plicatilis*	R[1]	℞	℞	26
320	*C. radiatus*	R[1]	℞	℞	26
321	*C. tergiversans*	R	℞	℞	48
322	*Corticium vagum*	R	℞	℞	38
323	*Cortinellus bulbiger*	R	℞	℞	56
324	*Cyathus striatus*	R	℞	℞	48,91
325	*Dacrymyces stellatus*	R	℞	℞	27,91
326	*Daedalea confragosa*	R	℞	℞	122

[1] Pyrimidine portion. [3] Nicotinic acid. [5] Or pyrimidine plus thiazole. [7] Vitamin B_6. [8] Inositol. [9] Partial requirement. [12] Either thiamine or biotin. [13] Pantothenic acid. [14] Nicotinic acid, vitamin B_6, inositol, and pantothenic acid. [15] Nicotinic acid, inositol, and pantothenic acid. [16] Not required by most isolates, but by certain isolates thiamine is required in addition to biotin. [17] Can be replaced by pyrimidine or thiazole.

continued

25. NUTRIENT REQUIREMENTS AND UTILIZATION: FUNGI

Part I. Vitamins

	Species (Synonym)	Thiamine	Biotin	Other	Reference
327	*D. quercina*	R	℞	℞	122
328	*D. unicolor*	R[9]	℞	℞	27,91
329	*Deconica inquilina*	R	℞	℞	48
330	*Entyloma arnoseridis*	℞	℞	℞	91,113
331	*Exobasidium vaccinii*	R	℞	℞	31
332	*Flammula carbonaria*	R	℞	℞	56
333	*F. penetrans*	R	℞	℞	56
334	*Fomes annosus*	R	℞	℞	86
335	*F. fraxineus*	℞	℞	℞	34,91
336	*F. igniarius*	R	℞	℞	86
337	*F. pinicola*	R	℞	℞	86
338	*Ganoderma lucidum*	R	℞	℞	122
339	*Gloeocystidium roseo-cremeum*	R	℞	℞	48
340	*Hydnum auriscalpium*	R	℞	℞	30
341	*H. coralloides*	℞	℞	℞	34,91
342	*H. corrugatum*	R	℞	℞	30
343	*H. erinaceus*	R	℞	℞	30
344	*Hypholoma capnoides*	R	℞	℞	56
345	*H. fasciculare*	R[5,9]	℞	℞	56
346	*H. sublateritium*	R	℞	℞	56
347	*Hypochnus solani*	℞	℞	℞	27,91
348	*Lactarius deliciosus*	R	℞	℞	63,66,91
349	*Lentinus omphalodes*	R	℞	℞	30
350	*L. tigrinus*	R[5]	℞	℞	47,91
351	*Lenzites abietina*	R[9]	℞	℞	30
352	*L. betulina*	R	℞	℞	30,48,91
353	*L. sepiaria*	R	℞	℞	27,43,48,91
354	*L. trabea*	R[9]	℞	℞	49
355	*Lepiota amianthina*	R	℞	℞	56
356	*L. procera*	R	℞	℞	56
357	*Marasmius alliaceus*	R[5]	℞	℞	53,55
358	*M. androsaceus*	R[5]	R[9]	℞	53-55
359	*M. chordalis*	R[5]	℞	℞	53,55
360	*M. epiphyllus*	R[1]	℞	℞	53,55
361	*M. foetidus*	R[5]	℞	℞	53,55
362	*M. fulvo-bulbillosus*	R[1,9]	℞	℞	53,55
363	*M. graminum*	R[5,9]	℞	℞	53,55
364	*M. perforans*	R	R	℞	53
365	*M. perniciosus*	R	℞	℞	58
366	*M. peronatus*	R[5,9]	℞	℞	53,55
367	*M. putillus*	R	℞	℞	105
368	*M. ramealis*	R[5,9]	℞	℞	53,55
369	*M. rotula*	R[5]	℞	℞	53,55
370	*M. scorodonius*	R[5]	℞	℞	53,55
371	*Melanconium betulinum*	R	R	R[8]	91
372	*Merulius lacrymans*	R	℞	℞	27,91
373	*Mycena alcalina*	R	℞	℞	29
374	*M. amicta*	R	℞	℞	29
375	*M. cinerella*	R	℞	℞	29
376	*M. debilis*	R[9]	℞	℞	29
377	*M. epipterygia*	R	℞	℞	56
378	*M. flavo-alba*	R	℞	℞	29,31
379	*M. galericulata*	R	℞	℞	29
380	*M. galopoda*	R	℞	℞	56
381	*M. lactea*	R	℞	℞	29
382	*M. metata*	R	℞	℞	56
383	*M. polygramma*	R	℞	℞	56
384	*M. rosella*	R	℞	℞	56
385	*M. rubromarginata*	℞	℞	℞	29
386	*M. sanguinolenta*	℞	℞	℞	29
387	*M. viscosa*	R	℞	℞	56
388	*M. vulgaris*	R	℞	℞	29,56
389	*M. zephyra*	R[9]	℞	℞	29
390	*Nyctalis asterophora*	R[1]	℞	℞	30,47
391	*Omphalia gracillima*	R	℞	℞	30
392	*Panaeolus campanulatus*	R[9]	℞	℞	30
393	*Panus stipticus*	R	℞	℞	30,56
394	*P. torulosus*	R	℞	℞	30,56
395	*Peniophora candida*	R	℞	℞	30
396	*P. cinctula*	R	℞	℞	30
397	*P. fraxinea*	R	℞	℞	30
398	*P. junipericola*	R	℞	℞	30
399	*P. septentrionalis*	R	℞	℞	30
400	*P. violaceo-livida*	R	℞	℞	30
401	*Pholiota adiposa*	R[9]	R[9]	R[7,9]	91,95
402	*P. mutabilis*	R	℞	℞	56
403	*P. squarrosa*	R	℞	℞	56
404	*Pleurotus corticatus*	R[1]	℞	℞	47
405	*Polyporus abietinus*	R[5]	℞	℞	27,30,43,113
406	*P. adustus*	R[1]	℞	℞	27,43,113,114
407	*P. anceps*	R	℞	℞	43,82
408	*P. annosus*	R[5]	℞	℞	27,30,86
409	*P. benzoinus*	R[5]	℞	℞	27,113
410	*P. cervinus*	R	℞	℞	30
411	*P. fomentarius*	R	℞	℞	27
412	*P. nidulans*	R	℞	℞	30
413	*P. spraguei*	℞	℞	℞	59,91,95,113
414	*P. squamosus*	R[5]	℞	℞	113
415	*P. versicolor*	R	℞	R[7,9]	113
416	*P. zonatus*	R[5]	℞	℞	27,113
417	*Rhizopogon roseolus*	R	R[9]	℞	63,66
418	*Schizophyllum commune*	R[1]	℞	℞	89,91,95
419	*Sistrotrema confluens*	R	℞	℞	30
420	*Sphaerobolus stellatus*	℞	℞	℞	34,91
421	*Stereum frustulosum*	R[4]	℞	℞	74,75,91
422	*S. murrayi*	℞	℞	℞	95
423	*Stropharia semiglobata*	R	℞	℞	30

[1] Pyrimidine portion. [4] Thiazole portion. [5] Or pyrimidine plus thiazole. [7] Vitamin B_6. [8] Inositol. [9] Partial requirement.

continued

Part I. Vitamins

	Species (Synonym)	Thiamine	Biotin	Other	Reference
424	*Tilletia horrida*	R[5]	Ɍ	Ɍ	91,113
425	*T. laevis*	Ɍ	Ɍ	Ɍ	91,113
426	*T. tritici*	R[18]	Ɍ	Ɍ	21,22,33, 44,99,113
427	*Trametes cinnabarina*	R	Ɍ	Ɍ	27,43
428	*T. heteromorpha*	R	Ɍ	Ɍ	30
429	*T. serialis*	R	Ɍ	Ɍ	27,43,91
430	*Tricholoma albobrunneum*	R[5,9]	Ɍ	Ɍ	63,65
431	*T. brevipes*	R[5,9]	Ɍ	R[19]	76
432	*T. flavobrunneum*	R[1]	Ɍ	Ɍ	76
433	*T. fumosum*	R[5,9]	Ɍ	R[20]	76
434	*T. gambosum*	R[1,9]	Ɍ	R[13]	76
435	*T. imbricatum*	R[5,9]	Ɍ	R[13]	63,76
436	*T. nudum*	R[1]	Ɍ	R[13]	27,43,76
437	*T. personatum*	R	Ɍ	Ɍ	76
438	*T. pessundatum*	R[1,9]	Ɍ	Ɍ	63,66,76
439	*T. vaccinum*	R[5,9]	Ɍ	Ɍ	76
440	*Tubaria furfuracea*	R	Ɍ	Ɍ	56
441	*Typhula variabilis*	R	Ɍ	Ɍ	48
442	*Ustilago avenae*	Ɍ	Ɍ	Ɍ	91,111,112
443	*U. bromivora*	Ɍ	Ɍ	Ɍ	91,111,112
444	*U. hordei*	Ɍ	Ɍ	Ɍ	111,112
445	*U. levis*	Ɍ	Ɍ	Ɍ	91,111,112
446	*U. longissima*	R[1,9]	Ɍ	Ɍ	91,111,112
447	*U. nuda*	Ɍ	Ɍ	Ɍ	91,111,112
448	*U. pinguiculae*	R[5]	Ɍ	Ɍ	7
449	*U. scabiosae*	R[5]	Ɍ	Ɍ	91,112,113
450	*U. striiformis*	Ɍ	Ɍ	Ɍ	52
451	*U. tritici*	Ɍ	Ɍ	Ɍ	111,112
452	*U. vinosa*	R[5]	Ɍ	Ɍ	7
453	*U. violacea*[21]	R[5]	Ɍ	Ɍ	91,111,112
454	*U. zeae*	Ɍ	Ɍ	Ɍ	80,91,111, 112
	Fungi Imperfecti				
455	*Acremoniella lutzi*	Ɍ	Ɍ	Ɍ	20
456	*Acremonium potronii*	R	Ɍ	Ɍ	20
457	*Aleurisma loboi (Glenosporella loboi)*	Ɍ	Ɍ	Ɍ	20
458	*Alternaria solani*	Ɍ	Ɍ	Ɍ	122
459	*Ascochyta pisi*	Ɍ	Ɍ	Ɍ	101
460	*Aspergillus aureus (A. area, A. foetidus)*	Ɍ	Ɍ	Ɍ	52,77,83,91
461	*A. awamori*	Ɍ	Ɍ	Ɍ	52,77,91
462	*A. carbonarius*	Ɍ	Ɍ	Ɍ	52,83,91
463	*A. chevalieri*	Ɍ	Ɍ	Ɍ	34,52,91
464	*A. cinnamomeus*	Ɍ	Ɍ	Ɍ	52,83,91
465	*A. citrosporus*	Ɍ	Ɍ	Ɍ	52,83,91
466	*A. clavatus*	Ɍ	Ɍ	Ɍ	52,83,91
467	*A. fischeri*	Ɍ	Ɍ	Ɍ	52,83,91
468	*A. flavipes*	Ɍ	Ɍ	Ɍ	52,83,91
469	*A. flavus*	Ɍ	Ɍ	Ɍ	52,73,91
470	*A. fumigatus*	Ɍ	Ɍ	Ɍ	52,78,91
471	*A. fuscus*	Ɍ	Ɍ	Ɍ	52,83,91
472	*A. giganteus*	Ɍ	Ɍ	Ɍ	40,52,91
473	*A. glaucus*	Ɍ	Ɍ	Ɍ	40,52,91
474	*A. gymnosardae*	Ɍ	Ɍ	Ɍ	52,77,91
475	*A. luchuensis (A. awamori)*	Ɍ	Ɍ	Ɍ	40,52,91
476	*A. lutea (A. flavus)*	Ɍ	Ɍ	Ɍ	52,83,91
477	*A. melleus*	Ɍ	Ɍ	Ɍ	52,83,91
478	*A. nidulans*	Ɍ	Ɍ	Ɍ	52,83,91
479	*A. niger*	Ɍ	Ɍ	Ɍ	52,91,101, 116
480	*A. ochraceus*	Ɍ	Ɍ	Ɍ	52,83,91
481	*A. oniki (A. ochraceus)*	Ɍ	Ɍ	Ɍ	52,77,91
482	*A. oryzae*	Ɍ	Ɍ	Ɍ	52,83,91
483	*A. ostianus*	Ɍ	Ɍ	Ɍ	40,52,91
484	*A. parasiticus*	Ɍ	Ɍ	Ɍ	5,52,91
485	*A. repens*	Ɍ	Ɍ	Ɍ	34,52,91
486	*A. soya (A. flavus)*	Ɍ	Ɍ	Ɍ	52,77,91
487	*A. sydowi*	Ɍ	Ɍ	Ɍ	52,83,91
488	*A. terreus*	Ɍ	Ɍ	Ɍ	16,52,91
489	*Basisporium gallarum*	Ɍ	Ɍ	Ɍ	52
490	*Blastomyces brasiliensis*	Ɍ	Ɍ	Ɍ	20
491	*B. dermatitidis*	Ɍ	Ɍ	Ɍ	20
492	*Botrytis allii*	Ɍ	Ɍ	Ɍ	18,52,91, 122
493	*B. cinerea*	Ɍ	Ɍ	Ɍ	18,52,91, 122
494	*Brettanomyces bruxellensis*	Ɍ	Ɍ	R[7]	14
495	*Candida albicans*	R	R	Ɍ	12
496	*C. aldoi*	R	R	Ɍ	12
497	*C. brumptii*	R	R	Ɍ	14
498	*C. chalmersi*	Ɍ	R	Ɍ	14
499	*C. chevalieri*	Ɍ	Ɍ	Ɍ	118
500	*C. deformans*	Ɍ	R	Ɍ	14
501	*C. flareri*	Ɍ	R	Ɍ	13
502	*C. guilliermondii*	Ɍ	R	Ɍ	12
503	*C. intermedia*	Ɍ	R	Ɍ	12
504	*C. krusei*	R	R	Ɍ	12
505	*C. mycotoruloidea*	Ɍ	R	Ɍ	13
506	*C. parakrusei*	Ɍ	R	Ɍ	13
507	*C. pseudotropicalis*	R	R	R[3,13]	12
508	*C. stellatoidea*	Ɍ	R	Ɍ	13
509	*C. suaveolens (C. humicola)*	R[22]	R[22]	Ɍ	12,14,20
510	*C. triadis*	R	R	Ɍ	12
511	*C. tropicalis*	R	R	Ɍ	12
512	*C. zeylanoides*	Ɍ	R	Ɍ	13

1/ Pyrimidine portion. 3/ Nicotinic acid. 5/ Or pyrimidine plus thiazole. 7/ Vitamin B_6. 9/ Partial requirement. 13/ Pantothenic acid. 18/ Conflicting reports on the replaceability of thiamine by pyrimidine plus thiazole, or by pyrimidine alone. 19/ *p*-Aminobenzoic acid. 20/ Nicotinamide. 21/ Also 7 closely related species. 22/ Conflicting reports on requirement for thiamine and biotin separately, or in combination.

continued

Part I. Vitamins

	Species (Synonym)	Thiamine	Biotin	Other	Reference
513	*Catenularia* sp.	Ɍ	Ɍ	Ɍ	113
514	*Cenococcum graniforme*	R[1]	R[9]	Ɍ	64-67
515	*Cephalosporium recifei*	Ɍ	Ɍ	Ɍ	1,20
516	*Cephalothecium roseum*	Ɍ	Ɍ	Ɍ	122
517	*Cercospora apii*	Ɍ	Ɍ	Ɍ	91
518	*C. beticola*	Ɍ	Ɍ	Ɍ	91
519	*Chalara quercina*	R[9]	R[9]	Ɍ	122
520	*Chalaropsis thielavioides*	R	Ɍ	Ɍ	95
521	*Cladosporium algeriensis (Hormodendrum algeriensis)*	R	Ɍ	Ɍ	15,20
522	*C. herbarum*	Ɍ	Ɍ	Ɍ	20,40
523	*C. langeronii (Hormodendrum langeronii)*	Ɍ	Ɍ	Ɍ	20
524	*C. pedroi (Hormodendrum pedroi)*	R	Ɍ	Ɍ	15,20
525	*C. wernecki*	Ɍ	Ɍ	Ɍ	20,40
526	*Colletotrichum circinans*	Ɍ	Ɍ	Ɍ	91,130
527	*C. lindemuthianum*	R[9,11]	Ɍ	Ɍ	52,83,122
528	*Cryptococcus* sp.	R	Ɍ	Ɍ	78
529	*Cytospora* sp.	R	Ɍ	Ɍ	23
530	*Dematium chodati*	Ɍ	Ɍ	Ɍ	113
531	*D. nigrum*	R	Ɍ	Ɍ	114
532	*D. pullulans*	Ɍ	Ɍ	Ɍ	113
533	*Dendrophoma obscurans*	R	Ɍ	Ɍ	52
534	*Diplodia macrospora*	Ɍ	R	Ɍ	60,91
535	*Epidermophyton floccosum*	Ɍ	Ɍ	Ɍ	20
536	*Fusarium avenaceum*	Ɍ	R[23]	Ɍ	92
537	*F. batatatis (F. oxysporum batatas)*	Ɍ	Ɍ	Ɍ	52,91
538	*F. conglutinans (F. oxysporum conglutinans)*	Ɍ	Ɍ	Ɍ	27,52,91
539	*F. niveum (F. oxysporum niveum)*	Ɍ	Ɍ	Ɍ	48,52,91
540	*F. oxysporum*	Ɍ	Ɍ	Ɍ	52,91
541	*F. radicicola (F. solani radicicola)*	Ɍ	Ɍ	Ɍ	52,91
542	*Glenosporopsis amazonica*	R	Ɍ	Ɍ	20
543	*Gliocladium fimbriatum*	Ɍ	Ɍ	Ɍ	121,125
544	*Helminthosporium gramineum*	Ɍ	Ɍ	Ɍ	24,101
545	*H. sativum*	Ɍ	Ɍ	Ɍ	91,101
546	*H. victoriae*	Ɍ	Ɍ	Ɍ	24
547	*Hemispora stellata*	Ɍ	Ɍ	Ɍ	20
548	*Hormiscium dermatitidis*	R	Ɍ	Ɍ	20
549	*Indiella americana*	R	Ɍ	Ɍ	78
550	*Kloeckera brevis*	R	R	R[14]	12
551	*Madurella americana*	Ɍ	Ɍ	Ɍ	20
552	*Malassezia furfur*	R	Ɍ	Ɍ	78
553	*Memnoniella echinata*	Ɍ	R	Ɍ	62,81
554	*Microsporum audouinii*	Ɍ	Ɍ	R[3,7]	20,91
555	*M. canis*	Ɍ	Ɍ	Ɍ	20
556	*M. ferrugineum*	Ɍ	Ɍ	Ɍ	20
557	*M. fulvum*	Ɍ	Ɍ	Ɍ	126
558	*Monosporium apiospermum*	Ɍ	Ɍ	Ɍ	20
559	*Mycelium radicis atrovirens*	Ɍ	Ɍ	Ɍ	65
560	*Mycoderma lipolytica*	R	Ɍ	Ɍ	12
561	*M. valida*	Ɍ	R	Ɍ	15
562	*Mycotorula lactis*	Ɍ	Ɍ	R[3]	99
563	*Penicillium aurantio-brunneum*	Ɍ	Ɍ	Ɍ	83,91
564	*P. brevicaule*	Ɍ	Ɍ	Ɍ	91,126
565	*P. camemberti*	Ɍ	Ɍ	Ɍ	46,91
566	*P. chrysogenum*	Ɍ	Ɍ	Ɍ	83,91
567	*P. citrinum*	Ɍ	Ɍ	Ɍ	3,91
568	*P. cyaneo-fulvum*	Ɍ	Ɍ	Ɍ	83,91
569	*P. cyaneum*	Ɍ	Ɍ	Ɍ	83,91
570	*P. digitatum*	R	R[9]	R[24]	129
571	*P. expansum*	Ɍ	Ɍ	Ɍ	91,126
572	*P. glaucum*	Ɍ	Ɍ	Ɍ	61,91
573	*P. islandicum*	Ɍ	Ɍ	Ɍ	52,91
574	*P. italicum*	Ɍ	Ɍ	Ɍ	61,91
575	*P. notatum*	Ɍ	Ɍ	Ɍ	27,91
576	*P. patulum*	Ɍ	Ɍ	Ɍ	8,91
577	*P. phoeniceum*	Ɍ	Ɍ	Ɍ	19,91
578	*P. puberulum*	Ɍ	Ɍ	Ɍ	6,91
579	*P. roqueforti*	Ɍ	Ɍ	Ɍ	72,91
580	*P. rubrum*	Ɍ	Ɍ	Ɍ	6,91
581	*P. rugulosum*	Ɍ	Ɍ	Ɍ	85,91
582	*P. spinulosum*	Ɍ	Ɍ	Ɍ	2,91
583	*P. terlikowskii*	Ɍ	Ɍ	Ɍ	9,91
584	*P. waksmanii*	Ɍ	Ɍ	Ɍ	39,91
585	*Phialophora compactum*	R	Ɍ	Ɍ	20
586	*P. jeanselmei*	R	Ɍ	Ɍ	20
587	*P. pedrosoi*	R	Ɍ	Ɍ	20
588	*P. verrucosa*	R	Ɍ	Ɍ	13,20
589	*Phoma betae*	Ɍ	Ɍ	Ɍ	52
590	*Phymatotrichum omnivorum*	Ɍ	Ɍ	Ɍ	117
591	*Piricularia oryzae*	R	R	Ɍ	45,52
592	*Pityrosporum ovale*	R	R	Ɍ	4
593	*Rhodotorula aurantiaca*	R	Ɍ	R[19]	96,109
594	*R. aurea*	Ɍ	Ɍ	Ɍ	109
595	*R. flava*	R	Ɍ	Ɍ	109

1/ Pyrimidine portion. 3/ Nicotinic acid. 7/ Vitamin B_6. 9/ Partial requirement. 11/ Requirement varies from "R" to "Ɍ," depending on the isolate. 14/ Nicotinic acid, vitamin B_6, inositol, and pantothenic acid. 19/ *p*-Aminobenzoic acid. 23/ One strain only. 24/ Partial requirement for vitamin B_6 and pantothenic acid.

continued

25. NUTRIENT REQUIREMENTS AND UTILIZATION: FUNGI

Part I. Vitamins

	Species (Synonym)	Thiamine	Biotin	Other	Reference
596	*R. glutinis*	℞	℞	℞	109
597	*R. mucilaginosa*	R	℞	℞	14,109
598	*R. rubra*	R	℞	℞	14,109
599	*R. sanniei*	R	℞	℞	32
600	*Sabouraudites gypseus*	℞	℞	℞	78
601	*S. radiolatus*	℞	℞	℞	78
602	*Sclerotium delphinii*	R[1/]	℞	℞	89,91
603	*S. rolfsii*	R[4/]	℞	℞	89,91
604	*Septoria apii*	R[1/]	℞	℞	113
605	*S. azaleae*	℞	℞	℞	36
606	*S. callistephi*	℞	℞	℞	71
607	*S. chrysanthemella*	℞	℞	℞	37
608	*S. nodorum*	℞	℞	℞	52
609	*Sporotrichum beurmanni*	℞	℞	℞	78
610	*S. councilmanni*	℞	℞	℞	78,91
611	*S. gougeroti*	℞	℞	℞	78,91
612	*S. schenckii*	R	℞	℞	20,89,91
613	*Stachybotrys atra*	℞	R	℞	62,81
614	*Thielaviopsis basicola*	R	℞	℞	48,91
615	*Torula* sp.	℞	℞	℞	90
616	*T. cremoris*	R	R	R[3/]	44,99
617	*T. fermentati*	R	℞	℞	90
618	*T. kefyr*	℞	R	℞	13
619	*T. lactis*	℞	℞	R[3/]	99
620	*T. laurentii*	R	℞	℞	90
621	*T. molischiana*	℞	R	℞	13
622	*T. rosea*	R	℞	℞	90
623	*T. sanguinea*	R	℞	℞	90
624	*T. sphaerica*	℞	R	R[3/]	13,99
625	*Torulopsis candida*	℞	R	℞	12
626	*T. dattila*	R	R	R[7/]	14
627	*T. kefyr*	℞	℞	R[3/]	99
628	*T. laurentii*	R	℞	℞	20
629	*T. minor*	℞	R	℞	12
630	*T. molischiana*	℞	R	℞	14
631	*T. neoformans*	R	℞	℞	20
632	*T. pulcherrima*	℞	R	℞	12
633	*Trichoderma lignorum*	℞	℞	℞	121,122
634	*Trichophyton acuminatum*	R	℞	℞	13
635	*T. concentricum (Endodermophyton concentricum)*	℞	℞	℞	20
636	*T. discoides*	R	R	R[7,8/]	98
637	*T. faviforme*	R	℞	R[8/]	13
638	*T. gallinae (Achorion gallinae)*	℞	℞	℞	20
639	*T. gypseum (Achorion gypseum)*	℞	℞	℞	20
640	*T. interdigitale*	R	℞	℞	70
641	*T. mentagrophytes*	R[11/]	℞	R[8,11/]	20,97
642	*T. rosaceum*	R	℞	℞	78
643	*T. rubrum*	℞	℞	℞	20
644	*T. sabouraudi*	℞	℞	℞	20
645	*T. schoenleini (Achorion schoenleini)*	℞	℞	℞	20
646	*T. sulfureum*	R	℞	℞	13,20
647	*T. tonsurans*	℞	℞	℞	20
648	*T. tropicale (Endodermophyton tropicale)*	℞	℞	℞	20
649	*T. violaceum*	R	℞	℞	13,20
650	*Trichosporon beigelii*	R	R	℞	20
651	*T. minor*	R	℞	℞	20

[1/] Pyrimidine portion. [3/] Nicotinic acid. [4/] Thiazole portion. [7/] Vitamin B_6. [8/] Inositol. [11/] Requirement varies from "R" to "℞," depending on the isolate.

Contributors: (a) Perlman, D., (b) Barnett, H. L., and Lilly, Virgil Greene, (c) Fries, Nils

References

[1] Almeida, F., and F. A. Sinoes Barbosa. 1940. Arquiv. Inst. Biol. (Sao Paulo) 11:1.

[2] Anslow, W. K., and H. Raistrick. 1938. Biochem. J. 32:687.

[3] Bailey, J. H., and C. J. Cavallito. 1943. J. Bacteriol. 45:30.

[4] Benham, R. W. 1941. Proc. Soc. Exptl. Biol. Med. 46:176.

[5] Berger, J., M. J. Johnson, and W. H. Peterson. 1937. J. Biol. Chem. 124:395.

[6] Birkinshaw, J. H., and H. Raistrick. 1932. Biochem. J. 26:441.

[7] Blumer, S. 1940. Mitt. Naturforsch. Ges. Bern, p. 19.

[8] Brack, A. 1947. Helv. Chim. Acta 30:1.

[9] Brian, P. W. 1946. Trans. Brit. Mycol. Soc. 29:211.

[10] Bronsart, H. V. 1919. Zentr. Bakteriol. Parasitenk., II, 49:51.

[11] Burgeff, H. 1934. Ber. Deut. Botan. Ges. 52:384.

[12] Burkholder, P. R. 1943. Am. J. Botany 30:206.

[13] Burkholder, P. R., and D. Moyer. 1943. Bull. Torrey Botan. Club 70:372.

[14] Burkholder, P. R., and D. Moyer. 1944. J. Bacteriol. 48:385.

[15] Butler, E. T., W. J. Robbins, and B. O. Dodge. 1941. Science 94:262.

[16] Calam, C. T., A. E. Oxford, and H. Raistrick. 1939. Biochem. J. 33:1488.

[17] Cantino, E. C. 1948. Am. J. Botany 35:238.

[18] Chrzaszcz, T., and K. Leonhard. 1936. Biochem. J. 30:1947.

continued

25. NUTRIENT REQUIREMENTS AND UTILIZATION: FUNGI

Part I. Vitamins

[19] Curtin, T. 1940. Ibid. 34:1605.
[20] De Area Leao, A. E., and A. Cury. 1950. Mycopathol. Mycol. Appl. 5:65.
[21] Defago, G. 1939. Ber. Schweiz. Botan. Ges. 49:413.
[22] Defago, G. 1940. Phytopathol. Z. 13:293.
[23] Dulaney, E. L., and F. H. Grutter. 1950. Mycologia 42:717.
[24] Elliott, E. S. 1949. Proc. West Va. Acad. Sci. 20:65.
[25] Farries, E. H. M., and A. F. Bell. 1930. Ann. Botany (London) 44:423.
[26] Fries, L. 1945. Arkiv Botan. 32A:1.
[27] Fries, N. 1938. Symbolae Botan. Upsaliensis 3(2):1.
[28] Fries, N. 1943. Ibid. 7(2):1.
[29] Fries, N. 1949. Svensk Botan. Tidskr. 43:316.
[30] Fries, N. 1950. Ibid. 44:379.
[31] Fries, N. Unpublished. Univ. Uppsala, Dept. Plant Physiology, Sweden, 1966.
[32] Fromageot, C., and J. L. Tchang. 1938. Arch. Mikrobiol. 9:434.
[33] Halbsguth, W. 1949. Planta 36:551.
[34] Hawker, L. E. 1936. Ann. Botany (London) 50:699.
[35] Hawker, L. E. 1938. Nature 142:1038.
[36] Hemmi, T., and S. Kurata. 1931. Mem. Coll. Agr. Kyoto Univ. 13:1.
[37] Hemmi, T., and H. Nakamura. 1927. Ibid. 3:1.
[38] Houston, B. R. 1930. Ph.D. Thesis. Univ. California, Berkeley.
[39] Hubert, B. 1938. Biol. Jaarboek Konink. Natuurw. Genoot. Dodonaea Gent 5:326.
[40] Huebner, E. 1938. Botan. Zentr. Beih., A, 58:175.
[41] Kerl, I. 1937. Z. Botan. 31:129.
[42] Knaysi, G. 1946. J. Bacteriol. 52:487.
[43] Kögl, F., and N. Fries. 1937. Z. Physiol. Chem. 249:93.
[44] Koser, S. A., M. H. Wright, and A. Dorfman. 1942. Proc. Soc. Exptl. Biol. Med. 51:204.
[45] Leaver, F. W., J. Leal, and C. R. Brewer. 1947. J. Bacteriol. 54:401.
[46] Leonian, L. H., and V. G. Lilly. 1937. Am. J. Botany 24:135.
[47] Leonian, L. H., and V. G. Lilly. 1938. Phytopathology 28:531.
[48] Leonian, L. H., and V. G. Lilly. 1940. Plant Physiol. 15:515.
[49] Lilly, V. G., and H. L. Barnett. 1948. J. Agr. Res. 77:287.
[50] Lilly, V. G., and H. L. Barnett. 1949. Mycologia 41:186.
[51] Lilly, V. G., and H. L. Barnett. 1949. Proc. West Va. Acad. Sci. 20:69.
[52] Lilly, V. G., and H. L. Barnett. 1951. Physiology of the fungi. McGraw-Hill, New York.
[53] Lindeberg, G. 1939. Svensk Botan. Tidskr. 33:85.
[54] Lindeberg, G. 1941. Arch. Mikrobiol. 12:58.
[55] Lindeberg, G. 1944. Symbolae Botan. Upsaliensis 8:1.
[56] Lindeberg, G. 1946. Botan. Notiser, p. 89.
[57] Lindeberg, G. 1946. Svensk Botan. Tidskr. 40:63.
[58] Lindeberg, G., and K. Molin. 1949. Physiol. Plantarum 2:138.
[59] Marczynski, R. 1943. Am. Midland Naturalist 30:164.
[60] Margolin, A. S. 1940. Proc. West Va. Acad. Sci. 14:56.
[61] Marloth, R. H. 1931. Phytopathology 21:169.
[62] Marsh, P. B., and K. Bollenbacher. 1946. Am. J. Botany 33:245.
[63] Melin, E., and G. Lindeberg. 1939. Botan. Notiser, p. 241.
[64] Melin, E., and P. Mikola. 1948. Physiol. Plantarum 1:109.
[65] Melin, E., and B. Norkrans. 1942. Svensk Botan. Tidskr. 36:271.
[66] Melin, E., and B. Nyman. 1940. Arch. Mikrobiol. 11:318.
[67] Mikola, P. 1948. Commun. Inst. Forestalis Fenniae 36:1.
[68] Molliard, M. 1903. Bull. Soc. Mycol. France 19:150.
[69] Molliard, M. 1903. Compt. Rend. 136:899.
[70] Mosher, W., et al. 1936. Plant Physiol. 11:795.
[71] Müller, W., and W. H. Schopfer. 1937. Compt. Rend. 205:687.
[72] Nielsen, N., and S. F. Fang. 1937. Compt. Rend. Trav. Lab. Carlsberg, Ser. Physiol., 22:141.
[73] Nikitinsky, J. 1904. Jahrb. Wiss. Botan. 40:1.
[74] Noecker, N. 1938. Am. J. Botany 25:345.
[75] Noecker, N., and M. Reed. 1943. Am. Midland Naturalist 30:171.
[76] Norkrans, B. 1950. Symbolae Botan. Upsaliensis 11(1):1.
[77] Okunuki, K. 1931. Japan. J. Botany 5:401.
[78] Oyama, T. 1937. Nagasaki Igakkai Zasshi 15:2601.
[79] Pehrson, S. O. 1948. Physiol. Plantarum 1:38.
[80] Perkins, D. D. 1949. Genetics 34:607.
[81] Perlman, D. 1948. Am. J. Botany 35:49.
[82] Perlman, D. 1949. Ibid. 36:180.
[83] Pruess, L. M., E. C. Eichinger, and W. H. Peterson. 1934. Zentr. Bakteriol. Parasitenk., II, 89:370.
[84] Quantz, L. 1943. Jahrb. Wiss. Botan. 91:120.
[85] Rennerfelt, E. 1938. Svensk Botan. Tidskr. 32:332.
[86] Rennerfelt, E. 1944. Ibid. 38:153.
[87] Ridings, W. H. 1966. M.S. Thesis. West Virginia Univ., Morgantown.
[88] Robbins, W. J. 1937. Bull. Torrey Botan. Club 65:267.
[89] Robbins, W. J., and F. Kavanagh. 1938. Am. J. Botany 25:229.
[90] Robbins, W. J., and F. Kavanagh. 1938. Plant Physiol. 3:611.
[91] Robbins, W. J., and V. W. Kavanagh. 1942. Botan. Rev. 8:411.
[92] Robbins, W. J., and R. Ma. 1941. Bull. Torrey Botan. Club 68:446.
[93] Robbins, W. J., and R. Ma. 1942. Ibid. 69:184.
[94] Robbins, W. J., and R. Ma. 1942. Am. J. Botany 29:835.
[95] Robbins, W. J., and R. Ma. 1942. Arch. Biochem. 1:219.
[96] Robbins, W. J., and R. Ma. 1944. Science 100:85.

continued

Part I. Vitamins

[97] Robbins, W. J., and R. Ma. 1945. Am. J. Botany 32:509

[98] Robbins, W. J., J. E. MacKinnon, and R. Ma. 1942. Bull. Torrey Botan. Club 69:509.

[99] Rogosa, M. 1943. J. Bacteriol. 46:435.

[100] Roncadori, R. W. 1964. Phytopathology 55:595.

[101] Ronsdorf, L. 1935. Arch. Mikrobiol. 6:309.

[102] Saksena, R. K. 1939. Natl. Acad. Sci. India (Allahabad) Business Matters, p. 97.

[103] Salvin, S. B. 1949. J. Infect. Diseases 84:275.

[104] Satoh, S. 1931. Mem. Coll. Agr. Kyoto Univ. 13:41.

[105] Schopfer, W. H. 1934. Arch. Mikrobiol. 5:511.

[106] Schopfer, W. H. 1934. Bull. Soc. Botan. Suisse 43:389.

[107] Schopfer, W. H. 1935. Z. Vitaminforsch. 4:187.

[108] Schopfer, W. H. 1937. Compt. Rend. Soc. Biol. 126:842.

[109] Schopfer, W. H. 1938. Protoplasma 31:105.

[110] Schopfer, W. H. 1944. Helv. Chim. Acta 27:1017.

[111] Schopfer, W. H., and S. Blumer. 1938. Compt. Rend. 206:1141.

[112] Schopfer, W. H., and S. Blumer. 1938. Arch. Mikrobiol. 9:305.

[113] Schopfer, W. H., and S. Blumer. 1940. Ibid. 11:205.

[114] Schopfer, W. H., and S. Blumer. 1940. Enzymologia 8:261.

[115] Snell, E. E., and A. N. Rannefelt. 1945. J. Biol. Chem. 157:475.

[116] Steinberg, R. A. 1936. J. Agr. Res. 52:439.

[117] Talley, P. J., and L. M. Blank. 1941. Plant Physiol. 16:1.

[118] Tanner, F. W., C. Vojnovich, and J. M. Van Lanen. 1945. Science 101:180.

[119] Treschow, C. 1944. Dansk Botan. Arkiv 11(6):1.

[120] Villela, G. G., and A. Cury. 1950. J. Bacteriol. 59:1.

[121] Weindling, R. 1937. Phytopathology 27:1175.

[122] West Virginia University Mycological Laboratory. Unpublished. Morgantown, 1951.

[123] Whiffen, A. J. 1938. Am. J. Botany 25:649.

[124] White, H. H. 1941. J. Council Sci. Ind. Res. 14:137.

[125] Wilkins, W. H., and G. C. M. Harris. 1944. Brit. J. Exptl. Pathol. 25:135.

[126] Williams, R. J., and J. M. Honn. 1932. Plant Physiol. 7:629.

[127] Wilson, E. E. 1927. Phytopathology 17:835.

[128] Windisch, S. 1937. Arch. Mikrobiol. 8:321.

[129] Wooster, R. C., and V. H. Cheldelin. 1945. Arch. Biochem. 8:311.

[130] Worley, C. L., and B. M. Duggar. 1938. Science 88:132.

[131] Wunschendorff, M., and C. Killian. 1928. Compt. Rend. 187:572.

Part II. Sugars

Interpretation of the amount of growth obtained on different sugars is often subject to error. Low yields may be due to slow utilization of the sugar involved, but are frequently due to other factors. It is possible that some organisms listed as not utilizing a certain sugar, or utilizing it poorly, will be found to utilize it well under different nutritional conditions. *Abbreviations:* U = utilized; Ʉ = utilized slightly or not at all; u = utilized slowly; v = utilized, but exhibits varying speeds of utilization.

	Species (Synonym)	Arabinose	Cellobiose	Fructose	Galactose	Glucose	Lactose	Maltose	Mannose	Raffinose	Sorbose	Sucrose	Xylose	Reference
	Phycomycetes													
1	*Achlya flagellata*	Ʉ 1/	...	Ʉ 2/	U 3/	Ʉ 4/	Ʉ	U	Ʉ	Ʉ	...	U	Ʉ 5/	61
2	*Aphanomyces euteiches*	Ʉ 6/	U	U	U	U	Ʉ	U	Ʉ	Ʉ	Ʉ	Ʉ	Ʉ	40
3	*Apodachlya brachynema*	...	...	U	U	U	u	U	...	U	...	U	...	17
4	*Blakeslea trispora*	...	...	U	U	U	U	U	U	U	u	U	U	30,33,35
5	*Blastocladia pringsheimii*	Ʉ 1/	...	U 2/	Ʉ 3/	U 4/	Ʉ	U	U 7/	...	Ʉ 8/	U	Ʉ 5/	9
6	*Choanephora circinans*	...	...	U	U	U	u	U	U	u	u	u	U	35
7	*C. conjuncta*	...	...	U	U	U	u	U	U	u	u	u	U	35
8	*C. cucurbitarum*	u 1/	U	U	U	U	Ʉ	U	U	U	Ʉ	Ʉ	U	31,35
9	*C. heterospora*	...	...	U	U	U	U	U	U	u	u	U	U	35
10	*C. infundibulifera*	...	...	U	U	U	U	U	U	u	u	U	U	35
11	*Cladochytrium replicatum*	Ʉ 6/	u	U	u	U	u	...	U	Ʉ	Ʉ	Ʉ	Ʉ	18
12	*Coccidioides immitis*	Ʉ 1/	U	U 2/	U 3/	U 4/	Ʉ	U	U 7/	u	...	Ʉ	u 5/	4

1/ L-Arabinose. 2/ D-Fructose. 3/ D-Galactose. 4/ D-Glucose. 5/ D-Xylose. 6/ D-Arabinose. 7/ D-Mannose. 8/ L-Sorbose.

continued

Part II. Sugars

	Species (Synonym)	Arabinose	Cellobiose	Fructose	Galactose	Glucose	Lactose	Maltose	Mannose	Raffinose	Sorbose	Sucrose	Xylose	Reference
13	*Delacroixia coronata (Entomophthora coronata)*	Ʉ[1]	Ʉ	U[2]	u[3]	U[4]	Ʉ	Ʉ	U[7]	Ʉ	Ʉ[8]	Ʉ	Ʉ[5]	64
14	*Dictyuchus monosporus*	Ʉ[1]	...	Ʉ[2]	Ʉ[3]	U[4]	Ʉ	Ʉ	Ʉ[7]	Ʉ	...	Ʉ	Ʉ[5]	61
15	*Entomophthora apiculata*	Ʉ[1]	Ʉ	u[2]	u[3]	U[4]	Ʉ	Ʉ	U[7]	Ʉ	u[8]	Ʉ	Ʉ[5]	64
16	*Gilbertella persicaria indica*	...	...	U	U	U	u	U	...	u	u	u	U	34
17	*Helicostylum piriforme*	...	...	U	U	U[4]	U	U	U[7]	U	u	U	U	30,33,36
18	*Leptomitus lacteus*	...	...	Ʉ[2]	Ʉ[3]	Ʉ[4]	...	Ʉ	...	...	...	Ʉ	...	47
19	*Mucor ramannianus*	u[1]	U	U[2]	U[3]	U[4]	U	U	U[7]	Ʉ	u[8]	Ʉ	Ʉ[5]	30,33
20	*Phycomyces blakesleeanus*	u[1]	u	U[2]	u[3]	U[4]	Ʉ	U	U[7]	Ʉ	Ʉ[8]	U	U[5]	30,31,33
21	*Phytophthora cactorum*	...	...	u[2]	Ʉ[3]	U[4]	Ʉ	U	u[7]	...	...	U	...	30,33
22	*P. erythroseptica*	...	...	u[2]	Ʉ[3]	U[4]	Ʉ	U	U[7]	...	...	U	...	30,33
23	*P. fagopyri*	...	...	u[2]	Ʉ[3]	U[4]	Ʉ	u	u[7]	...	...	U	...	30,33
24	*P. fragariae*	...	...	u	u	U	u	U	u	u	Ʉ	U	u	14
25	*P. gonapodyides (Pythiomorpha gonapodyoides)*	...	...	U[2]	Ʉ[3]	U[4]	Ʉ	u	u[7]	...	...	U	...	30,33
26	*Phytophthora infestans*	u[1]	...	u[2]	...	U	...	...	...	...	...	U	Ʉ[5]	19
27	*P. macrospora (P. parasitica macrospora)*	U[6]	...	U	U	U	U	U	...	U	...	U	U	45
28	*P. palmivora*	U[6]	...	U	U	u	U	U	...	U	...	U	u	44
29	*P. parasitica nicotianae*	Ʉ[6]	u	u	u	...	Ʉ	u	u	Ʉ	...	u	u	62
30	*Pilaira moreaui*	...	...	U[2]	U[3]	U[4]	U	U	U[7]	...	...	u	...	30,33
31	*Pythiogeton uniforme*	Ʉ[1]	U	U[2]	Ʉ[3]	U[4]	u	U	...	...	...	U	U[5]	9,10
32	*Pythium vexans (P. ascophallon)*	...	...	u[2]	Ʉ[3]	U[4]	Ʉ	U	U[7]	...	...	U	...	30,33
33	*Rhizophlyctis rosea*	Ʉ[1]	U	Ʉ[2]	Ʉ[3]	U[4]	Ʉ	Ʉ	Ʉ[7]	...	Ʉ[8]	Ʉ	Ʉ[5]	50
34	*Rhizopus stolonifer (R. nigricans)*	...	...	U[2]	U[3]	U[4]	Ʉ	U	U[7]	...	...	Ʉ	...	30,33
35	*R. suinus*	...	...	U[2]	U[3]	U[4]	Ʉ	u	U[7]	...	...	Ʉ	...	30,33
36	*Saprolegnia delica*	Ʉ[1]	...	U[2]	Ʉ[3]	U[4]	Ʉ	U	Ʉ[7]	Ʉ	...	Ʉ	Ʉ[5]	5
37	*S. ferax*	Ʉ[1]	...	Ʉ[2]	Ʉ[3]	U[4]	Ʉ	U	Ʉ[7]	Ʉ	...	Ʉ	Ʉ[5]	61
38	*Syncephalastrum racemosum*	u[1]	u	U[2]	U[3]	U[4]	Ʉ	U	U[7]	u	Ʉ[8]	Ʉ	u[5]	13,30
39	*Thraustotheca clavata*	Ʉ[1]	...	Ʉ[2]	Ʉ[3]	U[4]	Ʉ	U	Ʉ[7]	Ʉ	...	U	Ʉ[5]	61
	Ascomycetes													
40	*Arachniotus reticulatus*	...	...	U	U	U	U	U	...	u	...	U	U	16
41	*Arthroderma tuberculatum*	...	...	U	...	U	U	U	U	...	U	U	u	22
42	*Ceratocystis coerulescens*	...	...	...	...	...	u	U	...	U	...	U	...	63
43	*C. fagacearum (Chalara quercina; Endoconidiophora fagacearum)*	u[1]	U	u[2]	u[3]	U[4]	Ʉ	U	U[7]	u	Ʉ[8]	U	U[5]	31
44	*Ceratocystis fimbriata (Ceratostomella fimbriata)*	u[1]	u	u[2]	u[3]	U[4]	Ʉ	U	U[7]	Ʉ	Ʉ[8]	U	u[5]	31,63
45	*Ceratocystis pilifera*	U[6]	U	U	U	U	...	U	U	U	U	Ʉ	u	28
46	*Chaetomium convolutum*	U[1]	U	U[2]	U[3]	U[4]	u	U	U[7]	u	Ʉ[8]	U	U[5]	31
47	*C. globosum*	u[1]	u	U[2]	U[3]	U[4]	u	U	U[7]	u	u[8]	U	u[5]	31
48	*Claviceps purpurea*	...	U	U	...	U	...	Ʉ	U	...	...	U	Ʉ	53
49	*Cordyceps militaris*	u[1]	U	U[2]	U[3]	U[4]	Ʉ	U	U[7]	...	Ʉ[8]	u	Ʉ[5]	31
50	*Ctenomyces serratus*	...	...	U	U	U	u	U	...	...	...	u	U	16
51	*Diaporthe phaseolorum batatatis*	...	...	U[2]	...	U[4]	U	U	...	...	...	U	...	59
52	*Eidamella deflexa*	...	...	U	...	U	U	U	U	v	u	U	u	16,25
53	*Endothia parasitica*	u[1]	U	U[2]	u[3]	U[4]	Ʉ	U	U[7]	U	u[8]	U	u[5]	31
54	*Glomerella cingulata*	U[1]	U	U[2]	U[3]	U[4]	u	U	U[7]	U	u[8]	U	U[5]	31
55	*Gymnoascus reesii*	...	...	U	U	U	U	U	U	U	u	U	U	16,26,27
56	*Monilinia fructicola*	u[1]	U	U[2]	U[3]	U[4]	Ʉ	U	U[7]	u	U[8]	U	U[5]	31
57	*Morchella esculenta*	Ʉ[6]	U	U	U	U	u	U	U	U	u	U	u	8
58	*Myxotrichum uncinatum*	...	...	U	U	U	v	U	...	U	U	U	U	16,23
59	*Neocosmospora vasinfecta*	U[1]	u	U[2]	U[3]	U[4]	u	U	U[7]	u	Ʉ[8]	U	U[5]	31
60	*Ophiobolus graminis*	u[1]	u	u[2]	U[3]	U[4]	u	U	U[7]	u	Ʉ[8]	U	u[5]	31
61	*Pseudoarachniotus roseus*	...	U	U	...	U	u	U	U	u	u	U	U	24

[1] L-Arabinose. [2] D-Fructose. [3] D-Galactose. [4] D-Glucose. [5] D-Xylose. [6] D-Arabinose. [7] D-Mannose. [8] L-Sorbose.

continued

Part II. Sugars

	Species (Synonym)	Arabinose	Cellobiose	Fructose	Galactose	Glucose	Lactose	Maltose	Mannose	Raffinose	Sorbose	Sucrose	Xylose	Reference
62	*Rosellinia arcuata*	...	...	U[2]	u[3]	U[4]	u	U	U[7]	...	...	u	...	30,33
63	*Schizothecium longicolle*	Ʉ[1]	U	U[2]	Ʉ[3]	U[4]	Ʉ	U	U[7]	Ʉ	Ʉ[8]	Ʉ	U[5]	31
64	*Sordaria fimicola*	u[1]	U	U[2]	u[3]	U[4]	u	U	U[7]	Ʉ	Ʉ[8]	Ʉ	U[5]	30,31,33
65	*Sphaeropsis malorum*	u[1]	U	U[2]	U[3]	U[4]	u	U	U[7]	u	u[8]	U	u[5]	31
66	*Thielavia basicola*	...	...	U[2]	U[3]	U[4]	Ʉ	U	U[7]	...	...	U	...	30,33
67	*Venturia inaequalis*	U[6]	U	U	U	U	U	U	U	U	...	U	Ʉ	29
	Basidiomycetes													
68	*Calvatia fragilis*	u[6]	U	U	...	U	u	U	U	u	u	u	u	49
69	*C. gigantea*	u[6]	U	U	v	U	v	U	U	U	u	v	v	49
70	*Collybia velutipes*	u[1]	U	U[2]	u[3]	U[4]	u	U	U[7]	u	Ʉ[8]	U	u[5]	31
71	*Lenzites sepiaria*	Ʉ[1]	Ʉ	U[2]	u[3]	U[4]	u	U	U[7]	Ʉ	U[8]	u	U[5]	31
72	*L. trabea*	u[1]	U	u[2]	u[3]	U[4]	U	U	U[7]	u	u[8]	u	u[5]	31
73	*Melanconium fuligineum*	u[1]	U	U[2]	U[3]	U[4]	Ʉ	U	U[7]	u	u[8]	U	u[5]	31
74	*Polyporus albellus*	u[1]	u	u[2]	u[3]	U[4]	Ʉ	U	U[7]	Ʉ	Ʉ[8]	Ʉ	U[5]	31
75	*P. versicolor*	u[1]	U	U[2]	u[3]	U[4]	u	U	U[7]	u	u[8]	U	u[5]	31
76	*Schizophyllum commune*	u[1]	u	U[2]	u[3]	U[4]	u	u	U[7]	u	Ʉ[8]	u	u[5]	31
77	*Typhula variabilis*	...	...	U[2]	u[3]	U[4]	Ʉ	U	U[7]	...	...	U	...	30,33
78	*Ustilago violacea*	Ʉ[1]	U	U[2]	U[3]	U[4]	Ʉ	U	U[7]	Ʉ	...	U	Ʉ[5]	48
79	*U. zeae*	Ʉ[6]	u	U	u	U	U	U	U	U	Ʉ	U	U	65
	Fungi Imperfecti													
80	*Alternaria solani*	U[1]	u	U[2]	U[3]	U[4]	u	U	U[7]	u	u[8]	U	U[5]	31
81	*Aspergillus clavatus*	U[1]	U	U[2]	U[3]	U[4]	u	U	U[7]	U	Ʉ[8]	U	U[5]	31
82	*A. elegans*	U[1]	u	U[2]	u[3]	U[4]	u	U	U[7]	U	u[8]	U	U[5]	31
83	*A. nidulans*	...	...	...	...	U	...	...	...	U	...	U	...	2
84	*A. niger*	u[1]	...	U[2]	u[3]	U[4]	u	U	U[7]	...	U[8]	U	U[5]	51
85	*A. oryzae*	u[1]	...	U[2]	U[3]	U[4]	Ʉ	U	U[7]	u	...	...	u[5]	54
86	*A. quadrilineatus*	...	...	...	...	U	...	...	...	U	...	U	...	2
87	*A. rugulosus*	U[1]	u	U[2]	U[3]	U	u	U	U[7]	U	u[8]	U	U[5]	2,31
88	*A. variaecolor*	...	...	...	...	U	...	...	...	U	...	U	...	2
89	*A. violaceus*	...	...	...	...	U	...	...	...	U	...	U	...	2
90	*Botryodiplodia ananassae*	U[6]	...	U	U	U	...	...	U	...	u	...	U	55
91	*Botryosporium* sp.	...	...	U	U	U	U	U	...	...	...	U	U	39
92	*Botrytis cinerea*	U[1]	U	U[2]	U[3]	U[4]	U	U	U[7]	U	U[8]	U	U[5]	31
93	*Cephalosporium longisporum*	U[6]	...	U	U	U	u	...	U	U	U	U	...	43
94	*Colletotrichum gloeosporioides*	U[6]	...	U	U	U	U	U	U	U	U	U	U	11,58
95	*C. graminicola*	...	...	U	...	U	v	...	U	U	...	U	...	3
96	*C. lindemuthianum*	u[6]	U	U[2]	U[3]	U[4]	U	U	U[7]	U	Ʉ[8]	U	u[5]	31
97	*Curvularia penniseti*	u[6]	...	...	U	U	U	U	U	U	...	U	...	1
98	*Cytospora cincta*	...	...	U	U	U	u	U	...	...	Ʉ	U	...	21
99	*C. leucostoma*	...	...	U	U	U	...	U	...	...	Ʉ	U	...	21
100	*Darluca filum*	u[6]	U	U	U	U	u	U	U	u	u	U	U	39
101	*Dendrophoma obscurans*	...	...	...	u[3]	U	u	U	...	...	u[8]	U	...	31
102	*Diplodia macrospora*	...	...	U[2]	U[3]	U[4]	u	U	U[7]	...	...	U	...	33
103	*D. natalensis*	...	...	U[2]	u[3]	U[4]	u	U	U[7]	...	...	U	...	33
104	*Fusarium conglutinans*	U[1]	u	U[2]	U[3]	U[4]	u	U	U[7]	u	u[8]	U	U[5]	31
105	*F. culmorum*	u[1]	U	U[2]	U[3]	U[4]	u	u	U[7]	U	u[8]	u	u[5]	31
106	*F. lycopersici*	U[1]	u	U[2]	U[3]	U[4]	u	U	U[7]	u	U[8]	U	U[5]	31,33
107	*F. nivale*	U[1]	U	U[2]	U[3]	U[4]	u	U	U[7]	U	u[8]	U	U[5]	31
108	*F. niveum*	U[1]	U	U[2]	U[3]	U[4]	U	U	U[7]	U	U[8]	U	U[5]	31
109	*F. oxysporum*	...	...	U	...	U	...	U	...	...	...	U	...	38

[1] L-Arabinose. [2] D-Fructose. [3] D-Galactose. [4] D-Glucose. [5] D-Xylose. [6] D-Arabinose. [7] D-Mannose. [8] L-Sorbose.

continued

Part II. Sugars

	Species (Synonym)	Arabinose	Cellobiose	Fructose	Galactose	Glucose	Lactose	Maltose	Mannose	Raffinose	Sorbose	Sucrose	Xylose	Reference
110	*F. oxysporum medicaginis (F. medicaginis)*	U[1]	u	U[2]	U[3]	U[4]	u	U	U[7]	U	u[8]	U	U[5]	31
111	*F. oxysporum nicotianae*	u[6]	U	U	U	U	u	U	U	U	U	U	U	66
112	*F. roseum*	U[6]	U	...	U	U	u	U	...	U	...	U	U	32
113	*F. solani*	U[6]	...	U	U	U	...	...	U	...	u	...	U	55
114	*F. tracheiphilum*	U[1]	u	U[2]	U[3]	U[4]	U	U	U[7]	U	u[8]	u	U[5]	31
115	*Helminthosporium sorokinianum (H. sativum)*	u[1]	u	U[2]	u[3]	U[4]	u	U	U[7]	u	u[8]	U	u[5]	30,33
116	*Leptographium* sp.	u[6]	u	U	u	U	...	U	U	Ʉ	Ʉ	Ʉ	u	28
117	*Macrophomina phaseoli*	u[6]	...	U[2]	U[3]	U[4]	...	...	U	...	u	...	...	55
118	*Memnoniella echinata*	U[1]	U	U[2]	U[3]	U[4]	U	U	U[7]	U	...	U	U[5]	41
119	*Microsporum cookei*	U[6]	U	U	U	U	U	U	U	U	u	U	U	20
120	*M. distortum*	U[6]	U	U	U	U	U	U	U	U	u	U	U	20
121	*M. nanum*	U[6]	U	U	U	U	U	u	U	U	U	U	U	20
122	*Monosporium apiospermum*	u[1]	u	U[2]	U[3]	U[4]	u	u	U[7]	u	Ʉ[8]	U	U[5]	67
123	*Pencillium chrysogenum*	U[1]	u	U[2]	U[3]	U[4]	u	U	U[7]	U	u[8]	U	U[5]	31
124	*P. digitatum*	U[1]	U	U[2]	U[3]	U[4]	U	u	U[7]	...	...	U	U[5]	15
125	*P. expansum*	u[1]	U	U[2]	U[3]	U[4]	Ʉ	U	U[7]	U	U[8]	U	U[5]	31
126	*P. spiculisporum*	U[1]	U	U	U	U	u	U	U[7]	U	u[8]	U	U	16,31
127	*Pestalotia banksiana*	U[6]	u	U	U	U	u	U	U	U	u	U	U	56,57
128	*P. citri*	U[6]	u	U	U	U	u	U	U	U	u	U	U	56,57
129	*Pestalotiopsis glandicola*	...	U	U	U	U	U	U	U	U	U	U	U	6
130	*Phialophora cinerescens*	U[6]	...	U	U	...	...	U	...	U	...	...	U	12
131	*Phoma betae*	U[1]	U	U[2]	U[3]	U[4]	u	U	U[7]	U	u[8]	U	U[5]	31
132	*Phymatotrichum omnivorum*	...	...	U[2]	Ʉ[3]	U[4]	u	U	U[7]	u	...	U	Ʉ[5]	7
133	*Sclerotium delphinii*	U[1]	...	U[2]	...	U[4]	...	U	...	...	...	U	U[5]	42
134	*Septoria chrysanthemella*	...	...	...	U	U	U	U	U	...	...	U	...	60
135	*S. nodorum*	...	...	...	u[3]	U[4]	u	u	...	...	Ʉ[8]	u	...	46
136	*S. obesa*	...	...	...	U	U	U	U	U	...	...	U	...	60
137	*Stysanus stemonitis*	U[1]	U	u[2]	U[3]	U[4]	U	U	U[7]	U	Ʉ[8]	U	u[5]	31
138	*Thielaviopsis basicola*	...	u	U[2]	U[3]	U	Ʉ	U	...	u	Ʉ	U	Ʉ[5]	31,63
139	*Trichophyton tonsurans*	Ʉ[6]	U	U	U	U	Ʉ	Ʉ	U	Ʉ	u	Ʉ	Ʉ	52
140	*Trichurus spiralis minuta*	...	...	U	U	U	U	U	...	...	...	U	U	37

[1] L-Arabinose. [2] D-Fructose. [3] D-Galactose. [4] D-Glucose. [5] D-Xylose. [6] D-Arabinose. [7] D-Mannose. [8] L-Sorbose.

Contributors: (a) Wolf, Frederick T., (b) Lilly, Virgil Greene, and Barnett, H. L.

References

[1] Agarwal, G. P. 1958. Phyton (Buenos Aires) 11:143.
[2] Agnihotri, V. P. 1964. Mycopathol. Mycol. Appl. 24:305.
[3] Ali, M. M. 1962. Ibid. 17:261.
[4] Baker, E. E., and C. E. Smith. 1942. J. Infect. Diseases 70:51.
[5] Bhargava, K. S. 1945. Lloydia 8:60.
[6] Bhargava, S. N., and R. N. Tandon. 1964. Mycopathol. Mycol. Appl. 24:156.
[7] Blank, L. M., and P. J. Talley. 1941. Am. J. Botany 28:564.
[8] Brock, T. D. 1951. Mycologia 43:402.
[9] Cantino, E. C. 1949. Am. J. Botany 36:95.
[10] Cantino, E. C. 1949. Ibid. 36:747.
[11] Chaturvedi, C. 1965. Mycopathol. Mycol. Appl. 27:265.
[12] Chollet, M.-M., M. Moreau, and C. Moreau. 1965. Ibid. 25:223.
[13] Cutter, V. M. 1950. Farlowia 4:1.
[14] Davies, M. E. 1959. Brit. Mycol. Soc. Trans. 42:193.
[15] Fergus, C. L. 1952. Mycologia 44:183.
[16] Ghosh, G. R. 1960. Mycopathol. Mycol. Appl. 13:161.
[17] Gilpin, R. H. 1954. Mycologia 46:702.
[18] Goldstein, S. 1960. Ibid. 52:490.
[19] Hall, A. M. 1959. Brit. Mycol. Soc. Trans. 42:15.
[20] Koehne, G. W. 1962. Mycopathol. Mycol. Appl. 18:199.
[21] Konicek, D. E., and A. W. Helton. 1962. Ibid. 16:27.
[22] Kuehn, H. H. 1961. Ibid. 14:123.
[23] Kuehn, H. H. 1962. Ibid. 16:222.
[24] Kuehn, H. H., and P. F. Crosby. 1959. Ibid. 11:109.
[25] Kuehn, H. H., and P. F. Crosby. 1960. Ibid. 12:145.
[26] Kuehn, H. H., and P. F. Crosby. 1960. Ibid. 12:349.
[27] Kuehn, H. H., and G. F. Orr. 1962. Ibid. 16:351.
[28] Leaphart, C. D. 1956. Mycologia 48:25.

continued

25. NUTRIENT REQUIREMENTS AND UTILIZATION: FUNGI

Part II. Sugars

[29] Leben, C., and G. W. Keitt. 1948. Am. J. Botany 35:337.
[30] Lilly, V. G., and H. L. Barnett. 1951. Physiology of the fungi. McGraw-Hill, New York.
[31] Lilly, V. G., and H. L. Barnett. 1953. West Va. Univ. Agr. Expt. Sta. Tech. Bull. 362T.
[32] Lopez, M. E., and C. L. Fergus. 1965. Mycologia 57:897.
[33] Margolin, A. S. 1941. Ph.D. Thesis. West Virginia Univ., Morgantown.
[34] Mehrotra, B. S., and M. D. Mehrotra. 1963. Mycologia 55:582.
[35] Mehrotra, M. D. 1964. Mycopathol. Mycol. Appl. 23:167, 175.
[36] Mehrotra, M. D. 1964. Ibid. 23:223.
[37] Mehrotra, M. D. 1964. Ibid. 24:198.
[38] Naim, M. S., and H. H. Sharoubeem. 1964. Ibid. 22:59.
[39] Nicolas, G., and J. R. Villanueva. 1964. Mycologia 57:782.
[40] Papavisas, G. C., and W. A. Ayers. 1964. Ibid. 56: 816.
[41] Perlman, D. 1948. Am. J. Botany 35:36.
[42] Perlman, D. 1948. Ibid. 35:360.
[43] Pisano, M. A., and A. F. Plucker. 1958. Mycologia 50:223.
[44] Rao, V. G., M. K. Desai, and N. B. Kulkarni. 1966. Mycopathol. Mycol. Appl. 28:241.
[45] Rao, V. G., M. K. Desai, and N. B. Kulkarni. 1966. Ibid. 28:249.
[46] Richards, G. S. 1951. Phytopathology 41:571.
[47] Schade, A. L. 1940. Am. J. Botany 27:376.
[48] Schopfer, W. H., and S. Blumer. 1938. Arch. Mikrobiol. 9:305.
[49] Sedlmayr, M., E. S. Beneke, and J. A. Stevens. 1961. Mycologia 53:558.
[50] Stanier, R. Y. 1942. J. Bacteriol. 43:499.
[51] Steinberg, R. A. 1942. J. Agr. Res. 64:615.
[52] Swartz, H. E., and L. K. Georg. 1955. Mycologia 47:475.
[53] Taber, W. A., and L. C. Vining. 1957. Can. J. Microbiol. 3:1.
[54] Tamiya, H. 1932. Acta Phytochim. (Japan) 6:1.
[55] Tandon, R. N., and S. N. Bhargava. 1962. Lloydia 25:167.
[56] Tandon, R. N., and K. S. Bilgrami. 1958. Proc. Natl. Inst. Sci. India 24(B):118.
[57] Tandon, R. N., and K. S. Bilgrami. 1959. Ibid. 25(B):138.
[58] Tandon, R. N., and S. Chandra. 1962. Mycopathol. Mycol. Appl. 18:213.
[59] Timnick, M. B., V. G. Lilly, and H. L. Barnett. 1951. Phytopathology 41:327.
[60] Waddell, H. T., and G. F. Weber. 1963. Mycologia 55:442.
[61] Whiffen, A. J. 1945. J. Elisha Mitchell Sci. Soc. 61:114.
[62] Wills, W. H. 1954. Ibid. 70:231.
[63] Wilson, E. M., and V. G. Lilly. 1958. Mycologia 50: 376.
[64] Wolf, F. T. 1951. Bull. Torrey Botan. Club 78:211.
[65] Wolf, F. T. 1953. Mycologia 45:516.
[66] Wolf, F. T. 1955. Bull. Torrey Botan. Club 82:343.
[67] Wolf, F. T., R. R. Bryden, and J. A. MacLaren. 1950. Mycologia 42:233.

26. NUTRIENT UTILIZATION: YEASTS

Part I. Fermentation of Sugars

The ability of certain yeasts to produce gaseous fermentation of the six listed sugars is commonly used for taxonomic differentiation of the yeast species. Where raffinose is utilized, one-third of the molecule is fermented. *Abbreviations:* F = fermented, F̸ = not fermented; f = reaction varies.

	Species (Synonym)	Dextrose	Galactose	Lactose	Maltose	Raffinose	Sucrose	Reference
1	*Candida albicans*	F	f	F̸	F	F̸	F̸	1
2	*C. chodati (Endomycopsis chodati)*[1]	F	f	F̸	F	F	F	1
3	*C. krusei*	F	F̸	F̸	F̸	F̸	F̸	1
4	*C. lipolytica*	F̸	F̸	F̸	F̸	F̸	F̸	1
5	*C. membranaefaciens (C. melibiosi membranaefaciens)*	F	f	F̸	F̸	F[2]	F	1
6	*C. parapsilosis (C. krusoides)*	F	f	F̸	F̸	F̸	F̸	1
7	*C. pulcherrima*	F	F̸	F̸	F̸	F̸	F̸	1
8	*C. utilis (Torulopsis utilis)*	F	F̸	F̸	F̸	F	F	1
9	*Debaryomyces globosus*	F	F̸	F̸	F̸	F	F	1
10	*Endomycopsis ohmeri (Candida guilliermondii membranaefaciens; C. chalmersi)*	F	f	F̸	F̸	F	F	1

[1] Perfect state: *Pichia burtonii.* [2] Melibiose also fermented.

continued

26. NUTRIENT UTILIZATION: YEASTS

Part I. Fermentation of Sugars

	Species (Synonym)	Dextrose	Galactose	Lactose	Maltose	Raffinose	Sucrose	Reference
11	*Hanseniaspora valbyensis*	F	~~F~~	~~F~~	~~F~~	~~F~~	~~F~~	1
12	*Hansenula anomala*	F	f	~~F~~	f	F	F	1
13	*H. bimundalis*	F	~~F~~	~~F~~	~~F~~	~~F~~	~~F~~	3
14	*H. capsulata*	F	~~F~~	~~F~~	~~F~~	~~F~~	~~F~~	1
15	*H. fabianii*	F	~~F~~	~~F~~	F	F	F	2
16	*H. saturnus*	F	~~F~~	~~F~~	~~F~~	F	F	1
17	*Kloeckera apiculata*	F	~~F~~	~~F~~	~~F~~	~~F~~	~~F~~	1
18	*Pichia farinosa*	F	f	~~F~~	~~F~~	~~F~~	~~F~~	1
19	*P. guilliermondii*	F	~~F~~	~~F~~	~~F~~	F2/	F	4
20	*P. membranaefaciens*	f	~~F~~	~~F~~	~~F~~	~~F~~	~~F~~	1
21	*Saccharomyces cerevisiae*	F	F	~~F~~	F	F	F	1
22	*S. fragilis*	F	F	F	~~F~~	F	F	1
23	*S. lactis (Zygosaccharomyces lactis)*	F	F	F	~~F~~	F	F	1
24	*S. pastori (Z. pastori)*	F	~~F~~	~~F~~	~~F~~	~~F~~	~~F~~	1
25	*S. rosei (Torulaspora rosei)*	F	~~F~~	~~F~~	~~F~~	F	F	1
26	*S. veronae*	F	f	F	F	F	F	1
27	*Saccharomycodes ludwigii*	F	~~F~~	~~F~~	~~F~~	F	F	1
28	*Torulopsis colliculosa*	F	~~F~~	~~F~~	f	F	F	1
29	*T. lactis-condensi (T. caroliniana)*	F	~~F~~	~~F~~	~~F~~	F	F	1
30	*Zygosaccharomyces dobzhanskii*	F	f	~~F~~	F	F	F	1
31	*Z. pini*	f	~~F~~	~~F~~	~~F~~	~~F~~	~~F~~	1

2/ Melibiose also fermented.

Contributors: (a) Wickerham, Lynferd J., (b) Allgeier, R. J.

References

[1] Wickerham, L. J. 1951. U.S. Dept. Agr. Tech. Bull. 1029.

[2] Wickerham, L. J. 1965. Mycopathol. Mycol. Appl. 26:79.

[3] Wickerham, L. J. 1965. Ibid. 26:87.

[4] Wickerham, L. J. 1966. J. Bacteriol. 92(4):1269.

Part II. Assimilation of Carbohydrates

All species listed assimilate ammonium sulfate. Unless otherwise specified, nitrate is not assimilated, and vitamins are required for maintenance of growth. *Abbreviations:* A = assimilated; ~~A~~ = not assimilated; a = reaction varies; L = latent growth.

	Species (Synonym)	D-Arabinose	L-Arabinose	Cellobiose	Dextrose	Galactose	Lactose	Maltose	Melezitose	Melibiose	Raffinose	Rhamnose	D-Ribose	L-Sorbose	Sucrose	Trehalose	Xylose	Inulin	Soluble Starch	Reference
1	*Candida albicans*	~~A~~	a	~~A~~	A	A	~~A~~	A	A	~~A~~	~~A~~	~~A~~	~~A~~	L	A	A	A	~~A~~	A	1
2	*C. chodati (Endomycopsis chodati)*1,2/	~~A~~	A	a	A	A	~~A~~	A	a	~~A~~	A	~~A~~	A	a	A	A	A	~~A~~	A	1
3	*C. krusei*1/	~~A~~	~~A~~	~~A~~	A	~~A~~	~~A~~	~~A~~	~~A~~	~~A~~	~~A~~	~~A~~	~~A~~	~~A~~	~~A~~	~~A~~	~~A~~	~~A~~	~~A~~	1
4	*C. lipolytica*	a	~~A~~	~~A~~	A	a	~~A~~	~~A~~	~~A~~	~~A~~	~~A~~	~~A~~	a	a	~~A~~	~~A~~	~~A~~	~~A~~	~~A~~	1
5	*C. membranaefaciens (C. melibiosi membranaefaciens)*	A	A	A	A	A	~~A~~	A	A	A	A	a	A	A	A	A	A	A	~~A~~	1
6	*C. parapsilosis (C. krusoides)*	~~A~~	A	~~A~~	A	A	~~A~~	A	A	~~A~~	~~A~~	~~A~~	a	A	A	A	A	~~A~~	~~A~~	1
7	*C. pulcherrima*	~~A~~	~~A~~	A	A	A	~~A~~	A	A	~~A~~	~~A~~	~~A~~	A	A	A	A	A	~~A~~	~~A~~	1
8	*C. utilis (Torulopsis utilis)*1,3/	~~A~~	~~A~~	A	A	~~A~~	~~A~~	A	A	~~A~~	A	~~A~~	~~A~~	~~A~~	A	A	A	a	~~A~~	1

1/ Grows in a vitamin-free medium. 2/ Perfect state: *Pichia burtonii.* 3/ Assimilates nitrate.

continued

26. NUTRIENT UTILIZATION: YEASTS

Part II. Assimilation of Carbohydrates

	Species (Synonym)	D-Arabinose	L-Arabinose	Cellobiose	Dextrose	Galactose	Lactose	Maltose	Melezitose	Melibiose	Raffinose	Rhamnose	D-Ribose	L-Sorbose	Sucrose	Trehalose	Xylose	Inulin	Soluble Starch	Reference
9	*Debaryomyces globosus* [1]	Ⱥ	Ⱥ	Ⱥ	A	Ⱥ	Ⱥ	Ⱥ	Ⱥ	Ⱥ	A	Ⱥ	Ⱥ	Ⱥ	A	L	Ⱥ	a	Ⱥ	1
10	*Endomycopsis ohmeri (Candida guilliermondii membranaefaciens; C. chalmersi)*	Ⱥ	Ⱥ	A	A	A	Ⱥ	A	Ⱥ	Ⱥ	A	Ⱥ	a	A	A	A	Ⱥ	a	Ⱥ	1
11	*Hanseniaspora valbyensis*	Ⱥ	Ⱥ	A	A	Ⱥ	Ⱥ	Ⱥ	Ⱥ	Ⱥ	Ⱥ	Ⱥ	Ⱥ	Ⱥ	Ⱥ	Ⱥ	Ⱥ	Ⱥ	Ⱥ	1
12	*Hansenula anomala* [1,3]	Ⱥ	a	A	A	A	Ⱥ	A	A	Ⱥ	a	Ⱥ	a	Ⱥ	A	A	a	Ⱥ	A	1
13	*H. bimundalis* [3]	a	a	A	A	Ⱥ	Ⱥ	A	A	Ⱥ	Ⱥ	A	Ⱥ	Ⱥ	A	A	A	Ⱥ	Ⱥ	3
14	*H. capsulata* [3]	a	A	A	A	Ⱥ	Ⱥ	A	A	Ⱥ	Ⱥ	a	A	Ⱥ	Ⱥ	A	A	Ⱥ	A	1
15	*H. fabianii* [3]	Ⱥ	Ⱥ	A	A	Ⱥ	Ⱥ	A	A	Ⱥ	A	Ⱥ	Ⱥ	Ⱥ	A	A	A	Ⱥ	A	2
16	*H. saturnus* [1,3]	Ⱥ	Ⱥ	A	A	Ⱥ	Ⱥ	Ⱥ	Ⱥ	Ⱥ	A	A	Ⱥ	Ⱥ	A	Ⱥ	A	A	Ⱥ	1
17	*Kloeckera apiculata*	Ⱥ	Ⱥ	A	A	Ⱥ	Ⱥ	Ⱥ	Ⱥ	Ⱥ	Ⱥ	Ⱥ	Ⱥ	Ⱥ	Ⱥ	Ⱥ	Ⱥ	Ⱥ	Ⱥ	1
18	*Pichia farinosa* [1]	Ⱥ	Ⱥ	A	A	A	a	Ⱥ	Ⱥ	Ⱥ	Ⱥ	Ⱥ	A	Ⱥ	Ⱥ	a	a	Ⱥ	a	1
19	*P. guilliermondii*	A	A	A	A	A	Ⱥ	A	A	A	A	A	A	A	A	A	A	A	Ⱥ	4
20	*P. membranaefaciens* [1]	Ⱥ	Ⱥ	Ⱥ	A	Ⱥ	Ⱥ	Ⱥ	Ⱥ	Ⱥ	Ⱥ	Ⱥ	Ⱥ	Ⱥ	Ⱥ	Ⱥ	a	Ⱥ	Ⱥ	1
21	*Saccharomyces cerevisiae*	Ⱥ	Ⱥ	Ⱥ	A	A	Ⱥ	A	a	Ⱥ	A	Ⱥ	Ⱥ	Ⱥ	A	A	Ⱥ	a	Ⱥ	1
22	*S. fragilis*	Ⱥ	a	a	A	A	A	Ⱥ	Ⱥ	Ⱥ	A	Ⱥ	a	a	A	a	a	A	Ⱥ	1
23	*S. lactis (Zygosaccharomyces lactis)*	Ⱥ	Ⱥ	a	A	A	A	a	a	Ⱥ	A	Ⱥ	Ⱥ	a	A	a	a	Ⱥ	Ⱥ	1
24	*S. pastori (Z. pastori)*	Ⱥ	Ⱥ	Ⱥ	A	Ⱥ	Ⱥ	Ⱥ	Ⱥ	Ⱥ	Ⱥ	A	Ⱥ	Ⱥ	Ⱥ	L	Ⱥ	Ⱥ	Ⱥ	1
25	*S. rosei (Torulaspora rosei)* [1]	Ⱥ	Ⱥ	Ⱥ	A	Ⱥ	Ⱥ	a	Ⱥ	Ⱥ	A	Ⱥ	Ⱥ	A	A	A	Ⱥ	A	Ⱥ	1
26	*S. veronae*	Ⱥ	Ⱥ	Ⱥ	A	A	Ⱥ	A	A	Ⱥ	A	Ⱥ	Ⱥ	A	A	A	Ⱥ	A	Ⱥ	1
27	*Saccharomycodes ludwigii*	Ⱥ	Ⱥ	A	A	Ⱥ	Ⱥ	Ⱥ	Ⱥ	Ⱥ	a	Ⱥ	Ⱥ	Ⱥ	A	Ⱥ	Ⱥ	Ⱥ	Ⱥ	1
28	*Torulopsis colliculosa* [1]	Ⱥ	Ⱥ	Ⱥ	A	Ⱥ	Ⱥ	A	Ⱥ	Ⱥ	A	Ⱥ	Ⱥ	L	A	A	Ⱥ	A	Ⱥ	1
29	*T. lactis-condensi (T. caroliniana)* [3]	Ⱥ	Ⱥ	Ⱥ	A	Ⱥ	Ⱥ	Ⱥ	Ⱥ	Ⱥ	a	Ⱥ	Ⱥ	Ⱥ	A	Ⱥ	Ⱥ	Ⱥ	Ⱥ	1
30	*Zygosaccharomyces dobzhanskii*	Ⱥ	Ⱥ	A	A	A	Ⱥ	A	A	Ⱥ	A	Ⱥ	Ⱥ	A	A	A	a	Ⱥ	Ⱥ	1
31	*Z. pini*	Ⱥ	a	A	A	Ⱥ	Ⱥ	Ⱥ	Ⱥ	Ⱥ	Ⱥ	A	A	Ⱥ	Ⱥ	A	A	Ⱥ	Ⱥ	1

1/ Grows in a vitamin-free medium. 3/ Assimilates nitrate.

Contributors: (a) Wickerham, Lynferd J., (b) Allgeier, R. J.

References

[1] Wickerham, L.J. 1951. U.S. Dept. Agr. Tech. Bull. 1029.

[2] Wickerham, L.J. 1965. Mycopathol. Mycol. Appl. 26:79.

[3] Wickerham, L. J. 1965. Ibid. 26:87.

[4] Wickerham, L. J. 1966. J. Bacteriol. 92(4):1269.

Part III. Assimilation of Other Carbon Compounds

All species listed assimilate ammonium sulfate. Unless otherwise specified, nitrate is not assimilated, and vitamins are required for maintenance of growth. *Abbreviations:* A = assimilated; Ⱥ = not assimilated; a = reaction varies; L = latent growth.

	Species (Synonym)	Adonitol	Calcium 2-keto-gluconate	Dulcitol	Erythritol	Ethanol	Ethyl acetoacetate	D-Glucosamine HCl	Glycerol	Inositol	Mannitol	α-Methylglucoside	Potassium gluconate	Potassium 5-keto-gluconate	Potassium sodium saccharate	Salicin	Sodium citrate	Sodium lactate	Sodium pyruvate	Sodium succinate	Sorbitol	Reference
1	*Candida albicans*	A	A	Ⱥ	Ⱥ	A	a	a	A	Ⱥ	A	A	a	A	Ⱥ	Ⱥ	A	A	A	A	A	1
2	*C. chodati (Endomycopsis chodati)* [1,2]	A	A	Ⱥ	A	A	Ⱥ	A	A	Ⱥ	A	A	a	Ⱥ	Ⱥ	A	A	Ⱥ	L	A	A	1

1/ Grows in a vitamin-free medium. 2/ Perfect state: *Pichia burtonii.*

continued

Part III. Assimilation of Other Carbon Compounds

	Species (Synonym)	Adonitol	Calcium 2-keto-gluconate	Dulcitol	Erythritol	Ethanol	Ethyl acetoacetate	D-Glucosamine HCl	Glycerol	Inositol	Mannitol	α-Methylglucoside	Potassium gluconate	Potassium 5-keto-gluconate	Potassium sodium saccharate	Salicin	Sodium citrate	Sodium lactate	Sodium pyruvate	Sodium succinate	Sorbitol	Reference
3	*C. krusei*[1]	Ⱥ	Ⱥ	Ⱥ	Ⱥ	A	a	L	A	Ⱥ	Ⱥ	Ⱥ	Ⱥ	Ⱥ	Ⱥ	Ⱥ	a	A	A	A	Ⱥ	1
4	*C. lipolytica*	a	Ⱥ	Ⱥ	A	A	a	Ⱥ	A	Ⱥ	A	Ⱥ	A	Ⱥ	Ⱥ	a	A	A	A	A	A	1
5	*C. membranaefaciens (C. melibiosi membranaefaciens)*	A	A	A	A	A	Ⱥ	A	A	Ⱥ	A	A	A	Ⱥ	Ⱥ	A	A	A	A	A	A	1
6	*C. parapsilosis (C. krusoides)*	A	A	Ⱥ	Ⱥ	A	Ⱥ	a	A	Ⱥ	A	A	A	A	Ⱥ	Ⱥ	A	Ⱥ	A	A	A	1
7	*C. pulcherrima*	A	A	Ⱥ	Ⱥ	A	Ⱥ	A	A	Ⱥ	A	A	A	Ⱥ	Ⱥ	A	a	a	A	A	A	1
8	*C. utilis (Torulopsis utilis)*[1,3]	Ⱥ	Ⱥ	Ⱥ	Ⱥ	A	a	Ⱥ	A	Ⱥ	a	a	A	Ⱥ	Ⱥ	A	A	A	A	A	a	1
9	*Debaryomyces globosus*[1]	Ⱥ	A	Ⱥ	Ⱥ	A	Ⱥ	Ⱥ	a	Ⱥ	L	Ⱥ	Ⱥ	Ⱥ	Ⱥ	Ⱥ	Ⱥ	L	Ⱥ	Ⱥ	Ⱥ	1
10	*Endomycopsis ohmeri (Candida guilliermondii membranaefaciens; C. chalmersi)*	A	A	Ⱥ	Ⱥ	A	a	A	A	Ⱥ	A	A	a	Ⱥ	Ⱥ	A	A	Ⱥ	A	A	A	1
11	*Hanseniaspora valbyensis*	Ⱥ	a	Ⱥ	Ⱥ	Ⱥ	Ⱥ	Ⱥ	Ⱥ	Ⱥ	Ⱥ	Ⱥ	a	Ⱥ	Ⱥ	A	Ⱥ	Ⱥ	Ⱥ	Ⱥ	Ⱥ	1
12	*Hansenula anomala*[1,3]	a	Ⱥ	Ⱥ	A	A	Ⱥ	Ⱥ	A	Ⱥ	A	A	a	Ⱥ	Ⱥ	A	A	A	A	A	A	1
13	*H. bimundalis*[3]	Ⱥ	Ⱥ	Ⱥ	Ⱥ	A	Ⱥ	Ⱥ	A	Ⱥ	A	a	A	Ⱥ	Ⱥ	A	A	A	A	A	A	3
14	*H. capsulata*[3]	A	A	Ⱥ	A	A	Ⱥ	A	A	Ⱥ	A	a	a	Ⱥ	Ⱥ	A	Ⱥ	Ⱥ	a	a	A	1
15	*H. fabianii*[3]	Ⱥ	Ⱥ	Ⱥ	Ⱥ	A	a	Ⱥ	A	Ⱥ	A	A	A	Ⱥ	Ⱥ	A	A	A	A	A	A	2
16	*H. saturnus*[1,3]	Ⱥ	Ⱥ	Ⱥ	Ⱥ	A	Ⱥ	Ⱥ	A	Ⱥ	a	Ⱥ	A	Ⱥ	Ⱥ	A	A	A	A	A	a	1
17	*Kloeckera apiculata*	Ⱥ	A	Ⱥ	Ⱥ	Ⱥ	Ⱥ	Ⱥ	Ⱥ	Ⱥ	Ⱥ	Ⱥ	A	Ⱥ	Ⱥ	A	Ⱥ	Ⱥ	Ⱥ	Ⱥ	Ⱥ	1
18	*Pichia farinosa*[1]	A	Ⱥ	Ⱥ	A	a	Ⱥ	Ⱥ	A	Ⱥ	A	Ⱥ	A	Ⱥ	Ⱥ	A	A	Ⱥ	a	A	A	1
19	*P. guilliermondii*	A	A	A	Ⱥ	A	Ⱥ	A	A	Ⱥ	A	A	A	Ⱥ	Ⱥ	A	A	A	A	A	A	4
20	*P. membranaefaciens*[1]	Ⱥ	Ⱥ	Ⱥ	Ⱥ	A	Ⱥ	a	A	Ⱥ	Ⱥ	Ⱥ	Ⱥ	Ⱥ	Ⱥ	Ⱥ	a	a	a	a	Ⱥ	1
21	*Saccharomyces cerevisiae*	Ⱥ	Ⱥ	Ⱥ	Ⱥ	a	Ⱥ	Ⱥ	a	Ⱥ	Ⱥ	a	Ⱥ	Ⱥ	Ⱥ	Ⱥ	Ⱥ	L	L	Ⱥ	Ⱥ	1
22	*S. fragilis*	a	Ⱥ	Ⱥ	Ⱥ	A	Ⱥ	Ⱥ	A	Ⱥ	A	Ⱥ	Ⱥ	Ⱥ	Ⱥ	a	a	A	A	A	a	1
23	*S. lactis (Zygosaccharomyces lactis)*	a	Ⱥ	Ⱥ	Ⱥ	A	Ⱥ	Ⱥ	A	Ⱥ	A	a	Ⱥ	Ⱥ	Ⱥ	a	a	A	A	A	A	1
24	*S. pastori (Z. pastori)*	Ⱥ	Ⱥ	Ⱥ	Ⱥ	A	Ⱥ	Ⱥ	A	Ⱥ	A	Ⱥ	Ⱥ	Ⱥ	Ⱥ	Ⱥ	Ⱥ	L	A	A	L	1
25	*S. rosei (Torulaspora rosei)*[1]	Ⱥ	A	Ⱥ	Ⱥ	L	Ⱥ	Ⱥ	L	Ⱥ	A	a	A	Ⱥ	Ⱥ	Ⱥ	Ⱥ	A	A	Ⱥ	A	1
26	*S. veronae*	a	A	Ⱥ	Ⱥ	A	Ⱥ	Ⱥ	A	Ⱥ	A	A	a	Ⱥ	Ⱥ	Ⱥ	Ⱥ	Ⱥ	Ⱥ	A	A	1
27	*Saccharomycodes ludwigii*	Ⱥ	Ⱥ	Ⱥ	Ⱥ	L	Ⱥ	Ⱥ	L	Ⱥ	Ⱥ	Ⱥ	Ⱥ	Ⱥ	Ⱥ	L	Ⱥ	Ⱥ	Ⱥ	Ⱥ	Ⱥ	1
28	*Torulopsis colliculosa*[1]	...	A	Ⱥ	Ⱥ	A	Ⱥ	Ⱥ	A	Ⱥ	A	a	A	Ⱥ	Ⱥ	Ⱥ	Ⱥ	A	A	Ⱥ	A	1
29	*T. lactis-condensi (T. caroliniana)*[3]	Ⱥ	Ⱥ	Ⱥ	Ⱥ	Ⱥ	Ⱥ	Ⱥ	Ⱥ	Ⱥ	Ⱥ	Ⱥ	Ⱥ	Ⱥ	Ⱥ	Ⱥ	Ⱥ	Ⱥ	Ⱥ	Ⱥ	Ⱥ	1
30	*Zygosaccharomyces dobzhanskii*	Ⱥ	Ⱥ	Ⱥ	Ⱥ	A	Ⱥ	Ⱥ	A	Ⱥ	A	A	Ⱥ	Ⱥ	Ⱥ	A	A	A	A	A	A	1
31	*Z. pini*	A	a	Ⱥ	A	A	Ⱥ	Ⱥ	A	Ⱥ	A	Ⱥ	Ⱥ	Ⱥ	Ⱥ	A	a	a	a	a	A	1

1/ Grows in a vitamin-free medium. 3/ Assimilates nitrate.

Contributors: (a) Wickerham, Lynferd J., (b) Allgeier, R. J.

References

[1] Wickerham, L. J. 1951. U.S. Dept. Agr. Tech. Bull. 1029.

[2] Wickerham, L. J. 1965. Mycopathol. Mycol. Appl. 26:79

[3] Wickerham, L. J. 1965. Ibid. 26:87.

[4] Wickerham, L. J. 1966. J. Bacteriol. 92(4):1269.

27. NUTRIENT REQUIREMENTS AND UTILIZATION: ALGAE

Oxygen is essential for, and carbon dioxide is required by, all the species listed.

Part I. Vitamins, Sugars, and Alcohols

Vitamins are listed as "required" if the alga does not grow well in a purely mineral salts medium. Criterion for determining utilization of sugars and alcohols as a carbon source: growth of the alga in darkness on a given substrate (facultative heterotrophy). Stimulation of growth by a substance in the light does not indicate utilization. *Abbreviations:* R = required; R̸ = not required; U = utilized; U̸ = not utilized; u = poorly utilized.

	Species (Synonym)	Vitamins				Carbon Sources															Reference
						Sugars										Alcohols					
		Thiamine	Biotin	B_{12}	Other	Arabinose	Fructose	Galactose	Glucose	Lactose	Maltose	Mannose	Raffinose	Sucrose	Xylose	*n*-Butanol	Ethanol	Glycerol	Methanol	Other	
	Cyanophyta																				
1	*Agmenellum quadruplicatum*	R̸	R̸	R̸	...	...	...	...	U̸	...	...	...	...	...	...	...	...	...	...	...	67
2	*Anabaena cylindrica*	R̸	R̸	R̸	...	...	...	...	U̸	...	...	...	...	...	...	...	...	...	...	...	3
3	*A. gelatinosa*	R̸	R̸	R̸	...	...	...	...	...	...	...	...	...	...	...	...	...	...	...	...	9
4	*A. naviculoides*	R̸	R̸	R̸	...	...	...	...	...	...	...	...	...	...	...	...	...	...	...	...	9
5	*A. variabilis*	R̸	R̸	R̸	...	...	U̸	U̸	U̸	U̸	U̸	...	...	U̸	U̸	...	...	U̸	...	...	31
6	*Anacystis marina*	R̸	R̸	R̸	...	...	...	...	U̸	...	...	...	...	...	...	...	...	...	...	...	67
7	*A. nidulans*	R̸	R̸	R̸	...	...	U̸	U̸	U̸	U̸	U̸	...	...	U̸	U̸	...	...	U̸	...	...	31
8	*Aphanizomenon flos-aquae*	R̸	R̸	R̸	...	...	...	...	...	...	...	...	...	...	...	...	...	...	...	...	17
9	*Calothrix brevissima*	R̸	R̸	R̸	...	...	...	...	...	...	...	...	...	...	...	...	...	...	...	...	68
10	*C. parietina*	R̸	R̸	R̸	...	...	...	...	U̸	...	...	...	...	...	...	...	...	...	...	...	3
11	*C. scopulorum*	R̸	R̸	R̸	...	...	...	...	...	...	...	...	...	...	...	...	...	...	...	...	62
12	*Chroococcus turgidus*	R̸	R̸	R̸	...	...	...	...	U̸	...	...	...	...	...	...	...	...	...	...	...	3
13	*Coccochloris elabens*	R̸	R̸	R	...	...	...	...	U̸	...	...	...	...	...	...	...	...	...	...	...	67
14	*C. peniocystis*	R̸	R̸	R̸	...	...	...	...	...	...	...	...	...	...	...	...	...	...	...	...	17
15	*Gloeocapsa dimidiata*	R̸	R̸	R̸	...	...	...	...	...	...	...	...	...	...	...	...	...	...	...	...	17
16	*G. membranina*	R̸	R̸	R̸	...	...	...	...	...	...	...	...	...	...	...	...	...	...	...	...	71
17	*Lyngbya aestuarii*	R̸	R̸	R̸	...	...	...	...	U̸	...	...	...	...	...	...	...	...	...	...	...	67
18	*L. lagerheimii*	R̸	R̸	R	...	...	...	...	U̸	...	...	...	...	...	...	...	...	...	...	...	67
19	*Microcoleus chthonoplastes*	R̸	R̸	R̸	...	...	...	...	U̸	...	...	...	...	...	...	...	...	...	...	...	67
20	*M. tenerrimus*	R̸	R̸	R̸	...	...	...	...	...	...	...	...	...	...	...	...	...	...	...	...	67
21	*Microcystis aeruginosa (Diplocystis aeruginosa)*	R̸	R̸	R̸	...	...	...	...	...	...	...	...	...	...	...	...	...	...	...	...	17
22	*Nostoc entophytum*	R̸	R̸	R̸	...	...	...	...	...	...	...	...	...	...	...	...	...	...	...	...	62
23	*N. muscorum*	R̸	R̸	R̸	...	...	U̸	U̸	U̸[1]	U̸	U̸	...	...	U̸[1]	U̸	...	...	U̸	...	...	31
24	*Oscillatoria amphibia*	R̸	R̸	R	...	...	...	...	U̸	...	...	...	...	...	...	...	...	...	...	...	67
25	*O. brevis*	R̸	R̸	R̸	...	...	...	...	...	...	...	...	...	...	...	...	...	...	...	...	62
26	*O. subtillisima*	R̸	R̸	R	...	...	...	...	U̸	...	...	...	...	...	...	...	...	...	...	...	67
27	*Phormidium foveolarum*	R̸	R̸	R̸	...	...	...	...	U	...	...	...	...	...	...	...	...	...	...	...	3
28	*P. luridum*	R̸	R̸	R̸	...	...	...	...	U̸	...	...	...	...	...	...	...	...	...	...	...	3
29	*P. persicinum*[2]	R̸	R̸	R	...	...	...	...	...	...	...	...	...	...	...	...	...	...	...	...	46
30	*P. tenue*	R̸	R̸	R̸	...	...	...	...	...	...	...	...	...	...	...	...	...	...	...	...	17
31	*Plectonema nostocorum*	R̸	R̸	R̸	...	...	...	...	...	...	...	...	...	...	...	...	...	...	...	...	17
32	*P. notatum*	R̸	R̸	R̸	...	...	...	...	U[3]	...	...	...	...	...	...	...	...	...	...	...	3
33	*P. terebrans*	R̸	R̸	R̸	...	...	...	...	U̸	...	...	...	...	...	...	...	...	...	...	...	67
34	*Synechococcus cedrorum*	R̸	R̸	R̸	...	...	...	...	U̸	...	...	...	...	...	...	...	...	...	...	...	3
35	*Tolypothrix tenuis*	R̸?	R̸?	R̸?	...	...	U[4]	...	U[4]	...	...	...	...	u[4]	...	...	...	...	...	...	30
	Cryptophyta																				
36	*Chilomonas paramecium*[5]	R	R̸	R̸	R̸	...	...	...	U̸	...	...	...	...	...	...	U̸	U	U̸	U̸	U̸[6]	1,8,24,51

[1] By 1 strain; utilized by 1 strain. [2] Carbon sources tested for heterotrophic growth are not individually listed. [3] In presence of yeast autolysate. [4] In presence of casein hydrolysate. [5] Colorless. [6] *i*-Butanol, *i*-propanol, and *n*-propanol; however, *n*-hexanol is utilized.

continued

Part I. Vitamins, Sugars, and Alcohols

	Species (Synonym)	Vitamins				Carbon Sources															Reference
						Sugars										Alcohols					
		Thiamine	Biotin	B_{12}	Other	Arabinose	Fructose	Galactose	Glucose	Lactose	Maltose	Mannose	Raffinose	Sucrose	Xylose	*n*-Butanol	Ethanol	Glycerol	Methanol	Other	
37	*Cryptomonas ovata*	R̸	R̸	R	...	...	...	...	...	...	...	...	...	...	...	...	...	...	...	...	54
38	*Cyanaphora paradoza*	R̸	R̸	R	...	...	...	...	...	...	...	...	...	...	...	...	...	...	...	...	54
39	*Hemiselmis virescens*	R	R̸	R	...	...	...	...	...	...	...	...	...	...	...	...	...	...	...	...	12
40	*Rhodomonas lens*	R	R̸	?	...	...	...	...	...	...	...	...	...	...	...	...	...	...	...	...	51
	Pyrrophyta																				
41	*Amphidinium carteri*	R	R	R	...	...	...	...	...	...	...	...	...	...	...	...	...	...	...	...	41
42	*A. rhynchocephalum*	R	R	R	...	...	...	...	...	...	...	...	...	...	...	...	...	...	...	...	41
43	*Exuviaella cassubica*	R̸	R̸	R	...	...	...	...	...	...	...	...	...	...	...	...	...	...	...	...	53
44	*Glenodinium foliaceum*	R̸	R̸	R	...	...	...	...	...	...	...	...	...	...	...	...	...	...	...	...	12
45	*G. halli*	?	...	R	...	...	...	...	...	...	...	...	...	...	...	...	...	...	...	...	19
46	*Gonyaulax polyedra*	R̸	R̸	R	?	U̸	U̸	U̸	U̸	U̸	U̸	U̸	...	U̸	U̸	...	...	...	...	U̸[7]	22,51,65
47	*Gymnodinium brevis*	R	R	R	?	U̸	U̸	U̸	U̸	U̸	U̸	U̸	U̸	U̸	U̸	U̸	U̸	U̸	...	U̸[8]	2,72
48	*G. simplex*	?	?	?	?	...	...	...	...	...	...	...	...	...	...	...	...	...	...	...	66
49	*G. splendens*	R̸	R̸	R	...	...	...	...	...	...	...	...	...	...	...	...	...	...	...	...	64
50	*Gyrodinium californicum*	R̸	R̸	R	...	...	...	...	...	...	...	...	...	...	...	...	...	...	...	...	54
51	*G. cohnii*	?	R	R̸	...	...	...	...	...	...	...	...	...	...	...	...	...	...	...	...	52
52	*G. resplendens*	R̸	R̸	R	...	...	...	...	...	...	...	...	...	...	...	...	...	...	...	...	53
53	*G. uncatenum*	R̸	R̸	R	...	...	...	...	...	...	...	...	...	...	...	...	...	...	...	...	53
54	*Oxyrris marina*	R	R	R	...	...	...	...	...	...	...	...	...	...	...	...	...	...	...	...	12,13
55	*Peridinium balticum*	R̸	R̸	R	...	...	...	...	...	...	...	...	...	...	...	...	...	...	...	...	53
56	*P. chattoni*	R̸	R̸	R	...	...	...	...	...	...	...	...	...	...	...	...	...	...	...	...	53
57	*P. trochoideum*	R̸	R̸	R	...	...	...	...	...	...	...	...	...	...	...	...	...	...	...	...	12
58	*Prorocentrum micans*	R̸	R	R	...	...	...	...	...	...	...	...	...	...	...	...	...	...	...	...	11,29
59	*Woloszynskia limnetica (Peridinium* sp.)	R̸	R̸	R	...	...	...	...	...	...	...	...	...	...	...	...	...	...	...	...	54
	Bacillariophyta																				
60	*Achnanthes brevipes*	R̸	...	R	...	...	...	...	U̸	...	...	...	...	...	...	...	...	...	...	...	36
61	*Amphipleura rutilans*	R	...	R	...	...	...	...	U̸	...	...	...	...	...	...	...	...	...	...	...	36
62	*Amphiprora paludosa*	R	...	R̸	...	...	...	...	U̸	...	...	...	...	...	...	...	...	...	...	...	36
63	*Amphora coffaeiformis*	R̸[9]	...	R̸[10]	...	...	...	...	U[11]	...	...	...	...	...	...	...	...	...	...	...	36
64	*A. lineolata*	R̸	...	R	...	...	...	...	U	...	...	...	...	...	...	...	...	...	...	...	36
65	*A. perpusilla*	R̸	R̸	R	...	...	...	...	...	...	...	...	...	...	...	...	...	...	...	...	27
66	*Asterionella formosa*	R̸	R̸	R̸	...	...	...	...	...	...	...	...	...	...	...	...	...	...	...	...	51
67	*Chaetoceros ceratosporum*	...	...	...	...	...	...	...	U̸	...	...	...	...	...	...	...	...	...	...	...	34
68	*C. gracilis*	R̸	R̸	R̸	...	...	...	...	...	...	...	...	...	...	...	...	...	...	...	...	66
69	*C. lorenzianus*	...	...	R	...	...	...	...	...	...	...	...	...	...	...	...	...	...	...	...	20
70	*C. pelagicus*	R̸	...	R	...	...	...	...	U̸	...	...	...	...	...	...	...	...	...	...	...	20,34
71	*C. pseudocrinitus*	...	...	...	...	...	...	...	U̸	...	...	...	...	...	...	...	...	...	...	...	34
72	*Coscinodiscus asteromphalus*	...	...	R	...	...	...	...	U̸	...	...	...	...	...	...	...	...	...	...	...	20,34
73	*Cyclotella caspia*	...	...	R	...	...	...	...	U̸	...	...	...	...	...	...	...	...	...	...	...	20,34
74	*C. cryptica*	R̸	...	R	...	...	...	...	U	...	...	...	...	...	...	...	...	...	...	...	36,60
75	*C. nana*	R̸[12]	R̸[12]	R[12]	...	...	...	...	U̸[13]	...	...	...	...	...	...	...	...	...	...	...	21,34
76	*Cylindrotheca fusiformes (Nitzschia closterium)*	R[14]	...	R̸[15]	...	...	...	...	U[16]	...	...	...	...	...	...	...	...	...	...	...	35,36
77	*Detonula confervacea*	R̸	R̸	R̸	...	...	...	...	...	...	...	...	...	...	...	...	...	...	...	...	21
78	*Fragilaria brevistrata*	...	...	R	...	...	...	...	...	...	...	...	...	...	...	...	...	...	...	...	40
79	*F. capucina*	R̸	R̸	R̸	...	...	...	...	...	...	...	...	...	...	...	...	...	...	...	...	51

[7] Ribose. [8] Ribose and many other carbohydrates; also dulcitol, ethylene glycol, mannitol, and sorbitol. [9] By 7 strains; required by 3 strains. [10] By 6 strains; required by 4 strains. [11] By 8 strains; not utilized by 2 strains. [12] By 5 strains. [13] By 3 strains. [14] By 4 strains. [15] By 3 strains; required by 1 strain. [16] By 3 strains; not utilized by 1 strain.

continued

Part I. Vitamins, Sugars, and Alcohols

	Species (Synonym)	Vitamins				Carbon Sources															Reference
						Sugars										Alcohols					
		Thiamine	Biotin	B_{12}	Other	Arabinose	Fructose	Galactose	Glucose	Lactose	Maltose	Mannose	Raffinose	Sucrose	Xylose	*n*-Butanol	Ethanol	Glycerol	Methanol	Other	
80	*Gomphonema parvulum*	...	...	...	...	...	...	...	U̸	...	...	...	...	...	...	...	...	...	...	...	33
81	*Hantzschia amphionys*	...	...	...	...	...	...	...	U̸	...	...	...	...	...	...	...	...	...	...	...	33
82	*Licmophora hyalina*	...	...	R	...	...	...	...	...	...	...	...	...	...	...	...	...	...	...	...	40
83	*Melosira nummuloides*	...	...	...	...	...	...	...	U̸	...	...	...	...	...	...	...	...	...	...	...	34
84	*Navicula incerta*	R̸	...	R̸	...	...	...	...	U	...	...	...	...	...	...	...	...	...	...	...	36
85	*N. menisculus*	R̸	...	R̸	...	...	...	...	U̸	...	...	...	...	...	...	...	...	...	...	...	36
86	*N. minima*	...	...	...	...	...	...	...	U	...	...	...	...	...	...	...	...	...	...	...	33
87	*N. pelliculosa*	...	...	...	...	U̸	U	U̸	U	U̸	U̸	...	U̸	U̸	U̸	...	U̸	U	...	U̸[17]	33
88	*Nitzschia alba*[5]	R	...	R	...	...	...	...	U	...	...	...	...	...	...	...	...	...	...	...	32
89	*N. angularis affinis*	R̸	...	R̸	...	...	...	...	U	...	...	...	...	...	...	...	...	...	...	...	36
90	*N. curvilineata*	R̸	...	R̸	...	...	...	...	U̸	...	...	...	...	...	...	...	...	...	...	...	36
91	*N. filiformis*	R̸	...	R̸	...	...	...	...	U	...	...	...	...	...	...	...	...	...	...	...	36
92	*N. fonticola*	...	...	...	...	...	...	...	U	...	...	...	...	...	...	...	...	...	...	...	33
93	*N. frustulum*	R̸[18]	...	R̸[19]	...	...	...	...	U̸[20]	...	...	...	...	...	...	...	...	...	...	...	36
94	*N. hybridaeformis*	R̸	...	R̸	...	...	...	...	U̸	...	...	...	...	...	...	...	...	...	...	...	36
95	*N. laevis*	R̸[21]	...	R̸[21]	...	...	...	...	U	...	...	...	...	...	...	...	...	...	...	...	36
96	*N. leucosigma*[5]	R	...	R	...	...	...	...	U	...	...	...	...	...	...	...	...	...	...	...	32
97	*N. marginata*	R̸	...	R̸	...	...	...	...	U	...	...	...	...	...	...	...	...	...	...	...	36
98	*N. obtusa scalpelliformis*	R̸	...	R̸	...	...	...	...	U̸	...	...	...	...	...	...	...	...	...	...	...	36
99	*N. ovalis*	R̸	...	R	...	...	...	...	U̸	...	...	...	...	...	...	...	...	...	...	...	36
100	*N. palea*[22]	...	...	...	...	...	...	...	U̸	...	...	...	...	...	...	...	...	...	...	...	33
101	*N. punctata*	R̸	...	R	...	...	...	...	U	...	...	...	...	...	...	...	...	...	...	...	36
102	*N. putrida*[5]	R	...	R	...	...	...	...	U̸	...	...	...	...	...	...	...	...	...	...	...	32
103	*N. seriata*	...	...	R	...	...	...	...	...	...	...	...	...	...	...	...	...	...	...	...	20
104	*N. tenuissima*	?	...	?	...	...	...	...	U	...	...	...	...	...	...	...	...	...	...	...	36
105	*Phaeodactylum tricornutum*	R̸	R̸	R̸	...	...	...	...	...	...	...	...	...	...	...	...	...	...	...	...	25
106	*Rhizosolenia setigera*	...	...	R?	...	...	...	...	...	...	...	...	...	...	...	...	...	...	...	...	20
107	*Skeletonema costatum*	R̸	...	R[23]	...	...	...	...	U̸	...	...	...	...	...	...	...	...	...	...	...	10,34
108	*Stauroneis amphoroides*	R̸	...	R̸	...	...	...	...	U̸	...	...	...	...	...	...	...	...	...	...	...	36
109	*Stephanopyxis tunis*	R̸	R̸	R	...	...	...	...	...	...	...	...	...	...	...	...	...	...	...	...	51
110	*Synedra affinis*	R̸	...	R	...	...	...	...	U̸	...	...	...	...	...	...	...	...	...	...	...	36
111	*Tabellaria flocculosa*	R̸	R̸	R̸	...	...	...	...	...	...	...	...	...	...	...	...	...	...	...	...	51
112	*Thallasiosira fluviatilis*	...	...	R	...	...	...	...	U̸?	...	...	...	...	...	...	...	...	...	...	...	20,34,60
113	*T. nordenskioldii*	...	...	R?	...	...	...	...	...	...	...	...	...	...	...	...	...	...	...	...	20
	Chrysophyta																				
114	*Coccolithus huxleyi*	R[24]	...	R̸[25]	...	...	...	...	u	...	...	...	...	...	...	...	...	...	...	...	20,60
115	*Hymenomonas carterae*	R̸	R̸	R	...	...	...	...	...	...	...	...	...	...	...	...	...	...	...	...	54
116	*H. elongata*	R	R̸	R	...	...	...	...	...	...	...	...	...	...	...	...	...	...	...	...	10
117	*Isochrysis galbana*	R	R̸	R	...	...	...	...	...	...	...	...	...	...	...	...	...	...	...	...	51
118	*Microglena arenicola*	R	R̸	R	...	...	...	...	...	...	...	...	...	...	...	...	...	...	...	...	12
119	*Monochrysis lutherii*	R	R̸	R	...	...	...	...	...	...	...	...	...	...	...	...	...	...	...	...	12
120	*Ochromonas danica*	R	R	R̸	...	U̸	U	U	U	U̸	U	U	U̸	?	U̸	...	...	U̸	...	...	23,48
121	*O. malhamensis*	R	R	R	...	U̸	U	U	U	U̸	U?	U	U?	U	U̸	...	...	U	...	U?[7]	28,48
122	*Ochrosphaera neopolitana*	R	R̸	R̸	...	...	...	...	...	...	...	...	...	...	...	...	...	...	...	...	47
123	*Pavlova gyrans*	R	R̸	R	...	...	...	...	...	...	...	...	...	...	...	...	...	...	...	...	47
124	*Pleurochrysis scherffelii*	R	R̸	R̸	...	...	...	...	...	...	...	...	...	...	...	...	...	...	...	...	51
125	*Prymnesium parvum*	R	R̸	R	...	...	...	...	...	...	...	...	...	...	...	...	...	...	...	...	12

[5] Colorless. [7] Ribose. [17] Cellobiose, ethylene glycol, fucose, mannitol, melibiose, α-methylglucoside, rhamnose, sorbose, and trehalose. [18] By 6 strains. [19] By 4 strains; required by 2 strains. [20] By 3 strains; utilized by 3 strains. [21] By 2 strains. [22] 27 strains. [23] Several other compounds similar to B_{12} can be utilized in its place [15]. [24] By 2 strains; not required by 1 strain. [25] By 2 strains; required by 1 strain.

continued

Part I. Vitamins, Sugars, and Alcohols

	Species (Synonym)	Vitamins				Carbon Sources																Reference
						Sugars										Alcohols						
		Thiamine	Biotin	B_{12}	Other	Arabinose	Fructose	Galactose	Glucose	Lactose	Maltose	Mannose	Raffinose	Sucrose	Xylose	*n*-Butanol	Ethanol	Glycerol	Methanol		Other	
126	*Stichochrysis immobilis*	R̸	R̸	R̸	...	...	...	...	...	...	...	...	...	...	...	...	...	...	...		...	51
127	*Synochromonas korschikoffii*	R	...	R	...	...	...	...	...	...	...	...	...	...	...	...	...	...	...		...	49
128	*Synura caroliniana*	R̸	?	R	...	...	...	...	...	...	...	...	...	...	...	...	...	...	...		...	51
129	*S. petersenii*	R̸	R̸	R	...	...	...	...	...	...	...	...	...	...	...	...	...	...	...		...	54
	Xanthophyta																					
130	*Botrydiopsis intercedens*	R̸	R̸	R̸	...	...	U̸	...	U	...	...	U̸	...	U̸	...	...	U̸	U̸	...		...	6
131	*Bumilleriopsis brevis*	R̸	R̸	R̸	...	...	U	...	U	...	...	U	...	U	...	...	U	U	...		...	6
132	*Chlorellidium tetrabotrys*	R̸	R̸	R̸	...	...	U̸	...	U̸	...	...	U̸	...	U̸	...	...	U	U	...		...	6
133	*Monodus subterraneus*	R̸	R̸	R̸	...	...	U̸	...	U̸	U̸	U̸	...	U̸	U̸	...	...	...	U̸	...		...	42,43
134	*Polyedriella helvetica*	R̸	R̸	R̸	...	...	U̸	...	U̸	...	...	U̸	...	U̸	...	...	U̸	U̸	...		...	6
135	*Tribonema aequale*	R̸	R̸	R̸	...	U̸	U̸	U̸	U	U̸	...	U̸	...	U	U̸	...	U̸	U̸	...		...	5
136	*T. minus*	R̸	R̸	R̸	...	...	...	...	U	U̸	...	U̸	...	U̸	...	...	U̸	U̸	...		...	6
	Euglenophyta																					
137	*Astasia longa (A. chattoni, A. klebsii)*	R	R̸	R	R̸	...	...	...	U̸	...	...	...	...	...	...	U	U	...	U̸		U̸[26]	1,51
138	*A. quartana*	...	...	...	...	...	...	...	...	...	...	...	...	...	...	U̸	U̸	...	U̸		U̸[27]	1
139	*Euglena anabaena minor*[28]	R̸	...	R̸	R̸	...	...	...	U̸	...	...	...	...	U̸	...	...	...	U̸	...		...	1
140	*E. deses*[29]	...	...	...	...	...	...	...	U̸	...	...	...	...	U̸	...	...	U	U̸	...		...	1
141	*E. gracilis bacillaris*	R	R̸	R[30]	...	...	...	...	U	...	...	...	...	...	...	...	...	...	...		...	1
142	*E. gracilis typica*	R[31]	R̸	R[30]	...	...	...	...	U̸	...	...	...	...	U̸	...	U	U	...	U̸		U̸[32]	1,51
143	*E. gracilis urophora*	R	R̸	R[30]	...	...	...	...	U̸	...	...	...	...	...	...	U	U	...	U̸		U̸[33]	1,51
144	*E. klebsii*[28,34]	R	...	R	?	...	...	...	U̸	...	...	...	...	U̸	...	...	...	...	...		...	1
145	*E. mutabilis*	R	R̸	R	...	...	...	...	...	...	...	...	...	...	...	...	...	...	...		...	40
146	*E. pisciformis*	R[35]	R̸	...	...	...	...	...	U̸	...	...	...	...	U̸	...	...	...	U̸	...		...	1,51
147	*E. stellata*	R	R̸	R	...	...	...	...	...	...	...	...	...	...	...	...	...	U̸	...		...	1,51
148	*E. viridis*	R	R̸	R	...	...	...	...	...	...	...	...	...	...	...	...	...	...	...		...	51
149	*Peranema trichophorum*	R	R̸	R	R	...	...	...	...	...	...	...	...	...	...	...	...	...	...		...	63
150	*Phacus pyrum*	R	R̸	R	...	...	...	...	...	...	...	...	...	...	...	...	...	...	...		...	51
151	*Trachelomonas abrupta*	?	R̸	R	...	...	...	...	...	...	...	...	...	...	...	...	...	...	...		...	55
152	*T. pertyi*	?	R̸	R	...	...	...	...	...	...	...	...	...	...	...	...	...	...	...		...	51
	Chlorophyta																					
153	*Asterococcus superbus*	?	...	?	...	...	...	...	...	...	...	...	...	...	...	...	...	...	...		...	7
154	*Astrephomene gubernaculifera*	?	R̸	R̸	?	...	...	...	...	...	...	...	...	...	...	...	...	...	...		...	61
155	*Balticola buetschlii*	R̸	R̸	R	...	...	...	...	...	...	...	...	...	...	...	...	...	...	...		...	14
156	*B. droebakensis*[36]	R̸	R̸	R	...	...	...	...	...	...	...	...	...	...	...	...	...	...	...		...	14
157	*Brachiomonas submarina*	R	R̸	R	...	...	...	...	...	...	...	...	...	...	...	...	...	...	...		...	14
158	*Bracteacoccus cinnabarinus*	R̸	R̸	R̸	...	...	...	...	U	...	...	...	...	...	...	...	...	...	...		...	45
159	*B. engadiensis*	R̸	R̸	R̸	...	...	...	...	U	...	...	...	...	...	...	...	...	...	...		...	45
160	*B. minor*	R̸	R̸	R̸	...	...	...	...	U	...	...	...	...	...	...	...	...	...	...		...	45
161	*B. terrestris*	R̸	R̸	R̸	...	...	...	...	U	...	...	...	...	...	...	...	...	...	...		...	45

[26] *i*-Pentanol, *n*-pentanol, and *i*-propanol; however, *n*-hexanol and *n*-propanol are utilized, and *i*-butanol is poorly utilized. [27] *n*-Hexanol and *n*-propanol. [28] May require no vitamins after adaptation to media lacking vitamins, as with other species of *Euglena*. [29] According to E. G. Pringsheim, the organism used in these studies was *E. geniculata*. [30] Pseudocobalamin also utilized. [31] Can be replaced by pyrimidine. [32] *i*-Butanol, *i*-pentanol, *n*-pentanol, and *i*-propanol; however, *n*-hexanol and *n*-propanol are utilized. [33] *i*-Pentanol, *n*-pentanol, and *i*-propanol; however, *i*-butanol, *n*-hexanol, and *n*-propanol are utilized. [34] According to E. G. Pringsheim, the organism used in these studies was *E. mutabilis*. [35] Can be replaced by pyrimidine and thiazole. [36] Probably an obligate phototroph; substrates failing to support dark growth are not individually listed.

continued

27. NUTRIENT REQUIREMENTS AND UTILIZATION: ALGAE

Part I. Vitamins, Sugars, and Alcohols

	Species (Synonym)	Vitamins				Carbon Sources															Reference
						Sugars										Alcohols					
		Thiamine	Biotin	B_{12}	Other	Arabinose	Fructose	Galactose	Glucose	Lactose	Maltose	Mannose	Raffinose	Sucrose	Xylose	*n*-Butanol	Ethanol	Glycerol	Methanol	Other	
162	*Carteria crucifera*	?	...	?	...	...	...	...	...	...	...	...	...	...	...	...	...	...	...	...	7
163	*Chlamydomonas actinochloris*	?	...	?	...	...	...	...	...	...	...	...	...	...	...	...	...	...	...	...	7
164	*C. agloeformis*	℞	℞	℞	℞	...	...	...	...	...	...	...	...	...	...	...	...	...	...	...	1,51
165	*C. calyptrata*	?	...	?	...	...	...	...	...	...	...	...	...	...	...	...	...	...	...	...	7
166	*C. carrosa*[37]	?	...	?	...	...	...	...	...	...	...	...	...	...	...	...	...	...	...	...	7
167	*C. chlamydogama*	℞	℞	R	...	...	...	...	...	...	...	...	...	...	...	...	...	...	...	...	26
168	*C. dysosmos*	...	...	...	...	...	...	...	Ʉ	...	...	...	...	...	...	...	...	Ʉ	...	...	39
169	*C. eugametos*[38]	℞	℞	℞	...	...	...	...	...	...	...	...	...	...	...	...	...	...	...	...	70
170	*C. gloegama*	?	...	?	...	...	...	...	...	...	...	...	...	...	...	...	...	...	...	...	7
171	*C. gloeopara*	?	...	?	...	...	...	...	...	...	...	...	...	...	...	...	...	...	...	...	7
172	*C. inflexa*	?	...	?	...	...	...	...	...	...	...	...	...	...	...	...	...	...	...	...	7
173	*C. kakosmos*	?	...	?	...	...	...	...	...	...	...	...	...	...	...	...	...	...	...	...	7
174	*C. mexicana*	?	...	?	...	...	...	...	...	...	...	...	...	...	...	...	...	...	...	...	7
175	*C. microsphaera acuta*	?	...	?	...	...	...	...	...	...	...	...	...	...	...	...	...	...	...	...	7
176	*C. microsphaerella*	?	...	?	...	...	...	...	...	...	...	...	...	...	...	...	...	...	...	...	7
177	*C. minuta*	?	...	?	...	...	...	...	...	...	...	...	...	...	...	...	...	...	...	...	7
178	*C. moewusii*	℞	℞	℞	℞	Ʉ	...	...	Ʉ	...	Ʉ	...	...	Ʉ	Ʉ	Ʉ	Ʉ	Ʉ	...	...	1,26,51
179	*C. moewusii rotunda*	?	...	?	...	...	...	...	...	...	...	...	...	...	...	...	...	...	...	...	7
180	*C. mundana*	℞	℞	R	...	...	...	...	...	...	...	...	...	...	...	...	...	...	...	...	16
181	*C. mundana astigmata*	℞	℞	R	...	...	...	...	...	...	...	...	...	...	...	...	...	...	...	...	16
182	*C. mutabilis*	?	...	?	...	...	...	...	...	...	...	...	...	...	...	...	...	...	...	...	7
183	*C. peterfi*	?	...	?	...	...	...	...	...	...	...	...	...	...	...	...	...	...	...	...	7
184	*C. pulsatilla*[36]	℞	℞	R	...	...	...	...	...	...	...	...	...	...	...	...	...	...	...	...	14
185	*C. radiata*	?	...	?	...	...	...	...	...	...	...	...	...	...	...	...	...	...	...	...	7
186	*C. reinhardii*	℞	℞	℞[39]	...	...	...	...	...	...	...	...	...	...	...	...	...	...	...	...	40,51
187	*C. sectilis*	?	...	?	...	...	...	...	...	...	...	...	...	...	...	...	...	...	...	...	7
188	*C. typhlos*	?	...	?	...	...	...	...	...	...	...	...	...	...	...	...	...	...	...	...	7
189	*Chlorella autotrophica*	℞	℞	℞	...	Ʉ	Ʉ	Ʉ	Ʉ	Ʉ	Ʉ	Ʉ	Ʉ	Ʉ	...	...	...	...	...	...	58
190	*C. candida*	℞	℞	℞	...	Ʉ	Ʉ	Ʉ	U	Ʉ	Ʉ	Ʉ	Ʉ	Ʉ	...	...	...	...	...	...	58
191	*C. ellipsoidea*	℞	℞	℞	...	Ʉ	U	Ʉ	U	Ʉ	Ʉ	U	Ʉ	Ʉ	...	...	...	...	...	...	58
192	*C. emersonii*	℞	℞	℞	...	Ʉ	U	Ʉ	U	Ʉ	Ʉ	U	Ʉ	Ʉ	...	...	...	...	...	...	58
193	*C. emersonii globosa*	℞	℞	℞	...	Ʉ	U	Ʉ	U	Ʉ	Ʉ	U	Ʉ	Ʉ	...	...	...	...	...	...	58
194	*C. fusca*	℞	℞	℞	...	Ʉ	Ʉ	Ʉ	U	Ʉ	Ʉ	U	Ʉ	Ʉ	...	...	...	...	...	...	58
195	*C. fusca vacuolata*	℞	℞	℞	...	Ʉ	U	Ʉ	U	Ʉ	Ʉ	U	Ʉ	Ʉ	...	...	...	...	...	...	58
196	*C. infusionum*	℞	℞	℞	...	Ʉ	Ʉ	Ʉ	Ʉ[1]	Ʉ	Ʉ	Ʉ	Ʉ	Ʉ	...	...	...	...	...	...	58
197	*C. infusionum auxenophila*	℞	℞	℞	...	Ʉ	Ʉ	Ʉ	U	Ʉ	Ʉ	Ʉ	Ʉ	Ʉ	...	...	...	...	...	...	58
198	*C. miniata*	℞	℞	℞	...	?	U	U	U	?	Ʉ	U	Ʉ	U	...	...	...	...	...	...	58
199	*C. mutabilis*	℞	℞	℞	...	Ʉ	Ʉ	U	U	Ʉ	Ʉ	Ʉ	Ʉ	Ʉ	...	...	...	...	...	...	58
200	*C. nocturna*	℞	℞	℞	...	Ʉ	Ʉ	Ʉ	U	Ʉ	Ʉ	Ʉ	Ʉ	Ʉ	...	...	...	...	...	...	58
201	*C. photophila*	℞	℞	℞	...	Ʉ	Ʉ	Ʉ	Ʉ	Ʉ	Ʉ	Ʉ	Ʉ	Ʉ	...	...	...	...	...	...	58
202	*C. pringsheimii*	℞	℞	℞	...	Ʉ	u	u	u	Ʉ	Ʉ	Ʉ	Ʉ	Ʉ	...	...	...	...	...	...	58
203	*C. protothecoides*	R	℞	℞	...	Ʉ	U	U	U	Ʉ	Ʉ	Ʉ	Ʉ	Ʉ	...	...	...	...	...	...	58
204	*C. protothecoides communis*	R	℞	℞	...	Ʉ	U	U	U	Ʉ	Ʉ	Ʉ	Ʉ	Ʉ	...	...	...	...	...	...	58
205	*C. protothecoides galactophila*	R	℞	℞	...	Ʉ	U	U	U	Ʉ	Ʉ	Ʉ	Ʉ	Ʉ	...	...	...	...	...	...	58
206	*C. protothecoides mannophila*	R	℞	℞	...	Ʉ	U	U	U	Ʉ	Ʉ	U	Ʉ	Ʉ	...	...	...	...	...	...	58
207	*C. pyrenoidosa,* Emerson	℞	℞	℞	...	...	Ʉ	U	U	...	Ʉ	...	...	Ʉ	...	...	...	...	...	...	57
208	*C. regularis*	℞	℞	℞	...	Ʉ	U	U	U	Ʉ	Ʉ	Ʉ	Ʉ	Ʉ	...	...	...	...	...	...	58

[1] By 1 strain; utilized by 1 strain. [36] Probably an obligate phototroph; substrates failing to support dark growth are not individually listed. [37] 4 strains. [38] An obligate phototroph; individual compounds tested as carbon sources are not listed [69]. [39] By 1 strain; required by 1 strain.

continued

Part I. Vitamins, Sugars, and Alcohols

	Species (Synonym)	Vitamins				Carbon Sources															Reference
						Sugars										Alcohols					
		Thiamine	Biotin	B_{12}	Other	Arabinose	Fructose	Galactose	Glucose	Lactose	Maltose	Mannose	Raffinose	Sucrose	Xylose	*n*-Butanol	Ethanol	Glycerol	Methanol	Other	
209	*C. regularis aprica*	℞	℞	℞	...	U̸	U	U	U	U	U̸	U̸	U̸	U̸	...	...	...	...	...	...	58
210	*C. regularis imbricata*	℞	℞	℞	...	U̸	U	U	U	U	U̸	U̸	U̸	U̸	...	...	...	...	...	...	58
211	*C. saccharophila*	℞	℞	℞	...	U̸	U̸	U̸	U	U̸	U̸	U̸	U̸	U̸	...	...	...	...	...	...	58
212	*C. simplex*	℞	℞	℞	...	U̸	U̸	U̸	U	U̸	U̸	U̸	U̸	U̸	...	...	...	...	...	...	58
213	*C. sorokiniana*	℞	℞	℞	...	U̸	U̸	U̸	U	U̸	U̸	U̸	U̸	U̸	...	...	...	...	...	...	58
214	*C. vannielii*	℞	℞	℞	...	U̸	U̸	U	U	U̸	U̸	U̸	U̸	U̸	...	...	...	...	...	...	58
215	*C. variabilis*	℞	℞	℞	...	U̸	U̸	U̸	U̸	U̸	U̸	U̸	U̸	U̸	...	...	...	...	...	...	58
216	*C. vulgaris*	℞	℞	℞	...	U̸	U	U̸	U	U̸	U̸	U	U̸	U	...	...	...	...	...	...	51,58
217	*C. vulgaris luteoviridis*	℞	℞	℞	...	U̸	U	u	U	U̸	U̸	U	U̸	U	...	...	...	...	...	...	58
218	*Chlorococcum aplanosporum*	℞	℞	℞	...	...	...	...	U̸	...	...	...	...	...	...	...	...	...	...	...	45
219	*C. diplobionticum*	℞	℞	℞	...	...	...	...	U̸	...	...	...	...	...	...	...	...	...	...	...	45
220	*C. echinozygotum*	℞	℞	℞	...	...	...	...	U̸	...	...	...	...	...	...	...	...	...	...	...	45
221	*C. ellipsoideum*	℞	℞	℞	...	...	...	...	U̸	...	...	...	...	...	...	...	...	...	...	...	45
222	*C. hypnosporum*	℞	℞	℞	...	...	...	...	U̸	...	...	...	...	...	...	...	...	...	...	...	45
223	*C. macrostigmatum*	℞	℞	℞	...	...	...	...	U̸	...	...	...	...	...	...	...	...	...	...	...	45
224	*C. minutum*	℞	℞	℞	...	...	...	...	U̸	...	...	...	...	...	...	...	...	...	...	...	45
225	*C. multinucleatum*	℞	℞	℞	...	...	...	...	U̸	...	...	...	...	...	...	...	...	...	...	...	45
226	*C. oleofaciens*	℞	℞	℞	...	...	...	...	U̸	...	...	...	...	...	...	...	...	...	...	...	45
227	*C. perforatum*	℞	℞	℞	...	...	...	...	U̸	...	...	...	...	...	...	...	...	...	...	...	45
228	*C. pinguideum*	℞	℞	℞	...	...	...	...	U̸	...	...	...	...	...	...	...	...	...	...	...	45
229	*C. punctatum*	℞	℞	℞	...	...	...	...	U̸	...	...	...	...	...	...	...	...	...	...	...	45
230	*C. scabellum*	℞	℞	℞	...	...	...	...	U̸	...	...	...	...	...	...	...	...	...	...	...	45
231	*C. tetrasporum*	℞	℞	℞	...	...	...	...	U̸	...	...	...	...	...	...	...	...	...	...	...	45
232	*C. vacuolatum*	℞	℞	℞	...	...	...	...	U̸	...	...	...	...	...	...	...	...	...	...	...	45
233	*C. wimmeri*	℞	℞	℞	...	...	...	...	U̸	...	...	...	...	...	...	...	...	...	...	...	45
234	*Chlorosphaera consociata*	℞	℞	R	...	...	...	...	...	...	...	...	...	...	...	...	...	...	...	...	40
235	*Coelastrum morus* (?)	R	℞	℞	...	...	...	...	...	...	...	...	...	...	...	...	...	...	...	...	37
236	*Cyanidium caldarium* [40]	℞	℞	℞	...	...	U	U	U	U	U	...	...	U	...	...	U	U	...	...	3,4
237	*Dictyochloris fragrans*	℞	℞	℞	...	...	...	...	U	...	...	...	...	...	...	...	...	...	...	...	45
238	*Dunaliella primolecta*	℞	℞	℞	...	...	...	...	...	...	...	...	...	...	...	...	...	...	...	...	51
239	*D. salina*	℞	℞	℞	...	...	...	...	U̸	...	...	...	...	...	...	...	...	...	...	...	18,51
240	*D. viridis*	℞	℞	℞	...	...	...	...	U̸	...	...	...	...	...	...	...	...	...	...	...	18
241	*Gloeocystis gigas*	?	...	?	...	...	...	...	...	...	...	...	...	...	...	...	...	...	...	...	7
242	*G. maxima*	?	...	?	...	...	...	...	...	...	...	...	...	...	...	...	...	...	...	...	7
243	*Gonium pectorale*	℞	℞	R	...	...	...	...	...	...	...	...	...	...	...	...	...	...	...	...	61
244	*Haematococcus pluvialis*	℞	℞	℞	℞	...	...	...	...	...	...	...	...	...	...	...	...	...	...	...	1,51
245	*Lobomonas pyriformis*	℞	℞	℞	...	...	...	...	...	...	...	...	...	...	...	...	...	...	...	...	44
246	*L. rostrata*	℞	℞	R	...	...	...	...	...	...	...	...	...	...	...	...	...	...	...	...	37
247	*L. sphaerica*	℞	℞	R	...	...	...	...	u?	...	...	...	...	...	...	...	...	...	...	...	50
248	*Nannochloris atomus*	℞	℞	℞	...	...	...	...	...	...	...	...	...	...	...	...	...	...	...	...	56
249	*N. oculata*	℞	℞	℞	...	...	...	...	...	...	...	...	...	...	...	...	...	...	...	...	12
250	*Nautococcus pyriformis*	℞	℞	℞	...	...	...	...	U̸	...	...	...	...	...	...	...	...	...	...	...	45
251	*Neochloris alveolaris*	℞	℞	℞	...	...	...	...	U	...	...	...	...	...	...	...	...	...	...	...	45
252	*N. aquatica*	℞	℞	℞	...	...	...	...	U	...	...	...	...	...	...	...	...	...	...	...	45
253	*N. gelatinosa*	℞	℞	℞	...	...	...	...	U	...	...	...	...	...	...	...	...	...	...	...	45
254	*N. minuta*	℞	℞	℞	...	...	...	...	U̸	...	...	...	...	...	...	...	...	...	...	...	45
255	*N. pseudoalveolaris*	℞	℞	℞	...	...	...	...	U	...	...	...	...	...	...	...	...	...	...	...	45
256	*Platymonas tetrathele*	℞	℞	R	...	...	...	...	...	...	...	...	...	...	...	...	...	...	...	...	14
257	*Polytoma caudatum*	R [41]	℞	...	...	...	...	...	...	...	...	...	...	...	...	U̸	U̸	...	U̸	U̸ [42]	1,51
258	*P. obtusum*	℞	℞	...	℞	...	...	...	...	...	...	...	...	...	...	U̸	U̸	...	U̸	U̸ [43]	1,51
259	*P. ocellatum*	R [41]	℞	...	...	...	...	...	U̸	...	...	...	...	...	...	U	U	...	U̸	U [44]	1,51

[40] Genus of uncertain taxonomic position [59]. [41] Can be replaced by thiazole. [42] *i*-Butanol, *n*-pentanol, *i*-propanol, and *n*-propanol. [43] *i*-Butanol, *n*-pentanol, and *n*-propanol. [44] *i*-Butanol, *n*-hexanol, and *n*-propanol; however, *i*-pentanol and *i*-propanol are not utilized, and *n*-pentanol is poorly utilized.

continued

27. NUTRIENT REQUIREMENTS AND UTILIZATION: ALGAE

Part I. Vitamins, Sugars, and Alcohols

	Species (Synonym)	Vitamins				Carbon Sources																Reference
						Sugars										Alcohols						
		Thiamine	Biotin	B_{12}	Other	Arabinose	Fructose	Galactose	Glucose	Lactose	Maltose	Mannose	Raffinose	Sucrose	Xylose	*n*-Butanol	Ethanol	Glycerol	Methanol	Other		
260	*P. uvella*	R̸	R̸	...	R̸	U̸	...	...	U̸	...	...	...	...	...	U̸	U̸	U̸	...	U̸	U̸[42]		1,51
261	*Polytomella caeca*	R[35]	R̸	...	...	...	...	...	U̸	...	U̸	...	...	U̸	...	U	U	...	U̸	U̸[33]		1,51
262	*Prototheca zopfii*	R[35]	R̸	...	...	U̸	...	...	U	...	U̸	...	...	U̸	U̸	U	U	U	U̸	U[45]		1,51
263	*Pyramimonas inconstans*	R	R̸	R	...	...	...	...	...	...	...	...	...	...	...	...	...	...	...	...		51
264	*Radiosphaera dissecta*	R̸	R̸	R̸	...	...	...	...	U̸	...	...	...	...	...	...	...	...	...	...	...		45
265	*Scenedesmus obliquus*	R̸	R̸	R̸	...	...	...	...	...	...	...	...	...	...	...	...	...	...	...	...		51
266	*Selenastrum minutum*	R̸[46]	R̸	R̸	...	...	...	...	...	...	...	...	...	...	...	...	...	...	...	...		37
267	*Sphaerobotrys fluviatilis*	?	...	?	...	...	...	...	...	...	...	...	...	...	...	...	...	...	...	...		7
268	*Spongiochloris excentrica*	R̸	R̸	R̸	...	...	...	...	U	...	...	...	...	...	...	...	...	...	...	...		45
269	*S. lamellata*	R̸	R̸	R̸	...	...	...	...	U	...	...	...	...	...	...	...	...	...	...	...		45
270	*S. spongiosis*	R̸	R̸	R̸	...	...	...	...	U	...	...	...	...	...	...	...	...	...	...	...		45
271	*Spongiococcum alabamense*	R̸	R̸	R̸	...	...	...	...	U	...	...	...	...	...	...	...	...	...	...	...		45
272	*S. excentricum*	R̸	R̸	R̸	...	...	...	...	U	...	...	...	...	...	...	...	...	...	...	...		45
273	*S. multinucleatum*	R̸	R̸	R̸	...	...	...	...	U	...	...	...	...	...	...	...	...	...	...	...		45
274	*S. tetrasporum*	R̸	R̸	R̸	...	...	...	...	U̸	...	...	...	...	...	...	...	...	...	...	...		45
275	*Sporotetras pyriformis*	?	...	?	...	...	...	...	...	...	...	...	...	...	...	...	...	...	...	...		7
276	*Stephanoptera gracilis*	R̸	R̸	R̸	...	...	...	...	U̸	...	...	...	...	...	...	...	...	...	...	...		18
277	*Stephanosphaera pluvialis*	R	R̸	R	...	...	...	...	...	...	...	...	...	...	...	...	...	...	...	...		14
278	*Stichococcus cylindricus* (?)	R̸	R̸	R̸[39]	...	...	...	...	...	...	...	...	...	...	...	...	...	...	...	...		38,56
279	*Volvulina steinii*	?	R̸	R̸	?	...	...	...	...	...	...	...	...	...	...	...	...	...	...	...		61

[33] *i*-Pentanol, *n*-pentanol, and *i*-propanol; however, *i*-butanol, *n*-hexanol, and *n*-propanol are utilized. [35] Can be replaced by pyrimidine and thiazole. [39] By 1 strain; required by 1 strain. [42] *i*-Butanol, *n*-pentanol, *i*-propanol, and *n*-propanol. [45] *i*-Butanol, *n*-pentanol, and *n*-propanol; however, *i*-pentanol is poorly utilized, and *i*-propanol is not utilized. [46] By 6 strains; required by 1 strain.

Contributor: Thomas, William H.

References

[1] Albritton, E. C. 1954. Standard values in nutrition and metabolism. W. B. Saunders, Philadelphia.
[2] Aldrich, D. V. 1962. Science 137:988.
[3] Allen, M. B. 1952. Arch. Mikrobiol. 17:34.
[4] Allen, M. B. 1959. Ibid. 32:270.
[5] Belcher, J. H., and G. E. Fogg. 1958. Ibid. 30:17.
[6] Belcher, J. H., and J. D. A. Miller. 1960. Ibid. 36:219.
[7] Cain, J. 1965. Can. J. Botany 43:1367.
[8] Cosgrove, W. B., and B. K. Swanson. 1952. Physiol. Zool. 25:287.
[9] De, P. K. 1939. Proc. Roy. Soc. (London), B, 127: 121.
[10] Droop, M. R. 1955. J. Marine Biol. Assoc. U.K. 34: 229.
[11] Droop, M. R. 1957. J. Gen. Microbiol. 16:286.
[12] Droop, M. R. 1958. J. Marine Biol. Assoc. U.K. 37: 323.
[13] Droop, M. R. 1959. Ibid. 38:605.
[14] Droop, M. R. 1961. Rev. Algol. 5(4):247.
[15] Droop, M. R., et al. 1959. Preprints Abstr. Papers Intern. Oceanog. Congr., New York, p. 916.
[16] Eppley, R. W., and F. M. Macias. 1962. Physiol. Plantarum 15:72.
[17] Gerloff, G. C., G. P. Fitzgerald, and F. Skoog. 1950. Am. J. Botany 37:216.
[18] Gibor, A. 1956. Biol. Bull. 111:223.
[19] Gold, K. 1964. J. Protozool. 11:85.
[20] Guillard, R. R. L. 1963. Symp. Marine Microbiol., Chicago, 1961, p. 93.
[21] Guillard, R. R. L., and J. H. Ryther. 1962. Can. J. Microbiol. 8:229.
[22] Haxo, F. T., and B. M. Sweeney. 1955. Luminescence Biol. Systems Proc. Conf. Luminescence, Asilomar, Calif., 1954, p. 415.
[23] Heinrich, H. C. 1955. Naturwissenschaften 14:418.
[24] Holz, G. G. 1954. J. Protozool. 1:114.
[25] Hutner, S. H. 1948. Trans. N.Y. Acad. Sci. 10:136.
[26] Hutner, S. H., and L. Provasoli. 1951. Biochem. Physiol. Protozoa 1:27.
[27] Hutner, S. H., and L. Provasoli. 1953. Phycol. News Bull. 6:7.
[28] Hutner, S. H., L. Provasoli, and J. Filfus. 1953. Ann. N.Y. Acad. Sci. 56:852.
[29] Kain, J. M., and G. E. Fogg. 1960. J. Marine Biol. Assoc. U.K. 39:33.
[30] Kiyohara, T., et al. 1960. J. Gen. Appl. Microbiol. 6:176.
[31] Kratz, W. A., and J. Myers. 1955. Am. J. Botany 42:282.

continued

Part I. Vitamins, Sugars, and Alcohols

[32] Lewin, J., and R. A. Lewin. 1967. J. Gen. Microbiol. 46:361.
[33] Lewin, J. C. 1953. Ibid. 9:305.
[34] Lewin, J. C. 1963. Symp. Marine Microbiol., Chicago, 1961, p. 229.
[35] Lewin, J. C. 1965. Phycologia 4:142.
[36] Lewin, J. C., and R. A. Lewin. 1960. Can. J. Microbiol. 6:127.
[37] Lewin, R. A. 1952. Phycol. News Bull. 5:21.
[38] Lewin, R. A. 1954. J. Gen. Microbiol. 10:93.
[39] Lewin, R. A. 1954. Ibid. 11:459.
[40] Lewin, R. A. 1958. Sci. Studoj, p. 187.
[41] McLaughlin, J. J. A., and L. Provasoli. 1957. J. Protozool. 4(Suppl.):7.
[42] Miller, J. D. A., and G. E. Fogg. 1957. Arch. Mikrobiol. 28:1.
[43] Miller, J. D. A., and G. E. Fogg. 1958. Ibid. 30:1.
[44] Osterud, K. L. 1946. Physiol. Zool. 19:19.
[45] Parker, B. C., H. C. Bold, and T. R. Deason. 1961. Science 133:761.
[46] Pintner, I. J., and L. Provasoli. 1958. J. Gen. Microbiol. 18:190.
[47] Pintner, I. J., and L. Provasoli. 1963. Symp. Marine Microbiol., Chicago, 1961. p. 114.
[48] Pringsheim, E. G. 1955. Arch. Mikrobiol. 23:181.
[49] Pringsheim, E. G. 1958. Planta 52:405.
[50] Pringsheim, E. G. 1963. Arch. Mikrobiol. 46:227.
[51] Provasoli, L. 1958. Ann. Rev. Microbiol. 12:279.
[52] Provasoli, L., and K. Gold. 1957. J. Protozool. 4(Suppl.):7.
[53] Provasoli, L., and J. J. A. McLaughlin. 1955. Ibid. 2(Suppl.):10.
[54] Provasoli, L., and I. J. Pintner. 1953. Ann. N.Y. Acad. Sci. 56:839.
[55] Provasoli, L., and I. J. Pintner. 1955. Phycol. News Bull. 8:7.
[56] Ryther, J. H. 1954. Biol. Bull. 106:198.
[57] Samejima, H., and J. Myers. 1958. J. Gen. Microbiol. 18:107.
[58] Shihira, I., and R. W. Krauss. 1965. Chlorella: physiology and taxonomy of 41 isolates. Univ. Maryland Press, College Park.
[59] Silva, P. 1962. Physiol. Biochem. Algae, p. 827.
[60] Sloan, P. R., and J. D. H. Strickland. 1966. J. Phycol. 2:29.
[61] Stein, J. R. 1957. Ph. D. Thesis. Univ. California, Berkeley.
[62] Stewart, W. D. P. 1962. Ann. Botany (London), N.S. 26:439.
[63] Storm, J., and S. H. Hutner. 1953. Ann. N.Y. Acad. Sci. 56:901.
[64] Sweeney, B. M. 1954. Am. J. Botany 41:821.
[65] Thomas, W. H. 1955. J. Protozool. 2(Suppl.):2.
[66] Thomas, W. H. 1966. J. Phycol. 2:17.
[67] Van Baalen, C. 1962. Botan. Marina 4:129.
[68] Watanabe, A. 1951. Arch. Biochem. Biophys. 34:50.
[69] Wetherell, D. F. 1958. Physiol. Plantarum 11:260.
[70] Wetherell, D. F., and R. W. Krauss. 1957. Am. J. Botany 44:609.
[71] Williams, A. E., and R. H. Burris. 1952. Ibid. 39:340.
[72] Wilson, W. B., and A. Collier. 1955. Science 121:394.

Part II. Fatty Acids and Other Organic Acids

Criterion for determining utilization of fatty acids and other organic acids as a carbon source: growth of the alga in darkness on a given substrate (facultative heterotrophy). Stimulation of growth by a substance in the light does not indicate utilization. *Abbreviations:* U = utilized; U̸ = not utilized; u = poorly utilized.

	Species (Synonym)	Carbon Sources																			Reference
		Fatty Acids											Other Organic Acids 1/								
		Acetic	*i*-Butyric	*n*-Butyric	*n*-Caproic	*n*-Heptylic	*n*-Nonylic	*n*-Octylic	Propionic	*i*-Valeric	*n*-Valeric	Other	Citric	Fumaric	Lactic	Malic	Phosphoglyceric	Pyruvic	Succinic	Miscellaneous	
	Cyanophyta																				
1	*Agmenellum quadruplicatum*	U̸	...	...	...	...	...	...	...	...	...	...	...	...	U̸	...	...	...	...	...	28
2	*Anabaena variabilis*	...	...	U̸	...	...	...	...	U̸	...	...	...	...	U̸	U̸	U̸	...	...	U̸	...	12
3	*Anacystis marina*	U̸	...	...	...	...	...	...	...	...	...	...	...	...	U̸	...	...	...	...	...	28
4	*A. nidulans*	...	...	U̸	...	...	...	...	U̸	...	...	...	...	U̸	U̸	U̸	...	...	U̸	...	12
5	*Coccochloris elabens*	U̸	...	...	...	...	...	...	...	...	...	...	...	...	U̸	...	...	...	...	...	28
6	*Lyngbya aestuarii*	U̸	...	...	...	...	...	...	...	...	...	...	...	...	U̸	...	...	...	...	...	28
7	*L. lagerheimii*	U̸	...	...	...	...	...	...	...	...	...	...	...	...	U̸	...	...	...	...	...	28

1/ Negative results reported for organic acids may not be significant, since it has been shown that *Prototheca zopfii* and *Euglena gracilis* utilize them only at pH 3.5-5.5. Most of the negative results tabulated were obtained in media having a pH near neutrality.

continued

27. NUTRIENT REQUIREMENTS AND UTILIZATION: ALGAE

Part II. Fatty Acids and Other Organic Acids

	Species (Synonym)	Carbon Sources: Fatty Acids: Acetic	i-Butyric	n-Butyric	n-Caproic	n-Heptylic	n-Nonylic	n-Octylic	Propionic	i-Valeric	n-Valeric	Other	Other Organic Acids[1]: Citric	Fumaric	Lactic	Malic	Phospho-glyceric	Pyruvic	Succinic	Miscella-neous	Ref-er-ence
8	*Microcoleus chthonoplastes*	U̸	...	...	...	...	...	...	...	...	...	...	...	...	U̸	...	...	...	...	...	28
9	*M. tenerrimus*	U̸	...	...	...	...	...	...	...	...	...	...	...	...	U̸	...	...	...	...	...	28
10	*Nostoc muscorum*	...	...	U̸	...	...	...	...	U̸	...	...	...	...	U̸	U̸	U̸	...	...	U̸	...	12
11	*Oscillatoria amphibia*	U̸	...	...	...	...	...	...	...	...	...	...	...	...	U̸	...	...	...	...	...	28
12	*O. subtilissima*	U̸	...	...	...	...	...	...	...	...	...	...	...	...	U̸	...	...	...	...	...	28
13	*Plectonema terebrans*	U̸	...	...	...	...	...	...	...	...	...	...	...	...	U̸	...	...	...	...	...	28
	Cryptophyta																				
14	*Chilomonas paramecium*[2]	U	...	...	U	U̸	...	...	U̸	U̸	U̸	U[3]	U̸	U	U	U	...	...	U	...	6,10
	Pyrrophyta																				
15	*Gonyaulax polyedra*	U̸	...	U̸	...	...	...	...	U̸	...	...	...	U̸	...	...	U̸	...	...	U̸	U̸[4]	27
16	*Gymnodinium brevis*	U̸	...	U̸	...	...	...	...	U̸	...	U̸	U̸[5]	U̸	U̸	U̸	U̸	U̸	...	U̸	U̸[5]	2
17	*Oxyrris marina*	U	...	...	...	...	...	...	...	...	...	...	...	...	...	...	...	...	...	...	7
	Bacillariophyta																				
18	*Achnanthes brevipes*	U̸	...	...	...	...	...	...	...	...	...	...	...	...	U̸	...	...	...	...	...	16
19	*Amphipleura rutilans*	U̸	...	...	...	...	...	...	...	...	...	...	...	...	U̸	...	...	...	...	...	16
20	*Amphiprora paludosa*	U̸	...	...	...	...	...	...	...	...	...	...	...	...	U̸	...	...	...	...	...	16
21	*Amphora coffaeiformis*	U̸[6]	...	...	...	...	...	...	...	...	...	...	...	...	U̸[7]	...	...	...	...	...	16
22	*A. lineolata*	U̸	...	...	...	...	...	...	...	...	...	...	...	...	U̸	...	...	...	...	...	16
23	*Chaetoceros ceratosporum*	...	...	...	...	...	...	...	...	...	...	...	...	...	U̸	...	...	...	...	...	15
24	*C. pelagicus*	...	...	...	...	...	...	...	...	...	...	...	...	...	U̸	...	...	...	...	...	15
25	*C. pseudocrinitus*	...	...	...	...	...	...	...	...	...	...	...	...	...	U̸	...	...	...	...	...	15
26	*Coscinodiscus asteromphalus*	...	...	...	...	...	...	...	...	...	...	...	...	...	U̸	...	...	...	...	...	15
27	*Cyclotella caspia*	...	...	...	...	...	...	...	...	...	...	...	...	...	U̸	...	...	...	...	...	15
28	*C. cryptica*	U̸	...	...	...	...	...	...	...	...	...	...	...	...	U̸	...	...	...	...	...	16
29	*C. nana*	...	...	...	...	...	...	...	...	...	...	...	...	...	U̸[8]	...	...	...	...	...	15
30	*Cylindrotheca fusiformes (Nitzschia closterium)*	U̸[9]	...	...	...	...	...	...	...	...	...	...	...	...	U[10]	...	...	...	...	...	16
31	*Melosira nummuloides*	...	...	...	...	...	...	...	...	...	...	...	...	...	U̸	...	...	...	...	...	15
32	*Navicula incerta*	U̸	...	...	...	...	...	...	...	...	...	...	...	...	U̸	...	...	...	...	...	16
33	*N. menisculus*	U̸	...	...	...	...	...	...	...	...	...	...	...	...	U̸	...	...	...	...	...	16
34	*N. pelliculosa*	U̸	...	U̸	...	...	...	...	U̸	...	U̸	U̸[11]	U̸	U̸	U̸	U̸	U̸	U̸	U̸	U̸[12]	14
35	*Nitzschia alba*[2]	...	...	...	...	...	...	...	...	...	...	...	...	...	U	...	...	...	U	U̸[13]	13
36	*N. angularis affinis*	U̸	...	...	...	...	...	...	...	...	...	...	...	...	U̸	...	...	...	...	...	16
37	*N. curvilineata*	U̸	...	...	...	...	...	...	...	...	...	...	...	...	U	...	...	...	...	...	16
38	*N. filiformis*	U̸	...	...	...	...	...	...	...	...	...	...	...	...	U̸	...	...	...	...	...	16
39	*N. frustulum*	U̸[14]	...	...	...	...	...	...	...	...	...	...	...	...	U̸[15]	...	...	...	...	...	16
40	*N. hybridaeformis*	U̸	...	...	...	...	...	...	...	...	...	...	...	...	U̸	...	...	...	...	...	16
41	*N. laevis*	U̸	...	...	...	...	...	...	...	...	...	...	...	...	U	...	...	...	...	...	16
42	*N. leucosigma*[2]	...	...	...	...	...	...	...	...	...	...	...	...	...	U	...	...	...	U	U[13]	13
43	*N. marginata*	U̸	...	...	...	...	...	...	...	...	...	...	...	...	U̸	...	...	...	...	...	16
44	*N. obtusa scalpelliformis*	U̸	...	...	...	...	...	...	...	...	...	...	...	...	U̸	...	...	...	...	...	16
45	*N. ovalis*	U̸	...	...	...	...	...	...	...	...	...	...	...	...	U̸	...	...	...	...	...	16
46	*N. punctata*	U̸	...	...	...	...	...	...	...	...	...	...	...	...	U̸	...	...	...	...	...	16

[1] Negative results reported for organic acids may not be significant, since it has been shown that *Prototheca zopfii* and *Euglena gracilis* utilize them only at pH 3.5-5.5. Most of the negative results tabulated were obtained in media having a pH near neutrality. [2] Colorless. [3] *n*-Caprylic acid. [4] Malonate. [5] Several other fatty acids. [6] By 9 strains; utilized by 1 strain. [7] By 8 strains; utilized by 2 strains. [8] By 3 strains. [9] By 4 strains. [10] By 3 strains; not utilized by 1 strain. [11] Lauric, myristic, oleic, and stearic acids. [12] Formic, galacturonic, gluconic, glucuronic, glycolic, α-ketoglutaric, and oxalic acids. [13] Glutamic acid. [14] By 6 strains. [15] By 5 strains; utilized by 1 strain.

continued

Part II. Fatty Acids and Other Organic Acids

	Species (Synonym)	Carbon Sources																			Reference
		Fatty Acids											Other Organic Acids[1]								
		Acetic	*i*-Butyric	*n*-Butyric	*n*-Caproic	*n*-Heptylic	*n*-Nonylic	*n*-Octylic	Propionic	*i*-Valeric	*n*-Valeric	Other	Citric	Fumaric	Lactic	Malic	Phospho-glyceric	Pyruvic	Succinic	Miscella-neous	
47	*N. putrida*[2]	...	...	...	...	...	...	...	...	...	...	...	...	...	U	...	...	...	U	Ʉ[16]	13
48	*N. tenuissima*	U	...	...	...	...	...	...	...	...	...	...	...	...	U	...	...	...	...	...	16
49	*Skeletonema costatum*	Ʉ	...	...	...	...	...	...	...	...	...	...	...	...	Ʉ	...	...	...	...	Ʉ[13]	15,25
50	*Stauroneis amphoroides*	Ʉ	...	...	...	...	...	...	...	...	...	...	...	...	Ʉ	...	...	...	...	...	16
51	*Synedra affinis*	Ʉ	...	...	...	...	...	...	...	...	...	...	...	...	Ʉ	...	...	...	...	...	16
52	*Thallasiosira fluviatilis*	u	...	...	...	...	...	...	...	...	...	...	...	...	Ʉ	...	...	...	...	U[13]	15,25
	Chrysophyta																				
53	*Coccolithus huxleyi*	u	...	...	...	...	...	...	...	...	...	...	...	...	...	...	...	...	...	Ʉ[13]	25
54	*Ochromonas malhamensis*	...	...	...	...	...	...	...	...	...	...	...	...	...	...	...	...	...	...	Ʉ[13]	11
	Xanthophyta																				
55	*Botrydiopsis intercedens*	...	...	...	...	...	...	...	...	...	...	...	Ʉ	Ʉ	...	...	...	...	Ʉ	...	5
56	*Bumilleriopsis brevis*	U	...	...	...	...	...	...	...	...	...	...	U	U	...	...	...	...	U	...	5
57	*Chlorellidium tetrabotrys*	U	...	...	...	...	...	...	...	...	...	...	U	Ʉ	...	...	...	...	U	...	5
58	*Monodus subterraneus*	Ʉ	...	...	...	...	...	...	...	...	...	...	Ʉ	Ʉ	Ʉ	Ʉ	...	...	Ʉ	...	18
59	*Polyedriella helvetica*	Ʉ	...	...	...	...	...	...	...	...	...	...	Ʉ	Ʉ	...	...	...	...	Ʉ	...	5
60	*Tribonema aequale*	U	...	...	...	...	...	...	...	...	...	...	U	Ʉ	...	...	...	...	Ʉ	...	4
61	*T. minus*	Ʉ	...	...	...	...	...	...	...	...	...	...	Ʉ	Ʉ	...	...	...	...	Ʉ	...	5
	Euglenophyta																				
62	*Astasia longa (A. chattoni, A. klebsii)*	U	u	U	U	U	U	U	U	Ʉ	U	u[17]	...	...	U?	U?	...	Ʉ?	U?	...	1
63	*A. quartana*	U	u	U	U	U	...	...	U	u	U	U[18]	...	...	U	Ʉ	...	u	U	...	1
64	*Euglena anabaena minor*	Ʉ	Ʉ	Ʉ	Ʉ	Ʉ[19]	Ʉ[19]	Ʉ[19]	Ʉ	Ʉ	Ʉ	...	Ʉ	...	Ʉ	Ʉ	Ʉ	Ʉ	Ʉ	...	1
65	*E. deses*[20]	Ʉ	Ʉ	Ʉ	Ʉ[19]	Ʉ[19]	Ʉ[19]	Ʉ[19]	Ʉ	Ʉ	Ʉ	...	Ʉ	...	...	Ʉ	Ʉ	Ʉ	Ʉ	...	1
66	*E. gracilis bacillaris*	U	...	U	...	...	...	...	...	...	...	...	Ʉ	U	Ʉ	U	U	...	U	...	1
67	*E. gracilis typica*	U	Ʉ	U	U	Ʉ	U	U	U	Ʉ	U	U[21]	Ʉ	...	U	U	Ʉ	U	U	...	1
68	*E. gracilis urophora*	U	U	U	U	U	u	U	U	Ʉ	U	u[17]	Ʉ	U	U	U	...	U	Ʉ?	...	1
69	*E. klebsii*[22]	Ʉ	...	Ʉ	...	...	...	...	Ʉ	...	...	...	Ʉ	...	...	Ʉ	...	...	...	...	1
70	*E. pisciformis*	Ʉ	Ʉ	Ʉ	Ʉ[19]	Ʉ[19]	Ʉ[19]	Ʉ[19]	Ʉ	Ʉ	Ʉ	...	...	...	...	Ʉ	Ʉ	Ʉ	Ʉ	...	1
71	*E. stellata*	Ʉ	...	...	...	...	...	...	Ʉ	...	...	...	...	...	Ʉ	...	...	Ʉ	...	...	1
	Chlorophyta																				
72	*Astrephomene gubernaculifera*	U	...	...	...	...	...	...	...	...	...	...	...	...	...	...	...	...	...	...	26
73	*Balticola buetschlii*	Ʉ?	...	...	...	...	...	...	...	...	...	...	...	...	...	...	...	...	...	...	8
74	*B. droebakensis*[23]	Ʉ?	...	...	...	...	...	...	...	...	...	...	...	...	...	...	...	...	...	...	8
75	*Brachiomonas submarina*	Ʉ	...	...	...	...	...	...	...	...	...	...	...	...	...	...	...	...	...	...	8
76	*Bracteacoccus cinnabarinus*	U	...	...	...	...	...	...	...	...	...	...	...	...	...	...	...	...	...	...	20
77	*B. engadiensis*	Ʉ	...	...	...	...	...	...	...	...	...	...	...	...	...	...	...	...	...	...	20
78	*B. minor*	Ʉ	...	...	...	...	...	...	...	...	...	...	...	...	...	...	...	...	...	...	20
79	*B. terrestris*	U	...	...	...	...	...	...	...	...	...	...	...	...	...	...	...	...	...	...	20
80	*Chlamydomonas agloeformis*	U	Ʉ	U	Ʉ	...	...	...	Ʉ	...	Ʉ	...	Ʉ	...	Ʉ	Ʉ	Ʉ	...	Ʉ	...	1
81	*C. dysosmos*	U	...	...	...	...	...	...	...	...	...	...	Ʉ	...	u	Ʉ	Ʉ	u	Ʉ	...	17
82	*C. moewusii*	Ʉ	...	Ʉ	...	...	...	...	Ʉ	...	Ʉ	...	Ʉ	Ʉ	Ʉ	Ʉ	Ʉ	Ʉ	Ʉ	...	1

[1] Negative results reported for organic acids may not be significant, since it has been shown that *Prototheca zopfii* and *Euglena gracilis* utilize them only at pH 3.5-5.5. Most of the negative results tabulated were obtained in media having a pH near neutrality. [2] Colorless. [13] Glutamic acid. [16] Glutamate. [17] *i*-Caproic and *n*-decylic acids. [18] *i*-Caproic acid. [19] At toxic concentrations. [20] According to E. G. Pringsheim, the organism used in these studies was *E. geniculata*. [21] *n*-Decylic acid; however, *i*-caproic acid is poorly utilized. [22] According to E. G. Pringsheim, the organism used in these studies was *E. mutabilis*. [23] Probably an obligate phototroph; substrates failing to support dark growth are not individually listed.

continued

Part II. Fatty Acids and Other Organic Acids

	Species (Synonym)	Carbon Sources																				Reference
		Fatty Acids											Other Organic Acids[1]									
		Acetic	*i*-Butyric	*n*-Butyric	*n*-Caproic	*n*-Heptylic	*n*-Nonylic	*n*-Octylic	Propionic	*i*-Valeric	*n*-Valeric	Other	Citric	Fumaric	Lactic	Malic	Phospho-glyceric	Pyruvic	Succinic	Miscella-neous		
83	*Chlorella autotrophica*	?	...	...	...	...	...	...	...	...	...	...	...	...	...	...	...	...	...	...		23
84	*C. candida*	Ʉ	...	...	...	...	...	...	...	...	...	...	...	...	...	...	...	...	...	...		23
85	*C. ellipsoidea*	Ʉ	...	...	...	...	...	...	...	...	...	...	...	...	...	...	...	...	...	...		23
86	*C. emersonii*	Ʉ	...	...	...	...	...	...	...	...	...	...	...	...	...	...	...	...	...	...		23
87	*C. emersonii globosa*	Ʉ	...	...	...	...	...	...	...	...	...	...	...	...	...	...	...	...	...	...		23
88	*C. fusca*	Ʉ	...	...	...	...	...	...	...	...	...	...	...	...	...	...	...	...	...	...		23
89	*C. fusca vacuolata*	Ʉ	...	...	...	...	...	...	...	...	...	...	...	...	...	...	...	...	...	...		23
90	*C. infusionum*	Ʉ	...	...	...	...	...	...	...	...	...	...	...	...	...	...	...	...	...	...		23
91	*C. infusionum auxenophila*	Ʉ	...	...	...	...	...	...	...	...	...	...	...	...	...	...	...	...	...	...		23
92	*C. miniata*	Ʉ	...	...	...	...	...	...	...	...	...	...	...	...	...	...	...	...	...	...		23
93	*C. mutabilis*	U	...	...	...	...	...	...	...	...	...	...	...	...	...	...	...	...	...	...		23
94	*C. nocturna*	U	...	...	...	...	...	...	...	...	...	...	...	...	...	...	...	...	...	...		23
95	*C. photophila*	Ʉ	...	...	...	...	...	...	...	...	...	...	...	...	...	...	...	...	...	...		23
96	*C. pringsheimii*	Ʉ	...	...	...	...	...	...	...	...	...	...	...	...	...	...	...	...	...	...		23
97	*C. protothecoides*	U	...	...	...	...	...	...	...	...	...	...	...	...	...	...	...	...	...	...		23
98	*C. protothecoides communis*	U	...	...	...	...	...	...	...	...	...	...	...	...	...	...	...	...	...	...		23
99	*C. protothecoides galactophila*	U	...	...	...	...	...	...	...	...	...	...	...	...	...	...	...	...	...	...		23
100	*C. protothecoides mannophila*	U	...	...	...	...	...	...	...	...	...	...	...	...	...	...	...	...	...	...		23
101	*C. pyrenoidosa*	U	...	Ʉ	...	...	...	...	Ʉ	...	...	...	...	Ʉ	Ʉ	Ʉ	...	...	Ʉ	...		22
102	*C. regularis*	U	...	...	...	...	...	...	...	...	...	...	...	...	...	...	...	...	...	...		23
103	*C. regularis aprica*	U	...	...	...	...	...	...	...	...	...	...	...	...	...	...	...	...	...	...		23
104	*C. regularis imbricata*	U	...	...	...	...	...	...	...	...	...	...	...	...	...	...	...	...	...	...		23
105	*C. saccharophila*	Ʉ	...	...	...	...	...	...	...	...	...	...	...	...	...	...	...	...	...	...		23
106	*C. simplex*	Ʉ	...	...	...	...	...	...	...	...	...	...	...	...	...	...	...	...	...	...		23
107	*C. sorokiniana*	Ʉ	...	...	...	...	...	...	...	...	...	...	...	...	...	...	...	...	...	...		23
108	*C. vannielii*	Ʉ	...	...	...	...	...	...	...	...	...	...	...	...	...	...	...	...	...	...		23
109	*C. variabilis*	Ʉ	...	...	...	...	...	...	...	...	...	...	...	...	...	...	...	...	...	...		23
110	*C. vulgaris*	U	...	...	...	...	...	...	...	...	...	...	...	...	...	...	...	...	...	...		23
111	*C. vulgaris luteoviridis*	U	...	...	...	...	...	...	...	...	...	...	...	...	...	...	...	...	...	...		23
112	*Chlorococcum aplanosporum*	Ʉ	...	...	...	...	...	...	...	...	...	...	...	...	...	...	...	...	...	...		20
113	*C. diplobionticum*	Ʉ	...	...	...	...	...	...	...	...	...	...	...	...	...	...	...	...	...	...		20
114	*C. echinozygotum*	Ʉ	...	...	...	...	...	...	...	...	...	...	...	...	...	...	...	...	...	...		20
115	*C. ellipsoideum*	Ʉ	...	...	...	...	...	...	...	...	...	...	...	...	...	...	...	...	...	...		20
116	*C. hypnosporum*	Ʉ	...	...	...	...	...	...	...	...	...	...	...	...	...	...	...	...	...	...		20
117	*C. macrostigmatum*	Ʉ	...	...	...	...	...	...	...	...	...	...	...	...	...	...	...	...	...	...		20
118	*C. minutum*	Ʉ	...	...	...	...	...	...	...	...	...	...	...	...	...	...	...	...	...	...		20
119	*C. multinucleatum*	Ʉ	...	...	...	...	...	...	...	...	...	...	...	...	...	...	...	...	...	...		20
120	*C. oleofaciens*	Ʉ	...	...	...	...	...	...	...	...	...	...	...	...	...	...	...	...	...	...		20
121	*C. perforatum*	Ʉ	...	...	...	...	...	...	...	...	...	...	...	...	...	...	...	...	...	...		20
122	*C. pinguideum*	Ʉ	...	...	...	...	...	...	...	...	...	...	...	...	...	...	...	...	...	...		20
123	*C. punctatum*	Ʉ	...	...	...	...	...	...	...	...	...	...	...	...	...	...	...	...	...	...		20
124	*C. scabellum*	Ʉ	...	...	...	...	...	...	...	...	...	...	...	...	...	...	...	...	...	...		20
125	*C. tetrasporum*	Ʉ	...	...	...	...	...	...	...	...	...	...	...	...	...	...	...	...	...	...		20
126	*C. vacuolatum*	Ʉ	...	...	...	...	...	...	...	...	...	...	...	...	...	...	...	...	...	...		20
127	*C. wimmeri*	Ʉ	...	...	...	...	...	...	...	...	...	...	...	...	...	...	...	...	...	...		20

[1] Negative results reported for organic acids may not be significant, since it has been shown that *Prototheca zopfii* and *Euglena gracilis* utilize them only at pH 3.5-5.5. Most of the negative results tabulated were obtained in media having a pH near neutrality.

continued

Part II. Fatty Acids and Other Organic Acids

	Species (Synonym)	Carbon Sources																			Reference
		Fatty Acids											Other Organic Acids[1]								
		Acetic	i-Butyric	n-Butyric	n-Caproic	n-Heptylic	n-Nonylic	n-Octylic	Propionic	i-Valeric	n-Valeric	Other	Citric	Fumaric	Lactic	Malic	Phospho-glyceric	Pyruvic	Succinic	Miscella-neous	
128	*Cyanidium caldarium*[24]	U	...	...	...	...	...	...	...	...	...	...	U̸	...	U	...	U	...	...	...	3
129	*Dunaliella salina*	U̸	...	...	...	...	...	...	...	...	...	...	...	...	...	...	...	...	...	...	9
130	*D. viridis*	U̸	...	...	...	...	...	...	...	...	...	...	...	...	...	...	...	...	...	...	9
131	*Haematococcus pluvialis*	U	U̸	U	U̸	...	...	...	U̸	...	U̸	...	U̸	...	U	U	U̸	U	U		1,8
132	*Lobomonas pyriformis*	U	...	...	...	...	...	...	...	...	...	...	...	...	...	...	...	...	...	...	19
133	*L. sphaerica*	U	...	...	...	...	...	...	...	...	...	...	...	u?	u?	u?	...	...	...	...	21
134	*Neochloris alveolaris*	U	...	...	...	...	...	...	...	...	...	...	...	...	...	...	...	...	...	...	20
135	*Polytoma caudatum*	U	U̸	U	U̸	U̸	U̸	U̸	U̸	U̸	U̸	U̸[17]	...	...	U̸	...	...	U	...	...	1
136	*P. obtusum*	U	U̸	U	U̸	U̸	U̸	U̸	U̸	U̸	U̸	U̸[17]	U̸	...	U̸	U̸	U̸	u	U̸	...	1
137	*P. ocellatum*	U	U	U	U	U	U	U	U	u	U	U[17]	...	...	U	U̸?	...	U	U̸?	...	1
138	*P. uvella*	U	U̸	U	U	U̸	U̸	u	U̸	U̸	U	U[25]	...	...	U?	U̸	...	u	U?	...	1
139	*Polytomella caeca*	U	U̸	U	U	U	U	U	U	U̸	U	U[21]	...	...	U̸?	U̸	...	u	u	...	1
140	*Prototheca zopfii*	U	U	U	U	U	U	U	U	u	U	U[17]	U̸	U̸	U[26]	...	...	U[26]	U̸	...	1
141	*Radiosphaera dissecta*	U̸	...	...	...	...	...	...	...	...	...	...	...	...	...	...	...	...	...	...	20
142	*Stephanoptera gracilis*	U̸	...	...	...	...	...	...	...	...	...	...	...	...	...	...	...	...	...	...	9
143	*Stephanosphaera pluvialis*	U̸?	...	...	...	...	...	...	...	...	...	...	...	...	...	...	...	...	...	...	8

[1] Negative results reported for organic acids may not be significant, since it has been shown that *Prototheca zopfii* and *Euglena gracilis* utilize them only at pH 3.5-5.5. Most of the negative results tabulated were obtained in media having a pH near neutrality. [17] *i*-Caproic and *n*-decylic acids. [21] *n*-Decylic acid; however, *i*-caproic acid is poorly utilized. [24] Genus of uncertain taxonomic position **[**24**]**. [25] *i*-Caproic acid; however, *n*-decylic acid is not utilized. [26] Only at pH 3.0-5.5.

Contributor: Thomas, William H.

References

[1] Albritton, E. C. 1954. Standard values in nutrition and metabolism. W. B. Saunders, Philadelphia.

[2] Aldrich, D. V. 1962. Science 137:988.

[3] Allen, M. B. 1952. Arch. Mikrobiol. 17:34.

[4] Belcher, J. H., and G. E. Fogg. 1958. Ibid. 30:17.

[5] Belcher, J. H., and J. D. A. Miller. 1960. Ibid. 36: 219.

[6] Cosgrove, W. B., and B. K. Swanson. 1952. Physiol. Zool. 25:287.

[7] Droop, M. R. 1958. J. Marine Biol. Assoc. U.K. 37: 323.

[8] Droop, M. R. 1961. Rev. Algol. 5(4):247.

[9] Gibor, A. 1956. Biol. Bull. 111:223.

[10] Holz, G. G. 1954. J. Protozool. 1:114.

[11] Hutner, S. H., L. Provasoli, and J. Filfus. 1953. Ann. N.Y. Acad. Sci. 56:852.

[12] Kratz, W. A., and J. Myers. 1955. Am. J. Botany 42:282.

[13] Lewin, J., and R. A. Lewin. 1967. J. Gen. Microbiol. 46:361.

[14] Lewin, J. C. 1953. Ibid. 9:305.

[15] Lewin, J. C. 1963. Symp. Marine Microbiol., Chicago, 1961, p. 229.

[16] Lewin, J. C., and R. A. Lewin. 1960. Can. J. Microbiol. 6:127.

[17] Lewin, R. A. 1954. J. Gen. Microbiol. 11:459.

[18] Miller, J. D. A., and G. E. Fogg. 1958. Arch. Mikrobiol. 30:1.

[19] Osterud, K. L. 1946. Physiol. Zool. 19:19.

[20] Parker, B. C., H. C. Bold, and T. R. Deason. 1961. Science 133:761.

[21] Pringsheim, E. G. 1963. Arch. Mikrobiol. 46:227.

[22] Samejima, H., and J. Myers. 1958. J. Gen. Microbiol. 18:107.

[23] Shihira, I., and R. W. Krauss. 1965. Chlorella: physiology and taxonomy of 41 isolates. Univ. Maryland Press, College Park.

[24] Silva, P. 1962. Physiol. Biochem. Algae, p. 827.

[25] Sloan, P. R., and J. D. H. Strickland. 1966. J. Phycol. 2:29.

[26] Stein, J. R. 1957. Ph.D. Thesis. Univ. California, Berkeley.

[27] Thomas, W. H. 1955. J. Protozool. 2(Suppl.):2.

[28] Van Baalen, C. 1962. Botan. Marina 4:129.

continued

27. NUTRIENT REQUIREMENTS AND UTILIZATION: ALGAE

Part III. Amino Acids

Criterion for determining utilization of amino acids as a nitrogen source: growth of the alga on a given substrate in the absence of another nitrogen compound. *Abbreviations:* U = utilized; Ʉ = not utilized; u = poorly utilized.

	Species (Synonym)	Alanine	Arginine	Asparagine	Aspartic Acid	Glutamic Acid	Glutamine	Glycine	Histidine	Isoleucine	Leucine	Lysine	Ornithine	Phenylalanine	Proline	Serine	Tryptophan	Tyrosine	Valine	Other	Reference
	Cyanophyta																				
1	*Agmenellum quadruplicatum*	...	Ʉ	U	...	...	...	Ʉ	...	...	...	Ʉ	...	...	...	...	...	...	...	...	29
2	*Anabaena variabilis*	...	...	...	...	...	...	Ʉ	...	...	...	...	...	...	...	...	...	...	...	...	19
3	*Anacystis nidulans*	...	...	...	...	...	...	Ʉ	...	...	...	...	...	...	...	...	...	...	...	...	19
4	*Coccochloris elabens*	...	Ʉ	U	...	...	...	Ʉ	...	...	...	Ʉ	...	...	...	...	...	...	...	...	29
5	*Microcoleus chthonoplastes*	...	Ʉ	U	...	...	...	Ʉ	...	...	...	Ʉ	...	...	...	...	...	...	...	...	29
6	*Nostoc muscorum*	...	...	...	...	...	...	?	...	...	...	...	...	...	...	...	...	...	...	...	19
7	*Phormidium persicinum*	...	...	U	Ʉ	Ʉ	...	u	Ʉ	...	...	Ʉ	...	...	...	...	...	...	...	...	24
8	*Plectonema terebrans*	...	U	U	...	...	...	Ʉ	...	...	...	Ʉ	...	...	...	...	...	...	...	...	29
9	*Tolypothrix tenuis*	U	U	U	Ʉ	...	U	U	u	...	U	...	...	U	...	U	Ʉ	...	...	Ʉ[1]	18
	Cryptophyta																				
10	*Chilomonas paramecium*[2]	...	...	...	...	...	...	...	...	...	...	...	...	...	...	...	...	...	...	Ʉ[3]	16
11	*Hemiselmis virescens*	...	...	...	...	...	...	U	...	...	...	...	...	...	...	...	...	...	...	...	11
	Pyrrophyta																				
12	*Amphidinium carteri*	U	U	U	...	U	...	U	...	...	...	...	...	...	...	...	...	...	...	U[4]	26
13	*A. rhynchocephalum*	U	U	U	...	U	...	U	...	...	...	...	...	...	...	...	...	...	...	U[4]	26
14	*Gymnodinium brevis*	...	...	...	...	...	...	...	...	...	...	...	...	...	...	...	...	...	...	Ʉ[5]	2
15	*G. simplex*	...	...	u	...	u	...	U	...	...	...	...	...	...	...	...	...	...	...	...	28
16	*G. splendens*	U	...	...	...	U	...	U	...	...	...	...	...	...	...	...	...	...	...	...	26
17	*Gyrodinium californicum*	...	U	U	...	...	...	U	...	...	...	...	...	...	...	...	...	...	...	...	26
18	*G. resplendens*	...	U	U	...	...	...	...	...	...	...	...	...	...	...	...	...	...	...	...	26
19	*G. uncatenum*	...	U	U	...	...	...	...	...	...	...	...	...	...	...	...	...	...	...	...	26
	Bacillariophyta																				
20	*Chaetoceros gracilis*	...	...	U	...	u	...	U	...	...	...	...	...	...	...	...	...	...	...	...	28
21	*C. lorenzianus*	...	...	...	...	u	u	u	...	...	...	...	...	...	...	...	...	...	...	...	15
22	*C. pelagicus*	...	...	...	...	Ʉ	u	u[6]	...	...	...	...	...	...	...	...	...	...	...	...	15
23	*Coscinodiscus asteromphalus*	...	...	...	...	U	U	U	...	...	...	...	...	...	...	...	...	...	...	...	15
24	*Cyclotella caspia*	...	...	...	...	u	U	u	...	...	...	...	...	...	...	...	...	...	...	...	15
25	*C. nana*	...	...	...	...	Ʉ[7]	U[7]	U?[8]	...	...	...	...	...	...	...	...	...	...	...	...	15
26	*Cylindrotheca fusiformes* (*Nitzschia closterium*)	...	...	...	...	U	...	...	...	...	...	...	...	...	...	...	...	...	...	...	1
27	*Detonula confervacea*	...	...	...	...	u	u	u	...	...	...	...	...	...	...	...	...	...	...	...	15
28	*Nitzschia alba*[2]	...	...	...	...	U[9]	...	...	...	...	...	...	...	...	...	...	...	...	...	...	20
29	*N. leucosigma*[2]	...	...	...	...	U[9]	...	...	...	...	...	...	...	...	...	...	...	...	...	...	20
30	*N. putrida*[2]	...	...	...	...	U	...	...	...	...	...	...	...	...	...	...	...	...	...	...	20
31	*N. seriata*	...	...	...	...	u	U	Ʉ	...	...	...	...	...	...	...	...	...	...	...	...	15
32	*Rhizosolenia setigera*	...	...	...	...	Ʉ	u	u	...	...	...	...	...	...	...	...	...	...	...	...	15
33	*Skeletonema costatum*	...	...	...	...	Ʉ[9]	u	u	...	...	...	...	...	...	...	...	...	...	...	...	15
34	*Thallasiosira fluviatilis*	...	...	...	...	Ʉ[9]	u	u	...	...	...	...	...	...	...	...	...	...	...	...	15
35	*T. nordenskioldii*	...	...	...	...	U	u	u	...	...	...	...	...	...	...	...	...	...	...	...	15

1/ Threonine. 2/ Colorless. 3/ Various amino acids tested as carbon sources were not utilized. 4/ Methionine. 5/ Several amino acids tested as carbon sources were not utilized. 6/ Or not utilized. 7/ By 2 strains; poorly utilized by 1 strain. 8/ By 2 strains; not utilized by 1 strain. 9/ As a carbon source, *see* Part II.

continued

27. NUTRIENT REQUIREMENTS AND UTILIZATION: ALGAE

Part III. Amino Acids

	Species (Synonym)	Alanine	Arginine	Asparagine	Aspartic Acid	Glutamic Acid	Glutamine	Glycine	Histidine	Isoleucine	Leucine	Lysine	Ornithine	Phenylalanine	Proline	Serine	Tryptophan	Tyrosine	Valine	Other	Reference
	Chrysophyta																				
36	*Coccolithus huxleyi*	...	...	...	...	u[10]	u[11]	u[10]	...	...	...	...	...	...	...	...	...	...	...	...	15
37	*Hymenomonas elongata*	...	?	...	?	Ʉ	...	?	Ʉ	?	?	?	...	?	...	Ʉ	Ʉ	...	?	?[4]	10
38	*Monochrysis lutherii*	...	Ʉ	...	Ʉ	Ʉ	...	U	Ʉ	Ʉ	Ʉ	Ʉ	...	Ʉ	...	Ʉ	Ʉ	...	Ʉ	Ʉ[4]	10
39	*Ochromonas malhamensis*	...	...	...	...	...	...	...	U	...	...	...	...	...	...	...	...	...	...	...	17
40	*Prymnesium parvum*[12]	U	U	U	U	U[13]	...	U	U	U	U	U	...	U	...	?	Ʉ	U	U	U[4]	10,21
	Xanthophyta																				
41	*Monodus subterraneus*	Ʉ	Ʉ	Ʉ?	Ʉ	Ʉ	U	Ʉ	Ʉ	Ʉ	Ʉ	Ʉ?	Ʉ	Ʉ	Ʉ	Ʉ	u	Ʉ?	Ʉ	Ʉ?[14]	22
42	*Tribonema aequale*	Ʉ	U	...	Ʉ	Ʉ	U	...	...	...	U	Ʉ	...	U	...	U	U	U	U	U[15]	8
	Euglenophyta																				
43	*Euglena anabaena minor*	U	Ʉ	U	...	Ʉ	...	U	Ʉ	...	U	Ʉ	...	U	U	Ʉ	Ʉ	Ʉ	U	...	1
44	*E. deses*[16]	U	Ʉ	U	...	U	...	Ʉ	Ʉ	...	U	U	...	Ʉ	U	u	Ʉ	Ʉ	Ʉ	...	1
45	*E. gracilis bacillaris*	U	...	...	...	U[17]	...	...	...	...	...	...	...	...	...	...	...	...	...	...	1
46	*E. gracilis typica*	U	Ʉ	U	...	U	...	U	U	...	U	Ʉ	...	U	U	U	Ʉ	Ʉ	U	...	1
47	*E. gracilis urophora*	...	...	...	...	U[17]	...	...	...	...	...	...	...	...	...	...	...	...	...	...	1
48	*E. klebsii*[18]	U	Ʉ	U	...	U	...	U	U	...	U	U	...	Ʉ	U	U	Ʉ	Ʉ	U	...	1
49	*E. pisciformis*	Ʉ	Ʉ	U[19]	...	Ʉ	...	Ʉ	Ʉ	...	Ʉ	Ʉ	...	Ʉ	Ʉ	Ʉ	Ʉ	Ʉ	Ʉ	...	1
50	*E. stellata*	U	U	U	...	U	...	U	U	...	U	U	...	U	U	U	Ʉ	Ʉ	U	...	1
	Chlorophyta																				
51	*Asterococcus superbus*	U	...	...	U	Ʉ	Ʉ	Ʉ	...	...	...	Ʉ	U	...	...	Ʉ	...	...	...	...	9
52	*Balticola buetschlii*	Ʉ	U	Ʉ	Ʉ	Ʉ	...	Ʉ	U	Ʉ	Ʉ	U	Ʉ	Ʉ	Ʉ	Ʉ	U	Ʉ	Ʉ	Ʉ[1]	12
53	*B. droebakensis*	U	U	Ʉ	Ʉ	Ʉ	...	Ʉ	Ʉ	Ʉ	Ʉ	Ʉ	Ʉ	Ʉ	Ʉ	U	U	Ʉ	U	U[1]	12
54	*Brachiomonas submarina*	Ʉ	U	U	Ʉ	Ʉ	...	Ʉ	U	Ʉ	Ʉ	U	U	Ʉ	Ʉ	u	U	u	Ʉ	u[1]	12
55	*Carteria crucifera*	Ʉ	...	...	Ʉ	Ʉ	Ʉ	...	...	...	...	Ʉ	Ʉ	...	...	Ʉ	...	...	...	...	9
56	*Chlamydomonas actinochloris*	U[20]	...	...	U	Ʉ	U	U[20]	...	...	...	Ʉ	Ʉ	...	...	U[20]	...	...	...	...	9
57	*C. agloeformis*	...	...	U	...	...	...	U	...	...	...	...	...	...	...	...	...	...	...	...	1
58	*C. calyptrata*	Ʉ	...	...	Ʉ	Ʉ	Ʉ	Ʉ	...	...	...	Ʉ	Ʉ	...	...	Ʉ	...	...	...	...	9
59	*C. carrosa*[21]	U	...	...	U[13]	Ʉ	Ʉ	Ʉ[22]	...	...	...	Ʉ[22]	U	...	...	Ʉ	...	...	...	...	9
60	*C. chlamydogama*	Ʉ[23]	...	Ʉ	Ʉ	Ʉ	U	Ʉ	...	...	...	Ʉ	Ʉ	...	...	Ʉ	...	...	...	...	9
61	*C. eugametos*	Ʉ	...	...	Ʉ	Ʉ	Ʉ	Ʉ	...	...	...	Ʉ	Ʉ	...	...	Ʉ	...	...	...	...	9
62	*C. gloegama*	Ʉ	...	...	Ʉ	Ʉ	Ʉ	Ʉ	...	...	...	Ʉ	U	...	...	Ʉ	...	...	...	...	9
63	*C. gloeopara*	Ʉ	...	...	U	U	U	Ʉ	...	...	...	U	U	...	...	Ʉ	...	...	...	...	9
64	*C. inflexa*	U	...	...	u	Ʉ	U	U	...	...	...	Ʉ	U	...	...	U	...	...	...	...	9
65	*C. kakosmos*	Ʉ	...	...	Ʉ	Ʉ	U	Ʉ	...	...	...	Ʉ	Ʉ	...	...	Ʉ	...	...	...	...	9
66	*C. mexicana*	Ʉ	...	...	Ʉ	Ʉ	U	Ʉ	...	...	...	U	U	...	...	Ʉ	...	...	...	...	9
67	*C. microsphaera acuta*	U	...	...	Ʉ	Ʉ	Ʉ	Ʉ	...	...	...	Ʉ	Ʉ	...	...	Ʉ	...	...	...	...	9
68	*C. microsphaerella*	Ʉ	...	...	Ʉ	Ʉ	u	Ʉ	...	...	...	Ʉ	Ʉ	...	...	Ʉ	...	...	...	...	9
69	*C. minuta*	Ʉ	...	...	Ʉ	Ʉ	U	Ʉ	...	...	...	Ʉ	Ʉ	...	...	Ʉ	...	...	...	...	9
70	*C. moewusii*	Ʉ	...	U	U	Ʉ	Ʉ	Ʉ	...	...	...	Ʉ	U	...	...	Ʉ	...	...	...	...	9
71	*C. moewusii rotunda*	Ʉ	...	...	U	Ʉ	Ʉ	U	...	...	...	Ʉ	Ʉ	...	...	Ʉ	...	...	...	...	9
72	*C. mundana*	...	...	Ʉ	...	...	...	...	...	...	...	...	...	...	...	...	...	...	...	...	13

[1] Threonine. [4] Methionine. [10] By 3 strains. [11] By 2 strains; utilized by 1 strain. [12] Various strain differences. [13] By 3 strains; not utilized by 1 strain. [14] Cystine; however, threonine is not utilized. [15] Cystine and threonine. [16] According to E. G. Pringsheim, the organism used in these studies was *E. geniculata*. [17] Only at pH 3.0-5.5. [18] According to E. G. Pringsheim, the organism used in these studies was *E. mutabilis*. [19] Growth is obtained only if thiamine is present. [20] By 1 strain; not utilized by 1 strain. [21] 4 strains. [22] By 3 strains; utilized by 1 strain. [23] By 1 strain; poorly utilized by 1 strain.

continued

Part III. Amino Acids

	Species (Synonym)	Alanine	Arginine	Asparagine	Aspartic Acid	Glutamic Acid	Glutamine	Glycine	Histidine	Isoleucine	Leucine	Lysine	Ornithine	Phenylalanine	Proline	Serine	Tryptophan	Tyrosine	Valine	Other	Reference
73	*C. mundana astigmata*	...	...	U̸	...	...	...	...	...	...	...	...	...	...	...	...	...	...	...	...	13
74	*C. mutabilis*	U	...	...	U̸	U	U	U	...	...	...	U̸	U	...	...	U	...	...	...	...	9
75	*C. peterfi*	U̸	...	...	U̸	U̸	U	U̸	...	...	...	U̸	U̸	...	...	U̸	...	...	...	...	9
76	*C. radiata*	U̸	...	...	U̸	U̸	U̸	U̸	...	...	...	U̸	U̸	...	...	U̸	...	...	...	...	9
77	*C. reinhardii*	U̸	...	U̸	U̸	U̸	U̸	u	...	...	...	U̸	U	...	...	U̸	...	...	...	...	9
78	*C. sectilis*	U̸	...	...	U̸	U̸	u	U̸	...	...	...	U̸	U̸	...	...	U̸	...	...	...	...	9
79	*C. typhlos*	U̸	...	...	U̸	U̸	U̸	U̸	...	...	...	U̸	U	...	...	U̸	...	...	...	...	9
80	*Chlorella protothecoides*	U	...	U	U	...	...	...	...	...	...	...	...	...	...	...	...	...	...	...	4,5
81	*C. vulgaris*	U	U	U	U	...	...	u	U̸	u	u	u	U	u	U	U	...	u	u	u 1/	4,5,7
82	*Dunaliella salina*	...	...	U	U̸	U	...	U̸	...	...	...	...	...	...	...	...	...	...	...	...	14
83	*D. viridis*	...	...	U̸	U̸	U̸	...	U̸	...	...	...	...	...	...	...	...	...	...	...	...	14
84	*Gloeocystis gigas*	U̸	...	...	U̸	U̸	U̸	U̸	...	...	...	U̸	U̸	...	...	U̸	...	...	...	...	9
85	*G. maxima*	U̸	...	...	u	U̸	U	U̸	...	...	...	U̸	U̸	...	...	U̸	...	...	...	...	9
86	*Haematococcus pluvialis*	U̸	U	U̸	U̸	U̸	...	U	U̸	U̸	U̸	U̸	U	U̸	U̸	U̸	u	U̸	U̸	u 24/	12
87	*Lobomonas pyriformis*	...	...	U	...	...	...	U	...	...	...	...	...	U	...	...	...	...	...	...	23
88	*L. sphaerica*	...	...	U	...	U	...	...	...	...	...	...	...	...	...	...	...	...	...	...	25
89	*Nannochloris atomus*	...	...	U	...	...	...	U	...	...	...	...	...	...	...	...	...	...	...	U 25/	27
90	*N. oculata*	...	U̸	...	U̸	?	...	U̸	U̸	U̸	U̸	U̸	...	U̸	...	U̸	U	...	U̸	U̸ 4/	10
91	*Polytoma caudatum*	...	...	U	...	...	...	...	...	...	...	...	...	...	...	...	...	...	...	...	1
92	*P. obtusum*	u	u	U	...	...	...	U	u	...	u	u	...	u	u	u	u	...	...	...	1
93	*P. ocellatum*	U	...	...	...	...	...	...	...	...	...	...	...	...	...	...	...	...	...	...	1
94	*P. uvella*	U̸	...	U	...	...	...	U	u	...	U̸	...	...	...	...	u	...	...	u	...	1
95	*Scenedesmus obliquus*	U	...	U	U	U	U	U	...	...	...	...	...	...	...	...	...	...	...	...	3-6
96	*Sphaerobotrys fluviatilis*	U̸	...	...	U̸	U̸	U	U	...	...	...	U̸	U	...	...	U̸	...	...	...	...	9
97	*Sporotetras pyriformis*	U	...	...	U	U̸	U	U̸	...	...	...	U̸	U	...	...	U̸	...	...	...	...	9
98	*Stephanoptera gracilis*	...	...	u	U̸	U	...	U̸	...	...	...	...	...	...	...	...	...	...	...	...	14
99	*Stephanosphaera pluvialis*	U̸	U	U̸	U̸	U̸	...	U̸	U̸	U̸	U̸	U̸	U	U̸	U̸	U̸	U	U	U̸	U̸ 1/	12
100	*Stichococcus cylindricus ?*	...	...	U	...	...	...	U	...	...	...	...	...	...	...	...	...	...	...	U 25/	27

1/ Threonine. 4/ Methionine. 24/ Threonine: by 1 strain; not utilized by 1 strain. 25/ Cystine.

Contributor: Thomas, William H.

References

[1] Albritton, E. C. 1954. Standard values in nutrition and metabolism. W. B. Saunders, Philadelphia.

[2] Aldrich, D. V. 1962. Science 137:988.

[3] Algeus, S. 1948. Physiol. Plantarum 1:66.

[4] Algeus, S. 1949. Ibid. 2:266.

[5] Algeus, S. 1950. Ibid. 3:370.

[6] Algeus, S. 1951. Ibid. 4:459.

[7] Arnow, P., J. J. Oleson, and J. H. Williams. 1953. Am. J. Botany 40:100.

[8] Belcher, J. H., and G. E. Fogg. 1958. Arch. Mikrobiol. 30:17.

[9] Cain, J. 1965. Can. J. Botany 43:1367.

[10] Droop, M. R. 1955. J. Marine Biol. Assoc. U.K. 34: 229.

[11] Droop, M. R. 1957. J. Gen. Microbiol. 16:286.

[12] Droop, M. R. 1961. Rev. Algol. 5(4):247.

[13] Eppley, R. W., and F. M. Macias. 1962. Physiol. Plantarum 15:72

[14] Gibor, A. 1956. Biol. Bull. 111:223.

[15] Guillard, R. R. L. 1963. Symp. Marine Microbiol., Chicago, 1961, p. 93.

[16] Holz, G. G. 1954. J. Protozool. 1:114.

[17] Hutner, S. H., L. Provasoli, and J. Filfus. 1953. Ann. N.Y. Acad. Sci. 56:852.

[18] Kiyohara, T., et al. 1960. J. Gen. Appl. Microbiol. 6:176.

[19] Kratz, W. A., and J. Myers. 1955. Am. J. Botany 42:282.

[20] Lewin, J., and R. A. Lewin. 1967. J. Gen. Microbiol. 46:361.

[21] McLaughlin, J. J. A. 1958. J. Protozool. 5:75.

[22] Miller, J. D. A., and G. E. Fogg. 1958. Arch. Mikrobiol. 30:1.

[23] Osterud, K. L. 1946. Physiol. Zool. 19:19.

[24] Pintner, I. J., and L. Provasoli. 1958. J. Gen. Microbiol. 18:190.

[25] Pringsheim, E. G. 1963. Arch. Mikrobiol. 46:227.

[26] Provasoli, L., and J. J. A. McLaughlin. 1963. Symp. Marine Microbiol., Chicago, 1961, p. 105.

[27] Ryther, J. H. 1954. Biol. Bull. 106:198.

[28] Thomas, W. H. 1966. Limnol. Oceanog. 11:393.

[29] Van Baalen, C. 1962. Botan. Marina 4:129.

continued

Part IV. Other Nitrogenous Substances

Criterion for determining utilization of nitrogenous substances: growth of alga on a given substrate in the absence of another nitrogenous compound. *Abbreviations:* R = required; U = utilized; U̸ = not utilized; u = poorly utilized.

	Species (Synonym)	Acetamide	Adenine	Ammonium	Casein Hydrolysate	Cytosine	Nitrate	Nitrite	Nitrogen	Peptone	Succinamide	Uracil	Urea	Uric Acid	Miscellaneous	Reference
	Cyanophyta															
1	*Agmenellum quadruplicatum*	...	...	...	U	...	...	...	U̸	...	...	...	U	U	...	33
2	*Anabaena cylindrica*	...	...	U	u?	...	U	...	U	...	...	...	U̸	...	...	4
3	*A. gelatinosa*	...	...	...	...	...	...	...	...	...	...	...	...	...	U[1]	10
4	*A. naviculoides*	...	...	...	...	...	...	...	...	...	...	...	...	...	U[1]	10
5	*A. variabilis*	...	...	U	?	...	U	...	U̸[2]	...	...	...	U	...	...	20
6	*Anacystis marina*	...	...	...	...	...	...	...	U̸	...	...	...	...	...	...	33
7	*A. nidulans*	...	...	U	U̸	...	U	...	U̸	...	...	...	U̸	U̸	...	8,20
8	*Aphanizomenon flos-aquae*	...	...	...	...	...	...	...	U̸	...	...	...	...	...	...	36
9	*Calothrix brevissima*	...	...	...	...	...	...	...	U	...	...	...	...	...	...	34
10	*C. parietina*	...	...	U	U	...	U	...	U	...	...	...	U̸	...	...	4
11	*C. scopulorum*	...	...	...	...	...	...	...	U	...	...	...	...	...	...	31
12	*Chroococcus turgidus*	...	...	U	U	...	U	...	U̸	...	...	...	U̸	...	...	4
13	*Coccochloris elabens*	...	...	...	U	...	...	...	U̸	...	...	...	U	U	...	33
14	*C. peniocystis*	...	...	...	...	...	...	...	U̸	...	...	...	...	...	...	36
15	*Gloeocapsa dimidiata*	...	...	...	...	...	...	...	U̸	...	...	...	...	...	...	36
16	*G. membranina*	...	...	...	...	...	...	...	U̸	...	...	...	...	...	...	36
17	*Lyngbya aestuarii*	...	...	U	...	...	U	...	U	...	...	...	U̸	...	...	4,33
18	*L. lagerheimii*	...	...	...	...	...	...	...	U̸	...	...	...	...	...	...	33
19	*Microcoleus chthonoplastes*	...	...	...	U	...	...	...	U̸	...	...	...	U̸	U	...	33
20	*M. tenerrimus*	...	...	...	...	...	...	...	U̸	...	...	...	...	...	...	33
21	*Microcystis aeruginosa (Diplocystis aeruginosa)*	...	...	...	...	...	...	...	U̸	...	...	...	...	...	...	36
22	*Nostoc entophytum*	...	...	...	...	...	...	...	U	...	...	...	...	...	...	31
23	*N. muscorum*	...	...	U	?[3]	...	U	...	U	...	...	...	U	...	...	20
24	*Oscillatoria amphibia*	...	...	...	...	...	...	...	U̸	...	...	...	...	...	...	33
25	*O. brevis*	...	...	...	...	...	...	...	U̸	...	...	...	...	...	...	31
26	*O. subtilissima*	...	...	...	...	...	...	...	U̸	...	...	...	...	...	...	33
27	*Phormidium foveolarum*	...	...	U	U	...	U	...	U̸	...	...	...	U̸	...	...	4
28	*P. luridum*	...	...	U	U	...	U	...	U̸	...	...	...	U̸	...	...	4
29	*P. persicinum*	...	...	U	...	...	U	...	U̸	...	...	...	...	...	...	26
30	*P. tenue*	...	...	...	...	...	...	...	U̸	...	...	...	...	...	...	36
31	*Plectonema nostocorum*	...	...	...	...	...	...	...	U̸	...	...	...	...	...	...	36
32	*P. notatum*	...	...	U	U	...	U	...	U̸	...	...	...	U	...	...	4
33	*P. terebrans*	...	...	...	U	...	...	...	U̸	...	...	...	U	U	...	33
34	*Synechococcus cedrorum*	...	...	U[4]	U	...	U[4]	...	U̸	...	...	...	U̸	U̸	...	4,8,15
35	*Tolypothrix tenuis*	...	...	...	U	...	...	...	U	...	...	...	...	...	...	19,35
	Cryptophyta															
36	*Chilomonas paramecium*[5]	...	...	U	...	...	...	...	...	...	...	...	...	...	U̸[6]	18
	Pyrrophyta															
37	*Gymnodinium brevis*	...	...	...	...	...	...	...	...	...	...	...	...	...	U̸[7]	2
38	*G. simplex*	...	...	U	...	...	U	U	...	...	...	...	...	...	...	32
39	*Oxyrris marina*	...	...	...	...	...	...	...	...	...	...	...	...	...	R[8]	12

[1] Xanthine. [2] Some strains do fix nitrogen [15]. [3] Allen reports utilization [4]. [4] Allen reports nonutilization [4]. [5] Colorless. [6] Various amides tested as carbon sources were not utilized. [7] Several nitrogenous organic compounds tested as carbon sources were not utilized. [8] Amino nitrogen.

continued

Part IV. Other Nitrogenous Substances

	Species (Synonym)	Acetamide	Adenine	Ammonium	Casein Hy-drolysate	Cytosine	Nitrate	Nitrite	Nitrogen	Peptone	Succinamide	Uracil	Urea	Uric Acid	Miscellaneous	Refer-ence
	Bacillariophyta															
40	*Chaetoceros gracilis*	...	...	U	...	...	U	u	...	...	...	...	U	U	...	32
41	*C. lorenzianus*	...	...	...	...	...	...	...	...	...	...	...	?	u	...	17
42	*C. pelagicus*	...	...	...	...	...	...	...	...	...	...	...	U̸	U̸	...	17
43	*Coscinodiscus asteromphalus*	...	...	...	...	...	...	...	...	...	...	...	u	u	...	17
44	*Cyclotella caspia*	...	...	...	...	...	...	...	...	...	...	...	U	U	...	17
45	*C. nana*	...	...	...	...	...	...	...	...	...	...	...	U[9]	U[9]	...	17
46	*Cylindrotheca fusiformes*	...	...	U	...	...	U	...	...	U	...	...	...	...	...	1
47	*Detonula confervacea*	...	...	...	...	...	...	...	...	...	...	...	u	u	...	17
48	*Nitzschia alba*[5]	...	...	...	...	...	U	...	...	...	...	...	...	...	...	21
49	*N. leucosigma*[5]	...	...	...	...	...	U	...	...	...	...	...	...	...	...	21
50	*N. putrida*[5]	...	...	...	...	...	U	...	...	...	...	...	...	...	...	21
51	*N. seriata*	...	...	...	...	...	...	...	...	...	...	...	u	u	...	17
52	*Rhizosolenia setigera*	...	...	...	...	...	...	...	...	...	...	...	U	U̸	...	17
53	*Skeletonema costatum*	...	...	...	...	...	...	...	...	...	...	...	U	U	...	17
54	*Thallasiosira fluviatilis*	...	...	...	...	...	...	...	...	...	...	...	u	u	...	17
55	*T. nordenskioldii*	...	...	...	...	...	...	...	...	...	...	...	U	U	...	17
	Chrysophyta															
56	*Coccolithus huxleyi*	...	...	...	...	...	...	...	...	...	...	...	U̸[10]	u[10]	...	17
57	*Hymenomonas elongata*	...	...	U̸	...	...	U	...	...	...	...	...	?	U	...	11
58	*Monochrysis lutherii*	...	...	U	...	...	U	...	...	...	...	...	U	U	...	11
59	*Prymnesium parvum*	...	...	U[11]	...	...	U	...	...	...	...	...	U̸	?	...	11
	Xanthophyta															
60	*Monodus subterraneus*	...	...	U	...	...	U	...	...	u	U	...	U	u	...	23,24
61	*Tribonema aequale*	U	...	...	...	...	...	...	...	...	U	...	U	...	...	7
	Euglenophyta															
62	*Astasia longa (A. chattoni, A. klebsii)*	...	...	U	...	...	...	...	...	U	...	...	...	...	...	1
63	*A. quartana*	...	...	...	...	...	...	...	...	U	...	...	...	...	...	1
64	*Euglena anabaena minor*	...	...	U	...	...	U	...	...	U	...	...	...	...	...	1
65	*E. deses*[12]	...	...	U̸	...	...	U̸	...	...	U	...	...	...	...	...	1
66	*E. gracilis bacillaris*	...	...	U̸	...	...	U̸	...	...	U	...	...	...	...	...	1
67	*E. gracilis typica*	...	...	U	...	...	u	...	...	U	...	...	...	...	...	1
68	*E. gracilis urophora*	...	...	U	...	...	U̸	...	...	U	...	...	...	...	...	1
69	*E. klebsii*[13]	...	...	u	...	...	u	...	...	U	...	...	...	...	...	1
70	*E. pisciformis*	...	...	U	...	...	U̸	...	...	U	...	...	...	...	...	1
71	*E. stellata*	...	...	U	...	...	U	...	...	U	...	...	...	...	...	1
	Chlorophyta															
72	*Asterococcus superbus*	U	U	U	...	U̸	U	U	...	...	U̸	U̸	U	U̸	...	9
73	*Balticola buetschlii*	...	U̸	U	...	...	...	...	...	...	...	U̸	U	U	U[14]	13
74	*B. droebakensis*	...	U	U	...	...	...	...	...	...	...	U	U	U	U[14]	13
75	*Brachiomonas submarina*	...	U	U	...	...	U	...	...	...	...	U̸	U	U	U[14]	13
76	*Carteria crucifera*	U̸	U	U	...	U̸	U	U	...	...	U̸	U̸	U̸	U̸	...	9

[5] Colorless. [9] By 2 strains; poorly utilized by 1 strain. [10] By 3 strains. [11] Toxic under some conditions (e.g., basic pH and low salinity) and at high concentrations [22]. [12] According to E. G. Pringsheim, the organism used in these studies was *E. geniculata*. [13] According to E. G. Pringsheim, the organism used in these studies was *E. mutabilis*. [14] Guanine.

continued

27. NUTRIENT REQUIREMENTS AND UTILIZATION: ALGAE

Part IV. Other Nitrogenous Substances

	Species (Synonym)	Acetamide	Adenine	Ammonium	Casein Hydrolysate	Cytosine	Nitrate	Nitrite	Nitrogen	Peptone	Succinamide	Uracil	Urea	Uric Acid	Miscellaneous	Reference
77	*Chlamydomonas actinochloris*	Ʉ	U	U	...	Ʉ	U	U	...	...	U	Ʉ	Ʉ	Ʉ	...	9
78	*C. agloeformis*	...	...	U	...	...	U	...	...	U	...	...	...	...	...	1
79	*C. calyptrata*	U	U	U	...	Ʉ	U	U	...	...	Ʉ	Ʉ	U	U	...	9
80	*C. carrosa* [15]	U	U	U	...	Ʉ	U	U	...	...	Ʉ	Ʉ	U	Ʉ	...	9
81	*C. chlamydogama*	Ʉ	U	u	...	Ʉ	U	U	...	...	Ʉ	Ʉ	Ʉ	Ʉ	...	9
82	*C. eugametos*	Ʉ	Ʉ	Ʉ [16]	...	Ʉ	U	U	...	...	Ʉ	Ʉ	U	Ʉ	...	9
83	*C. gloegama*	U	U	U	...	Ʉ	U	U	...	...	Ʉ	Ʉ	U	Ʉ	...	9
84	*C. gloeopara*	U	U	U	...	Ʉ	U	U	...	...	U	U	U	U	...	9
85	*C. inflexa*	U	U	u	...	Ʉ	U	U	...	...	Ʉ	U	U	U	...	9
86	*C. kakosmos*	U	U	U	...	Ʉ	U	U	...	...	Ʉ	Ʉ	U	U	...	9
87	*C. mexicana*	U	U	u	...	Ʉ	U	U	...	...	U	Ʉ	U	Ʉ	...	9
88	*C. microsphaera acuta*	U	U	u	...	Ʉ	U	U	...	...	Ʉ	Ʉ	U	U	...	9
89	*C. microsphaerella*	U	U	u	...	Ʉ	U	Ʉ	...	...	Ʉ	Ʉ	U	U	...	9
90	*C. minuta*	U	U	u	...	Ʉ	U	U	...	...	U	Ʉ	U	U	...	9
91	*C. moewusii*	Ʉ	U	u	...	Ʉ	U	U	...	...	Ʉ	Ʉ	U	Ʉ	...	9
92	*C. moewusii rotunda*	Ʉ	U	u	...	Ʉ	U	U	...	...	Ʉ	Ʉ	U	U	...	9
93	*C. mundana*	...	...	U	...	...	Ʉ	...	...	...	...	...	u?	...	...	14
94	*C. mundana astigmata*	...	...	U	...	...	Ʉ	...	...	...	...	...	u?	...	...	14
95	*C. mutabilis*	Ʉ	U	U	...	Ʉ	U	U	...	...	Ʉ	Ʉ	U	Ʉ	...	9
96	*C. peterfi*	U	Ʉ	U	...	Ʉ	U	U	...	...	Ʉ	Ʉ	U	Ʉ	...	9
97	*C. pulsatilla*	...	...	...	...	...	...	...	...	...	...	...	...	...	U [17]	13
98	*C. radiata*	Ʉ	Ʉ	U	...	Ʉ	U	U	...	...	Ʉ	Ʉ	Ʉ	Ʉ	...	9
99	*C. reinhardii*	U	U	U	...	Ʉ	U	U	...	...	Ʉ	Ʉ	U	U	U [1]	8,9
100	*C. sectilis*	Ʉ	Ʉ	U	...	Ʉ	U	U	...	...	...	Ʉ	Ʉ	Ʉ	...	9
101	*C. typhlos*	U	U	U	...	Ʉ	U	U	...	...	Ʉ	Ʉ	U	U	...	9
102	*Chlorella autotrophica*	...	...	U	Ʉ	...	u	...	...	...	...	...	...	...	...	29
103	*C. candida*	...	...	U	U	...	U	...	...	...	...	...	...	...	...	29
104	*C. ellipsoidea*	...	...	U	U	...	U	...	...	...	...	...	...	...	...	29
105	*C. emersonii*	...	...	U	U	...	U	...	...	...	...	...	...	...	...	29
106	*C. emersonii globosa*	...	...	U	U	...	U	...	...	...	...	...	...	...	...	29
107	*C. fusca*	...	...	U	U	...	U	...	...	...	...	...	...	...	...	29
108	*C. fusca vacuolata*	...	...	U	U	...	U	...	...	...	...	...	...	...	...	29
109	*C. infusionum*	...	...	U	U	...	U	...	...	...	...	...	...	...	...	29
110	*C. infusionum auxenophila*	...	...	U	U	...	U	...	...	...	...	...	...	...	...	29
111	*C. miniata*	...	...	U	U	...	U	...	...	...	...	...	...	...	...	29
112	*C. mutabilis*	...	...	Ʉ	Ʉ	...	Ʉ	...	...	...	...	...	...	...	...	29
113	*C. nocturna*	...	...	U	U	...	U	...	...	...	...	...	...	...	...	29
114	*C. photophila*	...	...	U	U	...	U	...	...	...	...	...	...	...	...	29
115	*C. pringsheimii*	...	...	U	U	...	U	...	...	...	...	...	...	...	...	29
116	*C. protothecoides*	...	...	U	U	...	Ʉ	...	...	...	U	...	...	...	...	3,29
117	*C. protothecoides communis*	...	...	U	U	...	Ʉ	...	...	...	...	...	...	...	...	29
118	*C. protothecoides galactophila*	...	...	U	U	...	Ʉ	...	...	...	...	...	...	...	...	29
119	*C. protothecoides mannophila*	...	...	U	U	...	Ʉ	...	...	...	...	...	...	...	...	29
120	*C. pyrenoidosa*	...	...	U	...	...	U	...	...	...	...	...	U	U	U [1]	8,28
121	*C. regularis*	...	...	U	U	...	U	...	...	...	...	...	...	...	...	29
122	*C. regularis aprica*	...	...	U	U	...	U	...	...	...	...	...	...	...	...	29
123	*C. regularis imbricata*	...	...	U	U	...	U	...	...	...	...	...	...	...	...	29
124	*C. saccharophila*	...	...	U	U	...	U	...	...	...	...	...	...	...	...	29
125	*C. simplex*	...	...	U	U	...	U	...	...	...	...	...	...	...	...	29
126	*C. sorokiniana*	...	...	U	U	...	U	...	...	...	...	...	...	...	...	29
127	*C. vannielii*	...	...	U	U	...	U	...	...	...	...	...	...	...	...	29

[1] Xanthine. [15] 4 strains. [16] By male strain; poorly utilized by female strain. [17] Organic nitrogen; individual compounds not listed.

continued

Part IV. Other Nitrogenous Substances

	Species (Synonym)	Acetamide	Adenine	Ammonium	Casein Hydrolysate	Cytosine	Nitrate	Nitrite	Nitrogen	Peptone	Succinamide	Uracil	Urea	Uric Acid	Miscellaneous	Reference
128	*C. variabilis*	...	...	U	U̸	...	U̸	...	...	...	...	...	...	...	...	29
129	*C. vulgaris*	...	...	U	U	...	U	...	...	...	U	...	U	U	U[1]	3,6,8,29
130	*C. vulgaris luteoviridis*	...	...	U	U	...	U	...	...	...	...	...	...	...	...	29
131	*Cyanidium caldarium*[18]	...	...	U	U	...	U̸?	...	U̸	...	...	...	U	...	...	4,5
132	*Dunaliella salina*	...	...	U	...	...	U	...	...	...	...	...	U	U	...	16
133	*D. viridis*	...	...	U	...	...	U	...	...	...	...	...	U	U	...	16
134	*Gloeocystis gigas*	U̸	U	U	...	U̸	U	U	...	...	U̸	U̸	U	U̸	...	9
135	*G. maxima*	U	U	U	...	U̸	U	U	...	...	U	U̸	U	U	...	9
136	*Haematococcus pluvialis*	...	U	U	...	...	U	...	...	...	...	u[19]	U	U	U[14]	13
137	*Lobomonas pyriformis*	U	...	U	...	...	U	...	...	...	...	...	...	...	...	25
138	*Nannochloris atomus*	...	...	U	...	...	U	U	...	...	...	...	U	U	...	27
139	*N. oculata*	...	...	U	...	...	U	...	...	...	...	...	U	U	...	11
140	*Polytoma caudatum*	...	...	U	...	...	U̸	...	...	U	...	...	...	...	...	1
141	*P. obtusum*	...	...	U	...	...	U̸	...	...	U	...	...	...	...	...	1
142	*P. ocellatum*	...	...	U	...	...	U	...	...	U	...	...	...	...	...	1
143	*P. uvella*	...	...	U	...	...	U̸	...	...	U	...	...	...	...	...	1
144	*Polytomella caeca*	...	...	U	...	...	U̸	...	...	U	...	...	...	...	...	1
145	*Prototheca zopfii*	...	...	U	...	...	...	...	...	U	...	...	...	...	...	1
146	*Scenedesmus obliquus*	...	...	U	...	...	U	...	...	...	U	...	U	U	U[1]	3,8
147	*Sphaerobotrys fluviatilis*	U	U	u	...	U̸	U	U	...	...	U	U̸	U	U	...	9
148	*Sporotetras pyriformis*	U	U	U	...	U̸	U	U	...	...	U̸	U̸	U	U	...	9
149	*Stephanoptera gracilis*	...	...	U	...	...	U	...	...	...	...	...	U	U̸	...	16
150	*Stephanosphaera pluvialis*	...	U̸	U	...	...	...	...	...	...	...	U̸	U	U̸	U[14]	13
151	*Stichococcus cylindricus ?*	...	...	U	...	...	U	U	...	...	...	...	U	U	...	27

1/ Xanthine. 14/ Guanine. 18/ Genus of uncertain taxonomic position [30]. 19/ By 1 strain; not utilized by 1 strain.

Contributor: Thomas, William H.

References

[1] Albritton, E. C. 1954. Standard values in nutrition and metabolism. W. B. Saunders, Philadelphia.

[2] Aldrich, D. V. 1962. Science 137:988.

[3] Algeus, S. 1950. Physiol. Plantarum 3:370.

[4] Allen, M. B. 1952. Arch. Mikrobiol. 17:34.

[5] Allen, M. B. 1959. Ibid. 32:270.

[6] Arnow, P., J. J. Oleson, and J. H. Williams. 1953. Am. J. Botany 40:100.

[7] Belcher, J. H., and G. E. Fogg. 1958. Arch. Mikrobiol. 30:17.

[8] Birdsey, E., and V. Lynch. 1962. Science 137:763.

[9] Cain, J. 1965. Can. J. Botany 43:1367.

[10] De, P. K. 1939. Proc. Roy. Soc. (London), B, 127: 121.

[11] Droop, M. R. 1955. J. Marine Biol. Assoc. U.K. 34: 229.

[12] Droop, M. R. 1958. Ibid. 37:323.

[13] Droop, M. R. 1961. Rev. Algol. 5(4):247.

[14] Eppley, R. W., and F. M. Macias. 1962. Physiol. Plantarum 15:72.

[15] Fogg, G. E., and M. Wolfe. 1954. Symp. Soc. Gen. Microbiol. 4:99.

[16] Gibor, A. 1956. Biol. Bull. 111:223.

[17] Guillard, R. R. L. 1963. Symp. Marine Microbiol., Chicago, 1961, p. 93.

[18] Holz, G. G. 1954. J. Protozool. 1:114.

[19] Kiyohara, T., et al. 1960. J. Gen. Appl. Microbiol. 6:176.

[20] Kratz, W. A., and J. Myers. 1955. Am. J. Botany 42:282.

[21] Lewin, J., and R. A. Lewin. 1967. J. Gen. Microbiol. 46:361.

[22] McLaughlin, J. J. A. 1958. J. Protozool. 5:75.

[23] Miller, J. D. A., and G. E. Fogg. 1957. Arch. Mikrobiol. 28:1.

[24] Miller, J. D. A., and G. E. Fogg. 1958. Ibid. 30:1.

[25] Osterud, K. L. 1946. Physiol. Zool. 19:19.

[26] Pintner, I. J., and L. Provasoli. 1958. J. Gen. Microbiol. 18:190.

[27] Ryther, J. H. 1954. Biol. Bull. 106:198.

[28] Samejima, H., and J. Myers. 1958. J. Gen. Microbiol. 18:107.

[29] Shihira, I., and R. W. Krauss. 1965. Chlorella: physiology and taxonomy of 41 isolates. Univ. Maryland Press, College Park.

[30] Silva, P. 1962. Physiol. Biochem. Algae, p. 827.

[31] Steward, W. D. P. 1962. Ann. Botany (London), N.S. 26:439.

[32] Thomas, W. H. 1966. Limnol. Oceanog. 11:393.

[33] Van Baalen, C. 1962. Botan. Marina 4:129.

[34] Watanabe, A. 1951. Arch. Biochem. Biophys. 34:50.

[35] Watanabe, A., S. Nishigaki, and C. Konishi. 1951. Nature 168:748.

[36] Williams, A. E., and R. H. Burris. 1951. Am. J. Botany 39:340.

28. WATER REQUIREMENTS: HIGHER PLANTS

Part I. Transpiration Formulas

Transpiration, a physical process in which the wet leaf parenchyma loses water to the generally much drier surrounding air, accounts for the bulk of a plant's water requirements. An epidermis, perforated by stomata on one or both sides of the leaf, separates the parenchyma and the atmospheric environment, but unless the number of stomata is small, the stomata themselves closed, or the total leaf area limited, transpiration is not primarily controlled by this epidermal barrier. Two formulas, therefore, are necessary to determine the amount of transpiration and the resulting water requirement: one primarily for isolated leaf areas, the other for leaves in canopy situations. The two formulas given below are extreme simplifications. For detailed information on the transpiration of individual leaves, consult Raschke [3], and on the evaporation from plant stands, consult Monteith [2]. For reviews and discussions oriented to the practical problems of plant water requirements (e.g., irrigation), consult reference 1.

	Specification	Formula	Explanation	Remarks
1	Single leaves, or single plants with a relatively small number of leaves. (If the leaf has stomata on both sides, the calculation must be carried out for either side separately and the results added.)	$T = \frac{7 \times 10^{-7} A (e_l - e_a)}{(100/u + r_l)} g\ sec^{-1}$	A = total leaf area in cm^2 e_l = water vapor pressure inside the leaf in mb e_a = water vapor pressure of the ambient air u = air velocity in cm sec^{-1} r_l = stomatal diffusion resistance in sec cm^{-1}	The values of e_1 and r_1 must be determined experimentally; the first from a leaf temperature measurement, and the second with equipment suggested by Van Bavel, et al [4]. The formula is exact, except for the expression 100/u which represents a rule of thumb and which can be determined more accurately for individual cases. Nevertheless, the formula gives an accurate idea of the effect of the various environmental factors[1] on transpiration rate and, consequently, the water requirements.
2	Plant stands as they are found in fields. (In this case, no distinction can be made between transpiration and evaporation from the soil or plant surface.)	$E = \frac{(\epsilon H + 6 \times 10^{-9} d_a u_a)}{(\epsilon + 1)} g\ sec^{-1}\ cm^{-2}$	ϵ = physical constant, inversely proportional to ambient pressure and depending on the temperature (values at 1000 mb are given in Part II) H = radiation balance of the canopy in g sec^{-1} cm^{-2} (this is a latent heat equivalent of the radiative flux density) d_a = saturation vapor pressure deficit of the ambient air in mb u_a = windspeed at 2 m over the canopy in cm sec^{-1}	The factor, 6×10^{-9}, is again a rule of thumb figure and depends on the roughness parameter of the canopy and its displacement height. The formula applies reasonably well to pastures and closed crops. More importantly, it shows which are the principal environmental factors, and in which way they influence water requirements of plant stands.

[1] For instance, many plants under strong illuminance will exhibit low values of r_l (less than 0.2 sec cm^{-1}). This means that at low air velocities (less than 100 cm sec^{-1}), transpiration is entirely dependent on the environment and total leaf area. Stomatal closure due to low illuminance, high CO_2 levels, or desiccation will reverse this situation.

Contributor: Van Bavel, Cornelius H. M.

References

[1] Hagan, R. M., H. R. Haise, and T. W. Edminster, ed. 1967. Irrigation of agricultural lands. American Society of Agronomy, Madison, Wisc.

[2] Monteith, J.L. 1965. Symp. Soc. Exptl. Biol. 19:205.

[3] Raschke, K. 1956. Planta 48:200.

[4] Van Bavel, C. H. M., et al. 1965. Plant Physiol. 40: 535.

continued

28. WATER REQUIREMENTS: HIGHER PLANTS

Part II. Physical Constant ϵ (Dimensionless) and Temperature in °C

Temp	ϵ	Temp	ϵ	Temp	ϵ	Temp	ϵ	Temp	ϵ	Temp	ϵ
0.0	0.67	10.0	1.23	20.0	2.14	30.0	3.57	40.0	5.70	50.0	8.77
1.0	0.72	11.0	1.30	21.0	2.26	31.0	3.75	41.0	5.96	51.0	9.14
2.0	0.76	12.0	1.38	22.0	2.38	32.0	3.93	42.0	6.23	52.0	9.52
3.0	0.81	13.0	1.46	23.0	2.51	33.0	4.12	43.0	6.51	53.0	9.92
4.0	0.86	14.0	1.55	24.0	2.64	34.0	4.32	44.0	6.80	54.0	10.3
5.0	0.92	15.0	1.64	25.0	2.78	35.0	4.53	45.0	7.10	55.0	10.8
6.0	0.97	16.0	1.73	26.0	2.92	36.0	4.75	46.0	7.41	56.0	11.2
7.0	1.03	17.0	1.82	27.0	3.08	37.0	4.97	47.0	7.73	57.0	11.6
8.0	1.10	18.0	1.93	28.0	3.23	38.0	5.20	48.0	8.07	58.0	12.1
9.0	1.16	19.0	2.03	29.0	3.40	39.0	5.45	49.0	8.42	59.0	12.6
10.0	1.23	20.0	2.14	30.0	3.57	40.0	5.70	50.0	8.77	60.0	13.1

Contributor: Van Bavel, Cornelius H. M.

Reference: List, R. J. 1966. Smithsonian Misc. Collections 114:365,372.

29. CULTURE MEDIA: PLANTS

The media listed are not the only ones on which the various organisms will grow; also, the concentration of the constituents usually may be varied. Only in a few cases have actual requirements been quantitatively determined.

Part I. Bacteria

Amino acids are given as DL-isomers.

	Constituent	Concentration mg/liter
	Heterotrophic Bacteria[1,2]	
1	Peptone	5000
2	Yeast extract	3000
	Heterotrophic Bacteria[2,3]	
3	Peptone	5000
4	Yeast extract	3000
5	Agar	15,000
	Aerobic *Actinomyces* sp. [1]	
6	$CuSO_4 \cdot 5H_2O$	1
7	$Fe_2(SO_4)_3 \cdot 6H_2O$	10
8	$MgSO_4 \cdot 7H_2O$	500
9	$MnSO_4 \cdot H_2O$	1
10	K_2HPO_4	1000
11	NaCl	1000
12	$ZnSO_4 \cdot 7H_2O$	1
13	Agar	15,000
14	Glycerol	12,500
15	Arginine monohydrochloride	1000
16	pH = 6.9-7.1	
	Saprophytic *Actinomyces* sp. & *Streptomyces* sp.[4] [7]	
17	Dipotassium phosphate	1000
18	Agar	15,000
19	Glycerol	10,000
20	Asparagine	1000
	Photosynthetic Bacteria [4,5]	
21	NH_4Cl	1000
22	H_3BO_3	2.8
23	$CaCl_2$	100
24	$Co(NO_3)_2 \cdot 6H_2O$	0.05
25	$CuSO_4 \cdot 5H_2O$	0.02
26	$FeSO_4 \cdot 7H_2O$	20
27	$MgSO_4 \cdot 7H_2O$	250
28	$MnCl_2 \cdot 4H_2O$	0.05
29	K_2HPO_4	500
30	Na_2CO_3	2000[5]
31	NaCl	3000[6]
32	Na_2S	1000[5]
33	$ZnSO_4 \cdot 7H_2O$	0.5
34	Potassium acetate	1000[7]
35	Sodium succinate	4000[7]
36	Glycerol	2000[7]
37	Malic acid	3000[7]
38	Glutamic acid	2000[7]
39	Thiamine HCl	1.0[7]
40	Nicotinic acid	1.0[7]
41	D-Biotin	0.004[7]
42	pH = 7-9	
	***Haemophilus parainfluenzae* [2]**	
43	$CaCl_2$	3
44	$FeSO_4 \cdot 7H_2O$	12.8
45	$MgSO_4 \cdot 7H_2O$	82
46	KH_2PO_4	3120

1/ Nonsynthetic nutrient broth, prepared by adding specified ingredients to 1 liter of distilled water. 2/ Sugar broth or agar may be prepared by adding 5000 mg/liter of desired sugar. 3/ Nonsynthetic nutrient agar, prepared by adding specified ingredients to 1 liter of distilled water. 4/ Nonsynthetic medium, prepared by adding specified ingredients to 1 liter of distilled water. 5/ For purple and green sulfur bacteria. 6/ For marine forms. 7/ For purple nonsulfur bacteria.

continued

29. CULTURE MEDIA: PLANTS

Part I. Bacteria

	Constituent	Concentration mg/liter
47	Sodium acetate	6000
48	Glucose	1000
49	Alanine	1000
50	Arginine HCl	400
51	Aspartic acid	1000
52	Cystine	200
53	Glutamic acid	2000
54	Glycine	100
55	Histidine HCl	200
56	Isoleucine	200
57	Leucine	200
58	Lysine HCl	400
59	Methionine	200
60	Phenylalanine	200
61	Proline	200
62	Serine	200
63	Threonine	200
64	Tryptophan	200
65	Tyrosine	200
66	Valine	200
67	Adenine sulfate	10
68	Guanine HCl	10
69	Uracil	10
70	Nicotinamide adenine dinucleotide	0.1
71	Putrescine	500
72	Thiamine HCl	1
73	Riboflavin	0.1
74	Nicotinic acid	0.5
75	Pyridoxine HCl	2
76	D-Biotin	0.001
77	Calcium DL-pantothenate	1
78	Folic acid	0.01
79	*p*-Aminobenzoic acid	0.001
80	L-Inositol	20
81	Choline Cl	5
	Lactobacillus lactis[8] [6]	
82	NH_4Cl	280
83	$FeSO_4 \cdot 7H_2O$	10
84	$MgSO_4 \cdot 7H_2O$	1400
85	$MnSO_4$	203
86	K_2HPO_4	2000
87	KH_2PO_4	2000
88	Sodium acetate	3600
89	Sodium citrate	5000
90	Sodium ethyl oxalacetate	100
91	Glucose	20,000
92	Alanine	200
93	Arginine HCl	200
94	Asparagine	200
95	Aspartic acid	200
96	Cysteine	800
97	Cystine	400
98	Glutamic acid	400
99	Glutamine	100
100	Glycine	300
101	Histidine HCl	200
102	Hydroxyproline	50
103	Isoleucine	300
104	Leucine	100
105	Lysine HCl	600
106	Methionine	100
107	Norleucine	200
108	Phenylalanine	500
109	Proline	400
110	Serine	100
111	Threonine	100
112	Tryptophan	50
113	Tyrosine	400
114	Valine	200
115	Adenine sulfate	5
116	Cytidylic acid	10
117	Guanine HCl	5
118	Uracil	5
119	Xanthine	8
120	Polysorbate 80	1
121	Thiamine HCl	1
122	Riboflavin	1
123	Nicotinic acid	1
124	Pyridoxal HCl	2
125	Pyridoxal phosphate	1
126	Pyridoxamine HCl	0.4
127	Pyridoxine HCl	2
128	D-Biotin	0.005
129	Calcium DL-pantothenate	1
130	Folic acid	0.06
131	*p*-Aminobenzoic acid	0.04
132	Vitamin B_{12}	0.01
133	pH = 5.5	
	Streptococcus faecalis[8] [3]	
134	NH_4Cl	2500
135	$FeSO_4 \cdot 7H_2O$	27
136	$MgSO_4 \cdot 7H_2O$	512
137	$MnSO_4$	30
138	K_2HPO_4	5000
139	NaCl	15
140	Sodium acetate	5000
141	Sodium citrate	5000
142	Glucose	20,000
143	Alanine	500
144	Arginine HCl	400
145	Asparagine	500
146	Aspartic acid	500
147	Cystine	200
148	Glutamic acid	1000
149	Glycine	100
150	Histidine HCl	200
151	Isoleucine	200
152	Leucine	200
153	Lysine HCl	400
154	Methionine	200
155	Phenylalanine	200
156	Proline	400
157	Serine	500
158	Threonine	200
159	Tryptophan	200
160	Tyrosine	200
161	Valine	200
162	Adenine sulfate	10
163	Uridine	0.2
164	Glutathione	20
165	Polysorbate 80	10
166	Thiamine HCl	0.5
167	Riboflavin	0.5
168	Nicotinic acid	1
169	Pyridoxamine HCl	0.5
170	Pyridoxine HCl	0.5
171	D-Biotin	0.01
172	Calcium DL-pantothenate	0.5
173	Folic acid	0.02
174	*p*-Aminobenzoic acid	0.2

[8] Utilized for assay of vitamins or amino acids.

Contributors: (a) Clark, F. M., (b) Allen, Mary Belle

References

[1] el-Nakeeb, M. A., and H. A. Lechevalier. 1963. Appl. Microbiol. 11:75.

[2] Herbst, E. J., and E. E. Snell. 1949. J. Biol. Chem. 181:47.

continued

Part I. Bacteria

[3] Hoffmann, H. A., and P. L. Pavcek. 1952. J. Am. Chem. Soc. 74:344.

[4] Hutner, S. H. 1950. J. Gen. Microbiol. 4:286.

[5] Larsen, H. 1952. J. Bacteriol. 64:187.

[6] Shorb, M. S. 1952. Proc. Soc. Exptl. Biol. Med. 79: 611.

[7] Skinner, C. E., C. W. Emmons, and H. M. Tsuchiya, ed. 1947. Henrici's Molds, yeasts, and actinomyces. Ed. 2. J. Wiley, New York. p. 59.

Part II. Fungi

	Constituent	Concentration mg/liter[1]
	Molds & Yeasts[2] [4]	
1	Agar	15,000
2	Glucose	10,000
3	Potato extract[3]	1000 ml
	Molds & Yeasts[2,4] [6]	
4	Peptone	5000
5	Yeast extract	3000
6	Agar	20,000
7	Glucose	10,000
8	Malt extract	3000
	Yeasts[5] [5]	
9	$(NH_4)_2SO_4$	5000
10	H_3BO_3	10 μg
11	$CaCl_2 \cdot 2H_2O$	100
12	$CuSO_4 \cdot 5H_2O$	10 μg
13	$FeCl_3 \cdot 8H_2O$	50 μg
14	KI	100 μg
15	KH_2PO_4	1000
16	$MgSO_4 \cdot 7H_2O$	125
17	$MnSO_4 \cdot 4H_2O$	10 μg
18	NaCl	100
19	$Na_2MoO_4 \cdot 2H_2O$	1 μg
20	$ZnSO_4 \cdot 7H_2O$	70 μg
21	Glucose[6]	5000
22	DL-Methionine	5
23	Tryptophan	5
24	Thiamine	400 μg
25	Riboflavin	200 μg
26	Nicotinic acid	400 μg
27	Vitamin B_6	400 μg
28	Biotin	2 μg
29	Calcium pantothenate	400 μg
30	*p*-Aminobenzoic acid	200 μg
31	Inositol	2000 μg
	Aspergilli & Penicillia [3]	
32	$FeSO_4 \cdot 7H_2O$	10
33	$MgSO_4 \cdot 7H_2O$	500
34	KCl	500
35	K_2HPO_4	1000
36	$NaNO_3$	3000
37	Sucrose	30,000
38		pH = 6.8-6.9
	***Neurospora* sp. [1]**	
39	NH_4NO_3	1000
40	H_3BO_3	0.06
41	$CaCl_2$	100
42	$CuSO_4 \cdot 5H_2O$	0.40
43	$FeSO_4 \cdot 7H_2O$	0.98
44	$MgSO_4 \cdot 7H_2O$	500
45	$MnCl_2 \cdot 4H_2O$	0.07
46	KH_2PO_4	1000
47	NaCl	100
48	Na_2MoO_4	0.04
49	$ZnSO_4 \cdot 7H_2O$	8.8
50	Ammonium tartrate	5000
51	Sucrose	15,000
52	D-Biotin	0.005
53		pH = 5.6
	Basidiomycetes[7] [2]	
54	H_3BO_3	0.57
55	$CuSO_4 \cdot 5H_2O$	0.04
56	$FeSO_4 \cdot 7H_2O$	0.15
57	$MgSO_4 \cdot 7H_2O$	500
58	$MnCl_2 \cdot 4H_2O$	0.04
59	KH_2PO_4	1500
60	$ZnSO_4 \cdot 7H_2O$	0.31
61	Ammonium paramolybdate	0.02
62	Glucose	10,000
63	L-Glutamic acid	1200±[8]
64	Thiamine HCl	1
65		pH = 5.0-5.5

1/ Unless otherwise stated. 2/ Nonsynthetic medium. 3/ Boil 300 g sliced potatoes for 20 minutes and strain through cotton. 4/ Prepared by adding specified ingredients to 1 liter of distilled water. 5/ Synthetic medium for carbon assimilation tests. 6/ Or other carbon source equivalent to the carbon in glucose. 7/ Wood-rotting types. Biotin and/or riboflavin may be required by some species. 8/ Or DL-glutamic acid, 2400± mg/liter.

Contributors: (a) Clark, F. M., (b) Wolf, Frederick T., (c) Jennison, Marshall W.

References

[1] Beadle, G. W., and E. L. Tatum. 1945. Am. J. Botany 32:678.

[2] Jennison, M. W., et al. 1955. Mycologia 47:275.

[3] Raper, K. B., and D. I. Fennell. 1965. The genus *Aspergillus.* Williams and Wilkins. Baltimore.

[4] Skinner, C. E., C. W. Emmons, and H. M. Tsuchiya, ed. 1947. Henrici's Molds, yeasts, and actinomyces. Ed. 2. J. Wiley, New York. p. 53.

[5] Wickerham, L. J. 1951. U.S. Dept. Agr. Tech. Bull. 1029.

[6] Wickerham, L. J. Unpublished. Northern Regional Research Laboratory, Peoria, Ill., 1966.

continued

Part III. Algae

Variations of Pringsheim's soil-water medium are for nonsterile cultures, and are used especially for isolation purposes and for growing algae to secure "normal" growth forms. Success with soil-water media depends on the selection of a suitable garden soil. The soil should be of medium humus content and should not have had recent applications of commercial fertilizers. Soils with a high clay content are usually not the most suitable for most organisms. A variety of soil-water media can be made using a basic formula to which are added additional materials. The basic medium is made by placing one-quarter to one-half inch of garden soil in the bottom of a test tube, then adding pyrex-distilled water until the tube is three-quarters full. The tube is then plugged with cotton and steamed (not autoclaved) for one hour on two consecutive days. A few algae, such as *Spirogyra,* grow well in this basic medium. For most presumably phototrophic algae which thrive in an alkaline medium, a small pinch of powdered $CaCO_3$ is placed in the bottom of the test tube before the soil and water are added. Some algae (*Astasia, Euglena, Polytoma, Polytomella, Pyrobotrys,* and others) require additional complex nitrogenous or carbon compounds not present in the basic formula. In the case of *Euglena* and *Pyrobotrys,* the best results have been obtained by adding one-quarter of a garden pea cotyledon to the basic medium (including $CaCO_3$) before steaming. For the colorless forms, the addition of a barley grain before steaming supplies the necessary carbon source. A few strains, such as *Botryococcus,* grow best when a pinch of sterile ammonium magnesium phosphate is added after the basic medium (including $CaCO_3$) has been steamed. [6] Marine diatoms and blue-green algae grow well in the same medium as that used for marine flagellates (*see* page 177).

	Constituent	Concentration mg/liter[1]
	Marine Algae [7]	
1	B, as H_3BO_3	2
2	Ca, as Cl	150
3	Co, as Cl	10 μg
4	Cu, as Cl	20 μg
5	Fe, as Cl	2
6	$MgSO_4 \cdot 7H_2O$	8000
7	Mn, as Cl	1
8	Mo, as Na salt	0.5
9	KCl	700
10	NaCl	24,000
11	$NaNO_3$	300
12	$Na_2SiO_3 \cdot 9H_2O$	70
13	Zn, as Cl	0.5
14	Potassium glycerophosphate	100
15	Sodium versenol	30
16	Tris[2]	1000
17	Vitamin mix no. 8	1 ml
18	Thiamine HCl	0.2[3]
19	Riboflavin	5.0[4]
20	Nicotinic acid	0.1[3]
21	Pyridoxamine·2HCl	0.02[3]
22	Pyridoxine·2HCl	0.04[3]
23	Biotin	0.5[4]
24	Calcium pantothenate	0.1[3]
25	Folic acid	2.5[4]
26	Folinic acid	0.2[4]
27	*p*-Aminobenzoic acid	0.1[3]
28	Inositol	1.0[3]
29	Vitamin B_{12}	0.05[4]
30	Choline·H_2 citrate	0.5[3]
31	Orotic acid	0.26[3]
32	Thymine	0.8[3]
33	Putrescine·2HCl	0.04[3]
34	Vitamin B_{12}	0.5 μg
35	pH = 7.6	
	Cyanophyta [1]	
36	NH_4VO_3	0.02[5]
37	H_3BO_3	2.86
38	$CaCl_2$	55
39	$Co(NO_3)_2 \cdot 6H_2O$	0.05
40	$CuSO_4 \cdot 5H_2O$	0.08
41	$FeSO_4 \cdot 7H_2O$	20
42	$MgSO_4 \cdot 7H_2O$	250
43	$MnCl_2 \cdot 4H_2O$	1.8
44	KNO_3	2000[6]
45	K_2HPO_4	2580
46	NaCl	40
47	Na_2CO_3	1500[7]
48	Na_2MoO_4	0.2
49	$ZnSO_4 \cdot 7H_2O$	0.02
50	Sodium citrate	200
51	pH = 7-9	
	Cyanophyta [3]	
52	$Ca(NO_3)_2 \cdot 4H_2O$	10
53	$Fe_2(SO_4)_3 \cdot 6H_2O$	4
54	$MgSO_4 \cdot 7H_2O$	150
55	K_2HPO_4	1000
56	$NaNO_3$	1000
57	EDTA	50
58	H5 Microelements	1 ml
59	$Co(NO_3)_2 \cdot 6H_2O$	0.49[3]
60	$CuSO_4 \cdot 5H_2O$	1.57[3]
61	$MnCl_2 \cdot 4H_2O$	1.44[3]
62	MoO_3	0.71[3]
63	$ZnSO_4 \cdot 7H_2O$	8.82[3]
	***Oscillatoria rubescens* [9]**	
64	$Ca(NO_3)_2 \cdot 4H_2O$	59
65	K_2HPO_4	31
66	$MgSO_4 \cdot 7H_2O$	25
67	Na_2CO_3	21
68	$NaNO_3$	467
69	Fe EDTA complex	10 ml
70	$FeCl_3 \cdot 6H_2O$	2.7[8]
71	Disodium EDTA	3.7[8]
72	Trace element solution[9]	0.08 ml
73	pH = 7.6	
	***Navicula pelliculosa* [4]**	
74	B	0.1

[1] Unless otherwise stated. [2] Tris(hydroxymethyl)aminomethane. [3] mg/ml of mix or solution. [4] μg/ml of mix. [5] Not yet shown to be generally required. [6] May be omitted for nitrogen-fixing forms. [7] For those strains which grow only at an alkaline pH; 5% CO_2 in air should be supplied if Na_2CO_3 is added. [8] mg/10 ml of complex. [9] 100 ml of solution contains 47.4 mg $K_2Al_2(SO_4)_4 \cdot 24H_2O$, 8.8 mg $(NH_4)_6Mo_7O_{24} \cdot 4H_2O$, 310 mg H_3BO_3, 15.4 mg $Cd(NO_3)_2 \cdot 4H_2O$, 3.7 mg $Cr(NO_3)_3 \cdot 7H_2O$, 14.6 mg $Co(NO_3)_2 \cdot 6H_2O$, 12.5 mg $CuSO_4 \cdot 5H_2O$, 11.9 mg KBr, 8.3 mg KI, 223 mg $MnSO_4 \cdot 4H_2O$, 19.8 mg $NiSO_4(NH_4)_2SO_4 \cdot 6H_2O$, 3.3 mg $Na_2WO_4 \cdot 2H_2O$, 3.5 mg $V_2O_4(SO_4)_3 \cdot 16H_2O$, 28.7 mg $ZnSO_4 \cdot 7H_2O$. This formula is similar to Gaffron formula [2].

continued

Part III. Algae

	Constituent	Concentration mg/liter
75	$Ca(NO_3)_2 \cdot 4H_2O$	1000
76	Co	0.1
77	Cu	0.1
78	Fe	0.5
79	$MgSO_4 \cdot 7H_2O$	200
80	Mn	0.1
81	Mo	0.1
82	K_2HPO_4	200
83	Si, as orthosilicic acid	35
84	Zn	0.3
85	pH = 7.0-7.5	
	Chlorella pyrenoidosa [8]	
86	B	0.5
87	Ca	0.5
88	Co[10]	0.01
89	Cu[10]	0.04
90	Fe[10]	0.2
91	$MgSO_4 \cdot 7H_2O$	500
92	Mn[10]	0.5
93	Mo	0.02
94	KH_2PO_4	1310
95	V	0.01
96	Zn[10]	0.5
97	Urea[11]	440
98	pH = 6.0	
	Soil Algae [5]	
99	H_3BO_3	11.4
100	$CaCl_2 \cdot 2H_2O$	25
101	$Co(NO_3)_2 \cdot 6H_2O$	0.5
102	$CuSO_4 \cdot 5H_2O$	1.6
103	$FeSO_4 \cdot 7H_2O$	5
104	K_2HPO_4	75
105	KH_2PO_4	175
106	$MgSO_4 \cdot 7H_2O$	75
107	$MnCl_2 \cdot 4H_2O$	1.4
108	MoO_3	0.7
109	NaCl	25
110	$NaNO_3$	250
111	$ZnSO_4 \cdot 7H_2O$	8.8
112	EDTA[12]	50

[10] These metals were used as compounds chelated by EDTA. [11] Or KNO_3, 1440 mg/liter. [12] EDTA dissolved and neutralized with KOH.

Contributors: (a) Provasoli, Luigi, (b) Allen, Mary Belle, (c) Starr, Richard C.

References

[1] Allen, M. B., and D. I. Arnon. 1955. Plant Physiol. 30:366.

[2] Hughes, E. O., P. R. Gorham, and A. Zehnder. 1958. Can. J. Microbiol. 4:227.

[3] Kratz, W. A., and J. Myers. 1955. Am. J. Botany 42:282.

[4] Lewin, J. C. 1955. Plant Physiol. 30:129.

[5] Nichols, H. W., and H. C. Bold. 1966. J. Phycol. 1:34.

[6] Pringsheim, E. G. 1950. In J. Brunel, ed. The culturing of algae. C. F. Kettering Foundation, Dayton. p. 19.

[7] Provasoli, L., J. J. A. McLaughlin, and M. R. Droop. 1957. Arch. Mikrobiol. 25:408.

[8] Sorokin, C., and R. W. Krauss. 1962. Plant Physiol. 37:37.

[9] Staub, R. 1961. Schweiz. Z. Hydrobiol. 23:82.

Part IV. Higher Plants

	Constituent	Concentration mg/liter
1	H_3BO_3	0.57
2	$Ca(NO_3)_2 \cdot 4H_2O$	1180
3	$CuSO_4 \cdot 5H_2O$	0.04
4	$FeSO_4 \cdot 7H_2O$	2.5
5	$MgSO_4 \cdot 7H_2O$	493
6	$MnCl_2 \cdot 4H_2O$	0.90
7	H_2MoO_4	0.02
8	KH_2PO_4	136
9	K_2SO_4	349
10	$ZnSO_4 \cdot 7H_2O$	0.22

Contributor: Robbins, W. Rei

Reference: Robbins, W. R. Unpublished. Rutgers State Univ., New Brunswick, N.J., 1966.

30. CULTURE MEDIA: PLANT TISSUES

Part I. Balanced Salt Solutions

	Constituent	Concentration mg/liter
	White [3,4]	
1	H_3BO_3	1.5
2	$Ca(NO_3)_2 \cdot 4H_2O$	300
3	$Fe_2(SO_4)_3$	2.5
4	$MgSO_4 \cdot 7H_2O$	720
5	$MnSO_4 \cdot 4H_2O$	7
6	KCl	65
7	KI	0.75
8	KNO_2	80
9	$NaH_2PO_4 \cdot H_2O$	16.5
10	Na_2SO_4	200
11	$ZnSO_4 \cdot 7H_2O$	3
	Heller [1,2,4]	
12	$AlCl_3$	0.03
13	H_3BO_3	1
14	$CaCl_2 \cdot 2H_2O$	75
15	$CuSO_4 \cdot 5H_2O$	0.03
16	$FeCl_3 \cdot 6H_2O$	1
17	$MgSO_4 \cdot 7H_2O$	250
18	$MnSO_4 \cdot 4H_2O$	0.1
19	$NiO_2 \cdot 6H_2O$	0.03
20	KCl	750
21	KI	0.01
22	$NaNO_3$	600
23	$NaH_2PO_4 \cdot H_2O$	125
24	$ZnSO_4 \cdot 7H_2O$	1

Contributor: White, Philip R.

References

[1] Gautheret, R. J. 1959. La culture des tissus vegetaux. G. Masson, Paris.

[2] Heller, R. 1953. Ann. Sci. Nat. Botan. Biol. Vegetale, Ser. 11, 14:1.

[3] White, P. R. 1943. A handbook of plant tissue culture. J. Cattell Press, Lancaster, Penna.

[4] White, P. R. 1963. The cultivation of animal and plant cells. Ed. 2. Ronald Press, New York.

Part II. Tissue Culture Media

	Constituent	Concentration mg/liter
	Stem Tips1/ [1]	
1	Agar	10,000
2	Glucose	75,000
3	Gibberellin	1
	Root Tips2/ [3,4]	
4	Thiamine	0.1
5	Nicotinic acid	0.5
6	Vitamin B_6	0.1
7	Sucrose	20,000
8	Glycine	3
	Callus1/ [2,4]	
9	2,4-D	0.1
10	Thiamine	0.1
11	Nicotinic acid	0.5
12	Vitamin B_6	0.1
13	Agar	5,000
14	Sucrose	50,000
15	Glycine	3
	Tumor1/ [2,4]	
16	Thiamine	0.1
17	Nicotinic acid	0.5
18	Vitamin B_6	0.1
19	Agar	5,000
20	Sucrose	50,000

1/ Add specified ingredients to either White's or Heller's balanced salt solution (*see* Part I). 2/ Add specified ingredients to White's balanced salt solution only (*see* Part I).

Contributor: White, Philip R.

References

[1] Ball, E. 1960. Growth 24:91.

[2] Gautheret, R. J. 1959. La culture des tissus vegetaux. G. Masson, Paris.

[3] White, P. R. 1943. A handbook of plant tissue culture. J. Cattell Press, Lancaster, Penna.

[4] White, P. R. 1963. The cultivation of animal and plant cells. Ed. 2. Ronald Press, New York.

IV. DIGESTION AND ABSORPTION

31. COMPOSITION OF SALIVA

Part I. Man

Values are means, ± the standard deviation, and/or ranges, estimate "c" (*see* Introduction), unless otherwise specified.

	Property or Constituent	No. of Obser-vations	Source of Saliva	Stimulant	Value	Reference
	Physical Properties & General Chemical Constituents					
1	Freezing point depression	......	Mixed	None	(0.07-0.34)°C	15
2	pH	3405	Mixed	None	6.75(5.6-7.6)	3
3		39	Mixed	Paraffin	7.45(7.2-7.6)	32
4		154	Parotid	None	6.29 ± 0.34	49
5		72	Sublingual	None	6.49 ± 0.35	49
6		154	Submaxillary	None	6.38 ± 0.39	49
7	Secretion rate	148	Mixed	None	0.57(0.1-1.8) ml/min	46
8		148	Mixed	Paraffin	1.9(0.4-4.8) ml/min	46
9		527	Parotid	None	0.04 ± 0.036 ml/min	55
10		29	Parotid	Paraffin	0.7 ± 0.1(0.2-2.4) ml/min	30
11		28	Parotid	2% citric acid	1.2 ± 0.6(0.5-2.7) ml/min	42
12		30	Parotid	....	1.58(0.62-3.83) ml/min	6
13		28	Submaxillary	2% citric acid	1.2 ± 0.7(0.2-2.8) ml/min	42
14		30	Submaxillary	....	1.13(0.37-2.32) ml/min	6
15	Specific gravity	......	Mixed	None	(1.010-1.020)	10,15,29
16		450	Parotid	Acid	1.0033	43
17	Solids, total	69	Mixed	Paraffin	581(386-860) mg/100 ml	52
	Inorganic Substances					
18	Calcium, total	650	Mixed	None	5.8(5.2-9.7) mg/100 ml	1
19		100	Mixed	Paraffin	5.87(3.66-10.65) mg/100 ml	23
20		28	Parotid	2% citric acid	3.5 ± 1.4(2.1-6.7) mg/100 ml	42
21		28	Submaxillary	2% citric acid	8.0 ± 2.3(4.4-13.1) mg/100 ml	42
22	dialyzable	28	Parotid	2% citric acid	2.6 ± 1.0(0.7-4.8) mg/100 ml	42
23		28	Submaxillary	2% citric acid	6.3 ± 2.3(2.0-12.0) mg/100 ml	42
24	nondialyzable	28	Parotid	2% citric acid	1.0 ± 0.4(0.3-1.9) mg/100 ml	42
25		28	Submaxillary	2% citric acid	1.7 ± 0.9(0.5-3.5) mg/100 ml	42
26	Chloride	......	Mixed	None	15.5(8.4-17.7) mEq/liter	28
27		......	Mixed	Paraffin	11.8(8.7-17.7) mEq/liter	28
28		527	Parotid	None	24.8 ± 7.6 mEq/liter	48
29	Cobalt	37	Mixed	Paraffin	2.44(0-12.53) µg/100 ml	12
30	Copper	30	Mixed	None	31.7 ± 15.1(5.0-76.0) µg/100 ml	9
31		48	Mixed	Paraffin	25.9(10.0-47.5) µg/100 ml	12
32	Fluoride	......	Mixed	None	(0-0.005) mEq/liter	28
33	Iodide	21	Parotid	None	6.46 µg/100 ml	27
34		8	Submaxillary	None	3.65 µg/100 ml	
35	Iodine	......	Mixed	None	(0-350) µg/100 ml	4
36	Magnesium	67	Mixed	None	0.502 ± 0.31(0.157-0.934) mg/100 ml	23
37		116	Mixed	Paraffin	0.356 ± 0.18(0.151-0.878) mg/100 ml	
38	Phosphorus, total	50	Mixed	None	20.4 mg/100 ml	39
39	inorganic	180	Mixed	None	14.9(7.4-21.1) mg/100 ml	39
40		28	Parotid	2% citric acid	11.1 ± 2.8(7.0-16.5) mg/100 ml	42
41		28	Submaxillary	2% citric acid	9.0 ± 2.8(4.9-12.7) mg/100 ml	42

continued

31. COMPOSITION OF SALIVA

Part I. Man

	Property or Constituent	No. of Observations	Source of Saliva	Stimulant	Value	Reference
42	organic	50	Mixed	None	5.5 mg/100 ml	39
43		28	Parotid	2% citric acid	2.2 ± 1.5(0.6-5.6) mg/100 ml	42
44		28	Submaxillary	2% citric acid	1.6 ± 0.9(0.6-3.8) mg/100 ml	42
45	lipid	207	Mixed	None	0.119(0.02-0.24) mg/100 ml	37
46	Potassium	148	Mixed	None	80.3(56-148) mg/100 ml	46
47		148	Mixed	Paraffin	57.3(19-133) mg/100 ml	
48	Sodium	147	Mixed	None	23.2(8-56) mg/100 ml	46
49		148	Mixed	Paraffin	57.3(19-133) mg/100 ml	
50	Bicarbonate	25	Mixed	None	6.44(3.48-10.70) mEq/liter	13
51		25	Mixed	Paraffin	15.74(8.12-19.47) mEq/liter	13
52		502	Parotid	None	1.04 ± 0.94 mEq/liter	46,54
53	Carbon dioxide	......	Mixed	None	12(5-25) vol %	28
54		......	Mixed	Paraffin	25(8-44) vol %	
				Vitamins		
55	Thiamine	8	Mixed	None	0.7 μg/100 ml	22
56		23	Mixed	Paraffin	(0.2-1.4) μg/100 ml	21
57	Riboflavin	8	Mixed	None	5.0 μg/100 ml	22
58	Nicotinic acid	90	Mixed	Paraffin	11.5(2.34-40.90) μg/100 ml	11
59	B_6	17	Mixed	Paraffin	0.6(0.1-1.7) μg/100 ml	33
60	Biotin	8	Mixed	None	0.08 μg/100 ml	22
61	Pantothenic acid	41	Mixed	Paraffin	8.8(1.2-19.0) μg/100 ml	36
62	Folic acid	20	Mixed	Paraffin	2.4(0.3-7.5) μg/100 ml	33
63	B_{12}	2	Mixed	Paraffin	0.33(0.15-0.50) μg/100 ml	24
64	Choline	7	Mixed	None	0.65(0.47-0.99) mg/100 ml	14
65		87	Mixed	Paraffin	1.62(0.62-3.64) mg/100 ml	
66	Ascorbic acid	110	Mixed	Paraffin	0.07(0-0.372) mg/100 ml	26
67	K	8	Mixed	None	1.5 μg/100 ml	22
				Lipids, Carbohydrates, & Organic Acids		
68	Cholesterol	......	Mixed	None	7.5(3-15) mg/100 ml	28
	Carbohydrates, protein-bound					41
69	Deoxyribose	11	Parotid	Paraffin	0.19(0.17-0.22) mg/100 ml	
70	Galactose + mannose	43	Parotid	Paraffin	22.9 ± 10.3(4.7-47.6) mg/100 ml	
71	Glucose	4	Parotid	Paraffin	1.5(1.0-2.6) mg/100 ml	
72	Hexosamine	43	Parotid	Paraffin	7.5 ± 3.3(2.0-15.2) mg/100 ml	
73	Methylpentose	43	Parotid	Paraffin	5.9 ± 2.6(1.5-12.9) mg/100 ml	
74	Fucose	......	....	None	(54-133.1)[1] μg/ml	16
75	Glucose, total	16	Mixed	None	19.6(11.28-28.08) mg/100 ml	62
76		10	Mixed	Paraffin	20.7(14.04-30.0) mg/100 ml	62
77		507	Parotid	None	0.75 ± 0.68 mg/100 ml	59
78	free	43	Parotid	Paraffin	0.2 mg/100 ml	41
79	Citric acid	121	Mixed	Paraffin	1.05(0.20-3.15) mg/100 ml	63
80	Lactic acid	......	Mixed	None	0.17 mEq/L	28
81	Sialic acid	13	Parotid	....	0.27(0.11-0.36) mg/100 ml	41
82		18	Sublingual & submaxillary	Paraffin	13.1(5.7-25.4) mg/100 ml	40
				Nitrogenous Substances		
83	Protein	25	Mixed	None	386(156-630) mg/100 ml	13
84		25	Mixed	Paraffin	242(140-527) mg/100 ml	13
85		29	Parotid	Paraffin	125.7 ± 8.5(23.2-218.5) mg/100 ml	30

[1] Mean ranges.

continued

Part I. Man

	Property or Constituent	No. of Observations	Source of Saliva	Stimulant	Value	Reference
86	Mucin	30	Mixed	None	250 mg/100 ml	31
87		30	Mixed	Paraffin	270(80-600) mg/100 ml	
88	γ-Globulin, 1A	......	Parotid	None	28.0 mg/100 ml	7,18
89	2	......	Parotid	None	0	
90	Creatinine	3	Mixed	Paraffin	0.35(0.275-0.455) mg/100 ml	38
91	Ammonia	81[2]	Mixed	None	2.6 mM/liter	47
92		......	Mixed	Paraffin	3.5(0.8-7.1) mM/liter	15
93	Urea	9	Mixed	None	12.7(8.2-18.1) mg/100 ml	61
94		15	Mixed	Paraffin	8.8(0-14.3) mg/100 ml	60
95	Uric acid	......	Mixed	None	1.5(0.5-2.9) mg/100 ml	28,48
96		72	Mixed	Paraffin	4.8(1.5-8.7) mg/100 ml	60
97		29	Parotid	Paraffin	3.2 ± 0.2(1.3-5.3) mg/100 ml	30
98	Thiocyanate	35	Mixed	None	13.4(3.1-27.5) mg/100 ml	19
	Amino acids					
99	Alanine	9	Mixed	None	1.2(0.5-2.9) mg/100 ml	2
100	Arginine	18	Mixed	Paraffin	(3.3-10.0) mg/100 ml	35
101	Aspartic acid	9	Mixed	None	0.15(0.35-0.33) mg/100 ml	2
102	Cystine	18	Mixed	Paraffin	(0.16-0.45) mg/100 ml	35
103	Glutamic acid	9	Mixed	None	1.2(0.5-1.3) mg/100 ml	35
104		......	Mixed	Paraffin	(3.0-12.6) mg/100 ml	44
105	Glycine	9	Mixed	None	1.4(0.5-3.6) mg/100 ml	2
106		18	Mixed	Paraffin	(1.9-15.5) mg/100 ml	35
107	Histidine	18	Mixed	Paraffin	(0.35-2.00) mg/100 ml	35
108	Isoleucine	18	Mixed	Paraffin	(0.2-0.9) mg/100 ml	35
109	Leucine	18	Mixed	Paraffin	(0.025-0.300) mg/100 ml	35
110	Lysine	9	Mixed	None	0.77(0.15-1.50) mg/100 ml	2
111		18	Mixed	Paraffin	(0.4-1.5) mg/100 ml	34
112	Methionine	2	Mixed	Paraffin	(0.005-0.010) mg/100 ml	35
113	Phenylalanine	18	Mixed	Paraffin	(0.6-2.5) mg/100 ml	35
114	Proline	18	Mixed	Paraffin	(0.35-1.50) mg/100 ml	35
115	Serine	9	Mixed	None	0.66(0.33-1.20) mg/100 ml	2
116		18	Mixed	Paraffin	(1.0-1.8) mg/100 ml	34
117	Threonine	18	Mixed	Paraffin	(0.4-5.6) mg/100 ml	34
118	Tryptophan	18	Mixed	Paraffin	(0.2-0.9) mg/100 ml	34
119		29	Parotid	Paraffin	2.8 ± 0.2(1.3-5.2) mg/100 ml	30
120	Tyrosine	18	Mixed	Paraffin	(0.2-1.0) mg/100 ml	34
121		29	Parotid	Paraffin	5.2 ± 0.8(0.7-19.1) mg/100 ml	30
122	Valine	18	Mixed	Paraffin	(0.7-2.2) mg/100 ml	34
123	Nitrogen, total	20	Mixed	Paraffin	90.0(36.1-125.3) mg/100 ml	8
124	protein	20	Mixed	Paraffin	63.6(22.9-88.2) mg/100 ml	8
125	nonprotein	20	Mixed	Paraffin	36.4(8.2-62.4) mg/100 ml	8
126	ammonia	94[3]	Mixed	None	3.8(0.5-9.9) mg/100 ml	47
	Hormones & Enzymes[4]					
127	Cortisone	20	Mixed	Paraffin	0.45(0.15-0.85) μg/100 ml	25
128	Hydrocortisone	20	Mixed	Paraffin	0.11(0.05-0.2) μg/100 ml	25
129		18	Parotid	Sugared gum, 3 g	4.1 ± 1.6 mg/100 ml	58
130		10	Parotid	Sugared gum, 3 g	2.7 ± 0.8 mg/100 ml	57
131		206	Parotid	Sugared gum, 3 g	3.7 ± 1.7 mg/100 ml	56
132	Amylase	17	Mixed	Paraffin	40(17-102) units/ml[5]	45
133		17	Parotid	3% citric acid	50(25-120) units/ml[5]	45

[2] Subjects 12 years old. [3] Subjects 7 years old. [4] β-D-Galactosidase not demonstrable. [5] One unit of activity = approximately 1.8 × 10^{-2} mg amylase/ml saliva.

continued

31. COMPOSITION OF SALIVA

Part I. Man

	Property or Constituent	No. of Obser-vations	Source of Saliva	Stimulant	Value	Reference
134		17	Parotid	30% NaCl	53(17-116) units/ml 5/	45
135		16	Parotid	....	59.4 mg × 10^2 reducing sugar/ml	6
136		16	Submaxillary	....	14.4 mg × 10^2 reducing sugar/ml	6
137	Cholinesterase	......	Parotid	Paraffin	0.33(0.23-0.43) units/liter 6/	51
138	Esterase, total	......	Parotid	Paraffin	0.34(0.12-0.65) units/liter 7/	52
139		30	Parotid	....	0.065(0.049-0.101) units 8/	6
140		30	Submaxillary	....	0.118(0.059-0.455) units 8/	6
141	Glucose-6-phosphate de-hydrogenase	26	Mixed	....	8 ± 6.3(2-27) units/mg protein	50
142	β-Glucuronidase	......	Parotid	Paraffin	(170-1750) units/liter 9/	20
143		30	Parotid	....	81.56(12.12-150.00) units 10/	6
144		30	Submaxillary	....	54.28(5.88-123.52) units 10/	6
145	Lipase	......	Parotid	Paraffin	1.42(0.25-2.58) units/liter 11/	52
146	Lysozyme	......	Parotid	Paraffin	670(250-1360) units/liter	5
147	Phosphatase, acid	......	Parotid	Paraffin	4.23(2.5-7.7) units/liter 12/	53
148		30	Parotid	....	0.580(0.130-1.380) units 8/	6
149		30	Submaxillary	....	0.550(0.190-1.200) units 8/	6
150	alkaline	20	Mixed	Paraffin	1.04(0.08-1.94) units/100 ml	17
151	Pseudocholinesterase	30	Parotid	....	0.064(0.011-0.131) units 8/	6
152		30	Submaxillary	....	0.045(0-0.116) units 8/	6

5/ One unit of activity = approximately 1.8 × 10^{-2} mg amylase/ml saliva. 6/ β-Carbonaphthoxycholine iodide substrate. 7/ β-Naphthyl acetate substrate. 8/ One unit of activity = the quantity which liberated 10 mg β-naphthol or 6-bromo-2-naphthol per 1 hour incubation at 37°C. 9/ Sodium-8-benzoyl amino-2-naphthyl glucuronide substrate. 10/ One unit of activity = μg phenolphthalein liberated/100 ml saliva, in digest at 37°C for 17 hours. 11/ β-Naphthyl laurate substrate. 12/ Monosodium-β-naphthyl phosphate substrate.

Contributors: (a) Niedermeier, William, (b) Liebowitz, Daniel, and Ellis, Eldon E., (c) Grad, Bernard, (d) Frazer, A. C.; Sammons, H. G.; and Okunzua G.

References

[1] Becks, H., and W. W. Wainwright. 1946. J. Dental Res. 25:267.
[2] Berry, H. K. 1951. Texas Univ. Publ. 5109:157.
[3] Browley, R. E. 1935. J. Dental Res. 15:79.
[4] Cantarow, A., and B. Schepartz. 1967. Biochemistry. Ed. 4. W. B. Saunders, Philadelphia. p. 629.
[5] Chauncey, H. H., et al. 1954. J. Dental Res. 33:321.
[6] Chauncey, H. H., B. L. Henriques, and J. M. Tanzer. 1963. Arch. Oral Biol. 8:615.
[7] Chodirker, W. B., and T. B. Thomasi, Jr. 1963. Science 142:1080.
[8] Deakins, M., et al. 1941. J. Dental Res. 20:161.
[9] deJorge, F. B., et al. 1964. Clin. Chim. Acta 9:148.
[10] Dewar, J. R., and G. J. Parfitt. 1954. J. Dental Res. 33:596.
[11] Dreizen, S., A. I. Reed, and T. D. Spies. 1951. Intern. Z. Vitaminforsch. 22:396.
[12] Dreizen, S., H. A. Spies, and T. D. Spies. 1952. J. Dental Res. 31:137.
[13] Dreizen, S., et al. 1953. Ibid. 32:497.
[14] Eagle, E. 1941. J. Lab. Clin. Med. 27:103.
[15] Evans, C. L., and H. Hartridge. 1952. Principles of human physiology. Ed. 11. Lea and Febiger, Philadelphia. p.853.
[16] Evans, D. A. P. 1960. J. Lab. Clin. Med. 55:381.
[17] Ferrara, P. 1960. Ann. Stomatol. 9:287.
[18] Fisher, J. M., C. Ries, and K. B. Taylor. 1965. Science 150:1467.
[19] Fishman, E. J., and A. Fishman. 1948. J. Lab. Clin. Med. 33:772.
[20] Fishman, W. H., B. Springer, and R. Brunetti. 1948. J. Biol. Chem. 173:449.
[21] Fujishiro, I. 1951. Igaku To Seibutsugaku 23:59.
[22] Glavind, J. 1948. Intern. Z. Vitaminforsch. 20:234.
[23] Gow, B. S. 1965. J. Dental Res. 44:885.
[24] Granados, H., et al. 1950. Acta Pathol. Microbiol. Scand. 27:501.
[25] Greaves, M. S., and H. F. West. 1963. J. Endocrinol. 26:189.
[26] Hafkesbring, R., and J. T. Freeman. 1952. Am. J. Med. Sci. 224:324.
[27] Harden, R. McG., D. K. Mason, and W. W. Buchanon. 1965. J. Clin. Endocrinol. Metab. 25:957.
[28] Harrow, B., and Z. Mazur. 1954. Textbook of biochemistry. Ed. 6. W. B. Saunders, Philadelphia.
[29] Hawk, P. B., B. L. Oser, and W. H. Summerson. 1954. Practical physiological chemistry. Ed. 13. Blakiston, New York. p. 351.

continued

Part I. Man

[30] Hawkins, G. R., and I. Zipkin. 1964. Proc. Soc. Exptl. Biol. Med. 117:888.
[31] Inouye, J. M. 1930. J. Dental Res. 10:7.
[32] Karshan, M., F. Krasnow, and L. E. Krejci. 1931. Ibid. 11:573.
[33] Kauffman, S. L., G. J. Kasai, and S. A. Koser. 1953. Ibid. 32:840.
[34] Kesel, R. G., et al. 1947. Am. J. Orthodontics Oral Surg. 33:68.
[35] Kirch, E. R., et al. 1947. J. Dental Res. 26:297.
[36] Kniesner, A. H., A. W. Mann, and T. D. Spies. 1942. Ibid. 21:259.
[37] Krasnow, F. 1945. Ibid. 24:319.
[38] Ladell, W. S. S. 1947. J. Physiol. (London) 106:237.
[39] Luria, H. E. 1947. J. Dental Res. 26:203.
[40] Luria, H. E. 1961. Arch. Oral Biol. 4:141.
[41] Mandel, I. D., et al. 1961. Ibid. 3:278.
[42] Mandel, I. D., et al. 1964. Proc. Soc. Exptl. Biol. Med. 115:959.
[43] McAnear, J. F., I. L. Shannon, and G. F. Isbell. 1961. J. Dental Res. 40:720.
[44] Morris, J. L., and V. Jersey. 1923. J. Biol. Chem. 56:31.
[45] Newbrun, E. 1962. J. Dental Res. 41:459.
[46] Niedermeier, W. 1953. Federation Proc. 12:251.
[47] Nikifonk, G., et al. 1956. J. Pediat. 49:425.
[48] Pigman, W., and A. J. Reid. 1952. J. Am. Dental Assoc. 45:325.
[49] Raeder, A. 1966. N.Y. State Dental J. 32:365.
[50] Ramot, B., et al. 1960. Nature 185:931.
[51] Ravin, H. A., K. C. Tsou, and A. M. Seligman. 1951. J. Biol. Chem. 191:843.
[52] Seligman, A. M., and M. M. Nachlas. 1950. J. Clin. Invest. 29:31.
[53] Seligman, A. M., et al. 1951. J. Biol. Chem. 190:7.
[54] Shannon, I. L., W. A. Gibson, and H. H. Chauncey. 1963. J. Dental Res. 42:179.
[55] Shannon, I. L., and G. M. Isbell. 1962. Ibid. 41:496.
[56] Shannon, I. L., J. R. Prigmore, and S. C. Beering. 1964. J. Clin. Endocrinol. Metab. 23:1258.
[57] Shannon, I. L., J. R. Prigmore, and W. A. Gibson. 1963. U.S. Air Force School Aerospace Med. TDR 63-30.
[58] Shannon, I. L., et al. 1959. J. Clin. Endocrinol. Metab. 19:1477.
[59] Shannon, I. L., et al. 1963. Arch. Oral Biol. 8:419.
[60] Updegraff, H., and H. B. Lewis. 1924. J. Biol. Chem. 61:633.
[61] Wu, H., and D. Y. Wu. 1951. Proc. Soc. Exptl. Biol. Med. 76:130.
[62] Young, D. 1941. J. Dental Res. 20:597.
[63] Zipkin, I., and F. J. McClure. 1949. Ibid. 28:613.

Part II. Ruminants

Values in parentheses are ranges, estimate "c" (*see* Introduction).

	Animal	Source of Saliva	Property or Constituent	Method of Determination	Value	Remarks	Reference
1	Cattle	Mixed[1]	pH	....	8.4(8.3-8.5)	4 shorthorn cows, not lactating, eating, or ruminating; saliva collected from cardia through large rumen fistula which was closed by a rubber bung when not in use	3
2			Ash	....	0.88(0.85-0.90) g/100 ml		
3			Solids	....	1.0(0.97-1.07) g/100 ml		
4			Chloride	Sendroy, 1937	6.7(3.0-10.2) mEq/liter		
5			Potassium	Flame photometry	21(4-89) mEq/liter		
6			Sodium	Kramer & Gittlebaum, 1924	143(75-166) mEq/liter		
7			Bicarbonate	Conway, 1957 (for CO_2)	123(116-126) mEq/liter		
8			Phosphate	Allen, 1940	26(20-33) mEq/liter		
9			Nitrogen	Micro Kjeldahl	7.5(3.3-14.4) mg/100 ml		
10			Urea nitrogen	Conway, 1957 (for urea)	5.8(2.1-12.3) mg/100 ml		
11		Parotid	Chloride	Sendroy, 1937	6.5 mEq/liter	1 Friesian steer; papilla exteriorized	2
12			Phosphorus[2]	Allen, 1940	19 mEq/liter		
13			Potassium	Flame photometry	5.5 mEq/liter		
14			Sodium	Kramer & Gittlebaum, 1924	160 mEq/liter		
15			Bicarbonate	Conway, 1957 (for CO_2)	129 mEq/liter		
16			Nitrogen	Micro Kjeldahl	7.6 mg/100 ml		
17			Urea nitrogen	Conway, 1957 (for urea)	6.3 mg/100 ml		
18			Chloride	Sendroy, 1937	12 mEq/liter & 21 mEq/liter	2 calves, 5 & 8 months old[3]	5
19			Phosphorus[2]	Allen, 1940	47 mEq/liter & 17 mEq/liter		

[1] Lower and upper limits of ranges were determined from 16 to 25 recorded means, each mean the result of 12 observations.
[2] As HPO_4. [3] Anesthetized.

continued

31. COMPOSITION OF SALIVA

Part II. Ruminants

	Animal	Source of Saliva	Property or Constituent	Method of Determination	Value	Remarks	Reference
20			Potassium	Flame photometry	14 mEq/liter & 6 mEq/liter		
21			Sodium	Kramer & Gittlebaum, 1924	163 mEq/liter & 168 mEq/liter		
22			Bicarbonate	Conway, 1957 (for CO_2)	88 mEq/liter & 94 mEq/liter		
23	Goat	Parotid	pH	....	(8.12-8.32)	....	7
24			Ash	....	(20-1020) mg/100 ml	....	
25			Solids, total	....	(710-1960) mg/100 ml	....	
26			Nitrogen, total	....	(10-46) mg/100 ml	....	
27			Chloride	Buchler-Cotlove	12.5 ± 2.8 mEq/liter	4 adult animals; parotid duct cannulated	6
28			Potassium	Flame photometry	5.4 ± 0.79 mEq/liter		
29			Sodium	Flame photometry	181 ± 5.4 mEq/liter		
30	Sheep	Mixed	pH	....	8.5(8.4-8.6)	4 animals[3], 5 samples	7
31			Ash	....	0.88(0.8-0.9) g/100 g	3 animals[3], 4 samples	
32			Solids	....	1.05(1.0-1.2) g/100 g		
33			Calcium	Clark & Collip, 1925	1.1(0.8-1.5) mEq/liter	4 animals[3], 6 samples	
34			Chloride	Whitehorn, 1921 & Sendroy, 1925	10(7-12) mEq/liter	4 animals[3], 5 samples	
35			Magnesium	Denis, 1922	0.6(0.5-0.8) mEq/liter	3 animals[3], 6 samples	
36			Phosphorus[2]	Fiske & Subbarow, 1925	36(24-46) mEq/liter	4 animals[3], 6 samples	
37			Potassium	Kramer & Tisdall, 1921	6.9(4.1-12.0) mEq/liter		
38			Bicarbonate	....	104(89-126) mEq/liter[4]	4 animals[3], 7 samples	
39			Nitrogen	Micro Kjeldahl; McKenzie & Wallace, 1954	14.1(8.7-21.3) mg/100 ml	12 animals[3], 45 samples	8
40		Parotid	Secretion rate	Modification of Chauncey, et al, 1954	2.74(1.58-5.40) ml/min	6 adult ♂ animals[3]; direct intraoral cannulation	4
41			pH	....	8.04(7.69-8.23)	2 animals[5], 6 samples	7
42			Ash	....	1.06(0.95-1.15) g/100 ml		
43			Solids	....	1.31(1.28-1.38) g/100 ml		
44			Calcium	Modification of Wilson, 1955	0.74(0.30-1.70) mEq/liter	2 animals[5], 12 samples	9
45			Chloride	Whitehorn, 1921; Sendroy, 1937; Sanderson potentiometric	12(5-25) mEq/liter	13 animals[5], 17 samples	5,7
46			Magnesium	Wilson, 1955	0.45(0.17-1.32) mEq/liter	2 animals[5], 12 samples	9
47			Phosphorus[2]	Fiske & Subbarow, 1925	56(25-83) mEq/liter	13 animals[5], 18 samples	5,7
48			Potassium[6]	Kramer & Tisdall, 1921	10.5(3.1-31.0) mEq/liter		
49			Sodium[6]	Kramer & Gittlebaum, 1924	176(147-192) mEq/liter		
50			Bicarbonate	Van Slyke volumetric & Conway microdiffusion	107(47-125) mEq/liter		
51			Nitrogen[7]	Micro Kjeldahl	14.3(8.1-24.0) mg/100 ml	9 animals[5], 66 samples	7,8
52			Esterase, total[8]	Modification of Chauncey, et al, 1954	0.270(0.185-0.380) units[9]	6 adult ♂ animals[3]; direct intraoral cannulation	4
53			Phosphatase, acid	Modification of Chauncey, et al, 1954	0.022(0.006-0.032) units[9]		
54			Pseudocholinesterase	Modification of Chauncey, et al, 1954	0.384(0.320-0.480) units[9]		

[2] As HPO_4. [3] Anesthetized. [4] CO_2 content of saliva exposed to room air; equilibration with alveolar air increased CO_2 content by 10-20%. [5] Conscious, and with a cannulated parotid duct. [6] K:Na ratio is markedly influenced by sufficiency or insufficiency of Na in the body; during Na depletion, the ratio decreases. [7] Of the total nitrogen, from 10-25% was nondialyzable; urea accounted for 60-71% of the total nitrogen. [8] Pseudocholinesterase not demonstrable in submaxillary saliva; amylase and β-D-galactosidase not demonstrable in parotid and submaxillary saliva. [9] One unit of activity = the quantity which liberated 10 mg β-naphthol or 6-bromo-2-naphthol per 1 hour incubation at 37°C.

continued

31. COMPOSITION OF SALIVA

Part II. Ruminants

	Animal	Source of Saliva	Property or Constituent	Method of Determination	Value	Remarks	Reference
55		Submaxillary[10/]	Calcium	Modification of Wilson, 1955	1.88(0.96-2.66) mEq/liter	11 conscious animals; temporary cannulation of the duct	9
56			Magnesium	Wilson, 1955	0.50(0.10-1.00) mEq/liter		
57			Chloride	Sanderson potentiometric, 1952	11(7-15) mEq/liter	11 conscious animals; temporary cannulation of the duct	1,5
58			Phosphorus[2/]	Fiske & Subbarow, 1925	5(2-10) mEq/liter		
59			Potassium	Flame photometry	16(10-25) mEq/liter		
60			Sodium	Flame photometry	9(4-16) mEq/liter		
61			Bicarbonate	Conway microdiffusion	9(5-14) mEq/liter		
62			Esterase, total[8/]	Modification of Chauncey, et al, 1954	0.186(0.062-0.448) units[9/]	6 adult ♂ animals[3/]; direct intraoral cannulation	4
63			Phosphatase, acid	Modification of Chauncey, et al, 1954	0.024(0.012-0.029) units[9/]		
64		Sublingual	Chloride	Sanderson potentiometric, 1952	28(16-40) mEq/liter	6 animals[3/]	1,5
65			Phosphorus[2/]	Fiske & Subbarow, 1925	0.9(0.3-2.0) mEq/liter	6 animals[3/], 4 samples	
66			Potassium	Flame photometry	11(6-25) mEq/liter	6 animals[3/]	
67			Sodium	Flame photometry	30(16-47) mEq/liter		
68			Bicarbonate	Conway microdiffusion	12(8-18) mEq/liter	6 animals[3/], 5 samples	
69		Labial	Chloride	Sanderson potentiometric, 1952	34 mEq/liter	3 animals[3/], 2 samples	1,5
70			Phosphorus[2/]	Fiske & Subbarow, 1925	5(2-10) mEq/liter	3 animals[3/]	
71			Potassium	Flame photometry	6(3-9) mEq/liter		
72			Sodium	Flame photometry	39(29-47) mEq/liter		
73			Bicarbonate	Conway microdiffusion	3(2-4) mEq/liter	3 animals[3/], 5 samples	
74		Palatine	Chloride	Sanderson potentiometric, 1952	25 & 45 mEq/liter	2 animals[3/]	1,5
75			Phosphorus[2/]	Fiske & Subbarow, 1925	25 mEq/liter		
76			Potassium	Flame photometry	4 & 13 mEq/liter		
77			Sodium	Flame photometry	171 & 179 mEq/liter		
78			Bicarbonate	Conway microdiffusion	56 & 109 mEq/liter		

[2/] As HPO_4. [3/] Anesthetized. [8/] Pseudocholinesterase not demonstrable in submaxillary saliva; amylase and β-D-galactosidase not demonstrable in parotid and submaxillary saliva. [9/] One unit of activity = the quantity which liberated 10 mg β-naphthol or 6-bromo-2-naphthol per 1 hour incubation at 37°C. [10/] Rate of secretion influences composition of saliva and especially of submaxillary saliva: resting submaxillary secretion has high PO_4 and K concentrations and low Cl, Na, and HCO_2 concentrations, and as the rate of secretion increases, concentrations are reversed.

Contributors: (a) Phillipson, A. T., (b) Liebowitz, Daniel, and Ellis, Eldon E.

References

[1] Ash, R. W., and R. N. B. Kay. 1963. Progress in nutrition and allied sciences. Oliver and Boyd, Edinburgh.

[2] Bailey, C. B., and C. C. Balch. 1961. Brit. J. Nutr. 15:371.

[3] Bailey, C. B., and C. C. Balch. 1961. Ibid. 15:383.

[4] Chauncey, H. H., B. L. Henriques, and J. M. Tanzer. 1963. Arch. Oral Biol. 8:615.

[5] Kay, R. N. B. 1960. J. Physiol. (London) 150:515.

[6] Komi, N., and W. H. Snyder, Jr. 1963. Am. J. Physiol. 204:1055.

[7] McDougall, E. I. 1948. Biochem. J. 43:99.

[8] Somers, M. 1961. Australian J. Exptl. Biol. Med. Sci. 39:111.

[9] Storry, J. E. 1961. Nature 190:1197.

continued

31. COMPOSITION OF SALIVA

Part III. Mammals Other Than Man and Ruminants

Values in parentheses are ranges, estimate "c" (*see* Introduction).

	Animal	Property or Constituent	Source of Saliva	Value	Reference
1	Cat	pH	Mixed	7.5	4
2		Chloride	Submaxillary	(16.8-36.0) mEq/liter	7
3		Potassium	Submaxillary	8.6(7.7-9.2) mEq/liter	7
4		Sodium	Submaxillary	31.0(24.0-46.0) mEq/liter	7
5		Bicarbonate	Submaxillary	12.8(11.6-13.6) mEq/liter	7
6	Dog	pH	Mixed	(7.50-7.56)	4
7		Secretion rate	Parotid	0.55(0.14-1.40) ml/min	2
8			Submaxillary	1.31(0.20-3.84) ml/min	
9		Ash	Mixed	(290-610) mg/100 ml	1
10		Solids, total	Mixed	(440-1610) mg/100 ml	1
11		Calcium	Mixed	(2.9-6.6) mEq/liter	1
12			Parotid	8.6(5.0-10.3) mEq/liter	3
13		Chloride	Mixed	(16.3-69.3) mEq/liter	1
14			Parotid	81.9(37.5-103.7) mEq/liter	3
15		Phosphorus, total	Mixed	(1.2-3.0) mg/100 ml	1
16		Potassium	Mixed	(12.3-23.7) mEq/liter	1
17			Parotid	11.4(4.3-12.6) mEq/liter	3
18		Sodium	Parotid	108(48.8-132.9) mEq/liter	3
19		Bicarbonate	Parotid	55(34.7-69.1) mEq/liter	3
20		Amylase	Submaxillary[1]	$<0.010 \times 10^2$ mg/ml	2
21		Esterase, total	Parotid	0.416(0.238-0.831) units[2]	2
22			Submaxillary	1.296(0.488-3.575) units[2]	
23		β-D-Galactosidase	Parotid	0.076(0-0.130) units[2]	2
24			Submaxillary	0.334(0.160-0.575) units[2]	
25		Phosphatase, acid	Parotid	0.029(0.013-0.052) units[2]	2
26			Submaxillary	0.030(0.008-0.054) units[2]	
27		Pseudocholinesterase	Parotid	0.209(0.112-0.348) units[2]	2
28			Submaxillary	0.892(0.510-1.788) units[2]	
29	Horse	pH	Mixed	(7.31-8.62)	6
30		Specific gravity	Mixed	(1.001-1.008)	5
31			Parotid	(1.005-1.007)	
32		Ash	Mixed	(113-549) mg/100 ml	5
33		Solids, total	Mixed	1000 mg/100 ml	4
34		Water	Parotid	99.0%	4
35		Chloride	Mixed	(0.0056-0.0611) mEq/liter	4
36		Nitrogen	Mixed	(0.01-0.05) mM/liter	5
37	Rabbit	Secretion rate	Parotid	0.033(0.016-0.052) ml/min	2
38			Submaxillary	0.049(0.036-0.072) ml/min	
39		Amylase	Parotid	41.20(31.20-51.20 mg $\times 10^2$ reducing sugar/ml	2
40			Submaxillary	$<0.010 \times 10^2$ mg/ml	
41		Esterase, total[3]	Parotid	0.486(0.330-0.762) units[2]	2
42			Submaxillary	0.498(0.430-0.626) units[2]	
43		β-D-Galactosidase	Parotid	0.290(0.220-0.420) units[2]	2
44			Submaxillary	0.537(0.320-0.700 units[2]	
45		Phosphatase, acid	Parotid	0.200(0.126-0.360) units[2]	2
46			Submaxillary	0.077(0.033-0.121) units[2]	
47	Rat[4]	Amylase	Mixed	98.83(93.50-110.00) mg $\times 10^2$ reducing sugar/ml	2
48		Esterase, total	Mixed	7.267(5.320-8.720) units[2]	2
49		β-D-Galactosidase	Mixed	0.815(0.220-1.300) units[2]	2

[1] Amylase not demonstrable in parotid saliva. [2] One unit of activity = the quantity which liberated 10 mg β-naphthol or 6-bromo-2-naphthol per 1 hour incubation at 37°C. [3] Pseudocholinesterase not demonstrable. [4] Enzyme values for mixed saliva should be cautiously interpreted, since the enzyme measured may have originated from sources other than the salivary glands, e.g., bacteria and nasopharyngeal secretions.

continued

31. COMPOSITION OF SALIVA

Part III. Mammals Other Than Man and Ruminants

	Animal	Property or Constituent	Source of Saliva	Value	Reference
50		Phosphatase, acid	Mixed	0.220(0.149-0.290) units[2/]	2
51		Pseudocholinesterase	Mixed	2.040(0.800-2.700) units[2/]	2
52	Swine	pH	Mixed	(7.15-7.44)	5
53		Secretion rate	Parotid	2.98(0.62-4.88) ml/min	2
54			Submaxillary	1.18(0.90-1.78) ml/min	
55		Specific gravity	Parotid	(1.002-1.009)	5
56			Sublingual	(1.002-1.009)	
57			Submaxillary	(0.9996-1.001)	
58		Ash	Parotid	(120-360) mg/100 ml	5
59			Sublingual	320 mg/100 ml	
60			Submaxillary	164 mg/100 ml	
61		Nitrogen	Parotid	(0.004-0.099) mM/liter	5
62			Sublingual	(0.006-0.025) mM/liter	
63			Submaxillary	(0.006-0.025) mM/liter	
64		Amylase	Parotid[5/]	0.110(0.028-0.239) mg × 10^2 reducing sugar/ml	2
65		Esterase, total	Parotid	11.920(2.750-23.400) units[2/]	2
66			Submaxillary	0.984(0.535-2.380) units[2/]	
67		β-D-Galactosidase	Parotid	0.055(0-0.105) units[2/]	2
68			Submaxillary	0.108(0-0.150) units[2/]	
69		Phosphatase, acid	Parotid	0.027(0.007-0.041) units[2/]	2
70			Submaxillary	0.066(0.036-0.094) units[2/]	
71		Pseudocholinesterase	Parotid	68.250(24.600-112.000) units[2/]	2
72			Submaxillary	2.825(1.000-6.250) units[2/]	

2/ One unit of activity = the quantity which liberated 10 mg β-naphthol or 6-bromo-2-naphthol per 1 hour incubation at 37°C. 5/ Amylase not demonstrable in submaxillary saliva.

Contributors: (a) Liebowitz, Daniel, (b) Frazer, A. C.; Sammons, H. G.; and Okunzua, G., (c) Grad, Bernard

References

[1] Baxter, H. 1933. J. Biol. Chem. 102:203.

[2] Chauncey, H. H., B. L. Henriques, and J. M. Tanzer. 1963. Arch. Oral Biol. 8:615.

[3] De Beer, E. J., and D. W. Wilson. 1932. J. Biol. Chem. 95:671.

[4] Dukes, H. H. 1947. The physiology of domestic animals. Ed. 6. Comstock, Ithaca. pp. 260-278.

[5] Lenkeit, W. 1933. Ergeb. Physiol. 35:573.

[6] McDougall, E. I. 1948. Biochem. J. 43:99.

[7] Stavraky, G. W. 1940. Am. J. Physiol. 129:539.

32. COMPOSITION OF ESOPHAGEAL SECRETIONS: DOG

Values in parentheses are ranges, estimate "c" (*see* Introduction).

	Property or Constituent	Value		Property or Constituent	Value
1	Acid-combining power	(11.5-15.0) mEq/liter	7	Solids	(1.25-1.47) g/100 g
2	pH	(7.5-8.3)	8	Calcium	(6.2-6.9) mg/100 g
3	Secretion rate	(0.013-0.140) ml/min	9	Chloride	(501-618) mg/100 g
4	Specific gravity	1.007	10	Nitrogen, total	(52.5-142.4) mg/100 g
5	Ash	(0.96-1.05) g/100 g	11	Phosphorus, total	(0.9-1.2) mg/100 g
6	Organic material	(0.26-0.52) g/100 g	12	Potassium	(51.0-58.2) mg/100 g

Contributor: Liebowitz, Daniel

Reference: Babkin, B. P. 1950. Secretory mechanism of the digestive glands. Ed. 2. P. B. Hoeber, New York.

33. PROPERTIES OF THE CROP: BIRDS

The ingluvies is an expanded part of the esophagus or gullet (the term "crop" is usually associated with this organ in the chicken, pigeon, pheasant and turkey, and it is called the "craw" in the waterfowl). The ingluvies functions as a passageway, a producer of lubricating fluid, a storage area, a softening area, a producer of "milk" in doves and pigeons, a resonance chamber [4], a display organ [4], and a chemical digestion chamber. It is composed of five distinct layers: a mucous membrane layer covered by stratified squamous epithelium, a muscularis mucosa, a submucous tissue, an inner stratum of muscle, and an outer stratum of muscle [3].

	Species 1/	Crop					Remarks
		Type	pH 2/	Enzymes 3/	Food Movement	Motility Interval 4/	
1	*Anas platyrhynchos*	False	4.9 [7]	...	...	...	...
2	*Columba livia*	Double	4.3 [7]	Amylase, invertase [6]	...	10-20 sec [8]	"Pigeon milk" is composed of 58.6% protein [5], 33.8% fat, 4.6% ash, plus vitamins and growth factor [16] 5/
3	*Gallus domesticus* 6/	True 7/	4.5 [7]	Amylase [13], diastase [17], lactase [17]	2-24 hr	50-60 sec [8]	Movement of food out of crop is influenced by particle size [12], consistency, hardness and water content of feed
4	*Meleagris gallopavo*	True 7/	6.1 [7]	Amylase [9]	2-4 hr [14]	...	...
5	*Phasianus colchicus*	True 7/	5.8 [7]	...	...	...	...

1/ *Anser anser* has a rudimentary crop. 2/ Depends to some extent on mineral content of diet [11], and age of bird [15]. 3/ Enzymes listed are probably those from the crop, but otherwise the crop plays a minor role in enzymatic digestion; some enzymes identified in the crop are found in the feed or move up from the proventriculus or down from the mouth [2]. 4/ As the proventriculus becomes full, contractions slow down and eventually stop. 5/ "Pigeon milk" is produced by desquamation of fat-laden cells from the proliferated squamous epithelium of the crop [1]; the crop may also contain fragments of these cells plus small feed particles. 6/ Cropectomization does not affect survival or performance [10]. 7/ Crops may become pendulous under certain genetic, management, or nutritional conditions; glucose is absorbed by the crop [18].

Contributor: Sunde, M. L.

References

[1] Beams, H. W., and R. K. Meyer. 1931. Physiol. Zool. 4:486.
[2] Bolton, W. 1965. Brit. Poultry Sci. 6:97.
[3] Bradley, O. C. 1950. The structure of the fowl. Oliver and Boyd, London.
[4] Clarke, K. F., H. Rohn, and M. D. Martin. 1942. Wyoming Game Fish Dept. Bull. 2:13.
[5] Davies, W. L. 1939. Biochem. J. 33:898.
[6] Dulzetto, F. 1928. Arch. Biol. (Liege) 38:173.
[7] Farner, D. S. 1942. Poultry Sci. 21:445.
[8] Farner, D. S. 1960. In A. J. Marshall, ed. Biology and comparative physiology of birds. Academic Press, New York. v. 1, pp. 411-467.
[9] Fedorovskii, N. P. 1951. Sov. Zootekh. 1:50.
[10] Fisher, H., and H. S. Weiss. 1956. Poultry Sci. 35: 418.
[11] Heller, V. G., and R. Penquite. 1936. Ibid. 15:397.
[12] Heuser, G. F. 1945. Ibid. 24:20.
[13] Hewitt, F. A., and R. L. Schelkopf. 1955. Am. J. Vet. Res. 16:576.
[14] Hillerman, J. P., F. H. Kratzer, and W. O. Wilson. 1953. Poultry Sci. 32:332.
[15] Laerdal, O. A. 1960. Ph.D. Thesis. Univ. Wisconsin, Madison.
[16] Pace, D. M., P. A. Landott, and F. E. Mussehl. 1952. Growth 16:279.
[17] Plimmer, R. H. A., and J. L. Rosedale. 1922. Biochem. J. 16:23.
[18] Soldarmo, D., M. R. Kare, and R. H. Wasserman. 1961. Poultry Sci. 40:123.

34. COMPOSITION OF GASTRIC JUICE: VERTEBRATES

Values in parentheses are ranges, estimate "c" unless otherwise indicated (*see* Introduction).

Part I. Man

For information on the distribution of gastrin in the gastrointestinal tract of man and other mammals, consult reference 8.

	Property or Constituent	Experimental Conditions	Value	Reference
		Physical Properties & General Chemical Constituents		
1	Freezing point depression	....	(0.55-0.62)°C	12
2		Fasting	(0.298-0.816)°C	1
3	pH	....	(1.49-8.38)	7
4	Secretion rate	Dilution technique	1.0(0.7-9.5) ml/min	14,19,20
5	Specific gravity	....	1.006(1.004-1.010)	1
6	Water	Postmortem measurements in 7♂, 5♀	0.4(0.1-1.2)% of total body water	11
		Inorganic Substances		
7	Calcium	....	(1.04-7.00) mg/100 ml	3
8		Fasting	3.6(2.0-4.8) mEq/liter	2
9	Chloride	Fasting	(77.6-159.0) mEq/liter	15
10		Histamine stimulation	(131.4-170.0) mEq/liter	15
11	Magnesium	....	(2.2-9.4) mg/100 ml	3
12	Potassium	....	10(0.5-32.5) mEq/liter	22
13		Fasting	11.6(6.4-16.6) mEq/liter	2
14	Sodium	....	60(0-116) mEq/liter	22
15		Fasting	49(18.7-69.5) mEq/liter	2
16	Bicarbonate	....	(0-130) mg/100 ml	3
17	Hydrochloric acid	Basal secretion	3.6 mEq/hr	18
18		2 mg/kg body wt, 60-90 min after administration of histalog	28.6 mEq/hr	18
19		120 min after administration of insulin	36.9 mEq/hr	13
20	Total	Fasting	(46.0-118.3) mEq/liter	15
21		Histamine stimulation	(85.6-137.3) mEq/liter	15
22	Free	Fasting	(0-115.0) mEq/liter	15
23		Histamine stimulation	(78.1-135.0) mEq/liter	15
24	Phosphate	....	(1.17-4.20) mg/100 ml	3
		Vitamins, Carbohydrates, & Organic Acids		
25	Ascorbic acid	....	0.95(0.91-1.05) mg/100 ml	9
26	Fucose	....	13.8 mg/100 ml	25
27	Glucose	Fasting	(0.35-1.19) mg/ml	15
28		Histamine stimulation	(0.33-1.12) mg/ml	15
29	Hexosamine	Fasting	32.7 mg/100 ml	25
30	Hexose, total	....	32.1 mg/100 ml	25
31	Glucuronic acid	....	2.0 mg/100 ml	25
32	Sialic acid	....	7.31 mg/100 ml	25
		Nitrogenous Substances		
33	Protein	....	330 mg/100 ml	25
34	Mucoprotein	....	100(0-460) mg/100 ml	10
35	Mucin	....	0.36(0.15-1.50) g/100 g	5
36	γ-Globulin	....	(33-95) μg/ml or (33-384) mg/24 hr	6
37	Serum albumin	....	(17-451) μg/ml or (21-690) mg/24 hr	6
38	Histamine	....	(0.0013-0.0535) mg/100 ml	4
39	Urea	....	2.0 mg/100 ml	3

continued

34. COMPOSITION OF GASTRIC JUICE: VERTEBRATES

Part I. Man

	Property or Constituent	Experimental Conditions	Value	Reference
	Amino Acids			23
40	Alanine	Fasting	(1.8-2.7) mg/100 ml	
41		Caffeine stimulation	(2.0-2.6) mg/100 ml	
42	Arginine	Fasting	(3.3-3.6) mg/100 ml	
43		Caffeine stimulation	(3.5-5.0) mg/100 ml	
44	Aspartic acid	Fasting	(1.7-2.3) mg/100 ml	
45		Caffeine stimulation	(1.6-2.5) mg/100 ml	
46	Cystine	Fasting	(1.8-3.7) mg/100 ml	
47		Caffeine stimulation	(1.6-4.4) mg/100 ml	
48	Glutamic acid	Fasting	(2.0-3.2) mg/100 ml	
49		Caffeine stimulation	(2.6-4.7) mg/100 ml	
50	Glycine	Fasting	(1.3-1.6) mg/100 ml	
51		Caffeine stimulation	(1.2-2.1) mg/100 ml	
52	Histidine	Fasting	(1.3-2.0) mg/100 ml	
53		Caffeine stimulation	(1.3-1.8) mg/100 ml	
54	Isoleucine	Fasting	(0.7-1.4) mg/100 ml	
55		Caffeine stimulation	(2.3-2.5) mg/100 ml	
56	Leucine	Fasting	(1.2-2.2) mg/100 ml	
57		Caffeine stimulation	(1.2-3.3) mg/100 ml	
58	Lysine	Fasting	(1.4-1.8) mg/100 ml	
59		Caffeine stimulation	(1.3-1.6) mg/100 ml	
60	Methionine	Fasting	(0.8-1.5) mg/100 ml	
61		Caffeine stimulation	(0.9-1.9) mg/100 ml	
62	Phenylalanine	Fasting	(0.8-1.8) mg/100 ml	
63		Caffeine stimulation	(0.7-1.6) mg/100 ml	
64	Proline	Fasting	(1.7-3.2) mg/100 ml	
65		Caffeine stimulation	(2.2-3.3) mg/100 ml	
66	Serine	Fasting	(1.6-2.3) mg/100 ml	
67		Caffeine stimulation	(1.9-2.1) mg/100 ml	
68	Threonine	Fasting	(1.5-2.5) mg/100 ml	
69		Caffeine stimulation	2.0 mg/100 ml	
70	Tryptophan	Fasting	(1.4-1.9) mg/100 ml	
71		Caffeine stimulation	(1.2-1.9) mg/100 ml	
72	Tyrosine	Fasting	(1.0-1.1) mg/100 ml	
73		Caffeine stimulation	(0.9-1.3) mg/100 ml	
74	Nitrogen, total	Fasting	(0.91-2.18) mg/ml	15
75		Histamine stimulation	(0.73-1.34) mg/ml	15
76	α-amino	Fasting	(5.6-8.4) mg/100 ml	23
77		Caffeine stimulation	(7.2-14.4) mg/100 ml	23
		Enzymes		
78	Lipase	....	(7.0-8.4) units/ml	17
79	Lysozyme	....	7.57(2.6-19.2) μg/ml	21
80	Pepsin	Basal conditions; lyophilized bovine hemoglobin powder substrate	4119(0-8335) Hb units/hr	16
81		After test meal; plasma protein substrate	(9.7-62.8) units/ml	14,20
82	Ribonuclease	....	(0.03-0.07) μg/mg protein	24

Contributors: (a) Liebowitz, Daniel, and Ellis, Eldon E., (b) Frazer, A. C.; Sammons, H. G.; and Okunzua, G.

References

[1] Babkin, P. B. 1950. Secretory mechanism of the digestive glands. Ed. 2. P. B. Hoeber, New York.

[2] Bernstein, R. E. 1952. J. Lab. Clin. Med. 40:707.

[3] Bodansky, M., and O. Bodansky. 1952. Biochemistry of disease. Ed. 2. Macmillan, New York. pp. 302-393.

continued

34. COMPOSITION OF GASTRIC JUICE: VERTEBRATES

Part I. Man

[4] Brown, C. L., and R. G. Smith. 1935. Am. J. Physiol. 113:450.

[5] Brunner, P. 1946-47. Acta Med. Scand. 126:384.

[6] Cohen, N., M. I. Horowitz, and F. Hollander. 1962. Proc. Soc. Exptl. Biol. Med. 109:463.

[7] Dunham, L. J., and A. Brunschwig. 1946. Cancer Res. 6:54.

[8] Elwin, C. E., and B. Uvnäs. 1966. Univ. Calif. Los Angeles Forum Med. Sci. 5.

[9] Freeman, J. T., R. Hafkesbring, and E. K. Caldwell. 1951. Gastroenterology 18:224.

[10] Glass, G. B. J., and L. G. Boyd. 1949. Ibid. 12:821.

[11] Gotch, F., J. Nadell, and I. S. Edelman. 1957. J. Clin. Invest. 36:289.

[12] Houssay, B. A., et al. 1955. Human physiology. Ed. 2. McGraw-Hill, New York. p. 354.

[13] Hubel, K. A. 1966. Gastroenterology 50(1):24.

[14] Hunt, J. N. 1951. J. Physiol. (London) 113:169.

[15] Ihre, B. 1938. Acta Med. Scand., Suppl. 95.

[16] Janowitz, H. D., and F. Hollander. 1952. J. Clin. Invest. 31:338.

[17] Koningsberger, V. J., E. J. Slijper, and H. J. Vonk, ed. 1946. Tabulae Biol. 21(1):1.

[18] Laudano, O. M., and E. C. Roncoroni. 1965. Gastroenterology 40(4):372.

[19] Liebowitz, D. Unpublished. Univ. California, School Medicine, San Francisco, 1953.

[20] Liebowitz, D., et al. 1957. Gastroenterology 32:268.

[21] Lobstein, O. E., and S. J. Fogelson. 1951. Am. J. Digest. Diseases 18:282.

[22] Lockwood, J. S., and H. T. Randall. 1949. Bull. N.Y. Acad. Med. 25:228.

[23] Muting, D. 1954. Naturwissenschaften 41:580.

[24] Piper, D. W., M. L. Macoun, and B. Fenton. 1963. Am. J. Digest. Diseases 8:984.

[25] Richmond, V., R. Caputo, and S. Wolf. 1955. Gastroenterology 29:1017.

Part II. Dog

	Property or Constituent	Experimental Conditions	Value	Reference
	Physical Properties & General Chemical Constituents			
1	Freezing point depression	....	0.59(0.49-0.64)°C	6
2	pH	....	(1.0-4.5)	13
3	Secretion rate	Dilution technique	(0.30-1.45) ml/min	7
4	Specific gravity	....	(1.002-1.004)	4
5	Ash	....	132.5 mg/100 ml	4
6	Organic matter	....	294.4 mg/100 ml	4
7	Solids, total	....	(430-650) mg/100 ml	6
	Inorganic Substances & Vitamins			
8	Calcium	....	(0.95-3.30) mEq/liter	1
9	Chloride	....	172.9 mEq/liter	4
10		Sham feeding stimulation	123(98-143) mEq/liter	14
11	Magnesium	....	0.5 mg/100 ml	2
12	Potassium	....	7.2 mEq/liter	4
13		Sham feeding stimulation	15.2(10.3-22.0) mEq/liter	14
14	Sodium	....	22 mEq/liter	6
15		Sham feeding stimulation	64.0(46.3-79.0) mEq/liter	14
16	Hydrochloric acid	Histamine stimulation	455 ± 20 μEq/kg body wt	5
17		Gastrin stimulation	470 ± 18 μEq/kg body wt	5
18	Total	Sham feeding stimulation	32(0-50) mEq/liter	14
19	Free	Food stimulation	151(0-168.2) mEq/liter	4
20	Phosphate	....	0.25 mg/100 ml	2
21	Ascorbic acid	....	0.692(0.33-1.51) mg/100 ml	12
	Nitrogenous Substances			
22	Mucin	....	1.0(0.1-77.0) g/100 g	2
23	Ammonia	....	(1.2-4.6) mM/liter	1
24	Histamine	Sham feeding stimulation	(4-22) μg/liter	10

continued

34. COMPOSITION OF GASTRIC JUICE: VERTEBRATES

Part II. Dog

	Property or Constituent	Experimental Conditions	Value	Reference
	Amino acids			11
25	Arginine	Sham feeding stimulation	(0.08-0.26) M free amino acid/M threonine	
26	Aspartic acid	Sham feeding stimulation	(0.30-0.68) M free amino acid/M threonine	
27	Glutamic acid	Sham feeding stimulation	(0.81-2.36) M free amino acid/M threonine	
28	Histidine	Sham feeding stimulation	(0.04-0.08) M free amino acid/M threonine	
29	Isoleucine	Sham feeding stimulation	(1.11-1.93) M free amino acid/M threonine	
30	Leucine	Sham feeding stimulation	(1.30-3.58) M free amino acid/M threonine	
31	Lysine	Sham feeding stimulation	(0.15-0.26) M free amino acid/M threonine	
32	Methionine	Sham feeding stimulation	(0.13-0.22) M free amino acid/M threonine	
33	Phenylalanine	Sham feeding stimulation	(0.06-0.44) M free amino acid/M threonine	
34	Proline	Sham feeding stimulation	(0.05-0.21) M free amino acid/M threonine	
35	Serine	Sham feeding stimulation	(0.43-0.76) M free amino acid/M threonine	
36	Threonine	Sham feeding stimulation	1.00 M free amino acid/M threonine	
37	Tryptophan	Sham feeding stimulation	(0.03-0.04) M free amino acid/M threonine	
38	Tyrosinc	Sham feeding stimulation	(0.30-0.36) M free amino acid/M threonine	
39	Valine	Sham feeding stimulation	(1.07-1.30) M free amino acid/M threonine	
	Nitrogen			
40	Total N	....	(50-80) mg/100 ml	6
41	Protein N	Sham feeding stimulation	(18.0-19.9) mg/100 ml	8
42	Nonprotein N	....	(9.8-10.9) mg/100 ml	8
43	Total base N	....	(5.37-6.59) mg/100 ml	8
44	Volatile base N	....	(1.78-2.55) mg/100 ml	8
45	Nonvolatile base N	....	(3.59-4.04) mg/100 ml	8
46	Creatine N + creatinine N	....	(0.09-0.11) mg/100 ml	8
47	Histidine N + arginine N	....	(1.56-1.77) mg/100 ml	8
48	Humin bodies N	....	(3.29-3.73) mg/100 ml	8
49	Lysine fraction N	....	(1.88-2.17) mg/100 ml	8
50	Monoamino fraction N	Phosphotungstic acid filtrate	(0.70-1.02) mg/100 ml	8
51	Purine fraction N	....	(0.10-0.11) mg/100 ml	8
52	Urea N	....	(0.11-0.16) mg/100 ml	8
		Enzymes		
53	Lipase	....	(0.9-3900) units/ml	9
54	Pepsin	Sham feeding stimulation	81(41-164) units/ml	14
55		Histamine stimulation	132 ± 14 pepsin units/kg body wt	5
56		Gastrin stimulation	175 ± 24 pepsin units/kg body wt	5
57	Urease	....	3160 μg ammonia N released/g wet stomach tissue/hr at 37°C	3

Contributors: (a) Liebowitz, Daniel, and Ellis, Eldon E., (b) Frazer, A. C.; Sammons, H. G.; and Okunzua, G.

References

[1] Babkin, B. P. 1950. Secretory mechanism of the digestive glands. Ed. 2. P. B. Hoeber, New York.

[2] Bodansky, M., and O. Bodansky. 1952. Biochemistry of disease. Ed. 2. Macmillan, New York. pp. 302-393.

[3] Conway, E. J. 1953. The biochemistry of gastric acid secretion. C. C. Thomas, Springfield, Ill.

[4] Dukes, H. H. 1955. The physiology of domestic animals. Ed. 7. Comstock, Ithaca.

[5] Enias, S., and M. I. Grossman. 1967. Gastroenterology 52(1):29.

[6] Evans, C. L., and H. Hartridge, ed. 1952. Starling's Principles of human physiology. Ed. 11. Lea and Febiger, Philadelphia.

[7] Gray, J. S., and G. R. Bucher. 1941. Am. J. Physiol. 133:542.

[8] Komarov, S. A. 1937-38. J. Lab. Clin. Med. 23:828.

[9] Koningsberger, V. J., E. J. Slijper, and H. J. Vonk, ed. 1946. Tabulae Biol. 21(1):1.

[10] Macintosh, F. C. 1938. Quart. J. Exptl. Physiol. 28: 95.

[11] Nasset, E. S., and A. Davenport. 1954-55. J. Appl. Physiol. 7:447.

[12] Peters, G. A., and H. E. Martin. 1937. Proc. Soc. Exptl. Biol. Med. 36:76.

[13] Prosser, C. L. 1950. In C. L. Prosser, ed. Comparative animal physiology. W. B. Saunders, Philadelphia. pp. 152-153.

[14] Villareal, R., W. F. Ganong, and S. J. Gray. 1955. Am. J. Physiol. 183:485.

continued

34. COMPOSITION OF GASTRIC JUICE: VERTEBRATES

Part III. Vertebrates Other Than Man and Dog

Abbreviation: PU^{Hb} = number of pepsin units required to digest a given amount of hemoglobin substrate per unit of time or per unit of gastric content.

	Animal	Property or Constituent	Experimental Conditions	Value	Reference
1	Cat	Ash	Food stimulation	(121-384) mg/100 ml	2
2		Organic matter	Food stimulation	(48-265) mg/100 ml	2
3		Solids, total	Food stimulation	(169-649) mg/100 ml	2
4		Calcium	Food stimulation	(1.7-5.3) mEq/liter	2
5		Chloride	Food stimulation	(155.5-165.7) mEq/liter	2
6		Phosphorus	Food stimulation	(0.16-0.55) mg/100 ml	2
7		Potassium	Food stimulation	(11.5-13.6) mEq/liter	2
8		Sodium	Food stimulation	(12.17-55.65) mEq/liter	2
9		Hydrochloric acid	Histamine stimulation	349 ± 14 μEq/kg body wt	9
10			Gastrin stimulation	349 ± 20 μEq/kg body wt	9
11		Total	....	(127.5-154.7) mEq/liter	2
12		Free	Histamine & sham feeding stimulation	(97.25-122.20) mEq/liter	2
13		Histamine	....	(2.5-4.5) μg/100 ml	2
14		Nitrogen	Food stimulation	(10-41) mg/100 ml	2
15		Reducing sugar (as glucose)	....	(4.0-35.6) mg/100 ml	2
16		Lipase	....	(47-3000) units/ml	16
17		Pepsin	....	(0-400) Mett units	2
18			Histamine stimulation	123 ± 40 pepsin units/kg body wt	9
19			Gastrin stimulation	266 ± 80 pepsin units/kg body wt	9
20		Urease	....	1210 μg ammonia N released/g wet stomach tissue/hr at 37°C	6
21	Cattle	Secretion rate	Dilution technique	(0.5-2.0) ml/min	8
22		Specific gravity	....	(1.002-1.003)	8
23		Hydrochloric acid	....	(36-98) mEq/liter	19
24	Horse	pH	....	4.46(1.13-6.80)	8
25		Secretion rate	Dilution technique	(6.9-20.7) ml/min	8
26		Hydrochloric acid, free	....	(39-58) mEq/liter	8
27		Lipase	....	(5.5-400) units/ml	16
28	Macaque	pH	Basal state	>3.5	7
29		Chloride	....	81-109 mEq/liter	
30		Pepsin	....	104-536 units/ml	
31	Monkey, spider	Volume	Subjects restrained, fasting[1/]	5.0 ml/hr	21
32			Subjects moving freely, fasting[2/]	8.8 ml/hr	
33			Histamine stimulation[3/]	12.0 ml/hr	
34		Chloride	Subjects restrained, fasting[1/]	136.7 mEq/liter	
35			Subjects moving freely, fasting[2/]	145.0 mEq/liter	
36			Histamine stimulation[3/]	155.2 mEq/liter	
37		Potassium	Subjects restrained, fasting[1/]	16.8 mEq/liter	
38			Subjects moving freely, fasting[2/]	15.7 mEq/liter	
39			Histamine stimulation[3/]	12.6 mEq/liter	
40		Sodium	Subjects restrained, fasting[1/]	58.6 mEq/liter	
41			Subjects moving freely, fasting[2/]	48.6 mEq/liter	
42			Histamine stimulation[3/]	22.0 mEq/liter	
43		Hydrochloric acid	Subjects restrained, fasting[1/]	405.8 μEq/hr	
44			Subjects moving freely, fasting[2/]	946.7 μEq/hr	
45			Histamine stimulation[3/]	1634.7 μEq/hr	
46		Total	Subjects restrained, fasting[1/]	81.7 mEq/liter	
47			Subjects moving freely, fasting[2/]	111.0 mEq/liter	
48			Histamine stimulation[3/]	135.7 mEq/liter	
49		Free	Subjects restrained, fasting[1/]	61.2 mEq/liter	
50			Subjects moving freely, fasting[2/]	86.7 mEq/liter	
51			Histamine stimulation[3/]	127.5 mEq/liter	

[1/] 18 experiments on 4 monkeys. [2/] 17 experiments on 4 monkeys. [3/] 12 experiments on 4 monkeys.

continued

34. COMPOSITION OF GASTRIC JUICE: VERTEBRATES

Part III. Vertebrates Other Than Man and Dog

	Animal	Property or Constituent	Experimental Conditions	Value	Reference
52		Pepsin, output	Subjects restrained, fasting[1/]	1538.1 $PU^{Hb} \times 10^{-4}$/hr	
53			Subjects moving freely, fasting[2/]	2472.4 $PU^{Hb} \times 10^{-4}$/hr	
54			Histamine stimulation[3/]	5471.5 $PU^{Hb} \times 10^{-4}$/hr	
55		concentration	Subjects restrained, fasting[1/]	307.0 $PU^{Hb} \times 10^{-4}$/ml	
56			Subjects moving freely, fasting[2/]	299.2 $PU^{Hb} \times 10^{-4}$/ml	
57			Histamine stimulation[3/]	442.5 $PU^{Hb} \times 10^{-4}$/ml	
58	Monkey, squirrel	Volume	Subjects restrained, fasting	1.7(0.8-2.8) ml/hr	4
59		Chloride	Subjects restrained, fasting	155.9(105.0-181.6) mEq/liter	
60		Potassium	Subjects restrained, fasting	11.5(7.6-21.0) mEq/liter	
61		Sodium	Subjects restrained, fasting	60.9(26.5-103.0) mEq/liter	
62		Hydrochloric acid, total	Subjects restrained, fasting	81.7(38.6-118.3) mEq/liter	
63		free	Subjects restrained, fasting	59.6(8.0-102.0) mEq/liter	
64		Pepsin	Subjects restrained, fasting	796.1(363.0-1558.7) $PU^{Hb} \times 10^{-4}$/ml	
65	Rabbit	pH	....	(1-1.6)	3
66		Water	Deuterium oxide method	65(35-95)[b] ml or 4.1(2.3-5.9)[b]% of body water	11
67		Chloride	....	8.7(1.9-15.5)[b] mEq/liter	18
68		Potassium	....	0.7(0.1-1.3)[b] mEq/liter	18
69		Sodium	....	0.8(0-1.6)[b] mEq/liter	18
70		Lipase	....	(40-88) units/ml	16
71	Rat	pH	....	(2.0-4.0)	5
72		Lipase	....	130 units/ml	16
73		Urease	....	296 μg ammonia N released/g wet stomach tissue/hr at 37°C	6
74	Sheep	pH	....	(1.05-1.32)	19
75		Calcium	2 animals, 45 samples	1.7(1.0-2.2) mEq/liter	22
76		Chloride	1 animal, 121 samples	158(147-177) mEq/liter	19
77		Magnesium	2 animals, 45 samples	0.7(0.5-0.9) mEq/liter	22
78		Potassium	Flame photometry method	(1-19) mEq/liter	1
79		Sodium	Flame photometry method	(21-167) mEq/liter	1
80		Bicarbonate	Conway microdiffusion method	(0-10) mEq/liter	1
81		Hydrochloric acid	1 animal, 121 samples	86(9-128) mEq/liter	19
82		Lipase	....	(0.45-12.00) units/ml	16
83	Swine	pH	Fasting; gastric fistula	(3.75-4.00)	17
84		Secretion rate	Fasting; gastric fistula	1.05(0.73-1.40) ml/min	17
85		Ash	....	(400-800) mg/100 ml	15
86		Dry matter	....	(900-2400) mg/100 ml	15
87		Chloride	Fasting; gastric fistula	112(109-115) mEq/liter	17
88		Potassium	Fasting; gastric fistula	10 mEq/liter	17
89		Sodium	Fasting; gastric fistula	96(82-111) mEq/liter	17
90		Hydrochloric acid	....	100 mEq/liter	15
91		Lipase	....	(13-7500) units/ml	16
92		Pepsin	....	33.5(4.0-37.5) pepsin units[4/]	15
93	Wood-chuck	pH	....	3.8	2
94		Secretion rate	Dilution technique	(0.0013-0.0070) ml/min	
95		Hydrochloric acid, total	....	(30-56) mEq/liter	
96		free	....	(18.0-48.8) mEq/liter	
97	Chicken	pH	....	2.60	10
98		Hydrochloric acid, total	Histamine stimulation	(120-180) mEq/liter	20
99		free	Histamine stimulation	(80-150) mEq/liter	20
100		Lipase	....	(0.8-75.0) units/ml	16
101	Pigeon	pH	....	2.00	10
102		Hydrochloric acid, total	....	(60-148) mEq/liter	20
103			Histamine stimulation	(120-195) mEq/liter	20

1/ 18 experiments on 4 monkeys. 2/ 17 experiments on 4 monkeys. 3/ 12 experiments on 4 monkeys. 4/ Amount of pepsin that digests 1 ml of 1% edestin solution in 30 minutes.

continued

34. COMPOSITION OF GASTRIC JUICE: VERTEBRATES

Part III. Vertebrates Other Than Man and Dog

	Animal	Property or Constituent	Experimental Conditions	Value	Reference
104		free	....	(40-136) mEq/liter	20
105			Histamine stimulation	(70-160) mEq/liter	20
106		Pepsin	Histamine stimulation	(0-36) Mett units	20
107	Frog	pH	....	(1.6-2.5)	14
108		Secretion rate	In vitro mucosal chamber technique	(10-40) μl/1.4 cm^2 mucosa	12,13
109		Chloride	In vitro mucosal chamber technique	(2.5-3.5) mEq/1.4 cm^2 mucosa	12,13
110		Potassium	In vitro mucosal chamber technique	0.6(0.3-0.7) μEq/1.4 cm^2 mucosa	12,13
111		Hydrochloric acid	In vitro mucosal chamber technique	1.2(1-3) μEq/1.4 cm^2 mucosa	12,13

Contributors: (a) Liebowitz, Daniel, & Ellis, Eldon E., (b) Frazer, A. C.; Sammons, H. G.; & Okunzua, G., (c) Phillipson, A. T.

References

[1] Ash, R. W., and R. N. B. Kay. 1963. Progress in nutrition and allied sciences. Oliver and Boyd, Edinburgh.

[2] Babkin, B. P. 1950. Secretory mechanism of the digestive glands. Ed. 2. P. B. Hoeber, New York.

[3] Beauville, M., and P. Raynaud. 1964. J. Physiol. (Paris) 56:287.

[4] Brodie, D. A., and R. W. Marshall. 1963. Am. J. Physiol. 204:681.

[5] Broeck, C. J. H. van den, and A. P. de Groot. 1948. Physiol. Comp. Oecol. 1:148.

[6] Conway, E. J. 1953. The biochemistry of gastric acid secretion. C. C. Thomas, Springfield, Ill.

[7] De Los Santos, M. A., et al. 1962. Gastroenterology 42:595.

[8] Dukes, H. H. 1955. The physiology of domestic animals. Ed. 7. Comstock, Ithaca.

[9] Enias, A., and M. I. Grossman. 1967. Gastroenterology 52(1):29.

[10] Farner, D. S. 1942. Poultry Sci. 21:445.

[11] Gotch, F., J. Nadell, and I. S. Edelman. 1957. J. Clin. Invest. 36:289.

[12] Harris, J. B. Unpublished. Univ. California, School Medicine, San Francisco, 1959.

[13] Harris, J. B., and I. S. Edelman. 1959. Am. J. Physiol. 196:1266.

[14] Harris, J. B., H. Frank, and I. S. Edelman. 1958. Ibid. 195:499.

[15] Heyenga, H. 1939. Jahresber. Vet. Med. 65:299.

[16] Koningsberger, V. J., E. J. Slijper, and H. J. Vonk, ed. 1946. Tabulae Biol. 21(1):1.

[17] Liebowitz, D., and E. E. Ellis. Unpublished. Univ. California, School Medicine, San Francisco, 1959.

[18] Lockwood, J. S., and H. T. Randall. 1949. Bull. N.Y. Acad. Med. 25:228.

[19] Masson, M. J., and A. T. Phillipson. 1952. J. Physiol. (London) 116:98.

[20] Schmidt, C. R., and A. C. Ivy. 1939. J. Cellular Comp. Physiol. 13:219.

[21] Smith, G. P., et al. 1960. Am. J. Physiol. 199:889.

[22] Storrey, J. E. 1961. Nature 190:1197.

35. COMPOSITION OF BILE: VERTEBRATES

Values in parentheses are ranges, estimate "c" (*see* Introduction).

Part I. Man

	Property or Constituent	Bile: Gallbladder	Bile: Liver	Reference
	Physical Properties			
1	Freezing point depression	0.56°C 1/		14
2	pH	7.3(6.5-9.0)	7.15	8,9
3	Secretion rate	(0.13-0.20) ml/min	(2.6-15.0) ml/kg body wt/24 hr	21
4	Volume	....	(1000-2000) ml/24 hr	10
5	Specific conductivity	(99-137)/ohm cm at 30°C 1/		1
6	Specific gravity	1.026(1.010-1.032)	(1.008-1.015)	21,23
7	Surface tension	39.1(26.7-43.7) dynes/cm	....	24
8	Relative viscosity	2.85 ± 1.63	1.27 ± 0.24	3
9	Osmolarity	281 ± 10 milliosmoles/kg	284 ± 17 milliosmoles/kg	3

1/ Source of bile not specified.

continued

35. COMPOSITION OF BILE: VERTEBRATES

Part I. Man

	Property or Constituent	Bile: Gallbladder	Bile: Liver	Reference
	General Chemical Constituents			
10	Acids, total	5180(1400-9200) mg/100 ml	1090(420-1830) mg/100 ml	25
11		55.7(27.4-86.3) mg/ml	....	24
12	Trihydroxycholanic, total	....	1.53 mg/ml[2]; 3.26 mg/ml[3]	11
13	Cholic	24.2(8.6-49.4) mg/ml	1.52 mg/ml[2]; 3.26 mg/ml[3]	11,24
14	Dihydroxycholanic, total[4]	31.4(16-46.3) mg/ml	1.37 mg/ml[2]; 1.32 mg/ml[3]	11,24
15	Chenodeoxycholic	....	1.11 mg/ml[2]; 1.29 mg/ml[3]	11
16	Deoxycholic	....	0.34 mg/ml[2]; 0.24 mg/ml[3]	11
17	Base, total	....	(150-180) mEq/liter	5
18	Dry matter	136 ± 60 mg/ml	20 ± 9 mg/ml	3
19	Inorganic matter	(500-1100) mg/100 ml	(200-900) mg/100 ml	5
20	Salts	11,500 mg/100 ml	(650-1400) mg/100 ml	20
21	Solids, total	11,140(4,700-16,500) mg/100 ml	2600(1000-4000) mg/100 ml	25
22		163(82-223) mg/ml	....	24
23	Water	85.92%	97.48%	2,16
	Inorganic Substances			
24	Calcium	(5.0-7.0) mEq/liter	(2.0-4.5) mEq/liter	5
25	Chloride	(15-30) mEq/liter	(75-110) mEq/liter	5
26	Copper	(0.063-1.070) mg/100 ml[1]		17
27	Iodine, fasting subjects	(4-14) µg/100 ml[1]		6
28	fed subjects	50 µg/100 ml[1]		6
29	Iron	(0.031-1.680) mg/100 ml	6.8(4.8-7.8) mg/100 ml	15
30	Magnesium	....	1.5 mEq/liter	21
31	Phosphorus	140 mg/100 ml	(9.0-22.3) mg/100 ml	20
32	Potassium	12.8 ± 3.7 mEq/liter	(2.6-12.0) mEq/liter	3,18
33	Sodium	209 ± 34 mEq/liter	(131-164) mEq/liter	3,18
34	Bicarbonate	(8-12) mEq/liter	20-25 mEq/liter	23
	Vitamins, Lipids, & Carbohydrates			
35	Choline, total	550 mg/100 ml	(35-89) mg/100 ml	20
36	Cholesterol	5.8(2.6-9.6) mg/ml	120(80-170) mg/100 ml	24,25
37	Fat, neutral	370(150-560) mg/100 ml	110(40-300) mg/100 ml	25
38	Fatty acids	970(900-1090) mg/100 ml	110(80-140) mg/100 ml	25
39	Lecithin	3500 mg/100 ml	(100-575) mg/100 ml	20
40		92.2%[5]		22
41	Lysolecithin	3.9%[5]		22
42	Phosphatide	(200-500) mg/100 ml	(50-80) mg/100 ml	5
43	Phosphatidyl ethanolamine[6]	3.6%[5]		22
44	Phospholipid	38.1(17.3-46.0) mg/ml	(50-60) mg/100 ml	24,25
45	Hexosamine	8.3 ± 5.3 mg/100 ml	5.7 ± 4.9 mg/100 ml	3
46		182 ± 35 mg/100 ml[7]	....	13
47	Hexose	526 ± 89 mg/100 ml[7]	....	13
48	Glucides, total	240 mg/100 ml	(35-91) mg/100 ml	20
49	Reducing sugars	80 mg/100 ml	(17-52) mg/100 ml	20

[1] Source of bile not specified. [2] Bile obtained by intubation. [3] Bile obtained by external biliary drainage. [4] Determinations were made by using a standard of deoxycholic acid. [5] Percent of total phospholipids in mixed bile. [6] Phosphatidyl inositol, phosphatidyl serine, and sphingomyelin were not detected. [7] ± = plus or minus the standard error, not the standard deviation.

continued

35. COMPOSITION OF BILE: VERTEBRATES

Part I. Man

	Property or Constituent	Bile: Gallbladder	Bile: Liver	Reference
	Nitrogenous Substances			
50	Protein, total	(315-539) mg/100 ml	273 mg/100 ml	19
51	Mucin + pigment	3420(1800-4300) mg/100 ml	610 (430-930) mg/100 ml	25
52	Pigment	(200-1500) mg/100 ml	(50-170) mg/100 ml	5
53	Bilirubin	293.75 ± 193.57 mg/100 ml	64.68 ± 12.53 mg/100 ml	3
54		3.8(1.9-6.2) mg/ml	(20-200) mg/100 ml	24,26
55	Coproporphyrin	10.07 µg/100 ml	....	4
56	Urobilinogen	....	0.6 mg/24 hr	16
57	γ-Globulin, 1A	53.0 mg/100 ml[a]		7,12
58	2	143.0 mg/100 ml[a]		
59	Urea	(20-45) mg/100 ml	23.6 mg/100 ml	19
60	Nitrogen, total	349 ± 145 mg/100 ml	72 ± 31 mg/100 ml	3
61		828 mg/100 ml	....	13
62	amino acid	(6.0-21.6) mg/100 ml	5.4 mg/100 ml	19
63	peptide	(3.9-27.0) mg/100 ml	14.0 mg/100 ml	19

[a] In mixed bile.

Contributors: (a) Liebowitz, Daniel, and Ellis, Eldon E., (b) Frazer, A. C.; Sammons, H. G.; and Okunzua, G.

References

[1] Aenile, E. O., and S. Garcia Fernandez. 1952. Anais Fac. Farm. Porto 12:107.

[2] Bodansky, M., and O. Bodansky. 1952. Biochemistry of disease. Macmillan, New York. p. 398.

[3] Bouchier, I. A. D., S. R. Cooperband, and B. M. El Kodsi. 1965. Gastroenterology 49:343.

[4] Brugsch, J. 1952. Z. Ges. Inn. Med. Ihre Grenzgebiete 7:321.

[5] Cantarow, A., and B. Schepartz. 1967. Biochemistry. Ed. 4. W. B. Saunders, Philadelphia. p. 266.

[6] Cantarow, A., and M. Trumper. 1962. Clinical biochemistry. Ed. 6. W. B. Saunders, Philadelphia. p. 259.

[7] Chodirker, W. B., and T. B. Tomasi, Jr. 1963. Science 142:1080.

[8] Crawford, N. 1955. J. Med. Lab. Technol. 13:304.

[9] Dietrich, K. F., and C. Anders. 1957. Z. Physiol. Chem. 309:60.

[10] Doubilet, H., and L. Fishman. 1961. Am. J. Gastroenterol. 35:499.

[11] Failey, R. B., Jr., E. Brown, and M. E. Hodes. 1960. Arch. Pathol. 70:358.

[12] Fisher, J. M., C. Ries, and K. B. Taylor. 1965. Science 150:1467.

[13] Giles, R. B., Jr., et al. 1960. J. Lab. Clin. Med. 55: 38.

[14] Hawk, P. B., B. L. Oser, and W. H. Summerson. 1954. Practical physiological chemistry. Ed. 13. Blakiston, New York.

[15] Horrall, A. H. 1938. Bile, its toxicity and relation to disease. Univ. Chicago Press, Chicago.

[16] Houssay, B. A., et al. 1955. Human physiology. Ed. 2. McGraw-Hill, New York. pp. 368-369.

[17] Judd, E. S., and T. J. Dry. 1935. J. Lab. Clin. Med. 20:609.

[18] Lockwood, J. S., and H. T. Randall. 1949. Bull. N.Y. Acad. Med. 25:228.

[19] Nagl, F. 1953-54. Z. Klin. Med. 151:429.

[20] Polonovski, M., and R. Bourrillon. 1952. Bull. Soc. Chim. Biol. 34:703.

[21] Sobotka, H. 1937. Physiological chemistry of the bile. Williams and Wilkins, Baltimore.

[22] Spitzer, H. L., E. C. Kyriakides, and J. A. Balint. 1964. Nature 204:288.

[23] Sunderman, F. W., and F. Boerner. 1949. Normal values in clinical medicine. W. B. Saunders, Philadelphia.

[24] Tamesui, N., and K. Juniper. 1967. Gastroenterology 52(3):473.

[25] West, E. S., et al. 1966. Textbook of biochemistry. Ed. 4. Macmillan, New York. p. 510.

[26] With, T. K. 1954. Biology of bile pigments. A. Frost-Hansen, Copenhagen.

continued

35. COMPOSITION OF BILE: VERTEBRATES

Part II. Vertebrates Other Than Man

For additional information on the occurrence of bile acids and alcohols, consult reference 13.

	Animal	Property or Constituent	Bile: Gallbladder	Bile: Liver	Reference
1	Cat	pH	(5.0-6.0)	...	2
2		Secretion rate	...	14.0 ml/kg body wt/24 hr	19
3		Base, fixed	27.4(26.1-31.8) mEq/liter	17.2(15.7-19.4) mEq/liter	11
4		Chloride	5(0-20) mEq/liter	12(10-13) mEq/liter	11
5		Pigment	(238-1190) mg/100 ml	119(52-218) mg/100 ml	19
6		Coproporphyrin	95.8 μg/100 ml	...	4
7		Phosphatase, alkaline	(190-416) units[1] 100 ml	...	7
8	Cattle	pH	(6.74-7.47)	...	21
9		Secretion rate	...	15.4 ml/kg body wt/24 hr	19
10		Specific gravity	...	(1.022-1.025)	20
11		Acids	(1550-1700) mg/100 ml	...	21
12		Ash + alkali	(1250-1300) mg/100 ml	...	21
13		Water	90(83-91)%	...	21
14		Iron	...	(3-6) mg/100 ml	14
15		Lipids, total	(100-160) mg/100 ml	...	21
16		Cholesterol	60 mg/100 ml	...	21
17		Fat, neutral	(100-600) mg/100 ml	...	21
18		Lecithin	89.8%[2]		22
19		Lysolecithin	7.8%[2]		22
20		Phosphatidyl ethanolamine	1.1%[2]		22
21		Phosphatidyl serine[3]	1.2%[2]		22
22		Mucin	500 mg/100 ml	...	21
23		Mucin + pigment	76(24-102) mg/100 ml	95 mg/100 ml	19
24	Dog	pH	(5.18-6.97)	(7.1-8.5)	9,18
25		Secretion rate	...	12.0(5.2-52.5) mg/kg body wt/24 hr	19
26		Specific gravity	...	(1.008-1.015)	9
27		Surface tension	33.3 ± 1.54 dynes/cm	...	8
28		Acids	4.5(0.3-19.7) g/100 ml	...	21
29		Dry matter	(11,400-24,600) mg/100 ml	(2300-4500) mg/100 ml	17
30		Salts	(7,900-15,000) mg/100 ml	(500-2400) mg/100 ml	17
31		Water	91(76.0-97.1)%	95.9%	21
32		Calcium	26.1 mEq/liter	(3.7-7.2) mEq/liter	18,21
33		Chloride	...	70(59-105) mEq/liter	18
34		Iodine	(13-113) μg/100 ml[4]		21
35		Iron	(0.09-0.18) mg/100 ml	(1.8-16.0) mg/100 ml	4
36		Magnesium	...	3.6(2.2-5.0) mEq/liter	18
37		Phosphorus, total	(87-280) mg/100 ml	(10-15) mg/100 ml	17
38		Potassium	...	(5.1-6.0) mEq/liter	18
39		Sodium	...	168(150-203) mEq/liter	18
40		Bicarbonate	...	(14-68) mEq/liter	3,18
41		Choline, total	(340-1110) mg/100 ml	(39-58) mg/100 ml	17
42		Cholesterol	(80-100) mg/100 ml	(4-15) mg/100 ml	17
43		Fatty acids, total	(1600-5000) mg/100 ml	(175-270) mg/100 ml	17
44		Lecithin	(2250-7000) mg/100 ml	(250-400) mg/100 ml	17
45			95.8%[2]		22
46		Phosphatidyl serine[5]	1.8%[2]		22
47		Sphingomyelin	2.3%[2]		22
48		Glucides	(736-938) mg/100 ml	...	17
49		Reducing sugars	(64-72) mg/100 ml	...	17
50		Protein, total	(190-520) mg/100 ml	(130-210) mg/100 ml	17
51		Mucin + pigment	(96-387) mg/100 ml	107(16-387) mg/100 ml	19
52		Allantoin	18.9 mg/100 ml[4]		21
53		Ammonia	(0.4-0.6) mg/100 ml[4]		21

1/ King-Armstrong Units; phenylphosphate substrate, modified Bodansky method. 2/ Percent of total phospholipids in mixed bile. 3/ Trace of phosphatidyl inositol also present, sphingomyelin not detected. 4/ Source of bile not specified. 5/ Trace of phosphatidyl inositol also present; lysolecithin and phosphatidyl ethanolamine not detected.

continued

35. COMPOSITION OF BILE: VERTEBRATES

Part II. Vertebrates Other Than Man

	Animal	Property or Constituent	Bile: Gallbladder	Bile: Liver	Reference
54		Bilirubin	(92-170) mg/100 ml[6]	(42-55) mg/100 ml[6]	17
55		Coproporphyrin	146.7 μg/100 ml	...	4
56		Uric acid	...	(0.37-0.50) mg/100 ml[7]	21
57		Nitrogen, total	(255-635) mg/100 ml	(65-105) mg/100 ml	17
58		Phosphatase, alkaline	(0-900) units[1]	...	1,15,16
59	Goat	Secretion rate	...	11.8 ml/kg body wt/24 hr	19
60		Specific gravity	...	(1.004-1.010)	9
61		Ash	...	(480-760) mg/100 ml	9
62		Dry matter	...	(2880-4720) mg/100 ml	9
63		Pigment	...	126 mg/100 ml	19
64	Guinea pig	pH	(7.2-9.1)	...	21
65		Secretion rate	...	228 ml/kg body wt/24 hr	19
66		Acids	780 mg/100 ml	...	21
67		Ash + alkali	100 mg/100 ml	...	21
68		Solids, total	2160 mg/100 ml	...	21
69		Water	97.8%	...	21
70		Iron	(0.09-0.18) mg/100 ml	...	14
71		Lipids, total	140 mg/100 ml	...	21
72		Mucin	510 mg/100 ml	...	21
73		Mucin + pigment	(10-19) mg/100 ml	10 mg/100 ml	19
74	Horse[8]	Secretion rate	...	20.8 ml/kg body wt/24 hr	19
75		Specific gravity	...	1.010	6
76		Pigment	...	33(12.0-37.8) mg/100 ml	19
77	Rabbit	pH	(6.4-6.7)[7]	...	21
78		Secretion rate	...	118 ml/kg body wt/24 hr	19
79		Specific gravity	1.048	...	21
80		Acids	(1100-2600) mg/100 ml	...	21
81		Calcium	...	4.8(4.0-9.5) mEq/liter[7]	21
82		Chloride	...	82 mEq/liter	21
83		Iodine, fasting subjects	...	(4-14) μg/100 ml	21
84		fed subjects	...	(26-69) μg/100 ml	21
85		Iron	...	0.13 mg/100 ml	14
86		Magnesium	...	0.5 mEq/liter	21
87		Potassium	...	5.7 mEq/liter	21
88		Sodium	...	151 mEq/liter	21
89		Bicarbonate	...	46 mEq/liter	21
90		Phosphate	...	2.5 mEq/liter	21
91		Sulfate	...	4.4 mEq/liter	21
92		Cholesterol	(10-120) mg/100 ml	...	21
93		Reducing sugars	...	20 mg/100 ml	21
94		Ammonia	...	(0.022-0.070) mg/100 ml	21
95		Pigment	(87.2-131.4) mg/100 ml	21.8 mg/100 ml	19
96		Phosphatase, alkaline	(56-302) units[1] ml	...	15
97	Rat[8]	pH	...	8.3(7.9-8.5)	5
98		Secretion rate	...	(28.6-47.1) ml/kg body wt/24 hr	19
99		Specific gravity	...	1.011	5,10
100		Cholesterol	...	12.7 mg/100 ml/24 hr	10
101		Lecithin[9]	92.2%[2]		22
102		Phosphatidyl ethanolamine	6.0%[2]		22
103		Mucin + pigment	...	(11-19) mg/100 ml	19
104		Bilirubin	...	8.3 mg/100 ml/24 hr	10
105	Sheep	pH	(5.98-6.72)	...	21
106		Secretion rate	...	12.1 ml/kg body wt/24 hr	19
107		Specific gravity	...	(1.025-1.031)	20

[1] King-Armstrong Units; phenylphosphate substrate, modified Bodansky method. [2] Percent of total phospholipids in mixed bile. [6] Van den Bergh method [23]. [7] Fistula bile. [8] Gallbladder absent. [9] Traces of lysolecithin, phosphatidyl inositol, and sphingomyelin also present; phosphatidyl serine not detected.

continued

35. COMPOSITION OF BILE: VERTEBRATES

Part II. Vertebrates Other Than Man

	Animal	Property or Constituent	Bile		Reference
			Gallbladder	Liver	
108		Solids, total	8.66 ± 0.19 g/100 ml	...	12
109		Water	92%	95%	21
110		Chloride	73.6 ± 3.7 mEq/liter	...	12
111		Potassium	8.03 ± 0.27 mEq/liter	...	12
112		Sodium	196.6 ± 4.8 mEq/liter	...	12
113		Pigment	(50-110) mg/100 ml	107.5 mg/100 ml	19
114		Coproporphyrin	77.4 μg/100 ml	...	4
115		Nitrogen, total	247.7 mg/100 ml	...	12
116	Swine	Secretion rate	...	25.2 ml/kg body wt/24 hr	19
117		Acids	(7,900-12,000) mg/100 ml	...	21
118		Salts	7200 mg/100 ml	(8,500-12,000) mg/100 ml	17
119		Solids, total	10,600 mg/100 ml	(11,500-18,900) mg/100 ml	17
120		Phosphorus, total	20.5 mg/100 ml	(48-116) mg/100 ml	17
121		Choline, total	80 mg/100 ml	(180-450) mg/100 ml	17
122		Lipids, total	1800 mg/100 ml	...	21
123		Cholesterol	37 mg/100 ml	(130-180) mg/100 ml	17
124		Fat, neutral	(200-450) mg/100 ml	...	21
125		Fatty acids, total	370 mg/100 ml	(820-2000) mg/100 ml	17
126		Lecithin	520 mg/100 ml	(1200-2900) mg/100 ml	17
127		Glucides, total	...	(120-300) mg/100 ml	17
128		Reducing sugars	...	(37-150) mg/100 ml	17
129		Protein	420 mg/100 ml	(280-410) mg/100 ml	17
130		Mucin + pigment	24(20-60) mg/100 ml	33 mg/100 ml	19
131		Bilirubin	...	(32.0-61.5) mg/100 ml	17
132		Coproporphyrin	77.4 μg/100 ml	...	4
133		Nitrogen, total	266 mg/100 ml	(370-480) mg/100 ml	17
134	Chicken	pH	...	(6.0-6.2)	9
135		Secretion rate	...	14.2 ml/kg body wt/24 hr	19
136		Mucin + pigment	413 mg/100 ml	147 mg/100 ml	19
137	Goose	Acids	19,000 mg/100 ml	...	21
138		Ash + alkali	2100 mg/100 ml	...	
139		Solids, total	21,950 mg/100 ml	...	
140		Water	77.3%	...	
141		Mucin + pigment	3100 mg/100 ml	...	

Contributors: (a) Liebowitz, Daniel, and Ellis, Eldon E., (b) Frazer, A. C.; Sammons, H. G.; and Okunzua, G.

References

[1] Armstrong, A. R., and E. J. King. 1934. Can. Med. Assoc. J. 31:14.

[2] Best, C. H., and N. B. Taylor, ed. 1966. The physiological basis of medical practice. Ed. 8. Williams and Wilkins, Baltimore. p. 1142.

[3] Bodansky, M., and O. Bodansky. 1952. Biochemistry of disease. Ed. 2. Macmillan, New York. p. 337.

[4] Brugsch, J. 1952. Z. Ges. Inn. Med. Ihre Grenzgebiete 7:321.

[5] Byers, S. O., M. Friedman, and F. Michaelis. 1950. Federation Proc. 9:20.

[6] Carr, J. G. 1944. Vet. Bull. (Commonwealth Bur. Animal Health) 14:66.

[7] Dalgaard, J. B. 1949. Acta Physiol. Scand. 15:298.

[8] DePalma, R. G., and C. A. Hubay. 1964. Surg. Gynecol. Obstet. 118:1248.

[9] Dukes, H. H. 1955. The physiology of domestic animals. Ed. 7. Comstock, Ithaca.

[10] Friedman, M., S. O. Byers, and F. Michaelis. 1950. Am. J. Physiol. 162:577.

[11] Gamble, J. L., and M. A. McIver. 1928. J. Exptl. Med. 48:852.

[12] Harrison, F. A. 1962. J. Physiol. (London) 162:212.

[13] Haslewood, G. A. D. 1955. Physiol. Rev. 35:178.

[14] Horrall, A. H. 1938. Bile, its toxicity and relation to disease. Univ. Chicago Press, Chicago.

[15] Jacoby, F., and B. F. Martin. 1951. J. Anat. 85:391.

[16] King, E. J. 1964. Micro-analysis in medical biochemistry. Ed. 4. J. and A. Churchill, London.

[17] Polonovski, M., and R. Bourrillon. 1952. Bull. Soc. Chim. Biol. 34:703.

[18] Reinhold, J. G., and D. W. Wilson. 1934. Am. J. Physiol. 107:378.

[19] Schmidt, C. R., and A. C. Ivy. 1937. J. Cellular Comp. Physiol. 10:365.

continued

[20] Smith, F. 1921. A manual of veterinary physiology. Ed. 5. Eger, Chicago.

[21] Sobotka, H. 1937. Physiological chemistry of the bile. Williams and Wilkins, Baltimore.

[22] Spitzer, H. L., E. C. Kyriakides, and J. A. Balint. 1964. Nature 204:288.

[23] Van den Bergh, A. A. H., and W. Grotepass. 1934. Brit. Med. J. 1:1157.

36. COMPOSITION OF PANCREATIC SECRETION: MAMMALS

Values in parentheses are ranges, estimate "c" (*see* Introduction).

Part I. Man

Secretions were collected by external pancreatic fistula, unless otherwise specified.

	Property or Constituent	Value	Reference
	Physical Properties & General Chemical Constituents		
1	Freezing point depression	0.625°C	8
2	pH	(8.6-8.8)	6
3	Secretion rate	1.0(0.02-5.20) ml/min	14
4	Volume	(1500-3000) ml/24 hr[1]	4
5		(1.6-4.9) ml/kg body wt[2]	13
6	Specific gravity	(1.005-1.014)	14
7	Ash	(570-860) mg/100 ml	5,11
	Solids		
8	Total	(1240-1540) mg/100 ml	5,11,17
9	Organic	(380-690) mg/100 ml	11
10	Water	98.7%	9
	Inorganic Substances[3] & Carbohydrates		
11	Calcium	(2.2-3.2) mEq/liter	10
12	Chloride	76.6(54.1-95.2) mEq/liter	7
13	Magnesium	0.3 mEq/liter	15
14	Potassium	4.6(2.6-7.4) mEq/liter	3
15	Sodium	141(113-153) mEq/liter	3
16	Zinc	1.21(0-2.32) μg/ml[4]	12
17		0.91(0.22-1.65) μg/ml[4,5]	
18	Bicarbonate	9.1(2.0-16.1) mEq/liter[4]	12
19		80.0(48-124) mEq/liter[4,5]	12
20		>70 mEq/liter[2]	13
21	Phosphate	(0.026-1.220) mEq/liter	6,15
22	Sulfate	8.4 mEq/liter	15
23	Glucose	(8.5-18.0) mg/100 ml	6
	Nitrogenous Substances		
24	Protein, total	(190-340) mg/100 ml	10
25	Albumin	60 mg/100 ml	10
26	Globulin	40 mg/100 ml	10
27	Creatinine	Trace	6
28	Urea	(0.5-4.0) mg/100 ml	6
29	Uric acid	Trace	6
	Nitrogen		10
30	Total N	(190-340) mg/100 ml	
31	Nonprotein N	14.3 mg/100 ml	
32	Urea N	5.0 mg/100 ml	
33	Uric acid N	0.2 mg/100 ml	
	Enzymes		
34	Amylase	(6.4-31.1) units/100 ml	1
35		>93 Somogyi units[2]	13
36	Lipase	(300-2728) units/100 ml	1
37	Phosphatase	(0.8-12.7) Bodansky units/100 ml	6
	Proteolytic enzymes		16
38	Total	(9.4-139.0) mg trypsin/100 ml[6]	
39	Active	(0.04-16.50) mg trypsin/100 ml[6]	
40	Trypsin	(7.1-42.8) units/100 ml	2

[1] Unstimulated. [2] Duodenal aspirate after pancreozymin-secretin stimulation. [3] Traces of copper present; cobalt, iron, and nickel absent. [4] Contents of the duodenum were removed by constant suction through a double lumened tube. [5] 60 minutes after secretin stimulation. [6] Casein substrate.

Contributors: (a) Liebowitz, Daniel, and Ellis, Eldon E., (b) Frazer, A. C.; Sammons, H. G.; and Okunzua, G.

References

[1] Baxter, S. G. 1935-36. Am. J. Digest. Diseases 2: 109.

[2] Bodansky, O. 1933. J. Biol. Chem. 100:561.

[3] Bodansky, M., and O. Bodansky. 1952. Biochemistry of disease. Ed. 2. Macmillan, New York. p. 341.

[4] Doubilet, H., and L. Fishman. 1961. Am. J. Gastroenterol. 35:499.

[5] Glaessner, K. 1903-04. Z. Physiol. Chem. 40:465.

[6] Kogut, B., M. J. Matzner, and A. E. Sobel. 1936. J. Clin. Invest. 15:393.

continued

36. COMPOSITION OF PANCREATIC SECRETION: MAMMALS

Part I. Man

[7] Lockwood, J. S., and H. T. Randall. 1949. Bull. N.Y. Acad. Med. 25:228.

[8] Luckhardt, A. B., F. Stangl, and F. C. Koch. 1923. Am. J. Physiol. 63:397.

[9] Mattice, M. R. 1936. Chemical procedures for clinical laboratories. Lea and Febiger, Philadelphia.

[10] Miller, J. M., and T. B. Wiper. 1944. Ann. Surg. 120: 852.

[11] Schumm, O. 1902. Z. Physiol. Chem. 36:292.

[12] Sullivan, J. F., J. O'Grady, and H. G. Lankford. 1965. Gastroenterology 48:438.

[13] Sun, D. C. 1963. Ibid. 44:602.

[14] Sunderman, F. W., and F. Boerner. 1949. Normal values in clinical medicine. W. B. Saunders, Philadelphia.

[15] Tria, E., and G. Fabriani. 1941. Atti Reale Accad. Ital. Rend. Classe Sci. Fis. Mat. Nat. 2:381.

[16] Troll, W., H. Doubilet, and T. Cancro. 1951. Gastroenterology 19:326.

[17] Wohlgemuth, J. 1912. Biochem. Z. 39:302.

Part II. Mammals Other Than Man

	Animal	Property or Constituent	Value	Reference
1	Cat	Calcium	(4.6-5.1) mEq/liter	1
2		Chloride	(67-93) mEq/liter	8
3	Cattle	Secretion rate	4.2 ml/min	6
4		Calcium	(0.4-2.8) mEq/liter	7
5		Chloride	(93-124) mEq/liter	7
6		Magnesium	(Trace-0.7) mEq/liter	7
7		Potassium	(8-9) mEq/liter	7
8		Sodium	(148-156) mEq/liter	7
9	Dog	Acid-combining power [1/]	(58.8-80.4) mEq/liter	15
10		Freezing point depression	(0.56-0.66)°C	2,19
11		pH	(7.1-8.2)	2,5
12		Secretion rate	(0.2-1.1) ml/min	2,6
13		Specific gravity	(1.004-1.031)	14,22
14		Ash	(840-970) mg/100 ml	14,15
15		Solids, total	(1400-6390) mg/100 ml	2,14,15
16		organic	(480-2200) mg/100 ml	15
17		Water	98.04%	6
18		Calcium	(1.8-2.0) mEq/liter	2
19		Chloride	(71-106) mEq/liter	2
20		Magnesium	(0.2-1.4) mEq/liter	7,14
21		Potassium	(2.5-7.0) mEq/liter	2,8,14,15
22		Sodium	(149-162) mEq/liter	2
23		Bicarbonate	(93-143) mEq/liter	2,21
24		Phosphate	(0.7-3.6) mM/liter	2,8,12,14
25		Glucose	25 mg/100 ml	13
26		Protein	(500-4800) mg/100 ml	5
27		Urea	(24.0-58.5) mg/100 ml	12
		Nitrogen		
28		Total	(100-936) mg/100 ml	2,11,14, 15,22
29		Protein	(74.8-84.3) mg/100 ml	15
30		Nonprotein	(18-84) mg/100 ml	12,15
31		Lactate	(0.1-0.7) mEq/liter	12,13
32		Amylase [1/]	(23,900-47,500) mg maltose/ml [2/]	10
33		Lipase [1/]	(9,750-33,250) ml 0.05 *N* NaOH/ml [3/]	9
34		Pseudocholinesterase [1/]	(420-1080) units [4/]/ml	18
35		Trypsin [1/]	(407.5-2440.0) mg tyrosine/ml [5/]	9
36	Rabbit	Secretion rate	0.006 ml/min	21
37		Amylase	(1.6-8.3) units/min	4
38		Lipase	(0-0.4) units/min	4
39			(4.2-6.8) ml 0.01 *N* NaOH/ml [6/]	3
40		Trypsin	(7.50-24.15) units [7/]/min	4
41			(686-5140) units/ml	21
	Sheep	Secretion rate		16
42		Fasting 24-48 hr	0.9 ml/15 min	
43		Fed normally	3.1 ml/15 min	
44	Swine	Secretion rate	1.0 ml/min	6
45		Ash	(500-1900) mg/100 ml	20
46		Solids, total	(1200-2500) mg/100 ml	20
47		organic	(500-700) mg/100 ml	22
48		Amylase [8/]	(20-168) mg maltose/3 min [9/]	17
49		Lipase [8/]	(0.1-0.6) mEq acid/15 min [9/]	17

1/ Secretin-stimulated. 2/ Starch substrate. 3/ Olive oil emulsion substrate. 4/ Unit = amount of enzyme that liberates 1 μl CO_2/min; 0.06 M acetylcholine perchlorate substrate. 5/ Casein substrate. 6/ Vagus nerve cut. 7/ Unit = 0.1 ml juice capable of flocculating 2 ml milk. 8/ 10 minutes after secretin stimulation. 9/ Obtained under chloralose anesthesia.

Contributors: (a) Liebowitz, Daniel, and Ellis, Eldon E., (b) Frazer, A. C.; Sammons, H. G.; and Okunzua, G.

continued

36. COMPOSITION OF PANCREATIC SECRETION: MAMMALS

Part II. Mammals Other Than Man

References

[1] Agren, G. 1935. Biochem. Z. 281:358.
[2] Ball, E. G. 1930. J. Biol. Chem. 86:449.
[3] Baxter, S. G. 1931. Am. J. Physiol. 96:343.
[4] Baxter, S. G. 1935-36. Am. J. Digest. Diseases 2:109.
[5] Best, C. H., and N. B. Taylor. 1966. The physiological basis of medical practice. Ed. 8. Williams and Wilkins, Baltimore.
[6] Dukes, H. H. 1955. The physiology of domestic animals. Ed. 7. Comstock, Ithaca.
[7] Frouin, A., and P. Gerard. 1912. Compt. Rend. Soc. Biol. 72:98.
[8] Gamble, J. L., and M. A. McIver. 1928. J. Exptl. Med. 48:849.
[9] Grossman, M. I., H. Greengard, and A. C. Ivy. 1942-43. Am. J. Physiol. 138:676.
[10] Hallenbeck, G. A., M. Dworetzky, and C. F. Code. 1950. Ibid. 162:117.
[11] Hart, W. H., and J. E. Thomas. 1945. Gastroenterology 4:409.
[12] Hartmann, A. F., and R. Elman. 1929. J. Exptl. Med. 50:387.
[13] Hata, M. 1940. Mitt. Med. Akad. Kioto 30:279.
[14] Johnston, C. G., and E. G. Ball. 1930. J. Biol. Chem. 86:643.
[15] Komarov, S. A., G. O. Langstroth, and D. R. McRae. 1939. Can. J. Res. 17(D):113.
[16] Magee, D. F. 1961. J. Physiol. (London) 158:132.
[17] Magee, D. F., and T. T. White. 1965. Ann. Surg. 161:605.
[18] McCance, R. A., et al. 1951. Nature 168:788.
[19] Pincussohn, L. 1907. Biochem. Z. 4:484.
[20] Sineschekov, A. D. 1939. Fiziol. Zh. SSSR 27:70.
[21] Thomas, J. E. 1950. The external secretions of the pancreas. C. C. Thomas, Springfield, Ill.
[22] Thomas, J. E., and J. O. Crider. 1944. Am. J. Physiol. 140:574.

37. COMPOSITION OF GASTROINTESTINAL SECRETIONS: VERTEBRATES

Values in parentheses are ranges, estimate "c" (*see* Introduction).

	Animal	Specification	Property or Constituent	Value	Reference
			Duodenum		
1	Man	....	Sodium	(84.8-143.4) mEq/liter	28
2		In situ, duodenal bulb	pH	4.5(2.2-7.6)	3
3		post-bulbar duodenum	pH	6.7(5.2-8.0)	
4		Disodium phenylphosphate substrate, King method[1]	Phosphatase, alkaline	(10-30) Bodansky units/100 ml[2]	33
5		Intubation & aspiration; fasting	Osmotic pressure	200(138-276) milliosmoles/liter	18
6			Secretion rate	1.4(0.3-3.0) ml/min	35
7			Specific gravity	1.0078(1.0040-1.0107)	38
8			Calcium	12.4 mg/100 ml	18
9			Chloride	86.1(50.8-132.6) mEq/liter	18
10			Phosphorus, total	5.1(4.7-5.5) mg/100 ml	18
11			Zinc	1.21(0-2.32) µg/ml	35
12			Bicarbonate	9.1(2.0-16.1) mEq/liter	35
13			Ammonia	1217 µg/100 ml	36
14			Bilirubin	5.4(0.9-18.0) mg/100 ml	17
15			Urobilinogen	0.85(0-3.65) mg/100 g	17
16			Nitrogen, total	47(33-61) mg/100 ml	18
17			Cholesterol	36(0-315) mg/100 ml	38
18		Starch solution substrate, Agren & Lagerlöf method[3]	Amylase	(2-8) units/ml	2
19		Olive oil substrate, Frazer method[4]	Lipase	(2-6) units/ml	2

[1] For method, consult reference 20. [2] After fatty meal, value rises to 200 Bodansky units/100 ml. [3] For method, consult reference 1. [4] For method, consult reference 2.

continued

	Animal	Specification	Property or Constituent	Value	Reference
20		Tributyrin substrate, Lagerlöf method[5]	Lipase (as fatty acid)	179 units/hr	23
21		Azo-casein substrate, Charney & Tomarelli method[6]	Trypsin	(8-50) units/ml	2
22	1 day-10 yr old	Intubation & aspiration; fasting	Bile acids, free	0	11
23	1-4 days old	Intubation & aspiration; fasting	Bile salts, total	10.7(4.6-26.7) mEq/liter	11
24			G:T ratio[7]	0.47(0.21-0.86)	
25			C:CD:D ratio[8]	2.5:1.0:....	
26	5-7 days old	Intubation & aspiration; fasting	Bile salts, total	11.3(2.0-29.2) mEq/liter	11
27			G:T ratio[7]	0.95(0.34-2.30)	
28			C:CD:D ratio[8]	2.5:1.0:....	
29	7-12 mo old	Intubation & aspiration; fasting	Bile salts, total	8.8(2.2-19.7) mEq/liter	11
30			G:T ratio[7]	2.4(1.4-3.1)	
31			C:CD:D ratio[8]	1.1:1.0:....	
32	4-10 yr old	Intubation & aspiration; fasting	Bile salts, total	3.4(2.4-5.2) mEq/liter	11
33			G:T ratio[7]	1.7(1.3-2.4)	
34			C:CD:D ratio[8]	2.0:1.0:0.9	
35	ca. 20 yr old	Intubation & aspiration; fasting	Bile salts, total	8.1(2.8-20.0) mEq/liter	11
36			G:T ratio[7]	3.1(1.9-5.0)	
37			C:CD:D ratio[8]	1.2:1.0:1.6	
38	Cat	Brunner's glands & duodenal mucosa; fistula	pH	(8.7-8.9)	13
39			Secretion rate	0.9(0.5-1.4) ml/cm of fistula/hr	
40			Specific gravity	1.009	
41			Inorganic matter	8.42 mg/g	
42			Organic matter	4.88 mg/g	
43			Solids, total	13.30 mg/g	
44			Lipolytic enzymes	0	
45			Amylolytic enzymes	0	
46	Dog	Brunner's glands & duodenal mucosa; fistula	pH	8.4	13
47			Secretion rate	0.5 ml/cm of fistula/hr	13
48			Specific gravity	1.009	13
49			Inorganic matter	9.26 mg/g	13
50			Organic matter	6.15 mg/g	13
51			Solids, total	15.41 mg/g	13
52			Chloride	136(130-140) mEq/liter	8
53			Sodium	145(136-150) mEq/liter	8
54			Potassium	6.3(4.5-8.0) mEq/liter	8
55			Bicarbonate	17(14-22) mEq/liter	8
56			Amylolytic enzymes	0	13
57			Pepsin	1.5 units/ml	8
58		Intestinal contents; various diets; Bodansky method[9]	Phosphatase	(7.25-24.75) units/ml	22
59	Goat	Brunner's glands & duodenal mucosa; fistula	pH	(8.2-8.4)	13
60			Secretion rate	0.7(0.3-1.1) ml/cm of fistula/hr	
61			Specific gravity	(1.007-1.008)	
62			Inorganic matter	7.73 mg/g	
63			Organic matter	6.83 mg/g	
64			Solids, total	14.56 mg/g	
65			Lipolytic enzymes	0	
66			Amylolytic enzymes	0	

[5] For method, consult reference 23. [6] For method, consult reference 6. [7] Glycine to taurine-conjugated bile acids. [8] Cholic acid to chenodeoxycholic acid to deoxycholic acid. [9] For method, consult reference 5.

continued

37. COMPOSITION OF GASTROINTESTINAL SECRETIONS: VERTEBRATES

	Animal	Specification	Property or Constituent	Value	Reference
67	Horse	Duodenal juice	pH	7.13	10
68			Specific gravity	1.008	7
69			Water	98.47%	7
70			Mucus	0.95%	7
71	Rabbit	Brunner's glands & duodenal mucosa; fistula	pH	(8.6-9.0)	13
72			Specific gravity	1.009	13
73			Mucins	(0.8- 50) mg dry wt/ml	19
74			Proteolytic enzymes	0	13
75			Lipolytic enzymes	0	13
76		Acute experiment	Inorganic matter	10.23 mg/g	13
77			Organic matter	4.98 mg/g	
78			Solids, total	15.21 mg/g	
79	Sheep	Brunner's glands & duodenal mucosa; fistula	pH	(6.7-7.4)	16
80			Volume	(13.3-26.0) ml/hr	
81	Swine	Brunner's glands & duodenal mucosa; fistula	pH	(8.4-8.9)	13
82			Secretion rate	1.1(0.6-2.5) ml/cm of fistual/hr	13
83			Specific gravity	1.007	13
84			Inorganic matter	6.81 mg/g	13
85			Organic matter	4.99 mg/g	13
86			Solids, total	11.80 mg/g	13
87			Mucins	(0.80-1.50) mg/ml	19
88			Proteolytic enzymes	0	13
89			Lipolytic enzymes	0	13
90			Amylolytic enzymes	0	13
91	Chicken	Mucosal secretions; acute experiments	Osmolarity	346 milliosmoles/liter	21
92			pH	7.11	
93			Secretion rate	1.1 ml/hr	
94			Solids, mucus	11%	
95			RNA	0.85 μg/ml	
			Jejunum		
96	Man	Intubation & aspiration; fasting	Freezing point depression	0.507(0.400-0.577)°C	25
97			Osmolar concentration	268(212-305) milliosmoles/liter	25
98			pH	6.51(5.07-7.07)	15
99			Secretion rate	0.43(0.17-0.70) ml/min	27
100			Base, total	139(114-162) mEq/liter	25
101			Chloride	117(80-139) mEq/liter	25
102			Bicarbonate	13(2-32) mEq/liter	25
103			Bilirubin	6.0(0.8-18.5) mg/100 ml	17
104			Urobilinogen	0.62(0-2.96) mg/100 g	17
105		Upper jejunum	Calcium	7.6(5.2-11.6) mg/100 ml	18
106			Phosphorus, total	10.1(7.1-13.2) mg/100 ml	
107			Nitrogen, total	55(45-63) mg/100 ml	
108		Lower jejunum	Calcium	8.0(5.4-12.8) mg/100 ml	18
109			Phosphorus, total	7.2(7.1-7.3) mg/100 ml	
110			Nitrogen, total	56(45-73) mg/100 ml	
111	Cat	Perfused intestinal segment	DNA	(3-20) μg/hr/g intestine	14
112	Dog	Isolated loop or fistula; fasting	pH	6.83(6.30-7.28)	9
113			Volume	(0.01-0.3) ml/hr/in. of fistula	14
114			Ash	0.88(0.76-0.94) g/100 ml	9
115			Solids	1.65(1.22-2.34) g/100 ml	9
116			Calcium	2.7(1.6-5.4) mEq/liter	9
117			Chloride	147(141-153) mEq/liter	9
118			Magnesium	1.1(0.2-1.9) mEq/liter	9

continued

	Animal	Specification	Property or Constituent	Value	Reference
119			Phosphate	3.1(1.2-7.9) mEq/liter	9
120			Potassium	6.3(4.2-10.2) mEq/liter	9
121			Sodium	141(126-152) mEq/liter	9
122			Bicarbonate	21.7(5.2-30.0) mEq/liter	9
123			CO_2	10.0(5.5-16.0) mEq/liter	34
124			DNA	(200-600) μg/ml	14
125			Mucoprotein (as reducing sugar)	(0.13-0.29) g/100 ml	12
126			Amylase (as reducing sugar)	60(50-68) g/100 ml	34
127			Invertase (as reducing sugar)	68(56-78) g/100 ml	34
128			Lipase (as fatty acid)	6.1(4.9-7.4) g/100 ml	34
129			Peptidase (as amino N)	3.1(2.6-3.8) g/100 ml	34
130			Phosphatase (as inorganic P)	(1.9-3.3) g/100 ml	12
			Ileum		
131	Man	Intubation & aspiration; fasting	Osmotic pressure	277(238-299) milliosmoles/liter	18
132			Bilirubin	8.45(1.2-32.5) mg/100 ml	17
133			Urobilinogen	0.30(0-0.97) mg/100 g	17
134		90 cm beyond pylorus	pH	6.10	18
135			Calcium	5.3(5.2-5.4) mg/100 ml	
136			Chloride	128.6 mEq/liter	
137			Phosphorus, total	5.8(4.5-7.1) mg/100 ml	
138			Bicarbonate	2.3 mEq/liter	
139			Nitrogen, total	47(40-54) mg/100 ml	
140		120 cm beyond pylorus	pH	7.05(6.77-7.21)	18
141			Secretion rate	0.56(0.18-1.05) ml/min	
142			Calcium	7.9(5.0-12.8) mg/100 ml	
143			Chloride	118.3(101.0-132.6) mEq/liter	
144			Phosphorus, total	5.7(4.5-7.3) mg/100 ml	
145			Bicarbonate	19.8(3.9-39.8) mEq/liter	
146			Nitrogen, total	70(53-86) mg/100 ml	
147		160 cm beyond pylorus	pH	7.23(7.16-7.31)	18
148			Secretion rate	0.37(0.28-0.47) ml/min	
149			Calcium	7.4(5.0-9.8) mg/100 ml	
150			Chloride	126.6(123.9-128.2) mEq/liter	
151			Phosphorus, total	6.3 mg/100 ml	
152			Bicarbonate	14.6(10.4-17.0) mEq/liter	
153			Nitrogen, total	55(34-86) mg/100 ml	
154		Sammons method[10]	Lipase	2.5(1.4-4.3) units/ml	30
		Ileostomy discharge			
155		Sammons method[11]	Mucinase	(150-1000) units/24 hr	29
156		Tomarelli method[12]	Proteolytic activity	242(40-685) units	32
157		Ileostomy; fistula	Ash	0.866 g/100 ml	4
158			Potassium	11.2(5.9-29.3) mEq/liter	24
159			Sodium	129.4(105.4-143.7) mEq/liter	24
160	Dog	Ileal loop or transplant; after fasting	pH	(7.61-8.66)	9
161			Ash	(0.89-0.98) g/100 ml	9
162			Solids	(1.31-1.78) g/100 ml	9
163			Calcium	(5.0-5.5) mEq/liter	9
164			Chloride	78.4(68.1-87.9) mEq/liter	9
165				101(98-104) mEq/liter	34
166			Potassium	(4.7-6.8) mEq/liter	9
167			Sodium	151(146-156) mEq/liter	9

[10] For method, consult reference 31. [11] For method, consult reference 29. [12] For method, consult reference 37.

continued

37. COMPOSITION OF GASTROINTESTINAL SECRETIONS: VERTEBRATES

	Animal	Specification	Property or Constituent	Value	Reference
168			Bicarbonate	91.9(69.8-114.0) mEq/liter	9
169			CO_2	62.9(55.9-69.1)	34
170			Amylase (as reducing sugar)	24(20-30) g/100 ml	34
171			Invertase (as reducing sugar)	27(23-34) g/100 ml	34
172			Lipase (as fatty acid)	2.2(1.8-2.9) g/100 ml	34
173			Peptidase (as amino N)	1.3(1.1-1.6) g/100 ml	34
	Whole Small Intestine				
174	Man	Estimates from data on structure & activity of gastrointestinal tract	Total secretory volume	(10-20) liter/day	26
175			Protein, sloughed mucosal cells	(77-91) g/day	
176			Protein, intestinal secretions	(40-200) g/day	

Contributors: (a) Goldsmith, Dale P. J., (b) Cummins, Alvin J., (c) Frazer, A. C.; Sammons, H. G.; and Okunzua, G., (d) Forrest, Andrew P. M., (e) Senior, John R.

References

[1] Agren, G., and H. O. Lagerlöf. 1936. Acta Med. Scand. 90:1.

[2] Anderson, C. M., et al. 1952. Lancet 262:836.

[3] Archambault, A. P., R. A. Rovelstad, and H. C. Carlson. 1967. Gastroenterology 52:940.

[4] Bickel, A., and H. R. Kanitz. 1934. Biochem. Z. 270:378.

[5] Bodansky, A. 1933. J. Biol. Chem. 101:93.

[6] Charney, J., and R. M. Tomarelli. 1947. Ibid. 171: 501.

[7] Colin, G. 1872. Traite Physiol. Comp. Animaux 1: 818.

[8] Cooke, A. R., and M. I. Grossman. 1966. Gastroenterology 51:506.

[9] DeBeer, E. J., C. G. Johnston, and D. W. Wilson. 1935. J. Biol. Chem. 108:113.

[10] Dukes, H. H. 1955. The physiology of domestic animals. Ed. 7. Comstock, Ithaca.

[11] Encrantz, J., and J. Sjövall. 1959. Clin. Chim. Acta 4:793.

[12] Fink, K. 1944. Am. J. Physiol. 141:598.

[13] Florey, H. W., and H. E. Harding. 1934. J. Pathol. Bacteriol. 39:255.

[14] Goldsmith, D. P. J. Unpublished. Univ. Nebraska, College Medicine, Omaha, 1967.

[15] Gotschlick, E. 1928. Deut. Arch. Klin. Med. 159: 288.

[16] Harrison, F. A., and K. J. Hill. 1962. J. Physiol. (London) 162:225.

[17] Hollan, O. R. 1950. Gastroenterology 16:418.

[18] Karr, W. G., and W. O. Abbott. 1935. J. Clin. Invest. 14:893.

[19] Kent, P. W. 1962. Gastroenterology 43:292.

[20] King, E. J. 1964. Micro-analysis in medical biochemistry. Ed. 4. J. and A. Churchill, London. pp. 102-103.

[21] Kokas, E., J. L. Phillips, Jr., and W. D. Brunson, Jr. 1967. Comp. Biochem. Physiol. 22:81.

[22] Kosman, A. J., J. W. Kaulbersz, and S. Freeman. 1942. Am. J. Physiol. 138:236.

[23] Lagerlöf, H. O. 1942. Acta Med. Scand., Suppl. 128.

[24] Lockwood, J. S., and H. T. Randall. 1949. Bull. N.Y. Acad. Med. 25:228.

[25] McGee, L. C., and A. B. Hastings. 1945. Gastroenterology 4:243.

[26] Nasset, E. S. 1965. Federation Proc. 24(4):953.

[27] Owles, W. H. 1937. Clin. Sci. 3:21.

[28] Ross, C. A. C., and H. G. Sammons. Unpublished. Univ. Birmingham, Dept. Pharmacology, Birmingham, England, 1967.

[29] Sammons, H. G. 1951. Lancet 261:239.

[30] Sammons, H. G. Unpublished. Univ. Birmingham, Dept. Pharmacology, Birmingham, England, 1967.

[31] Sammons, H. G., A. C. Frazer, and M. Thompson. 1956. J. Clin. Pathol. 9:379.

[32] Sammons, H. G., C. A. C. Ross, and W. A. Wood. 1955. Clin. Sci. 14:157.

[33] Sammons, H. G., and M. D. Thompson. Unpublished. Univ. Birmingham, Dept. Pharmacology, Birmingham, England, 1967.

[34] Schiffrin, M. J., and E. S. Nasset. 1939. Am. J. Physiol. 128:70.

[35] Sullivan, J. F., J. O'Grady, and H. G. Lankford. 1965. Gastroenterology 48:438.

[36] Summerskill, W. H. J., T. Aoyagi, and W. B. Evans. 1966. Gut 7:497.

[37] Tomarelli, R. M., J. Charney, and M. L. Harding. 1949. J. Lab. Clin. Med. 34:428.

[38] Voegtlin, W. L., H. Greengard, and A. C. Ivy. 1934. Am. J. Physiol. 110:198.

38. COMPOSITION OF CONTENTS OF GERMFREE GASTROINTESTINAL TRACT: VERTEBRATES

Part I. Stomach and Intestine

	Animal	Sex, Age, & Wt	Gastro-intestinal Segment	Property or Constituent	Value: Conventional	Value: Germfree	Reference
				Contents of Stomach			
1	Rat	....	....	pH	5.8	2.7	6
2		1-2 mo	....	Lactic acid, mg/g fresh contents	....	0.85	3
3		♂, 100	....	Histamine, μg/g fresh contents	12.3 ± 1.3	6.0 ± 0.5	2
4	Sheep	2-4 mo	Rumen	pH	....	6.5[1]; 6.8[1]; 6.9[1]	7
5			Abomasum	pH	....	5.3[1]; 6.5[1]; 6.7[1]	
6	Chicken	12 days	....	pH	3.4[1]; 3.5[1]	3.3[1]; 4.6[1]; 5.0[1]	6
				Contents of Small Intestine			
7	Rabbit, Dutch[2]	1-3 yr	Whole	Amylase, mM maltose/30 min/g fresh contents	5.89[1]; 8.84[1]	8.08[1]; 8.66[1]	10
8	Rat	....	Duodenum	pH	6.4	6.3	6
9			Jejunum	pH	5.8	6.3	
10			Ileum, upper	pH	7.0	6.5	
11			lower	pH	7.0	6.9	
12		100 days	Middle third	Thiamine, μg/g dry matter	8.7 ± 0.8	4.5 ± 1.0	9
13			Lower third	Thiamine, μg/g dry matter	4.5 ± 0.7	2.3 ± 0.4	
14		♂, 100 days	Upper half	Dry weight, % of wet wt	20.5 ± 1.1[3]	18.9 ± 0.8[3]	2
15				Histamine, μg/g wet wt	3.7 ± 0.7[1,3]; 6.5 ± 0.7[1,3]	2.0 ± 0.2[3]	
16			Third quarter	Dry weight, % of wet wt	25.2 ± 2.1[3]	26.2 ± 0.9[3]	2
17				Histamine, μg/g wet wt	3.1 ± 0.4[1,3]; 5.3 ± 0.4[1,3]	1.3 ± 0.1[3]	
18			Fourth quarter	Dry weight, % of wet wt	28.5 ± 1.5[3]	27.0 ± 1.0[3]	2
19				Histamine, μg/g wet wt	1.3 ± 0.1[1,3]; 4.8 ± 1.0[1,3]	1.1 ± 0.1[3]	
20			Lower	Dry weight, % of wet wt	26.3 ± 0.7[3]	24.1 ± 0.8[3]	8
21		♂, 300-400 g	Terminal ileum	Dry weight, % of wet wt	24.2 ± 1.4[4]	25.4 ± 2.6	1
22				Osmolarity, milliosmoles/liter	446 ± 28[4]	423 ± 59	
23				Conductivity, mM NaCl	153 ± 5.9[4]	146 ± 14.2	
24				Chloride, mM	4.12 ± 1.38[4]	5.20 ± 4.19	
25				Potassium, mM	9.86 ± 1.45[4]	9.20 ± 1.49	
26				Sodium, mM	124 ± 18[4]	132 ± 21	
27		♀, 4 mo	Upper	Total N, % of solids	10.5 ± 0.7	10.6 ± 1.6	5
28				Amylase, g starch/15 min/g dry matter	113 ± 40	79.0 ± 26	
29				Lipase, mEq free fatty acids/20 min/g dry matter	17.3 ± 4.5	11.2 ± 4.1	
30				Protease, mEq tyrosine/10 min/g dry matter	0.92 ± 0.21	0.75 ± 0.28	
31			Middle	Total N, % of solids	7.4 ± 0.6	7.3 ± 1.6	
32				Amylase, g starch/15 min/g dry matter	113.0 ± 69	119.0 ± 20	
33				Lipase, mEq free fatty acids/20 min/g dry matter	17.3 ± 3.1	14.6 ± 3.9	
34				Protease, mEq tyrosine/10 min/g dry matter	1.96 ± 0.60	1.79 ± 0.54	
35			Lower	Total N, % of dry matter	5.1 ± 0.6	4.1 ± 1.0	
36				Amylase, g starch/15 min/g dry matter	112.0 ± 45	16.0 ± 4.0	
37				Lipase, mEq free fatty acids/20 min/g dry matter	9.2 ± 2.5	8.7 ± 4.7	
38				Protease, mEq tyrosine/10 min/g dry matter	1.22 ± 0.26	1.50 ± 0.28	

1/ For one subject. 2/ Fitted with coprophagy-preventing collar. 3/ Standard deviation of the mean. 4/ Monoinoculated with *Clostridium difficile*.

continued

38. COMPOSITION OF CONTENTS OF GERMFREE GASTROINTESTINAL TRACT: VERTEBRATES

Part I. Stomach and Intestine

	Animal	Sex, Age, & Wt	Gastro-intestinal Segment	Property or Constituent	Value: Conventional	Value: Germfree	Reference
39	Sheep	2-4 mo	Duodenum	pH	....	6.3[1/]; 6.5[1/]; 6.9[1/]	7
40			Jejunum	pH	....	6.5[1/]; 6.5[1/]; 6.6[1/]	
41			Ileum	pH	....	6.6[1/]; 6.7[1/]; 6.9[1/]	
42	Chicken, Leghorn	12 days	Duodenum	pH	6.3[1/]; 6.5[1/]	6.3[1/]; 6.4[1/]; 6.6[1/]	6
43			Ileum, lower	pH	6.51[1/]; 6.53[1/]	6.3[1/]; 6.3[1/]; 6.4[1/]	
44		10 wk	Upper	Amylase, g starch/15 min/g dry matter	105 ± 53	90 ± 28	4
45				Lipase, mEq free fatty acids/20 min/g dry matter	6.53 ± 2.41	5.64 ± 1.17	
46				Protease, mEq tyrosine/10 min/g dry matter	1.23 ± 0.24	1.19 ± 0.23	
47			Lower	Total N, % of contents	3.1 ± 0.10	3.8 ± 0.23	
48				Protein N, % of contents	0.6 ± 0.24	0.6 ± 0.26	
49				Nonprotein N, % of contents	2.5 ± 0.14	3.2 ± 0.14	
50				Amylase, g starch/15 min/g dry matter	104 ± 38	90 ± 20	
51				Lipase, mEq free fatty acids/20 min/g dry matter	4.40 ± 1.12	3.98 ± 1.02	
52				Protease, mEq tyrosine/10 min/g dry matter	1.73 ± 0.23	1.43 ± 0.16	

[1/] For one subject.

Contributor: Pleasants, Julian R.

References

[1] Asano, T. 1967. Proc. Soc. Exptl. Biol. Med. 124: 424.

[2] Beaver, M. H., and B. S. Wostmann. 1962. Brit. J. Pharmacol. 19:385.

[3] Ducluzeau, R., et al. 1966. Compt. Rend. 262(D): 321.

[4] Lepkovsky, S., et al. 1964. Poultry Sci. 43:722.

[5] Lepkovsky, S., et al. 1966. Brit. J. Nutr. 20:257.

[6] Luckey, T. D. 1963. Germfree life and gnotobiology. Academic Press, New York.

[7] Smith, C. K. 1966. Ph.D. Thesis. Univ. Notre Dame, Indiana.

[8] Wostmann, B., and E. Bruckner-Kardoss. 1959. Am. J. Physiol. 197:1345.

[9] Wostmann, B. S., P. L. Knight, and D. F. Kan. 1962. Ann. N.Y. Acad. Sci. 98:516.

[10] Yoshida, T., et al. 1968. Brit. J. Nutr. 22(4).

Part II. Cecum, Colon, and Rectum

Values in parentheses are ranges, estimate "c" (*see* Introduction).

	Animal	Sex, Age, & Wt	Property or Constituent	Value: Conventional	Value: Germfree	Reference
	Contents of Cecum					
1	Guinea pig	....	Oxidation-reduction potential (*E*) at pH 7 in mv	−367	−90	16
2			Histamine, μg/g fresh contents	10.3	2.5	22
3		3 wk[1/]	Free ammonia, μg/100 g wet wt	....	430	20
4		4 wk	pH	6.1	6.5	25
5			Ash, % of dry matter	0.711 ± 0.28	0.648 ± 0.29	

[1/] 40% protein diet.

continued

38. COMPOSITION OF CONTENTS OF GERMFREE GASTROINTESTINAL TRACT: VERTEBRATES

Part II. Cecum, Colon, and Rectum

	Animal	Sex, Age, & Wt	Property or Constituent	Value		Reference
				Conventional	Germfree	
6			Dry weight, % of wet wt	18.0 ± 3.5	13.9 ± 1.2	
7			Crude fiber, % of dry matter	13.2 ± 3.0	11.7 ± 0.90	
8			Total N, % of dry matter	4.89 ± 0.59	4.17 ± 0.74	
9			Total amino N, % of dry matter	4.06 ± 0.36	2.58 ± 0.4	
10			Free amino N, % of dry matter	0.714 ± 0.13	0.616 ± 0.12	
11			Total lipids, % of dry matter	9.33 ± 3.3	4.56 ± 2.0	
12			Fatty acids, % of dry matter	4.89 ± 1.32	1.72 ± 0.24	
13			Ether-soluble acids, mEq/g dry matter	0.25 ± 0.09	0.18 ± 0.06	
14		2 mo[2]	Fresh weight, % of body wt	5.8(3.0-7.1)	8.8(6.0-14.1)	10
15		♂, 5 mo[3]	Fresh weight, % of body wt[4]	3.32 ± 1.0	15.9 ± 2.8	17
16		♀, 5 mo[3]	Fresh weight, % of body wt[4]	4.77 ± 3.4	32.6 ± 11.2	17
17	Mouse, Swiss	♂, 80 days	Histamine, μg/g fresh contents	3.4 ± 0.3[5]	1.0 ± 0.1[5]	2
18		11 mo	Fresh weight, % of body wt[4]	0.66 ± 0.16	15.6 ± 1.3	3
19		♀, 80 days	Fresh weight, % of body wt[4]	0.79 ± 0.40	9.8 ± 1.7	3
20		....	Lethal substance, LD_{50}/total contents	<1	(5-8)	7
21	Rabbit, Dutch	3 mo	Fresh weight, % of body wt	3.17 ± 0.20	11.5 ± 2.1	18
22	Rabbit, Dutch[6]	1-3 yr	Ash, % of dry matter	8.63 ± 1.50	6.36 ± 0.69	26
23			Dry weight, % of wet wt	24.7[7]; 26.7[7]	14.5[7]; 15.2[7]	
24			Crude fat, % of dry matter	0.96 ± 0.34	0.91 ± 0.014	
25			Crude fiber, % of dry matter	24.43 ± 9.08	27.18 ± 4.44	
26			Calcium, % of dry matter	0.816 ± 0.022	0.484 ± 0.076	
27			Phosphorus, % of dry matter	1.435 ± 0.111	0.545 ± 0.056	
28			Total N, % of dry matter	6.75 ± 1.7	4.24 ± 0.51	
29			Protein N, % of dry matter	4.47 ± 1.42	1.26 ± 0.15	
30			Nonprotein N, % of dry matter	2.28 ± 0.41	2.98 ± 0.25	
31			Amylase, mM maltose/30 min/g fresh contents	0.36[7]; 0.85[7]	2.35[7]; 2.75[7]	
32	Rat	....	Free ammonia, mg/100 g wet wt	(32-79)	(6-10)	6
33			Urea, mg/100 g wet wt	0	(40-45)	6
34			Sterols, presence or absence	Present[8]	Present[9]	9
35			Musculoactive substance, μg bradykinin equivalent/ml contents	2.5	16.6	21
36			Lethal substance, LD_{50}/total contents	<1	(5-8)	7
37		1-2 mo	Lactic acid, mg/g ingested diet	1.12	0.75	5
38			Residual sugar, mg lactose/g ingested diet	12.8	16.1	
39		1-3 mo	Hexosamine, % of dry matter	(1.0-1.9)	(5.7-10.6)	13
40		1-8 mo	Ash, % of dry matter	22.6 ± 2.16	15.3 ± 1.71	15
41			Dry weight, % of wet wt	25.3 ± 2.70	18.2 ± 3.94	
42		3 mo	pH	6.6 ± 0.1	7.5 ± 0.1	23
43			Oxidation-reduction potential *(E)* at pH 7 in mv	−183 ± 36[10]	+60 ± 15[10]	
44		♂, 3 mo	Fresh weight, % of body wt[4]	0.797 ± 0.1	5.3 ± 0.67	8
45			Dry weight, % of wet wt	26.3 ± 1.7	16.1 ± 1.3	22
46		100 days	Thiamine, μg/g dry matter	8.5 ± 1.8	1.9 ± 0.4	24
47		♂, 100 days	Histamine, μg/g fresh contents	4.7 ± 0.7[5]	1.5 ± 0.1[5]	2
48		♀, 4 mo	Total N, % of dry matter	(3.5-4.7)	(5.3-5.9)	12
49				(5.5-9.1)	(5.0-8.4)	13
50			Protein N, % of dry matter	(1.8-2.4)	(0.5-2.0)	12

[2] First generation. [3] Second generation. [4] Corrected for cecal contents. [5] Standard deviation of the mean. [6] Fitted with coprophagy-preventing collar. [7] For one subject. [8] Coprostanol was the major sterol found in the cecum, but was present only in small amounts in the small intestine. [9] Cholesterol, lathosterol, methostenol, campesterol, stigmasterol, and β-sitosterol were present in the cecum and small intestine; coprostanol or coprostanol analogues of the plant sterols were not found. [10] 50 minutes after anesthesia.

continued

Part II. Cecum, Colon, and Rectum

	Animal	Sex, Age, & Wt	Property or Constituent	Value: Conventional	Value: Germfree	Reference
51			Nonprotein N, % of dry matter	(1.7-2.3)	(3.3-4.9)	12
52			Amylase, g starch/15 min/g dry matter	9.7 ± 4.7	2.2 ± 0.3	12
53			Lipase, mEq free fatty acids/20 min/g dry matter	5.7 ± 1.9	5.1 ± 1.0	12
54			Protease, mEq tyrosine/10 min/g dry matter	0.77 ± 0.27	1.15 ± 0.20	12
55		260 g[11]	Free ammonia, mg/100 g wet wt	22	(2-4)	4
56			Urea, mg/100 g wet wt	0	(17-26)	
57		♂, 260 g	Potassium, mg/100 g wet wt	(292-770)	(48-153)	4
58			Sodium, mg/100 g wet wt	(400-585)	(390-650)	
59			Total N, mg/260 g subject	23	59	
60			Alcohol-sol N, mg/260 g subject	5	40	
61			Residue N, mg/260 g subject	13	6.5	
62			Trichloroacetic acid-sol N, mg/260 g subject	5	12.5	
63			Free amino acids, mg/g wet wt	0.52	5.2	
64		300-400 g	Osmolarity, milliosmoles/liter	321 ± 14.9[12]	318 ± 12.5	1
65			Conductivity, mM NaCl	114.4 ± 8.7[12]	84.6 ± 5.9	
66			Carbon dioxide, mM	18.98 ± 10.41[12]	4.17 ± 0.37	
67			Chloride, mM	13.78 ± 8.72[12]	1.66 ± 0.29	
68			Potassium, mM	13.40 ± 1.49[12]	11.59 ± 1.56	
69			Sodium, mM	87.8 ± 21[12]	49.0 ± 6.9	
70	Sheep	2-4 mo	pH	....	6.8[7]; 6.9[7]; 7.0[7]	19
	Chicken[13]					
71	Leghorn	12 days	pH	(6.3-6.7)	(6.3-6.5)	15
72		1 mo	Fresh weight, % of body wt	0.347	0.343	15
73		4-7 wk	Riboflavin, μg/g fresh contents	7.3 ± 2.38	10.9 ± 7.57	14
74			Nicotinic acid, μg/g fresh contents	37.2 ± 18.7	12.1 ± 6.7	
75			Biotin, μg/g fresh contents	0.488 ± 1.59	0.241 ± 0.182	
76			Calcium pantothenate, μg/g fresh contents	7.74 ± 3.12	5.47 ± 2.40	
77			Folic acid, μg/g fresh contents	1.83 ± 0.94	2.29 ± 0.46	
78		10 wk	Total N, % of dry matter	8.1 ± 0.18	4.3 ± 0.49	11
79			Protein N, % of dry matter	4.00 ± 0.70	0.09 ± 0.02	
80			Nonprotein N, % of dry matter	4.2 ± 0.56	4.2 ± 1.2	
81			Amylase, g starch/15 min/g dry matter	4.5 ± 2.3	9.0 ± 4.1	
82			Lipase, mEq free fatty acids/20 min/g dry matter	2.51 ± 0.61	1.64 ± 0.52	
83			Protease, mEq tyrosine/10 min/g dry matter	0.23 ± 0.04	1.48 ± 0.11	
84		11 wk	Ash, % of dry matter	22.3 ± 1.23	18.4 ± 4.19	15
85			Dry weight, % of wet wt	16.2 ± 2.0	11.1 ± 1.1	
86			Total N, % of dry matter	7.13 ± 1.26	7.35 ± 0.47	
87	Wyandotte	8 wk	Ash, % of dry matter	12.9 ± 2.2	12.9 ± 4.0	15
88	Bantam		Dry weight, % of wet wt	25.6 ± 2.72	13.2 ± 0.83	
			Contents of Colon			
89	Rabbit, Dutch[6]	1-3 yr	Amylase, mM maltose/30 min/g fresh contents	0.25[7]; 0.41[7]	1.47[7]; 1.91[7]	26
90	Rat	....	pH	6.5	6.5	15
91		100 days	Thiamine, μg/g dry matter	8.0 ± 1.6	1.7 ± 0.4	24
92		♀, 4 mo	Total N, % of dry matter	3.9 ± 0.2	4.3 ± 0.3	12
93			Amylase, g starch/15 min/g dry matter	6.7 ± 2.6	1.6 ± 0.3	
94			Lipase, mEq free fatty acids/20 min/g dry matter	4.3 ± 2.1	6.2 ± 1.5	
95			Protease, mEq tyrosine/10 min/g dry matter	0.82 ± 0.11	0.93 ± 0.27	
96	Sheep	2-4 mo	pH	6.9[7]; 6.9[7]; 7.0[7]	....	19

[6] Fitted with coprophagy-preventing collar. [7] For one subject. [11] 22% protein diet. [12] Monoinoculated with *Clostridium difficile*. [13] Other data on germfree chickens of various ages, too detailed to collate for this table, may be found in Lobund Reports No. 3, 1960, Univ. of Notre Dame Press, Notre Dame, Indiana.

continued

38. COMPOSITION OF CONTENTS OF GERMFREE GASTROINTESTINAL TRACT: VERTEBRATES

Part II. Cecum, Colon, and Rectum

	Animal	Sex, Age, & Wt	Property or Constituent	Value		Reference
				Conventional	Germfree	
97	Chicken,	12 days	pH	6.2[7]; 6.5[7]	6.1[7]; 6.2[7]; 6.5[7]	15
98	Leghorn	10 wk	Amylase, g starch/15 min/g dry matter	12.2	13.7	11
99			Lipase, mEq free fatty acids/20 min/g dry matter	2.11	1.68	
100			Protease, mEq tyrosine/10 min/g dry matter	1.54	1.04	
	Contents of Rectum					
101	Chicken,	10 wk	Ash, % of dry wt	8.09 ± 1.06	17.53 ± 3.74	15
102	Leghorn		Dry weight, % of wet wt	18.7 ± 2.9	15.5 ± 3.0	

7/ For one subject.

Contributor: Pleasants, Julian R.

References

[1] Asano, T. 1967. Proc. Soc. Exptl. Biol. Med. 124:424.
[2] Beaver, M. H., and B. S. Wostmann. 1962. Brit. J. Pharmacol. 19:385.
[3] Bruckner-Kardoss, E., and B. S. Wostmann. Unpublished. Univ. Notre Dame, Dept. Biology, Indiana, 1967.
[4] Combe, E., and E. Sacquet. 1966. Compt. Rend. 262(D):685.
[5] Ducluzeau, R., et al. 1966. Ibid. 262(D):321.
[6] Ducluzeau, R., et al. 1966. Ibid. 262(D):944.
[7] Gordon, H. A. 1965. Nature 205:571.
[8] Gordon, H. A., and B. S. Wostmann. 1960. Anat. Record 137:65.
[9] Gustafsson, B. E., J. A. Gustafsson, and J. Sjovall. 1966. Acta Chem. Scand. 20:1827.
[10] Horton, R. E., and J. L. S. Hickey. 1961. Proc. Animal Care Panel 11:93.
[11] Lepkovsky, S., et al. 1964. Poultry Sci. 43:722.
[12] Lepkovsky, S., et al. 1966. Brit. J. Nutr. 20:257.
[13] Lindstedt, G., S. Lindstedt, and B. E. Gustafsson. 1965. J. Exptl. Med. 121:201.
[14] Luckey, T. D. 1959. Ann. N.Y. Acad. Sci. 78:127.
[15] Luckey, T. D. 1963. Germfree life and gnotobiology. Academic Press, New York.
[16] Phillips, B. P., P. A. Wolfe, and H. A. Gordon. 1959. Ann. N.Y. Acad. Sci. 78:308.
[17] Pleasants, J. R., et al. 1967. Z. Versuchstierk. 9:195.
[18] Reddy, B. S., et al. 1965. J. Nutr. 87:189.
[19] Smith, C. K. 1966. Ph.D. Thesis. Univ. Notre Dame, Indiana.
[20] Warren, K. S., and W. L. Newton. 1959. Am. J. Physiol. 197:717.
[21] Wiseman, R. F., and H. A. Gordon. 1965. Nature 205:572.
[22] Wostmann, B., and E. Bruckner-Kardoss. 1959. Am. J. Physiol. 197:1345.
[23] Wostmann, B. S., and E. Bruckner-Kardoss. 1966. Proc. Soc. Exptl. Biol. Med. 121:1111.
[24] Wostmann, B. S., P. L. Knight, and D. F. Kan. 1962. Ann. N.Y. Acad. Sci. 98:516.
[25] Wynngate, A. E., R. E. Horton, and M. Forbes. 1958. Germfree animal studies. Walter Reed Army Medical Center, Washington, D.C.
[26] Yoshida, T., et al. 1968. Brit. J. Nutr. 22(4).

39. GASTRIC SECRETION TESTS: MAN

Tubes used in testing should be positioned in the gastric antrum and checked fluoroscopically. For additional information, consult references 2, 5, 6, 8-15, and 17.

	Test	Subjects			Volume ml/hr	Free HCl Output[1] mEq/hr	Total HCl Output[1] mEq/hr	HCl Concentration mEq/liter	Reference
		Sex	No.	Age, yr					
1	Basal secretion	♂	30	<20->60[2]	64 ± 21.4	2.59 ± 1.97	3.7 ± 2.12	....	3
2			20	19-66	38.7 ± 23.01	....	1.3 ± 1.59	29.8 ± 21.68	1
3			4	<30	50.1 ± 31.22	....	2.8 ± 2.18	35.8 ± 14.04	
4			16	>30	35.6 ± 19.83	....	1.0 ± 1.13	28.3 ± 22.96	

1/ There is a recent trend to avoid the arbitrary division of acid into free and total; a single titration to pH 7.0-7.4 with a glass electrode or phenol red is recommended [1,11,13,14]. 2/ Average age, 36.5 years.

continued

	Test	Subjects: Sex	No.	Age, yr	Volume ml/hr	Free HCl Output[1] mEq/hr	Total HCl Output[1] mEq/hr	HCl Concentration mEq/liter	Reference
5			25	20-29	73	2.22[3]	...	31	7
6			80	30-39	80	2.58[3]	...	32	
7			80	40-49	83	2.66[3]	...	29	
8			79	50-59	69	1.95[3]	...	23	
9			40	60+	64	1.73[3]	...	23	
10			615	20-60+	...	2.44 ± 2.85	...	...	4
11			74	20-29	...	2.50 ± 2.81	...	...	
12			157	30-39	...	2.63 ± 2.70	...	...	
13			156	40-49	...	2.83 ± 3.01	...	...	
14			158	50-59	...	2.25 ± 3.04	...	...	
15			70	60+	...	1.48 ± 2.18	...	...	
16			75	<30->70	58	1.8	...	31	16
17		♀	12	<20->60[2]	54.2 ± 24.2	1.48 ± 1.33	2.24 ± 1.76	...	3
18			20	19-65	40.6 ± 38.8	...	1.1 ± 1.75	20.3 ± 18.27	1
19			5	<30	72.8 ± 53.49	...	3.0 ± 2.44	34.6 ± 18.31	
20			15	>30	29.9 ± 24.37	...	0.5 ± 0.75	15.6 ± 15.59	
21			22	20-29	77	2.17[3]	...	27	7
22			66	30-39	65	1.59[3]	...	22	
23			80	40-49	65	1.26[3]	...	19	
24			80	50-59	56	0.99[3]	...	14	
25			32	60+	44	0.93[3]	...	15	
26			634	20-60+	...	1.33 ± 2.00	...	...	4
27			65	20-29	...	1.74 ± 2.06	...	...	
28			145	30-39	...	1.58 ± 2.32	...	...	
29			184	40-49	...	1.45 ± 2.24	...	...	
30			162	50-59	...	0.98 ± 1.53	...	...	
31			78	60+	...	0.95 ± 1.43	...	...	
	Maximal histamine response[4]								
32	Maximal acid output[5]	♂	24	<20->60[2]	201.6 ± 53.4	20.5 ± 6.8	23.3 ± 6.9	...	3
33			20	19-66	177 ± 73.3	...	17.1 ± 11.94	...	1
34			4	<30	248 ± 71.1	...	29.4 ± 10.69	...	
35			16	>30	159 ± 68.1	...	14.0 ± 10.08	...	
36		♀	12	<20->60[2]	153.7 ± 33.3	15.7 ± 5.1	17.7 ± 5.4	...	3
37			20	19-65	107 ± 57.7	...	9.4[3] ± 7.20[6]	...	1
38			5	<30	188 ± 42.9	...	19.7 ± 5.16	...	
39			15	>30	80 ± 30.5	...	5.8[4] ± 3.16[7]	...	
40	15-45 minutes[8]	♂	18	19-66	203 ± 97.6	...	20.3 ± 14.24	...	1
41			3	<30	279 ± 98.4	...	32.5 ± 13.53	...	
42			15	>30	188 ± 90.1	...	17.8 ± 13.12	...	
43		♀	19	19-65	121 ± 77.5	...	11.7 ± 9.28	...	1
44			5	<30	225 ± 51.4	...	25.1 ± 5.78	...	
45			14	>30	86 ± 47.9	...	7.0 ± 4.54	...	
46	Peak acid output[9]	♂	20	19-66	214.9 ± 91.48	...	21.6 ± 13.79	94.7 ± 35.06	1
47			4	<30	279.0 ± 85.33	...	33.4 ± 11.75	120.8 ± 6.42	
48			16	>30	198.9 ± 85.76	...	18.7 ± 12.65	88.2 ± 36.26	
49		♀	20	19-65	138.2 ± 68.70	...	12.3 ± 8.95	87.2 ± 32.79	1
50			5	<30	225.2 ± 51.4	...	25.3 ± 5.51	119.4 ± 7.36	
51			15	>30	109.2 ± 45.28	...	8.0 ± 4.72	76.5 ± 30.88	

[1] There is a recent trend to avoid the arbitrary division of acid into free and total; a single titration to pH 7.0-7.4 with a glass electrode or phenol red is recommended [1,11,13, 14]. [2] Average age, 36.5 years. [3] Calculated from milligram values. [4] An antihistamine is administered intramuscularly during the basal collection, followed in 15 minutes by a standard dose of 0.04 mg of histamine acid phosphate/kg body wt [1,2]. [5] Output during the 60 minutes following histamine injection [1,2]. [6] 19 subjects. [7] 14 subjects. [8] Values are doubled to obtain the output for times between 15 and 45 minutes after histamine injection [1,2]. [9] Output is double the value obtained for the maximum 30 minute output following injection of the stimulant [1, 2].

continued

39. GASTRIC SECRETION TESTS: MAN

	Test	Subjects			Volume ml/hr	Free HCl Output[1/] mEq/hr	Total HCl Output[1/] mEq/hr	HCl Concentration mEq/liter	Reference
		Sex	No.	Age, yr					
	Histalog response[10/]								
52	0.5 mg/kg dose	♂	25	20-29	167	14.81[3/]	...	85	7
53			80	30-39	167	14.04[3/]	...	83	
54			80	40-49	171	14.48[3/]	...	79	
55			79	50-59	142	11.51[3/]	...	75	
56			40	60+	120	8.69[3/]	...	65	
57			615	20-60+	...	11.64 ± 7.62	...	...	4
58			74	20-29	...	11.46 ± 6.69	...	...	
59			157	30-39	...	12.83 ± 6.69	...	...	
60			156	40-49	...	13.29 ± 8.66	...	...	
61			158	50-59	...	10.67 ± 7.11	...	...	
62			70	60+	...	7.67 ± 7.56	...	...	
63		♀	22	20-29	117	8.69[3/]	...	73	7
64			66	30-39	123	8.69[3/]	...	72	
65			80	40-49	126	9.04[3/]	...	68	
66			80	50-59	104	7.02[3/]	...	58	
67			32	60+	92	6.48[3/]	...	54	
68			634	20-60+	...	7.53 ± 5.20	...	...	4
69			65	20-29	...	7.79 ± 4.57	...	...	
70			145	30-39	...	7.83 ± 4.51	...	...	
71			184	40-49	...	8.12 ± 5.42	...	...	
72			162	50-59	...	6.90 ± 5.59	...	...	
73			78	60+	...	6.67 ± 5.40	...	...	
74	1.5 mg/kg dose	♂	75	<30->70	264[11/]	...	30.9[11/]	109[12/]	16
75			75	<30->70	284[13/]	...	34.4[13/]	123[14/]	

[1/] There is a recent trend to avoid the arbitrary division of acid into free and total; a single titration to pH 7.0-7.4 with a glass electrode or phenol red is recommended [1,11,13, 14]. [3/] Calculated from milligram values. [10/] There is evidence that a dose of histalog of about 2.0 mg/kg body wt is necessary to produce a maximal response [9]. This dose, 50 times that of histamine, is 25 times less toxic and need not be accompanied by an antihistamine [7]. [11/] Peak 60-minute output (105-minute collection). [12/] Mean concentration (105 minutes after histalog). [13/] Peak acid output (*see* footnote 9). [14/] Peak concentration (105 minutes after histalog).

Contributor: Livermore, George R., Jr.

References

[1] Baron, J. H. 1963. Gut 4:136.

[2] Carniero de Moura, M., and J. Pinto Correia. 1964. Am. J. Digest. Diseases 9:669.

[3] Dotevall, G. 1961. Acta Med. Scand. 170:59.

[4] Grossman, M. I., J. B. Kirsner, and I. A. Gillespie. 1963. Gastroenterology 45:14.

[5] Hirschowitz, B. I. 1961. Am. J. Digest. Diseases 6: 199.

[6] Kay, A. W. 1953. Brit. Med. J. 2:77.

[7] Kirsner, J. B., and H. Ford. 1955. J. Lab. Clin. Med. 46:307.

[8] Laudano, O. M. 1966. Gastroenterology 50:653.

[9] Laudano, O. M., and E. C. Roncoroni. 1965. Ibid. 49:372.

[10] Marks, I. N. 1961. Ibid. 41:599.

[11] Rosenberg, J. 1964. Am. J. Gastroenterol. 42:391.

[12] Scobie, B. A. 1965. Brit. Med. J. 2:1287.

[13] Sparberg, M., and J. B. Kirsner. 1964. Am. J. Digest. Diseases 9:567.

[14] Sparberg, M., and J. B. Kirsner. 1964. Arch. Internal Med. 114:508.

[15] Ward, S., et al. 1963. Gastroenterology 44:620.

[16] Wormsley, K. G., and M. I. Grossman. 1965. Gut 6:427.

[17] Zaterka, S., and D. P. Neves. 1964. Gastroenterology 47:251.

40. LIVER FUNCTION TESTS: MAN

For renal function tests, *see* Table 113.

	Test	Normal Value	Remarks	Reference
	Bilirubin Excretion[1]			
1	Bilirubin, urine	Negative	Only direct-reacting bilirubin appears in urine of man	3,11
2	Bilirubin clearance	5% retention in 4 hr	Injections of bilirubin not excreted in bile outflow	7,8
3	Bilirubin partition	Total bilirubin, 1 mg/100 ml; direct bilirubin, 0.2 mg/100 ml	Approximately 3% of population normally have high total bilirubin and indirect levels due to familial jaundice of Gilbert	3,6,20
4	Icterus index	1-5 units	Serum must be free from hemolysis	21
5	Urobilinogen, feces	Present	Decreased or absent during obstruction of biliary tract	30
6	urine	1.0 Ehrlich unit in 2 hr	Increased in advanced hepatitis and cirrhosis; often decreased or absent in total duct obstruction	
7	Van den Bergh reaction, ring test technique	Negative	Any degree of positivity is abnormal	9
	Excretion of Crystalloid Dyes			
8	Rose Bengal, tagged with ^{131}I	?	Still under evaluation	22,27
9	Sulfobromophthalein sodium	$\not>$5% retention in 45 min	Dosage, 5 mg/kg iv. Test especially useful for Laennec's cirrhosis, in which compensation causes clinical or latent jaundice to be undetectable	24
	Carbohydrate Metabolism			
10	Galactose tolerance	Urine, <3 g in 5-6 hr; blood, 0 in 75 min	Used for assay of liver damage in acute phase; other sugar tolerance test rarely used	2,25
11	Glucagon tolerance	Blood sugar rise $\not>$60 mg/100 ml	Test under development; may be useful in glycogen storage disease	29
12	Lactic acid tolerance	<5 mg in 30 min	Not in general use	26
	Lipid Metabolism			
13	Cholesterol, total	150-250 mg/100 ml	Increased during duct obstruction	18
14	esters	70-74% of total	In liver damage, <50% of total cholesterol level	
	Protein Metabolism			
15	Ammonia	20-120 µg/100 ml[2]	Blood level elevated in severe liver damage	10
16	Cephalin flocculation	$\not>$2+ in 48 hr		14
17	Hippuric acid	>2.5 g in urine/24 hr[3]; >1 g in urine[4]	Sodium benzoate is conjugated with glycine in liver to form hippuric acid. In liver damage, output in urine is decreased.	12,32
18	Prothrombin time	12-14 sec	Prolonged in severe liver damage (e.g., yellow fever) and obstructive jaundice in absence of bile in intestine; usually responds to vitamin K in cases of duct obstruction	23,28
19	Serum protein	Total protein, 6.5-8%; albumin, 3.5-5%; globulin, 2.3-3.9%	Albumin decreases and globulin[5] increases in liver disease. Electrophoretogram may be used.	1,16
20	Thymol turbidity	<4 units		19
21	Zinc turbidity	<12 units		17
	Serum Enzyme Levels			
22	Alkaline phosphatase	1-4 units	Increases during many diseases, especially duct obstruction of liver. Normal levels indicate absence of duct obstruction.	4,13
23	Cholinesterase	55-100 units/ml	Decreases during liver damage	5

[1] The liver has little, if any, reserve capacity in excreting bilirubin. Jaundice may be defined as a qualitative and/or quantitative abnormality in serum bilirubin. [2] As ammonia nitrogen. [3] After oral administration of sodium benzoate. [4] After intravenous administration of sodium benzoate. [5] Usually γ-globulin.

continued

40. LIVER FUNCTION TESTS: MAN

	Test	Normal Value	Remarks	Reference
24	Glutamic oxaloacetic transaminase	6-40 units	Very high levels occur during acute hepatitis	15
25	Glutamic pyruvic transaminase	6-36 units	Used in early diagnosis of hepatitis	15,31

Contributor: Elton, Norman W.

References

[1] Annino, J. S. 1964. Clinical chemistry. Ed. 3. Little, Brown; Boston. pp. 190-193.
[2] Bauer, R. 1906. Wien. Med. Wochschr. 66:2537.
[3] Bergh, A. A. H. van den. 1928. Der Gallenfarbstoff im Blute. Ed. 2. S. C. Van Doesburgh, Leyden; J. A. Barth, Leipzig. (*Translation:* U.S. Army Chem. Corps Med. Lab. Spec. Rept. 40:CMLRE-ML-52, 1954.)
[4] Bodansky, A. 1933. J. Biol. Chem. 101:93.
[5] Caraway, W. T. 1956. Am. J. Clin. Pathol. 26:945.
[6] Ducci, H., and C. J. Watson. 1945. J. Lab. Clin. Med. 30:293.
[7] Eilbott, W. 1927. Z. Klin. Med. 106:529.
[8] Elton, N. W. 1936. Am. J. Clin. Pathol. 6:81.
[9] Elton, N. W. 1950. Ibid. 20:901.
[10] Faulkner, W. R., and R. C. Britton. 1960. Cleveland Clinic Quart. 27:202.
[11] Free, A. H., and H. M. Free. 1953. Gastroenterology 24:414.
[12] Griffith, W. H. 1926. J. Biol. Chem. 69:197.
[13] Gutman, A. B. 1959. Am. J. Med. 27:875.
[14] Hanger, F. M. 1939. J. Clin. Invest. 18:261.
[15] Karmen, A. 1955. Ibid. 34:131.
[16] Kingsley, G. R. 1940. J. Biol. Chem. 133:731.
[17] Kunkel, H. G. 1947. Proc. Soc. Exptl. Biol. Med. 66:217.
[18] Leffler, H. H. 1959. Am. J. Clin. Pathol. 31:310.
[19] Maclagan, N. F., N. H. Martin, and J. B. Lunnon. 1952. J. Clin. Pathol. 5:1.
[20] Malloy, H. T., and K. A. Evelyn. 1937. J. Biol. Chem. 119:481.
[21] Meulengracht, E. 1932. Acta Med. Scand. 79:32.
[22] Nordyke, R. A., and W. H. Blahd. 1959. J. Am. Med. Assoc. 170:1159.
[23] Quick, A. J. 1945. Am. J. Clin. Pathol. 15:560.
[24] Rosenthal, S. M., and E. C. White. 1925. J. Am. Med. Assoc. 84:112.
[25] Shay, H., and P. Fieman. 1937. Ann. Internal Med. 10:1297.
[26] Soffer, L. J., et al. 1937. Arch. Internal Med. 60:882.
[27] Taplin, G. V., O. M. Meredith, and H. Kade. 1955. J. Lab. Clin. Med. 45:665.
[28] Unger, P. N., and S. Shapiro. 1948. J. Clin. Invest. 27:39.
[29] Van Itallie, T. B., and W. B. A. Bentley. 1955. Ibid. 34:1730.
[30] Watson, C. J., et al. 1944. Am. J. Clin. Pathol. 14: 605.
[31] Wroblewski, F., and J. S. LaDue. 1956. Proc. Soc. Exptl. Biol. Med. 91:569.
[32] Zieve, L., E. Hill, and S. Nesbitt. 1950. J. Lab. Clin. Med. 36:705.

41. ANTIMETABOLITES

Listed are selected examples of molecular modifications changing metabolites to cytotoxic compounds or to inhibitors of biochemical functions in certain microbial or mammalian cells. In most cases, a competitive relationship or reversal of toxic action by the metabolite has been demonstrated. In some cases, biological antagonism extends to metabolites other than the one most similar in structure.

	Metabolite	Antimetabolite	Structural Alteration or Name	Antimetabolite Action
	Vitamins			
	Water-soluble			
1	Thiamine	Aminobenzyl-methylthiazolium chloride	2 C for 2 N, loss of side chains	Inhibits fish thiaminase
2		Butylthiamine	Butyl for CH_3	....
3		Oxythiamine	OH for NH_2	Inhibits cocarboxylase synthesis
4		Pyrithiamine	CH=CH for S	Inhibits cocarboxylase synthesis
5	Riboflavin	Corresponding phenazine	2 C for 2 N, 2 NH_2 for 2 OH	Inhibitory effects in microorganisms & animals readily reversed by riboflavin
6		5-Deoxyriboflavin	H for OH	
7		6,7-Dichlororiboflavin	2 Cl for 2 CH_3	
8		Galactoflavin	Dulcityl for ribityl	
9		Hydroxyethyldimethylisoalloxazine	Replacement of side chain	

continued

41. ANTIMETABOLITES

	Metabolite	Antimetabolite	Structural Alteration or Name	Antimetabolite Action
10	Nicotinic acid (or amide)	3-Acetylpyridine	$COCH_3$ for COOH	Induces deficiency in animals
11		6-Aminonicotinamide	NH_2 for H	Forms cofactor analogue
12		5-Fluoronicotinamide	F for H	Forms cofactor analogue
13		Pyridine-3-sulfonic acid or amide	SO_3H for COOH	Activity in microorganisms & animals
14	B_6	4-Deoxypyridoxine	H for OH	Activity in microorganisms & animals
15		5-Homopyridoxine	CH_2 added	Activity in microorganisms
16		ω-Methylpyridoxine	C_2H_5 for CH_3	Replaces B_6 in some test systems
17		Toxopyrimidine	Pyrimidine portion of thiamine	Convulsant activity
18	Biotin	Biotin sulfone	SO_2 for S	Inhibition of various microorganisms prevented by biotin; in some species, analogues can replace biotin (rows 18–21)
19		Dethiobiotin	2 H for S	
20		Homobiotin	Extra CH_2 group in side chain	
21		Ureylenecyclohexylbutyric acid	2 C for S	
22	Pantothenic acid	ω-Methylpantothenic acid	CH_3 for H	Induces deficiency in animals
23		Pantothenyl alcohol	CH_2OH for COOH	Inhibits microorganisms, not animals
24		Pantoyltaurine & derivatives	SO_3H & derivatives for COOH	Inhibits microorganisms, pantothenate-utilizing enzymes
25		Phenylpantothenone	COC_6H_5 for COOH	Inhibits microorganisms
26		Salicylyl β-alanine	*o*-Hydroxybenzoyl for pantoyl	Inhibits microorganisms
27	Folic acid	4-Amino-N^{10}-methylpteroylglutamic acid	NH_2 for OH, CH_3 for H	Antileukemic drug; Inhibitors of dihydrofolate reductase (rows 27–31)
28		4-Aminopteroylglutamic acid	NH_2 for OH	Antileukemic drug
29		Diaminopteridines	2,4-Diamino-6-methyl pteridine	...
30		Diaminopyrimidines	2,4-Diamino-5-*p*-chlorophenyl-6-ethylpyrimidine	Antimalarial drug
31		Diaminotriazines	2,4-Diamino-5-*p*-chlorophenyl-6-dimethyl-*s*-dihydrotriazine	...
32		Homofolic acid	Additional CH_2 in side chain	Substrates for dihydrofolate reductase (rows 32–35)
33		9-Methylpteroylglutamic acid	CH_3 for H	
34		10-Methylpteroylglutamic acid	CH_3 for H	
35		Pteroylaspartic acid	Replacement of glutamic acid	
36	*p*-Aminobenzoic acid	*p*-Aminoacetophenone & derivatives	COR for COOH	...
37		*p*-Aminobenzamide	$CONH_2$ for COOH	...
38		*p*-Aminosalicylic acid	OH for H	Antitubercular drug
39		Arsanilic acid	$AsO(OH)_2$ for COOH	...
40		Heterocyclic acids	N or S for C	...
41		*p*-Nitrobenzoic acid	NO_2 for NH_2	...
42		Sulfanilamide & derivatives	SO_2NH_2 or derivatives for COOH	Antimicrobial drugs
43	Inositol	Hexachlorocyclohexane	6 Cl for 6 OH	Acts on fungi & plants
44		Lindane	γ isomer of analogue	Insecticide
45	B_{12}	5,6-Dichlorobenzimidazole	2 Cl for 2 CH_3	Replaces benzimidole of B_{12} in some bacteria
46	Choline	2-Amino-2-methylpropanol	...	...
47		α,α-Dimethylcholine	...	...
48		Triethylcholine	Ethyl for methyl	Competes with or replaces choline
49	Ascorbic acid	Glucoascorbic acid	Addition of CHOH & optical inversion	Inhibits growth of animals
	Fat-soluble			
50	α-Tocopherol	α-Tocopherol quinone	Opening of ring by addition of O	Antagonizes both vitamins E and K
51	K	Bishydroxycoumarin & derivatives	O for C, side-chain alterations	Anticoagulant
52		2-Chloro-1, 4-naphthoquinone	...	...
53		2,3-Dichloronaphthoquinone	2 Cl for alkyl side chains	...
54		Methoxynaphthoquinone	OCH_3 for CH_3	...

continued

41. ANTIMETABOLITES

	Metabolite	Antimetabolite	Structural Alteration or Name	Antimetabolite Action
			Amino Acids	
55	α-Alanine	Cycloserine	4-Amino-3-isoxazolidine	Antibiotic, inhibits D-alanine utilization for cell wall formation
56	β-Alanine	β-Aminobutyric acid	CH_3 for H	...
57		Propionic acid	H for NH_2	...
58	Arginine	Canavanine	O for CH_2	...
59	Asparagine	β-Aspartylhydrazine	NH_2 for H	Antagonist of asparagine & glutamine
60	Aspartic acid	α-Aspartophenone	C_6H_5 for OH	...
61		β-Hydroxyaspartic acid	OH for H	...
62		β-Methylaspartic acid	CH_3 for H	...
63	Glutamic acid	*N*-Alkylglutamines	*N*-Alkyl for OH	...
64		β-Hydroxyglutamic acid	OH for H	...
65		δ-Hydroxyglycine	Aminomethyl carbinol group for COOH	Inhibits glutamine synthetase
66		Methionine sulfoxide	$SOCH_3$ for COOH	Convulsant
67	Glutamine	Azaserine	*O*-Diazoacetyl-L-serine	Inhibits glutamine utilization for purine biosynthesis
68		*N*-Benzylglutamine	*N*-Benzyl derivative	...
69		DON	6-Diazo-5-oxo-L-norleucine	Inhibits glutamine utilization for purine biosynthesis
70		*N*-Ethylglutamine	*N*-Ethyl derivative	...
71		α-Glutamylhydrazine	NH_2 for H	...
72	Histidine	2-Thiazolealanine	Replacement of imidazole	Many analogues have antihistamine activity
73		1,2,4-Triazole-3-alanine	Replacement of imidazole	
74	Isoleucine	Cyclopentaneglycine	Bridging methyl groups with methylene group	Valine acts as antagonist in microbial & mammalian systems; some analogues are antagonists of both valine & isoleucine
75		*O*-Methylthreonine	*O*-Methyl for ethyl	
76		α-Amino-3-chlorobutyric acid	Replacement of side chain by halogen	
77		2- & 3-Cyclohexeneglycine	Replacement of branched chain	
78		ω-Dehydroisoleucine	2-Amino-3-methyl pentanoic acid	
79	Leucine	2-Amino-4-methylhexanoic acid	CH_3 extension of branched chain	Competitive antagonists in microbial metabolism; optical isomer D-leucine acts as an antimetabolite
80		Cyclopentanealanine	Replacement of branched chain	
81		Methallylglycine	2-Amino-4-methyl-4-pentanoic acid	
82	Lysine	α-Amino-ε-hydroxycaproic acid	OH for NH_2	...
83	Methionine	Ethionine	C_2H_5 for CH_3	...
84		Methionine sulfone	...	...
85		Methionine sulfoximine	...	Convulsant, inhibits glutamine synthesis
86		Methoxinine	O for S	Replaces methionine for some organisms
87		Norleucine	CH_2 for S	...
88		Selenomethionine	Se for S	...
89	Phenylalanine	4-Chlorophenylalanine	...	Many related modifications of phenyl group or side chain; toxic effects of some analogues reversed by tyrosine; studied mainly in microbial & cell culture systems; several show antiviral activity
90		1-Cyclopentenealanine	Cyclopentene for benzene ring	
91		3- & 4-Fluorophenylalanine	F for H	
92		2- & 3-Furylalanine	O for CH=CH	
93		β-Hydroxyphenylalanine	OH for H	
94		2-Thiophenealanine	S for CH=CH	
95	Proline	3,4-Dehydroproline	Unsaturated bond in ring	Competitive inhibitor in bacteria
96		Hydroxyproline	...	Inhibits some fungi
97	Serine	α-Methylserine	CH_3 for H	Threonine acts as antagonist of serine

continued

	Metabolite	Antimetabolite	Structural Alteration or Name	Antimetabolite Action
98	Tryptophan	2-Azatryptophan	...	Competitive antagonism (Other methylated, halogenated & ring modifications studied; several analogues of indole & anthranilic acid competitive with tryptophan; studied mainly in microbial metabolism — applies to entries 98–105)
99		7-Azatryptophan	N for C of indole ring	Competitive antagonism
100		2-Benzimidazolealanine	Replacement of indole ring	...
101		Benzothienylalanine	S for N	...
102		5-Fluorotryptophan	F for H	Inhibits anthranilic acid conversion
103		Indoleacrylic acid	Loss of NH_3	...
104		5-Methyltryptophan	CH_3 for H	Noncompetitive in bacteria
105		1-Naphthyleneacrylic acid	Loss of NH_3, C=C for N	...
106	Tyrosine	*p*-Aminophenylalanine	NH_2 for OH	Antagonizes
107		3,5-Difluorotyrosine	F for H	Less toxic than monofluoro
108		3-Fluorotyrosine	F for H	Toxic for rats & mice
109		5-Hydroxy-2-pyridinealanine	Pyridine for benzene ring	Competitive antagonist
		Purines[1]		
110	Adenine	Adenine arabinoside	...	Arabinosides of adenine, thymine, & uracil isolated from sponges
111		3′-Amino-3-deoxyadenosine	...	Antibiotic
112		2-Azaadenine	Ring N for CH	...
113		Benzimidazole	...	...
114		7-Deazaadenosine	4-Amino-7-(D-ribofuranosyl)-7H-pyrrolo[2,3-*d*] pyrimidine	Antibiotic
115		Decoyinine	CH for 6′CH_2OH of psicofuranine	Antibiotic
116		3′-Deoxyadenosine	...	Antibiotic
117		2,6-Diaminopurine	NH_2 for H	...
118		2,6-Diaminopurine riboside	...	...
119		Nebularine[2]	...	Antibiotic; also occurs in mushrooms
120		Psicofuranine	CH_2OH for 1′H of adenosine	Antibiotic
121		Purine	H for NH_2	...
122		Pyrazolopyrimidines	4-Aminopyrazolo[3,4-*d*] pyrimidine	...
123		Toyocamycin	4-Amino-5-cyano-7(D-ribofuranosyl)pyrrolo[2,3-*d*] pyrimidine	Antibiotic
124	Hypoxanthine	7-Deazainosine	CH for N	...
125		6-Mercaptopurine	SH for O	Antileukemic agent
126		6-Mercaptopurine arabinoside	2′-Epimer	...
127		6-Mercaptopurine riboside	...	Substrate for inosine kinase
128		6-(1-Methyl-4-nitro-5-imidazolyl)thiopurine	Derivative of 6-mercaptopurine	Immunosuppressive agent
129	Guanine	8-Azaguanine	5-Amino-7-hydroxy-triazolo[4,5-*d*] pyrimidine	...
130		6-Thiodeoxyguanosine	...	...
131		6-Thioguanine	...	...
132		6-Thioguanosine	...	...
133	Xanthine	4-Hydroxypyrazolo[3,4-*d*] pyrimidine	...	Xanthine oxidase inhibitor

[1] Generally substrates for anabolic and catabolic enzymes. Diverse metabolic effects on biosynthesis and function of nucleic acids after conversion to nucleotides. Primarily of interest as potential anticancer and antiviral agents. [2] Purine riboside.

continued

41. ANTIMETABOLITES

	Metabolite	Antimetabolite	Structural Alteration or Name	Antimetabolite Action
			Pyrimidines[1]	
134	Cytosine	6-Azacytidine	…	…
135		6-Azacytosine	Ring N for CH	…
136		Cytosine arabinoside	2′-Epimer of cytidine	Antagonist of deoxycytidine; inhibits DNA viruses
137		5-Fluorocytosine	F for H	…
138		5-Iododeoxycytidine	I for H	…
139	Orotic acid	5-Fluoroorotic acid	F for H	More potent than bromine or chlorine analogues
140		Uracil-6-methylsulfone	SO_2CH_3 for COOH	Inhibits formation of orotidylate
141		Uracil-6-sulfonic acid	SO_3H for COOH	Inhibits formation of orotidylate
142	Thymine	6-Azathymidine	…	Nucleosides inhibit DNA viruses & act as antagonists of thymidine (142–149)
143		6-Azathymine	Ring N for CH	
144		5-Bromodeoxyuridine	…	
145		5-Bromouracil	Br for CH_3	
146		5-Iododeoxyuridine	…	
147		5-Iodouracil	I for CH_3	
148		5-Trifluoromethyldeoxyuridine	…	
149		5-Trifluoromethyluracil	CF_3 for CH_3	
150	Uracil	5-Azauracil	Ring N for CH	…
151		6-Azauracil	Ring N for CH	Nucleotide inhibits orotidylate decarboxylase
152		6-Azauridine	Ring N for CH	…
153		5-Fluorodeoxyuridine	F for H	…
154		5-Fluorouracil	F for H	Nucleotide inhibits thymidylate synthetase
155		5-Fluorouridine	F for H	…
156		5-Mercaptodeoxyuridine	SH for OH	…
157		5-Mercaptouracil	SH for H	…
158		2-Thiouracil	S for O	…
			Miscellaneous[3]	
159	Acetate	Fluoroacetate	…	Condenses with oxalacetate to form fluorocitrate
160	Glucose	D-Glucosamine	…	Inhibits anaerobic glycolysis
161	Mevalonate	Fluoromevalonate	…	Inhibits cholesterol synthesis

[1] Generally substrates for anabolic and catabolic enzymes. Diverse metabolic effects on biosynthesis and function of nucleic acids after conversion to nucleotides. Primarily of interest as potential anticancer and antiviral agents. [3] Hormone analogues comprise large groups of synthetic compounds, some of which have either antagonistic or enhanced hormonal activity. Other classes of drugs provide many examples of biological antagonism by structural analogues; examples (not listed in the table) include antihistamines, antagonists of 5-hydroxytryptamine, and inhibitors of amine oxidase and cholinesterase. Hexose and pentose antimetabolites, inhibitory analogues of intermediates on pathways of carbohydrate and lipid metabolism, and analogues retaining metabolite activity also do not appear in the table.

Contributor: Nichol, Charles A.

General References

[1] Fox, J. J., K. A. Watanabe, and A. Bloch. 1966. Progr. Nucleic Acid Res. Mol. Biol. 5:251.

[2] Hochster, R. M., and J. H. Quastel, ed. 1963. Metabolic inhibitors. Academic Press, New York. v. 1 & 2.

[3] Montgomery, J. A. 1965. Progr. Drug Res. 8:431.

[4] Schnitzer, R. J., and F. Hawking, ed. 1963-66. Exptl. Chemotherapy 1-4.

[5] Sexton, W. A. 1963. Chemical constitution and biological activity. Van Nostrand, Princeton.

[6] U.S. Public Health Service, National Cancer Institute. 1959-67. Cancer Chemotherapy Rept. 1-51.

[7] Woolley, D. W. 1952. A study of antimetabolites. J. Wiley, New York.

42. PROPERTIES OF PROTEOLYTIC ENZYMES AND THEIR PRECURSORS

Part I. Physical

	Enzyme or Precursor [Code number] 1/	Source	$S_{20,w}$ 2/ sec × 10^{13}	$D_{20,w}$ 2/ $cm^2\ sec^{-1}$ × 10^{-7}	Molecular Weight	Isoelectric Point 3/ pH	$E^{1\%}_{1cm}$ 4/ Value	$E^{1\%}_{1cm}$ 4/ λ, nm	Reference
1	Bromelain [3.4.4.24]	Pineapple plant	2.73	7.77	33,000	9.55	19.0	280	26
2	Carboxypeptidase A [3.4.2.1]	Cattle pancreatic juice	3.06	8.82	34,300	5.60 5/	19.4	278	2,18,29, 31,36,39
3	Carboxypeptidase B [3.4.2.2]	Swine pancreas	3.23	8.16	34,300		21.4	278	10
4	α-Chymotrypsin [3.4.4.5]	Cattle pancreas	2.56	10.2	25,000	8.1-8.6 6/	20.4	280	1,20,33, 35,43
5	Chymotrypsinogen A	Cattle pancreas	2.54	9.5	25,100	9.1	20.0	282	7,27,32, 40,41
6	Papain [3.4.4.10]	Papaya latex	2.42	10.27	20,700; 22,000	8.75	25.0	278	11,19,22
7	Pepsin [3.4.4.1]	Swine stomach mucosa	2.88	8.71	32,700	<1.0	14.3	280	4,8,28, 30,42
8	Pepsinogen	Swine stomach mucosa	3.24		40,400; 38,944	3.7	12.5	278	3,16,27, 30,42
9	Streptococcal proteinase [3.4.4.18]	Group A streptococci, 5797			32,000		16.4	280	9,23,24
10	Streptococcal proteinase zymogen	Group A streptococci, 5797			44,000		13.7	280	9,23,24
11	Subtilisin-type Carlsberg [3.4.4.16]	*Bacillus subtilis,* Carlsberg	2.85		27,600	9.4	8.6	280	13,14,37
12	Subtilisin-type BPN′ [3.4.4.16]	*Bacillus subtilis,* N′	2.76	9.04	27,600	7.80	11.7	278	15,25
13	Trypsin [3.4.4.4]	Bovine pancreas	2.50	9.40	23,800	10.5	15.4	280	5,6,20,21
14	Trypsinogen	Bovine pancreas	2.7	9.7	24,500	9.3	15.2	280	12,17,27, 34,38

1/ Code numbers recommended in the 1964 Report of the International Union of Biochemistry: *Enzyme Nomenclature,* 1965, Elsevier Publishing Co., New York. 2/ Values for sedimentation ($S_{20,w}$) and diffusion ($D_{20,w}$) coefficients are for data normalized to standard conditions of water at 20°C and extrapolated to zero protein concentration. 3/ Apparent values determined from electrophoretic mobility measurements. 4/ Absorbance of a 1% protein solution in a 1-cm light path cell at the wavelength specified. 5/ Determined at 0.3 ionic strength. 6/ Depends on ionic strength of the buffer.

Contributor: Glazer, A. N.

References

[1] Anderson, E. A., and R. A. Alberty. 1948. J. Phys. Colloid Chem. 52:1345.
[2] Anson, M. L. 1937. J. Gen. Physiol. 20:663.
[3] Arnon, R., and G. E. Perlmann. 1963. J. Biol. Chem. 238:653.
[4] Blumenfeld, O. O., J. Leonis, and G. E. Perlmann. 1960. Ibid. 235:379.
[5] Cunningham, L. W., Jr. 1954. Ibid. 211:13.
[6] Cunningham, L. W., Jr., et al. 1953. Discussions Faraday Soc. 13:58.
[7] Desnuelle, P., and M. Rovery. 1961. Advan. Protein Chem. 16:139.
[8] Edelhoch, H. 1957. J. Am. Chem. Soc. 79:6100.
[9] Elliott, S. D. 1950. J. Exptl. Med. 92:201.
[10] Folk, J. E., et al. 1960. J. Biol. Chem. 235:2272.
[11] Glazer, A. N., and E. L. Smith. 1961. Ibid. 236: 2948.
[12] Green, N. M., and H. Neurath. 1954. In H. Neurath and K. Bailey, ed. The proteins. Academic Press, New York. v. 2, pt. B, p. 1057.
[13] Güntelberg, A. V. 1954. Compt. Rend. Trav. Lab. Carlsberg 29:27.
[14] Güntelberg, A. V., and M. Ottesen. 1954. Ibid. 29: 36.
[15] Hagihara, B., et al. 1958. J. Biochem. (Tokyo) 45: 185.
[16] Herriott, R. M. 1938. J. Gen. Physiol. 21:501.
[17] Kay, C. M., L. B. Smillie, and F. A. Hilderman. 1961. J. Biol. Chem. 236:118.
[18] Keller, P. J., E. Cohen, and H. Neurath. 1956. Ibid. 223:457.
[19] Kimmel, J. R., and E. L. Smith. 1954. Ibid. 207:515.
[20] Kunitz, M., and J. H. Northrop. 1936. J. Gen. Physiol. 19:991.

continued

Part I. Physical

[21] Laskowski, M. 1961. In C. Long, ed. Biochemists' handbook. Van Nostrand, New York. p. 301.
[22] Light, A., et al. 1964. Proc. Natl. Acad. Sci. U.S. 52:1276.
[23] Liu, T.-Y., and S. D. Elliott. 1965. J. Biol. Chem. 240:1138.
[24] Liu, T.-Y., et al. 1963. Ibid. 238:251.
[25] Matsubara, H., et al. 1965. Ibid. 240:1125.
[26] Murachi, T., M. Yasui, and Y. Yasuda. 1964. Biochemistry 3:48.
[27] Northrop, J. H., M. Kunitz, and R. M. Herriott. 1948. Crystalline enzymes. Ed. 2. Columbia Univ. Press, New York.
[28] Perlmann, G. E. 1955. Advan. Protein Chem. 10:23.
[29] Putnam, F. W., and H. Neurath. 1946. J. Biol. Chem. 166:603.
[30] Rajagopalan, T. G., S. Moore, and W. H. Stein. 1966. Ibid. 241:4940.
[31] Rupley, J. A., and H. Neurath. 1960. Ibid. 235:609.
[32] Schwert, G. W. 1951. Ibid. 190:799.
[33] Schwert, G. W., and S. Kaufman. 1951. Ibid. 190:807.
[34] Smillie, L. B., and C. M. Kay. 1961. Ibid. 236:112.
[35] Smith, E. L., and D. M. Brown. 1952. Ibid. 195:525.
[36] Smith, E. L., D. M. Brown, and H. T. Hanson. 1949. Ibid. 180:33.
[37] Smith, E. L., et al. 1966. Ibid. 241:5974.
[38] Tietze, F. 1953. Ibid. 204:1.
[39] Vallee, B. L., et al. 1960. Ibid. 235:64.
[40] Wilcox, P. E., E. Cohen, and W. Tan. 1957. Ibid. 228:999.
[41] Wilcox, P. E., et al. 1957. Biochim. Biophys. Acta 24:72.
[42] Williams, R. C., and T. G. Rajagopalan. 1966. J. Biol. Chem. 241: 4951.
[43] Worthington Biochemical Corporation. 1967. Enzymes and enzyme reagents. Freehold, N.J.

Part II. Kinetic

	Enzyme	Source	Optimum pH	Substrate	Temp °C	pH	K_m 1/ moles/liter	V_{max} 2/ sec^{-1}	Reference
1	Bromelain	Pineapple plant	5-8	Benzoyl-L-arginine ethyl ester	25	6.0	0.17	0.50	11,18
2				Benzoyl-L-argininamide	25	6.0	1.2×10^{-3}	0.0035	
3	Carboxypeptidase A	Cattle pancreatic juice	7.4	Benzyloxycarbonylglycyl-L-phenylalanine	25	7.5	5.83×10^{-3}	106	1,21, 23
4	Carboxypeptidase B	Swine pancreas	7.9-8.0	Hippuryl-L-arginine	23	8.0	2.1×10^{-4}	105	4,24
5				Hippuryl-L-arginic acid	23	8.0	0.4×10^{-4}	238	
6	α-Chymotrypsin	Cattle pancreas	7-9	Acetyl-L-tyrosine ethyl ester	25	8.0	0.7×10^{-3}	193	2,9,16
7	Papain	Papaya latex	5-8	Benzoyl-L-arginine ethyl ester	25	6.0	1.33×10^{-2}	16.1	15,22
8	Pepsin	Swine stomach mucosa	1.8-4 3/	*N*-Acetyl-L-phenylalanyl-L-tyrosine	37	2.0	2.2×10^{-3}	0.085	13,14, 19,20
9				Benzyloxycarbonyl-L-His-L-Phe-L-Trp ethyl ester	37	4.0	2.3×10^{-4}	0.51	
10	Streptococcal proteinase	Group A streptococci, 5797	7.4-7.7	Benzyloxycarbonyl-L-phenylalanyl-L-leucine	37	7.6	1.2×10^{-3}	1.02	3,5
11	Subtilisin-type Carlsberg	*Bacillus subtilis,* Carlsberg	8-10	Benzoyl-L-arginine ethyl ester	37	8.0	7×10^{-3}	16.1	6,8
12	Subtilisin-type BPN′	*Bacillus subtilis,* N′	8-10	Benzoyl-L-arginine ethyl ester	37	8.0	1×10^{-2}	4.6	6,10
13	Trypsin	Bovine pancreas	7.6-8	Benzoyl-L-arginine ethyl ester	25	8.0	8×10^{-5}	14.3	7,12, 16,17

1/ K_m (Michaelis constant) = $\frac{K_{-1} + K_{+2}}{K_{+1}}$, where K_{+1} = velocity constant for formation of the enzyme-substrate complex, K_{-1} = velocity constant for dissociation of this complex into substrate and enzyme, and K_{+2} = velocity constant for the breakdown of the enzyme-substrate complex into products. 2/ V_{max} (maximal velocity) = $v(1 + K_m/S)$, where v is the measured velocity at a substrate concentration S. 3/ pH optimum depends on type of substrate.

Contributor: Glazer, A. N.

continued

42. PROPERTIES OF PROTEOLYTIC ENZYMES AND THEIR PRECURSORS

Part II. Kinetic

References

[1] Anson, M. L. 1937. J. Gen. Physiol. 20:663.
[2] Cunningham, L. W., Jr., and C. S. Brown. 1956. J. Biol. Chem. 221:287.
[3] Elliott, S. D. 1950. J. Exptl. Med. 92:201.
[4] Folk, J. E., et al. 1960. J. Biol. Chem. 235:2272.
[5] Gerwin, B. I., W. H. Stein, and S. Moore. 1966. Ibid. 241:3331.
[6] Glazer, A. N. 1967. Ibid. 242:433.
[7] Green, N. M., and H. Neurath. 1953. Ibid. 204:379.
[8] Güntelberg, A. V. 1954. Compt. Rend. Trav. Lab. Carlsberg 29:27.
[9] Gutfreund, H., and J. M. Sturtevant. 1956. Biochem. J. 63:655.
[10] Hagihara, B., et al. 1958. J. Biochem. (Tokyo) 45: 185.
[11] Inagami, T., and T. Murachi. 1963. Biochemistry 2: 1439.
[12] Inagami, T., and J. M. Sturtevant. 1960. Biochim. Biophys. Acta 38:64.
[13] Inouye, K., et al. 1966. Biochemistry 5:2473.
[14] Jackson, W. T., M. Schlamowitz, and A. Shaw. 1966. Ibid. 5:4105.
[15] Kimmel, J. R., and E. L. Smith. 1954. J. Biol. Chem. 207:515.
[16] Kunitz, M., and J. H. Northrop. 1936. J. Gen. Physiol. 19:991.
[17] Laskowski, M. 1961. In C. Long, ed. Biochemists' handbook. Van Nostrand, New York. p. 301.
[18] Murachi, T., M. Yasui, and Y. Yasuda. 1964. Biochemistry 3:48.
[19] Northrop, J. H. 1922. J. Gen. Physiol. 5:263.
[20] Rajagopalan, T. G., S. Moore, and W. H. Stein. 1966. J. Biol. Chem. 241:4940.
[21] Smith, E. L., and H. T. Hanson. 1949. Ibid. 176:997.
[22] Whitaker, J. R., and M. L. Bender. 1965. J. Am. Chem. Soc. 87:2728.
[23] Whitaker, J. R., F. Menger, and M. L. Bender. 1966. Biochemistry 5:386.
[24] Wolff, E. C., E. W. Schirmer, and J. E. Folk. 1962. J. Biol. Chem. 237:3095.

43. COMPOSITION OF DIGESTIVE ENZYMES AND THEIR PRECURSORS

Data are for crystalline or electrophoretically homogeneous enzymes. Values are grams per 100 grams enzyme, unless otherwise indicated.

Part I. Elements

	Enzyme or Precursor	Source	Carbon	Hydrogen	Nitrogen	Amino N	Phosphorus	Sulfur	Other Minerals	Reference
1	α-Amylase	Swine pancreas	49.46	7.18	15.52	....	0.05	1.33	....	3,4
2	Carboxypeptidase A	Cattle pancreatic juice	....	.....	15.4	....	......	.....	....	16
3		Cattle pancreas	56.2	7.2	14.4	....	0	0.47	Zn, 0.182	1,14
4	α-Chymotrypsin	Cattle pancreatic juice	50.0	7.06	15.5	1.22	0	1.85	Cl, 0.16	11
5	β-Chymotrypsin	Cattle pancreatic juice	....	.....	16.24	1.31	......	1.56	....	11
6	γ-Chymotrypsin	Cattle pancreatic juice	....	.....	16.0	1.34	......	1.59	....	11
7	Chymotrypsinogen	Cattle pancreas	50.6	7.0	15.8	0.97	0	1.9	Cl, 0.17	11
8	Deoxyribonuclease	Cattle pancreas	50.16	6.91	14.88	2.25	0	1.09	....	6,8
9	Lecithinase	Pancreatic juice	50.77	6.41	15.88	....	......	4.0	....	13
10	Pepsin	Cattle	51.7	6.86	14.6	0.162	0.09	0.94	....	2,11
11		Salmon	51.9	6.48	15.62	....	0.03	1.58	....	10
12	Pepsinogen	Cattle	52.8	6.88	15.9	....	......	0.09	....	15
13		Swine	....	.....	....	39 1/	1 1/	.....	....	17
14	Rennin	....	51.4	7.19	14.51	1.11	0.04	1.46	Cu, 0.0035	7
15	Ribonuclease	Cattle pancreas	48.2	6.2	16.1	17 1/	Trace	1.1	....	11,12
16	Trypsin	Swine pancreas	50.2	6.6	16.13	....	0	1.1	Cl, 2.85	9,11
17	Trypsinogen	Swine pancreas	50.1	6.9	15.3	20-26 1/	......	1.1	....	5,9

1/ Number of amino residues per molecule of enzyme.

Contributor: Dianzani, Mario U.

References

[1] Anson, M. L. 1937. J. Gen. Physiol. 20:663.
[2] Bovey, F. A., and S. S. Yanari. 1960. Enzymes 4:63.
[3] Caldwell, M. L., et al. 1952. J. Am. Chem. Soc. 74: 4003.

continued

43. COMPOSITION OF DIGESTIVE ENZYMES AND THEIR PRECURSORS

Part I. Elements

[4] Caldwell, M. L., et al. 1954. Ibid. 76:143.
[5] Desnuelle, P. 1960. Enzymes 4:119.
[6] Gehrmann, G., and S. Okada. 1957. Biochim. Biophys. Acta 23:621.
[7] Hankinson, C. L. 1943. J. Dairy Sci. 26:53.
[8] Kunitz, M. 1950. J. Gen. Physiol. 33:349.
[9] Kunitz, M., and J. H. Northrop. 1936. Ibid. 19:991.
[10] Norris, E. R., and D. W. Elam. 1940. J. Biol. Chem. 134:443.
[11] Northrop, J. H., M. Kunitz, and R. M. Herriott. 1948. Crystalline enzymes. Columbia Univ. Press, New York. p. 26.
[12] Scheraga, H. A., and J. A. Rupley. 1961. Advan. Enzymol. 24:175.
[13] Slotta, K. H., and H. L. Fraenkel-Conrat. 1938. Ber. Deut. Chem. Ges. 71B:1076.
[14] Smith, E. L., and A. Stockell. 1954. J. Biol. Chem. 207:501.
[15] Sumner, J. B. 1930. Ber. Deut. Chem. Ges. 63B:582.
[16] Vallee, B. L., and H. Neurath. 1954. J. Am. Chem. Soc. 75:5006.
[17] Van Vunakis, H., and R. M. Herriott. 1957. Biochim. Biophys. Acta 22:600.

Part II. Essential Amino Acids

	Enzyme or Precursor	Source	His	Ile	Leu	Lys	Met	Phe	Thr	Trp	Val	Reference
1	α-Amylase	Human saliva	3.24	5.80	5.77	6.33	2.4	7.20	4.5	7.2	6.89	10
2		Swine pancreas	3.9	11.5[1/]		4.9	2.1	10.1	3.9	6.7	7.8	3,4
3	Carboxypeptidase A	Cattle pancreatic juice	3.07	6.60	8.12	6.85	0.39	6.38	7.82	3.30	4.72	15
4		Cattle pancreas	3.47	7.65	9.41	7.81	0.44	7.16	9.21	3.62	5.58	1,13
5	α-Chymotrypsin	Cattle pancreatic juice	1.26	.....	9.1	.....	1.25	.....	11.2	5.81	.....	11
6	β-Chymotrypsin	Cattle pancreatic juice	1.22	.....	9.4	.....	1.29	.....	10.6	6.40	.....	11
7	γ-Chymotrypsin	Cattle pancreatic juice	1.26	.....	8.5	.....	1.28	.....	10.7	6.27	.....	11
8	Chymotrypsinogen A[2/]	Cattle pancreas	2	10	19	23	2	6-7	23	7	22	2
9	Deoxyribonuclease	Cattle pancreas	5.31	4.28	8.62	7.72	2.77	5.25	6.94	1.57	7.71	6,8
10	Lipoxidase	....	3.6	8.1	11.4	7.8	1.8	4.9	8.9	0.41	7.8	7
11	Pepsin[2/]	Cattle	1	27	28	1	5	14	28	6	21	2,11
12	Pepsinogen[2/]	Cattle	4	64[1/]		12	5	20	.....	.....	.....	14
13		Swine	.....	.....	.....	.....	.....	.....	25	6	27	16
14	Ribonuclease[2/]	Cattle pancreas	4	3	2	10	4	3	10	.....	9	11,12
15	Trypsin	Swine pancreas	.....	.....	.....	.....	.....	.....	.....	3.65	.....	9,11
16	Trypsinogen[2/]	Swine pancreas	3	12	12	14	1	4	9-11	X[3/]	15	5,9

[1/] Isoleucine plus leucine. [2/] Values are number of amino acid residues per molecule of enzyme. [3/] Undetermined number of residues, destroyed by acid hydrolysis.

Contributor: Dianzani, Mario U.

References

[1] Anson, M. L. 1937. J. Gen. Physiol. 20:663.
[2] Bovey, F. A., and S. S. Yanari. 1960. Enzymes 4:63.
[3] Caldwell, M. L., et al. 1952. J. Am. Chem. Soc. 74: 4033.
[4] Caldwell, M. L., et al. 1954. Ibid. 76:143.
[5] Desnuelle, P. 1960. Enzymes 4:119.
[6] Gehrmann, G., and S. Okada. 1957. Biochim. Biophys. Acta 23:621.
[7] Holman, R. T., et al. 1950. Arch. Biochem. 26:199.
[8] Kunitz, M. 1950. J. Gen. Physiol. 33:349.
[9] Kunitz, M., and J. H. Northrop. 1936. Ibid. 19:991.
[10] Muus, J. 1954. J. Am. Chem. Soc. 76:5163.
[11] Northrop, J. H., M. Kunitz, and R. M. Herriott. 1948. Crystalline enzymes. Columbia Univ. Press, New York. p. 26.
[12] Scheraga, H. A., and J. A. Rupley. 1961. Advan. Enzymol. 24:175.
[13] Smith, E. L., and A. Stockell. 1954. J. Biol. Chem. 207:501.
[14] Sumner, J. B. 1930. Ber. Deut. Chem. Ges. 63B:582.
[15] Vallee, B. L., and H. Neurath. 1954. J. Am. Chem. Soc. 75:5006.
[16] Van Vunakis, H., and R. M. Herriott. 1957. Biochim. Biophys. Acta 22:600.

continued

43. COMPOSITION OF DIGESTIVE ENZYMES AND THEIR PRECURSORS

Part III. Nonessential Amino Acids

	Enzyme or Precursor	Source	Ala	Arg	Asp	Cys	Cystine 1/	Glu	Gly	Pro	Ser	Tyr	Reference
1	α-Amylase	Human saliva	4.43	8.75	19.3	.....	4.4	9.6	6.82	3.6	7.8	5.51	11
2		Swine pancreas	6.9	5.8	14.5	.....	2.3	10.5	6.7	3.6	4.1	5.3	3,4
3	Carboxypeptidase A	Cattle pancreatic juice	4.12	4.54	10.12	.....	1.19	9.36	3.85	3.09	8.36	9.32	16
4		Cattle pancreas	5.16	5.06	11.7	.....	1.40	10.7	5.06	3.66	10.1	10.3	1,14
5	α-Chymotrypsin	Cattle pancreatic juice	.....	.....	....	1.22	3.66	....	.....	.....	....	2.83	12
6	β-Chymotrypsin	Cattle pancreatic juice	.....	.....	....	1.29	3.51	....	.....	.....	....	2.87	12
7	γ-Chymotrypsin	Cattle pancreatic juice	.....	.....	....	1.27	3.59	....	.....	.....	....	3.09	12
8	Chymotrypsinogen A 2/	Cattle pancreas	22	4	8.	.....	10	3	23	9	30	4	2
9	Deoxyribonuclease	Cattle pancreas	4.87	7.04	13.88	1.28 3/		10.04	3.06	3.50	10.35	8.33	6,9
10	Lipoxidase	....	.....	4.7	6.2	0	0	10.4	6.3	5.1	....	6.2	8
11	Pepsin 2/	Cattle	18	2	44	.....	6	27	38	15	44	18	2,12
12	Pepsinogen 2/	Cattle	.....	.....	....	.....	.....	....	.....	.....	53	16	17
13		Swine	27	3	46	.....	6	32	36	20	....	.....	15
14	Ribonuclease 2/	Cattle pancreas	12	4	5 4/	.....	8	5 5/	3	4 6/	15	6	12,13
15	Trypsin	Swine pancreas	.....	.....	....	.....	.....	....	.....	.....	....	7.8	10,12
16	Trypsinogen 2/	Swine pancreas	13	2	24	.....	12	10	21	7	38	9	5,10

1/ Determined after oxidation to cysteic acid. One molecule of cysteic acid is formed from one-half of the symmetrical cystine molecule or from one molecule of cysteine; the values in this column, therefore, do not distinguish between cysteine and cystine. 2/ Values are number of amino acid residues per molecule of enzyme. 3/ Cysteine plus cystine. 4/ Also reported as 16 [7]. 5/ Also reported as 12 [7]. 6/ Also reported as 5 [7].

Contributor: Dianzani, Mario U.

References

[1] Anson, M. L. 1937. J. Gen. Physiol. 20:663.
[2] Bovey, F. A., and S. S. Yanari. 1960. Enzymes 4:63.
[3] Caldwell, M. L., et al. 1952. J. Am. Chem. Soc. 74:4033.
[4] Caldwell, M. L., et al. 1954. Ibid. 76:143.
[5] Desnuelle, P. 1960. Enzymes 4:119.
[6] Gehrmann, G., and S. Okada. 1957. Biochim. Biophys. Acta 23:621.
[7] Hirs, C. H. W., S. Moore, and W. H. Stein. 1956. J. Biol. Chem. 219:623.
[8] Holman, R. T., et al. 1950. Arch. Biochem. 26:199.
[9] Kunitz, M. 1950. J. Gen. Physiol. 33:349.
[10] Kunitz, M., and J. H. Northrop. 1936. Ibid. 19:991.
[11] Muus, J. 1954. J. Am. Chem. Soc. 76:5163.
[12] Northrop, J. H., M. Kunitz, and R. M. Herriott. 1948. Crystalline enzymes. Columbia Univ. Press, New York. p. 26.
[13] Scheraga, H. A., and J. A. Rupley. 1961. Advan. Enzymol. 24:175.
[14] Smith, E. L., and A. Stockell. 1954. J. Biol. Chem. 207:501.
[15] Sumner, J. B. 1930. Ber. Deut. Chem. Ges. 63B:582.
[16] Vallee, B. L., and H. Neurath. 1954. J. Am. Chem. Soc. 75:5006.
[17] Van Vunakis, H., and R. M. Herriott. 1957. Biochim. Biophys. Acta 22:537.

44. CATALYTIC ACTION OF DIGESTIVE ENZYMES

Conditions suitable for enzyme action vary with the method used and with the source of the enzyme. **Method:** Chem = chemical; Col = colorimetric; Mano = manometric; Pol = polariscopic; Phys = physical; Titr = titrimetric.

	Catalytic Action		Conditions Suitable for Enzyme Action					
	Enzyme	Substrate→Product	pH	Substrate Concentration	Temp °C	Cofactor	Method	Occurrence in
1	Acetylcholine esterase	Acetylcholine→acetate + choline	7.4	3 mg/ml	37		Mano	Pancreas
2	Adenosine triphosphatase	Adenosine triphosphate→adenosine diphosphate + PO_4	7.5	1 mg P/ml	37	Ca^{2+}	Chem	Pancreas, intestinal mucosa
3	Amino acid carboxylase	Amino acid→amines + CO_2	4-5.5	0.001 *M*	30	Pyridoxal phosphate	Mano	Pancreas

continued

44. CATALYTIC ACTION OF DIGESTIVE ENZYMES

	Catalytic Action		Conditions Suitable for Enzyme Action					
	Enzyme	Substrate→Product	pH	Substrate Concentration	Temp °C	Cofactor	Method	Occurrence in
4	α-Amylase (animal)	Starch or glycogen→dextrins + maltose	7	1%	37	NaCl	Chem	Saliva, pancreas, intestinal mucosa
5	Arginase	L-Arginine→L-ornithine + urea	9.5	0.66%	38	Ca^{2+}, Mn^{2+}	Mano	Pancreas, intestinal mucosa
6	Carbonic anhydrase	H_2CO_3→CO_2 + H_2O	5-9	0.08 *M*	15		Mano	Gastric mucosa
7	Carboxypeptidase	Peptide (free COOH)→amino acid + peptide	8.5	6% edestin	25		Titr	Pancreas (as zymogen)
8	Cholesterol esterase	Cholesterol esters→cholesterol + acids	5.3 or 7					Intestinal mucosa, pancreas
9	Chymotrypsin	Proteins→polypeptides + amino acids	7.6	5% casein	38		Chem	Pancreas
10	Conjugase	Pteroylglutamate→pterine + glutamic acid	7-8		37	Ca^{2+}		Pancreas
11	Deoxyribonuclease	Thymonucleic acid→nucleotides	6-7	0.5%	37	Mg^{2+}, Mn^{2+}	Phys	Intestinal mucosa, pancreas
12	Esterase, simple	Ethyl butyrate→ethanol + butyrate	8.0	Saturated	20		Titr	Gastric & intestinal mucosa, pancreas
13	β-Galactosidase 1/	Lactose→glucose + galactose	5.6	2.5%	38		Chem	Intestinal mucosa, pancreas
14	α-Glucosidase 2/	Maltose→glucose	7.2	50 mg/ml	30		Pol	Intestinal mucosa, pancreas
15	β-Glucosidase	β-Glucosides→glucose + aglycon	4.4-5.0	1 mg/ml	30		Pol	Intestinal mucosa
16	Guanase	Guanine→xanthine + NH_3	8.7	Saturated	40		Chem	Pancreas
17	Invertase 3/	Sucrose→glucose + fructose	4.5	4 g/25 ml	20		Pol	Intestinal mucosa
18	Lecithinase A	Lecithin→lysolecithin + fatty acid	7	Egg yolk	38	Ca^{2+}	Chem	Pancreas
19	Lecithinase B	Lysolecithin→glycerylphosphorylcholine + fatty acid	4		41		Chem	Pancreas
20	Leucylpeptidase	Leucyl peptides→leucine + other amino acids	8-9	0.05 *M*	40	Mg^{2+}, Mn^{2+}		Intestinal mucosa
21	Lipase, pancreatic	Fats→glycerol + fatty acids	9	2.5 g/15 ml	30	$CaCl_2$	Titr	Pancreas
22	Lipoxidase	Linoleic acid, etc. →oxidized fatty acids	6.5	0.02%	25		Col	Intestinal mucosa
23	Nucleoside phosphorylase	Inosine→hypoxanthine + ribose-1-phosphate	7.5	0.001 *M*	30		290 nm 4/	Intestinal mucosa
24	Pepsin	Proteins→proteoses, peptones, amino acids	1.5-2.0	2%	20		Col	Gastric mucosa
25	Phosphoglucomutase	Glucose-1-phosphate→glucose-6-phosphate	7.5-9.2	10^{-6} *M*	30	Co^{2+}, Mg^{2+}, Mn^{2+}	Chem	Pancreas
26	Phosphoglyceromutase	3-Phosphoglycerate→2-phosphoglycerate	7	10^{-5} *M*	24		Chem	Pancreas
27	Phytase	Phytate→inositol + phosphate	5.5-7.8	0.1%	37	Mg^{2+}	Chem	Intestinal mucosa
28	Rennin	Casein→paracasein	5.8	Raw milk	40		Phys	Stomach 5/
29	Ribonuclease	Ribonucleic acid→ribonucleotides	4-5	0.25 mg P/ml	25		Chem	Pancreas
30	Trypsin	Proteins (especially denatured)→polypeptides and amino acids	8-9	2.2%	25		Col	Pancreatic juice
31	Urease	Urea→CO_2 + NH_3	7.0	1.5%	20		Chem	Gastric mucosa
32	Xanthine oxidase	Xanthine or aldehyde→uric or other acids	7.5	0.003 *M*	20		Mano	Intestinal mucosa, pancreas

1/ Lactase. 2/ Maltase. 3/ Sucrase or saccharase. 4/ Wavelength used for measuring light absorption. 5/ Young ruminants only.

continued

44. CATALYTIC ACTION OF DIGESTIVE ENZYMES

Contributors: (a) Somers, G. Fred, (b) Perlman, D., (c) Campbell, Jack J. R.

General References

[1] Boyer, P. D., H. Lardy, and K. Myrbäck, ed. 1959-63. The enzymes. Ed. 2. Academic Press, New York.

[2] Dixon, M., and E. C. Webb. 1964. Enzymes. Ed. 2. Academic Press, New York.

[3] Sumner, J. B., and G. F. Somers, ed. 1953. Chemistry and methods of enzymes. Ed. 3. Academic Press, New York.

45. DIGESTIVE ENZYMES: VERTEBRATE TISSUES AND SECRETIONS

Abbreviations: T = tissue; S = secretion. *Symbols:* + = present; − = absent; ± = doubtful.

	Animal	Enzyme	Salivary Gland		Esophagus	Stomach		Pancreas		Small Intestine		Cecum & Colon	
			T	S	T	T	S	T	S	T	S	T	S
1	Man	Amylase	....	+[17]	....	....	....	....	+[4]	+[17]	±[24]	....	....
2		Enteropeptidase 1/	....	....	....	....	....	....	....	....	+[31]	....	....
3		Erepsin; peptidases	....	+[17]	....	....	....	+[24]	+[24]	+[24]	+[24]	....	....
4		β-Fructofuranosidase 2/	....	....	....	....	....	....	....	....	+[31]	....	....
5		α-Glucosidase 3/	....	....	....	....	....	....	+[4]	....	....	....	....
6		Lipase; esterases	+[5]	+[17]	+[5]	+[5]	+[24]	+[24]	+[24]	....	±[31]	....	....
7		Pepsin	....	....	....	+[17]	+[17]	....	....	....	....	....	....
8		Phosphatases	....	+[17]	....	+[17]	....	....	....	+[26]	....	+[26]	....
9		Rennin	....	....	....	....	−4/[11]	....	....	....	....	....	....
10		Trypsin 5/	....	....	....	....	....	....	+[4]	....	....	....	....
11		Urease	....	....	....	+[10]	....	....	....	....	....	....	....
12	Cat	Amylase	....	−[17]	....	....	....	....	+[4]	....	+[31]	....	....
13		Carbonic anhydrase	....	....	....	+[4]	....	+[4]	....	+[4]	....	....	....
14		Enteropeptidase 1/	....	....	....	....	....	....	....	+[17]	+[17]	....	....
15		Erepsin; peptidases	....	....	....	....	....	+[17]	....	±[17]	±[31]	....	....
16		β-Fructofuranosidase 2/	....	....	....	....	....	....	....	....	±[31]	....	....
17		α-Glucosidase 3/	....	....	....	....	....	+[4]	....	....	....	....	....
18		Lipase; esterases	....	....	....	+[17]	....	....	+[4]	....	−[26]	+[22]	−6/[22]
19		Pepsin	....	....	....	....	+[4]	....	....	....	....	....	....
20		Phosphatases	+[26]	....	....	+[26]	....	±[26]	....	+[26]	....	+[26]	....
21		Trypsin 5/	....	....	....	....	....	....	....	+[17]	−[31]	....	....
22		Urease	....	....	....	+[10]	....	....	....	....	....	....	....
23	Cattle, ♀	Amylase	....	+[8]	....	+[26]	....	+[24]	+[24]	....	....	....	....
24		Enteropeptidase 1/	....	....	....	....	....	....	....	....	+[17]	....	....
25		β-Galactosidase 7/	+[8]	....	....	....	....	....	....	....	....	....	....
26		Lipase; esterases	+[8]	+[8]	....	+[17]	....	+[17]	....	....	....	....	....
27		Pepsin	....	....	−[24]	....	+[4]	....	....	−[24]	....	....	....
28		Phosphatases	+[8]	....	....	....	....	....	....	+[15]	....	....	....
29		Ribonuclease	....	....	....	....	....	+[5]	....	....	....	....	....
30		Rennin	....	....	....	+8/[5]	±8/[17]	....	....	....	....	....	....

1/ Enterokinase. 2/ Invertase. 3/ Maltase. 4/ In adult. 5/ And other nonacid proteases. 6/ Colon. 7/ Lactase. 8/ Only in young.

continued

45. DIGESTIVE ENZYMES: VERTEBRATE TISSUES AND SECRETIONS

	Animal	Enzyme	Salivary Gland		Esophagus	Stomach		Pancreas		Small Intestine		Cecum & Colon	
			T	S	T	T	S	T	S	T	S	T	S
31		Trypsin 5/	...	...	...	...	...	+[5]	+[24]	...	...	...	...
32		Urease	...	...	...	+[26]	...	...	...	...	...	...	...
33	Dog	Amylase	...	+[8]	...	...	±[24]	+[4]	+[4]	...	+[31]	...	±[24]
34		Carbonic anhydrase	+[6]	...	...	+[4]	...	...	...	...	...	...	...
35		Enteropeptidase 1/	...	...	...	...	...	...	...	+[4]	+[4]	...	−[19]
36		Erepsin; peptidases	...	...	...	...	...	+[4]	+[4]	+[24]	+[4]	...	±[19]
37		β-Fructofuranosidase 2/	...	...	...	...	...	...	...	...	±[31]	...	...
38		β-Galactosidase 7/	+[8]	...	...	...	...	...	...	...	...	...	...
39		α-Glucosidase 3/	...	...	...	...	...	...	+[4]	...	...	...	...
40		Lipase; esterases	+[8]	+[17]	...	+[24]	+[24]	+[4]	+[4]	+[24]	±[31]	...	+[24]
41		Pancreatopeptidase E 9/	...	...	...	...	...	+[7]	...	...	...	...	...
42		Pepsin	...	...	−[24]	...	+[3]	...	...	...	...	...	...
43		Phosphatases	+[8]	...	...	...	...	...	...	+[26]	...	...	...
44		Ribonuclease	...	...	...	...	...	+[25]	...	...	...	...	...
45		Rennin	...	...	...	...	±8/[3]	...	...	...	...	...	...
46		Trypsin 5/	...	...	...	...	...	+[4]	+[4]	...	±[31]	...	...
47		Urease	...	...	...	+[10]	...	...	...	...	...	...	...
48	Goat	Amylase	...	−[24]	...	...	...	...	...	...	±[31]	...	...
49		Enteropeptidase 1/	...	...	...	...	...	...	...	...	+[17]	...	...
50		Erepsin; peptidases	...	...	...	...	...	...	...	...	−[31]	...	...
51		β-Fructofuranosidase 2/	...	...	...	...	...	...	...	...	±[31]	...	...
52		Lipase; esterases	...	...	...	...	...	...	...	...	±[31]	...	...
53		Rennin	...	...	...	...	+8/[26]	...	...	...	...	...	...
54		Trypsin 5/	...	...	...	...	...	...	...	...	−[31]	...	...
55		Urease	...	...	...	...	...	...	...	−[26]	...	...	...
56	Guinea pig	Amylase	...	+[17]	...	...	...	...	...	...	...	...	...
57		Carbonic anhydrase	...	...	...	+[18]	...	+[18]	...	...	...	...	...
58		Erepsin; peptidases	...	...	...	...	...	+[17]	...	+[17]	...	...	...
59		Lipase; esterases	...	...	...	+[17]	...	...	+[24]	...	...	...	...
60		Pancreatopeptidase E 9/	...	...	...	...	...	+[9]	...	...	...	...	...
61		Phosphatases	...	...	...	...	...	...	...	+[23]	...	...	...
62	Horse	Amylase	...	±[24]	...	...	...	...	...	...	+[1]	+[29]	...
63		Enteropeptidase 1/	...	...	...	...	...	...	...	...	+[17]	...	...
64		β-Fructofuranosidase 2/	...	...	...	...	...	...	...	...	+[1]	...	...
65		β-Galactosidase 7/	...	...	...	...	...	...	...	...	+[1]	...	...
66		α-Glucosidase 3/	...	...	...	...	...	...	...	...	+[1]	...	...
67		Lipase; esterases	...	+[26]	...	+[17]	...	...	...	...	−[1]	...	...
68		Pepsin	...	...	...	...	...	...	...	−[24]	...	...	...
69		Trypsin 5/	...	...	...	...	...	...	...	...	+[1]	...	...
70	Monkey	Amylase	...	+[17]	...	...	...	...	...	...	...	...	...
71		Enteropeptidase 1/	...	...	...	...	...	...	...	...	+[17]	...	...

1/ Enterokinase. 2/ Invertase. 3/ Maltase. 5/ And other nonacid proteases. 7/ Lactase. 8/ Only in young. 9/ Elastase.

continued

45. DIGESTIVE ENZYMES: VERTEBRATE TISSUES AND SECRETIONS

	Animal	Enzyme	Salivary Gland		Esophagus	Stomach		Pancreas		Small Intestine		Cecum & Colon	
			T	S	T	T	S	T	S	T	S	T	S
72		Erepsin; peptidases	...	+[3]	...	...	...	...	...	...	...	...	...
73		Pepsin	...	...	...	...	+[28]	...	...	...	...	...	...
74	Mouse	Carbonic anhydrase	...	...	...	+[18]	...	+[18]	...	...	...	...	...
75		Phosphatases	...	...	...	...	...	+[23]	...	...	...	...	...
76	Rabbit	Amylase	...	+[8]	...	...	...	...	+[4]	...	+[31]	...	...
77		Carbonic anhydrase	...	...	...	+[4]	...	+[4]	...	+[4]	...	...	...
78		Enteropeptidase 1/	...	...	...	...	...	...	...	...	+[17]	...	...
79		Erepsin; peptidases	...	...	...	...	...	+[17]	...	+[24]	−[31]	...	...
80		β-Galactosidase 7/	+[8]	...	...	...	...	...	...	...	...	...	...
81		Lipase; esterases	+[8]	...	...	+[17]	+[24]	...	+[4]	...	±[31]	...	...
82		Pepsin	...	...	...	+[24]	...	...	...	−[24]	...	+[26]	...
83		Phosphatases	+[8]	...	...	+[26]	...	...	...	+[26]	...	...	...
84		Trypsin 5/	...	...	...	...	...	...	+[4]	...	−[31]	...	...
85		Urease	...	...	...	+[10]	...	...	...	...	...	...	...
86	Rat	Amylase	...	+[27]	...	+[21]	...	+[4]	+[4]	+[30]	...	+6/[21]	...
87		Carbonic anhydrase	...	...	...	+[4]	...	+[4]	...	+[4]	...	...	...
88		Enteropeptidase 1/	...	...	...	...	...	...	...	+[23]	...	...	...
89		Erepsin; peptidases	...	...	...	...	...	...	...	+[30]	...	...	...
90		β-Galactosidase 7/	+[8]	...	...	...	...	...	...	...	...	...	...
91		α-Glucosidase 3/	...	...	...	...	...	...	...	+[30]	...	...	...
92		Lipase; esterases	+[8]	...	...	+[17]	...	+[4]	...	...	...	...	...
93		Pancreatopeptidase E 9/	...	...	...	...	...	+[9]	...	...	...	...	...
94		Pepsin	...	...	...	+[26]	+[16]	...	...	...	...	...	...
95		Phosphatases	+[8]	...	...	...	...	...	...	+[23]	...	...	...
96		Trypsin 5/	...	...	...	...	...	+[4]	...	...	...	...	...
97		Urease	...	...	...	+[10]	...	...	...	...	...	...	...
98	Sheep	Amylase	...	−[17]	...	...	...	+[17]	+[17]	...	...	...	...
99		Enteropeptidase 1/	...	...	...	...	...	...	...	...	+[17]	...	...
100		β-Galactosidase 7/	+[8]	...	...	...	...	...	...	...	...	...	...
101		Lipase; esterases	+[8]	+[17]	...	+[17]	...	+[17]	...	...	...	−[24]	...
102		Pepsin	...	...	−[24]	+[26]	...	...	...	...	...	...	...
103		Phosphatases	+[8]	...	...	...	...	...	...	...	...	...	...
104		Ribonuclease	...	...	...	...	...	+[2]	...	...	...	...	...
105		Rennin	...	...	...	+8/[5]	...	...	...	...	...	...	...
106		Trypsin 5/	...	...	...	...	...	+[26]	+[26]	...	...	...	...
107		Urease	...	...	...	+[26]	...	...	...	...	...	...	...
108	Swine	Amylase	...	+[17]	...	...	−[12]	+[17]	+[24]	...	+[31]	...	...
109		Enteropeptidase 1/	...	...	...	...	...	...	...	+[25]	+[17]	...	...
110		Erepsin; peptidases	...	...	...	+[17]	...	+[17]	...	−[31]	...	...	...
111		β-Fructofuranosidase 2/	...	...	...	...	...	...	...	...	±[31]	...	...
112		β-Galactosidase 7/	+[8]	...	...	...	...	...	...	...	...	...	...
113		Lipase; esterases	+[8]	...	...	±[13]	...	+[14]	...	+[17]	±[31]	...	...
114		Pancreatopeptidase E 9/	...	...	...	...	...	+[20]	+[20]	...	...	...	...

1/ Enterokinase. 2/ Invertase. 3/ Maltase. 5/ And other nonacid proteases. 6/ Colon. 7/ Lactase. 8/ Only in young. 9/ Elastase.

continued

45. DIGESTIVE ENZYMES: VERTEBRATE TISSUES AND SECRETIONS

	Animal	Enzyme	Salivary Gland		Esophagus	Stomach		Pancreas		Small Intestine		Cecum & Colon	
			T	S	T	T	S	T	S	T	S	T	S
115		Pepsin	......	......	−[24]	+[17]	+[12]	......	......	±[24]	......	......	......
116		Phosphatases	+[8]	......	......	......	......	+[18]	......	+[26]	......	......	......
117		Ribonuclease	......	......	......	......	......	+[25]	......	......	......	......	......
118		Rennin	......	......	......	......	+[8/][17]	......	......	......	......	......	......
119		Trypsin[5/]	......	......	......	......	......	+[17]	+[24]	......	−[31]	......	......
120		Urease	......	......	......	+[10]	......	......	......	......	......	......	......
121	Chicken	Amylase	......	+[17]	......	......	......	+[17]	......	+[17]	......	......	......
122		Lipase; esterases	......	......	......	+[17]	......	......	......	......	......	......	......
123		Pepsin	......	......	......	+[5]	......	......	......	......	......	......	......
124		Phosphatases	......	......	......	......	......	......	......	+[23]	......	......	......
125	Frog	Amylase	......	+[17]	......	......	......	......	......	......	......	......	......
126		Erepsin; peptidases	......	......	......	......	......	+[17]	......	+[17]	......	......	......
127		α-Glucosidase[3/]	......	......	......	......	......	+[26]	......	−[26]	......	......	......
128		Pepsin	......	......	+[24]	+[17]	+[17]	......	......	......	......	......	......
129		Trypsin[5/]	......	......	......	......	......	+[26]	......	......	......	......	......
130		Urease	......	......	......	+[10]	......	......	......	......	......	......	......

[3/] Maltase. [5/] And other nonacid proteases. [8/] Only in young.

Contributor: Hollander, Franklin

References

[1] Alexander, F., and A. K. Chowdhury. 1958. Nature 181:190.

[2] Aqvist, S. E. G., and C. B. Anfinsen. 1959. J. Biol. Chem. 234:1112.

[3] Babkin, B. P. 1929. Die äussere Sekretion der Verdauungsdrüsen. Ed. 2. J. Springer, Berlin.

[4] Babkin, B. P. 1950. Secretory mechanism of the digestive glands. Ed. 2. P. B. Hoeber, New York.

[5] Boyer, P. D., H. Lardy, and K. Myrbäck, ed. 1959-63. The enzymes. Ed. 2. Academic Press, New York.

[6] Brusilow, S. W., and C. L. Diaz. 1962. Am. J. Physiol. 202:158.

[7] Carter, A. E. 1956. Science 123:669.

[8] Chauncey, H. H., and G. Quintarelli. 1961. Am. J. Anat. 108:263.

[9] Cohen, H., H. Megel, and W. Kleinberg. 1958. Proc. Soc. Exptl. Biol. Med. 97:8.

[10] Conway, E. J. 1953. The biochemistry of gastric acid secretion. C. C. Thomas, Springfield, Ill.

[11] Dotti, L. B., and I. S. Kleiner. 1942. Am. J. Physiol. 138:557.

[12] Dukes, H. H. 1955. The physiology of domestic animals. Ed. 7. Comstock, Ithaca.

[13] Evans, R. A., and D. A. Stansfield. 1961. Nature 190:1110.

[14] Gjessing, E., and J. C. Hartnett. 1960. Federation Proc. 19:49.

[15] Harris, E. S., et al. 1952. Proc. Soc. Exptl. Biol. Med. 81:593.

[16] Hirschowitz, B. I., and W. G. Underhill. 1959. Am. J. Physiol. 196:837.

[17] Koningsberger, V. J., E. J. Slijper, and H. J. Vonk, ed. 1946. Tabulae Biologicae 21(1).

[18] Kurata, Y. 1953. Stain Technol. 28:231.

[19] Kuvaeva, I. B. 1957. Fiziol. Zh. SSSR 43:311.

[20] Lewis, U. J., D. E. Williams, and N. G. Brink. 1956. J. Biol. Chem. 222:705.

[21] McGeachin, R. L., and K. F. Norwood, Jr. 1959. Am. J. Physiol. 196:972.

[22] Martin, B. F. 1959. Nature 183:1464.

[23] Moog, F. 1962. Federation Proc. 21:51.

[24] Oppenheimer, C. 1925-26. Die Fermente und ihre Wirkungen. Ed. 5. G. Thieme, Leipzig. v. 1,2.

[25] Oppenheimer, C., and L. Pincussen, ed. 1929. Ibid. G. Thieme, Leipzig. v. 3.

[26] Oppenheimer, C. 1935-39. Ibid. W. Junk, Haag. suppl.

[27] Schneyer, L. H., and C. A. Schneyer. 1956. Federation Proc. 15:164.

[28] Smith, G. P., and F. P. Brooks. 1959. Ibid. 18:147.

[29] Sym, E. A., W. Stankiewicz, and F. Zielinski. 1939. Enzymologia 6:113.

[30] Van Genderen, H., and C. Engel. 1938. Ibid. 5:71.

[31] Wright, R. D., et al. 1940. Quart. J. Exptl. Physiol. 30:73.

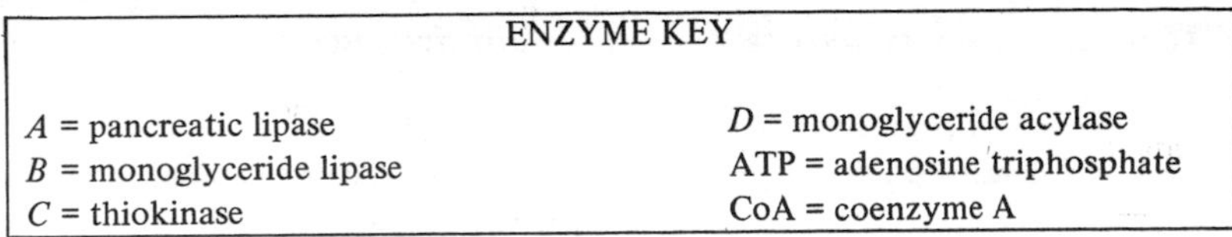

ENZYME KEY
A = pancreatic lipase
B = monoglyceride lipase
C = thiokinase
D = monoglyceride acylase
ATP = adenosine triphosphate
CoA = coenzyme A

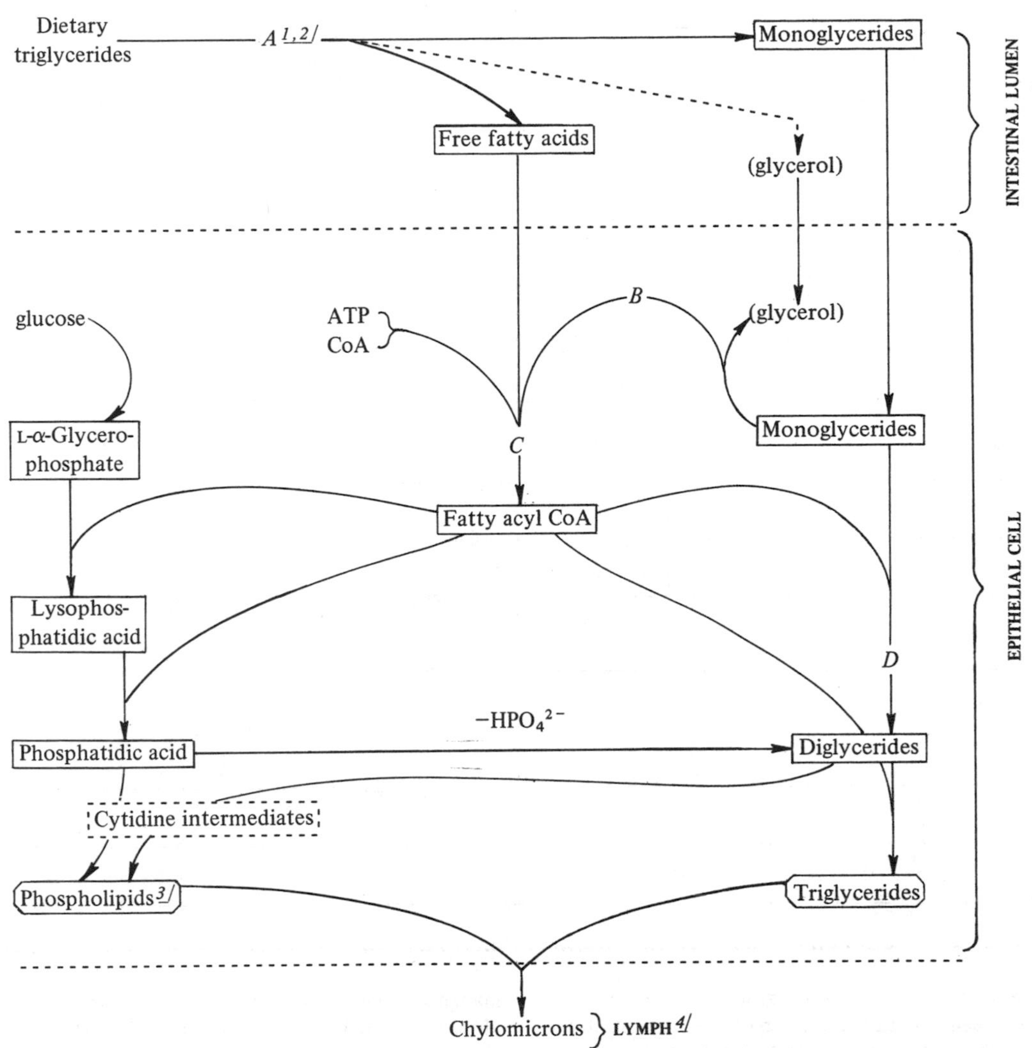

1/ Pancreatic lipase acts preferentially on ester linkages at the terminal or 1 position of glycerol. Thus the major products of digestion are fatty acids and monoglycerides. 2/ Bile salts in their conjugated form participate in at least three reactions during fat digestion and absorption: (i) as a cofactor for pancreatic lipase; (ii) to form micelles containing monoglyceride and fatty acid, as well as other lipids (these micelles are probably the form in which lipid is absorbed into the cell); (iii) as a cofactor for thiokinase in the intestinal mucosal cell. 3/ Absorbed fatty acids go mainly into the triglycerides of chylomicrons, but small amounts are synthesized into cholesterol esters and phospholipids which also are constituents of chylomicrons. 4/ Fatty acids with chain lengths shorter than 10 carbon atoms are absorbed mainly into the portal blood, those with longer chain lengths mainly into the lymph.

Contributor: Grossman, Morton I.

Reference: Senior, J. R., and K. J. Isselbacher. 1962. J. Biol. Chem. 237:1454.

47. PATHWAYS OF CARBOHYDRATE DIGESTION: MAN AND LABORATORY MAMMALS

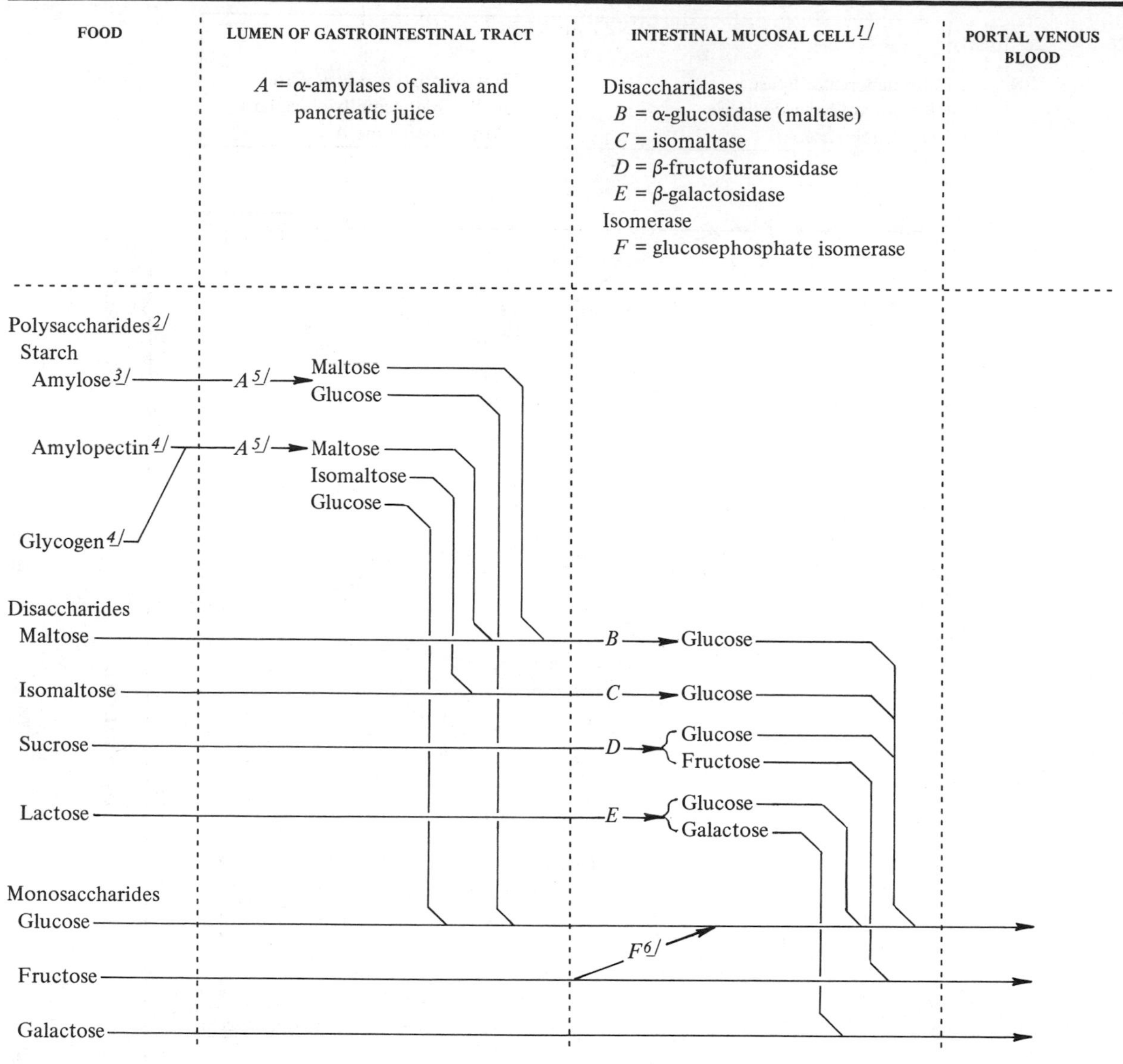

1/ Dihexoses and monohexoses are absorbed into the intestinal mucosal cell. Within the microvilli of the intestinal mucosal cell, the dihexoses are split to monohexoses. Apart from the small fraction of hexose metabolized (oxidized) during passage through the intestinal mucosal cell, phosphorylation of hexoses does not occur as a mechanism for absorption of hexoses into the cell or for delivery from the cell into the portal blood. 2/ A number of so-called structural polysaccharides occurring in foods are not digestible in the alimentary tract of vertebrates and so pass into the feces essentially unaltered. These include cellulose, lignin, mannan, xylan, pectic acids, alginic acid, and chitin. 3/ Amylose is a straight chain polymer of glucose with alpha 1-4 glucosidic linkages. 4/ Amylopectin and glycogen are branched chain polymers of glucose with alpha 1-4 linkages in the straight chain portions and alpha 1-6 linkages at the points of branching. 5/ α-Amylase hydrolyzes 1-4 glucosidic linkages in chains of glucose containing 3 or more residues; it does not split maltose. α-Amylase does not split the 1-6 linkages in amylopectin. 6/ Some fructose is transformed to glucose in the intestinal mucosal cell and some passes through unchanged.

Contributor: Grossman, Morton I.

Reference: Dahlquist, A. 1962. Gastroenterology 43:694.

48. PATHWAYS OF PROTEIN DIGESTION: MAN AND LABORATORY MAMMALS

Pepsin, trypsin, and chymotrypsin are endopeptidases, i.e., they hydrolyze peptide bonds in the interior of peptide chains as well as terminal bonds. Carboxypeptidase and leucine aminopeptidase are exopeptidases and can act only on terminal peptide bonds.

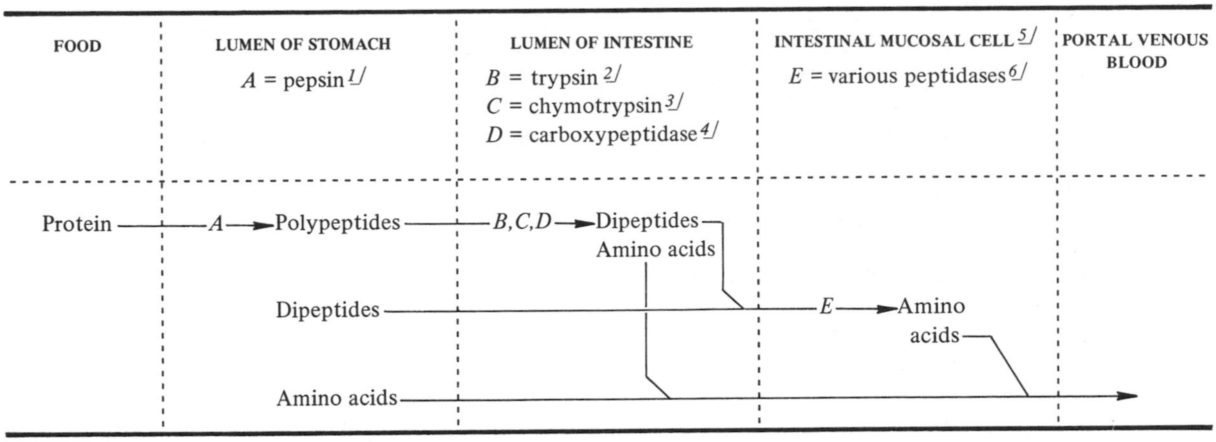

FOOD	LUMEN OF STOMACH	LUMEN OF INTESTINE	INTESTINAL MUCOSAL CELL 5/	PORTAL VENOUS BLOOD
	A = pepsin 1/	*B* = trypsin 2/ *C* = chymotrypsin 3/ *D* = carboxypeptidase 4/	*E* = various peptidases 6/	
Protein ———	*A* ——► Polypeptides ———	*B,C,D* ——► Dipeptides, Amino acids		
	Dipeptides ———	———	*E* ——► Amino acids	——►
	Amino acids ———	———	———	——►

1/ Pepsin hydrolyzes many types of peptide bonds but splits most rapidly those in which an aromatic amino acid provides the amino group. 2/ Trypsin hydrolyzes peptide bonds to which L-arginine, or L-lysine, contributes the carbonyl group. 3/ Chymotrypsin hydrolyzes many types of peptide bonds, but splits most rapidly those in which an aromatic amino acid contributes the carbonyl group. 4/ Carboxypeptidase does not exhibit absolute specificity with respect to the terminal amino acid forming the bond being split; it acts most rapidly on those linkages in which aromatic amino acids are in the terminal position. The terminal amino acid must have a free carboxyl group. 5/ Amino acids and dipeptides enter the intestinal mucosal cells. Amino acids pass through unaltered (with a few exceptions, such as transamination of glutamic acid), and dipeptides are split to amino acids in the microvilli of the cell where the peptidases are localized. 6/ Only a few of the intestinal mucosal peptidases have been characterized. The best known is leucine aminopeptidase.

Contributor: Grossman, Morton I.

Reference: Fruton, J. S., and S. Simmonds. 1958. General biochemistry. Ed. 2. J. Wiley, New York.

49. APPARENT DIGESTIBILITY AND ABSORBABILITY OF NUTRIENTS: VERTEBRATES

Values are grams of fat, carbohydrate, or protein digested and absorbed per 100 grams of the nutrient ingested as a component of the food or feed listed. The quantity digested and absorbed is the quantity of the nutrient ingested minus the quantity subsequently found in the feces. Fecal fat (= ether extract) includes bacterial lipids and lipids excreted through the intestinal wall. Fecal protein (= 6.25 × fecal nitrogen) includes amino acids and other nitrogen compounds. Values for man are for food as commonly prepared for ingestion. Values are subject to marked change with variation in the diet. High dietary cellulose content increases fecal losses of other nutrients. **Carbohydrate:** NFE = nitrogen-free extract.

<table>
<tr><th rowspan="2"></th><th rowspan="2">Animal</th><th rowspan="2">Food or Feed</th><th rowspan="2">Fat</th><th colspan="2">Carbohydrate</th><th rowspan="2">Protein</th><th rowspan="2">Reference</th></tr>
<tr><th>Fiber</th><th>NFE</th></tr>
<tr><td>1</td><td>Man 1/</td><td>Animal products 2/</td><td>95</td><td colspan="2">98</td><td>97</td><td>10</td></tr>
<tr><td>2</td><td></td><td>Eggs</td><td>95</td><td colspan="2">98</td><td>97</td><td>16</td></tr>
<tr><td>3</td><td></td><td>Fats</td><td>95 3/</td><td colspan="2">....</td><td>........</td><td>9</td></tr>
<tr><td>4</td><td></td><td>Meat or fish</td><td>95</td><td colspan="2">....</td><td>97</td><td>16</td></tr>
<tr><td>5</td><td></td><td>Milk or milk products</td><td>95</td><td colspan="2">98</td><td>97</td><td>16</td></tr>
</table>

1/ For additional information on the coefficients of digestibility for fat, carbohydrate, and protein in selected foods, consult references 10 and 16. 2/ Weighted by kinds used. 3/ Digestibility varies inversely with saturation and length of carbon chain, and is less in infants than in adults [8].

continued

49. APPARENT DIGESTIBILITY AND ABSORBABILITY OF NUTRIENTS: VERTEBRATES

	Animal	Food or Feed	Fat	Carbohydrate		Protein	Reference
				Fiber	NFE		
6		Plant products[2]	94	97		82	10
7		Cornmeal, whole, ground	90	96		60	16
8		degermed	90	99		76	16
9		Fat, separated	95	....		....	16
10		Fruit, except lemons & limes	90	90		85	16
11		Macaroni or spaghetti	90	98		86	16
12		Oats, rolled	90	98		76	16
13		Potatoes	90	96		74	16
14		Rice, brown	90	98		75	16
15		white or polished	90	99		84	16
16		Sugar	....	98		....	16
17		Wheat, 97-100% extraction	90	90		79	16
18		85-93% extraction	90	94		83	16
19		70-74% extraction	90	98		89	16
	Cattle	Animal products					14
20		Fish meal, tuna	97	....	....	76	
21		Milk	100	....	99	96	
22		Milk, skim, centrifuged	38	....	100	96	
		Plant products					
23		Alfalfa, hay	35	44	71	70	14
24		meal	61	52	69	78	14
25		Barley grains	63	6	88	70	14
26		Clover hay	58	56	69	63	14
27		Corn, silage	70	64	69	45	14
28		grains	83	13	88	63	14
29		gluten feed	74	70	88	86	14
30		Cottonseed meal	92	57	80	81	14
31		Fat, separated	77	....	....	....	1-3,5,6,11
32		Grass, Kentucky blue-, pasture	51	70	65	68	14
33		pasture, mixed, green	42	74	77	75	14
34		Linseed meal, old process	93	−11[4,5]	78	85	14
35		Oat grains	84	13	76	74	14
36		Peanut meal, 39% protein	97	55	79	94	14
37		Potato tubers	1	−23[4]	91	55	14
38		Soybean meal, solvent process	38	57	91	90	14
39		Sugar, feeding	....	....	97	−59[4]	14
40		Timothy, green	57	68	72	59	14
41		hay	46	58	57	46	14
42		Wheat, bran	74	30	76	76	14
43		mixed feed, winter	87	50	76	77	14
44		Yeast, dried	−89[4]	0	89	92	14
	Goat	Plant products					14
45		Alfalfa, hay	19	41	69	74	
46		meal, dehydrated	22	33	66	67	
47		Corn grains	98	−41[4]	101[6]	59	
48		Cottonseed meal, 36% protein, low fiber	92	41	63	91	
49		Grass, mixed, green, Europe	64	66	79	70	

[2] Weighted by kinds used. [4] Some feedstuffs when ingested either stimulate intestinal excretion of nutrients, specifically nitrogen (protein) or lipid, or decrease the digestibility of nutrients, e.g., fiber. The negative percentage digestibility refers to either of these actions. [5] Ingestion of linseed meal causes more fiber to be lost in the feces than was originally contained in the quantity of linseed meal ingested. The additional fiber lost comes from other roughages of known digestibility which are fed with the linseed meal, resulting in a negative value. [6] Addition, particularly in small proportion, of a feeding material which greatly increases the digestibility of the basal ration may increase the digestibility of a nutrient to more than 100 percent.

continued

	Animal	Food or Feed	Fat	Carbohydrate		Protein	Reference
				Fiber	NFE		
50		Potato peelings	39	14	93	40	
51		Soybean meal, solvent process	47	101[6]	89	91	
52		Wheat bran	58	60	75	76	
	Horse	Animal products					14
53		Milk, mare's	90	....	90	91	
		Plant products					14
54		Alfalfa hay	−6[4]	39	68	74	
55		Barley grains	25	39	87	88	
56		Clover hay	29	38	64	56	
57		Corn grains	59	−31[4]	89	69	
58		Cottonseed meal, 36% protein, high fiber	90	29	49	85	
59		Grass, pasture, mixed, Europe	−59[4]	33	62	66	
60		Linseed meal, old process	35	....	53	84	
61		Oat grains	66	10	74	77	
62		Potato tubers	42	75	101[6]	63	
63		Sugar, feeding	50	32	83	70	
64		Timothy hay	13	43	53	43	
65		Wheat bran	27	22	53	73	
66		Yeast, wet	....	....	103[6]	91	
	Sheep	Animal products					14
67		Bone meal	−171[4]	....	....	69	
68		Buttermilk, dried	98	1	94	90	
69		Fish meal	95	....	....	89	
70		Meat scrap, beef	97	....	....	82	
71		Milk, skim, dried	102[6]	....	93	90	
		Plant products					14
72		Alfalfa, hay	31	45	69	72	
73		meal	36	47	72	72	
74		Barley grains	80	45	91	79	
75		Clover hay	43	56	64	62	
76		Corn, silage	71	64	68	47	
77		grains	85	93	93	70	
78		gluten feed, low ash, high fat	80	78	90	83	
79		Cottonseed meal	96	31	70	61	
80		Grass, mixed, medium protein, green	50	75	77	72	
81		Linseed meal, old process	92	50	79	84	
82		Oat grains	80	32	78	78	
83		Oats, rolled	96	80	98	90	
84		Peanut meal	91	56	90	91	
85		Potato tubers	55	−53[4]	93	63	
86		Soybean meal, solvent process	52	101[6]	96	94	
87		Timothy, green	59	51	57	39	
88		hay	47	55	61	47	
89		Wheat, grains	72	33	92	78	
90		middlings	89	38	75	78	
91		bran	55	36	72	75	
92		Yeast, dried	7	−105[4]	88	85	
	Swine	Animal products					14
93		Bone meal	−116[4]	0	−104[4]	78	
94		Buttermilk, dried	−30[4]	....	98	93	

[4] Some feedstuffs when ingested either stimulate intestinal excretion of nutrients, specifically nitrogen (protein) or lipid, or decrease the digestibility of nutrients, e.g., fiber. The negative percentage digestibility refers to either of these actions. [6] Addition, particularly in small proportion, of a feeding material which greatly increases the digestibility of the basal ration may increase the digestibility of a nutrient to more than 100 percent.

continued

	Animal	Food or Feed	Fat	Carbohydrate		Protein	Reference
				Fiber	NFE		
95		Fish meal	81	....	....	92	
96		Meat & bone scrap	100	....	−46[4/]	89	
97		Milk, cow's	96	....	97	9	
98		skim, dried	122[6/]	....	97	98	
		Plant products					14
99		Alfalfa, hay	14	22	49	47	
100		meal	11	22	47	46	
101		Barley grains	44	11	89	77	
102		Corn grains	46	21	69	56	
103		Cottonseed meal	90	31	69	86	
104		Grass, mixed, prebloom, green, Europe	84	39	52	52	
105		Linseed meal, old process	62	20	80	90	
106		Oat grains	76	14	74	78	
107		Peanut meal	84	70	84	94	
108		Potato tubers	0	79	96	15	
109		Soybean meal, solvent process	58	83	91	91	
110		Sugar, cane	....	....	99	....	
111		Wheat, grains	80	24	94	92	
112		middlings	73	20	74	79	
113		bran	58	23	69	76	
114		Yeast, wet	30	....	78	89	
	Chicken	Animal products					4,7,13,15
115		Bone meal	90	....	90	95	
116		Buttermilk, dried	96	....	35	96	
117		Fish meal	93	....	87	91	
118		Liver meal	97	....	88	92	
119		Meat scrap	92	....	90	84	
120		Milk, skim, dried	95	....	37	96	
		Plant products					
121		Alfalfa meal	54	....	36	58	4,7,13,15
122		Barley	78	....	72	74	4,7,13,15
123		Corn, meal, whole, ground	92	....	95	88	4,7,13,15
124		gluten meal	91	....	84	88	4,7,13,15
125		Cottonseed meal	88	....	78	86	4,7,13,15
126		Fat, separated	95	....	....	....	4,7,13,15
127		Macaroni or spaghetti	85	....	97	78	7
128		Oats, whole grain	91	....	62	66	4,7,13,15
129		Peanut meal	93	....	78	82	4,7,13,15
130		Rice, white	100	....	95	100	12
131		Soybean meal	92	....	36	92	4,7,13,15
132		Wheat, whole grain	91	....	90	89	4,7,13,15
133		middlings	78	....	62	70	4,7,13,15
134		bran	74	....	35	60	4,7,13,15
135		Yeast	86	....	78	90	4,7,13,15

[4/] Some feedstuffs when ingested either stimulate intestinal excretion of nutrients, specifically nitrogen (protein) or lipid, or decrease the digestibility of nutrients, e.g., fiber. The negative percentage digestibility refers to either of these actions. [6/] Addition, particularly in small proportion, of a feeding material which greatly increases the digestibility of the basal ration may increase the digestibility of a nutrient to more than 100 percent.

Contributors: (a) Swanson, Eric W., (b) Runnels, Tom D., (c) Watt, Bernice K., (d) Pearson, Paul B.

References

[1] Armsby, H. P. 1917. The nutrition of farm animals. Macmillan, New York.

[2] Armsby, H. P., and J. A. Fries. 1917. J. Agr. Res. 10:599.

[3] Armsby, H. P., and J. A. Fries. 1917. Ibid. 11:451.

[4] Ewing, W. R. 1963. Poultry nutrition. Ed. 5. R. Ewing, Pasadena, Calif.

continued

[5] Forbes, E. B., et al. 1928. J. Agr. Res. 37:253.
[6] Forbes, E. B., et al. 1930. Ibid. 40:37.
[7] Fraps, G. S. 1946. Texas Agr. Expt. Sta. Bull. 678.
[8] Mattil, K. F. 1946. Oil Soap (Chicago) 23:244.
[9] Maynard, L. A. 1944. J. Nutr. 28:443.
[10] Merrill, A. L., and B. K. Watt. 1955. U.S. Dept. Agr. Agr. Handbook 74.
[11] Mitchell, H. H., and T. S. Hamilton. 1932. J. Agr. Res. 45:163.
[12] Morrison, F. B. 1948. Feeds and feeding. Morrison, Ithaca, N.Y.
[13] New Jersey Feed Laboratory. Unpublished. Protein digestibility tests over a ten year period. Trenton, N.J., 1967.
[14] Schneider, B. H. 1947. Feeds of the world. Univ. West Virginia, Morgantown.
[15] Titus, H. W. 1961. The scientific feeding of chickens. Ed. 4. Interstate, Danville, Ill.
[16] Watt, B. K., and A. L. Merrill. 1963. U.S. Dept. Agr. Agr. Handbook 8.

50. MEMBRANE TRANSPORT OF NUTRIENTS

Part I. Classification of Transport Processes

The processes by which water, ions, and organic nutrients move across biological membranes are described in the table below. Kinetic approaches to transport phenomena, using equations identical or similar to those employed in enzyme kinetics, have been helpful in determining whether two substrates compete for some common part of the transport system or whether other types of interactions are taking place. [15,19] The irreversible thermodynamics approach to membrane biophysics has been used to evaluate active transport, electrokinetic phenomena, and water flow across membranes in series [2,4,7,8]. The biochemical and molecular basis of active transport has been under intensive study, and the theories that have evolved may be found in references 6, 9-13, and 16. Perhaps the most recent development concerns observations on the release of nondialyzable factors that may function in membrane transport [1, 3,5,18].

	Type of Transport	Process	Explanation	
1	Simple diffusion	A nonelectrolyte traverses the membrane in accordance with a modification of Fick's equation: $J_i = -p_i \Delta C_i$ [14]	J_i = flux of species i, measured in moles per unit area per unit time; ΔC = concentration difference across the membrane; and p = permeability coefficient (contains terms for the membrane thickness and the equilibrium distribution coefficient of substrate between the membrane and the solution)	The direction of the net flux of a diffusing species is down its electrochemical potential gradient, and represents the difference between two opposing unidirectional fluxes: $J_{net} = J_{12} - J_{21}$, where J_{net} = net flux of the species, J_{12} = unidirectional flux from side 1 to side 2, and J_{21} = unidirectional flux from side 2 to side 1
2		An electrolyte traverses the membrane in accordance with a modification of Fick's equation, but the electropotential gradient must be considered in addition to the concentration gradient: $J_k = -p_k (\Delta C_k + \frac{Z\bar{c}F}{RT} \Delta\psi)$ [14]	J_k = flux of the ionic species k, measured in equivalents per unit area per unit time; p and ΔC as above; Z = valency; $\bar{c}$ = mean concentration of ion; F = Faraday; R = gas constant; T = absolute temperature; and $\Delta\psi$ = electropotential difference	
3	Facilitated diffusion	An interaction between a membrane component and the diffusing species, which results in an enhanced rate of transport; however, the direction of J_{net} is always down its electrochemical potential	Due to the interaction between membrane carrier and substrate, this type of diffusion shows saturation kinetics and competitive inhibition, and has been inhibited by protein affectors (e.g., Cu^{2+} and phlorizin). Direct inhibition by metabolic poisons (e.g., iodoacetate and cyanide) does not occur.	
4	Exchange diffusion	A special mechanism defined by Ussing, in which there is a one-for-one exchange of an ionic species across the membrane [17]	A membrane carrier is saturated with the particular ion because of the carrier's high affinity constant. Due to thermal agitation, the carrier-ion complex rapidly interchanges its ion with the same species of ion at the two interfaces of the membrane.	

continued

50. MEMBRANE TRANSPORT OF NUTRIENTS

Part I. Classification of Transport Processes

	Type of Transport	Process	Explanation
5	Active transport	A net movement of substrate against an electrochemical gradient	Energy input is required, and the transport process must be closely coupled to an energy-yielding process. Active transport, like facilitated diffusion, appears to be carrier-mediated and shows saturation kinetics; it also has a high degree of specificity and shows competitive inhibition between structurally similar substances. Metabolic inhibitors and inhibiting conditions (e.g., 2,4-dinitrophenol, cyanide, and depressed temperature) decrease or inhibit transport.
6	Pinocytosis	Transfer of macromolecules across a membrane [20]	The macromolecule may attach to the membrane which invaginates, forming a pinocytic vesicle or vacuole. If the membrane is ruptured or dissolved, the macromolecule will then be in direct contact with the cytoplasm. A vaçuolated macromolecule can be expelled from the cell by reverse pinocytosis.

Contributor: Wasserman, Robert H.

References

[1] Bobinski, H., and W. D. Stein. 1966. Nature 211: 1366.

[2] Dainty, J., and B. Z. Ginzburg. 1963. J. Theoret. Biol. 5:256.

[3] Fox, C. F., and E. P. Kennedy. 1965. Proc. Natl. Acad. Sci. U.S. 54:891.

[4] Ginzburg, B. Z., and A. Katchalsky. 1963. J. Gen. Physiol. 47:403.

[5] Heppel, L. A. 1967. Science 156:1451.

[6] Hokin, L. E., and M. R. Hokin. 1963. Federation Proc. 22:8.

[7] Katchalsky, A., and P. F. Curran. 1965. Nonequilibrium thermodynamics in biophysics. Harvard Univ. Press, Cambridge.

[8] Kedem, O., and A. Essig. 1965. J. Gen. Physiol. 48: 1047.

[9] Ling, G. N. 1962. A physical theory of the living state. Blaisdell, New York.

[10] Ling, G. N. 1965. Federation Proc. 24:5.

[11] Mitchell, P. 1963. Biochem. Soc. Symp. (Cambridge, Engl.) 22:142.

[12] Post, R. L., et al. 1960. J. Biol. Chem. 235:1796.

[13] Skou, J. C. 1965. Physiol. Rev. 45:596.

[14] Snell, F. M., et al. 1965. Biophysical principles of structure and function. Addison-Wesley, Reading, Mass.

[15] Stein, W. D. 1964. Recent Progr. Surface Sci. 1:300.

[16] Troschin, A. S. 1958. Das Problem der Zellpermeabilitat. G. Fischer, Jena.

[17] Ussing, H. H. 1949. Physiol. Rev. 29:132.

[18] Wasserman, R. H., and A. N. Taylor. 1966. Science 119:536.

[19] Wilbrandt, W., and T. Rosenberg. 1961. Pharmacol. Rev. 13:109.

[20] Woodin, A. M. 1963. Biochem. Soc. Symp. (Cambridge, Engl.) 22:126.

Part II. Rate of Transport Across the Small Intestine: Vertebrates

Data have been selected from studies which illustrate different experimental approaches made in the investigation of nutrient transport across the intestine. Because of different experimental conditions and different reference bases, it would be difficult to make direct comparisons between reports or to arrive at summation values that would be meaningful. **Flux** refers to flux of substrate across the intestine. **M → S** represents the unidirectional flux from mucosa to serosa, or from intestinal lumen to plasma or lymph, unless otherwise stated. **S → M** represents the unidirectional flux in the opposite direction. **Net:** the difference between the unidirectional fluxes, which is equivalent to net absorption. **Flux Units:** millimoles (mM), micromoles (μM), milliequivalents (mEq), or microequivalents (μEq) per unit time per unit measure of tissue. For recent monographs concerned with nutrient transport in a variety of biological systems, consult references 3, 6, 19, 26, 27, 31-33, 35, 36, 44, 47, 49-51, 54, 55, and 57.

continued

Part II. Rate of Transport Across the Small Intestine: Vertebrates

	Animal	Intestinal Segment [Length, cm]	Substrate [Concentration]	Flux M → S	Flux S → M	Flux Net	Flux Units	Remarks	Reference
					Water[1/]				
1	Man, adult	Jejunum [30]	H_2O	....	....	109.0	mM/hr/cm	In vivo perfusion by intubation; 140 mM NaCl, 16.7 mM glucose, 10 g/liter polyethylene glycol	53
2		Ileum [30]	H_2O	....	....	66.7	mM/hr/cm		
3		Jejunum [30]	H_2O	....	....	90.0	mM/hr/cm	In vivo perfusion by intubation; 140 mM NaCl, 16.7 mM mannitol, 10 g/liter polyethylene glycol	53
4		Ileum [30]	H_2O	....	....	105.4	mM/hr/cm		
5		Jejunum [30]	H_2O	888.9	[611.1]	277.8	mM/hr/cm	In vivo perfusion by intubation; 150 mM saline	20
6	Dog	Duodenum [10-15]	H_2O	2.33	[3.00]	−0.67	$mM/hr/cm^2$	In situ infusion into isolated loop; isotonic saline (^{22}Na, deuterium oxide); absorption or secretion measured	23
7		Jejunum [10-15]	H_2O	3.33	2.67	0.67	$mM/hr/cm^2$		
8		Ileum [10-15]	H_2O	4.33	3.67	0.67	$mM/hr/cm^2$		
9		Colon [10-15]	H_2O	16.35	12.68	3.67	$mM/hr/cm^2$		
10	Rat	Jejunum	H_2O	....	....	190.0	mM/hr/g dry wt	In vitro, everted sacs; Krebs-Ringer-HCO_3^- + 11 mM glucose	7
11		Jejunum, ileum	H_2O	....	....	200.0	mM/hr/g dry wt		
12		Ileum	H_2O	....	....	75.5	mM/hr/g dry wt		
13		Jejunum [30]	H_2O	....	....	1005	mM/hr/g dry wt	In vivo perfusion of cannulated intestinal segments; Krebs-Henseleit with 25 mM PO_4 buffer pH 6.9	38
14		Ileum [30]	H_2O	....	....	1045	mM/hr/g dry wt		
15	220-250 g	Jejunum	H_2O	....	....	86.1	mM/hr/g wet wt	In vitro, everted sacs; Krebs-Henseleit buffer + 27.8 mM glucose	13
16		Ileum	H_2O	....	....	60.6	mM/hr/g wet wt		
17		Jejunum	H_2O	....	....	23.3	mM/hr/g wet wt	In vitro, everted sacs; Krebs-Henseleit buffer	13
18		Ileum	H_2O	....	....	41.7	mM/hr/g wet wt		
19	250-350 g	Jejunum [4-8]	H_2O	....	3100	....	mM/hr/g dry wt	In vivo perfusion through intact blood supply of jejunal loop; isotonic saline	40
					Ions				
20	Man, adult	Jejunum [30]	K^+ [0 mEq]	....	....	−0.010	mEq/hr/cm	In vivo perfusion by intubation; 140 mM NaCl, 16.7 mM glucose, 10 g/liter polyethylene glycol	53
21			Na^+ [140 mEq]	....	....	0.249	mEq/hr/cm		
22		Ileum [30]	Na^+ [140 mEq]	....	....	0.238	mEq/hr/cm		
23		Jejunum [30]	Na^+ [140 mEq]	....	....	0.263	mEq/hr/cm	In vivo perfusion by intubation; 140 mM NaCl, 16.7 mM mannitol, 10 g/liter polyethylene glycol	53
24		Ileum [30]	Na^+ [140 mEq]	....	....	0.282	mEq/hr/cm		
25			K^+ [0 mEq]	....	....	−0.028	mEq/hr/cm		
26		Colon [30]	K^+ [3.95 mEq]	0.005	0.075	−0.070	mEq/hr/cm	In vivo perfusion of isolated segment; Tyrode's solution; 2 subjects	46
27		Jejunum [30]	Na^+ [150 mEq]	1.82	1.08	0.74	mEq/hr/cm	In vivo perfusion by intubation; isotonic saline	20
28		Colon [30]	Na^+ [154 mEq]	0.26	0.08	0.18	mEq/hr/cm	In vivo perfusion of isolated segment; Tyrode's solution	46

1/ Water transfer occurs in response to osmotic pressure differences, hydrostatic pressure differences, electroosmosis, etc., but water is not actively transported directly. Membranes in series with different permeability properties allow fluid to move against an *apparent* activity gradient. [41]

continued

Part II. Rate of Transport Across the Small Intestine: Vertebrates

	Animal	Intestinal Segment [Length, cm]	Substrate [Concentration]	Flux M → S	Flux S → M	Flux Net	Flux Units	Remarks	Reference
29	Dog	Duodenum [10-15]	Cl^- [Isotonic NaCl]	....	....	−1.20	μEq/hr/cm²	In situ, isolated loop; isotonic NaCl, 10-min absorption period	23
30		Jejunum [10-15]	Cl^- [Isotonic NaCl]	....	....	1.98	μEq/hr/cm²		
31		Ileum [10-15]	Cl^- [Isotonic NaCl]	....	....	3.84	μEq/hr/cm²		
32		Colon [10-15]	Cl^- [Isotonic NaCl]	....	....	13.50	μEq/hr/cm²		
33		Duodenum [10-15]	Na^+ [149 mEq]	2.7×10^{-3}	4.26×10^{-3}	-1.56×10^{-3}	mEq/hr/cm²	In situ infusion into isolated loop; isotonic saline (^{22}Na, deuterium oxide); absorption or secretion measured	23
34		Jejunum [10-15]	Na^+ [149 mEq]	4.86×10^{-3}	3.18×10^{-3}	1.68×10^{-3}	mEq/hr/cm²		
35		Ileum [10-15]	Na^+ [149 mEq]	6.9×10^{-3}	4.5×10^{-3}	2.40×10^{-3}	mEq/hr/cm²		
36		Colon [10-15]	Na^+ [149 mEq]	25.2×10^{-3}	15.9×10^{-3}	9.30×10^{-3}	mEq/hr/cm²		
37	Young, adult	Jejunum [75]	Ca^{2+} [10 mEq]	....	....	7	μEq/hr/cm	In vivo perfusion of Thiry-Vella fistulas; 220 ml/hr calcium lactate, pH 6.5-7.0, 1 hr	9
38			[20 mEq]	....	....	10	μEq/hr/cm		
39			[40 mEq]	....	....	12	μEq/hr/cm		
40	8-15 kg	Ileum [22]	K^+ [3.47 mEq]	3.8×10^{-3}	11.5×10^{-3}	-7.6×10^{-3}	mEq/hr/cm	In vivo perfusion of Thiry-Vella fistual; 40 ml/hr Tyrode's solution; 5% dextrose intravenous infusion administered simultaneously	46
41		Colon [16]	K^+ [3.67 mEq]	5.25×10^{-3}	10.1×10^{-3}	-4.9×10^{-3}	mEq/hr/cm		
42	Rabbit, 2.5-4 kg	Ileum [5-8]	Na^+ [137 mEq]	9.6	5.7	3.9	μEq/hr/cm²	In vitro perfusion; physiological salt solution, bicarbonate phosphate buffer, pH 7.2, 38.5°C	45
43	Rat	Jejunum	HCO_3^- [25 mM]	....	....	106	μM/hr/g dry wt	In vitro, everted sacs; Krebs-Ringer-HCO_3^-, 37°C, 1 hr	7
44		Ileum	HCO_3^- [25 mM]	....	....	29	μM/hr/g dry wt		
45		Proximal jejunum	Cl^- [100 mM]	0.668	0.239	0.429	mEq/hr/g dry wt	In vitro, everted sacs; Krebs-Ringer-HCO_3^--glucose solution with 30 mM acetate, 37°C, 1 hr	7
46		Distal jejunum	Cl^- [100 mM]	0.356	0.178	0.178	mEq/hr/g dry wt		
47		Ileum	Cl^- [100 mM]	0.630	0.350	0.280	mEq/hr/g dry wt		
48		Jejunum	PO_4^{3-} [15.6 mM]	32	20	12	μM/hr/g dry wt	In vitro, everted sacs; Krebs-Ringer-PO_4-glucose solution, 37°C, 1 hr	7
49		Ileum	PO_4^{3-} [15.6 mM]	6	2	4	μM/hr/g dry wt		
50	120-150 g	Small intestine [2]	F^- [0.26 mM]	....	....	0.39	μM/hr/cm	In vitro, everted sacs; Ringer's solution, 37°C, 30 min	48
51	200 g	Duodenum [5]	PO_4^{3-} [$H_2PO_4^-$, 2 mEq]	0.087	0.061	0.026	μEq/hr/cm²	In vitro, everted sacs; Krebs-Ringer-HCO_3^--glucose solution, 37°C, 1 hr	39
52		Jejunum [5]	PO_4^{3-} [$H_2PO_4^-$, 2 mEq]	0.076	0.038	0.038	μEq/hr/cm²		
53		Ileum [5]	PO_4^{3-} [$H_2PO_4^-$, 2 mEq]	0.042	0.036	0.006	μEq/hr/cm²		
54	200-250 g	Duodenum [10-15]	Ca^{2+} [4.0 mEq]	0.34	0.03	0.31	μEq/hr/cm	In vivo perfusion; isotonic saline	52

[2] Part not specified.

continued

Part II. Rate of Transport Across the Small Intestine: Vertebrates

	Animal	Intestinal Segment [Length, cm]	Substrate [Concentration]	Flux M → S	Flux S → M	Flux Net	Flux Units	Remarks	Reference
55	200-450 g	Jejunum [30]	PO_4^{3-} [25 mM]	....	....	0.28	mM/hr/g dry wt	In situ perfusion of isolated segment	37
56			[100 mM]	....	....	0.77	mM/hr/g dry wt		
57		Jejunum [30]	Na^+ [160 mEq]	....	....	1.91	mEq/hr/g dry wt	In situ, cannulated intestinal segments; Krebs-Henseleit-glucose with phosphate buffer, pH 6.9, 38°C	38
58		Ileum [30]	Na^+ [160 mEq]	....	....	2.74	mEq/hr/g dry wt		
59	250 g	Jejunum	HCO_3^- [25 mM]	....	....	105	µM/hr/g wet wt	In vitro, everted sacs; Krebs-Henseleit solution, 28°C, 1.5 hr	5
60			Na^+ [143.5 mEq]	....	....	0.188	mEq/hr/g wet wt	In vitro, everted sacs; Krebs-Henseleit with 13.9 mM glucose, 28°C	5
61				....	....	0.190	mEq/hr/g wet wt	In vitro, everted sacs; Krebs-Henseleit with 13.9 mM glucose, 28°C	4
62				....	....	0.138	mEq/hr/g wet wt	In vitro, everted sacs; Krebs-Henseleit with 13.9 mM glucose, 38°C	4
63	250-350 g	Jejunum [10]	F^- [0.167 mM]	0.48	0.72	....	µM/hr/g dry wt	In vitro, everted sacs; Krebs-HCO_3-saline, 1.9 mM Ca^{++}, 37°C, 1 hr	42
64		Ileum [10]	F^- [0.167 mM]	0.36	0.78	....	µM/hr/g dry wt		
65		Colon [10]	F^- [0.167 mM]	0.15	0.10	....	µM/hr/g dry wt		
66	250-450 g	Ileum [10]	Na^+ [150 mEq]	54.0	38.0	16.0	µEq/hr/cm	In vivo perfusion; 300 milliosmols/liter unbuffered saline	12
67	300-400 g	Ileum, some jejunum [45-55]	Ca^{2+} [9.9 mEq]	0.16	0.06	0.10	µEq/hr/cm	In vivo perfusion; NaCl, HCO_3^- buffer	14
68		Jejunum [30]	Cl^- [135 mM]	....	....	1.49	mEq/hr/g dry wt	In situ perfusion of intestinal segment; 160 mM Na, 135 mM Cl, 25 mM HCO_3^-	43
69		Ileum [30]	Cl^- [135 mM]	....	....	1.63	mEq/hr/g dry wt		
70		Colon [12]	Cl^- [135 mM]	....	....	1.82	mEq/hr/g dry wt		
71		Ileum [10]	Na^+ [150 mEq]	20.9	9.3	11.9	µEq/hr/cm	In vitro perfusion; NaCl-$NaHCO_3$ buffer, 14 mM glucose	11
					Carbohydrates				
72	Man, young	Duodenum [30]	Suc [73 mM]	....	....	0.88; 0.55[3,4]	mM/hr/cm	In vivo intubation; 2 subjects	21
73		Jejunum [30]	Suc [73 mM]	....	....	1.45; 0.96[3,4]	mM/hr/cm	In vivo intubation; 11 subjects	21
74		Ileum [30]	Suc [73 mM]	....	....	0.84; 0.40[3,4]	mM/hr/cm	In vivo intubation; 8 subjects	21
75	adult	Jejunum [30]	Glc [80 mM] + Gal [80 mM]	....	....	1.6; 1.0[5]	mM/hr/cm	In vivo intubation	22
76			Glc [80 mM]	....	....	2.5	mM/hr/cm		
77			Lac [80 mM]	....	....	1.0; 0.7[4,5]	mM/hr/cm		
78			Mal [80 mM]	....	....	1.4[4]	mM/hr/cm		
79			Suc [80 mM]	....	....	1.7; 1.3[3,4]	mM/hr/cm		

[3] Glucose; fructose. [4] Values given in terms of hydrolytic products. [5] Glucose; galactose.

continued

Part II. Rate of Transport Across the Small Intestine: Vertebrates

	Animal	Intestinal Segment [Length, cm]	Substrate [Concentration]	Flux M → S	Flux S → M	Flux Net	Flux Units	Remarks	Reference
80	Dog	Upper jejunum [~20]	Fru [70 mM]	....	....	0.15	mM/hr/cm	In vivo perfusion of Thiry-Vella fistula; NaCl added to give 310 milliosmols/liter, 2 ml/min	2
81			[280 mM]	....	....	0.46	mM/hr/cm		
82			Gal [70 mM]	....	....	0.32	mM/hr/cm		
83			[280 mM]	....	....	0.60	mM/hr/cm		
84			Glc [70 mM]	....	....	0.36	mM/hr/cm		
85			[280 mM]	....	....	0.48	mM/hr/cm		
86			Sor [70 mM]	....	....	0.04	mM/hr/cm		
87			[280 mM]	....	....	0.31	mM/hr/cm		
88		Lower ileum	Gal [70 mM]	....	....	0.14	mM/hr/cm		
89			[280 mM]	....	....	0.30	mM/hr/cm		
90			Glc [70 mM]	....	....	0.11	mM/hr/cm		
91			[280 mM]	....	....	0.28	mM/hr/cm		
92	Hamster	Jejunum	Glc [11.1 mM]	....	....	0.540	mM/hr/g dry wt	In vitro, everted sac; Krebs-Henseleit-HCO_3	17
93		Small intestine [3-4]	Ara [30.0 mM]	0.080	0.169	−0.089	mM/hr/g dry wt	In vitro, everted sacs; bicarbonate saline, 95% O_2:5% CO_2, 37°C, 1 hr	56
94			Fru [30.0 mM]	0.120	0.134	−0.014	mM/hr/g dry wt		
95			Gal [30.0 mM]	0.670	0.071	0.599	mM/hr/g dry wt		
96			Glc [30.0 mM]	0.760	0.027	0.733	mM/hr/g dry wt		
97			Man [30.0 mM]	0.089	0.169	−0.080	mM/hr/g dry wt		
98			Rib [30.0 mM]	0.112	0.272	−0.160	mM/hr/g dry wt		
99			Sor [30.0 mM]	0.076	0.214	−0.138	mM/hr/g dry wt		
100			Xyl [30.0 mM]	0.210	0.174	0.036	mM/hr/g dry wt		
101	Rat	Stomach & small intestine [Entire]	Fru [27.7 mM]	....	....	0.78	mM/hr/cm	5 ml of 6% sugar solution per os; absorption determined by difference	10
102		Jejunum	Glc [2.78 mM]	....	....	0.384	mM/hr/g dry wt	In vitro, everted sac; Krebs-Henseleit-HCO_3^-, 37°C	16
103			[5.55 mM]	....	....	0.810	mM/hr/g dry wt		
104			Glc [11.1 mM]	....	....	0.402	mM/hr/g dry wt	In vitro, everted sac; Krebs-Henseleit-HCO_3^-	17
105	~250 g	Jejunum	Glc [14 mM]	....	....	0.146	mM/hr/g wet wt	In vitro, everted sac; Krebs-Henseleit, 28°C	15
106	~500 g	Jejunum [5-7]	Glc [28 mM]	....	....	0.027	mM/hr/cm	In vivo, isolated segments; hexose in isotonic saline	8
107			*O*-Methyl glc [25.8 mM]	....	....	0.026	mM/hr/cm		
108			D-Xyl [33 mM]	....	....	0.011	mM/hr/cm		
109		Ileum [5-7]	Glc [28 mM]	....	....	0.022	mM/hr/cm		
110			*O*-Methyl glc [25.8 mM]	....	....	0.020	mM/hr/cm		
111			D-Xyl [33 mM]	....	....	0.009	mM/hr/cm		
			Amino Acids						
112	Man, young adult	Jejunum [30]	Ile [5 mM]	....	....	0.130	mM/hr/cm	In vivo perfusion by intubation; mixtures 8 amino acids, each at same molarity, 15 ml/min	1
113			[20 mM]	....	....	0.322	mM/hr/cm		
114			Leu [5 mM]	....	....	0.127	mM/hr/cm		
115			[20 mM]	....	....	0.314	mM/hr/cm		
116			Lys [5 mM]	....	....	0.105	mM/hr/cm		
117			[20 mM]	....	....	0.232	mM/hr/cm		
118			Met [5 mM]	....	....	0.136	mM/hr/cm		
119			[20 mM]	....	....	0.366	mM/hr/cm		
120			Phe [5 mM]	....	....	0.107	mM/hr/cm		
121			[20 mM]	....	....	0.209	mM/hr/cm		

continued

Part II. Rate of Transport Across the Small Intestine: Vertebrates

	Animal	Intestinal Segment [Length, cm]	Substrate [Concentration]	Flux M → S	Flux S → M	Flux Net	Flux Units	Remarks	Reference
122			Thr [5 mM]	....	....	0.083	mM/hr/cm		
123			[20 mM]	....	....	0.155	mM/hr/cm		
124			Trp [5 mM]	....	....	0.098	mM/hr/cm		
125			[20 mM]	....	....	0.168	mM/hr/cm		
126			Val [5 mM]	....	....	0.120	mM/hr/cm		
127			[20 mM]	....	....	0.238	mM/hr/cm		
128	Hamster, 100-150 g	Lower jejunum or upper ileum	D-Ala [5 mM]	....	....	0	mM/hr/g dry wt	In vitro, everted sacs; Krebs-Henseleit-HCO_3^- buffer, 37°C, 1 hr	34
129			L-Ala [5 mM]	....	....	46.0×10^{-3}	mM/hr/g dry wt		
130			Gly [5 mM]	....	....	20.0×10^{-3}	mM/hr/g dry wt		
131			D-Met [5 mM]	....	....	19.0×10^{-3}	mM/hr/g dry wt		
132			L-Met [5 mM]	....	....	47.0×10^{-3}	mM/hr/g dry wt		
133			D-Trp [5 mM]	....	....	0	mM/hr/g dry wt		
134			L-Trp [5 mM]	....	....	18.0×10^{-3}	mM/hr/g dry wt		
135			D-Tyr [5 mM]	....	....	0	mM/hr/g dry wt		
136			L-Tyr [5 mM]	....	....	49.0×10^{-3}	mM/hr/g dry wt		
137			L-Arg [1 mM]	....	....	2.1×10^{-3}	mM/hr/g dry wt	In vitro, everted sacs; Krebs-Henseleit-HCO_3^- buffer, 37°C, 1 hr	25
138			L-Lys [1 mM]	....	....	7.7×10^{-3}	mM/hr/g dry wt		
139			DL-Orn [1 mM]	....	....	5.1×10^{-3}	mM/hr/g dry wt		
140			Betaine [5 mM]	....	....	14.0×10^{-3}	mM/hr/g dry wt	In vitro, everted sacs; Krebs-Henseleit-HCO_3^- buffer, 37°C, 1 hr	24
141			L-Pro [5 mM]	....	....	12.0×10^{-3}	mM/hr/g dry wt		
142			Sarcosine [5 mM]	....	....	8.0×10^{-3}	mM/hr/g dry wt		
143	Rat, ♂, adult	Upper small intestine [10]	L-Ala [407 µM]	....	....	0.286	mM/hr/cm	In situ perfusion; mixture of amino acids in NaCl or Krebs-Ringer-HCO_3^- buffer. Concentration of amino acids simulates plasma concentration.	28-30
144			L-Asp [10 µM]	....	....	−0.009	mM/hr/cm		
145			L-Glu [123 µM]	....	....	0.010	mM/hr/cm		
146			Gly [288 µM]	....	....	0.122	mM/hr/cm		
147			L-Ile [81 µM]	....	....	0.065	mM/hr/cm		
148			L-Leu [145 µM]	....	....	0.113	mM/hr/cm		
149			L-Met [52 µM]	....	....	0.043	mM/hr/cm		
150			L-Phe [54 µM]	....	....	0.038	mM/hr/cm		
151			L-Pro [97 µM]	....	....	0.079	mM/hr/cm		
152			L-Ser [172 µM]	....	....	0.090	mM/hr/cm		
153			L-Thr [191 µM]	....	....	0.111	mM/hr/cm		
154			L-Tyr [48 µM]	....	....	0.033	mM/hr/cm		
155			L-Val [168 µM]	....	....	0.143	mM/hr/cm		
156	♀, 120-170 g	Small intestine[2]	L-Ala [1 mM]	....	....	0.170[6]	mM/hr/g dry wt	In vitro; Krebs-Ringer-HCO_3^--0.5% glucose, single amino acid added, 95% O_2:5% CO_2, 4 min	18
157			[10 mM]	....	....	0.680[6]	mM/hr/g dry wt		
158			L-Arg [1 mM]	....	....	0.117[6]	mM/hr/g dry wt		
159			[10 mM]	....	....	0.251[6]	mM/hr/g dry wt		
160			L-Asn [1 mM]	....	....	0.129[6]	mM/hr/g dry wt		
161			[10 mM]	....	....	0.860[6]	mM/hr/g dry wt		

[2] Part not specified. [6] Net accumulation of the amino acid by incubated tissue.

continued

Part II. Rate of Transport Across the Small Intestine: Vertebrates

	Animal	Intestinal Segment [Length, cm]	Substrate [Concentration]	Flux M → S	Flux S → M	Flux Net	Flux Units	Remarks	Reference
162			L-Asp [1 mM]	....	....	0.024[6]	mM/hr/g dry wt		
163			[10 mM]	....	....	0.216[6]	mM/hr/g dry wt		
164			L-Glu [1 mM]	....	....	0.027[6]	mM/hr/g dry wt		
165			[10 mM]	....	....	0.204[6]	mM/hr/g dry wt		
166			L-Gln [1 mM]	....	....	0.170[6]	mM/hr/g dry wt		
167			[10 mM]	....	....	0.765[6]	mM/hr/g dry wt		
168			L-Gly [1 mM]	....	....	0.041[6]	mM/hr/g dry wt		
169			[10 mM]	....	....	0.535[6]	mM/hr/g dry wt		
170			L-His [1 mM]	....	....	0.110[6]	mM/hr/g dry wt		
171			[10 mM]	....	....	0.621[6]	mM/hr/g dry wt		
172			L-Ile [1 mM]	....	....	0.191[6]	mM/hr/g dry wt		
173			[10 mM]	....	....	0.378[6]	mM/hr/g dry wt		
174			L-Leu [1 mM]	....	....	0.209[6]	mM/hr/g dry wt		
175			[10 mM]	....	....	0.322[6]	mM/hr/g dry wt		
176			L-Lys [1 mM]	....	....	0.102[6]	mM/hr/g dry wt		
177			[10 mM]	....	....	0.150[6]	mM/hr/g dry wt		
178			L-Met [1 mM]	....	....	0.206[6]	mM/hr/g dry wt		
179			[10 mM]	....	....	0.360[6]	mM/hr/g dry wt		
180			L-Orn [1 mM]	....	....	0.080[6]	mM/hr/g dry wt		
181			[10 mM]	....	....	0.348[6]	mM/hr/g dry wt		
182			L-Phe [1 mM]	....	....	0.164[6]	mM/hr/g dry wt		
183			[10 mM]	....	....	0.533[6]	mM/hr/g dry wt		
184			L-Pro [1 mM]	....	....	0.117[6]	mM/hr/g dry wt		
185			[10 mM]	....	....	0.654[6]	mM/hr/g dry wt		
186			L-Ser [1 mM]	....	....	0.122[6]	mM/hr/g dry wt		
187			[10 mM]	....	....	0.821[6]	mM/hr/g dry wt		
188			L-Val [1 mM]	....	....	0.204[6]	mM/hr/g dry wt		
189			[10 mM]	....	....	0.521[6]	mM/hr/g dry wt		

[6] Net accumulation of the amino acid by incubated tissue.

Contributors: Wasserman, Robert H., and Franklin, Margery H.

References

[1] Adibi, S. A., and S. J. Gray. 1967. Gastroenterology 52:837.

[2] Annegers, J. H. 1964. Am. J. Physiol. 206:1095.

[3] Bell, D. J., and J. K. Grant, ed. 1963. Biochem. Soc. Symp. (Cambridge, Engl.) 22.

[4] Capraro, V., A. Bianchi, and C. Lippe. 1963. Experientia 19:347.

[5] Capraro, V., E. Milla, and A. Bianchi. 1963. Nature 199:1099.

[6] Christensen, H. N. 1962. Biological transport. W. A. Benjamin, New York.

[7] Clarkson, T. W., A. Rothstein, and A. Cross. 1961. Am. J. Physiol. 200:781.

[8] Cocco, A. E., and T. R. Hendrix. 1965. Bull. Johns Hopkins Hosp. 117:296.

[9] Cramer, C. F., and J. Dueck. 1962. Am. J. Physiol. 202:161.

[10] Csaky, T. Z., and J. H. Humm. 1956. Arch. Biochem. Biophys. 62:411.

[11] Curran, P. F. 1960. J. Gen. Physiol. 43:1137.

[12] Curran, P. F., and A. K. Solomon. 1957. Ibid. 41:143.

[13] Detheridge, J. F., J. Matthews, and D. H. Smyth. 1966. J. Physiol. (London) 183:369.

[14] Dumont, P. A., P. F. Curran, and A. K. Solomon. 1960. J. Gen. Physiol. 43:1119.

[15] Esposito, G., A. Faelli, and V. Capraro. 1964. Experientia 20:122.

[16] Faust, R. G. 1964. J. Cellular Comp. Physiol. 63:55.

[17] Faust, R. G., and S. L. Wu. 1965. Ibid. 65:435.

[18] Finch, L. R., and F. J. R. Hird. 1960. Biochim. Biophys. Acta 43:278.

[19] Fishman, A. P., ed. 1962. Circulation 26(5):983.

[20] Fordtran, J. S., et al. 1961. Trans. Assoc. Am. Physicians 74:195.

[21] Gray, G. M., and F. J. Ingelfinger. 1966. J. Clin. Invest. 45:388.

[22] Gray, G. M., and N. A. Santiago. 1966. Gastroenterology 51:489.

[23] Grim, E. 1962. Am. J. Digest. Diseases 7:17.

continued

Part II. Rate of Transport Across the Small Intestine: Vertebrates

[24] Hagihira, H., T. H. Wilson, and E. C. C. Lin. 1962. Am. J. Physiol. 203:637.
[25] Hagihira, H., et al. 1961. Biochem. Biophys. Res. Commun. 4:478.
[26] Harris, E. J. 1960. Transport and accumulation in biological systems. Academic Press, New York.
[27] Hoffman, J. F., ed. 1964. The cellular functions of membrane transport. Prentice-Hall, Englewood Cliffs, N.J.
[28] Jacobs, F. A. 1965. Federation Proc. 24:946.
[29] Jacobs, F. A. Unpublished. Univ. North Dakota, Dept. Biochemistry, Grand Fords, 1967.
[30] Jacobs, F. A., and A. H. Lang. 1965. Proc. Soc. Exptl. Biol. Med. 118:772.
[31] Kavanau, J. L. 1966. Structure and function in biological membranes. Holden-Day, San Francisco. v. 1 & 2.
[32] Kleinzeller, A., and A. Kotyk, ed. 1961. Membrane Transport Metab. Proc. Symp., Prague, 1960.
[33] Kruhøffer, P., J. Hess Thaysen, and N. A. Thorn. 1960. Handbuch Exptl. Pharmakol. Ergaenz. 13:196.
[34] Lin, E. C. C., H. Hagihira, and T. H. Wilson. 1962. Am. J. Physiol. 202:919.
[35] Locke, M., ed. 1964. Cellular membranes and development. Academic Press, New York.
[36] Lowenstein, W. R., ed. 1966. Ann. N.Y. Acad. Sci. 137:403.
[37] McHardy, G. J. R., and D. S. Parsons. 1956. Quart. J. Exptl. Physiol. 41:398.
[38] McHardy, G. J. R., and D. S. Parsons. 1957. Ibid. 42:33.
[39] Noble, H. M., and A. J. Matty. 1967. J. Endocrinol. 37:111.
[40] Ochsenfahrt, H., et al. 1966. Arch. Exptl. Pathol. Pharmakol. 254:461.
[41] Ogilvie, J. T., J. R. McIntosh, and P. F. Curran. 1963. Biochim. Biophys. Acta 66:441.
[42] Parkins, F. M., et al. 1966. Ibid. 126:513.
[43] Parsons, D. S. 1956. Quart. J. Exptl. Physiol. 41: 410.
[44] Roche, M., ed. 1960. J. Gen. Physiol. 43(5-2).
[45] Schultz, S. G., and R. Zalusky. 1964. Ibid. 47:567.
[46] Shields, R., A. T. Mulholland, and R. G. Elmslie. 1966. Gut 7:686.
[47] Snell, F. M., and W. K. Noell, ed. 1964. Transcellular membrane potentials and ionic fluxes. Gordon and Breach, New York.
[48] Stookey, G. K., E. L. Dellinger, and J. C. Muhler. 1964. Proc. Soc. Exptl. Biol. Med. 115:298.
[49] Ussing, H. H. 1960. Handbuch Exptl. Pharmakol. Ergaenz. 13:1.
[50] Van Deenan, L. L. M. 1965. Progr. Chem. Fats Lipids 8(1).
[51] Wasserman, R. H., ed. 1963. The transfer of calcium and strontium across biological membranes. Academic Press, New York.
[52] Wasserman, R. H., F. A. Kallfelz, and C. L. Comar. 1961. Science 133:883.
[53] Whalen, G. E., et al. 1966. Gastroenterology 51:975.
[54] Whittam, R. 1964. Transport and diffusion in red blood cells. Williams and Wilkins, Baltimore.
[55] Wilson, T. H. 1962. Intestinal absorption. W. B. Saunders, Philadelphia.
[56] Wilson, T. H., and T. N. Vincent. 1955. J. Biol. Chem. 216:851.
[57] Wiseman, G. 1964. Absorption from the intestine. Academic Press, New York.

Part III. Sources of Information for Transport Across Other Membranes

	Nutrient	Organ or Tissue	Reference
1	Water	Liver	30,78
2		Gallbladder	31,46,92
3		Kidney	6,24,78,87,110,128
4		Urinary bladder	13,46
5		Skin	61
6		Muscle	135
7		Uterus	111
8		Salivary gland	104
9		Nerve	114
10		Erythrocytes	108
11	Calcium	Liver	16,68,91,100,119
12		Gallbladder	94
13		Kidney	2,63,101,120
14		Muscle	50,126
15		Heart	11,90
16		Bone	5,123,133
17		Uterus	118
18		Placenta	49
19		Erythrocytes	103
20	Chloride	Liver	41
21		Kidney	41,83,96
22		Urinary bladder	13
23		Salivary gland	104
24		Mammary gland	81
25		Cornea	45
26		Brain or blood-brain barrier	59
27		Erythrocytes	74
28	Copper	Liver & kidney	40
29	Fluoride	Placenta	42,82,136
30	Iodide	Salivary gland	1
31		Thyroid	35,124
32		Placenta	80
33		Brain or blood-brain barrier	8

continued

50. MEMBRANE TRANSPORT OF NUTRIENTS

Part III. Sources of Information for Transport Across Other Membranes

	Nutrient	Organ or Tissue	Reference
34	Iron	Intestine	4,25,29
35		Placenta	60
36	Phos-	Kidney	85
37	phate	Muscle	18
38		Heart	11
39		Placenta	39
40	Potas-	Liver	14,17,41
41	sium	Gallbladder	94
42		Kidney	41,83,112,116
43		Skin	27
44		Muscle	51,97,109,115,135
45		Heart	62,115
46		Salivary gland	56,104
47		Mammary gland	81
48		Nerve	57,65
49		Brain or blood-brain barrier	34
50		Erythrocytes	28,52,58,76,95
51		Ascites cells	43,54
52	Sodium	Liver	17,41
53		Gallbladder	46,92,94
54		Kidney	6,24,41,44,67,75, 83,110,116
55		Urinary bladder	13,26,38,71,107
56		Skin	9,26,70,117
57		Muscle	33,115,135
58		Heart	93,115
59		Salivary gland	56,104
60		Salt gland	20
61		Mammary gland	81
62		Nerve	3,57,65,113
63		Cornea	45
64		Brain or blood-brain barrier	36,134
65		Erythrocytes	74,76,95,129
66		Ascites cells	54
67	Carbo-	Liver	14,48
68	hy-	Kidney	19
69	drates	Muscle	15,23,69,88
70		Heart	66,88,89
71		Mammary gland	53,81
72		Brain or blood-brain barrier	37
73		Erythrocytes	12,77,79,86,89
74	Amino	Liver	72
75	acids	Kidney	84,98,106,122,125
76		Urinary bladder	55
77		Muscle	32,47,69,73,131
78		Placenta	7
79		Brain or blood-brain barrier	102,132
80		Erythrocytes	121,127,130
81		Leucocytes	99
82		Lymphocytes	10
83		Ehrlich tumor cells	21,22,64,105

Contributors: Wasserman, Robert H., and Franklin, Margery H.

References

[1] Alexander, W. D., et al. 1967. Proc. Nutr. Soc. (Engl. Scot.) 26:62.

[2] Anast, C., et al. 1967. J. Clin. Invest. 46:57.

[3] Asano, T., and W. P. Hurlbut. 1958. J. Gen. Physiol. 41:1187.

[4] Aschkenasy, A. 1966. Rev. Franc. Etudes Clin. Biol. 11:1010.

[5] Au, W. Y. W., and F. C. Bartter. 1966. Endocrinology 78:1100.

[6] Aukland, K., and J. Kjekshus. 1966. Am. J. Physiol. 210:971.

[7] Barnabei, O., and A. Ninni. 1963. Biochim. Biophys. Acta 70:586.

[8] Becker, B. 1961. Am. J. Physiol. 201:1149.

[9] Biber, T. U. L., R. A. Chez, and P. F. Curran. 1966. J. Gen. Physiol. 49:1161.

[10] Blecher, M. 1963. Am. J. Physiol. 205:446.

[11] Brierley, G., E. Murer, and E. Bachmann. 1964. Arch. Biochem. Biophys. 105:89.

[12] Britton, H. G. 1964. J. Physiol. (London) 170:1.

[13] Brodsky, W. A., and T. P. Schilb. 1966. Am. J. Physiol. 210:987.

[14] Burton, S. D., and T. Ishida. 1965. Ibid. 209:1145.

[15] Carlin, H., and O. Hechter. 1961. J. Gen. Physiol. 45:309.

[16] Carvalho, A. P., H. Sanui, and N. Pace. 1965. J. Cellular Comp. Physiol. 66:57.

[17] Cascarano, J., and I. Seidman. 1965. Biochim. Biophys. Acta 100:301.

[18] Causey, G., and E. J. Harris. 1951. Biochem. J. 49: 176.

[19] Chan, S. S., and W. D. Lotspeich. 1962. Am. J. Physiol. 203:975.

[20] Chance, B., et al. 1964. Ibid. 206:461.

[21] Christensen, H. N., and M. Liang. 1966. J. Biol. Chem. 241:5542.

[22] Christensen, H. N., et al. 1955-56. Ann. N.Y. Acad. Sci. 63:983.

[23] Clausen, T. 1965. Biochim. Biophys. Acta 109:164.

[24] Cole, D. F. 1957. Quart. J. Exptl. Physiol. 42:15.

[25] Cowan, J. W., et al. 1966. J. Nutr. 90:423.

[26] Crabbe, J., and P. De Weer. 1964. Nature 202:298.

[27] Curran, P. F., and M. Cereijido. 1965. J. Gen. Physiol. 48:1011.

[28] D'Amico, G., et al. 1966. Experientia 22:32.

[29] Davis, P. S., and D. J. Deller. 1967. Gastroenterology 52:691.

[30] DeVenuto, F., and U. Westphal. 1965. Arch. Biochem. Biophys. 112:187.

[31] Diamond, J. M., and J. McD. Tormey. 1966. Nature 210:817.

[32] Diehl, J. F. 1966. Biochim. Biophys. Acta 115:239.

[33] Dockry, M., R. P. Kernan, and A. Tangney. 1966. J. Physiol. (London) 186:187.

continued

Part III. Sources of Information for Transport Across Other Membranes

[34] Dower, F. R. 1961. Ibid. 158:366.
[35] Fawcett, D. M. 1966. Can. J. Biochem. 44:1669.
[36] Fishman, R. A. 1959. J. Clin. Invest. 38:1698.
[37] Fishman, R. A. 1964. Am. J. Physiol. 206:836.
[38] Frazier, H. S., and A. Leaf. 1963. J. Gen. Physiol. 46:491.
[39] Fuchs, A., and F. Fuchs. 1961. Acta Physiol. Scand. 52:65.
[40] Gaballah, S. S., et al. 1965. Proc. Soc. Exptl. Biol. Med. 120:733.
[41] Gamble, J. L. 1963. Biochim. Biophys. Acta 66:158.
[42] Gedalia, I., et al. 1961. Proc. Soc. Exptl. Biol. Med. 106:147.
[43] Glick, J. L., and S. Githens. 1965. Nature 208:88.
[44] Gottschalk, C. W., et al. 1963. Am. J. Physiol. 204: 532.
[45] Green, K. 1965. Ibid. 209:1311.
[46] Grim, E. 1962. Am. J. Digest. Diseases 7:17.
[47] Guroff, G., and S. Udenfriend. 1960. J. Biol. Chem. 235:3518.
[48] Haft, D. E., and L. L. Miller. 1958. Am. J. Physiol. 192:33.
[49] Hansard, S. L., et al. 1966. J. Nutr. 89:335.
[50] Harris, E. J. 1957. Biochim. Biophys. Acta 23:80.
[51] Harris, E. J. 1957. J. Gen. Physiol. 41:169.
[52] Harris, E. J., and T. A. J. Prankerd. 1957. Ibid. 41: 197.
[53] Hartmann, P. E. 1966. Australian J. Biol. Sci. 19: 495.
[54] Hempling, H. G. 1966. Biochim. Biophys. Acta 112: 503.
[55] Henderson, C. B., and W. A. Webber. 1964. Can. J. Physiol. Pharmacol. 42:275.
[56] Henriques, B. L. 1961. Am. J. Physiol. 201:935.
[57] Hodgkin, A. L. 1951. Biol. Rev. Cambridge Phil. Soc. 26:339.
[58] Hoffman, J. F. 1966. Am. J. Med. 41:666.
[59] Hogben, C. A. M., P. Wistrand, and T. H. Maren. 1960. Am. J. Physiol. 199:124.
[60] Hoskins, F. H., and S. L. Hansard. 1964. J. Nutr. 83:10.
[61] Huf, E. G., N. S. Doss, and J. P. Wills. 1957. J. Gen. Physiol. 41:397.
[62] Hutter, O. F. 1957. Brit. Med. Bull. 13:176.
[63] Jackson, W. P. U., and C. P. Dancaster. 1962. J. Clin. Endocrinol. Metab. 22:195.
[64] Jacquez, J. A. 1963. Biochim. Biophys. Acta 71:15.
[65] Keynes, R. D., and P. R. Lewis. 1951. J. Physiol. (London) 114:151.
[66] Kien, G. A., A. W. Gomoll, and T. R. Sherrod. 1960. Proc. Soc. Exptl. Biol. Med. 103:682.
[67] Kiil, F., K. Aukland, and H. E. Refsum. 1961. Am. J. Physiol. 201:511.
[68] Kimberg, D. V., and S. A. Goldstein. 1966. J. Biol. Chem. 241:95.
[69] Kipnis, D. M., and J. E. Parrish. 1965. Federation Proc. 24:1051.
[70] Kirschner, L. B. 1955. J. Cellular Comp. Physiol. 45:61.
[71] Klahr, S., and N. S. Bricker. 1964. Am. J. Physiol. 206:1333.
[72] Korner, A., and H. Tarver. 1957. J. Gen. Physiol. 41:219.
[73] Kostyo, J. L., and J. E. Schmidt. 1963. Am. J. Physiol. 204:1031.
[74] LaCelle, P. L., and A. Rothstein. 1966. J. Gen. Physiol. 50:171.
[75] Lassen, N. A., O. Munck, and J. H. Thaysen. 1961. Acta Physiol. Scand. 51:371.
[76] Lee, P., A. Woo, and D. C. Tosteson. 1966. J. Gen. Physiol. 50:379.
[77] LeFevre, P. G., et al. 1964. Science 143:955.
[78] Lehninger, A. L. 1962. Physiol. Rev. 42:467.
[79] Levine, M., D. L. Oxender, and W. D. Stein. 1965. Biochim. Biophys. Acta 109:151.
[80] London, W. T., W. L. Money, and R. W. Rawson. 1964. J. Endocrinol. 28:247.
[81] MacKenzie, D. D. S., and A. K. Lascelles. 1965. Australian J. Biol. Sci. 18:1035.
[82] Maplesden, D. C., et al. 1960. J. Nutr. 71:70.
[83] Marsh, D. J., and S. Solomon. 1965. Am. J. Physiol. 208:1119.
[84] Maude, D. L., et al. 1965. Arch. Ges. Physiol. 285: 313.
[85] Michael, A. F., and K. N. Drummond. 1967. Can. J. Physiol. Pharmacol. 45:103.
[86] Miller, D. M. 1966. Biochim. Biophys. Acta 120: 156.
[87] Morel, F., M. Mylle, and C. W. Gottschalk. 1965. Am. J. Physiol. 209:179.
[88] Morgan, H. E., D. M. Regen, and C. R. Park. 1964. J. Biol. Chem. 239:369.
[89] Morgan, H. E., et al. 1965. Federation Proc. 24: 1040.
[90] Nayler, W. G. 1966. J. Pharmacol. Exptl. Therap. 153:479.
[91] Ogata, E., and H. Rasmussen. 1966. Biochemistry 5:57.
[92] Onstad, G. R., L. J. Schoenfield, and J. A. Higgins. 1967. J. Clin. Invest. 46:606.
[93] Page, E., and S. R. Storm. 1965. J. Gen. Physiol. 48:957.
[94] Peters, C. J., and M. Walser. 1966. Am. J. Physiol. 210:677.
[95] Post, R. L., et al. 1960. J. Biol. Chem. 235:1796.
[96] Rehberg, P. 1926. Biochem. J. 20:461.
[97] Renkin, E. M. 1959. Am. J. Physiol. 197:1025.
[98] Rosenberg, L. E., I. Albrecht, and S. Segal. 1967. Science 155:1426.
[99] Rosenberg, L. E., and S. Downing. 1965. J. Clin. Invest. 44:1382.
[100] Rossi, C., A. Azzi, and G. F. Azzone. 1966. Biochem. J. 100:4c.
[101] Rossi, C. S., and A. L. Lehninger. 1963. Biochem. Biophys. Res. Commun. 11:441.
[102] Schanberg, S. M. 1963. J. Pharmacol. Exptl. Therap. 139:191.
[103] Schatzmann, H. J. 1966. Experientia 22:364.

continued

Part III. Sources of Information for Transport Across Other Membranes

[104] Schneyer, L. H., and C. A. Schneyer. 1963. Am. J. Physiol. 205:1058.
[105] Scholefield, P. G. 1961. Can. J. Biochem. Physiol. 39:1717.
[106] Schwartzman, L., A. Blair, and S. Segal. 1966. Biochem. Biophys. Res. Commun. 23:220.
[107] Sharp, G. W. G., and A. Leaf. 1965. J. Biol. Chem. 240:4816.
[108] Sidel, V. W., and A. K. Solomon. 1957. J. Gen. Physiol. 41:243.
[109] Sjodin, R. A. 1965. Ibid. 48:777.
[110] Solomon, A. K. 1959. Colloq. Biol. Saclay 1:106.
[111] Spaziani, E., and C. M. Szego. 1959. Am. J. Physiol. 197:355.
[112] Sullivan, L. P., W. S. Wilde, and R. L. Malvin. 1960. Ibid. 198:244.
[113] Tasaki, I. 1963. J. Gen. Physiol. 46:755.
[114] Tasaki, I., T. Teorell, and C. S. Spyropoulos. 1961. Am. J. Physiol. 200:11.
[115] Ulrich, F. 1959. Ibid. 197:997.
[116] Ulrich, F. 1961. Biochem. J. 80:532.
[117] Ussing, H. H. 1959. Colloq. Biol. Saclay 1:139.
[118] Van Breemen, C., E. E. Daniel, and D. Van Breemen. 1966. J. Gen. Physiol. 49:1265.
[119] Vasington, F. D. 1966. Biochim. Biophys. Acta 113:414.
[120] Vasington, F. D., and J. V. Murphy. 1962. J. Biol. Chem. 237:2670.
[121] Vidaver, G. A. 1964. Biochemistry 3:795.
[122] Vishwakarma, P. 1963. Can. J. Biochem. Physiol. 41:1099.
[123] Wasserman, R. H. 1962. J. Nutr. 77:69.
[124] Wasserman, R. H., et al. 1956. Am. J. Vet. Res. 17:149.
[125] Webber, W. A. 1963. Can. J. Biochem. Physiol. 41:131.
[126] Weber, A., R. Herz, and I. Reiss. 1966. Biochem. Z. 345:329.
[127] Wheeler, K. P., and H. N. Christensen. 1967. J. Biol. Chem. 242:1450.
[128] Whittembury, G., et al. 1959. Am. J. Physiol. 197:1121.
[129] Wieth, J. O., and J. Funder. 1965. Scand. J. Clin. Lab. Invest. 17:399.
[130] Winter, C. G., and H. M. Christensen. 1964. J. Biol. Chem. 239:872.
[131] Wool, I. G. 1965. Federation Proc. 24:1060.
[132] Yoshida, H., et al. 1963. Japan. J. Pharmacol. 13:1.
[133] Young, V. R., J. R. Luick, and G. P. Lofgreen. 1966. Brit. J. Nutr. 20:727.
[134] Zadunaisky, J. A., and P. F. Curran. 1963. Am. J. Physiol. 205:949.
[135] Zierler, K. L., E. Rogus, and C. F. Hazlewood. 1966. J. Gen. Physiol. 49:433.
[136] Zipkin, I., and W. L. Babeaux. 1965. J. Oral Therap. Pharmacol. 1:652.

V. NUTRIENT FUNCTION, DEFICIENCY, AND EXCESS

51. FUNCTION, DEFICIENCY, AND EXCESS OF CHEMICAL ELEMENTS: ANIMALS

Carbon, hydrogen, nitrogen, oxygen, phosphorus, and sulfur are required in the synthesis of structural proteins, carbohydrates, fats, and other organic compounds, and in the formation of the end products of metabolism.

	Element	Occurrence	Ingestion & Absorption	Body Distribution	Function, Deficiency, or Excess	Excretion
1	Arsenic	In food of animal & plant origin; in foods treated with arsenical insecticides [6,25]	Readily absorbed from intestine [6,25]	Throughout human body tissues, but more concentrated in nails & hair. Very high concentrations in crustaceans (up to 100 ppm). 0.5 ppm in animal & plant tissues. [6,25]	Promotes growth in swine & poultry; coccidiostat; may be beneficial in bone formation; controls selenium toxicity & cariogenicity; possible thyroid anatagonist; some antitumor effect; catalyst of phosphorylation [6,25]	Organically bound arsenic in urine; inorganic arsenic in urine & feces; excreted through hair & nails; noncumulative in tissues [6,25]
2	Boron	Significant quantities in plant foods, particularly legumes, fruits, & vegetables [25]	Normal human intake, 10-20 mg/day; readily absorbed from GI tract [25]	Bone has highest concentration; after boron intoxication, brain has largest amount. Essential element for certain vascular plants & algae. [25]	No known function in animals. Increased amounts toxic to plants & animals. [17, 25]	Mainly in urine. Appears in milk. [17,25]
3	Bromine	Traces in many foods [15,22]	Readily absorbed from GI tract [15,22]	Same distribution as chloride in mammals; some concentration in thyroid; saliva has 1.5 times the concentration in blood. In Tyrian purple (brominated indigo) derived from viscera of marine gastropod *(Purpura aperta)*; in dibromotyrosine in protein gorgonin from coral *(Primnoa lepadifera)*. [15,22,24]	Not known[1/] [2]	Mainly in urine [2,15,22,24]
4	Cadmium	Trace quantities in many plant & animal tissues [25]	Poorly absorbed from GI tract [23]	Maximal tissue uptake in liver & kidney. Component of certain enzymes. Metallothionein (protein of horse kidney) contains up to 5.9%. [23]	No known biological function. Toxic to man in certain industrial exposures. [23]	In feces, mostly unabsorbed; insignificant urinary excretion [23]
5	Calcium	In many foods, particularly milk & dairy products, grains & starches [3]	Intake of 200-1500 mg/day for most humans (about 75-80% from milk & dairy products) is absorbed largely from upper part of small intestine. Absorption is aided by vitamin D. [3,21]	Small amount in blood & fluids (biologically active) and large amount (99%) in bone & teeth (bone-blood equilibrium). Exists as free ion, bound to protein and coupled with citrate, sulfate, or phosphate. One of the more abundant elements (approx 1.1 kg/70 kg body wt). Present as $CaCO_3$ in exoskeleton of invertebrates and in shells of certain eggs. Component of supporting structure (skeleton) of body as phosphate & carbonate. Vital electrolyte of cell & extracellular fluid. [3,21]	Plays basic role in determining excitability of nerve & muscle. Provides protective shell of certain eggs. [3, 21]	In urine & feces in varying proportions; amount related to intake [3,21]

[1/] Used medically as sedative.

continued

51. FUNCTION, DEFICIENCY, AND EXCESS OF CHEMICAL ELEMENTS: ANIMALS

	Element	Occurrence	Ingestion & Absorption	Body Distribution	Function, Deficiency, or Excess	Excretion
6	Chlorine	Widely distributed in food as chloride. More in foods of animal origin. Added to food of man & domestic animals as NaCl. [2,7]	Absorbed from GI tract [2,7]	Principal anion of extracellular fluid, distribution of which is similar to sodium in extracellular fluid, but milliequivalent concentrations are generally lower. Minimal intracellular quantities in most cells. Chief anion of gastric juice; also present in all other gastrointestinal secretions.2/ [2,7]	Involved in maintenance of fluid and electrolyte homeostasis [2]	Chiefly in urine. Variable amount in sweat; excessive loss in sweat in cystic fibrosis. [2,7]
7	Chromium	Minute quantities in most foods [13]	Most forms, even soluble salts, poorly absorbed from GI tract [13]	Probably essential element. Nucleoprotein isolated from beef liver contains 1080 ppm. Present in other nucleoproteins.3/ [13]	May activate or inhibit certain enzyme systems. May be functional in certain impairments of carbohydrate metabolism in humans. Deficiency results in alteration of glucose tolerance in experimental animals. [13]	Excreted in urine. Fecal chromium represents unabsorbed component. [13]
8	Cobalt	Trace constituent of most foods of plant & animal origin [2,25]	Absorbed from GI tract [2,25]	Trace distribution in many tissues, particularly glands & visceral organs, e.g., liver. Component of vitamin B_{12} (cobalamin)4/ required by animal species from lowest to highest forms. [2,25]	Can activate or enhance activity of certain enzymes. Deficiency disease occurs in ruminants. [2,25]	In urine & feces [2,25]
9	Copper	Minute amounts in food as copper protein complexes [11,25]	Poorly absorbed from intestine [11,25]	Higher concentration in invertebrates than in vertebrates. High concentration in hepatopancreas & gonads of Mollusca; also in gut of insects. Present in turacin (red pigment in feathers of turaco bird). Component of hemocyanin (respiratory pigment in numerous marine animals), & hemocuprein (a protein found in the liver of certain mammals). Liver is principal site of storage. [2,11,25]	Functional in erythropoiesis, elastin formation, myelinization of certain nerves, pigmentation, & certain enzyme synthesis (tyrosinase, laccase, & ascorbic acid oxidase). Nutritional deficiency disease in cattle & sheep due to inadequate intake. Molybdenum and zinc are antagonistic to proper copper metabolism. [2,8,11,25]	Most of orally administered copper appears in feces due to poor absorption. Parenterally administered copper slowly excreted in feces, with small amount in urine. [11]
10	Fluorine	Traces in various foods. Significant quantities in water in certain areas; added to public drinking water in some communities. [3]	Absorbed from GI tract [3]	Present in bones & teeth. High concentration (0.6-1.6%) in bones of marine animals. [3]	Diminishes solubility of bones & teeth in weakly acid solutions. Decreases caries incidence. [3]	Primarily in urine [3]

2/ Variation in chlorine concentration tolerated better than most other electrolytes. 3/ Used as tag or marker for coupling with red cells in blood volume measurements. 4/ A cobalt-containing vitamin; originates only in microorganisms.

continued

	Element	Occurrence	Ingestion & Absorption	Body Distribution	Function, Deficiency, or Excess	Excretion
11	Iodine	Trace amounts in foods, mostly as inorganic iodide; amount in food related to soil content [2,25]	Absorption takes place throughout GI tract; in lower forms, through cell membranes [2,25]	Estimated at 10-25 mg in human adult; 70-80% concentrated in the thyroid as in other vertebrates. Only approx 0.1% is free iodine, the rest being grouped as PBI (protein-bound iodine), including thyroxine, diiodotyrosine, & thyroglobulin. More iodide present in shellfish & other marine fish. [2,25]	Minute intake necessary for growth (essential part of thyroid hormones) & prevention of goiter [2,25]	Mainly in urine. In milk of lactating mammals. [2,25]
12	Iron	In many foods, particularly meats, eggs, shellfish, & leguminous plants [25]	Mainly as ferrous compounds from GI tract. More absorption when iron-deficiency exists. Absorbed mostly from small intestine and to lesser extent from stomach & lower GI tract. [1,14]	Human body contains 3-5 g, approx 50% as hemoglobin, 10% as muscle myoglobin, with remainder stored as ferritin & hemosiderin mainly in liver & spleen. In blood hemoglobin, muscle myoglobin, cytochromes, & enzyme systems. [1,14]	Respiratory pigments in higher & lower forms. Cytochromes present in nearly all cells. Mobilized through small pool of ferric iron circulating in plasma bound to the globulin, transferrin. [1,14]	Only traces in excreta, normally <1 mg/day; increased amounts excreted during hemorrhage. Fecal iron is primarily unabsorbed dietary iron. [1,14]
13	Magnesium	Widely distributed in foods. High concentration in green vegetables as part of porphyrin group of chlorophyll. [3,23]	Avg human intake approx 300 mg/day. Salts readily absorbed from small intestine. [3,23]	Essential element for all animal species. Minute amounts in plasma & extracellular fluid, larger amounts in intracellular fluid. Approx 60% in bones. [3,23]	Low concentrations increase cell irritability. Required for activity of several animal enzymes. [3,23]	Approx one-third in urine. Unabsorbed form excreted in feces. [3,23]
14	Manganese	Traces present in most plant & animal food [10,23]	Poorly absorbed from intestine [10,23]	Particularly in liver, bone, & lactating mammary gland. Present in blood plasma as transmanginin (a specific protein complex). In blood pigment of shellfish (*Pinna nobilis*[5/]). Associated with nucleic acid. [2,10,23,25]	Deficiency disease produced in many species. Required for mucopolysaccharide synthesis in chick. [2,10,23,25]	Mainly in feces; traces in urine [2]
15	Molybdenum	Trace quantities widely distributed in foods [2,25]	Readily absorbed from GI tract [2,25]	Essential element in certain mammals. Concentrations greater in liver, kidney, & adrenal gland. Present in certain enzymes, including xanthine oxidase & nitrate reductase. [2,25]	High intake causes copper deficiency [2,25]	Mainly in urine. Passes mammary & placental barrier. [2,25]
16	Phosphorus	Occurs as inorganic phosphate in most foods, also as organic complexes [12]	Rapidly absorbed from intestine. Absorbed through cell membranes in lower forms. [21]	Large quantities as phosphate complex of calcium in bones & teeth of vertebrates. Component of phospholipids (intermediates in lipid metabolism) in nerve & other tissues, phosphocreatinine or phosphoarginine in muscle. Present as inorganic PO_4 in body fluids; as nucleoprotein in all cells, and as component of DNA & RNA, basic to genetic code & cell messenger systems; as adenosine triphosphate (ATP) in many cells of higher & lower species. Intracellular phosphate present mainly as organic complexes. [12,18]	High-energy phosphorus compounds basic in energy conversions. Combines with intermediates in carbohydrate metabolism. Buffer in urine. Constituent of phospholipids which are intermediates in lipid metabolism. [12,18]	Excreted in urine & feces [12]

[5/] Synonym: *P. squamosa.*

continued

	Element	Occurrence	Ingestion & Absorption	Body Distribution	Function, Deficiency, or Excess	Excretion
17	Potassium	In variety of foods [5]	Ingested as inorganic salt; absorbed from intestine. Absorbed through gills & cell membranes in many lower marine forms. [5]	Principal & essential cation of intracellular fluid; small amount in extracellular fluid [2,5,7]	Controls water shifts between cells and extracellular fluid; necessary for growth (amino acid metabolism) [2]	Almost entirely in urine. Minute amounts in feces & sweat. [2,5,7]
18	Selenium	In most animal tissues. Certain plants have very high concentrations which arise from soil. [2,25]	Poorly absorbed from intestine [2,25]	Essential nutrient; highest concentrations in liver, kidneys, heart, & spleen [2,25]	Functional relation to vitamin E. Deficiency in rat results in liver degeneration; in chick, in exudate diathesis; in lambs, in nutritional muscular dystrophy. Toxic in increased amounts to most species. [2,25]	Excreted largely in urine; small amount in feces [2,25]
19	Silicon	High content in soils, plants, & atmospheric dust [25]	Absorbed from intestine, and through cell membranes [9]	In skeletal structures & in supporting structures of certain Protozoa, Porifera, & higher forms. Also concentrated in fibrin, muscle, & aorta. [9]	May contribute to elasticity of tissue, including skin. May relate to aging. Serious effects from inhaled particles deposited in lungs. [9,20]	Primarily in urine of vertebrates. Also in hair & nails. [9]
20	Sodium	Widely distributed in foods as inorganic salt. More in foods of animal origin than in foods of plant origin. [2,7,16]	Taken as NaCl by many higher vertebrates, including man. Absorbed from intestine in higher forms, and through gills & cell membranes in lower forms. [2,7,16]	Chief cation of extracellular fluid. Major part of body sodium is extracellular, much in bone; some intracellular. Tissues vary in concentration of intracellular sodium, muscle containing only small amounts. Chief cation of intestinal secretions. [2,7,16]	Essential for proper external environment of cells. Principal cation of seawater, external environment of marine animals. Salts are important buffers of plasma, extracellular fluid, & urine. [2,7,16]	Primarily in urine. Variable quantities in sweat; small amounts in feces. [2]
21	Sulfur	In many foods [2,22]	Ingested as inorganic & organic sulfates, & sulfhydryl sulfur of cystine & methionine. Organic sulfur predominates. [2,22]	Small amount of sulfate in extracellular fluid. Essential component of many proteins. Relatively large amount of sulfur in proteins, and small amount in certain lipids, sulfated polysaccharides, & glutathione. Sulfuric acid secreted as digestive fluid in *Ascidia.* [2,22]	Sulfate used in detoxification; used in taurocholic acid to promote fat emulsification, in heparin to prevent blood clotting, & in chondroitin sulfate to promote wound healing [2,22]	Excreted in urine, mostly as inorganic sulfate with small amount of organic sulfate [22]
22	Vanadium	In small quantities in most terrestrial and marine plants [25]	Extracted from marine muds by *Ascidia.* Not readily absorbed from intestine of mammals. [15]	Present in high concentrations in various ascidians & in holothurians. In tunicates, high proportion is in blood as hemovanadium (respiratory protein). In apatite of teeth, isomorphous with phosphorus. In most biological lipids. Essential element for a species of green algae. [4,15]	May stimulate certain crops. May suppress dental caries. Inhibits cholesterol biosynthesis. [4,15]	Mostly in feces of man & other animals [15]

continued

51. FUNCTION, DEFICIENCY, AND EXCESS OF CHEMICAL ELEMENTS: ANIMALS

	Element	Occurrence	Ingestion & Absorption	Body Distribution	Function, Deficiency, or Excess	Excretion
23	Zinc	In all plant & animal tissue [2,19, 25]	Typical human diet, 10-15 mg/day. Poorly absorbed from GI tract. [2, 19,25]	Human body contains approx 2 g. Eye, male sex glands & secretions, hair, & bones have higher levels than other tissues. [2,19,25]	Cofactor of many enzyme systems, including carbonic anhydrase. Involved with synthesis of nucleic acid. Required for growth of rat. Antagonistic to proper copper metabolism. Deficiency symptoms in man produced by chelating agents.[6/] [2,8,11,19,25]	Most of dietary zinc in feces. Very small urinary excretion. Some excreted in hair. [2,19, 25]

[6/] Spontaneous human deficiency widespread in Egypt.

Contributors: Free, Alfred H., and Free, Helen M.

References

[1] Bothwell, T. H., and C. A. Finch. 1962. Iron metabolism. Little, Brown; Boston.
[2] Comar, C. L., and F. Bronner, ed. 1962. Mineral metabolism. Academic Press, New York, v. 2, pt. B.
[3] Comar, C. L., and F. Bronner, ed. 1964. Ibid. v. 2, pt. A.
[4] Curran, G. L. 1954. J. Biol. Chem. 210:765.
[5] Fenn, W. O. 1940. Physiol. Rev. 20:377.
[6] Frost, D. V. 1967. Federation Proc. 26:194.
[7] Gamble, J. L. 1950. Chemical anatomy, physiology, and pathology of extracellular fluid. Harvard Univ. Press, Cambridge.
[8] Hill, C. H., B. Starcher, and C. Kim. 1967. Federation Proc. 26:129.
[9] King, E. J., and T. H. Belt. 1938. Physiol. Rev. 18:329.
[10] Leach, R. M. 1967. Federation Proc. 26:118.
[11] McElroy, W. D., and B. Glass. 1950. Symposium on Copper metabolism. Johns Hopkins Press, Baltimore.
[12] McElroy, W. D., and B. Glass. 1951-52. Phosphorus metabolism. Johns Hopkins Press, Baltimore. v. 1 & 2.
[13] Mertz, W. 1967. Federation Proc. 26:186.
[14] Moore, C. V. 1958. In R. O. Wallerstein and S. R. Mettier, ed. Iron in clinical medicine. Univ. California Press, Berkeley. pp. 5-8.
[15] Monier-Williams, G. W. 1949. Trace elements in foods. J. Wiley, New York.
[16] Overman, R. R. 1951. Physiol. Rev. 31:285.
[17] Pfeiffer, C. C., L. F. Hallman, and I. Gersh. 1945. J. Am. Med. Assoc. 128:266.
[18] Potter, V. R. 1960. Nucleic acid outlines. Burgess, Minneapolis. v. 1, pp. 53-91.
[19] Prasad, A. S. 1967. Federation Proc. 26:172.
[20] Robinson, T. N., and W. W. Robinson. 1965. Military Med. 130:1082.
[21] Schmidt, C. L. A., and D. M. Greenberg. 1935. Physiol. Rev. 15:297.
[22] Shohl, A. T. 1939. Mineral metabolism. Reinhold, New York.
[23] Stefanini, M., ed. 1966. Progress in clinical pathology. Grune and Stratton, New York.
[24] Ucko, H. 1936. Biochem. J. 30:992.
[25] Underwood, E. J. 1962. Trace elements in human and animal nutrition. Ed. 2. Academic Press, New York.

52. FUNCTION, DEFICIENCY, AND EXCESS OF ESSENTIAL VITAMINS: VERTEBRATES

	Substance	Required in Diet by	Functions	Signs of Deficiency	Signs of Excess
			Water-soluble Vitamins		
1	Thiamine	Most or all vertebrates investigated[1/]	Essential for normal growth, appetite, digestion, gastrointestinal tonus, nerve activity, carbohydrate metabolism. As cocarboxylase, participates in α-keto acid decarboxylation oxidations, dismutations, & condensations leading to CO_2 formation; as transketolase, participates in metabolism of glucose through the shunt system which generates reduced nicotinamide adenine dinucleotide phosphate (NADPH) & ribose.	Retarded growth, anorexia (man, other animals). Neuron degeneration (man, other animals), but no peripheral nerve degeneration. Convulsions, hyperesthesia, anesthesia. Opisthotonos (chicken, pigeon, turkey). Heart dilation, myocardial lesions (dog, fox, rat, swine); bradycardia (cat, dog, monkey, rat, swine). Edema (dog, fox, rat, swine). Gastrointestinal disturbances (man). Pyruvic acid accumulation in blood & tissues. Decreased urinary citric acid (rat). Beriberi (man).	Vascular hypotension (man, dog, rabbit). Acute toxicity: individual sensitivity to injections 1000 times the daily requirement.

[1/] Bacterial synthesis in the rumen wholly, or in great part, provides the requirements of the B vitamins for ruminating animals.

continued

	Substance	Required in Diet by	Functions	Signs of Deficiency	Signs of Excess
2	Riboflavin	All vertebrates investigated 1/	Appears as coenzyme flavin mononucleotide (FMN) or flavin adenine dinucleotide (FAD) in a number of flavoprotein enzymes functioning as proton & electron carriers, e.g., L- & D-amino acid oxidases, xanthine oxidase, succinic dehydrogenase, cytochrome reductase, "Warburg's yellow enzyme." Has role in visual mechanism of the retina. Acts closely with nicotinic acid, both being components of important biological oxidation-reduction systems.	Retarded or halted growth (rat, other animals). Epidermal atrophy, dermatitis, greasy scaling especially of nasolabial folds, cheeks, chin (man); cheilosis, angular stomatitis, lesions of lip & mouth corners (man). Myelin degeneration of nerves (dog, mouse, rat, swine, chicken); central neuritis (man); lack of coordination, faulty grasp reflex (monkey); curled-toe paralysis (chicken); partial leg paralysis (rat). Muscle weakness (dog, monkey). Mild photophobia, dimmed vision & diminished visual acuity, sore eyes & lids (man); corneal cloudiness, vascularization, cataract, opacity & ulceration (man, dog, rat). Congenital skeletal malformations in offspring of riboflavin-deficient females (rat). Requirement increases in pregnancy & lactation.	Paresthesia, itching (man). Toxic amounts administered intraperitoneally cause anuria, renal concretions (rat). Dose 5000 times the therapeutic amount is tolerated (mouse, rat).
3	Nicotinic acid 2/	All vertebrates investigated 1/	Component of nicotinamide adenine dinucleotide (NAD^+) & nicotinamide adenine dinucleotide phosphate ($NADP^+$), which function as hydrogen transfer agents in more than 50 metabolic reactions. Stimulates gastric secretion.	Delayed growth & development in young. Bilateral, symmetrical dermatitis, aggravated by sunlight, heat, inflammation (man); rarefaction of corium, keratinization, atrophy of sebaceous glands, desquamation (man). Swollen gills (trout). Poor feathering (chick). Stomatitis (man, dog, fox, swine, chicken, turkey); smooth glossitis (man); salivary drooling (dog). Atrophy, ulceration, & cyst formation of large intestine (man, dog, swine); diarrhea (man, calf, dog, rabbit, chick, duck, turkey). Achlorhydria (man, swine). Macrocytic anemia (dog, rabbit, swine); leukopenia (rabbit). Retrobulbar neuritis, encephalopathy, headache, dizziness, depression, delusions, dementia, locomotor difficulties, tremors, jerky movements, rigidity, altered tendon reflexes, numbness, paralysis (man). Perosis (chick, turkey poult). Pellegra (man), blacktongue (cat, dog, other animals).	Burning & itching skin, elevated skin temp, peripheral vasodilation (man). Respiratory center paralysis (rat). Decreased serum cholesterol. Death after very large doses; 2 g/day causes death within 20 days (dog). Diet containing 2% nicotinamide inhibits growth (chick); 1% causes fatty liver. Large doses of nicotinic acid cause ketosis (rat). Therapeutic:toxic dose ratio = 1:1000.
4	B_4	Most or all vertebrates. May be formed within the organism from all substances containing adenine.	With the other essential B-complex constituents, an essential factor in normal growth, development, and maintenance. A component of nucleoproteins and as such an essential factor in cell activity. A constituent of nicotinamide adenine dinucleotide, amino acid dehydrase, lipodehydrase, with activity in nerve tissue. Therapeutic use: treatment of agranulocytosis and certain polyneuritis (gravidic). Synergistic with nicotinic acid in catabolism of alcohol.	Insufficient development. Leukocytic disturbance and anemia. Neuritic syndrome. Enzymatic problems (malnutrition) and dermatosis.	No effects reported

1/ Bacterial synthesis in the rumen wholly, or in great part, provides the requirements of the B vitamins for ruminating animals. 2/ Animal products contain nicotinamide; plant products contain mainly nicotinic acid.

continued

52. FUNCTION, DEFICIENCY, AND EXCESS OF ESSENTIAL VITAMINS: VERTEBRATES

	Substance	Required in Diet by	Functions	Signs of Deficiency	Signs of Excess
5	B_6[3/]	All vertebrates investigated[1/]. Requirement by animals is increased with increased dietary protein.	Coenzyme (pyridoxal phosphate) for transaminase & codecarboxylase systems, kynurinase, cystathionase, serine & threonine dehydrases, cysteine desulfhydrase, racemizing enzymes; deamination of amino acids & formation of urea N; conversion of tryptophan to nicotinic acid; metabolism of fatty acids. Necessary for normal adrenocortical function. Therapeutic uses: treatment of hyperemesis gravidarum, seborrheic dermatitis (man).	Retarded growth (man, infant; guinea pig, monkey, rabbit, rat, chick); decreased availability of growth hormone & insulin (rat); anorexia (calf, chick); unthriftiness (calf); weight loss, reduced egg production, death (chicken). Hypochromic anemia (man, infant); polymorphonuclear leukocytosis, lymphopenia (man); hypochromic, microcytic anemia with anisocytosis & irregular reticulocytosis (dog, monkey, swine, chick, duck); poikilocytosis (calf); cardiovascular dilation, hypertrophy of right auricle & ventricle; increased plasma urea & nonprotein N; tachycardia & cardiac embarrassment (rat); mucus accumulation in thorax (dog); impaired antibody production (rat); degeneration in myelin sheaths of peripheral nerves & spinal cord (dog, swine); convulsions (man, infant; rat, swine, chicken); epileptiform fits (rat, swine, chicken); ataxia (swine). Denudation of hair from paws, snout, & eartips, thickening of ears (rat); dermatitis, bald patches (monkey). Increased oxalic acid urea, ammonia, uric acid, & creatinine (dog); calcium oxalate deposition in kidneys (cat, rat); tryptophan metabolites in urine (dog, hamster, mouse, rat); large amounts of xanthurenic acid (man). Deficiency signs produced by ingestion of desoxypyridoxine: weakness, nervousness, irritability, insomnia, seborrhea-like lesions about eyes, nose, & mouth, cheilosis, glossitis, stomatitis (man).	LD_{50} (rat): subcutaneously, 3 g/kg body wt; orally, 4 g/kg. Convulsions 24 hr after LD_{50} dose (rat). Abnormal encephalograms after 200 mg/day for 33 days (man, adult). Doses of 10 mg/kg body wt/day for 3 mo had no effect (dog, monkey, rat).
6	Biotin	Man, calf, dog, monkey, rat, mouse, rabbit, chicken, turkey. Synthesis by intestinal bacteria in mammals may partially or wholly meet requirements.	Growth factor for all vertebrates studied; may be required by all rapidly growing tissues. Affects CO_2 fixation, carboxylation & decarboxylation of tricarboxylic acid cycle, deamination of aspartic acid, serine, & threonine, synthesis of citrulline, synthesis of long-chain fatty acids by mitochondria.	Seborrheic skin pathology, scaly & greasy dermatitis followed by extreme hyperkeratosis after long deficiency (dog, monkey, rabbit, rat, chicken). Scaly dermatitis in volunteers fed 200 g egg white/day (man). Spectacle alopecia (rodents); alopecia (monkey) may be extreme. Atrophy of lingual papillae (man). Spasticity, paralysis of hindquarters (rat). Precordial distress, changes in electrocardiogram (man). Anorexia, lassitude, sleeplessness, muscle pain (man). Perosis (chick). Spontaneous deficiency in chick; rare in other animals, unless fed avidin which combines with biotin, making biotin unavailable to the animal.	Relatively nontoxic to all animals. Dose of 1 g/kg body wt not toxic (mouse).
7	Pantothenic acid	All vertebrates investigated, including calf, dog, fox, guinea pig, hamster, monkey, rat, mouse, swine, chicken, duck, pigeon, turkey	Growth factor. As component of coenzyme A, functions in enzymatic acylation; fat, protein, carbohydrate metabolism; phospholipid & steroid synthesis.	Retarded growth in all animals. Specific dermatitis of mouth & feet (chicken); eczematous dermatitis (rat). Burning sensations in hands, feet (man). Achromotrichia (dog, fox, monkey, mouse, rat); spectacle alopecia (rat). Myelin degeneration of peripheral nerves (chick); chromatolysis of dorsal root ganglion cells (swine, chick). Spastic abnormalities of hindquarters, abnormal gait, ataxia (dog, mouse, swine); convulsions (dog). Hemorrhagic necrosis of adrenals, secretion of red pigment by harderian glands (rat). Diarrhea with bloody stools (dog); anorexia, diarrhea, colitis (monkey, swine); necrosis of intestinal epithelium, abscesses followed by ulceration (rat). Anemia (dog, monkey, rat, swine). Necrosis of kidney (rat). Increased deposition of liver fat (dog, chick). Increased nonprotein N in severe deficiency (dog); death in severe deficiency. Abnormalities & failure in reproduction; ocular changes.	LD_{50} (mouse): subcutaneously, 2.7 g; orally, 10 g; intraperitoneally, 0.9 g. LD_{50} (rat): subcutaneously, 3.4 g/kg body wt. Doses of 100 g had no ill effects (man).

1/ Bacterial synthesis in the rumen wholly, or in great part, provides the requirements of the B vitamins for ruminating animals. 3/ Occurs largely as pyridoxal in animal products and as pyridoxamine in plant products. The 3 forms (pyridoxine, pyridoxal, pyridoxamine) are equally active when given to animals by injection, but pyridoxine is the most active when administered orally.

continued

52. FUNCTION, DEFICIENCY, AND EXCESS OF ESSENTIAL VITAMINS: VERTEBRATES

	Substance	Required in Diet by	Functions	Signs of Deficiency	Signs of Excess
8	Folic acid	Man, dog, fox, guinea pig, sulfa-treated lamb[1], rat, mink, chicken, duck, goose, turkey, fish	Growth & hematopoietic factor (fox, mink, monkey, chick, on purified rations). Production & utilization of formate. Transfer of methyl, hydroxymethyl, & formyl groups, e.g., ethanolamine to choline, homocysteine to methionine, nicotinamide to *N*-methyl nicotinamide, pyrimidine ring to thymine, glycine to serine. Introduction of 2- & 8-carbon atoms into purine ring, and amidine carbon into histidine. Tyrosine oxidation. Therapeutic uses: treatment of sprue, nutritional macrocytic anemia, certain megaloblastic & macrocytic anemias of infancy, macrocytic anemias of pregnancy (man); additive in practical rations as growth stimulant (mink).	Retarded growth. Sprue (man, monkey); megaloblastic bone marrow (man, monkey, other animals); macrocytic, hyperchromic anemia (man, monkey); macrocytic anemia with ultimate anisocytosis (chick, turkey); cytopenia (monkey, chick); leukocyte abnormalities (monkey, rat, chick); infarction of spleen (rat). Poor feather structure (chicken, turkey); abnormal feather pigmentation (chicken); graying of pelage (rat). Perosis (chick, turkey). Impaired reproduction (rat, chicken); lowered hatchability of eggs (chicken). Impaired lactation (mouse, rat). Neck paralysis (goose, turkey). Diarrhea & absorptive difficulties associated with sprue, e.g., disorders of calcium metabolism, impaired absorption of fat & vitamins. Abnormal histidine metabolism, resulting in high levels of urinary formiminoglutamic acid.	Relatively nontoxic. Males more resistant than females (mouse). Death by obstruction of renal tubules with precipitated folic acid after intake of toxic amounts. Intravenous LD_{50}: 120 mg/kg body wt (guinea pig); 600 mg/kg (mouse); 410 mg/kg (rabbit); 500 mg/kg (rat).
9	B_{12}	Most or all vertebrates investigated[1]	Growth factor (mouse, rat, swine, chicken, turkey). Utilization of small amounts of orally administered B_{12} potentiated by gastric juice (man), implying that an "intrinsic" factor may be necessary for utilization of small amounts of B_{12}, the "extrinsic" factor. When large amounts of B_{12} are administered orally, it can be absorbed in the absence of the intrinsic factor. Methylation reactions (rat, chick). Combined action with folic acid group. B_{12} coenzymes involved in synthesis of methionine & deoxyribonucleotides. Therapeutic uses: in pernicious anemia (man), relieves lingual manifestations & reverses degenerative changes in spinal cord unless damage is irreversible; sprue (man).	Megaloblastic marrow, macrocytic & hyperchromic anemia, glossitis (man). Degenerative changes in spinal cord.	Polycythemia (nonruminants)
10	Choline[4]	Dog, guinea pig, rat, chicken, turkey; most or all vertebrate young	Source of transferable (labile) methyl (CH_3) groups; enzymatically transformed to betaine which transfers the methyl group.[5] Donor of methyl groups--in presence of homocysteine--for synthesis of methionine, purines. Synthesis of lecithin. Creatine formation (rat). Precursor of acetylcholine. Essential for normal nutrition & egg production (chicken), lactation (hamster), normal liver function (dog, mouse, rat, chicken). Direct catalytic role of choline in intermediate metabolism not demonstrated. Therapeutic uses: treatment of fatty liver & certain forms of liver cirrhosis (dog, rat); prevention of perosis (chicken, turkey).	Increased mortality (chicken, turkey). Liver: fatty degeneration & cirrhosis (dog, rabbit, rat); prolonged prothrombin & bromsulphalein times, especially in animals on high protein diets (rat); necrosis from chronic deficiency (mouse, rat, chick). Enlargement & hemorrhagic congestion of kidney (rat); necrosis of renal tubule, epithelium, & glomerulus (rat); granular atrophy, hypertension resulting from early kidney lesions, decreased alkaline phosphatase activity & fat deposition (rat). Increased serum phosphatase (rat). Paralysis (young rat); muscle weakness (guinea pig). Decreased egg production, ovarian abortion (chicken, turkey). Intracranial bleeding in offspring of choline-deficient females (rat). Small subcutaneous & adrenal hemorrhages, marked anemia (guinea pig).	Inhibition of erythrocyte formation (dog). Diarrhea (man).

1/ Bacterial synthesis in the rumen wholly, or in great part, provides the requirements of the B vitamins for ruminating animals. 4/ No single analogue can carry out all functions of choline; several compounds can replace it in one or more of its functions. 5/ Choline may readily be replaced as a methyl donor by betaine, dimethyl thetine, or methionine.

continued

52. FUNCTION, DEFICIENCY, AND EXCESS OF ESSENTIAL VITAMINS: VERTEBRATES

	Substance	Required in Diet by	Functions	Signs of Deficiency	Signs of Excess
11	Ascorbic acid	Man & other primates, guinea pig	Protects adrenal oxysteroids from destruction by liver (rat). As antioxidant, protects hydrogen carriers. Promotes oxidation of fatty acids & aromatic amino acids, conversion of folic acid to folinic acid, formation of intercellular substances, i.e., collagen, ossein, dentine. Increases phagocytic activity. Prevents & cures scurvy (primates, guinea pig).	Loss of appetite, decline in physical activity, defective healing of wounds. Follicular keratosis (man); loss of luster & roughening of hair. Disorientation of cells in growing region of bones & teeth; beading of ribs; failure of chondroblast, osteoblast, & ameloblast differentiation & maturation. Loosening of teeth, swollen gums. Anemia with decreased red cells; increase in circulating leukocytes. Failure of fibroblasts to differentiate and mature. Capillary hemorrhages, especially in subcutaneous & intramuscular areas. Swelling, atrophy, soreness of muscles, leading to "face ache posture." Increased adrenal cholesterol in early deficiency, decreased in late deficiency. Reduction of cytoplasm & indistinctness of cell membrane. Increased respiration rate early in deficiency, decreased in late stages. Lowered temp in late stages.	Hypervitaminosis doubtful if calcium content of diet sufficient. Massive doses by injection lead to sudden death.
	Fat-soluble Vitamins				
12	A[6]	All vertebrates and many invertebrates. May be formed within the organism from one of the carotenoid provitamins, α-, β-, γ-carotene, or cryptoxanthin.	Stimulates growth & development; maintains epithelium; important in biosynthesis of mucopolysaccharides. Vitamin A is a precursor for retinene which with the visual proteins forms the photosensitive visual pigments, i.e., rhodopsin, porphyropsin, iodopsin.	Retarded growth (man, rat, chick, turkey); inability to stand on hind legs (swine). Localized overgrowth of bone (cattle, rat). Night blindness, photophobia (man). Optic nerve degeneration, possibly resulting from skull overgrowth & pressure (cattle, rat). Degenerative changes in epithelium of eye, xerophthalmia, keratomalacia in severe deficiency (man, rat). Metaplasia, hyperkeratinization, cornification, & desquamation of skin (man, rat), & of mucosa (man). Decreased egg production (chicken); irregular estrus, male sterility (rat). Odontoblast atrophy (man, rat). Deficiency accentuated by impaired digestion or absorption of fat, excessive ingestion of mineral oil, hyperthyroidism (inhibits conversion of provitamins to vitamin A_1).	Hypoprothrombinemia (rat); increased serum lipids & phosphatase; decreased serum proteins (man). Fragility, hyperostosis, cortical thickening of long bones, periosteal swellings, pain (man, cat, rat). Dry & exfoliated epithelium, mouth desquamation, hyperemia of skin & mucosa, liver enlargement, severe headache (man). Telangiectasis (cattle). Acute toxicity: >300 times the daily requirement; chronic toxicity: 100 times the daily requirement.
13	D[7]	Most vertebrates investigated	Essential to normal bone development. Enhances absorption of calcium & phosphorus; promotes phosphorus reabsorption by renal tubules. Maintains alkaline phosphatase at bone site.	Retarded growth (man, others). Rickets. Skeletal abnormalities & deformities, varying with degree & duration of deficiency (man, rat, others).[8] Rapidly growing regions of bones most affected. Persistent overproliferation of cartilage; enlargement of ends of long bones; soft, weak bones, with deformation by stress & posture; osteomalacia, causing decalcification & fragility of nongrowing bone. Faulty calcification of teeth, similar to deficiencies of vitamins A & C. Hypocalcemia, hypophosphatemia. Increased plasma phosphatase. Myasthenia; atony of skeletal & gut muscle. Tetany, convulsions, spasmodic closure of glottis (man, rat). Deficiency accentuated by impaired digestion or absorption of fat, excessive ingestion of mineral oil & polyunsaturated fats, lack of exposure to sunlight; pregnancy, lactation.	Early symptoms: anorexia, thirst, lassitude. Later symptoms: nausea, vomiting, diarrhea, abdominal discomfort, weight loss & debility. Hypercalcemia, hyperphosphatemia. Deposition of calcium salts in various organs. Dense calcification in long bone metaphyses at the expense of diaphyseal calcification (man, infant & growing young). Calcium deposits, causing kidney damage & renal dysfunction: increased urinary excretion of calcium & phosphorus. Continued hypervitaminosis leads to death. Excessive doses may be cumulative. Hypercalcemia, high urinary calcium & renal damage after doses of 125,000 units/day for 8 mo.[9]

[6] Exists as vitamin A_1 in marine fishes and land vertebrates; as both A_1 and A_2 in amphibia, anadromus and catadromus fishes; and as A_2 in place of, or in addition to, A_1 in freshwater species. [7] Ultraviolet light converts the provitamins ergosterol and 7-dehydrocholesterol to vitamins D_2 and D_3, respectively. [8] Skeletal abnormalities are scars of functional and structural change, and may persist long after the deficiency has been relieved. Degree of restoration may be extensive and continue over long periods. [9] The amount of dietary vitamin D which will produce signs of excess varies with individuals within the same species, and at different times within the same individual.

continued

52. FUNCTION, DEFICIENCY, AND EXCESS OF ESSENTIAL VITAMINS: VERTEBRATES

	Substance	Required in Diet by	Functions	Signs of Deficiency	Signs of Excess
14	E	Cattle, dog, guinea pig, hamster, mink, mouse, rabbit, rat, swine, chicken, duck, turkey	Biological antioxidant; protects unsaturated fatty acids & vitamin A against peroxidation. Participates in oxidation-reduction reactions. Therapeutic uses: treatment of skin collagenoses (man); protection against toxic agents, e.g., carbon tetrachloride, chloroform, alloxan.	Irreparable degeneration of testicular germinal epithelium (cattle, mouse, rat, chicken); uterine necrosis, seminal vesicle necrosis (rat). Reproductive failure (rat, swine). Reduced egg hatchability, death of embryo (chick). Acute muscle degeneration (dog, guinea pig, hamster, rabbit, rat, chicken, duck, turkey). Acute encephalomalacia, cerebellum & nerve cell degeneration (chick). Ataxia, tremors, weakness, opisthotonos (chicken). Paralysis (suckling rat, born of vitamin E-deficient mother). Creatinuria. Generalized exudative diathesis (chick). Liver necrosis, degeneration (mouse, rat, swine). Steatitis (cat, mink, rat). Deficiency produces an increased fragility of erythrocytes in presence of hyaluronic acid. Additional causes of deficiency: impaired digestion or absorption of fat resulting from inflammation of intestinal mucosa, sprue, & chronic diarrhea; excessive ingestion of mineral oil. Requirement is related to the level of polyunsaturated fatty acids in the diet; the requirement increases during pregnancy & lactation.	No effects reported
15	K[10]	Man, dog, mouse, rabbit, rat, canary, chicken, duck, goose, pigeon, turkey. Synthesis by intestinal bacteria in mammals may partially or wholly meet requirements.	Essential for production of prothrombin in liver and of other blood coagulation factors. Involved in electron transport & oxidative phosphorylation in mitochondria	Decline or failure of prothrombin synthesis. Decreased blood prothrombin content, resulting in increased bleeding tendency after slight trauma & multiple hemorrhages throughout all tissues (man, chicken); increased clotting time (man, others). Deficiency produced by sulfa drugs (rats) and by biliary obstruction (man); bile is essential for absorption of vitamin K.	Toxicity relatively low. Vomiting (man); vomiting after oral dose of 180 mg menadione (dog). Porphyrinuria (man, dog); albuminuria (dog). Prolonged clotting time (rabbit); cytopenia, hemoglobinemia (mouse). LD = 350-500 mg/kg body wt (rat).
			Unsaturated Fatty Acids		
16	Arachidonic, linoleic, & linolenic acids	Most vertebrates investigated	Essential to growth & reproduction (rat). Serve as building units of phospholipids. Decrease serum cholesterol levels (man, other animals).	Retarded or halted growth, elevated metabolic rate (rat). Eczema (man); scaliness on feet & tail (rat). Alopecia, disturbances in reproduction, kidney & urinary tract lesions, increased water intake (rat).	Changes from normal in composition of stored fat

10/ A number of synthetic products with a quinoid nucleus have vitamin K activity, e.g., menadione (2-methyl-1,4-naphthoquinone).

Contributors: (a) Mayer, Jean, and Gershoff, Stanley N., (b) Lecoq, Raoul, (c) Mickelsen, Olaf

General References

[1] American Medical Association. 1951. Handbook of nutrition. Ed. 2. Blakiston, Philadelphia.

[2] Clark, G. W. 1953. A vitamin digest. C. C. Thomas, Springfield, Ill.

[3] Follis, R. H. 1958. Deficiency disease. C. C. Thomas, Springfield, Ill.

[4] Harris, R. S., and D. J. Ingle, ed. 1960. Vitamins Hormones 18.

[5] Harris, R. S., I. G. Wool, and J. A. Loraine, ed. 1963-64. Ibid. 21 & 22.

[6] Kleiner, I. S., and J. M. Orten. 1966. Biochemistry. Ed. 7. C. V. Mosby, St. Louis.

[7] Lecoq, R. 1952. Therapie 7:431.

[8] Lecoq, R. 1959. Les vitamines. G. Doin, Paris.

[9] Moore, T. 1957. Vitamin A. Elsevier, Amsterdam.

[10] Nutrition Foundation. 1967. Newer knowledge in nutrition. Nutrition Foundation, New York.

[11] Robinson, F. A. 1951. The vitamin B complex. J. Wiley, New York.

[12] Rosenberg, H. R. 1952. Chemistry and physiology of vitamins. Interscience, New York.

[13] Sebrell, W. H., Jr., and R. S. Harris. 1954. The vitamins. Academic Press, New York. v. 1-3.

[14] Shafer, J. 1949. Vitamins in medical practice. Staples Press, London.

[15] U.S. Department of Agriculture. 1959. Food. Yearbook of agriculture. U.S. Gov't. Printing Office, Washington, D.C.

[16] Williams, R. J., et al. 1950. The biochemistry of B vitamins. Reinhold, New York.

53. CORRELATION OF WEIGHT GAIN TO FEED CONSUMED: VERTEBRATES

Values are grams gained in body weight per gram of feed consumed. Values were calculated by dividing total gain (from birth to percent of specified mature weight) by the total weight of the feed consumed since birth. Except in the case of milk fed to cattle (*see* footnote 2), total weight of feed included natural moisture content.

	Animal	Grams Gained/Gram of Feed at								Reference
		10% Mature Wt		25% Mature Wt		50% Mature Wt		90% Mature Wt		
		♂	♀	♂	♀	♂	♀	♂	♀	
1	Cattle, beef[1,2]/	0.50	0.61	0.30	0.40	0.21	0.20	...	0.08	1-3,6
2	dairy, large[2]/	0.44	0.55	0.25	0.31	0.16	0.15	0.05	0.09	3,6
3	small[2]/	0.41	0.65	0.23	0.33	0.13	0.16	0.08	0.09	3,6
4	Rat, Sprague-Dawley[3]/	1.0	...	0.57	1.0	0.38	0.35	0.13	0.13	4
5	Swine[4]/	0.47[5]/	0.47	0.30[5]/	0.30	0.19[5]/	0.19	...	...	7
6	Chicken, White Leghorn	0.55	0.55	0.47	0.47	0.36	0.36	...	0.21	5
7	heavy breeds	0.55	0.55	0.50	0.50	0.41	0.41	...	0.25	5
8	Turkey, small type	0.57	0.57	0.46	0.46	0.37	0.37	0.28	0.28	5
9	large type	0.57	0.57	0.46	0.46	0.37	0.37	0.28	0.28	5

[1]/ Estimates based on feeding experience with calves up to weaning age. [2]/ Feed corrected to an "air dry" basis: 12% for whole milk and 10% for skim milk, as used in calf feeding. [3]/ No allowance made for amount of milk consumed before weaning. [4]/ Age at maturity estimated at 24 months. Values extrapolated from feed consumption data calculated for the following age periods: 50-84 days, 84-112 days, 112-140 days, 140-168 days, 168-224 days, 224-280 days, 280-336 days, and 336-392 days. [5]/ Castrated.

Contributors: (a) Swanson, Eric W., (b) Bird, H. R., (c) Warner, R. G., (d) Davey, R. J.

References

[1] Bailey, C. M., et al. 1966. J. Animal Sci. 25:132.

[2] Bogart, R., et al. 1963. Ibid. 22:993.

[3] Green, W. W., and J. Buric. 1953. Ibid. 12:561.

[4] National Research Council, Committee on Animal Nutrition. 1962. Natl. Acad. Sci. Natl. Res. Council Publ. 990.

[5] National Research Council, Committee on Animal Nutrition. 1966. Ibid. 1345.

[6] Ragsdale, A. C. 1934. Missouri Univ. Agr. Expt. Sta. Bull. 336 & 338.

[7] U.S. Dept. of Agriculture, Agricultural Research Service, Swine Research Branch. Unpublished. Beltsville, Md., 1966.

54. FUNCTION, DEFICIENCY, AND EXCESS OF CHEMICAL ELEMENTS: HIGHER PLANTS

Data are applicable primarily to herbaceous crop plants. Carbon, hydrogen, and oxygen were intentionally omitted, since these elements are constituents of the carbohydrates, fats, proteins, vitamins, hormones, chlorophyll, and other organic compounds occurring in plants. The bicarbonate ion is involved in ion absorption or exchange. Oxygen is the final receptor of hydrogen in aerobic respiration. Many of the metallic elements (as ions) that are indicated as being associated with enzymes serve as activators for enzymes. [1,3,9,14,15] Symptoms of certain species may vary widely from those described below.

	Element	Occurrence and/or Function	Symptoms of Deficiency	Symptoms of Excess	Reference
1	Boron	Inverse relationship between boron level and water permeability of membranes and moisture content of tissues. (May be a constituent of cytoplasmic membranes). Necessary for cell division, and translocation of sucrose and possibly other sugars.	Terminal leaves necrotic, shed prematurely; internodes of terminal shoots shortened, usually rosetting; apical meristems blacken and die, general breakdown of meristematic tissue; roots short, stubby. Plants dwarfed, stunted; flower development and seed production usually impaired or lacking.	Marginal chlorosis and/or necrosis in leaves; defoliation. Considerable concentration causes death of most plants.	1,3,4,6, 7,9,10, 14,15, 18,20, 23

continued

	Element	Occurrence and/or Function	Symptoms of Deficiency	Symptoms of Excess	Reference
2	Calcium	Involved in cross-binding in cell walls	Leaves chlorotic, rolled, curled; breakdown of meristematic tissues in stems and roots (death in acute cases); roots poorly developed, lack fiber, and may appear gelatinous. Symptoms appear near growing points of stems and roots. Little or no fruiting.	Chlorosis similar to that in iron or manganese deficiency[1/]. Zinc and boron deficiency may be induced when soil reaction (pH) and calcium are high.	1,3,7,9, 10,14, 15,18, 20,23
3	Copper	Associated with tyrosinase, a polyphenol oxidase involved in reduction of molecular oxygen. In ascorbic acid oxidase, which may be concerned in respiratory oxidation[2/]. In laccase (this enzyme has limited distribution in plants, and its function has not been established).	Wilting of terminal shoots, frequently followed by death. Leaf color often faded. Carotene and other pigments reduced.	Chlorosis, similar to that in iron deficiency, followed by necrosis; permanent wilting of upper leaves; leaves may become wrinkled and necrotic at margins. Fibrous roots stubby, poorly developed, brownish at tips. Reduced growth; death in extreme cases.	1-3,5,7-10,12, 14-16, 18,20, 22,23
4	Iron	Associated with peroxidase, which breaks down peroxides and transfers active oxygen to oxidizable substances. In cytochrome oxidase, which plays a role in reduction of molecular oxygen[2/]. In catalase, which effects the release of molecular oxygen from hydrogen peroxide.	Interveinal white chlorosis, appearing first on young leaves; tendency for chlorosis of all aerial parts, often becoming necrotic; in some cases leaves may be completely bleached, margins and tips scorched. Usually has an overall effect.		1,3,7,9, 10,14-16,18, 20,23
5	Magnesium	In chlorophyll, which is essential for photosynthesis. Associated with cocarboxylase, which is the coenzyme for the carboxylases; in enolase, which is necessary in glycolysis (from 2-phosphoglyceric acid to 2-phosphopyruvic acid); in hexokinase, which brings about transphosphorylation of glucose.	Mottled chlorosis with veins green and leaf web tissue yellow or white, appearing first on old leaves; severely affected leaves may wilt and shed, or may abscise without the wilting stage; brittleness of leaves common; necrosis often occurs	Usually an interveinal necrosis	1,3,7,9, 10,14-16,18, 20,23
6	Manganese	Associated with arginase (?), which converts arginine to urea. In an unidentified enzyme, which brings about catabolism of oxaloacetic acid to pyruvic acid and carbon dioxide in respiration.	Mottled chlorosis with veins green and leaf web tissue yellow or white, appearing first on young leaves; may spread to old leaves. Stems yellowish green, often hard and woody. Carotene reduced.	Leaves pale, necrotic, bronzing at margins; symptoms similar to those in iron deficiency. Small black spots on stem of potato.	1,3,7,9, 10,14-16,18, 20,23
7	Molybdenum	Associated with an unidentified enzyme (?), which is apparently required in ascorbic acid synthesis. It is a cofactor for nitrate reductase; required also for nitrogen fixation.	Light yellow chlorosis of leaves; leaf blade may fail to expand	Lower leaves yellow with brown necrotic areas; in severe cases upper leaves may be stunted, chlorotic, and may abscise	4,7,9-11,15, 18,20, 23
8	Nitrogen	In proteins, the chief organic constituents of protoplasm. In chlorophyll, which is essential for photosynthesis. Important in the utilization of sugars. In many organic compounds.	In young plants, stunted growth and yellowish green leaves; older leaves light green, followed by yellowing and drying or shedding, often with abundant anthocyanins in veins. Shoots short, thin, growth upright and spindly; flowering reduced. Apple and peach fruit highly colored, developing slowly, small when mature.	Excessive vegetative growth; leaves dark green; high transpiration. Reduced yield of seed and fruit crops; may secure satisfactory yield of leafy vegetables of reduced quality.	1,3,7,9, 10,14, 15,18, 20,23

[1/] Chlorosis due to the physiological unavailability of iron and manganese or reduced potassium. [2/] Terminal process in aerobic respiration.

continued

54. FUNCTION, DEFICIENCY, AND EXCESS OF CHEMICAL ELEMENTS: HIGHER PLANTS

	Element	Occurrence and/or Function	Symptoms of Deficiency	Symptoms of Excess	Reference
9	Phosphorus	In phospholipids, e.g., lecithin, which are constituents of cytoplasmic membranes. In nucleoprotein, a constituent of the nucleus and chromosomes. In adenosine di- and triphosphates, which are required for phosphorylation reactions, glycolysis and synthesis of sucrose, starch and proteins. Di- and triphosphopyridine nucleotide, coenzymes which accept and/or donate hydrogen in oxidation-reduction reactions.	Young plants stunted, leaves dark blue-green, sometimes purplish (potato and certain other vegetables have pale green leaves); stems slender; often anthocyanins in veins, and may become necrotic. Meristematic growth ceases in potato. Fruits ripen slowly; plants often dwarfed at maturity.		1,3,7,9, 10,13-15,18, 20,23
10	Potassium	May be involved in action of fructokinase and other enzyme systems	Leaves of potato usually dark blue-green and leaves of monocotyledons pale green or streaked with yellow, with marginal chlorosis and necrosis appearing first on old leaves; usually wrinkled, corrugated, or crinkled between veins	Leaves yellowish green; reduced growth; tendency toward calcium and magnesium deficiency	1,3,7,9, 10,14, 15,18, 20,23
11	Sulfur	In cystine and cysteine, which are present in all plant proteins. In glutathione, which may function as a hydrogen carrier in respiration. In mustard oil glycosides, which may tie up reserve food substances which would otherwise be toxic to cells.	Leaves light green to yellow, appearing first along veins of young leaves; stems often slender	Necrosis or firing of older leaves of certain species or varieties	1,3,7,9, 10,14, 15,18, 20,23
12	Zinc	Associated with an unidentified enzyme which is directly necessary for synthesis of tryptophan, the precursor of indoleacetic acid	Leaves chlorotic and necrotic, young growth first affected; rosetting; premature shedding; whitish chlorotic streaks between veins in older leaves and whitening of upper leaves in monocotyledons; chlorosis of lower leaves in dicotyledons	Leaves yellow from zinc-induced iron chlorosis	1,2,7-10,15-23

Contributors: (a) Gauch, Hugh G., (b) Carolus, Robert L., (c) Reuther, Walter, (d) Judkins, Wesley P.

References

[1] Bonner, J. F. 1950. Plant biochemistry. Academic Press, New York.

[2] Chapman, H. D., G. F. Liebig, Jr., and A. P. Vanselow. 1939. Soil Sci. Soc. Am. Proc. 4:196.

[3] Curtis, O. F., and D. G. Clark. 1950. Introduction to plant physiology. McGraw-Hill, New York.

[4] Devlin, R. M. 1966. Plant physiology. Reinhold, New York.

[5] Forbes, R. H. 1917. Univ. Calif. (Berkeley) Publ. Agr. Sci. 1:395.

[6] Gauch, H. G., and W. M. Dugger, Jr. 1954. Maryland Univ. Agr. Expt. Sta. Tech. Bull. A-80.

[7] Hambridge, G., ed. 1949. Hunger signs in crops. National Fertilizer Association, Washington, D.C.

[8] Hewitt, E. J. 1948. Nature 161:489.

[9] Hewitt, E. J. 1951. Ann. Rev. Plant Physiol. 2:25.

[10] Kitchen, K. B., ed. 1948. Diagnostic techniques for soils and crops. American Potash Institute, Washington, D.C.

[11] Lyon, C. B., and K. C. Beeson. 1948. Botan. Gaz. 109:506.

[12] McElroy, W. D., and H. B. Glass, ed. 1950. Copper metabolism. Johns Hopkins Press, Baltimore.

[13] McElroy, W. D., and H. B. Glass, ed. 1951. Phosphorus metabolism. Johns Hopkins Press, Baltimore.

[14] Meyer, B. S., and D. B. Anderson. 1952. Plant physiology. Ed. 2. Van Nostrand, New York.

[15] Mulder, E. G. 1950. Ann. Rev. Plant Physiol. 1:1.

[16] Sumner, J. B., and K. Myrbäck, ed. 1950-52. The enzymes. Academic Press, New York. v. 1 & 2.

[17] Tsui, C. 1948. Am. J. Botany 35:172.

[18] U.S. Department of Agriculture. 1938. Better plants and animals. Yearbook of agriculture. U.S. Gov't. Printing Office, Washington, D.C.

[19] Viets, F. J. 1951. J. Am. Soc. Agron. 43:150.

[20] Wallace, T. 1951. Diagnosis of mineral deficiencies in plants. H.M. Stationery Office, London.

[21] Wallace, T., and E. J. Hewitt. 1946. J. Pomol. Hort. Sci. 22:153.

[22] Willis, L. F., and J. R. Piland. 1936. J. Agr. Res. 52:467.

[23] Young, R. S. 1935. Cornell Univ. Agr. Expt. Sta. Mem. 174.

55. CORRELATION BETWEEN SOIL pH AND CHEMICAL ELEMENT AVAILABILITY: TABULAR

The effects of soil pH on chemical element availability, uptake, or toxicity, are manifested by the appearance of deficiency or excess symptoms in the indicator organisms growing in the soil. In soils high in organic matter, the presence of organically complexed or chelated trace elements may change the pH relationship which occurs in mineral soils. **Correlation:** a reciprocal relationship between soil pH and symptoms of deficiency or excess of a given element occurring in the indicator organism: high = symptoms rarely occur outside the stated pH range; medium = symptoms occur usually within, but sometimes outside, the stated pH range; low = symptoms occur at all pH levels, i.e., little or no correlation exists between soil pH and symptoms of deficiency or excess of the element.

Part I. Element Deficiency

Organisms Indicating Deficiency: plants and animals most sensitive to a lack of the element, and therefore most likely to respond when the element is added to the soil.

	Element	Organisms Indicating Deficiency	Soil: Specification	Soil: pH	Correlation	Reference
1	Aluminum	Hydrangea[1], tea; pteridophytes	Neutral soils	5.5-8.0	High	5,16
2	Boron[2]	Apples, beets, cauliflower, celery, kale, tobacco, turnips; legumes	Calcareous, droughty soils having high calcium-boron ratio; leached, acid, sandy soils low in organic matter	5.0-8.0	Medium to low	3,4,20, 25,31, 33
3	Calcium	Alfalfa, beets, celery, clover, flax, peas, potatoes, tomatoes	Light, sandy soils; highly acid soils	<4.5	High	12,18, 31,32
4		Flax	Waterlogged soils in Australia	5.5-6.3	High	
5	Chlorine	Lettuce	Leached soils in inland areas	....	....	17
6	Cobalt[2]	Legumes; ruminants & other animals feeding on cobalt-deficient plants	Soils derived from sandstones & granite	>7.0	Medium	1,2,19, 23,30
7	Copper[3]	Apples, citrus, lettuce, onions, peaches, pears, plums, tomatoes; cereals, various grasses, legumes	Peaty soils; reclaimed heath soils; acid & calcareous sands & gravels	<5.0; >7.5	Low	2,3,9, 15,21, 31
8	Iodine	Animals feeding on iodine-deficient plants	Areas of calcareous rocks; river flats & alluvial soils	....	Low	6,30
9	Iron	Strawberries, sugar beets; tree & bush fruits	Mainly calcareous soils; acid soils given a high concentration of heavy metals	>7.0	Medium to high	3,11, 13,31
10	Magnesium	Apples, citrus, cauliflower, kale, lettuce, oats, potatoes, sugar beets, tobacco, tomatoes	Light, acid, sandy soils; soils given a heavy application of potassium & calcium fertilizers	<5.0	Low	3,12, 27,31, 32
11	Manganese[2]	Beans, beets, oats, potatoes, tomatoes; grasses, tree & bush fruits[4]	Soils high in organic matter; reclaimed heaths; calcareous soils	6.5-8.0	High	3,22,31
12	Molybdenum[5]	Cauliflower & other *Brassica* crops, sugar beets; legumes	Light, leached, acid soils	4.5-6.0	High	2,3,14, 21,23, 24,26
13	Nitrogen	Nonlegumes; molybdenum-deficient legumes at low pH	Mainly light, acid soils, but also other soils	<5.5	Low	3,31
14	Phosphorus	Beets, cotton, potatoes, rutabagas, turnips; cereals, legumes	Mainly acid soils, clay, & certain calcareous soils; unimproved soils	<6.0; 7.0-8.0	Medium	3,31,35
15	Potassium	Beets, corn, potatoes, tobacco, tomatoes, tung trees; legumes, tree & bush fruits	Sandy soils, especially when leached; light, calcareous soils	<5.5	Low	3,31
16	Selenium[5]	Cattle & sheep	Soils derived from acid igneous & arenaceous rocks	....	....	7,20,30
17	Sodium[6]	Beets, carrots, celery, rutabagas, turnips	Nonsaline, inland soils	<7.5	Low	29,31
18	Sulfur	Cotton, flax, tea; legumes	Mainly leached, eroded soils of areas remote from urban & industrial districts	<6.0	Low	8,31,34
19	Zinc[2]	Castor beans, corn, flax, hop, lima beans, pecans, soybeans; fruit trees	Soils high in organic matter; leached sands & gravels	6.0-8.0	Medium	3,10,21, 23,25, 28

[1] Aluminum required for production of blue pigment in hydrangea flowers. [2] Availability reduced by liming. [3] Availability usually reduced by liming. [4] Except citrus. [5] Availability increased by liming. [6] Utilized by certain higher plants; essential for beets.

continued

55. CORRELATION BETWEEN SOIL pH AND CHEMICAL ELEMENT AVAILABILITY: TABULAR

Part I. Element Deficiency

Contributor: Wild, Alan

References

[1] Ahmed, S., and H. J. Evans. 1960. Soil Sci. 90:205.
[2] Bear, F. E. 1954. J. Agr. Food Chem. 2:244.
[3] Bear, F. E., et al. 1949. Hunger signs in crops. American Society of Agronomy and National Fertilizer Association, Washington, D.C.
[4] Berger, K. C. 1949. Advan. Agron. 1:321.
[5] Chenery, E. M. 1955. Plant Soil 6:174.
[6] Chilean Iodine Bureau. 1952. Iodine content of foods. Chilean Iodine Educational Bureau, London.
[7] Gardiner, M. R., et al. 1962. Australian J. Exptl. Agr. Animal Husbandry 2:261.
[8] Gilbert, F. A. 1951. Botan. Rev. 17:671.
[9] Gilbert, F. A. 1952. Advan. Agron. 4:147.
[10] Greenwood, M., and R. K. Djokoto. 1952. J. Hort. Sci. 27:223.
[11] Haas, A. R. C. 1942. Plant Physiol. 17:27.
[12] Hewitt, E. J. 1952. Intern. Soc. Soil Sci. Comm. 2 & 4, Dublin, Trans. 1:107.
[13] Hewitt, E. J. 1953. J. Exptl. Botany 4:59.
[14] Hewitt, E. J., and E. W. Bolle-Jones. 1952. J. Hort. Sci. 27:257.
[15] Hodgson, J. F. 1963. Advan. Agron. 15:119.
[16] Hutchinson, G. E. 1945. Soil Sci. 60:29.
[17] Johnson, C. M., et al. 1957. Plant Soil 8:337.
[18] Millikon, C. R. 1944. J. Dept. Agr. Victoria 42:79.
[19] Mitchell, R. L. 1963. J. Roy. Agr. Soc. Engl. 124:75.
[20] Mitchell, R. L. 1964. In F. E. Bear, ed. Chemistry of the soil. Ed. 2. Reinhold, New York. pp. 320-368.
[21] Mitchell, R. L., et al. 1957. J. Sci. Food Agr. 8(Suppl.):51.
[22] Mulder, E. G., and F. C. Gerretsen. 1952. Advan. Agron. 4:221.
[23] Price, N. O., and W. W. Moschler. 1965. J. Agr. Food Chem. 13:163.
[24] Rubins, E. J. 1956. Soil Sci. 81:191.
[25] Stiles, W. 1958. Encycl. Plant Physiol. (Berlin) 4: 558.
[26] Stout, P. R., and C. M. Johnson. 1956. Soil Sci. 81:183.
[27] Thompson, F. C., et al. 1949. Wye Coll. Dept. Hop Res. Ann. Rept. 34.
[28] Thorne, W. 1957. Advan. Agron. 9:31.
[29] Truog, E., et al. 1953. Soil Sci. 76:41.
[30] Underwood, E. J. 1960. Trace elements in human and animal nutrition. Ed. 2. Academic Press, New York.
[31] Wallace, T. 1961. The diagnosis of mineral deficiencies in plants by visual symptoms. H. M. Stationery Office, London.
[32] Wallace, T. Unpublished. Univ. Bristol, Agricultural and Horticultural Research Station, Long Ashton, 1961.
[33] Wear, J. I., and R. M. Patterson. 1962. Soil Sci. Soc. Am. Proc. 26:344.
[34] Whitehead, D. C. 1964. Soils Fertilizers 27:1.
[35] Williams, E. G. 1949. Natl. Agr. Advisory Serv. Gt. Brit. Quart. Rev. (4):149.

Part II. Element Excess

Organisms Indicating Excess: plants and animals most sensitive to high concentrations of the element.

	Element	Organisms Indicating Excess	Soil & Toxicity Specifications	Soil pH	Correlation	Reference
1	Aluminum	Barley, carrots, celery, cotton, flax, French beans[1/], leeks, lettuce, sugar beets	Acid soils, often phosphorus-deficient. Toxicity aggravated by steam sterilization.	<5.5	High	10,11,18, 19,32
2	Arsenic	Alfalfa, apricots, barley, lemons, peaches, tomatoes	Continued use of arsenical sprays[2/]	....	Low	17,28,29
3	Boron	Avocados, blackberries, citrus, peaches, plums, potatoes	Sandy soils irrigated with boron-rich water; excessive use of boron fertilizer; reclamation of some industrial dusts (fly ash)	<5.5; >8.2	....	7,13,26, 31
4	Cobalt[3/]	Cauliflower, sugar beets, tomatoes	Pollution by industrial effluent or mining operations	<5.5	High	1,12,24, 31

1/ Some varieties. 2/ Toxicity reported in oats when minerals containing arsenic are present in the soil. 3/ Uptake reduced by liming.

continued

55. CORRELATION BETWEEN SOIL pH AND CHEMICAL ELEMENT AVAILABILITY: TABULAR

Part II. Element Excess

	Element	Organisms Indicating Excess	Soil & Toxicity Specifications	Soil pH	Correlation	Reference
5	Copper[3/]	Alfalfa, cauliflower, citrus, corn, sugar beets, tomatoes, wheat	Sandy soils polluted by industrial effluent or mining operations; fungicide residues	<6.0	Medium high	1,4,6,9, 25
6	Fluorine[3/]	Barley, buckwheat, collards, tomatoes	Pollution by industrial fumes	<6.5	High	15,23
7	Lithium	Avocados, citrus, red kidney beans	Certain irrigated soils	>8.2	....	2,28
8	Manganese[3/]	Alfalfa, barley, kale, lespedeza, potatoes, rutabagas, sweet clover, tomatoes, vetch	Acid soils. Toxicity aggravated by steam sterilization.	<5.5	High	11,20-22, 32
9	Molybdenum[4/]	Ruminants feeding on molybdenum-rich plants	Soils derived from rocks high in molybdenum content	7.0-7.5	High	5,24,30
10	Nickel[3/]	Beets, cabbage, clover, corn, kale, oats, potatoes, tobacco, tomatoes, turnips	Soils derived from serpentine rocks; pollution by industrial effluent or mining operations	<6	High	1,9,12, 14,21, 27
11	Selenium	Animals feeding on selenium-rich plants	Soils high in organic matter & derived from Upper Cretaceous rocks (United States) & Upper Carboniferous limestone (Ireland)	....	....	8,16,30, 33
12	Zinc[3/]	Cauliflower, sugar beets, tomatoes	Sandy soils polluted by industrial effluent or mining operations; proximity to galvanized metal	....	....	3,9,12,24

3/ Uptake reduced by liming. 4/ Uptake increased by liming.

Contributor: Wild, Alan

References

[1] Bear, F. E. 1954. J. Agr. Food Chem. 2:244.
[2] Bradford, G. R. 1963. Soil Sci. 96:77.
[3] Davies, W. M. 1952. Intern. Soc. Soil Sci. Comm. 2 & 4, Dublin, Trans. 1:136.
[4] Delas, J. 1963. Agrochimica 7:258.
[5] Dick, A. T. 1956. Soil Sci. 81:229.
[6] Drovineau, G., and R. Mazoyer. 1962. Ann. Agron. 13:31.
[7] Eaton, F. M. 1944. J. Agr. Res. 69:237.
[8] Fleming, G. A. 1962. Soil Sci. 94:28.
[9] Forster, W. A. 1954. Ann. Appl. Biol. 41:637.
[10] Hewitt, E. J. 1948. Long Ashton (Bristol) Agr. Hort. Res. Sta. Rept. 58.
[11] Hewitt, E. J. 1952. Intern. Soc. Soil Sci. Comm. 2 & 4, Dublin, Trans. 1:107.
[12] Hewitt, E. J. 1953. J. Exptl. Botany 4:59.
[13] Hodgson, D. R., et al. 1963. J. Agr. Sci. 61:299.
[14] Hunter, J. G., and O. Vergnano. 1952. Ann. Appl. Biol. 39:279.
[15] Hurd-Karrer, A. M. 1950. Soil Sci. 70:153.
[16] Lakin, H. W., and H. G. Byers. 1948. U.S. Dept. Agr. Tech. Bull. 950.
[17] Liebig, G. F., Jr., et al. 1959. Soil Sci. 88:342.
[18] McCart, G. D., and E. J. Kamproth. 1965. Agron. J. 57:404.
[19] Messing, J. H. L. 1965. Nature 207:439.
[20] Messing, J. H. L. 1965. Plant Soil 23:1.
[21] Mitchell, R. L. 1951. Proc. Intern. Congr. Pure Appl. Chem., 11th, London, 1947, 3:157.
[22] Mulder, E. G., and F. C. Gerretsen. 1952. Advan. Agron. 4:221.
[23] Prince, A. L., et al. 1949. Soil Sci. 67:269.
[24] Reith, J. W. S., and R. L. Mitchell. 1964. Plant Anal. Fertilizer Probl., 4th, Brussels, 1962, 4:241.
[25] Reuther, W., and P. F. Smith. 1953. Soil Sci. 75: 219.
[26] Russell, E. W. 1961. Soil conditions and plant growth. Longmans, London.
[27] Soane, B. D., and D. H. Saunder. 1959. Soil Sci. 88:322.
[28] Stiles, W. 1958. Encycl. Plant Physiol. (Berlin) 4: 558.
[29] Thompson, A. H., and L. P. Batjer. 1950. Soil Sci. 69:281.
[30] Underwood, E. J. 1960. Trace elements in human and animal nutrition. Ed. 2. Academic Press, New York.
[31] Wallace, T. 1961. The diagnosis of mineral deficiencies in plants by visual symptoms. H. M. Stationery Office, London.
[32] Wallace, T. Unpublished. Univ. Bristol, Agricultural and Horticultural Research Station, Long Ashton, 1961.
[33] Walsh, T., et al. 1951. Nature 168:881.

56. CORRELATION BETWEEN SOIL pH AND CHEMICAL ELEMENT AVAILABILITY: GRAPHIC

The width of the element band at a particular pH value indicates the relative favorability for the presence of the element in readily available form in the soil, but does not indicate the relative amount necessarily present (cropping and fertilization are also influential factors). The darker area between the curved lines is proportional to the hydrogen-ion concentration to the left of pH 7, and to the hydroxyl-ion concentration to the right of pH 7.

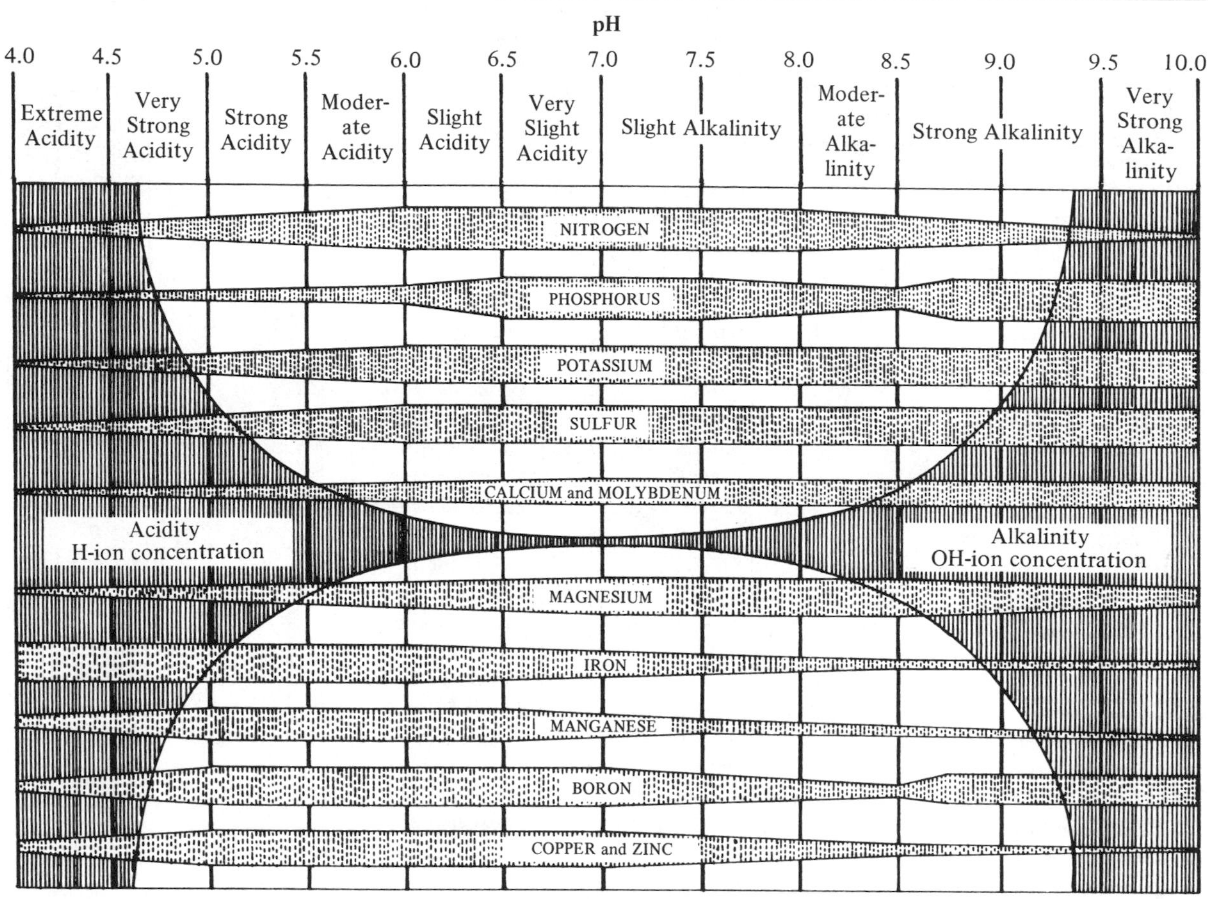

Contributor: Truog, Emil

Reference: Truog, E. 1949. In V. Ignatieff, ed. Food Agr. Organ. U. N. Agr. Studies 9:15.

57. OPTIMUM SOIL pH FOR GROWTH: SPERMATOPHYTES

	Species (Synonym)	pH	Reference
	Gymnospermae		
1	*Abies* spp.	4.5-6.5	6
2	*Chamaecyparis thyoides*	4.5-6.0	6
3	*Ginkgo biloba*	5.5-7.0	6
4	*Juniperus* spp.	5.5-7.5	6
5	*J. communis*	5.0-6.5	6
6	*J. communis saxatilis*	4.5-5.5	6
7	*J. virginiana*	5.0-8.0	6
8	*Larix* spp.	4.5-7.5	6
9	*Picea* spp.	4.5-6.5	6
10	*P. pungens*	5.0-6.5	6
11	*P. sitchensis*	5.0-6.5	6
12	*Pinus* spp.	4.5-6.5	6
13	*P. palustris*	4.5-6.0	6
14	*P. resinosa*	5.0-6.0	4

continued

57. OPTIMUM SOIL pH FOR GROWTH: SPERMATOPHYTES

	Species (Synonym)	pH	Reference
15	*Pseudotsuga taxifolia*	5.0-6.5	6
16	*Taxodium distichum*	6.0-7.5	6
17	*Taxus* spp.	5.0-7.5	6
18	*Thuja occidentalis*	6.0-7.5	4
19	*Tsuga canadensis*	4.5-6.0	6
	Angiospermae		
	Monocotyledoneae		
20	*Agrostis alba*	5.0-6.5	6
21	*Allium cepa*	6.0-7.5	6
22	*Ananas comosus*	4.5-6.0	5
23	*Asparagus officinalis*	6.0-8.0	4
24	*Avena sativa*	5.0-7.5	3,4
25	*Canna indica*	6.0-8.0	4
26	*Cynodon dactylon*	5.5-7.5	1
27	*Gladiolus* spp.	6.0-8.0	1
28	*Hemerocallis* spp.	6.0-8.0	1
29	*Hordeum vulgare*	6.0-7.5	6
30	*Hyacinthus orientalis*	6.0-7.5	6
31	*Iris* spp.	6.0-8.0	1
32	*Lilium longiflorum*	6.0-7.0	4
33	*Musa paradisiaca*	5.0-7.5	5
34	*Narcissus* spp.	5.0-7.0	1
35	*Oryza sativa*	5.0-6.5	3,4
36	*Paspalum dilatatum*	6.0-7.0	1
37	*Phleum pratense*	6.0-8.0	4
38	*Poa pratensis*	5.5-7.5	3,4
39	*Saccharum officinarum*	6.0-8.0	3,4
40	*Secale cereale*	5.0-7.0	3,4
41	*Setaria italica*	5.0-6.5	3,4
42	*Sorghum vulgare*	5.5-7.5	3,4
43	*S. vulgare caffrorum*	6.0-7.5	3,4
44	*S. vulgare sudanense*	6.0-7.5	1
45	*Tradescantia virginiana*	5.0-7.5	4
46	*Triticum aestivum*	5.5-7.5	3
47	*Tulipa gesneriana*	6.0-7.5	6
48	*Zea mays*	5.5-7.5	3,4
49	Dicotyledoneae		
49	*Abelia* spp.	6.0-8.0	1
50	*Acacia* spp.	6.5-8.0	6
51	*Acer* spp.	5.5-7.5	6
52	*A. spicatum*	4.5-6.0	6
53	*Aesculus glabra*	6.0-7.5	6
54	*A. hippocastanum*	5.5-7.0	6
55	*A. pavia*	5.0-6.5	6
56	*Ailanthus altissima*	6.0-8.0	6
57	*Alnus* spp.	6.0-7.5	6
58	*Althaea* spp.	6.0-8.0	1
59	*Alyssum* spp.	6.0-8.0	1
60	*Amelanchier* spp.	5.0-7.5	6
61	*Anthyllis vulneraria*	5.5-8.0	2
62	*Antirrhinum majus*	6.0-7.5	4
63	*Apium graveolens dulce*	6.0-7.5	6
64	*Arachis hypogaea*	5.0-6.5	4
65	*Begonia* spp.	5.5-7.0	6
66	*Beta saccharifera (B. vulgaris)*	6.5-8.0	4
67	*B. vulgaris*	6.0-7.5	4
68	*Betula lenta*	4.5-6.0	6
69	*Brassica napobrassica*	5.0-7.5	2
70	*B. nigra*	6.0-7.5	4
71	*B. oleracea botrytis*	5.5-7.5	1
72	*B. oleracea capitata*	6.0-7.5	4
73	*B. oleracea gemmifera*	6.0-7.5	1
74	*B. oleracea italica*	6.0-7.0	4
75	*B. rapa*	5.5-7.0	1
76	*Buddleia* spp.	6.0-8.0	1
77	*Buxus sempervirens*	6.0-7.5	6
78	*Calendula* spp.	6.0-8.0	1
79	*Callistephus chinensis*	6.0-7.5	6
80	*Camellia japonica*	4.5-6.0	6
81	*Cannabis sativa*	6.0-7.5	6
82	*Capsicum frutescens (C. annum)*	5.5-7.0	1
83	*Carpinus* spp.	6.0-7.5	6
84	*Carya ovata*	6.0-6.5	6
85	*Castanea dentata*	4.5-6.5	6
86	*C. pumila*	4.5-6.5	6
87	*Catalpa* spp.	6.0-7.5	6
88	*Celtis* spp.	6.0-7.5	6
89	*Cercis canadensis*	6.0-7.5	6
90	*Chrysanthemum morifolium*	6.0-7.5	4
91	*Citrullus vulgaris*	5.0-6.5	6
92	*Citrus limon*	6.0-7.5	4
93	*C. paradisi*	6.0-8.0	1
94	*C. sinensis*	6.0-7.5	4
95	*Clematis* spp.	6.0-7.5	1
96	*Coleus blumei*	6.0-7.5	6
97	*Cornus florida*	5.0-6.5	6
98	*Cucumis melo*	6.0-8.0	1
99	*C. sativus*	5.5-7.0	4
100	*Cucurbita maxima*	5.5-7.0	4
101	*C. pepo*	5.5-7.0	1
102	*Dahlia* spp.	6.0-8.0	1
103	*Datura stramonium*	6.0-7.5	4
104	*Daucus carota*	5.5-7.0	4
105	*Delphinium* spp.	6.0-8.0	1
106	*Dianthus caryophyllus*	6.0-7.5	4
107	*Eucalyptus* spp.	6.5-8.0	6
108	*Fagopyrum sagittatum (F. esculentum)*	5.5-7.0	3,4
109	*Fagus grandifolia*	5.0-6.5	4
110	*F. sylvatica*	6.0-7.5	6
111	*Fragaria* spp.	5.0-6.5	1,4
112	*Gaillardia* spp.	6.0-8.0	1
113	*Gardenia jasminoides*	5.0-7.0	1
114	*Gleditsia triacanthos*	6.0-7.5	6
115	*Glycine max (G. soja)*	6.0-7.5	6
116	*Gossypium hirsutum*	5.0-6.5	6
117	*Gymnocladus dioicus*	6.0-7.5	6
118	*Hedera helix*	6.0-8.0	4
119	*Helianthus annuus*	6.0-7.5	3,4
120	*H. tuberosus*	6.5-7.5	4

continued

57. OPTIMUM SOIL pH FOR GROWTH: SPERMATOPHYTES

	Species (Synonym)	pH	Reference
121	*Heliotropium* spp.	6.0-8.0	1
122	*Hibiscus esculentus*	6.0-7.5	1
123	*H. rosa-sinensis*	6.0-8.0	4
124	*Iberis* spp.	6.0-7.0	1
125	*Ilex aquifolium*	5.0-6.5	6
126	*I. cornuta*	6.0-7.5	1
127	*I. opaca*	4.5-6.0	6
128	*I. vomitoria*	5.5-7.5	1
129	*Impatiens balsamina*	6.0-7.5	4
130	*Ipomoea batatas*	5.0-6.5	6
131	*Juglans* spp.	6.0-7.5	6
132	*Kalanchoe blossfeldiana*	6.0-7.5	4
133	*Kalmia latifolia*	4.5-6.0	6
134	*Lactuca sativa*	6.0-7.5	6
135	*Lepidium sativum*	6.0-7.0	4
136	*Lespedeza* spp.	5.0-6.5	1
137	*Ligustrum* spp.	6.0-7.5	1
138	*Linum usitatissimum*	5.0-7.0	3,4
139	*Liquidambar styraciflua*	5.0-6.5	6
140	*Liriodendron tulipifera*	5.5-7.5	6
141	*Lycopersicon esculentum*	5.5-7.5	4
142	*Magnolia grandiflora*	5.0-7.0	1
143	*Malus pumila*	5.0-6.5	4
144	*Matthiola incana*	6.0-7.5	4
145	*Medicago sativa*	6.2-7.8	3,4
146	*Melilotus alba*	6.0-7.5	6
147	*M. indica*	6.0-7.5	1
148	*Morus* spp.	6.0-7.5	6
149	*Nicotiana tabacum*	5.5-7.5	3,4
150	*Nyssa sylvatica*	4.5-6.0	6
151	*Oenothera biennis*	6.0-8.0	4
152	*Ostrya virginiana*	6.0-7.0	6
153	*Paulownia tomentosa*	5.5-7.5	6
154	*Pelargonium domesticum*	6.0-8.0	1,4
155	*Petroselinum crispum (P. hortense)*	5.0-7.0	4
156	*Petunia* spp.	6.0-8.0	1
157	*Phaseolus limensis*	6.0-7.5	6
158	*P. vulgaris*	6.0-7.5	3,4
159	*Pisum sativum*	6.0-8.0	1
160	*Platanus* spp.	5.5-7.5	6
161	*Populus* spp.	5.5-7.5	6
162	*P. tremuloides*	4.5-5.5	6
163	*Prunus cerasus*	6.0-7.0	4
164	*P. glandulosa*	6.0-7.5	6
165	*P. persica (Amygdalus persica)*	6.0-7.5	4
166	*P. virginiana*	6.0-7.5	6
167	*Pyrus communis*	6.0-7.5	4
168	*Quercus alba*	6.0-8.0	1
169	*Q. borealis*	4.5-6.5	6
170	*Q. coccinea*	4.5-6.5	6
171	*Q. falcata*	4.5-5.0	6
172	*Q. laevis*	4.5-5.0	6
173	*Q. marilandica*	4.5-5.0	6
174	*Q. palustris*	6.0-7.0	1
175	*Q. phellos*	4.5-6.5	6
176	*Q. prinus*	6.0-7.0	1
177	*Q. robur*	6.0-7.5	6
178	*Q. stellata*	4.5-5.0	6
179	*Q. velutina*	4.5-6.5	6
180	*Raphanus sativus*	5.5-7.0	6
181	*Rhododendron obtusum amoenum*	4.5-6.0	4
182	*Ricinus communis*	6.0-7.5	4
183	*Robinia* spp.	5.5-7.5	6
184	*Rosa* sp.	5.5-7.0	4
185	*Rubus* spp.[1/]	6.0-8.0	1
186	*Saintpaulia ionantha*	5.5-7.0	6
187	*Salix* spp.	5.5-7.5	6
188	*S. repens*	4.5-6.0	6
189	*Solanum tuberosum*	5.0-6.5	3,4
190	*Sorbus americana*	4.5-6.5	6
191	*S. aucuparia*	5.5-7.5	6
192	*Spinacia oleracea*	6.0-7.5	4
193	*Tilia* spp.	6.0-7.5	6
194	*Trifolium pratense*	6.0-7.5	3,4
195	*T. repens*	5.5-7.5	5
196	*Tropaeolum majus*	5.5-7.5	4
197	*Ulmus americana*	6.0-8.0	1
198	*U. parvifolia*	6.0-8.0	1
199	*Vaccinium* spp.	4.5-6.0	6
200	*Vicia* spp.	5.5-7.5	1
201	*V. faba equina*	6.0-7.0	4
202	*V. villosa*	5.0-7.0	4
203	*Vigna* spp.[2/]	5.5-7.5	1
204	*Viola* spp.	6.0-7.5	1
205	*Vitis* spp.	6.0-8.0	1
206	*Zinnia* spp.	6.0-8.0	1

[1/] Most species. [2/] Many species.

Contributors: (a) Walker, Richard B., (b) Wherry, Edgar T., (c) Welch, C. D., (d) Larsen, Sigurd

References

[1] Bennett, W. F. 1953. Texas Agr. Expt. Sta. Leaflet L-164.

[2] Dorph-Petersen, K. 1947. Tidsskr. Planteavl 51:1.

[3] Ignatieff, V. 1949. Food Agr. Organ. U. N. Agr. Studies 9:108.

[4] Spurway, C. H. 1941. Mich. State Univ. Agr. Expt. Sta. Spec. Bull. 306.

[5] Sutton, C. D. Unpublished. Levington Research Station, Ipswich, England, 1962.

[6] Wherry, E. T. Unpublished. Univ. Pennsylvania, Philadelphia, 1965.

58. CONTROL OF TRANSPIRATION WITH FOLIAR SPRAYS OF INHIBITORS OF STOMATAL MOVEMENT: HIGHER PLANTS

	Species	Inhibitor [Common Name]	Concentration	Effect			Reference
				Stomata	% Decrease in Transpiration	Duration	
1	*Festuca rubra*	Phenylmercuric acetate	3.3×10^{-4} *M*	Closed	20	8 days	3
2	*Glycine max*	2-Chloro-4-ethylamino-6-isopropylamino-*s*-triazine [Atrazine]	14 ppm	Closed	Not stated	At least 6 hr	10
3	*Gossypium* sp.	Phenylmercuric acetate	10^{-3} *M*	Closed	40	12 days	8,9
4			10^{-4} *M*	Closed	35-40	12-27 days	
5			10^{-5} *M*	Closed	10	12 days	
6		8-Hydroxyquinoline sulfate	10^{-2} *M*	....	20	12 days	
7			10^{-3} *M*	....	10	12 days	
8		Hydroxylamine hydrochloride	10^{-4} *M*	....	20	12 days	
9			10^{-3} *M*	....	40	12 days	
10		3-(*p*-Chlorophenyl)-1,1-dimethylurea	10^{-3} *M*	....	30	12 days	
11		[Monuron]	10^{-4} *M*	....	20	12 days	
12	*Helianthus annuus*	Phenylmercuric acetate	0.9×10^{-4} *M*	Closed	14	37 days	6
13	*Hordeum vulgare*	Kinetin	10^{-6} *M*	Opened	Increased	2 hr	5
14		Monomethyl ester of nonenylsuccinic acid	10^{-3} *M*	Closed	13-30	2 days	13
15	*Lycopersicon esculentum*	Sodium azide	10^{-3} *M*	Closed	40	45 min	2
16	*Nicotiana tabacum*	Phenylmercuric acetate	0.9×10^{-4} *M*	Closed	10	5-11 days	6
17			10^{-4} *M*	Closed	....	14 days	16
18			0.33×10^{-4} *M*	....	16	9-16 days	17
19			10^{-4} *M*	....	43	9-16 days	17
20		8-Hydroxyquinoline	10^{-3} *M*	Closed	....	4 hr	16
21		Sodium α-hydroxydecanesulfonate	10^{-3} *M*	Closed	....	4 hr	16
22		Monomethyl ester of decenylsuccinic acid	10^{-3} *M*	Closed	21-43	5 days	15
23	*Phaseolus vulgaris*	Ammonium 2,4-dichlorophenoxyacetate	10-1000 ppm	Closed	....	50 hr	1
24		2,4-Dichlorophenoxyacetic acid	125 ppm	....	50	13 days	14
25		2-Chloro-4-ethylamino-6-isopropylamino-	20 ppm	....	40	5 hr	11
26		*s*-triazine [Atrazine]	300 ppm	....	53	5 hr	11
27		Isopropyl-*N*-phenylcarbamate	300 ppm	....	25	5 hr	11
28		*N*-(3,4-Dichlorophenyl)-2-methylpentanamide [Karsil]	300 ppm	....	25	5 hr	11
29		3,4-Dichloropropionanilide	300 ppm	....	52	5 hr	11
30		5-Bromo-3-isopropyl-6-methyluracil	300 ppm	....	48	5 hr	11
31		Phenylmercuric acetate	300 ppm	....	55	5 hr	11
32	*Pinus resinosa*	Phenylmercuric acetate	10^{-3} *M*	Closed	Saving soil moisture	35 days	12
33	*Tropaeolum majus*	β-Naphthoxyacetic acid	300 ppm	Closed	Lowered	2 hr	4
34	*Zea mays*	Phenylmercuric acetate	0.9×10^{-4} *M*	Closed	10-26	2 hr	7
35			10^{-4} *M*	Closed	....	14 days	16

Contributor: Zelitch, Israel

References

[1] Bradbury, D., and W. B. Ennis, Jr. 1952. Am. J. Botany 39:324.

[2] Cook, G. D., J. R. Dixon, and A. C. Leopold. 1964. Science 144:546.

[3] Davenport, D. C. 1966. Nature 212:7077.

[4] Ferri, M. G., and A. Lex. 1948. Contrib. Boyce Thompson Inst. 15:283.

[5] Livne, A., and Y. Vaadia. 1965. Physiol. Plantarum 18:658.

[6] Shimshi, D. 1963. Plant Physiol. 38:709.

[7] Shimshi, D. 1963. Ibid. 38:713.

[8] Slatyer, R. O., and J. F. Bierhuizen. 1964. Agr. Meteorol. 1:42.

[9] Slatyer, R. O., and J. F. Bierhuizen. 1964. Australian J. Biol. Sci. 17:131.

[10] Smith, D., and K. P. Buchholtz. 1962. Science 136: 263.

[11] Smith, D., and K. P. Buchholtz. 1964. Plant Physiol. 39:572.

[12] Waggoner, P. E., and B.-A. Bravdo. 1967. Proc. Natl. Acad. Sci. U.S. 57:1096.

[13] Waggoner, P. E., J. L. Monteith, and G. Szeicz. 1964. Nature 201:97.

[14] Williams, G. G., et al. 1961. U.S. Army Electronic Proving Ground (Fort Huachuca, Ariz.) Ann. Rept. Res. Transpiration.

[15] Zelitch, I. 1964. Science 143:692.

[16] Zelitch, I., and P. E. Waggoner. 1962. Proc. Natl. Acad. Sci. U.S. 48:1101.

[17] Zelitch, I., and P. E. Waggoner. 1962. Ibid. 48:1297.

VI. ANIMAL ENERGY EXCHANGE

59. BODY TEMPERATURES

The body temperature of a homoiotherm is affected by time of day, age, sex, activity, and adaptation to climate extremes. All measurements are diurnal, unless otherwise indicated. Values in parentheses are ranges, estimates "b" or "c" (*see* Introduction).

Part I. Mammals

	Species (Synonym)	Temperature		Reference
		Site	°C	
	Primates			
1	*Homo sapiens*	Rectum	36.9(36.2-37.6)	4
2	*Aotus trivirgatus*	Rectum	38.2(37.4-40.0)	20
3	*Callithrix jacchus*	Rectum or colon	(35.5-41)	89
4	*Cebuella pygmaea*	Rectum or colon	(34-38.5)	89
5	*Cercopithecus pygerythrus*	Rectum	38.7(37.2-40.1)	20
6	*Cynopithecus* sp.	Rectum	37.9(37.1-38.8)	39
7	*Erythrocebus patas (Cercopithecus pattus)*	Axilla	38.0(37.4-38.5)	69
8	*Lemur variegatus*	Rectum	38.2(37.5-38.9)	20
9	*Macaca irus (M. cynomolgus)*	Axilla	37.7(36.7-38.6)	69
10	*M. mulatta (M. rhoesus)*	Axilla	38.4(37.4-39.2)	69
11	*Pan troglodytes*	Rectum	(36.3-37.8)	49
12	*Papio hamadryas*	Axilla	38.1(37.3-38.7)	69
13	*(P. hamadragus)*	Abdomen	(37.3-38.7)	115
14	*Perodicticus potto*	Rectum	36.9(34.9-38.9)	123
15	*Pongo pygmaeus (P. satyrus)*	Rectum	(36.2-37.8)	39
16	*Saimiri sciurea*	Rectum	39.5	25
	Artiodactyla			
17	*Alces americana*	Rectum	39.4	29
18	*Bison bison*	Rectum	39.0	39
19	*Bos indicus*	Intramuscular[1]	38.5(37.7-39.2)	14
20	*B. taurus*	Intramuscular[1]	38.4(37.3-39.2)	14
21	*B. taurus*[2]	Rectum	38.3(36.7-39.1)	31
22	*B. taurus*[3]	Rectum	38.6(38.0-39.3)	31
23	Holstein	Rectum	39.6(38.2-41.0)	114
24	Jersey	Rectum	39.3(37.9-40.7)	113
25	*Bubalus* spp.	Rectum	38.2(37.4-38.7)	84
26	*Camelus bactrianus*	Rectum	37.5(36.9-38.0)	39
27	*C. dromedarius*	Intramuscular[1]	(35.1-39.1)	13
28		Rectum or colon	37.5(34-41)	110
29		Rectum	(34.5-35.6)[4]	27
30		Rectum	(37.4-38.5)[5]	27
31	*Capra* sp.	Rectum	38.6(37.8-39.4)	57
32	*Capra* sp.[6]	Rectum	38.6(35.2-40.5)	109
33	*Giraffa camelopardalis*	Intramuscular[1]	38.5(37.8-39.1)	13
34	*Hippopotamus amphibius*	Rectum	35.4(34.0-39.0)	24,76
35	*Lama guanicoe*	Rectum	38.8(38.2-39.4)	105
36	*Muntiacus muntjac*	Rectum	38.6	20
37	*Odocoileus hemionus*	Rectum	38.3(37.9-39.8)	28
38	*Oreamnos americanus*	Rectum	38.6(37.8-39.0)	63
39	*Oryx beisa*	Intramuscular[1]	38.5(36.6-40.0)	13
40	*Ovibos moschatus*	Rectum	40.0	3
41	*Ovis aries*	Rectum	38.9	84
42	Awassi	Rectum	(36.4-38.4)	78
43	East African	Intramuscular[1]	39.6(38.5-40.7)	15
44	Merino	Rectum	(38.3-40.9)	78
45	Welsh Mountain	Intramuscular[1]	(37.9-39.8)	15

1/ In neck. 2/ Beef cattle. 3/ Dairy cattle. 4/ At 7:00 a.m. 5/ At 6:00 p.m. 6/ Indian species.

continued

59. BODY TEMPERATURES

Part I. Mammals

	Species (Synonym)	Temperature		Reference
		Site	°C	
46	*Rangifer tarandus*	Rectum	39.0(38.1-40.0)	80
47	*R. tarandus arcticus (R. arcticus)*	Rectum or colon	39.3(38.8-40.5)	47
48	*R. tarandus stonei*	Rectum	39.0(38.5-40.0)	63
49	*Redunca arundinum*	Rectum	38.4	121
50	*Sus scrofa*	Rectum	(39.0-40.3)	49
51	*Syncerus caffer*	Intramuscular[1]	38.7(36.9-40.1)	13
52	*Taurotragus oryx*	Intramuscular[1]	39.1(38.3-39.9)	13
53		Rectum	38.8	121
54	*Tayassu tajacu angulatus (T. angulatus)*	Rectum	38.5	17
	Perissodactyla			
55	*Ceratotherium simum*	Rectum or colon	35.2(33.6-37.5)	1
56	*Diceros bicornis*	Intramuscular[1]	38.7(37.6-39.8)	13
57	*Equus caballus*	Rectum	38	18
58	*Rhinoceros* sp.	Rectum	37.7(37.6-37.8)	12
	Proboscidea			
59	*Elephas maximus*	Rectum	36.4(36.2-36.7)	11
	Carnivora			
60	*Alopex lagopus*	Rectum	38.6(36.6-41.5[7])	102,111
61	*Bassariscus astutus*	Rectum	37.6(37.2-37.9)	20
62	*Canis aureus indicus*	Rectum	38.3	29
63	*Canis familiaris*	Rectum	38.7(38.1-39.3)	32
64	*C. lupus*	Rectum	40.5	69
65	*Enhydra lutris*	Rectum	38.5	63
66	*Felis catus*	Rectum	(37.2-39.0)	104
67	*F. concolor*	Rectum	(38.5-39.8)	29,30
68	*Mephitis mephitis mesomelas (M. mesomelas)*	Rectum	36.4(36.3-36.5)	20
69	*Mustela putorius*	Rectum	40.0	96,108
70	*M. rixosa*	Rectum	40.4(38.4-42.4)	96,108
71	*Nasua nasua (N. rufa)*	Rectum	38.2(37.1-39.2)	20
72	*Nyctereutes procyonoides*	Rectum	37.4(37.0-37.8)	101
73	*Potos caudiovolvus*	Rectum	37.2	17
74	*Procyon cancrivorus*	Rectum	39.0	17
75	*Thalarctos maritimus*	Rectum	37.4(37.0-38.0)	55
76	*Ursus americanus*	Rectum	38.0(31.3-39.0)	54
77	*U. arctos*	Rectum	38.0(37.0-38.0)	55,63
78	*Vulpes fulva*	Rectum	38.8(37.5-40.1)	96,108
79	*V. vulpes*	Rectum	37.8(37.6-38.0)	101
80	*V. vulpes alascensis*	Rectum	40.1	63
	Pinnipedia			
81	*Callorhinus ursinus*	Heart	38.6(37.4-39.5)	43
82	*Erignathus barbatus*	Rectum	37.2(36.8-37.3)	63
83	*Eumetopias jubata*	Rectum	38.5	63
84	*Mirounga angustirostris*	Rectum or colon	35.9(33.0-37.5)	5
85	*Odobenus rosmarus divergens (O. divergens)*	Rectum	36.1[8]	55
86	*Phoca vitulina*	Intramuscular	37.0(36-38)	62
	Cetacea			
87	*Balaenoptera musculus*[9]	Belly	35.7(35.6-35.8)	126
88	*B. physalus*	Belly	38.4	126
89	*Eschrichtius gibbosus (Rhachianectes glaucus)*[10]	Belly	36.5(35.0-38.0)	126

[1] In neck. [7] Upper limit of range probably represents readings taken after violent activity. [8] Recorded after subject had spent half hour on ice floe. [9] Dead 12-16 hours. [10] 30 subjects, dead 0-9 hours.

continued

59. BODY TEMPERATURES

Part I. Mammals

	Species (Synonym)	Temperature		Reference
		Site	°C	
90	*Megaptera novaeangliae*	Intramuscular	36.0(34.5-37.7)	90
91	*(M. nodosa)*	Belly	38.1	126
92	*Physeter catodon*	Belly	38.2	126
	Rodentia			
93	*Baiomys taylori*	Abdomen	(32-36)	60
94	*Capromys pilorides*	Rectum	38.3(36.2-40.4)	2
95	*Castor fiber*	Rectum or colon	37.0(36.6-37.4)	118
96	*Cavia porcellus*	Rectum	38.1(36.6-39.6)	42
97	*Citellus citellus*	Rectum or colon	37.7(35.7-39.0)	40
98	*C. franklini*	Rectum	36.6(33.9-39.3)	96,108
99	*C. lateralis*	Rectum	37.7(35.0-39.0)	55
100	*C. leucurus*	Rectum or colon	36.7(35.5-38.5)	58
101	*C. pygmaeus*	Rectum or colon	37.2(35.0-38.7)	68
102	*C. tereticaudus*	Rectum or colon	37(35.5-39.5)	59
103	*C. tridecemlineatus*	Rectum	36.9(33.0-40.8)	96,108
104	*C. undulatus*	Rectum	38.8(33.0-41.0)	54
105	*C. undulatus parryii (C. parryii)*	Rectum	38.1(35.5-40.7)	96,108
106	*Clethrionomys gapperi*	Rectum	37.3(35.3-39.3)	96,108
107	*C. rutilus*	Rectum	38.3(36.6-40.0)	98
108	*Coendou villosus*	Rectum	35.3	37
109	*Cricetus cricetus*	Rectum	39.0(37.7-40.3)	79
110	*Dasyprocta aguti*	Rectum	38.5(37.9-39.0)	20
111	*D. azarae*	Rectum	39.0(38.9-39.1)	20
112	*D. prymnolopha*	Rectum	38.9(38.7-39.0)	20
113	*Dicrostonyx groenlandicus*	Rectum or colon	38.7(38-39.5)	45
114	*D. groenlandicus rubricatus (D. rubricatus)*	Rectum	38.3(35.4-41.2)	98
115	*Dipodomys agilis & D. merriami*	Rectum or colon	37(35-38)	23
116	*Erethizon dorsatum*	Rectum	37.5(36.0-38.2)	63
117	*Eutamias minimus*	Rectum	37.6(36.6-38.0)	55
118	*Geomys bursarius*	Rectum	34.8(33.8-35.8)	67
119	*G. pinetis*	Rectum or colon	36.3(35.9-36.7)	81
120	*Glaucomys volans*	Rectum	39.0(36.6-41.4)	96,108
121	*Glis glis*	Rectum	35.5(35.1-35.9)	69
122	*Heliophobius argenteocinereus kapiti (H. kapiti)*	Rectum or colon	35.1(34.9-35.3)	81
123	*Heterocephalus glaber*	Rectum or colon	30.0(29.4-30.6)	81
124	*Hydromys chrysogaster*	Rectum or colon	36.6	105
125	*Jaculus jaculus*	Rectum or colon	36.9(36.2-37.3)	71
126	*Lagurus curtatus*	Rectum	35.6(33.8-38.5)	55
127	*Lemmus lemmus*	Skin	35.6 11/	52
128	*Liomys irroratus*	Rectum or colon	36.6(36.0-37.7)	61
129	*L. salvini*	Rectum or colon	37.1(36.5-37.8)	61
130	*Marmota caligata*	Rectum	36.4(33.5-39.3)	96,108
131	*M. marmota*	Rectum	38.3	63
132	*Melomys littoralis*	Rectum or colon	37.5	105
133	*Meriones unguiculatus*	Rectum or colon	38.2	106
134	*Mesocricetus auratus*	Rectum	36.4(35.8-37.6)	38
135	*Microdipodops pallidus*	Rectum or colon	38.8(37-41)	9
136	*Microtus arvalis*	Rectum or colon	37(28-38)	10
137	*M. longicaudus*	Rectum	37.2	55
138	*M. pennsylvanicus*	Rectum	39.3(34.7-43.1)	96,108
139	*Mus musculus*	Rectum or colon	37.2(36.6-38.8)	44
140	*Muscardinus avellanarius*	Rectum	34.5(31.0-37.9)	103
141	*Myocastor coypus*	Rectum	38.0(37.2-38.8)	20
142	*Myoprocta acouchy (Dasyprocta acouchy)*	Rectum	38.9(38.7-39.0)	20
143	*Napaeozapus insignis*	Rectum or colon	37.0(36.5-37.5)	19
144	*Neotoma fuscipes*	Rectum or colon	36.6(36-38)	74

11/ Mean skin temperature.

continued

59. BODY TEMPERATURES

Part I. Mammals

	Species (Synonym)	Temperature		Reference
		Site	°C	
145	*N. lepida*	Rectum or colon	36.8(36-38)	74
146	*Ondatra zibethicus*	Rectum	38.0(37.0-39.1)	63
147	*Perognathus hispidus*	Rectum	36.5(34.9-38.1)	95
148	*P. longimembris*	Subcutaneous	34.7(33.7-36)	26
149	*Peromyscus californicus*	Rectum or colon	37.3(36-38.5)	120
150	*P. crinitus*	Rectum or colon	35.7(35.1-36.3)	82
151	*P. eremicus*	Rectum or colon	36.7(33.3-38.6)	99
152	*P. leucopus*	Rectum	37.4(33.6-41.2)	93
153	♂	Esophagus	37.6(36.2-38.8)	112
154	♀	Esophagus	38.1(36.6-39.5)	112
155	*P. maniculatus*	Rectum	37.5(37.1-37.9)	56
156	*P. maniculatus artemisiae*	Rectum or colon	37.2	48
157	*P. maniculatus austerus*	Rectum or colon	36.3	48
158	*P. maniculatus nebrascensis*	Rectum or colon	35.9	48
159	*P. maniculatus oreas*	Rectum or colon	36.0	48
160	*P. maniculatus sonoriensis*	Rectum or colon	36.7(34.9-38.3)	99
161	*P. polionotus*	Rectum or colon	37.1(31.7-41)	117
162	*P. sitkensis*	Rectum or colon	36.3	48
163	*P. thomasi*	Rectum or colon	37.8(36-39)	100
164	*P. truei*	Rectum or colon	36.6(36.4-36.8)	82
165	*Pitymys subterraneus (Microtus subterraneus)*	Rectum or colon	(34.8-39)	116
166	*Proechimys semispinosus*	Rectum	37.9(36.5-39.3)	106
167	*Rattus conatus*	Rectum or colon	37.3	105
168	*R. norvegicus*	Rectum	37.3(34.5-40.0)	51
169	*R. rattus*	Rectum	(32.1-38.1)	69
170	*Reithrodontomys megalotis*	Rectum	37.5(37.0-38.0)	55
171	*Sicista betulina*	Rectum or colon	(36-38)[12]	66
172	*Spalax leucodon*	Rectum or colon	37.0(36.6-37.4)	81
173	*Tachyoryctes splendens*	Rectum or colon	36.0(35.8-36.2)	81
174	*Tamias striatus*	Rectum	38.6(36.5-40.1)	70
175	*Tamiasciurus hudsonicus*	Rectum or colon	39.5(38.5-40.5)	89
176	*Uromys sherrini*	Rectum or colon	37.1	105
177	*Zapus hudsonius*	Rectum	37.3(35.3-39.3)	94
	Lagomorpha			
178	*Lepus americanus*	Pericardium	38.9(37.5-40)	46
179		Rectum	38.5(38.0-39.0)	63
180	*L. timidus*	Rectum	38.7(38.1-39.3)	101
181	*Ochotona collaris*	Rectum	39.0	86
182	*Oryctolagus cuniculus*	Rectum or colon	38.2(38-38.4)	41
183	*Sylvilagus floridanus*	Rectum	39.4(38.7-40.1)	96,108
	Pholidota			
184	*Manis tricuspis*	Rectum or colon	(32.2-35.2)	36
	Edentata			
185	*Bradypus griseus*	Rectum	33.2(29.2-37.2)	16,17,37,85,123
186	*B. tridactyla (B. cuculliger)*	Rectum	31.0(24.4-37.6)	72
187	*Chaetophractus villosus (Dasypus villosus)*	Rectum	33.4(31.8-35.0)	33
188	*Choloepus hoffmanni*	Rectum	34.5(33.4-35.8)	16,17,20,37
189	*Cyclopes* sp.	Rectum	30.7(30.2-31.1)	37
190	*Dasypus novemcinctus*	Rectum or colon	35.0(34.0-36.4)	64,65
191	*D. sexcinctus*	Rectum	33.2(32.2-34.1)	20
192	*Myrmecophaga tridactyla (M. jubata)*	Rectum or colon	(32-34)	124
193	*Tamandua tetradactyla*	Rectum	33.5(32.0-35.0)	37

[12] Recorded while subject was active.

continued

59. BODY TEMPERATURES

Part I. Mammals

	Species (Synonym)	Temperature		Reference
		Site	°C	
		Chiroptera		
194	*Antrozous pallidus*	Intraclavicular depression	36.3(33.0-38.5)	73
195	*Artibeus* sp.	Rectum or colon	37.0(34-40)	89
196	*Asellia tridens*	Intraclavicular depression	37.3(23.2-39.8)	73
197	*Carollia perspicillata*	Rectum	37.2(36.4-37.8)	123
198	*Desmodus rotundus*	Rectum	37.3(30.0-40.2)	77
199	*Epomophorus anurus*	Rectum	39.2(36.0-41.1)	73
200	*Eptesicus fuscus*	Intraclavicular depression	38.2(24.0-41.0)	73
201		Rectum	35.3	96,108
202	*E. serotinus*	Rectum	38.1(36.2-40.0)	34
203	*E. tenuipinnis*	Rectum	35.7(32.2-39.2)	34
204	*Eumops perotis*	Rectum	38.2(27.7-40.0)[13]	75
205	*Hipposideros bicolor*	Intraclavicular depression	34.9[14]; 35.5[15]	73
206	*H. caffer*	Rectum	34.9(31.4-38.4)	34
207	*H. cyclops*	Rectum	34.8(31.4-38.2)	34
208	*H. speoris*	Intraclavicular depression	34.5[14]; 37.2[15]	73
209	*Megaderma lyra*	Intramuscular[1]	39.3[14]; 40.0[15]	73
210	*Miniopterus blepotis*	Rectum or colon	(22.1-41.7)	88
211	*Myotis lucifugus*	Rectum	39.0(31.0-42.0)	50
212		Subcutaneous[16]	37.5(31.2-41.5)	53
213	*M. myotis*	Intraclavicular depression	39.5(23.4-41.7)	73
214		Rectum	37.6(35.6-39.6)	34
215	*M. mystacinus*	Rectum	37.2(36.2-38.2)	34
216	*M. nattereri*	Intraclavicular depression	39.8[14]; 41.3[15]	73
217	*M. sodalis*	Rectum	39.0(31.0-40.0)	50
218	*M. yumanensis*	Intraclavicular depression	38.3(24.2-41.3)	73
219	*Nyctalus noctula*	Intraclavicular depression	38.2(23.0-40.0)	73
220	*(Pipistrellus noctula)*	Skin[17]	31.5(30.0-33.0)[11]	21
221	*Pipistrellus pipistrellus*	Intraclavicular depression	37.3(23.0-41.6)	73
222	*Plecotus auritus*	Intraclavicular depression	38.5(24.5-39.3)	73
223		Rectum	36.6(35.0-38.2)	34
224	*Pteropus geddiei*	Rectum	35.4(32.2-38.6)	21
225	*P. giganteus*	Rectum	36.8(34.9-38.0)	73
226	*P. poliocephalus*	Rectum or colon	35.9(35-39)	8
227	*P. scapulatus*	Rectum	(35.0-40.2)	8
228	*Rhinolophus ferrum-equinum*	Intraclavicular depression	38.3(25.0-40.9)	73
229	*R. hipposideros*	Intraclavicular depression	37.0[14]; 38.5[15]	73
230		Rectum	35.9(34.4-37.4)	34
231	*R. landeri*	Rectum	32.8(28.0-37.6)	34
232	*Rhinopoma hardwickei*	Intraclavicular depression	34.0(27.6-38.2)	73
233	*R. microphyllum*	Intraclavicular depression	33.9(27.0-36.2)	73
234	*Rousettus aegyptiacus*	Rectum	40.1(37.9-41.7)	73
235	*R. angolensis*	Rectum	39.1[14]; 39.8[15]	73
236	*Sturnira lilium*	Rectum or colon	(34-39)	89
237	*Syconycteris australis*	Rectum	36.4(35.3-37.6)	8
238	*Tadarida condylura*	Intraclavicular depression	36.8(23.2-40.0)	73
239	*T. hindei*	Intraclavicular depression	39.4(33.0-41.7)	73
240	*T. pumila*	Intraclavicular depression	39.1[14]; 40.8[15]	73
241	*T. teniotis*	Intraclavicular depression	36.0(23.7-39.2)	73
242	*Taphozous melanopogon*	Intraclavicular depression	37.5(34.2-40.8)	73
243	*Thylacomys lagotis (Macrotis lagotis)*	Rectum or colon	(33.5-37.5)	89
		Insectivora		
244	*Blarina brevicauda*	Rectum	35.7(34.5-37.7)	70
245	*Erinaceus europaeus*	Rectum or colon	35.6(34.8-36.4)	87

[1] In neck. [11] Mean skin temperature. [13] In flight. [14] Mean temperature. [15] Upper limit. [16] On abdomen. [17] Thermocouple placed on shaved skin of back.

continued

59. BODY TEMPERATURES

Part I. Mammals

	Species (Synonym)	Temperature		Reference
		Site	°C	
246	*Hemiechinus auritus*	Rectum or colon	(33.4-36.4)	36
247	*Paraechinus aethiopicus*	Rectum or colon	(31.2-36.2)	36
248	*Scalopus aquaticus*	Rectum	35.8(34.6-37.0)	96,108
249	*Sorex cinereus*	Rectum or colon	38.8(36-40.5)	97
250	*Tenrec ecaudatus (Centetes ecaudatus)*	Rectum or colon	(24.1-34.8)	35
	Marsupialia			
251	*Antechinus flavipes*	Rectum or colon	37.5(37.1-38.7)	91
252	*Cercartetus nanus*	Rectum or colon	34.9(32.4-37.9)	7
253	*Dasycercus cristicauda*	Rectum or colon	35.9(33.9-37.9)	91
254	*Dasyurus maculatus*	Rectum	33.3(32.2-34.3)	20
255	*Didelphis marsupialis*	Rectum	35.5(34.1-36.9)	86
256	*D. marsupialis virginiana (D. virginiana)*	Rectum	35.0	92
257	*Isoodon obesulus (Thylacis obesulus)*	Rectum or colon	(31.0-37.0)	89
258	*Macropus giganteus*	Rectum	35.4(34.7-36.0)	20
259	*M. major*	Rectum or colon	37.1(36.5-37.5)	89
260	*Marmosa cinerea*	Rectum or colon	34.7(29.3-37.8)	35
261	*M. mexicana*	Rectum	32.7(28.9-36.5)	123
262	*Metachirus nudicaudatus*	Rectum	33.8(32.4-36.4)	86
263	*Petrogale xanthopus*	Rectum	35.9	119
264	*Phascogale tapoatafa*	Rectum or colon	38.0(36.7-38.8)	91
265	*Phascolarctos cinereus*	Rectum	36.4(34.9-38.4)	119
266	*Potorus tridactylus*	Rectum or colon	36.5	105
267	*Sarcophilus harrisii*	Rectum or colon	37.1(36.1-37.7)	91
268	*Satanellus hallucatus*	Rectum or colon	36.0(33.8-37.6)	91
269	*Setonix brachyurus*	Rectum or colon	37(36.6-37.6)	6
270	*Sminthopsis crassicaudata*	Rectum or colon	37.3(37.0-38.1)	91
271	*S. larapinta*	Rectum or colon	36.5(35.1-38.3)	91
272	*Trichosurus caninus & T. vulpecula*	Rectum or colon	36.9	105
273	*Wallabia dorsalis*	Rectum or colon	37.3(36.5-38)	89
274	*W. rufogrisea (Macropus ruficollis)*	Rectum	35.8	20
	Monotremata			
275	*Ornithorhynchus* sp.	Cloaca	30.3(25.7-34.9)	22
276	*Tachyglossus* sp.	Abdomen & cloaca	29.9(24.9-34.9)	22,83,125
277	*T. aculeatus (Echidna aculeata)*	Rectum or colon	31.0(27.5-33.9)	122
278	*Zaglossus* sp.	Rectum	29.0(26.2-31.8)	107

Contributors: (a) Hock, Raymond J., (b) Hart, J. Sanford, (c) Morrison, Peter R.

References

[1] Allbrook, D. B., et al. 1958. J. Physiol. (London) 143:51P.
[2] Angulo, J. J. 1949. J. Mammal. 30:54.
[3] Back, G. 1836. Compt. Rend. 2:621.
[4] Baldwin, S. P., and S. C. Kendeigh. 1932. Sci. Publ. Cleveland Museum Nat. Hist. 3:1.
[5] Bartholomew, G. A. 1954. J. Mammal. 35:211.
[6] Bartholomew, G. A. 1956. Physiol. Zool. 29:26.
[7] Bartholomew, G. A., and J. W. Hudson. 1962. Ibid. 35:94.
[8] Bartholomew, G. A., P. Leitner, and J. E. Nelson. 1964. Ibid. 37:179.
[9] Bartholomew, G. A., and R. E. MacMillen. 1961. Ibid. 34:177.
[10] Bashemina, N. V. 1963. Ref. Zh. Biol. 101234.
[11] Benedict, F. G. 1936. Carnegie Inst. Wash. Publ. 474.
[12] Benedict, F. G., F. L. Fox, and M. L. Baker. 1921. Am. J. Physiol. 56:464.
[13] Bligh, J., and A. M. Harthoorn. 1965. J. Physiol. (London) 176:145.
[14] Bligh, J., and G. N. Lampkin. 1965. J. Agr. Sci. 64:221.
[15] Bligh, J., et al. 1965. J. Physiol. (London) 176:130.
[16] Britton, S. W., and W. E. Atkinson. 1938. J. Mammal. 19:94.
[17] Britton, S. W., and R. F. Kline. 1939. Am. J. Physiol. 125:730.
[18] Brody, S. 1945. Bioenergetics and growth. Reinhold, New York.
[19] Brower, J. E., and T. J. Cade. 1966. Ecology 47:46.

continued

Part I. Mammals

[20] Brown, A. E. 1909. Proc. Zool. Soc. London, p. 81.
[21] Burbank, R. C., and J. Z. Young. 1934. J. Physiol. (London) 82:459.
[22] Burrell, H. 1927. The platypus. Angus and Robertson, Sydney.
[23] Carpenter, R. E. 1966. Univ. Calif. (Berkeley) Publ. Zool. 78.
[24] Cena, K. 1964. Intern. J. Biometeorol. 8:57.
[25] Chaffee, R. R. J., et al. 1966. J. Appl. Physiol. 21:151.
[26] Chew, R. M., R. G. Lindberg, and P. Hayden. 1967. Comp. Biochem. Physiol. 21:487.
[27] Cleland, J. B. 1909. Proc. Linnean Soc. N.S. Wales 34:268.
[28] Cowan, I. McT., and A. J. Wood. 1955. J. Wildlife Mgt. 19:154.
[29] Davy, J. 1826. Edinburgh Phil. J. 14:38.
[30] Despretz, C. 1824. Ann. Chim. Phys. (Paris) 26:337.
[31] Dukes, H. H. 1955. The physiology of domestic animals. Ed. 7. Comstock, Ithaca.
[32] Eagan, C. J., J. L. Durrer, and W. M. Millard. 1963. Arctic Aeromed. Lab. TDR 63-40:1.
[33] Eisentraut, M. 1932. Z. Vergleich. Physiol. 16:39.
[34] Eisentraut, M. 1940. Biol. Zentr. 60:199.
[35] Eisentraut, M. 1955. Mammalia 19:437.
[36] Eisentraut, M. 1956. Z. Saeugetierk. 21:49.
[37] Enders, R. K., and D. E. Davis. 1936. J. Mammal. 17:165.
[38] Folk, G. E., R. R. Schellinger, and D. Snyder. 1961. Proc. Iowa Acad. Sci. 68:594.
[39] Fox, H. 1923. Disease in captive wild mammals and birds. J. B. Lippincott, Philadelphia.
[40] Gelineo, S. 1939. Serb. Acad. Sci. Bull. Math. Nat. 5:197.
[41] Gelineo, S. 1956. Ibid. 16(4):1.
[42] Gosselin, R. E. 1949. Am. J. Physiol. 157:103.
[43] Hanna, G. D. 1924. Ibid. 68:52.
[44] Hart, J. S. 1951. Can. J. Zool. 29:224.
[45] Hart, J. S., and O. Heroux. 1955. Can. J. Biochem. Physiol. 33:428.
[46] Hart, J. S., H. Pohl, and J. S. Tener. 1965. Can. J. Zool. 43:731.
[47] Hart, J. S., et al. 1961. Ibid. 39:845.
[48] Hayward, J. S. 1965. Ibid. 43:309.
[49] Heitman, A. F., and E. H. Hughes. 1949. J. Animal Sci. 8:171.
[50] Henshaw, R. E., and G. E. Folk. 1966. Physiol. Zool. 39:223.
[51] Hill, R. M. 1947. Am. J. Physiol. 149:650.
[52] Hissa, R. 1964. Experientia 20:326.
[53] Hock, R. J. 1951. Biol. Bull. 101:289.
[54] Hock, R. J. 1960. Bull. Harvard Museum Comp. Zool. 124:155.
[55] Hock, R. J. Unpublished. Northrop Space Laboratories, Hawthorn, Calif., 1968.
[56] Hock, R. J., and J. C. Roberts. 1966. Can. J. Zool. 44:365.
[57] Hornby, H. E. 1942. Trans. Soc. Trop. Med. Hyg. 35:239.
[58] Hudson, J. W. 1962. Univ. Calif. (Berkeley) Publ. Zool. 64.
[59] Hudson, J. W. 1964. Ann. Acad. Sci. Fennicae, A-IV, 71 15.
[60] Hudson, J. W. 1965. Physiol. Zool. 38:243.
[61] Hudson, J. W., and J. A. Rummel. 1966. Ecology 47:345.
[62] Irving, L., and J. S. Hart. 1957. Can. J. Zool. 35:497.
[63] Irving, L., and J. Krog. 1954. J. Appl. Physiol. 6:667.
[64] Johansen, K. 1961. Physiol. Zool. 34:126.
[65] Johansen, K. 1962. Symp. Arctic Biol. Med., 2nd, p. 73.
[66] Johansen, K., and J. Krog. 1959. Am. J. Physiol. 196:1200.
[67] Johnson, G. E. 1931. Quart. Rev. Biol. 5:439.
[68] Kalabukhov, N. I. 1946. Animal sleep. Ed. 2. Kharkov State Univ. Press, U.S.S.R.
[69] Kanitz, A. 1925. Tabulae Biol. 1:371.
[70] Kendeigh, S. C. 1945. J. Mammal. 26:86.
[71] Kirmiz, J. P. 1962. Soc. Publ. Egypt. S.A.E., p. 1.
[72] Kredel, F. E. 1928. J. Pathol. Bacteriol. 31:517.
[73] Kulzer, E. 1965. Z. Vergleich. Physiol. 50:1.
[74] Lee, A. K. 1963. Univ. Calif. (Berkeley) Publ. Zool. 64:57.
[75] Leitner, P. 1966. Comp. Biochem. Physiol. 19:431.
[76] Luck, C. P., and P. G. Wright. 1962. Proc. Intern. Bioclimatol. Congr., 2nd, p. 334.
[77] Lyman, C. P., and W. A. Wimsatt. 1966. Physiol. Zool. 39:101.
[78] MacFarlane, W. V., R. J. H. Morris, and H. B. Howard. 1958. Australian J. Agr. Res. 19:217.
[79] Malan, A., and G. Hildwein. 1965. Compt. Rend. Soc. Biol. 159:473.
[80] McEwan, E. H., A. J. Wood, and H. C. Nordan. 1965. Can. J. Zool. 43:683.
[81] McNab, B. K. 1966. Ecology 47:712.
[82] McNab, B. K., and P. R. Morrison. 1963. Ecol. Monographs 33:63.
[83] Miklouho-Maclay, N. 1883. Proc. Linnean Soc. N.S. Wales 9:1204.
[84] Minett, F. C. 1947. J. Animal Sci. 6:35.
[85] Morrison, P. R. 1945. J. Mammal. 26:272.
[86] Morrison, P. R. 1946. J. Cellular Comp. Physiol. 27:125.
[87] Morrison, P. R. 1957. J. Mammal. 38:254.
[88] Morrison, P. R. 1959. Biol. Bull. 116:484.
[89] Morrison, P. R. 1962. Symp. Arctic Biol. Med., 2nd, p. 381.
[90] Morrison, P. R. 1962. Biol. Bull. 123:154.
[91] Morrison, P. R. 1965. Australian J. Zool. 13:173.
[92] Morrison, P. R., and J. H. Petajan. 1962. Physiol. Zool. 35:52.
[93] Morrison, P. R., and F. A. Ryser. 1959. Ibid. 32:90.
[94] Morrison, P. R., and F. A. Ryser. 1962. J. Cellular Comp. Physiol. 60:109.
[95] Morrison, P. R., and F. A. Ryser. 1962. J. Mammal. 43:529.
[96] Morrison, P. R., and F. A. Ryser. Unpublished. Univ. Alaska, College, 1967.

continued

59. BODY TEMPERATURES

Part I. Mammals

[97] Morrison, P. R., F. A. Ryser, and A. R. Dawe. 1959. Physiol. Zool. 32:256.

[98] Morrison, P. R., F. A. Ryser, and R. L. Strecker. 1954. J. Mammal. 35:376.

[99] Murie, M. 1961. Ecology 42:723.

[100] Muser, G. G., and V. H. Shoemaker. 1965. Univ. Mich. Museum Zool. Occasional Papers 643.

[101] Olnianskaya, R. R., and A. D. Slonim. 1947. Bull. Acad. Sci. URSS 2:245.

[102] Parry, W. E. 1827. Ann. Chim. Phys. (Paris) 34:111.

[103] Pembrey, M. S. 1903. J. Physiol. (London) 29:195.

[104] Robinson, K. W. 1941. Proc. Roy. Soc. Queensland 53:161.

[105] Robinson, K. W., and P. R. Morrison. 1957. J. Cellular Comp. Physiol. 49:455.

[106] Robinson, P. F. 1959. Sciencc 130:502.

[107] Rynberk, G. van. 1913. Amst. Bijdragen Dierk. 19:187.

[108] Ryser, F. A. 1952. Ph.D. Thesis. Univ. Wisconsin, Madison.

[109] Sadiq, M. N. 1943. Indian J. Vet. Sci. Animal Husbandry 13:247.

[110] Schmidt-Nielsen, K. 1964. Desert animals. Clarendon Press, Oxford.

[111] Scholander, P. F., et al. 1950. Biol. Bull. 99:237.

[112] Sealander, J. A. 1953. Ibid. 104:87.

[113] Seath, D. M., and G. D. Miller. 1946. J. Dairy Sci. 29:465.

[114] Seath, D. M., and G. D. Miller. 1947. Ibid. 30:957.

[115] Simpson, S., and J. J. Galbraith. 1906. Trans. Roy. Soc. Edinburgh 45:65.

[116] Smirnov, P. K. 1962. Vestn. Leningr. Univ., Ser. Biol., 16(4):72.

[117] Smith, M. H., and W. E. Criss. 1967. Physiol. Zool. 40:314.

[118] Steen, I., and J. B. Steen. 1965. Comp. Biochem. Physiol. 15:267.

[119] Sutherland, A. 1897. Proc. Roy. Soc. Victoria 9: 57.

[120] Tucker, V. A. 1965. J. Cellular Comp. Physiol. 65: 393.

[121] Vanderplank, F. L. 1941. Trans. Roy. Soc. Trop. Med. Hyg. 35:43.

[122] Wardlaw, H. S. H. 1915. Proc. Linnean Soc. N.S. Wales 40:231.

[123] Wislocki, G. B. 1933. Quart. Rev. Biol. 101:385.

[124] Wislocki, G. B., and R. K. Enders. 1935. J. Mammal. 16:328.

[125] Wood Jones, F. 1923. The mammals of South Australia. Rogers, Adelaide.

[126] Zenkovic, B. A. 1938. Compt. Rend. Acad. Sci. URSS 18:685.

Part II. Birds

	Species (Synonym)	Temperature		Reference
		Site	°C	
	Passeriformes			
1	*Acanthis hornemanni exilipes*	Cloaca	40.5(40.0-41.0)	35
2	*Agelaius phoeniceus*	Proventriculus	42.6(42.1-43.0)	9
3	*Aimophila cassinii*	Proventriculus	42.2[1,2]	63
4	*A. ruficeps*	Proventriculus	(42.1-43.4)	63
5	*Ammodramus savannarum*	Proventriculus	42.6	63
6	*Anthus spinoletta*	Cloaca	39.9	60
7	*Bombycilla cedrorum*	Proventriculus	42.9(42.0-44.4)	9
8	*B. garrulus*	Proventriculus	42.5[1]	63
9	*Calcarius lapponicus*	Proventriculus	41.7	63
10	*C. ornatus*	Proventriculus	43.1[1,2]	63
11	*Carpodacus purpureus*	Proventriculus	43.2(42.5-43.8)	9
12	*Certhia familiaris*	Proventriculus	41.9(42.7-42.5)	63
13	*Chamaea fasciata*	Proventriculus	42.0(41.5-42.3)	63
14	*Chloris chloris (Ligurinus chloris)*	Cloaca	41.5(41.2-42.2)[1]	63
15	*Cinclus mexicanus*	Proventriculus	41.8	63
16	*Contopus virens (Myiochanes virens)*	Skin	41.6[3]; 39.6-43.0[3,4]	1,39
17	*Corvus brachyrhynchos*	Cloaca	43.0[2]	9
18	*C. corax*	Cloaca	42.6(41.9-43.1)	63
19	*C. corax principalis*	Cloaca	41.3(40.5-42.0)	35
20	*C. monedula (Coloeus monedula)*	Cloaca	41.8(41.0-42.6)	57
21	*Cyanocitta cristata*	Cloaca	43.6(42.0-44.4)	9
22		Proventriculus	42.4	63

1/ Recorded after bird was shot. 2/ For one subject. 3/ Recorded by thermocouples in nest; 0.7°C was added to skin temperature to bring it up to body temperature. 4/ Mean daily minimum and maximum temperatures [1].

continued

59. BODY TEMPERATURES

Part II. Birds

	Species (Synonym)	Temperature		Reference
		Site	°C	
23	*C. cristata bromia*	Cloaca	40.3	49
24	*C. stelleri*	Proventriculus	42.1	63
25	*Dendroica auduboni*	Proventriculus	42.1	63
26	*D. caerulescens & D. magnolia*	Proventriculus	42.2	63
27	*D. tigrina*	Proventriculus	42.7	63
28	*Dolichonyx oryzivorus*	Proventriculus	42.6(40.9-43.4)	9
29	*Dumetella carolinensis*	Skin	41.2[3]; 40.0-42.3[3,4]	1,39
30	*Emberiza citrinella*	Cloaca	39.2	60
31		Proventriculus	40.5	60
32	*Empidonax flaviventris*	Proventriculus	42.3(41.9-42.8)	63
33	*E. minimus*	Proventriculus	42.4(41.9-42.8)	63
34	*E. traillii*	Proventriculus	42.3(41.8-43.1)	63
35	*Eremophila alpestris alpestris (Otocoris alpestris)*	Proventriculus	43.9[1,2]	9
36	*Erithacus rubecula*	Proventriculus	40.6	60
37	*Estrilda troglodytes*	Cloaca	39.8	11
38	*Euphagus carolinus*	Proventriculus	42.3[2]	9
39	*E. cyanocephalus*	Proventriculus	42.2(41.2-42.7)	63
40	*Geothlypis trichas*	Proventriculus	42.3(41.4-42.8)	63
41	*Guiraca caerulea*	Proventriculus	42.2(41.7-42.6)	63
42	*Gymnorhinus cyanocephala (Cyanocephalus cyanocephalus)*	Proventriculus	(41.4-42.4)	63
43	*Hedymeles ludovicianus*	Proventriculus	43.6(43.2-43.9)	9
44	*Hesperiphona vespertina*	Cloaca	(40.6-41.5)	16
45		Proventriculus	43.3(42.8-43.9)	9
46	*Hirundo rustica erythrogaster (H. erythrogaster)*	Proventriculus	41.4	63
47	*Hylocichla guttata*	Proventriculus	42.9(42.0-43.2)	63
48	*H. mustelina*	Proventriculus	42.8	63
49		Skin	40.9[3]; 39.2-42.1[3,4]	1,39
50	*Icteria virens*	Proventriculus	42.9(42.2-43.6)	63
51	*Icterus bullockii*	Proventriculus	42.2	63
52	*I. galbula*	Proventriculus	42.8	63
53	*Iridoprocne bicolor*	Proventriculus	41.5(41.1-42.2)	63
54	*Junco hyemalis*	Proventriculus	43.0(41.3-44.0)	9
55	*J. oreganus*	Proventriculus	42.8(42.5-43.7)	63
56	*Lanius ludovicianus*	Proventriculus	42.2(41.8-42.9)	63
57	*Loxia curvirostra*	Cloaca	(38.5-40.0)	17
58	*L. curvirostra pusilla*	Proventriculus	43.3(43.1-43.6)	9
59	*L. leucoptera leucoptera*	Cloaca	41.0(40.5-41.0)	35
60	*Melospiza lincolnii*	Proventriculus	43.6[2]	9
61	*M. melodia*	Proventriculus	43.6(42.0-44.6)	9
62	*M. melodia melodia*	Skin	41.1[3]; 40.2-43.0[3,4]	1,39
63	*Mimus polyglottos*	Proventriculus	42.7(42.3-43.6)	63
64	*Molothrus ater*	Proventriculus	43.2(42.5-43.6)	9
65	*Motacilla alba*	Proventriculus	40.6	60
66	*Muscicapa striata*	Proventriculus	40.9	60
67	*Myadestes townsendi*	Proventriculus	42.9(42.6-43.3)	63
68	*Nucifraga columbiana*	Proventriculus	41.5	63
69	*Nuttallornis borealis*	Proventriculus	42.7(42.2-43.3)	63
70	*Oporornis agilis*	Proventriculus	42.5[1,2]	63
71	*O. philadelphia*	Proventriculus	42.1	63
72	*O. tolmiei*	Proventriculus	42.1(41.7-43.0)	63
73	*Parus atricapillus*	Proventriculus	42.4(42.2-43.1)	63
74	*P. atricapillus atricapillus (Penthestes atricapillus)*	Proventriculus	43.8(43.2-44.3)	9
75	*P. atricapillus turneri*	Cloaca	40.0(39.5-40.0)	35
76	*P. carolinensis*	Proventriculus	42.3	63
77	*P. cinctus*	Proventriculus	40.6	41

1/ Recorded after bird was shot. 2/ For one subject. 3/ Recorded by thermocouples in nest; 0.7°C was added to skin temperature to bring it up to body temperature. 4/ Mean daily minimum and maximum temperatures [1].

continued

59. BODY TEMPERATURES

Part II. Birds

	Species (Synonym)	Temperature Site	°C	Reference
78	*Passer domesticus*	Cloaca	41.5(37.3-43.5)	38
79		Pectoral muscle	38.6[5]	33
80	*Passerculus sandwichensis*	Proventriculus	42.4(41.4-43.3)	63
81	*Passerella iliaca*	Proventriculus	43.8(42.7-44.3)	9
82	*Passerherbulus caudacutus*	Proventriculus	42.9[1]	63
83	*Passerina amoena*	Proventriculus	42.5	63
84	*Perisoreus canadensis*	Cloaca	(40.0-42.6)	61
85	*P. canadensis pacificus*	Cloaca	41.0	35
86	*Petrochelidon pyrrhonota (P. lunifrons)*	Proventriculus	41.2(40.6-41.8)	63
87	*Phainopepla nitens*	Proventriculus	41.9	63
88	*Phoenicurus phoenicurus*	Proventriculus	41.0	60
89	*Phylloscopus trochilus*	Proventriculus	40.4	60
90	*Pica pica*	Cloaca	(40.0-42.5)	36
91	*P. pica hudsonia*	Proventriculus	41.5(41.0-42.6)	35
92	*Pinicola enucleator alascensis*	Cloaca	41.6(40.0-42.7)	35
93	*P. enucleator leucura*	Proventriculus	42.6(42.0-43.2)	9
94	*Pipilo aberti*	Pectoral muscle	42.0	14
95		Proventriculus	39.5	14
96	*P. fuscus*	Pectoral muscle	41.7	14
97		Proventriculus	39.5	14
98	*Piranga ludoviciana*	Proventriculus	42.4	63
99	*Plectrophenax nivalis*	Cloaca	39.8[6]; 33.7[7]	26
100	*P. nivalis nivalis*	Cloaca	40.0(39.5-41.0)	35
101	*Poephila castanotis (Taeniopygia castanotis)*	Cloaca	40.2	12
102	*Polioptila caerulea*	Proventriculus	42.1(41.1-42.6)	63
103	*Poroaria coronata (P. cristata)*	Proventriculus	44.1[2]	9
104	*Progne subis*	Proventriculus	41.7	63
105	*Psaltriparus minimus*	Proventriculus	41.1	63
106	*Pyrrhula pyrrhula*	Proventriculus	42.2[1]	63
107	*Quiscalus quiscula*	Proventriculus	43.1	63
108	*Q. quiscula aeneus*	Proventriculus	43.5(42.7-44.0)	9
109	*Regulus satrapa*	Proventriculus	41.8(41.3-42.1)	63
110	*Richmondena cardinalis*	Cloaca	(41-42.5)[8]; (38.5-40.0)[5]	15
111		Proventriculus	42.9(42.0-43.3)	63
112	*Riparia riparia*	Proventriculus	41.4	58
113	*Sayornis phoebe*	Proventriculus	43.3	63
114	*Seiurus aurocapillus*	Proventriculus	41.9	63
115	*Setophaga ruticilla*	Proventriculus	42.2	63
116	*Sialia sialis*	Proventriculus	42.6(42.2-43.0)	9
117	*Sitta carolinensis*	Proventriculus	42.1(41.1-42.7)	63
118	*Spinus pinus*	Proventriculus	42.1(41.5-42.7)	63
119	*Spiza americana*	Proventriculus	42.4	63
120	*Spizella arborea*	Proventriculus	43.0(42.3-44.0)	9
121	*S. passerina passerina*	Skin	41.7[3]; 39.8-42.9[3,4]	1,39
122	*Stelgidopteryx ruficollis*	Proventriculus	42.7	63
123	*Sturnella neglecta*	Proventriculus	42.2	63
124	*Sturnus vulgaris*	Proventriculus	41.5	60
125	*Tachycineta thalassina*	Proventriculus	40.9	63
126	*Telmatodytes palustris*	Proventriculus	41.6(40.7-42.9)	63
127	*Thyromanes bewickii*	Proventriculus	42.1	63
128	*Toxostoma curvirostre*	Proventriculus	42.7	63
129	*Troglodytes aedon aedon*	Skin	41.1[3]; 39.5-42.7[3,4]	1,39

[1] Recorded after bird was shot. [2] For one subject. [3] Recorded by thermocouples in nest; 0.7°C was added to skin temperature to bring it up to body temperature. [4] Mean daily minimum and maximum temperatures [1]. [5] Nocturnal measurement. [6] Ambient temperature, −22 to −20°C. [7] Ambient temperature, −60°C for 90 minutes. [8] Diurnal measurement.

continued

59. BODY TEMPERATURES

Part II. Birds

	Species (Synonym)	Temperature Site	°C	Reference
130	*T. troglodytes*	Proventriculus	39.7	60
131	*Turdus migratorius*	Proventriculus	43.2(42.0-44.2)	63
132	*T. musicus*	Cloaca	41.0(38.4-42.7)	57
133	*Tyrannus tyrannus*	Proventriculus	42.1	63
134	*Vermivora celata*	Proventriculus	41.9(41.3-42.8)	63
135	*V. peregrina*	Proventriculus	42.3	63
136	*Vireo gilvus*	Proventriculus	41.9	63
137	*V. olivaceus*	Proventriculus	42.5(42.2-43.2)	63
138	*V. solitarius*	Proventriculus	42.1(41.8-42.4)	63
139	*Wilsonia pusilla*	Proventriculus	42.1(41.4-42.6)	63
140	*Xanthocephalus xanthocephalus*	Proventriculus	42.4(41.4-43.5)	63
141	*Zonotrichia albicollis*	Proventriculus	43.2(41.5-44.3)	9
142	*Z. leucophrys*	Proventriculus	42.8(41.5-43.5)	63
143	*Z. leucophrys gambelii*	Cloaca	42.0	40
	Piciformes			
144	*Asyndesmus lewis*	Proventriculus	42.2	63
145	*Centurus carolinus*	Proventriculus	43.0	63
146	*Colaptes auratus*	Proventriculus	42.8(42.4-43.3)	63
147	*Dendrocopos pubescens (Dryobates pubescens)*	Proventriculus	42.1(41.2-42.6)	63
148	*Dendrocopos villosus septentrionalis*	Cloaca	43.0[1,2]	35
149	*(Dryobates villosus)*	Proventriculus	42.4(42.2-42.8)	63
150	*Dryocopus pileatus (Phloeotomus pileatus)*	Proventriculus	41.7	63
151	*Melanerpes erythrocephalus*	Proventriculus	42.4	63
152	*Picoides arcticus*	Cloaca	39.0	35
153	*P. tridactylus (P. americanus)*	Proventriculus	41.7	63
154	*P. tridactylus fasciatus*	Cloaca	42.2(42.0-42.5)	35
155	*Sphyrapicus varius*	Proventriculus	42.2(41.5-43.0)	63
	Coraciiformes			
156	*Megaceryle alcyon*	Cloaca	40.0(39.2-40.7)	63
	Apodiformes			
157	*Aeronautes melanoleucus*	Proventriculus	41.0(40.7-41.3)	63
158	*A. saxatilis*	Cloaca	38.6	6
159	*Amazilia fimbriata (Agyrtria viridissima)*	....	43.0	25
160	*Amazilia leucogaster bahiae*	Axilla	39.4(31.6-40.0)	50
161	*Aphantocroa cirrochloris*	Throat	44.6	55
162	*Archilochus alexandri*	Pectoral muscle	40.0	42
163		Proventriculus	39.4(38.8-40.2)	63
164	*A. colubris*	Proventriculus	38.9(38.2-41.1)	63
165	*Calypte anna*	Cloaca	41.9	6
166		Pectoral muscle	38.0	42
167	*C. costae*	Pectoral muscle	40.0	42
168	*Chaetura pelagica*	Proventriculus	41.8	63
169	*Chlorestes notatus cyanogenys*	Axilla	38.8(30.0-39.2)	50
170	*Clytolaema rubricauda*	Throat	42.2	55
171	*Colibri serrirostris*	Throat	42.5	55
172	*Cynanthus latirostris*	Proventriculus	41.1(40.7-41.4)	63
173	*Eupetomena macroura*	Throat	40.6	55
174	*Hylocharis cyanus cyanus*	Axilla	38.8(30.0-39.2)	50
175	*Lampornis clemenciae*	Pectoral muscle	35.6	45
176	*Lophornis magnifica*	Throat	39.5	55
177	*Melanotrochilus fuscus*	Throat	42.2	55
178	*Oreotrochilus estella*	Proventriculus	36.4	51
179		Cloaca	38.8	51

[1] Recorded after bird was shot. [2] For one subject.

continued

59. BODY TEMPERATURES

Part II. Birds

	Species (Synonym)	Temperature Site	Temperature °C	Reference
180	*Polytmus guainumbi*	Throat	41.0	35
181	*Selasphorus platycercus*	Proventriculus	38.7	63
182	*S. rufus*	Proventriculus	39.0(38.8-39.2)	63
183	*Thalurania furcata*	Throat	39.6	55
184	*T. glaucopis*	Throat	41.2	55
	Caprimulgiformes			
185	*Caprimulgus europaeus*	Cloaca	(37.4-40.5)	52
186	*C. vociferus (Antrostomus vociferans)*	Proventriculus	42.4	63
187	*Chordeiles minor minor*	Cloaca	(34.0-40.0)	44
188	*Phalaenoptilus nuttalli*	Cloaca	(35.0-43.5)[9]	7
189	*Podargus strigoides*	Cloaca	37.6	43
	Strigiformes			
190	*Asio flammeus flammeus*	Cloaca	41.2(38.8-42.2)	36
191	*A. otus wilsonianus (A. wilsonianus)*	Cloaca	40.1	63
192	*Bubo virginianus*	Cloaca	40.5(40.3-40.8)	9
193	*Nyctea scandiaca*	Cloaca	40.9(40.6-41.5)	35
194	*Otus asio*	Proventriculus	39.6(38.0-40.8)	63
195	*O. asio naevius*	Cloaca	40.1[2]	9
196	*O. flammeolus*	Proventriculus	39.2	63
197	*Speotyto cunicularia*	Cloaca	40.3	27
198	*Strix varia*	Cloaca	40.0(39.6-40.5)	9
199	*Tyto alba*	Cloaca	39.5(38.7-40.3)	27
	Cuculiformes			
200	*Coccyzus americanus*	Proventriculus	42.3(41.6-42.9)	63
201	*Geococcyx californianus*	Cloaca	41.9[1]	63
	Psittaciformes			
202	*Amazona aestiva aestiva*	Cloaca	41.0[2]	9
	Columbiformes			
203	*Columba livia*	Cloaca	40.0	60
204	*Scardafella inca*	Pectoral muscle	40.2	46
205	*Streptopelia decaocto*	Cloaca	43.3(43.1-43.9)	9
206	*Zenaida asiatica*	Cloaca	42.6(41.8-44.5)	63
207	*Zenaidura macroura*	Cloaca	40.6	32
208		Pectoral muscle	42.5	4
	Charadriiformes			
209	*Actitis macularia*	Proventriculus	42.4	63
210	*Aethia cristatella*	Cloaca	41.6[2]	35
211	*Alca torda*	Cloaca	40.5(39.9-41.1)	63
212	*Catharacta skua*	Cloaca	41.2	18
213	*Catoptrophorus semipalmatus*	Cloaca	41.4	63
214	*Cepphus grylle*	Cloaca	40.4	41,56
215	*Charadrius hiaticula*	Cloaca	38.3	60
216		Proventriculus	39.9	60
217	*C. vociferus*	Proventriculus	41.7	63
218	*Chlidonias niger (Hydrochelidon nigra)*	Cloaca	41.6	63
219	*Ereunetes mauri*	Proventriculus	41.8(41.1-42.4)	63
220	*Erolia alpina (Calidris alpina)*	Proventriculus	39.8	60
221	*E. bairdii*	Proventriculus	42.2(41.4-42.6)	63
222	*E. ferruginea (Calidris ferruginea)*	Proventriculus	40.2	60

[1] Recorded after bird was shot. [2] For one subject. [9] Cloacal temperature of 17.5°C reported for subject in torpid state [47].

continued

59. BODY TEMPERATURES

Part II. Birds

	Species (Synonym)	Temperature: Site	Temperature: °C	Reference
223	*Himantopus mexicanus*	Cloaca	41.0(39.8-42.4)	63
224	*Larus argentatus*	Cloaca	42.3(41.6-43.0)	48,63
225	*L. argentatus smithsonianus*	Cloaca	41.4(40.8-41.9)	9
226	*L. atricilla*	Cloaca	42.3(41.7-42.8)	9
227	*L. canus brachyrhynchos*	Cloaca	40.7(40.2-41.3)	35
228	*L. dominicanus*	Cloaca	40.9	18
229	*L. fuscus*	Cloaca	41.7(41.3-42.1)1/	63
230	*L. glaucescens*	Cloaca	41.7(38.2-42.7)	36
231	*L. hyperboreus*	Cloaca	(40.0-42.6)	36
232	*L. hyperboreus barrovianus*	Cloaca	42.1(41.2-42.5)	35
233	*L. marinus*	Cloaca	41.9(41.2-42.5)	9
234	*L. pipixcan*	Cloaca	40.9	63
235	*L. ridibundus*	Cloaca	41.41,2/	63
236	*Limnodromus griseus*	Cloaca	40.9	63
237	*Limosa fedoa*	Cloaca	40.7	63
238	*Lobipes lobatus*	Proventriculus	41.8(39.6-42.8)	63
239	*Lunda cirrhata*	Cloaca	41.32/	35
240	*Numenius americanus*	Proventriculus	40.9(40.2-41.3)	63
241	*Pagophila eburnea*	Cloaca	40.4(39.9-41.2)1/	63
242	*Philomachus pugnax*	Cloaca	38.7	60
243		Proventriculus	40.3	60
244	*Recurvirostra americana*	Cloaca	41.0(40.1-42.7)	63
245	*Rhynocops nigra*	Cloaca	40.6	63
246	*Rissa tridactyla*	Cloaca	41.4(39.9-42.4)	63
247	*Squatarola squatarola*	Cloaca	41.2(40.7-42.2)	63
248	*Steganopus tricolor*	Proventriculus	41.1(39.9-42.6)	63
249	*Stercorarius parasiticus*	Cloaca	41.21,2/	9
250	*Sterna forsteri*	Cloaca	41.4(40.9-41.8)	63
251	*S. fuscata*	Proventriculus	40.58/; 39.45/	31
252	*Totanus flavipes*	Cloaca	41.4	63
253	*T. melanoleucus*	Cloaca	41.5(40.8-42.2)	63
254	*Uria aalge*	Cloaca	40.9(40.4-41.5)	9
255	*U. lomvia*	Cloaca	40.5(39.7-41.5)1/	63
	Gruiformes			
256	*Anthropoides paradisea (Tetrapteryx paradisea)*	Cloaca	40.5	8
257	*A. virgo*	Cloaca	41.2	9
258	*Aramus guarauna (A. vociferus)*	Cloaca	40.3	63
259	*Fulica americana*	Cloaca	41.5(41.2-41.8)	63
260	*F. atra*	Cloaca	40.51,2/	63
261	*Grus canadensis canadensis*	Cloaca	41.3(41.0-41.5)	9
262	*Rallus limicola (R. virginianus)*	Proventriculus	40.9	63
263	*R. longirostris crepitans (R. crepitans)*	Cloaca	40.11/	63
	Galliformes			
264	*Bonasa umbellus togata*	Cloaca	42.52/	9
265	*Canachites canadensis canadensis*	Cloaca	42.0(41.0-43.0)1/	35
266	*Chrysolophus amherstiae*	Cloaca	42.2(41.9-42.4)	9
267	*C. pictus*	Cloaca	42.4(42.3-42.6)	9
268	*Colinus virginianus*	Cloaca	41.7	63
269	*Coturnix coturnix japonica*	Cloaca	41.8	65
270	*Crax alector (C. nigra)*	Cloaca	42.1	9
271	*C. rubra (C. globicera)*	Cloaca	41.3	63
272	*Francolinus natalensis*	Cloaca	42.2	63
273	*Gallus gallus*	Cloaca	41.4	34

1/ Recorded after bird was shot. 2/ For one subject. 5/ Nocturnal measurement. 8/ Diurnal measurement.

continued

Part II. Birds

	Species (Synonym)	Temperature		Reference
		Site	°C	
274	*Gennaeus nycthemerus nycthemerus*	Cloaca	42.3(42.2-42.4)	9
275	*Lagopus lagopus*	Cloaca	(41.3-42.0)	36
276	*L. leucurus leucurus*	Cloaca	41.5(40.5-42.5)	35
277	*L. mutus nelsoni*	Cloaca	42.3(41.8-42.8)	35
278	*Lophortyx californicus*	Cloaca	40.5	32
279		Pectoral muscle	41.0(40.0-41.5)	5
280	*L. gambelii*	Proventriculus	(40.0-41.5)	5
281	*Meleagris gallopavo*	Cloaca	41.5	64
282	*Numida meleagris*	Cloaca	42.2(42.0-43.3)	9
283	*Oreortyx pictus*	Cloaca	41.9(41.5-42.3)	63
284	*Pavo cristatus*	Cloaca	40.0(39.5-40.3)	9
285	*Phasianus colchicus*	Cloaca	41.9	62
286	*P. colchicus mongolicus*	Cloaca	42.1(41.7-42.4)	9
287	*P. torquatus*	Cloaca	42.1	63
	Falconiformes			
288	*Accipiter nisus nisus (A. nisus)*	Cloaca	41.2	60
289	*A. striatus velox (A. velox)*	Cloaca	42.8(42.2-43.3)	63
290	*Buteo jamaicensis borealis (B. borealis borealis)*	Cloaca	41.2(40.9-41.5)	9
291	*B. lagopus (Archibuteo lagopus)*	Cloaca	41.0[1,2]	63
292	*B. lagopus s.johannis*	Cloaca	42.0(41.9-42.0)	9
293	*B. platypterus*	Cloaca	41.0[2]	9
294	*B. swainsoni*	Cloaca	40.7	63
295	*Cathartes aura*	Cloaca	39.9	63
296	*Circus cyaneus hudsonius (C. hudsonius)*	Cloaca	41.9(41.4-42.4)	9
297	*Falco mexicanus*	Cloaca	41.4[1,2]	63
298	*F. peregrinus*	Cloaca	40.7(40.1-41.8)	63
299	*F. sparverius*	Cloaca	42.5(42.0-42.8)	9
300		Proventriculus	40.5	3
301	*Geranoaetus melanoleucus*	Cloaca	40.3	8
302	*Gypaetus barbatus*	Cloaca	39.7	8
303	*Haliaeetus leucocephalus*	Cloaca	41.0	35
	Anseriformes			
304	*Aix sponsa*	Cloaca	42.0	63
305	*Anas acuta*	Cloaca	41.1(40.2-42.2)	63
306	*A. acuta tzitzihoa (Dafila acuta tzitzihoa)*	Cloaca	43.0(42.8-43.2)	9
307	*A. carolinensis*	Cloaca	41.3(40.1-42.2)	63
308	*A. crecca nimia*	Cloaca	40.4(39.5-41.6)	35
309	*A. cyanoptera*	Cloaca	41.7	63
310	*A. platyrhynchos*	Cloaca	41.3(40.6-42.2)	63
311	*A. rubripes*	Cloaca	41.0(40.7-41.5)	63
312	*A. strepera (Chaulelasmus streperus)*	Cloaca	42.9[2]	9
313	*Anser albifrons*	Cloaca	40.6(40.5-40.7)	9
314	*A. anser domesticus*	Cloaca	41.3(40.2-42.0)	63
315	*A. fabalis*	Cloaca	40.9	9
316	*Aythya affinis*	Cloaca	41.4(41.0-41.7)	63
317	*A. marila (Marila marila)*	Cloaca	42.7(42.2-43.2)	63
318	*Branta bernicla*	Cloaca	(41.0-42.7)	36
319	*B. canadensis canadensis*	Cloaca	40.5(39.8-41.3)	9
320	*B. canadensis hutchinsii*	Cloaca	40.5(40.0-41.0)	9
321	*B. canadensis minima*	Cloaca	41.1(40.7-41.5)	9
322	*B. leucopsis*	Cloaca	40.2(39.9-41.5)	9
323	*B. nigricans (B. bernicla nigricans)*	Cloaca	40.5(39.0-42.0)	35
324	*Bucephala clangula (Clangula clangula)*	Cloaca	40.4[2]	63

[1] Recorded after bird was shot. [2] For one subject.

continued

59. BODY TEMPERATURES

Part II. Birds

	Species (Synonym)	Temperature		Reference
		Site	°C	
325	*B. clangula americana*	Cloaca	41.5[2]	35
326	*Cairina moschata*	Cloaca	42.0(40.8-42.3)	63
327	*Chen caerulescens*	Cloaca	40.4(40.2-40.7)	9
328	*C. hyperborea*	Cloaca	42.1	63
329	*C. hyperborea atlantica*	Cloaca	40.8(40.6-41.3)	9
330	*Cygnus atratus (Chenopis atrata)*	Cloaca	40.6(40.0-41.0)	9
331	*Cygnus olor (Sthenelides olor)*	Cloaca	40.4	9
332	*Dendrocygna autumnalis*	Cloaca	42.3[2]	9
333	*Lophodytes culcullatus*	Cloaca	42.2[1,2]	35
334	*Mareca americana*	Cloaca	41.5[2]	35
335	*M. penelope*	Cloaca	42.5(41.4-43.1)	48,63
336	*Mergus serrator*	Cloaca	41.9(41.3-42.6)	63
337	*Oidemia nigra*	Cloaca	41.3(40.9-41.7)[1]	63
338	*Olor buccinator (Cygnus buccinator)*	Cloaca	40.1	8
339	*Oxyura jamaicensis (Erismatura jamaicensis)*	Cloaca	41.8	63
340	*Philacte canagica*	Cloaca	(41.0-42.5)	36
341	*Somateria mollissima dresseri*	Cloaca	42.7(42.5-43.0)	9
342	*Spatula clypeata*	Cloaca	41.4(40.3-42.8)	63
343	*Tadorna tadorna*	Cloaca	42.7(42.4-42.9)	63
	Ciconiiformes			
344	*Ardea herodias*	Cloaca	39.6	8
345	*Botaurus lentiginosus*	Cloaca	40.2[1]	9
346	*Butorides virescens*	Cloaca	41.0	63
347	*Egretta thula candidissima (E. candidissima)*	Cloaca	40.2	63
348	*Eudocimus albus (Guara alba)*	Cloaca	42.3(42.2-42.4)	9
349	*Jabiru mycteria*	Cloaca	40.1	8
350	*Leptoptilos javanicus*	Cloaca	39.6	8
351	*Mycteria americana*	Proventriculus	40.7	37
352	*Nycticorax nycticorax*	Cloaca	39.5(38.7-40.8)	63
353	*N. nycticorax hoactli*	Cloaca	42.3(41.9-42.5)	9
354	*Phoenicopterus chilensis*	Cloaca	40.5(40.4-40.6)	9
355	*P. ruber roseus (P. antiquorum)*	Cloaca	40.2	8
356	*Plegadis falcinellus*	Cloaca	40.6(40.2-40.9)	63
	Pelecaniformes			
357	*Anhinga anhinga*	Cloaca	41.0	63
358	*Morus bassanus*	Cloaca	41.0	9
359	*Pelecanus erythrorhynchos*	Cloaca	40.5[2]	9
360	*P. occidentalis*	Cloaca	40.3(39.7-41.3)	63
361	*Phaethon rubricauda*	Proventriculus	39.0[8]; 37.1[5]	30
362	*Phalacrocorax aristotelis*	Cloaca	40.4	41,56
363	*P. auritus*	Cloaca	41.3(41.0-41.5)	9
364	*P. carbo*	Cloaca	39.8	56
365	*P. pelagicus resplendens*	Cloaca	40.5[1,2]	35
366	*Sula dactylatra*	Proventriculus	40.7(39.9-41.2)[8]; 38.3 (37.1-39.5)[5]	2
367	*S. sula*	Proventriculus	40.3[8]; 38.0[5]; 40.9[10]	30
	Procellariiformes			
368	*Daption capense*	Cloaca	39.1	53
369	*Diomedea chlororhynchos (Thalassogeron chlororhynchus)*	Cloaca	41.0(40.7-41.3)	63
370	*D. exulans*	Cloaca	39.6	19,41
371	*D. immutabilis*	Proventriculus	37.5	29
372	*D. nigripes*	Proventriculus	38.1	29

1/ Recorded after bird was shot. 2/ For one subject. 5/ Nocturnal measurement. 8/ Diurnal measurement. 10/ Recorded during flight.

continued

59. BODY TEMPERATURES

Part II. Birds

	Species (Synonym)	Temperature: Site	Temperature: °C	Reference
373	*Fulmarus glacialis*	Cloaca	38.8(38.1-39.6)	63
374	*Oceanodroma leuchorhoa*	Cloaca	39.9	24
375	*Pachyptila turtur*	Cloaca	39.9	20,41
376	*Pagodroma nivea*	Cloaca	38.7	53
377	*Pterodroma leucoptera hypoleuca (P. hypoleuca hypoleuca)*	Proventriculus	38.5 8/; 39.9 5/	28
378	*Puffinus nativitatis*	Proventriculus	38.1 8/; 38.6 5/	28
379	*P. pacificus*	Proventriculus	39.5 8/; 37.7 5/	28
380	*P. tenuirostris*	Cloaca	40.9 8/; 39.9 5/	23
	Podicipediformes			
381	*Aechmophorus occidentalis*	Cloaca	38.5	63
382	*Podiceps auritus (Colymbus auritus)*	Cloaca	39.9	63
383	*P. caspicus*	Cloaca	40.2	41,63
384	*Podilymbus podiceps*	Cloaca	39.3	63
	Gaviiformes			
385	*Gavia arctica pacifica*	Cloaca	39.0	35
	Tinamiformes			
386	*Nothura maculosa*	Cloaca	40.5(39.2-42.4) 1/	63
	Apterygiformes			
387	*Apteryx australis*	Cloaca	39.0	22,41
388	*A. australis mantelli (A. mantelli)*	Cloaca	37.8(37.4-38.2)	63
389	*A. haasti*	Cloaca	38.1 1/	63
	Casuariformes			
390	*Casuarius bennetti*	Cloaca	39.0	8
391	*C. bicarunculatus intensus (C. intensus)*	Cloaca	38.8	63
392	*C. casuarius beccarii (C. beccarii)*	Cloaca	39.2 1/	63
393	*Dromiceius novaehollandiae*	Cloaca	39.0	59,63
	Struthioniformes			
394	*Struthio camelus*	Cloaca	39.2(38.0-40.4) 8/; 38.3 (37.9-38.7) 5/	13
395		Thoracic cavity	39.1(38.3-40.2)	10
	Sphenisciformes			
396	*Aptenodytes forsteri*	Cloaca	(36.0-38.0)	54
397	*A. patagonica*	Cloaca	37.7	41
398	*Eudyptula minor*	Cloaca	38.9(37.8-40.1)	63
399	*Megadyptes antipodes*	Cloaca	37.8	21,41
400	*Pygoscelis adeliae*	Cloaca	(37.0-38.0)	18
401	*P. papua*	Cloaca	38.1	41

1/ Recorded after bird was shot. 5/ Nocturnal measurement. 8/ Diurnal measurement.

Contributors: (a) Neumann, Richard L., and Hudson, Jack W., (b) Hock, Raymond J.

References

[1] Baldwin, S. P., and S. C. Kendeigh. 1932. Sci. Publ. Cleveland Museum Nat. Hist. 3.

[2] Bartholomew, G. A. 1966. Condor 68:523.

[3] Bartholomew, G. A., and T. J. Cade. 1957. Wilson Bull. 69:149.

[4] Bartholomew, G. A., and W. R. Dawson. 1954. Ecology 35:181.

[5] Bartholomew, G. A., and W. R. Dawson. 1958. Auk 75:150.

continued

59. BODY TEMPERATURES

Part II. Birds

[6] Bartholomew, G. A., T. R. Howell, and T. J. Cade. 1957. Condor 59:145.

[7] Bartholomew, G. A., J. W. Hudson, and T. R. Howell. 1962. Ibid. 64:117.

[8] Benedict, F. G., and E. L. Fox. 1927. Proc. Am. Phil. Soc. 66:511.

[9] Bernard, R., R. Cayouette, and J. A. Brassard. 1944. Rev. Can. Biol. 3:251.

[10] Bligh, J., and T. C. Hartley. 1965. Ibis 107:104.

[11] Cade, T. J., C. A. Tobin, and A. Gold. 1965. Physiol. Zool. 38:9.

[12] Calder, W. A. 1964. Ibid. 37:400.

[13] Crawford, E. C., and K. Schmidt-Nielsen. 1967. Am. J. Physiol. 212:347.

[14] Dawson, W. R. 1954. Univ. Calif. (Berkeley) Publ. Zool. 59:81.

[15] Dawson, W. R. 1958. Physiol. Zool. 31:37.

[16] Dawson, W. R., and H. B. Tordoff. 1959. Condor 61:388.

[17] Dawson, W. R., and H. B. Tordoff. 1964. Auk 81:26.

[18] Eklund, C. R. 1942. Ibid. 59:544.

[19] Eydoux, F., and L. F. A. Souleyet. 1838. Compt. Rend. 6:456.

[20] Farner, D. S. 1956. J. Appl. Physiol. 8:546.

[21] Farner, D. S. 1958. Auk 75:249.

[22] Farner, D. S., N. Chivers, and T. Riney. 1956. Emu 56:199.

[23] Farner, D. S., and R. L. Serventy. 1959. Condor 61:426.

[24] Folk, G. E. 1951. Anat. Record 111:541.

[25] Groebbels, F. 1932. Der Vogel. Gebrüder Bornträger, Berlin. v. 1.

[26] Hock, R. J. Unpublished. Northrop Space Laboratories, Hawthorne, Calif., 1967.

[27] Howell, T. R. 1964. Wilson Bull. 76:28.

[28] Howell, T. R., and G. A. Bartholomew. 1961. Auk 78:343.

[29] Howell, T. R., and G. A. Bartholomew. 1961. Condor 63:185.

[30] Howell, T. R., and G. A. Bartholomew. 1962. Ibid. 64:6.

[31] Howell, T. R., and G. A. Bartholomew. 1962. Ibis 104:98.

[32] Hudson, J. W., and A. Brush. 1964. Comp. Biochem. Physiol. 12:157.

[33] Hudson, J. W., and S. Kimzey. 1966. Ibid. 17:203.

[34] Hutchinson, J. C. D. 1954. J. Agr. Sci. 45:48.

[35] Irving, L., and J. Krog. 1954. J. Appl. Physiol. 6:667.

[36] Irving, L., and J. Krog. 1954. Physiol. Zool. 35:224.

[37] Kahl, M. 1963. Ibid. 36:141.

[38] Kendeigh, S. C. 1944. J. Exptl. Zool. 96:1.

[39] Kendeigh, S. C. Unpublished. Univ. Illinois, Dept. Zoology, Champaign, 1967.

[40] King, J. R. 1964. Comp. Biochem. Physiol. 12:13.

[41] King, J. R., and D. S. Farner. 1961. In A. J. Marshall, ed. Biology and comparative physiology of birds. Academic Press, New York. v. 2, pp. 215-288.

[42] Lasiewski, R. C. 1964. Physiol. Zool. 37:212.

[43] Lasiewski, R. C., and G. A. Bartholomew. 1966. Condor 68:253.

[44] Lasiewski, R. C., and W. R. Dawson. 1964. Ibid. 66:477.

[45] Lasiewski, R. C., and R. J. Lasiewski. 1967. Auk 84:34.

[46] MacMillen, R. E., and C. H. Trost. 1967. Comp. Biochem. Physiol. 20:263.

[47] Marshall, J. T., Jr. 1955. Condor 57:129.

[48] Martins, C. 1856. Compt. Rend. 42:515.

[49] Misch, M. 1960. Physiol. Zool. 33:252.

[50] Morrison, P. 1962. Condor 64:315.

[51] Pearson, O. P. 1953. Ibid. 55:17.

[52] Peiponen, V. A. 1966. Ann. Acad. Sci. Fennicae, A-IV, 101:1.

[53] Prevost, J. 1964. Oiseau 34(Suppl.):91.

[54] Prevost, J., and F. Bourliere. 1957. Alauda 25:167.

[55] Ruschi, A. 1949. Bol. Museu Biol. Santa Theresa (Espirito Santo) 1(7).

[56] Simpson, S. 1912. Proc. Roy. Soc. Edinburgh 32:19.

[57] Simpson, S., and J. J. Galbraith. 1905. J. Physiol. (London) 33:225.

[58] Stoner, D. K. 1937. N.Y. State Museum Cir. 19.

[59] Sutherland, A. 1899. Proc. Zool. Soc. London, p. 787.

[60] Udvardy, M. D. F. 1953. Zool. Bidrag Uppsala 30:25.

[61] Veghte, J. H. 1964. Physiol. Zool. 37:316.

[62] Westerkov, K. 1956. Emu 56:405.

[63] Wetmore, A. 1921. Smithsonian Inst. Misc. Collections 72(12).

[64] Wilson, W. O., and A. Woodard. 1955. Poultry Sci. 34:369.

[65] Yousef, M. K., L. Z. MacFarland, and W. O. Wilson. 1966. Life Sci. (Oxford) 5:1887.

60. ENERGY METABOLISM AT VARIOUS WEIGHTS: MAN

Part I. Basal: Infants and Children

Values for infants less than 38 months old are based on "basal" heat production, including the specific dynamic action of food; measurements were made while the infant was sleeping quietly. All data are for normal weight-for-height subjects. Normal weight-for-height, defined as within ±10% of average weight, was derived from the following equations: under 11 months, $Wt = 0.323e^{0.047\ ht}$; 11 months and over, $Wt = 2.6e^{0.018\ ht}$ (e = 2.718, the basis of natural logarithms). Other weight-for-height categories: slender, 80-90% of average; underweight, <80%; stocky, 110-120%; overweight, 120-140%; obese, >140%.

	Weight kg	Metabolic Rate kcal/hr ♂[1] or ♀[1]
	Age, 1 wk-10 mo[2]	
1	3.5	8.4
2	4.0	9.5
3	4.5	10.5
4	5.0	11.6
5	5.5	12.7
6	6.0	13.8
7	6.5	14.9
8	7.0	16.0
9	7.5	17.1
10	8.0	18.2
11	8.5	19.3
12	9.0	20.4
13	9.5	21.4
14	10.0	22.5
15	10.5	23.6
16	11.0	24.7

	Weight kg	Metabolic Rate kcal/hr ♂[3]	♀[4]
	Age, 11-38 mo[2]		
17	9.0	22.0	21.2
18	9.5	22.8	22.0
19	10.0	23.6	22.8
20	10.5	24.4	23.6
21	11.0	25.2	24.4
22	11.5	26.0	25.2
23	12.0	26.8	26.0
24	12.5	27.6	26.9
25	13.0	28.4	27.7
26	13.5	29.2	28.5
27	14.0	30.0	29.3
28	14.5	30.8	30.1
29	15.0	31.6	30.9
30	15.5	32.4	31.7
31	16.0	33.2	32.6
32	16.5	34.0	33.4

	Weight kg	Metabolic Rate kcal/hr ♂[5]	♀[6]
	Age, 3-16 yr		
33	15	35.8	33.3
34	20	39.7	37.4
35	25	43.6	41.5
36	30	47.5	45.5
37	35	51.3	49.6
38	40	55.2	53.7
39	45	59.1	57.8
40	50	63.0	61.9
41	55	66.9	66.0
42	60	70.8	70.0
43	65	74.7	74.0
44	70	78.6	78.1
45	75	82.5	82.2

[1] Computed from the equation: kcal/hr = 2.18 × wt in kg + 0.737. SE, 1.6 kcal/hr. [2] For infants in slender classification, heat production would be 1 kcal/hr higher; underweight, >2 SE higher; overweight, >2 SE lower. [3] Computed from the equation: kcal/hr = 1.59 × wt in kg + 7.74. SE, 2.2 kcal/hr. [4] Computed from the equation: kcal/hr = 1.63 × wt in kg + 6.48. SE, 1.9 kcal/hr. [5] Computed from the equation: kcal/hr = 0.778 × wt in kg + 24.11. SE, 2.4 kcal/hr. [6] Computed from the equation: kcal/hr = 0.815 × wt in kg + 21.09. SE, 2.2 kcal/hr.

Contributor: Johnson, Herman L.

General References: **[1]** Sargent, D. W. 1961. U.S. Dept. Agr. Home Econ. Res. Rept. 14. **[2]** Sargent, D. W. 1962. Ibid. 18.

Part II. Resting: Adults

There is no difference between the metabolic rates of the two sexes if the rate is expressed in units of either lean cell mass or active tissue. Resting metabolism is related to body weight and fat content. Since there is at present no agreed rapid method of measuring the fat content of the body, the following table—which presents a range of normal values for the resting rate of metabolism and includes clinical assessments of body fat content—is new and awaits confirmation. **Fat Content of Body**, ♂: 5% = thin, 10% = average, 15% = plump, >20% = fat; ♀: 5-15% = thin, 20% = average, 25% = plump, >30% = fat.

	Body Wt kg	Fat Content of Body 5%	10%	15%	20%	25%	30%
		Metabolic Rate, kcal/min					
1	45	.....	.....	0.82	0.78	.....	.....
2	50	0.99	0.94	0.89	0.84	0.80	.....
3	55	1.06	1.01	0.96	0.91	0.86	0.81
4	60	1.12	1.08	1.03	0.98	0.93	0.88

	Body Wt kg	Fat Content of Body 5%	10%	15%	20%	25%	30%
		Metabolic Rate, kcal/min					
5	65	1.19	1.14	1.09	1.05	1.00	0.95
6	70	1.26	1.21	1.16	1.11	1.07	1.02
7	75	1.32	1.28	1.23	1.18	1.13	1.08
8	80	1.39	1.34	1.30	1.25	1.20	1.15

continued

60. ENERGY METABOLISM AT VARIOUS WEIGHTS: MAN

Part II. Resting: Adults

Contributor: Passmore, R.

Reference: Passmore, R. 1966. Nutr. Dieta 8:163.

61. BASAL ENERGY METABOLISM AT VARIOUS AGES: MAN

Values are smoothed means of basal kilogram calories per square meter per hour from the three largest and most authoritative sets of original data: (i) The Mayo Foundation Standards of Boothby, Berkson, and Dunn [2], based on measurements of 639 males and 828 females; (ii) the British measurements of Robertson and Reid [6], 987 males and 1323 females; and (iii) The Carnegie Nutrition Laboratory data of Harris and Benedict [3], 136 males and 103 females. The height-weight formula of DuBois and DuBois was used in computing body surface area: surface area in m^2 = $0.007184 \times \text{wt in kg}^{0.425} \times \text{ht in cm}^{0.725}$. Somewhat higher values are to be expected on first tests (i.e., on persons unaccustomed to the procedures). Values in parentheses are ranges (estimate "b", *see* Introduction), calculated by E. F. DuBois from an average coefficient of variation of 6.9% [1, 3-6].

	Age yr	Males Metabolic Rate, kcal/m²/hr	Females Metabolic Rate, kcal/m²/hr
1	3	60.1(51.8-68.3)	54.5(47.0-62.0)
2	4	57.9(49.9-65.9)	53.9(46.5-61.3)
3	5	56.3(48.5-64.1)	53.0(45.7-60.3)
4	6	54.0(46.5-61.5)	51.2(44.1-58.3)
5	7	52.3(45.1-59.5)	49.7(42.8-56.6)
6	8	50.8(43.8-57.8)	48.0(41.4-54.6)
7	9	49.5(42.7-56.3)	46.2(39.8-52.6)
8	10	47.7(41.1-54.3)	44.9(38.7-51.1)
9	11	46.5(40.1-52.9)	44.1(38.0-50.2)
10	12	45.3(39.0-51.6)	42.0(36.2-47.8)
11	13	44.5(38.4-50.6)	40.5(34.9-46.1)
12	14	43.8(37.8-49.8)	39.2(33.8-44.6)
13	15	43.7(37.7-49.7)	38.3(33.0-43.6)
14	16	42.9(37.0-48.8)	37.7(32.5-42.9)
15	17	41.9(36.1-47.7)	36.2(31.2-41.2)
16	18	40.5(34.9-46.1)	35.7(30.8-40.6)
17	19	40.1(34.6-45.6)	35.4(30.5-40.3)
18	20	39.8(34.3-45.3)	35.3(30.4-40.2)
19	21	39.4(34.0-44.8)	35.2(30.3-40.1)
20	22	39.2(33.8-44.6)	35.2(30.3-40.1)
21	23	39.0(33.6-44.4)	35.2(30.3-40.1)
22	24	38.7(33.4-44.0)	35.1(30.3-39.9)
23	25	38.4(33.1-43.7)	35.1(30.3-39.9)
24	26	38.2(32.9-43.5)	35.0(30.2-39.8)
25	27	38.0(32.8-43.2)	35.0(30.2-39.8)
26	28	37.8(32.6-43.0)	35.0(30.2-39.8)
27	29	37.7(32.5-42.9)	35.0(30.2-39.8)
28	30	37.6(32.4-42.8)	35.0(30.2-39.8)
29	31	37.4(32.2-42.6)	35.0(30.2-39.8)
30	32	37.2(32.1-42.3)	34.9(30.1-39.7)
31	33	37.1(32.0-42.2)	34.9(30.1-39.7)
32	34	37.0(31.9-42.1)	34.9(30.1-39.7)
33	35	36.9(31.8-42.0)	34.8(30.0-39.6)
34	36	36.8(31.7-41.9)	34.7(29.9-39.5)
35	37	36.7(31.6-41.8)	34.6(29.8-39.4)
36	38	36.7(31.6-41.8)	34.5(29.7-39.3)
37	39	36.6(31.5-41.7)	34.4(29.7-39.1)
38	40	36.5(31.5-41.5)	34.3(29.6-39.0)
39	45	36.3(31.3-41.3)	33.9(29.2-38.6)
40	50	36.0(31.0-40.0)	33.4(28.8-38.0)
41	55	35.4(30.5-40.3)	32.9(28.4-37.4)
42	60	34.8(30.0-39.6)	32.4(27.9-36.9)
43	65	34.0(29.3-38.7)	31.8(27.4-36.2)
44	70	33.1(28.5-37.7)	31.3(27.0-35.6)
45	75+	31.8(27.4-36.2)	31.1 1/(26.8-35.4) 1/

1/ Extrapolated from smooth curve.

Contributor: DuBois, Eugene F.

References

[1] Berkson, J., and W. M. Boothby. 1938. Am. J. Physiol. 121:669.

[2] Boothby, W. M., J. Berkson, and H. L. Dunn. 1936. Ibid. 116:468.

[3] Harris, J. A., and F. G. Benedict. 1919. Carnegie Inst. Wash. Publ. 279.

[4] Lewis, R. C., A. M. Duvall, and A. Iliff. 1943. J. Pediat. 23:1.

[5] Lewis, R. C., G. M. Kinsman, and A. Iliff. 1937. Am. J. Diseases Children 53:348.

[6] Robertson, J. D., and D. D. Reid. 1952. Lancet 2:940.

62. BASAL AND RESTING ENERGY METABOLISM AT VARIOUS AGES: FARM AND LABORATORY ANIMALS

Resting Metabolism: heat production when the animal is at rest, but not in a strictly thermoneutral environment nor in a postabsorptive state. The values for resting metabolism therefore will be greater than those for basal metabolism, exact values depending on the nature of the diet, time after feeding, level of lactation, and environmental temperature. Beef cattle, goats, horses, swine, and chickens were measured in a recumbent position. Growing and mature lactating dairy cattle were measured in a thermoneutral environment. **O_2 Cons.**: oxygen consumption at standard temperature and pressure.

	Animal	Sex	Age	Body Wt kg	Body Surface Area[1/] m^2	Basal: Metabolism kcal/kg/day	Basal: Metabolism kcal/m^2/day	Basal: O_2 Cons. liters/kg/day	Resting: Metabolism kcal/kg/day	Resting: Metabolism kcal/m^2/day	Resting: O_2 Cons. liters/kg/day	Reference
	Cattle, beef											
1	Hereford	♂	1.0 mo	40	1.02	.....	......	...	53.9	2104	11.2	2,5
2			1.6 mo	60	1.29	.....	......	...	46.4	2165	9.6	
3			3.0 mo	100	1.71	.....	......	...	38.4	2243	8.0	
4			7.0 mo	200	2.53	.....	......	...	29.7	2352	6.2	
5			11.0 mo	300	3.17	.....	......	...	25.6	2420	5.3	
6			1.3 yr	400	3.72	.....	......	...	23.0	2471	4.8	
7			1.7 yr	500	4.21	.....	......	...	21.2	2513	4.4	
8		♀	....	40	1.02	.....	......	...	61.8	2411	12.8	
9			1.8 mo	60	1.29	.....	......	...	51.1	2386	10.6	
10			5.0 mo	100	1.71	.....	......	...	40.3	2354	8.4	
11			9.0 mo	200	2.53	19.9	1575	4.1	29.2	2310	6.1	
12			1.2 yr	300	3.17	17.0	1610	3.5	24.1	2286	5.0	
13			1.7 yr	400	3.72	15.2	1635	3.2	21.1	2270	4.4	
14			2.0 yr	450	3.97	14.5	1646	3.0	20.0	2136	4.1	
	Cattle, dairy											
15	Brown Swiss	♀	1.5 mo	50	1.26	.....	......	...	48.0	1905	10.1	6,12
16			4.3 mo	100	1.98	.....	......	...	60.0	3030	12.0	
17			7.3 mo	200	2.92	.....	......	...	49.1	3362	9.7	
18			11.0 mo	300	3.66	.....	......	...	41.6	3410	8.2	
19			1.4 yr	417	4.40	21.7	2056	4.6	32.5	3076	6.4	
20			2.9 yr	500	4.87	.....	......	...	32.4	3321	6.5	
21	Holstein	♀	1.1 mo	50	1.26	.....	......	...	47.5	1886	10.1	6,7, 12
22			2.9 mo	100	1.98	.....	......	...	60.0	3054	12.5	
23			5.7 mo	200	2.92	.....	......	...	52.9	3624	10.6	
24			9.6 mo	300	3.66	.....	......	...	44.2	3619	8.7	
25			1.2 yr	400	4.30	.....	......	...	39.6	3683	7.5	
26			1.4 yr	431	4.48	20.5	1977	4.4	36.5	3514	7.2	
27			3.9 yr	500	4.87	.....	......	...	33.0	3386	6.8	
28			4.3 yr	600	5.39	.....	......	...	34.1	3068	6.3	
29	Jersey	♀	0.7 mo	25	0.91	.....	......	...	62.4	1714	12.5	6,12
30			2.4 mo	50	1.26	.....	......	...	55.7	2210	13.9	
31			5.1 mo	100	1.98	.....	......	...	64.1	3236	13.0	
32			10.6 mo	200	2.92	.....	......	...	47.5	3255	9.5	
33			1.4 yr	266	3.42	21.3	1656	4.5	34.6	3455	6.9	
34			6.5 yr	400	4.30	.....	......	...	40.1	3734	8.0	
35	Goat, Angora &	♂	....	2	....	.....	......	...	132	......	.....	1
36	Toggenburg			4	....	.....	......	...	106	......	.....	
37				8	....	.....	......	...	85	......	.....	
38				16	....	.....	......	...	68	......	.....	
39				30	....	.....	......	...	55	......	.....	
40				50	....	.....	......	...	47	......	.....	
41				70	....	.....	......	...	42	......	.....	
42		♀	....	2	....	.....	......	...	124	......	.....	
43				4	....	.....	......	...	97	......	.....	
44				8	....	.....	......	...	75	......	.....	
45				16	....	.....	......	...	59	......	.....	

1/ Calculated from the following equations: beef cattle, 0.13 × wt in $kg^{0.56}$; dairy cattle, 0.15 × wt in $kg^{0.56}$.

continued

62. BASAL AND RESTING ENERGY METABOLISM AT VARIOUS AGES: FARM AND LABORATORY ANIMALS

	Animal	Sex	Age	Body Wt kg	Body Surface Area[1] m^2	Basal Metabolism kcal/kg/day	Basal Metabolism kcal/m^2/day	Basal O_2 Cons. liters/kg/day	Resting Metabolism kcal/kg/day	Resting Metabolism kcal/m^2/day	Resting O_2 Cons. liters/kg/day	Reference
46				30	....	.....	......	...	47	......	.....	
47				50	....	.....	......	...	39	......	.....	
48				70	....	.....	......	...	34	......	.....	
49	Guinea pig	♂	Birth	0.08	0.0164	.....	......	...	154	751	.....	10
50			19-22 days	0.15	0.0243	117	722	...	122	753	.....	
51			30-34 days	0.20	0.0293	108	737	23	114	778	23	
52			75-82 days	0.40	0.0456	86	754	18	91	798	29	
53			137-145 days	0.60	0.0591	71	721	...	75	761	.....	
54			290 days	0.80	0.0710	60	676	13	63	710	13	
55		♀	Birth	0.08	0.0164	.....	......	...	160	781	.....	
56			19-22 days	0.15	0.0243	120	741	...	128	790	.....	
57			30-34 days	0.20	0.0293	112	765	24	118	805	24	
58			80-87 days	0.40	0.0456	90	789	19	94	825	19	
59			154-170 days	0.60	0.0591	74	751	...	79	802	.....	
60			270 days	0.80	0.0710	63	710	13	68	766	14	
61	Horse, Percheron	♂[2]	0.6 mo	100	1.82	.....	......	...	44.8	2460	9.3	4
62			2.8 mo	200	2.82	.....	......	...	32.2	2280	6.7	
63			6.0 mo	300	3.63	.....	......	...	26.5	2180	5.5	
64			1.2 yr	400	4.35	.....	......	...	23.0	2120	4.8	
65			2.0 yr	500	5.02	.....	......	...	24.1	2400	5.0	
66			2.9 yr	600	5.63	.....	......	...	24.9	2650	5.2	
67			4.8 yr	700	6.21	.....	......	...	25.6	2880	5.3	
68			....	800	6.75	.....	......	...	26.2	3100	5.4	
69		♀	0.7 mo	100	1.82	.....	......	...	45.0	2470	9.3	
70			2.9 mo	200	2.82	.....	......	...	32.7	2320	6.8	
71			6.0 mo	300	3.63	.....	......	...	27.1	2240	5.6	
72			1.2 yr	400	4.35	.....	......	...	23.8	2180	4.9	
73			1.9 yr	500	5.02	.....	......	...	24.9	2480	5.2	
74			2.4 yr	600	5.63	.....	......	...	24.8	2640	5.1	
75			3.3 yr	700	6.21	.....	......	...	24.6	2780	5.1	
76			5.0 yr	800	6.75	.....	......	...	24.5	2910	5.1	
77	Mule	♂♀	1 wk	60	1.35	.....	......	...	60.5	2685	12.5	11
78			4 wk	100	1.87	.....	......	...	50.3	2689	10.4	
79			4 mo	200	2.91	.....	......	...	39.2	2697	8.1	
80			8 mo	300	3.76	.....	......	...	33.9	2701	7.0	
81			13 mo	400	4.52	.....	......	...	30.6	2705	6.3	
82			26 mo	500	5.21	.....	......	...	28.2	2706	5.8	
83			38 mo	600	5.85	.....	......	...	26.4	2709	5.5	
84			5 yr	700	6.45	.....	......	...	25.0	2710	5.2	
85	Rat, albino	♂♀	5 days	0.010	0.0047	.....	......	...	290	617	.....	8,13
86			10 days	0.015	0.0060	.....	......	...	200	500	.....	
87			19 days	0.025	0.0084	.....	......	...	216	643	.....	
88			29-31 days	0.050	0.0129	240	930	51	280	1085	60	
89		♂	40-42 days	0.100	0.0200	210	1050	...	260	1300	.....	
90			60-64 days	0.200	0.0310	140	903	30	155	1000	32	
91			100-120 days	0.300	0.0400	107	802	...	113	848	.....	
92			175 days	0.500	0.0552	.....	......	...	119	1076	24	
93			350 days	0.600	0.0619	.....	......	...	108	1045	22	
94		♀	42-45 days	0.100	0.0200	210	1050	...	240	1200	.....	
95			120-140 days	0.200	0.0310	118	761	25	135	871	28	
	Swine[3]											
96	Chester White &	♂♀	1.5 mo	5	0.27	.....	......	...	77.2	1440	.....	3
97	Duroc-Jersey	♂	3.3 mo	10	0.42	.....	......	...	67.6	1620	.....	
98			5.3 mo	25	0.75	38.6	1300	8.0	61.8	2070	12.8	

[1] Calculated from the following equations: guinea pig, 9.85 × wt in $g^{0.64}$; horse, 0.1 × wt in $kg^{0.63}$; mule, 0.1 × wt in $kg^{0.636}$; rat, 0.0011 × wt in $g^{0.63}$; swine, 0.097 × wt in $kg^{0.633}$. [2] Geldings. [3] Basal metabolism is actually 24-hr fasting metabolism.

continued

62. BASAL AND RESTING ENERGY METABOLISM AT VARIOUS AGES: FARM AND LABORATORY ANIMALS

	Animal	Sex	Age	Body Wt kg	Body Surface Area[1/] m^2	Basal Metabolism kcal/kg/day	Basal Metabolism kcal/m^2/day	Basal O_2 Cons. liters/kg/day	Resting Metabolism kcal/kg/day	Resting Metabolism kcal/m^2/day	Resting O_2 Cons. liters/kg/day	Reference
99			7.3	50	1.15	33.8	1460	7.0	57.9	2510	12.0	
100			11.0 mo	100	1.79	26.5	1480	5.5	.....	......	.....	
101			1.8 yr	200	2.78	19.3	1390	4.0	.....	......	.....	
102			2.1 yr	250	3.19	17.4	1360	3.6	.....	......	.....	
103		♀	3.0 mo	10	0.42	43.4	1040	9.0	72.4	1740	15.0	
104			5.1 mo	25	0.74	36.7	1230	7.6	65.6	2205	13.6	
105			6.6 mo	50	1.16	31.8	1380	6.6	60.8	2630	12.6	
106			10.0 mo	100	1.79	23.2	1290	4.8	.....	......	.....	
107			1.5 yr	200	2.77	15.9	1150	3.3	.....	......	.....	
108			2.1 yr	250	3.19	14.1	1100	2.9	.....	......	.....	
109	Chester White	♂	11.0 mo	100	1.79	.....	......	...	38.6	2160	8.0	
110			1.8 yr	200	2.78	.....	......	...	32.8	2360	6.8	
111			2.1 yr	250	3.19	.....	......	...	31.1	2430	6.4	
112		♀	10.0 mo	100	1.79	.....	......	...	36.2	2020	7.5	
113			1.5 yr	200	2.77	.....	......	...	27.3	1960	5.6	
114			2.1 yr	250	3.19	.....	......	...	25.1	1960	5.2	
115	Duroc-Jersey	♂	11.0 mo	100	1.79	.....	......	...	33.8	1890	7.0	
116			1.8 yr	200	2.78	.....	......	...	25.8	1860	5.3	
117			2.1 yr	250	3.19	.....	......	...	23.7	1860	4.9	
118		♀	10.0 mo	100	1.79	.....	......	...	33.3	1860	6.9	
119			1.5 yr	200	2.77	.....	......	...	20.8	1500	4.3	
120			2.1 yr	250	3.19	.....	......	...	17.8	1390	3.7	
121	Chicken[3/], Rhode Island Red	♂♀	Hatching	0.04	0.011	.....	......	...	200	727	.....	9
122		♂	15 days	0.10	0.021	.....	......	...	220	1048	.....	
123			4 wk	0.25	0.040	.....	......	...	196	1220	40	
124			13 wk	1.10	0.114	90	868	19	105	1020	21	
125			25 wk	2.60	0.209	86	1077	18	93	1160	19	
126		♀	20 days	0.10	0.021	.....	......	...	220	1048	.....	
127			4 wk	0.20	0.034	.....	......	...	210	1230	43	
128			13 wk	0.90	0.099	91	828	19	99	900	20	
129			25 wk	2.00	0.174	70	799	15	76	880	16	

[1/] Calculated from the following equation: chicken, 8.19 × wt in $g^{0.705}$. [3/] Basal metabolism is actually 24-hr fasting metabolism.

Contributor: Kibler, Hudson H.

References

[1] Brody, S. 1938. Missouri Univ. Agr. Expt. Sta. Res. Bull. 291.

[2] Brody, S., J. E. Comfort, and J. S. Matthews. 1928. Ibid. 115.

[3] Brody, S., and H. H. Kibler. 1944. Ibid. 380.

[4] Brody, S., H. H. Kibler, and E. A. Trowbridge. 1943. Ibid. 368.

[5] Brody, S., et al. 1947. Ibid. 404.

[6] Kibler, H. H. 1960. Ibid. 743.

[7] Kibler, H. H. 1964. Ibid. 862.

[8] Kibler, H. H., and S. Brody. 1942. J. Nutr. 24:461.

[9] Kibler, H. H., and S. Brody. 1944. Ibid. 28:27.

[10] Kibler, H. H., and S. Brody. 1947. Ibid. 33:331.

[11] Kibler, H. H., and S. Brody. 1949. Missouri Univ. Agr. Expt. Sta. Res. Bull. 438.

[12] Kibler, H. H., and S. Brody. 1953. Ibid. 522.

[13] Kibler, H. H., and H. D. Johnson. 1961. J. Gerontol. 16:13.

63. ENERGY METABOLISM

When oxygen consumption values were not given in the references, they were calculated by dividing heat production (kcal/24 hr) by the weight of the animal, by 4.8 (caloric equivalence of one liter of oxygen), and by 24 hours. *Abbreviation:* RQ = respiratory quotient.

Part I. Mammals

The relationship between weight and standard metabolism in mammals can be determined by the formula, log M = 1.83 + 0.756 log W ± 0.05, where M = standard metabolism in kcal/day, and W = weight in kilograms [23].

	Species (Synonym)	Weight g	Ambient Temp °C	Oxygen Consumption ml/g/hr	Reference
1	*Homo sapiens*	70 X 10^3	28	0.25 ± 0.09	10
2	*Alopex lagopus*	4500	18	0.73[1/]	37
3	*Blarina brevicauda*	21	15-25	5.3	30
4	*Bos indicus*	364 X 10^3	18	0.14	21
5	*B. taurus*	272 X 10^3	20	0.17	35
6	*Canis familiaris*	....	....	0.83	10
7	*Cavia* sp.	861	30	0.58	22
8	*Cebuella pygmaea*	100	30	1.0	31
9	*Citellus undulatus*	600	6	0.063[2/]	14
10			20	0.8[3/]	14
11		700	20	1.2[4/]	14
12	*Clethrionomys gapperi*	24	15-25	3.6	30
13	*Cricetus cricetus*[5/]	340	32	0.77[3/]	27
14		435	32	0.87[4/]	27
15	*Dasypus novemcinctus*	....	30	0.20	20
16	*Dicrostonyx groenlandicus*	76	20	3.94	6
17	*Dipodomys merriami*	35	31-34	1.2	5
18	*Elephas maximus*	3600 X 10^3	20.2	0.15[6/]	2
19	*Equus caballus*	....	....	0.25	10
20	*Felis catus*	....	....	0.71	10
21	*Meriones unguiculatus*	....	30	1.0	34
22	*Mesocricetus auratus*	....	....	0.07[2/]; 2.9[7/]	26
23	*Microsorex hoyi*	3.5	....	16.7[8/]	3
24	*Microtus pennsylvanicus*	32	15-25	3.2	30
25	*Mus musculus,* white	16	15-25	3.4	30
26	*Mustela rixosa*	37.5	15	8.15[9/]	37
27	*Myotis lucifugus*	5.2	2	0.030 ± 0.008[7/]	13
28		5.9	10	0.071 ± 0.022[7/]	13
29		6.2	20	0.39 ± 0.161	13
30		6.9	37	2.89 ± 0.89	13
31	*Oreamnos americanus*	32 X 10^3	−20 to +20	0.26[10/]	24
32	*Ornithorhynchus anatinus (O. paradoxus)*	....	....	0.46	29
33	*Oryctolagus cuniculus*	3300	28	0.68	11
34	*Ovis aries*	....	....	0.34	10
35	*Peromyscus leucopus*	21	15-25	4.4	30
36	*P. maniculatus*	20	25	8.0[11/]	16
37	At sea level	20	32	3.0[3/]; 4.0[4/]	17
38	At 3800 m[12/]	20	32	3.0[3/]; 2.0[4/]	17
39	*Phoca vitulina*	27-41 X 10^3	20	0.42-0.50[3/,13/]	9,18,19
40		30-44 X 10^3	10	0.45-0.52[4/,14/]	9,18,19
41	*Phocoena phocoena*	19 X 10^3	....	0.30[14/]	36
42	*Pteropus poliocephalus*	598	5	1.0	1
43			15	0.5	1
44			30	0.45	1
45	*Rangifer tarandus*	100 X 10^3	−16 ± 3	0.36[15/]; 1.43[11/]	8

[1/] CO_2 production, 0.55 ml/g/hr; RQ, 0.75. [2/] During hibernation or period of lethargy. [3/] Winter. [4/] Summer. [5/] Acclimated to 23°C. [6/] RQ, 1.02. [7/] During activity or nonhibernation. [8/] CO_2 production, 14.2 ml/g/hr; RQ, 0.85. [9/] CO_2 production, 6.11 ml/g/hr; RQ, 0.75. [10/] RQ, 0.88. [11/] During exercise. [12/] Subjects native to high altitude. [13/] RQ, 0.73. [14/] RQ, 0.75. [15/] During rest.

continued

Part I. Mammals

	Species (Synonym)	Weight g	Ambient Temp °C	Oxygen Consumption ml/g/hr	Reference
46	*Rattus norvegicus,* white	423	30	1.045	12
47	wild	225	−40	6.5	25
48	*Reithrodontomys megalotis*	9	33	2.5	33
49	*Saimiri sciurea*	840	....	0.83	28
50	*Sorex cinereus*	3.5	27	16.8	32
51	*S. cinereus cinereus (S. araneus)*	7.2	20	7.72 3/	7
52		8.1	20	11.63 4/	7
53	*Sus scrofa*	169 X 10^3	24	0.11	4
54	*Tamiasciurus hudsonicus*	175	20 16/	1.70 4,17/	19
55		229	20 16/	1.50 3/	19
56	*Thalarctos maritimus* 18/	25 X 10^3	24.5	0.49	15
57	*Ursus americanus*	50 X 10^3	20	0.36 7/	14
58		150 X 10^3	5	0.05 2/; 0.10 7/	14
59	*Vulpes vulpes alascensis*	4.44	8 16/	0.55 4,14/	19
60		5.01	−13 16/	0.50 3/	19

2/ During hibernation or period of lethargy. 3/ Winter. 4/ Summer. 7/ During activity or nonhibernation. 14/ RQ, 0.75. 16/ Critical temperature. 17/ RQ, 0.85. 18/ Young subject.

Contributor: Hock, Raymond J.

References

[1] Bartholomew, G. A., Jr., P. Leitner, and J. E. Nelson. 1964. Physiol. Zool. 37:179.
[2] Benedict, F. G. 1936. Carnegie Inst. Wash. Publ. 474.
[3] Buckner, C. H. 1964. Can. J. Zool. 42:259.
[4] Capstick, J. W., and T. B. Wood. 1922. J. Agr. Sci. 12:257.
[5] Dawson, W. R. 1955. J. Mammal. 36:543.
[6] Fisher, K. C., and M. E. Needler. 1957. J. Cellular Comp. Physiol. 50:293.
[7] Gebczynski, M. 1965. Acta Theriol. 10:303.
[8] Hammel, H. T., et al. 1962. Arctic Aeromed. Lab. TDR 61-54.
[9] Hart, J. S., and L. Irving. 1959. Can. J. Zool. 37:447.
[10] Heilbrun, L. V. 1952. Outline of general physiology. W. B. Saunders, Philadelphia.
[11] Heroux, O. 1967. Can. J. Biochem. Physiol. 45:451.
[12] Heroux, O., F. Depocas, and J. S. Hart. 1959. Ibid. 37:473.
[13] Hock, R. J. 1951. Biol. Bull. 101:289.
[14] Hock, R. J. 1960. Bull. Harvard Museum Comp. Zool. 124:155.
[15] Hock, R. J. 1968. Z. Saeugetierk. 33:57.
[16] Hock, R. J. Unpublished. Northrop Space Laboratories, Hawthorne, Calif., 1968.
[17] Hock, R. J., and J. C. Roberts. 1966. Can. J. Zool. 44:365.
[18] Irving, L., and J. S. Hart. 1957. Ibid. 35:497.
[19] Irving, L., H. Krog, and M. Monson. 1955. Physiol. Zool. 28:173.
[20] Johansen, K. 1961. Ibid. 34:126.
[21] Kibler, H. H. 1957. Missouri Univ. Agr. Expt. Sta. Res. Bull. 648.
[22] Kibler, H. H., S. Brody, and D. Worstell. 1947. J. Nutr. 33:331.
[23] Kleiber, M. 1947. Physiol. Rev. 27:511.
[24] Krog, H., and M. Monson. 1954. Am. J. Physiol. 178:515.
[25] Krog, H., M. Monson, and L. Irving. 1955. J. Appl. Physiol. 7:349.
[26] Lyman, C. P. 1948. J. Exptl. Zool. 109:55.
[27] Malan, A., and G. Hildwein. 1965. Compt. Rend. Soc. Biol. 159:473.
[28] Malinow, M. R., and R. Wagner. 1966. Lab. Animal Care 16:105.
[29] Martin, C. J. 1903. Phil. Trans. Roy. Soc. London, B, 195:1.
[30] Morrison, P. R. 1948. J. Cellular Comp. Physiol. 31:69.
[31] Morrison, P. R., and E. H. Middleton. 1967. Folia Primatol. 6:70.
[32] Morrison, P. R., and O. P. Pearson. 1947. Science 104:287.
[33] Pearson, O. P. 1960. Physiol. Zool. 33:152.
[34] Robinson, P. F. 1959. Science 130:502.
[35] Rogerson, A. 1960. J. Agr. Sci. 55:359.
[36] Scholander, P. F. 1940. Hvalradets Skrifter Norske Videnskaps-Akad. Oslo 22:1.
[37] Scholander, P. F., et al. 1950. Biol. Bull. 99:259.

continued

63. ENERGY METABOLISM

Part II. Birds

The relationship between weight and metabolism in passerines can be determined by the formula, $\log M = \log 129 + 0.724 \log W \pm 0.113$, where M = heat production in kcal/day, and W = weight in kilograms. The formula for determining the relationship between weight and metabolism in nonpasserines is $\log M = \log 78.3 + 0.723 \log W \pm 0.068$. [18] Data are for birds at thermoneutrality.

	Species (Synonym)	Weight kg	Heat Production kcal/24 hr	Oxygen Consumption ml/g/hr	Reference
1	*Aquila chrysaetos*	3.0	102	0.30	8
2	*Archilochus colubris*	0.0032	1.6	4.34	16
3	*Ardea herodias*	1.87	128	0.59	3
4	*Asio flammeus*	0.406	26.6	0.57	9
5	*A. otus*	0.252	19.7	0.68	9
6	*Branta bernicla*	1.130	108.5	0.83[1]	13
7		1.168	93.4	0.69[2]	13
8	*Bubo virginianus*	1.450	108	0.65	3
9	*Calypte anna*	0.0048	2.2	3.98	16
10		0.0043	....	0.8[3]	22
11	*Casuarius bennetti*	17.6	516	0.25	3
12	*Chloris chloris*	0.031	11.2	3.14	24
13	*Chordeiles minor*	0.075	9.5	1.10	17
14	*Colinus virginianus*	0.194	23.0	1.03	18
15	*Corvus caurinus*	0.282	73.2	2.25[1]	13
16		0.306	96.7	2.74[2]	13
17	*C. corax*	0.850	92	0.94[4]	23
18	*C. cryptoleucus*	0.640	79	1.07	18
19	*Coturnix coturnix*	0.097	23	2.06	8
20	*Cyanocitta cristata*	0.081	17.6	1.89	21
21	*Estrilda troglodytes*	0.0061	2.8	3.98	19
22	*Grus canadensis*	3.89	168	0.37	3
23	*Junco hyemalis*	0.018	6.1	2.94	18
24	*Larus hyperboreus*	1.60	304	1.65[5]	23
25	*Lophortyx californicus*	0.137	16.0	1.01	11
26	*Loxia curvirostra*	0.029	10.5	3.14	5
27	*Molothrus ater*	0.034	11.0	2.80	18
28	*Nyctidromus albicollis*	0.043	7.7	1.55	23
29	*Olor buccinator (Cygnus buccinator)*	8.88	418	0.41	3
30	*Parus major*	0.0185	8.4	3.94	24
31	*Passer domesticus*	0.0224	9.5	3.68[2]	6
32		0.0235	11.0	4.06[6]	6
33		0.0255	6.9	2.35	12
34	*Pelecanus conspicillatus*	5.09	374	0.64	3
35	*Perisoreus canadensis*	0.071	14.3	1.75	25
36	*Phalaenoptilus nuttalli*	0.040	3.7	0.80	1
37	*Plectrophenax nivalis*	0.042	11.4	2.36[7]	23
38	*Richmondena cardinalis*	0.040	12.2	2.65	4
39	*Scardafella inca*	0.0405	5.2	1.15	20
40	*Stellula calliope*	0.0023	....	66.3[8]	16
41		0.003	1.4	4.05	16
42	*Struthio camelus*	100	2350	0.20	18
43	*Troglodytes aedon*	0.009	5.3	5.11	14
44	*Zenaidura macroura*	0.091	13.4	1.28	11
45	*Zonotrichia albicollis*	0.029	8.0	2.43	15
46	Domestic duck	1.87	157	0.73	8
47	Domestic fowl	2.006	130.7	0.57	10
48	Domestic goose	5.0	2.80	0.49	7
49	Domestic pigeon	0.300	30	0.87	2
50	Domestic turkey	3.7	184	0.43	7

[1] Summer. [2] Winter. [3] Subject torpid at 24°C. [4] CO_2 production, 0.67 ml/g/hr; RQ, 0.71. [5] CO_2 production, 1.25 ml/g/hr; RQ, 0.76. [6] Spring. [7] CO_2 production, 1.72 ml/g/hr; RQ, 0.73. [8] During flight, at 24°C.

Contributor: Hock, Raymond J.

References

[1] Bartholomew, G. A., J. W. Hudson, and T. R. Howell. 1962. Condor 64:117.

[2] Benedict, F. G. 1938. Carnegie Inst. Wash. Publ. 503.

[3] Benedict, F. G., and E. L. Fox. 1927. Proc. Am. Phil. Soc. 66:511.

[4] Dawson, W. R. 1954. Univ. Calif. (Berkeley) Publ. Zool. 59:81.

[5] Dawson, W. R., and H. B. Tordoff. 1964. Auk 81:26.

[6] Fonberg, A. 1932. Sprawozdania Posiedzen Towarz. Nauk. Warszaw., IV, 25:59.

[7] Giaja, J. 1931. Ann. Physiol. Physicochim. Biol. 7:12.

[8] Giaja, J., and B. Males. 1928. Ibid. 4:875.

[9] Graber, R. R. 1962. Condor 64:473.

[10] Herzog, D. 1930. Wiss. Arch. Landwirtsch., B, 3:610.

[11] Hudson, J. W., and A. H. Brush. 1964. Comp. Biochem. Physiol. 12:157.

[12] Hudson, J. W., and S. L. Kimzey. 1964. Am. Zoologist 4:294.

[13] Irving, L., H. Krog, and M. Monson. 1955. Physiol. Zool. 28:173.

[14] Kendeigh, S. C. 1939. J. Exptl. Zool. 82:419.

[15] King, J. R. 1964. Comp. Biochem. Physiol. 12:13.

[16] Lasiewski, R. C. 1963. Physiol. Zool. 36:122.

[17] Lasiewski, R. C., and W. R. Dawson. 1964. Condor 66:477.

[18] Lasiewski, R. C., and W. R. Dawson. 1967. Ibid. 69:13.

[19] Lasiewski, R. C., S. H. Hubbard, and W. R. Moberly. 1964. Ibid. 66:212.

[20] MacMillen, R. E., and C. H. Trost. 1965. Am. Zoologist 5:208.

[21] Misch, M. S. 1960. Physiol. Zool. 33:252.

[22] Pearson, O. P. 1950. Condor 52:145.

[23] Scholander, P. F., et al. 1950. Biol. Bull. 99:259.

[24] Steen, J. 1958. Ecology 39:625.

[25] Veghte, J. H. 1964. Physiol. Zool. 37:316.

64. FACTORS AFFECTING ENERGY EXCHANGE

Part I. Age, Work, Feed Intake, and Gravity

	Factor	Metabolic Process Affected	Animal	Equation & Explanation	Remarks	Reference
1	Age	Basal metabolic rate	Man, adult ♂	$B = 71W^{0.75}[1 + 0.004(30 - a) + 0.01(s - 43.4)]$ B = basal metabolic rate in kcal day^{-1} W = body weight in kg a = age in years s = specific stature, i.e., (height in cm)$W^{-0.33}$	Calculated by M. Kleiber (from data of Harris, J. S., and F. G. Benedict, 1919, Carnegie Inst. Wash. Publ. 279) to obtain physiologically meaningful parameters	2
2			adult ♀	$B = 66W^{0.75}[1 + 0.004(30 - a) + 0.018(s - 42.1)]$		
3		Fasting catabolic rate	Rat, ♀, 77-1000 days old	$B = 72.6W^{0.75}(1 + 0.55e^{-0.014a} + 0.008e^{0.0034a})$ B = metabolic rate in kcal day^{-1} W = body weight in kg e = 2.718, the basis of natural logarithms a = age in days	The results of 700 three-hour respiration trials are summarized as the sum of a negative and a positive exponential function of age	5
4	Work Horizontal walking	Energy cost	Man	$C = 0.8v + 0.5$ C = metabolic rate in kcal $minute^{-1}$ v = velocity of horizontal walking in km $hour^{-1}$	In this equation, energy expenditure is linearly proportional to speed between the velocities of 3.0-6.5 km/hr (consult p. 806, fig. 1, of reference). However, the parameters in this equation have no proper physiological meaning because the metabolic rate for standing (v = 0) amounts to 1.7 or 1.9 kcal/min, nearly four times the constant, 0.5 (consult p. 811 of reference).	6
5				$C = 1.6e^{0.20v}$ C = metabolic rate in kcal $minute^{-1}$ e = 2.718, the basis of natural logarithms v = velocity of horizontal walking in km $hour^{-1}$	This exponential equation with physiologically meaningful parameters for the entire range of speeds from 0 to 9 km/hr, better summarizes the relation of metabolic rate and velocity of walking than does the equation in entry 4. The linear logarithmic regression from which the exponential equation was derived has a correlation coefficient of 0.97. The calculated rate for v = 0 (of 1.6 kcal/min) is in good agreement with the independently measured rate for standing.	4
6	Partial efficiency	Energy cost	Horse	$\text{Partial efficiency} = \frac{\text{Change in work}}{\text{Corresponding change in catabolism}}$	According to Zuntz, N., and O. Hagemann, 1898, Landw. Jahrb., v. 27, suppl III, p. 180, horses utilize body substance as fuel for work with a partial efficiency of 28%. If horses are fed mainly roughages with a net energy content amounting to 50% of the feed energy, then the partial efficiency of feed energy utilization for work amounts to 14%.	3
7	Feed intake	Energy utilization	Cattle, Holstein, ♀, lactating	$Y = -92.1 + 0.656X \pm 0.0112$ Y = energy balance, i.e., energy in milk & gain in body substance $day^{-1}kg^{-0.75}$ X = metabolizable food energy $day^{-1}kg^{-0.75}$	Pooled regression of measurements for energy balance on metabolizable energy	1

continued

64. FACTORS AFFECTING ENERGY EXCHANGE

Part I. Age, Work, Feed Intake, and Gravity

	Factor	Metabolic Process Affected	Animal	Equation & Explanation	Remarks	Reference
8				$Q = 92.1 + 0.344X$ Q = heat production day^{-1} $kg^{-0.75}$	Derived regression for heat production on metabolizable energy	
9				$\Delta Q = Q - 92.1 = 0.344X$	Calorigenic effect showing increase in heat production per day	
10				$\frac{\Delta Q}{X}$ 100	Roughage content of ration vs calorigenic effect Average ration: 34% of metabolizable energy 60% alfalfa ration: 36% of metabolizable energy 40% alfalfa ration: 33% of metabolizable energy 20% alfalfa ration: 33% of metabolizable energy	
11	Gravity[1]	Energy expenditure	Chicken	Body mass in kg = $2.29 - 0.23\,g$ $g = 1$, acceleration in terms of earth gravity	By measuring feed intake and body gain, and then analyzing the bodies, it was determined that centrifuged chickens ate more food and gained less weight than noncentrifuged chickens. As indicated by the equation, body mass is a linear function of the centrifugal force up to 3 g.	7
12				% body fat = $12 - 4\,g$	Fat content also decreased linearly with increasing centrifugal force. At 1 g, body fat = 8%, and at 2 g, 4%.	
13				Maintenance feed/kg body mass = $28 + 9.7\,g$	Feed requirement for maintenance was determined by plotting gain in body substance against feed intake. Feed and carcass analyses indicate that the partial efficiency of energy utilization for growth was independent of acceleration.	

[1] Since at earth gravity ($g = 1$) the basal metabolic rate is proportional to the 0.75 power of body weight (which in this case expresses directly body mass), and since the effect of gravity on energy requirement is directly proportional to body mass, the relative effect of gravity as part of the basal metabolic rate must increase with increasing body size.

Contributor: Kleiber, Max

References

[1] Flatt, W. P., et al. 1968. Symp. Energy Metab., 4th, Jablonna, Poland, 1967.

[2] Kleiber, M. 1932. Hilgardia 6:345.

[3] Kleiber, M. 1961. The fire of life. J. Wiley, New York.

[4] Kleiber, M. Unpublished. Univ. California, Davis, 1967.

[5] Kleiber, M., A. H. Smith, and T. N. Chernikoff. 1956. Am. J. Physiol. 186:11.

[6] Passmore, R., and J. V. G. A. Durnin. 1955. Physiol. Rev. 35:801.

[7] Smith, A. H. Unpublished. Univ. California, Davis, 1967.

Part II. Altitude

	Metabolic Process Affected	Subjects	Altitude	Value	Remarks
1	Basal metabolic rate	6 scientists	Sea level[1]	37.6 kcal m^{-2} surface area hr^{-1}	$\frac{\text{Observed} - \text{Predicted}}{\text{Predicted}} \times 100 = 11\%$
2			5800 m[2]	41.7 ± 1.57 kcal m^{-2} surface area hr^{-1}	
3		3 Sherpas	Sea level[1]	38.0 kcal m^{-2} surface area hr^{-1}	$\frac{\text{Observed} - \text{Predicted}}{\text{Predicted}} \times 100 = 22\%$
4			5800 m[2]	46.1 ± 1.01 kcal m^{-2} surface area hr^{-1}	

[1] Predicted value according to DuBois, and Boothby and DuBois. [2] Observed value.

continued

Part II. Altitude

	Metabolic Process Affected	Subjects	Altitude	Value	Remarks
5	Oxygen uptake	33, ages 22-29 yr	Sea level	4.02 ml $min^{-1}kg^{-1}$ lean body mass	Data of Brozek
6		16 Indians	Sea level	4.07 ml $min^{-1}kg^{-1}$ lean body mass	Data of Banerjee and Sen
7		48 students	Sea level	3.97 ml $min^{-1}kg^{-1}$ lean body mass	Data of Miller and Blyth
8		17 miners	4500 m	5.06 ml $min^{-1}kg^{-1}$ lean body mass	In Peru
9		5 scientists	5800 m	4.48 ml $min^{-1}kg^{-1}$ lean body mass	In the Himalayas

Contributor: Kleiber, Max

Reference: Gill, M. B., and L. G. C. E. Pugh. 1964. J. Appl. Physiol. 19:949.

Part III. Environmental Temperature

At a physiologically low environmental temperature, below the critical temperature (T_C), the metabolic rate is determined by the thermostatic heat requirement. Above the critical temperature, the metabolic rate is essentially independent of temperature changes as long as the body temperature remains constant. If at low environmental temperature the thermal insulation of the animal, or its reciprocal (heat transmissivity), is independent of changes in temperature, then the thermostatic heat requirement and consequently the metabolic rate are proportional to the difference between body and environmental temperatures (Fourier's law of heatflow). $\Delta Q/\Delta t = q\ (T_B - T_E)$, where Q/t = metabolic rate in cal hr^{-1}, T_B = body temperature, T_E = environmental temperature, and q = heat transmissivity. At a physiologically high environmental temperature, above the critical temperature, the metabolic rate is independent of changes in environmental temperature, so that $Q/t = M$, and M = minimal metabolic rate. At the critical temperature, the thermostatic heat requirement is equal to the minimal metabolic rate, thus $q\ (T_B - T_C) = M$. From this relationship, the critical temperature can be calculated when M and a metabolic rate at a low environmental temperature are known. [8]

	Animal 1/	B kcal $d^{-1}m^{-2}$	q 2/ (in cold)	B/q 3/ °C	T_C 4/ °C	Reference
	Man					
1	Nude, in water	......	....	.....	33	1
2	in air	......	....	.....	26	2,12
3	Clothed	890	43	20.7	16	14
4	Cattle 5/	1465	50	29.3	8	3
5	Rabbit	438	20	21.9	15	7
6	Rat	600	59	10.2	27	10
7	Sheep	1160	36	32.2	5	11

1/ A very good example of the rectilinear relation between metabolic rate and environmental temperature in the Arctic fox has been reported [4,6]. In many cases, however, heat transmissivity seems to increase with decreasing environmental temperature, as has been clearly shown in man [9]. This can be explained as the result of shivering, a wasteful method of chemical temperature regulation, which earlier was regarded as obligatory. Recently, however, more and more observations on nonshivering calorigenesis in the cold have been reported. Up to 20% of such calorigenesis may be contributed by brown adipose tissue [13], but it is now believed that muscles also can increase the metabolic rate without shivering. The agent regarded to be responsible for the regulation of nonshivering calorigenesis is noradrenalin [5]. 2/ $\frac{Q/t}{T_B - T_E}$. 3/ $T_B - T_C$. 4/ $T_B - B/q$. 5/ Steer.

Contributor: Kleiber, Max

References

[1] Burton, A. C., and H. C. Bazett. 1936. Am. J. Physiol. 117:36.
[2] Erikson, H., et al. 1956. Acta Physiol. Scand. 37:35.
[3] Forbes, E. B., M. Kriss, and W. Braman. 1927. J. Agr. Res. 34:167.
[4] Hart, J. S. 1957. Rev. Can. Biol. 16:156.

continued

64. FACTORS AFFECTING ENERGY EXCHANGE

Part III. Environmental Temperature

[5] Hsieh, A. C. L., and L. D. Carlson. 1957. Am. J. Physiol. 188:40.

[6] Irving, L., H. Krog, and H. Monson. 1955. Physiol. Zool. 128:173.

[7] Kleiber, M. 1928. Habilitation thesis. Technische Hochschule, Zurich.

[8] Kleiber, M. 1967. Der Energiehaushalt von Mensch und Haustier. P. Parey, Hamburg. p. 143.

[9] Lefevre, J. 1911. Chaleur animale et bioenergetique. G. Masson, Paris. p. 433.

[10] Mitchell, H. H., and G. G. Carman. 1926. Am. J. Physiol. 76:385.

[11] Ritzman, E. G., and F. G. Benedict. 1931. New Hampshire Agr. Expt. Sta. Bull. 45.

[12] Scholander, P. F., et al. 1957. J. Appl. Physiol. 10:231.

[13] Smith, R. E., and R. J. Hock. 1963. Science 140:199.

[14] Swift, R. W. 1932. J. Nutr. 5:213.

Part IV. Circadian Cycle

For information on circadian cycle nomenclature, consult reference 1.

	Species	Weight g	Ambient Temp °C	Animal Activity a	O_2 Consumption Rate ml hr^{-1} Night	Day	Change	Reference
1	*Peromyscus*	27	30	....	120	50	80% maximum change	3
2	*Rattus*	234	30	0-100	255 + 1.2a	203 + 0.9a	....	2
3				0	255	203	23% mean change	
4				50	315	249	23% mean change	

Contributor: Kleiber, Max

References

[1] Halberg, F. 1959. Z. Vitamin. Hormon. Ferment-forsch. 10:225.

[2] Heusner, A. A. 1963. Doctoral Thesis. Univ. Strasbourg, France. p. 71.

[3] Kayser, C., and A. A. Heusner. 1967. J. Physiol. (Paris) 59:3.

65. ENERGY COST OF WORK: MAN

Energy Expenditure: Values in kcal/min are based on an average body surface area of 1.8 m^2 for men (height, 173 cm and weight, 68 kg), and 1.65 m^2 for women (height, 165 cm and weight, 60 kg).

	Activity	No. of Subjects	No. of Tests	Age yr	Wt kg	Energy Expenditure kcal/min	% over supine	Reference
	Male							
	Relaxation & personal grooming							
1	Resting, supine, basal	82	....	....	....	1.17	......	5
2	Basal	9	....	....	....	1.19	......	18,37
3		5	10	91-100	43-67	0.89	−24	43
4		5	15	19-25	....	1.19	......	38
5	Lying, at ease	5	15	19-25	....	1.5	28	38
6	Sitting, relaxed & fasting	1	3	....	....	1.19	......	4
7	at ease	5	5	19-25	....	1.8	54	38
8	calculating	5	7	19-25	....	1.78	52	38
9	writing	4	4	19-25	....	1.91	63	38
10	listening to boat race	2	2	19-25	....	1.97	68	38
11	reading	2	2	19-25	....	1.98	69	38
12	eating	8	32	20-24	73	1.44	23	7

continued

65. ENERGY COST OF WORK: MAN

	Activity	No. of Subjects	No. of Tests	Age yr	Wt kg	Energy Expenditure kcal/min	Energy Expenditure % over supine	Reference
13	Kneeling	2	4	20-24	73	1.22	4	7
14	Squatting	1	2	20-24	73	2.02	73	7
15	Standing, at ease	5	8	19-25	....	1.98	69	38
16	relaxed	2	47	....	....	1.25	7	4
17	Showering	8	16	20-24	73	3.31	183	7
18	Dressing	8	24	20-24	73	3.30	182	7
19		9	....	18-20	69	4.0	242	14
20	Brushing boots & clothes; polishing buttons	1	3	28	....	2.57	120	10
21	Washing face, neck, & hands; brushing hair	1	3	28	....	2.74	134	10
22	Personal toilet	8	32	20-24	73	1.97	68	7
23	Washing, shaving, dressing	5	8	19-25	....	3.56	204	38
24	Cleaning shoes	2	2	19-25	....	3.49	198	38
25	Shining shoes	7	21	20-24	73	3.10	165	7
	Transportation & sports							
	Climbing ladder, 17-cm step							
26	50° angle, 9.1 m/min, no load	....	....	....	....	7.7	558	33
27	50-lb load	....	....	....	....	14.3	1122	33
28	70° angle, 11.1 m/min, no load	....	....	....	....	9.0	669	33
29	50-lb load	....	....	....	....	17.1	1362	33
30	90° angle, 11.9 m/min, no load	....	....	....	....	11.5	883	33
31	50-lb load	....	....	....	....	25.4	2071	33
32	Climbing stairs, up & down, 97/min	5	10	19-25	....	8.4	618	38
33	116/min	5	5	19-25	....	9.3	695	38
34	15-cm step, 14.8 m/min	....	....	....	75	9.8	736	1
35	17.6 m/min	....	....	....	75	10.3	780	1
36	Walking, up stairs, normal	8	16	20-24	73	18.08	1445	7
37	down stairs, normal	8	16	20-24	73	6.94	494	7
38	indoors, 2.4 mi/hr	4	4	19-25	....	4.3	268	38
39	3.0 mi/hr	4	6	19-25	....	5.1	336	38
40	outdoors, 4.0 mi/hr	1	1	19-25	....	8.2	601	38
41	4.2 mi/hr	4	5	19-25	....	9.1	678	38
42	4.4 mi/hr	4	8	19-25	....	9.5	712	38
43	4.6 mi/hr	3	4	19-25	....	9.9	746	38
44	4.8 mi/hr	5	6	19-25	....	10.7	815	38
45	hard snow, 6 km/hr	1	....	....	83	11.9	917	12
46	loose snow, 4 km/hr, 20-kg load	1	....	....	83	20.2	1627	12
47	snow shoes, soft snow, 4 km/hr	1	....	....	83	13.8	1080	12
48	Skiing, hard snow, level, 6 km/hr	1	....	....	83	9.9	746	12
49	Ski running	4	4	23-35	72	21.8	1765	25
50	Driving car	3	19	....	64	2.8	139	14
51	Driving motorcycle	3	19	....	64	3.4	191	14
52	Bicycling, 5.5 mi/hr	1	....	....	71	4.5	285	49
53	9.4 mi/hr	1	....	....	71	7.0	498	49
54	13.1 mi/hr	1	....	....	71	11.1	849	49
55	Rowing, 22 strokes/min	2	2	....	....	12.3	951	26
56	26 strokes/min	3	3	....	....	15.9	1259	26
57	33 strokes/min	5	7	....	....	19.0	1524	26
58	Football	1	2	20-24	73	9.07	675	7
59	Basketball	2	4	20-24	73	7.76	563	7
60	Table tennis	1	2	20-24	73	4.36	273	7
61	Bowling	1	2	20-24	73	7.31	525	7
62	Swimming	1	2	20-24	73	10.90	832	7
	Domestic work							
63	Peeling potatoes	1	1	19-25	....	2.7	131	38
64	Washing dishes	3	3	19-25	....	3.3	182	38
65	Laboratory work	5	5	19-25	....	3.2	174	38
66	Cleaning windows	1	3	28	....	3.3	182	10
67		10	....	27	61	3.7	216	41
68	Scrubbing floors	1	3	28	....	3.8	225	10
69	Washing socks	1	1	19-25	....	4.1	250	38
70	Washing clothes	2	4	20-24	73	2.62	124	7
71	Making beds	1	1	19-25	....	7.0	498	38
72	Making bunks	8	24	20-24	73	4.74	305	7
73	Sweeping	8	24	20-24	73	3.80	225	7

continued

65. ENERGY COST OF WORK: MAN

	Activity	No. of Subjects	No. of Tests	Age yr	Wt kg	Energy Expenditure kcal/min	Energy Expenditure % over supine	Reference
74	Mopping	8	16	20-24	73	4.73	304	7
	Craft activities							
75	Copper tooling, sitting	2	2	41	....	1.8	54	20
76	Handloom weaving, sitting	1	1	40	....	1.9	62	20
77	Chip carving, reclining	1	2	40	....	2.0	71	20
78	Chisel carving, hardwood, sitting	1	1	40	....	2.5	114	20
79	softwood, sitting	1	1	40	....	2.6	122	20
80	Making link belts	6	24	18-30	66-89	1.40	20	30
81	Sanding	6	24	18-30	66-89	2.31	97	30
	Office work							
82	Miscellaneous, sitting	10	36	....	55-72	1.6	37	17
83	standing	10	45	....	55-72	1.8	55	17
	Industrial trades							
84	Shoemaking: fixing soles	1	2	27	45	2.2	88	15
85	filing soles	1	....	27	45	2.3	97	15
86	polishing shoes	1	....	27	45	1.8	54	15
87	repair	6	17	....	....	2.7	131	34
88	manufacture	4	16	....	....	3.0	156	34
89	Locksmithing	1	5	19	53	2.5	114	15
90	Filing	1	2	19	53	3.5	199	15
91	Tailoring: cutting	2	....	21	63	2.6	122	15
92	machine sewing	2	....	....	....	2.7	131	15
93	hand sewing	2	....	....	....	1.9	62	15
94	pressing	2	....	....	....	3.9	233	15
95	Armature winding	2	8	....	....	2.2	88	34
96	Radio work, mechanical	4	8	....	....	2.7	131	34
97	Printing: hand composing	1	1	....	....	2.2	88	34
98	machine	1	1	....	....	2.2	88	34
99	paper layer	1	1	....	....	2.5	114	34
100	bookbinder at guillotine	1	1	....	....	2.3	97	34
101	Watch & clock repairing (trainee)	....	8	....	....	1.6	37	48
102	Inspecting wooden separators	....	4	....	....	1.8	54	48
103	Assembly line work, light	....	3	....	....	1.8	54	48
104	medium	....	14	....	....	2.7	131	48
105	Drilling (trainee)	....	3	....	....	1.8	54	48
106	Drafting	....	5	....	....	1.8	54	48
107	Machine fitting	....	12	....	....	4.2	259	48
108	Machine work (engineering), light	....	8	....	....	2.4	105	48
109	medium	....	12	....	....	3.1	165	48
110	Typewriter work, mechanic (trainee)	....	6	....	....	2.1	80	48
111	Joining work	....	18	....	....	3.6	208	48
112	(trainee)	....	8	....	....	3.0	156	48
113	Turning work	....	4	....	....	3.7	216	48
114	Toolroom work	....	4	....	....	3.9	233	48
115	Sheet metal work	....	8	....	....	3.0	156	48
116	Punching battery plates to size	....	5	....	....	3.3	182	48
117	Cutting battery plates	....	14	....	....	3.3	182	48
118	Light battery plate casting	....	6	....	....	3.6	208	48
119	Heavy battery plate casting	....	4	....	....	4.2	259	48
120	Machine molding battery plates	....	2	....	....	5.1	336	48
121	Trimming battery plates	....	3	....	....	4.4	276	48
122	Fixing rubber insulation to battery plates	....	3	....	....	2.2	88	48
123	Loading battery plates into charging vat	....	8	....	....	3.9	233	48
124	Unloading battery boxes from oven	....	4	....	....	6.8	481	48
125	Straightening lead contact bars	....	3	....	....	4.6	293	48
126	Molding plastic	....	9	....	....	3.3	182	48
127	Molding ebonite	....	7	....	....	3.6	208	48
128	Lead rolling on roller mill	....	3	....	....	3.9	233	48
129	Casting lead balls in mold	....	2	....	....	4.8	310	48
130	Loading chemicals into mixer	....	2	....	....	6.0	413	48
	Building trades							
131	Shoveling, 8-kg load, 1-m lift, 12/min	....	....	....	....	7.5	541	33
132	Hewing with pick	....	....	....	....	7.0	498	17
133	Pushing wheelbarrow, 57-kg load, 4.5 km/hr	....	....	....	....	5.0	327	33

continued

65. ENERGY COST OF WORK: MAN

	Activity	No. of Subjects	No. of Tests	Age yr	Wt kg	Energy Expenditure kcal/min	% over supine	Reference
134	Bricklaying	....	....	....	....	4.0	242	2
135	Mixing cement	....	....	....	....	4.7	302	21
136	Stonemasonry, shaping stones	....	....	....	....	3.8	225	21
137	Plaster lathing	....	....	....	....	3.1	165	21
138	Plastering walls	....	....	....	....	4.1	250	21
139	Carpentry: measuring wood	1	35	....	62	2.4	105	15
140	machine sawing	1	35	....	62	2.4	105	15
141	joining floorboards	1	35	....	62	4.4	276	15
142	chiseling	1	31	....	65	5.7	387	15
143	sawing, softwood	1	31	....	65	6.3	439	15
144	hardwood	1	31	....	65	7.5	541	15
145	drilling hardwood	1	35	....	62	7.0	498	15
146	planing, softwood	1	31	....	65	8.1	592	15
147	hardwood	1	31	....	65	9.1	678	15
	Farming							
148	Mowing: horse-drawn reaper	15	....	15-55	....	4.3	268	8
149	Threshing: throwing sheaves to thresher	7	....	15-41	....	5.6	379	23
150	Hoeing	....	12	....	....	4.4	276	39
151	Deep ridging	5	13	24-36	57	9.5	712	16
152	Ploughing, horse	7	16	18-39	57-86	5.9	404	27
153	tractor	7	22	18-39	57-86	4.2	259	27
154	Milking, hand	1	....	28	64	4.7	302	28
155	machine	1	....	28	64	3.7	216	28
156	Cleaning milk pails	1	....	28	64	4.4	276	28
	Heavy industry							
157	Lumbering: tree felling	11	....	....	....	10.7	815	35
158	tree trimming	11	....	....	....	10.2	772	35
159	tree barking	11	....	....	....	10.1	763	35
160	crosscutting with bucksaw	11	....	....	....	9.0	669	35
161	tree felling with bucksaw	2	....	....	....	9.6	721	35
162	crosscutting on sawhorse	2	....	....	....	7.8	567	35
163	splitting softwood	2	....	....	....	9.7	729	35
164	splitting birch billets	2	....	....	....	8.9	661	35
165	stacking firewood	2	....	....	....	6.3	439	35
166	Chopping, vertical, 1.25-kg ax, 19/min	1	....	23	82	6.9	490	19
167	34/min	1	....	23	82	11.9	917	19
168	horizontal, 1.25-kg ax, 34/min	1	....	23	82	13.2	1028	19
169	2.0-kg ax, 33/min	1	....	23	82	12.3	951	19
170	Coal mining: hewing	18	....	....	....	7.0	498	17
171	loading	20	....	....	....	7.1	507	17
172	timbering	18	....	....	....	5.7	387	17
173	drilling	30	....	....	....	5.8	396	22
174	pushing tubs	12	....	....	....	8.0	584	22
175	Walking in mine, normal, 3.10 mi/hr	10	20	23-45	55-92	5.05	332	29
176	2.58 mi/hr	4	9	....	....	4.25	263	29
177	slight stoop, 2.44 mi/hr	6	12	....	....	4.04	245	29
178	full stoop, 1.96 mi/hr	10	21	....	....	5.56	375	29
179	up 5% grade, normal, 2.72 mi/hr	4	10	....	....	5.76	393	29
180	full stoop, 1.98 mi/hr	4	11	....	....	5.66	384	29
181	up 11.4% grade, normal, 2.40 mi/hr	10	17	....	....	7.89	574	29
182	full stoop, 2.21 mi/hr	8	18	....	....	8.70	643	29
183	down 5% grade, normal, 2.96 mi/hr	3	7	....	....	4.35	272	29
184	full stoop, 2.13 mi/hr	4	11	....	....	4.95	323	29
185	normal, 2.82 mi/hr	4	5	....	....	3.94	237	29
186	full stoop, 2.27 mi/hr	4	5	....	....	5.16	341	29
187	Steelwork, open hearth: slag removal	....	....	....	....	11.6	892	11
188	dolomite shoveling	....	....	....	....	10.9	832	11
189	heavy mill, tending furnace	....	....	....	....	10.2	772	11
190	hand rolling	....	....	....	....	8.9	661	11
191	tending sawpits	....	....	....	....	6.5	456	11
192	wire rod mill, roughing	....	....	....	....	8.2	600	11
193	wire bundling	....	....	....	....	10.2	772	11
194	14-in. merchant mill: mill rolling	....	....	....	....	9.4	703	11
195	forging	....	....	....	....	6.5	455	11
196	fletting	....	....	....	....	4.9	319	11

continued

	Activity	No. of Subjects	No. of Tests	Age yr	Wt kg	Energy Expenditure kcal/min	% over supine	Reference
197	Steel fabrication: bar cleaner	....	....	....	....	3.8	225	34
198	furnaceman	....	....	....	....	3.6	208	34
199	wagonsmith	....	....	....	....	3.6	208	34
200	striker	....	....	....	....	4.0	242	34
201	wire drawer	....	....	....	....	4.6	293	34
202	wire washer	....	....	....	....	5.1	336	34
203	forgesmith	....	....	....	....	2.4	105	34
204	forgesmith's mate	....	....	....	....	2.6	122	34
205	molder	....	....	....	....	3.9	233	34
206	core layer (molding)	....	....	....	....	3.0	156	34
	Female							
	Relaxation & personal grooming							
207	Supine, basal	49	265	22	55	.98	......	40
208	Sitting	57	338	22	55	1.09	11	40
209	Standing	16	47	22	55	1.11	13	40
210	Dressing, undressing	12	....	8-12	34	2.3	135	47
211	Washing, dressing, undressing	3	....	43-55	70	3.3	237	13
	Domestic work							
212	Washing dishes, top of pan 30 in. from floor[1]	1	3	....	....	1.53	56	31
213	36 in. from floor[1]	1	6	....	....	1.41	44	31
214	42 in. from floor[1]	1	3	....	....	1.37	40	31
215	46 in. from floor[1]	1	5	....	....	1.38	41	31
216	Brush scrubbing, 28 in. from floor	2	20	40	60	1.73	48	42
217	40 in. from floor	2	20	40	60	1.68	44	42
218	Peeling potatoes, sitting on chair	7	24	27	....	1.23	26	46
219	sitting on stool, turned at waist	7	24	27	....	1.32	35	46
220	standing	7	26	27	....	1.29	32	46
221	after 2 hr standing	2	11	26	....	1.42	45	46
222	Chopping, 1-handed, 28 in. from floor	2	20	40	60	1.48	26	42
223	40 in. from floor	2	20	40	60	1.38	18	42
224	2-handed, 28 in. from floor	2	20	40	60	1.61	38	42
225	40 in. from floor	2	20	40	60	1.43	22	42
226	Rotary mixing, 28 in. from floor	2	20	40	60	1.69	44	42
227	40 in. from floor	2	20	40	60	1.54	32	42
228	Spoon beating, 28 in. from floor	2	20	40	60	1.54	32	42
229	40 in. from floor	2	20	40	60	1.40	20	42
230	Beating batter, standing, bowl at normal level	7	....	22	....	1.43	46	46
231	bowl 2 in. above normal level	7	....	22	....	1.42	45	46
232	bowl 2 in. below normal level	7	....	22	....	1.45	48	46
233	Kneading dough, standing, at normal level	7	....	22	....	2.04	108	46
234	2 in. above normal level	7	....	22	....	2.01	105	46
235	2 in. below normal level	7	....	22	....	2.17	121	46
236	Stepping up 7 in.	9	36	26	....	2.77	183	6
237	Arm reach, 46 in. above floor[2]	9	36	26	....	1.39	42	6
238	56 in. above floor[2]	9	36	26	....	1.52	55	6
239	72 in. above floor[2]	9	36	26	....	1.82	86	6
240	& trunk bend to 22 in. above floor[2]	9	36	26	....	1.92	96	6
241	& trunk bend to 3 in. above floor[2]	9	36	26	....	2.88	194	6
242	& knee bend to 3 in. above floor[2]	7	28	26	....	4.12	320	6
243	& body pivot 36 in. above floor[2]	9	36	26	....	1.75	77	6
244	Hand sewing, blanket, 18 stitches/min	1	11	....	....	1.16	18	31
245	sheets, 18 stitches/min	1	5	....	....	1.18	20	31
246	30 stitches/min	1	6	....	....	1.25	28	31
247	Machine sewing, motor-operated	1	10	....	....	1.24	27	31
248	foot-operated	1	8	....	....	1.43	46	31
249	Darning	1	2	22	....	1.26	29	32
250	Crocheting, 32 stitches/min	1	5	22	....	1.27	30	32
251	Knitting, 23 stitches/min	1	4	22	....	1.29	31	32
252	Washing towels, by hand	1	4	22	....	2.02	106	32
253	Washing clothes, by hand	7	25	22	....	2.69	175	46
254	Rinsing clothes	7	21	22	....	2.42	147	46

[1] Height of subject, 168 cm. [2] Average height of subjects, 157 cm.

continued

65. ENERGY COST OF WORK: MAN

	Activity	No. of Subjects	No. of Tests	Age yr	Wt kg	Energy Expenditure kcal/min	Energy Expenditure % over supine	Reference
255	Wringing clothes: by hand	7	23	22	....	2.21	125	46
256	hand wringer	2	7	23	....	2.71	177	46
257	electric wringer	7	23	22	....	1.85	89	46
258	Drying clothes in extractor	7	21	22	....	2.08	112	46
259	Emptying washing machine, carrying 2 gal water from tub to floor	2	6	23	....	2.19	124	46
260	Cleaning laundry equipment, wiping & scouring	2	6	23	....	2.28	133	46
261	Putting up & removing clothesline	2	7	23	....	2.14	118	46
262	Hanging up clothes, from basket on utility table	7	22	22	....	2.00	104	46
263	from basket on floor	7	21	22	....	2.63	168	46
264	Ironing napkins, sitting on chair, 27-in.-high board	4	12	23	....	1.51	54	46
265	sitting on stool, 32.5-in.-high board	5	26	23	....	1.52	55	46
266	standing, very high board	7	7	22	....	1.58	61	46
267	electric rotary ironer	5	50	23	....	1.35	38	46
268	Ironing, standing, normal board	7	7	22	....	1.69	72	46
269	high board	7	7	22	....	1.64	67	46
270	3.5-lb iron	4	13	23	....	1.64	67	46
271	4.6-lb iron, sloping handle	4	14	23	....	1.67	70	46
272	straight handle	4	13	23	....	1.72	76	46
273	5.9-lb iron	4	13	23	....	1.68	71	46
274	6.2-lb iron	4	12	23	....	1.68	71	46
275	Putting wash through mangle	1	....	44	65	6.0	512	46
276	Washing floor on knees	1	3	22	....	1.63	66	32
277	Sweeping floor	1	4	22	....	1.85	89	32
278	Vacuum-cleaning rug, 0.5 ft/sec	1	9	....	....	1.53	56	45
279	1 ft/sec	1	10	....	....	1.63	66	45
280	2 ft/sec	1	10	....	....	2.02	106	45
281	3 ft/sec	1	12	....	....	2.58	163	45
282	4 ft/sec	1	9	....	....	4.02	310	45
283	Stripping & making beds	1	....	55	80	5.4	451	46
	Transportation & sports							
284	Walking, 1.1 mi/hr	9	60	24	....	1.99	103	44
285	2.2 mi/hr	9	64	24	....	2.84	190	44
286	3.4 mi/hr	9	51	24	....	2.90	196	44
287	2.8 mi/hr, carrying 20-lb load	1	3	29	....	2.00	104	3
288	with shoulder yoke	1	3	29	....	1.94	98	3
289	on 1 shoulder	1	3	29	....	2.07	111	3
290	in 2 bundles in either hand	1	3	29	....	2.19	124	3
291	on tray in front of body	1	3	29	....	2.25	130	3
292	with shoulder strap	1	3	29	....	2.28	133	3
293	on head	1	3	29	....	2.49	154	3
294	in rucksack fairly low on back	1	3	29	....	2.64	169	3
295	on hip	1	3	29	....	2.72	178	3
296	Skiing, hard snow, level, moderate speed	1	....	....	57	10.8	1002	12
297	uphill, maximum speed	1	....	....	68	18.6	1798	12
	Stenographic work							
298	Typing, 59 words/min	1	4	18	....	1.34	37	9
299	115 words/min	1	3	31	....	1.72	76	9
300	electric, 40 words/min	6	....	....	45-52	1.31	34	36
301	mechanical, 40 words/min	6	....	....	45-52	1.48	51	36
	Craft activities							
302	Leather carving, sitting	11	44	23	....	1.65	68	40
303	Leather lacing, sitting	12	27	22	....	1.39	42	40
304	Leather stamping, sitting	14	38	20	....	1.33	36	40
305	Leather tooling, sitting	16	41	20	....	1.28	31	40
306	reclining	3	3	36	....	1.13	15	20
307	Weaving link belt, reclining, soft leather	4	4	33	....	1.18	20	20
308	stiff leather	4	4	33	....	1.33	36	20
309	Leather punching & lacing, reclining	4	4	33	....	1.20	22	20
310	Copper tooling, sitting	3	3	29	....	1.39	42	20
311	Chip carving, sitting	17	53	22	....	1.61	64	40
312	reclining	4	4	33	....	1.39	42	20
313	Weaving, hand loom	3	3	29	....	1.58	61	20
314	table loom	17	47	22	....	1.69	72	40

continued

65. ENERGY COST OF WORK: MAN

	Activity	No. of Subjects	No. of Tests	Age yr	Wt kg	Energy Expenditure kcal/min	% over supine	Reference
315	floor loom	2	24	22	......	2.05	109	40
316		3	4	42	......	2.12	116	20
317	Chisel carving, sitting, hardwood	5	5	32	......	2.14	118	20
318	softwood	5	5	33	......	2.16	120	20
319	Printing, floor press, standing	5	26	22	......	2.31	136	40
320	Bicycle grinding	6	35	22	......	2.91	197	40
321	Hand sawing, standing	16	47	22	......	3.27	234	40
	Industrial activity							
322	Light turning	8	37	18-33	48-77	2.5	155	24
323	Heavy turning	5	21	23-44	49-62	3.3	237	24
324	Turning & finishing	8	36	19-33	47-65	3.0	206	24
325	Forging	4	20	22-32	55-69	3.1	216	24
326	Stamping	2	12	35-44	44-55	3.2	227	24
327	Hoisting shelf with pulley	1	5	54	56	3.3	237	24
328	Tool setting	5	25	21-26	45-59	3.4	247	24
329	Finishing copper bands	2	6	42-44	55-57	3.4	247	24
330	Gauging	4	19	18-44	52-55	4.0	308	24
331	Laboring, general industrial	5	14	35-51	44-86	5.1	420	24

Contributor: Kottke, Frederic J.

References

[1] Abbott, B. C., B. Bigland, and J. M. Ritchie. 1952. J. Physiol. (London) 117:380.
[2] Baader, E., and G. Lehmann. 1929. Arbeitsphysiologie 1:40.
[3] Bedale, E. M. 1924. Ind. Fatigue Res. Board Biomed. Rept. 29.
[4] Benedict, F. G., and H. Murschhauser. 1915. Carnegie Inst. Wash. Publ. 231.
[5] Benedict, F. G., et al. 1914. J. Biol. Chem. 18:139.
[6] Bratton, E. C. 1951. Cornell Univ. Agr. Expt. Sta. Bull. 873.
[7] Brockett, J. E., et al. 1957. U.S. Army Med. Nutr. Lab. (Denver) Rept. 212.
[8] Busca, L., and A. Granati. 1945. Boll. Soc. Ital. Biol. Sper. 20:30.
[9] Carpenter, T. M. 1911. J. Biol. Chem. 9:231.
[10] Cathcart, E. P., and F. J. Trafford. 1919. J. Physiol. (London) 53:xcix.
[11] Christensen, E. H. 1953. Ergonomics Soc. Symp. Fatigue, p. 93.
[12] Christensen, E. H., and P. Hogberg. 1950. Arbeitsphysiologie 14:292.
[13] Droese, W., et al. 1949. Ibid. 14:63.
[14] Edholm, O. G., et al. 1955. Brit. J. Nutr. 9:286.
[15] Farkas, G., and J. Geldrich. 1930. Arch. Hyg. Bacteriol. 104:1.
[16] Fox, R. H. 1953. Ph.D. Thesis. London Univ., England.
[17] Garry, R. C., et al. 1955. Brit. Med. Res. Council Spec. Rept. Ser. 289.
[18] Gephart, F. C., and E. F. DuBois. 1916. Arch. Internal Med. 17:902.
[19] Glaser, H. 1952. Arbeitsphysiologie 14:448.
[20] Gordon, E. E. 1952. Arch. Phys. Med. Rehabil. 33:201.
[21] Granati, A. 1946. Boll. Soc. Ital. Biol. Sper. 22:267.
[22] Granati, A., and L. Busca. 1941. Quaderni Nutr. 8:1.
[23] Granati, A., and L. Busca. 1945. Boll. Soc. Ital. Biol. Sper. 20:51.
[24] Greenwood, M., C. Hodson, and A. E. Tebb. 1919. Proc. Roy. Soc. (London), B, 91:62.
[25] Hedman, R. 1957. Acta Physiol. Scand. 40:305.
[26] Henderson, Y., and H. W. Haggard. 1925. Am. J. Physiol. 72:220.
[27] Hettinger, T., and W. Wirths. 1953. Arbeitsphysiologie 15:41.
[28] Hettinger, T., and W. Wirths. 1953. Ibid. 15:103.
[29] Humphreys, P. W., and A. R. Lind. 1962. Brit. J. Ind. Med. 19:264.
[30] Kottke, F. J., et al. 1962. Arch. Phys. Med. Rehabil. 43:228.
[31] Langworthy, C. F. 1922. J. Home Econ. 14:621.
[32] Langworthy, C. F., and H. G. Barott. 1920. Am. J. Physiol. 52:400.
[33] Lehmann, G. 1953. Praktische Arbeitsphysiologie. G. Thieme, Stuttgart.
[34] Lehmann, G., E. A. Müller, and H. Spitzer. 1950. Arbeitsphysiologie 14:166.
[35] Lundgren, N. P. V. 1946. Acta Physiol. Scand. 13 (Suppl. 41).
[36] Marro, F., V. Milani, and E. C. Vigliani. 1954. Med. Lavoro 45:12.
[37] Means, J. H. 1915. J. Med. Res. 32:121.
[38] Passmore, R., J. G. Thomson, and G. M. Warnoch. 1952. Brit. J. Nutr. 6:253.
[39] Phillips, P. G. 1954. J. Trop. Med. Hyg. 57:12.
[40] Quiggle, A. B., and F. J. Kottke. 1954. Bull. Univ. Minn. Hosp. Minn. Med. Found. 26(4).
[41] Richardson, D. T., and W. Campbell. 1927. Report on the investigation of the energy expenditure of the British soldier in India. Government of India Press, Calcutta.
[42] Richardson, M., and E. McCracken. 1966. J. Am. Dietet. Assoc. 48:192.
[43] Robertson, J. D. 1958. Lancet 1:296.
[44] Smith, H. M., and D. B. Doolittle. 1925. J. Biol. Chem. 65:665.
[45] Swartz, V. 1929. J. Home Econ. 21:439.
[46] Swartz, V. 1933. Wash. State Coll. Agr. Expt. Sta. Bull. 282.
[47] Taylor, C. M., O. F. Pye, and A. B. Caldwell. 1948. J. Nutr. 36:123.
[48] Turner, D. 1955. Brit. J. Ind. Med. 12:237.
[49] Zuntz, L. 1899. Untersuchungen über den Gaswechsel und Energieumsatz des Radfahrers. A. Hirschwald, Berlin.

66. OXYGEN CONSUMPTION: ANIMALS

Oxygen consumption values should be used with caution, as the figures reflect order of magnitude only. **Rate**: Values are cubic millimeters oxygen per gram fresh weight per hour for adult animals, unless otherwise indicated.

Part I. Mammals and Birds

	Species (Synonym)	Rate	Reference
	Mammalia		
1	*Homo sapiens*	220[1]	6
2		4000[2]	25
3	*Alopex lagopus*	505	29
4	*Aotus trivirgatus*	510	29
5	*Bettongia* sp.	950	17
6	*Blarina brevicauda kirtlandi*	5200	20
7	*Bos taurus*, ♀	184	6
8		390	9,30
9	*Bradypus* sp.	168	13
10	*Canis familiaris*	580	9
11	Young	250	15
12	Eskimo, young	785	29
13	*Cavia porcellus*	816	6
14	*Choloepus* sp.	216	13
15	*Citellus undulatus parryii*	600	29
16	*Clethrionomys gapperi gapperi*	3600[1]	20
17	*C. gapperi rhoadsi*	3800[1]	20
18	*Dasypus* sp.	201	28
19	*Dasyurus* sp.	560	17
20	*Dicrostonyx groenlandicus*	1700	29
21	*Elephas maximus*, ♀, 37 yr old	155	1
22	*Eliomys quercinus (Myoxus arbor)*	15[3]	14
23		852[4]	
24	*Eptesicus fuscus*	800	20
25	*Equus caballus*	250	9
26	*Felis catus*	710	9
27	*Glaucomys volans volans*	2000	20
28	*Marmota* sp.	14[3]	3
29		262[4]	
30	*Mesocricetus auratus*	70[3]	16
31		2900[4]	16
32	*(Cricetus auratus)*	1050	14
	Microdipodops megacephalus nasutus		21
33	♂	3700	
34	♀	3400	
35	*Microtus pennsylvanicus pennsylvanicus*	3300[1]	20
36	*Mus* sp.	2500[1]	9
37		20,000[5]	
38	*M. musculus*, house mouse	1530[6]	18
39		3500[1]	20
40	white mouse	1600[6]	18
41		3600[1]	20
42	*Mustela rixosa*	5000	29
43	*Myotis lucifugus*	1500	20
44	*Napaeozapus insignis insignis*	3100	20
45	*Nasua narica*	500	29
46	*Ornithorhynchus* sp.	460	17
47	*Oryctolagus cuniculus*	640-850	9
48	*Ovis aries*	220	6
49		340	9,30
50	*Peromyscus maniculatus*	1650[6]	18
51		3600[1]	20
52	*P. maniculatus gracilis*	3000[1]	20
53	*Phoca vitulina*	540	11
54	*Phocoena phocoena*	300	26
55	*Pitymys pinetorum scalopsoides*	4300[1]	20
56	*Procyon cancrivorus*	395	29
57	*Proechimys semispinosus*	1270	29
58	*Rattus* sp.	2000	17
59	♂, 6-9 mo old	692	19
60	*R. rattus*	770	10
61	*Reithrodontomys megalotis longicaudus*	3800[1]	21
62	*Saguinus geoffroyi (Leontocebus geoffroyi)*	1040	29
63	*Sorex cinereus*	13,700	21
64	*S. trowbridgii montereyensis*	7200	21
65	*S. vagrans sonomae*, ♂	6100	21
66	♀	5500	
67	*S. vagrans vagrans*	8600	21
68	*Sus scrofa*	220	30
69	*Tachyglossus* sp. *(Echidna* sp.)	1100	17
70	*Thalarctos maritimus*, cubs	700	29
71	*Trichechus manatus latirostris*	120	27
72	*Trichosurus* sp.	700	17
73	*Tursiops truncatus*	360	12
74	*Zapus hudsonius americanus*	4200[1]	20
	Aves		
75	*Acanthis cannabina (Carduelis cannabina)*	4508[7]	5
76	*(C. linaria)*	5566[7]	
77	*Alauda arvensis*	3512[7]	5
78	*Anas* sp.	800	8
79	*Anser* sp.	547	7
80		592	30
81	*Anthus pratensis*	3614[7]	5
82	*Calypte anna*	12,300[8]	22
83	*Carduelis carduelis*	5336[7]	5
84	*Chloris chloris*	4671[7]	5
85	*Columba* sp.	710	24
86	*Corvus corax*[9]	940	29
87	*Coturnix coturnix*	2080[7]	5

[1] Resting. [2] Maximum work. [3] Hibernating. [4] Awake. [5] Running. [6] Basal. [7] Ambient temperature, 10°C. [8] Ambient temperature, 24°C. [9] In Arctic habitat.

continued

66. OXYGEN CONSUMPTION: ANIMALS

Part I. Mammals and Birds

	Species (Synonym)	Rate	Reference
88	*Emberiza calandra*	3222 7/	5
89	*E. citrinella*	4551 7/	5
90	*Fringilla coelebs*	3621 7/	5
91	*Gallus domesticus*, ♀	630	30
92	*G. domesticus*, Rhode Island Red	497 10/	4
93	*Larus hyperboreus* 9/	1640	29
94	*Lullula arborea*	3672 7/	5
95	*Nyctidromus albicollis* 11/	1750	29
96	*Passer domesticus*	2100	2
97	*P. montanus*	4427 7/	5
98	*Perisoreus canadensis* 9/	2725	29
99	*Pipra mentalis* 11/	4620	29
100	*Plectrophenax nivalis* 9/	3350	29
101	*Selasphorus sasin*	13,900 12/	22
102	*Serinus canarius*	2900	2
103	Dove	950	24
104	Hummingbird, at noon	17,000	23
105	at midnight	1000	

7/ Ambient temperature, 10°C. 9/ In Arctic habitat. 10/ Day and night measurement. 11/ In tropical habitat. 12/ Ambient temperature, 22°C.

Contributor: Flemister, Launce J.

References

[1] Benedict, F. G. 1936. Carnegie Inst. Wash. Publ. 474.
[2] Benedict, F. G., and E. L. Fox. 1933. Arch. Ges. Physiol. 322:357.
[3] Benedict, F. G., and R. C. Lee. 1938. Carnegie Inst. Wash. Publ. 497.
[4] Benedict, F. G., et al. 1932. Conn. Univ. Storrs Agr. Expt. Sta. Bull. 177.
[5] Bont, A. F. de. 1944. Ann. Soc. Roy. Zool. Belg. 75:75.
[6] Brody, S. 1945. Bioenergetics and growth. Reinhold, New York.
[7] Hari, Y. 1917. Biochem. Z. 87:313.
[8] Hari, Y., and A. Kriwuscha. 1918. Ibid. 88:345.
[9] Heilbrunn, L. V. 1952. An outline of general physiology. Ed. 3. W. B. Saunders, Philadelphia.
[10] Herrington, L. P. 1940. Am. J. Physiol. 129:123.
[11] Irving, L., et al. 1935. J. Cellular Comp. Physiol. 7: 137.
[12] Irving, L., et al. 1941. Ibid. 17:145.
[13] Irving, L., et al. 1942. Ibid. 20:189.
[14] Kayser, C. 1939. Ann. Physiol. Physicochim. Biol. 15:1087.
[15] Krogh, A. 1914. Intern. Z. Physik. Chem. Biol. 1: 491.
[16] Lyman, C. P. 1948. J. Exptl. Zool. 109:55.
[17] Martin, C. J. 1903. Phil. Trans. Roy. Soc. London, B, 195:1.
[18] Morrison, P. R. 1948. J. Cellular Comp. Physiol. 31: 281.
[19] Moses, S. 1947. Proc. Soc. Exptl. Biol. Med. 64:54.
[20] Pearson, O. P. 1947. Ecology 28:127.
[21] Pearson, O. P. 1948. Science 108:44.
[22] Pearson, O. P. 1950. Condor 52:145.
[23] Pearson, O. P. 1953. Sci. Am. 188(1):69.
[24] Riddle, O. 1932. Missouri Univ. Agr. Expt. Sta. Res. Bull. 166:59, 86.
[25] Robinson, S., A. T. Edwards, and D. B. Dill. 1937. Science 85:409.
[26] Scholander, P. F. 1940. Hvalradets Skrifter Norske Videnskaps-Akad. Oslo 22.
[27] Scholander, P. F., and L. Irving. 1941. J. Cellular Comp. Physiol. 17:169.
[28] Scholander, P. F., et al. 1943. Ibid. 21:53.
[29] Scholander, P. F., et al. 1950. Biol. Bull. 99:259.
[30] Voit, E. 1901. Z. Biol. 41:113.

Part II. Lower Chordates and Other Metazoa

Oxygen consumption values should be used with caution, as the figures reflect order of magnitude only. **Rate**: Values are cubic millimeters oxygen per gram fresh weight per hour for mature animals, unless otherwise indicated.

	Class & Species (Synonym)	Temp °C	Rate	Reference
	Chordata			
	Reptilia			
1	*Alligator mississippiensis*	19.5	7.5	8
2		22	8.9	8
3	*(A. lucius)*	25	64	53
4	*Amphibolurus barbatus*	15	60	4
5		20	130	
6		30	160	
7		35	175	
8		40	200	
9	*Anguis fragilis*	20	40	87

continued

Part II. Lower Chordates and Other Metazoa

	Class & Species (Synonym)	Temp °C	Rate	Reference
10	*Constrictor constrictor*	16	4.9	8
11		22	10.0	
12		30	24.0	
13	*Crotalus atrox*	16	6.8	8
14		22	16.4	78
15		30	35.5	78
16	*Crotaphytus collaris*	10	16	29
17		20	75	
18		30	200	
19		40	350	
20	*Dipsosaurus dorsalis*	21	40	64
21		26	60	64
22		31	95	64
23		36	120	64
24		41	150	64
25		32	100	80
26		36	180	80
27		40	240	80
28		44	350	80
29	*Drymarchon corais cou-*	16	10.1	8
30	*peri*	22	20.0	
31		30	47.0	
32	*Eumeces obsoletus*	20	57	27
33		30	166	
34		40	478	
35	*Iguana tuberculata*	22	22.2	8
36		30	52.0	
37	*Lacerta agilis*	20	1980	69
38	*L. viridis*	25	170	53
39	*Malaclemys terrapin*	24	35	58
	centrata			
40	*Natrix natrix (Coluber*	20	92	45
41	*natrix)*	20	150	22
42	*Python molurus*	16	6.2	8
43	*P. reticulatus*	22	12.2	8
44	*P. sebae*	30	26.7	8
45	*Sceloporus occidentalis*	20	250	28
46		30	550	
47		40	920	
48	*Storeria dekayi*, ♂	20	266	21
49	♀	20	183	
50	*Testudo elephantopus el-*	17.2	8.9	8
51	*ephantopus (T. vicina)*	22	22.0	
52	*Uta stansburiana*	20	370	28
53		30	620	
54		40	1100	
55	*Varanus gouldii & V. va-*	20	70	5
56	*rius*	30	170	
57		40	480	
	Amphibia			
58	*Ambystoma maculatum*	5	24	91
59		15	106	
60		25	130	

	Class & Species (Synonym)	Temp °C	Rate	Reference
61	*Ensatina eschscholtzii*	12	50	42
62		14	60	
63		16	70	
64		18	80	
65	*Eurycea bislineata bis-*	1	14.4	84
66	*lineata*	10	41.0	
67	*E. nana*[1]	15	48	67
68		20	71	
69		25	86	
70	*E. neotenes*[1]	15	44	67
71		20	79	
72		25	106	
73		30	105	
74	*E. pterophila*[1]	15	84	67
75		20	116	
76		25	90	
77		30	82	
	Pelobates fuscus (Rana fusca)			13
78	Winter	20	100	
79	Summer	20	210	
80	*Plethodon cinereus ci-*	1	16.0	84
81	*nereus*	10	33.7	
82	*Rana catesbeiana (R.*	25.3	106	53
	mugiens)			
83	*R. esculenta*	20	70	87
84	Winter	20	85	12
85	Summer	20	437	12
86	*R. temporaria*	16	86	87
87		20	89	87
88	Winter	19	85	12
89	Summer	19	554	12
90	*Triturus* sp. *(Molge* sp.)	20	110	45
91	*T. vulgaris*	20	123	87
92	*Typhlonectes compres-*	20	33	74
	sicauda			
	Pisces			
93	*Anguilla anguilla (A.*	25	128	65
	vulgaris)			
94	*Arapaima gigas*	25	9	72
95	*Astronotus ocellatus*	20	1.3	73
96	*Carassius auratus (Cy-*	10	23	41
97	*prinus carassius)*	20	80	41
98		30	175	41
99		10	138	40
100		20	96.6	40
101		30	75.6	40
102		40	0	40
103		20	113	33
104	Resting	20	85	41
105	Active	20	160	41
106	*Carassius carassius*	5	15	10
107		10	25	
108		15	50	

1/ Neotenic salamander.

continued

66. OXYGEN CONSUMPTION: ANIMALS

Part II. Lower Chordates and Other Metazoa

	Class & Species (Synonym)	Temp °C	Rate	Reference
109		20	120	
110		25	180	
111	*Chromis chromis (Heli-*	16	93	86
112	*asis chromis)*	20	162	
113	*Cichla temensis*	20	0.9	73
114	*Crenichthys baileyi*	21	284	78
115		37	546	
116	*Cyprinus carpio*	19.5	100	50
117	*Diplodus sargus (Sargus rondeletti)*	25	375	65
118	*Esox lucius*	18	102	57
119	*Fundulus parvipinnis*	10	66[2], 55[3]	89
120		12	91[2], 71[3]	
121		14	130[2], 85[3]	
122		16	152[2], 93[3]	
123		18	206[2], 148[3]	
124		20	267[2], 148[3]	
125		22	295[2], 165[3]	
126		24	318[2], 217[3]	
127	*Gillichthys*	10	27	3
128		17	48	
129		24	93	
130	*Lepidosiren paradoxa*	20	42	72
131	*Misgurnus fossilis (Cobites fossilis)*	20	51	7
	Protopterus aethiopicus			77
132	Fasting	20	10	
133	Feeding	20	52	
134	*Salmo trutta*	15	226	57
135	*Scomber scombrus*	20	726	2
136	*Serranus scriba*	16	116	86
137		20	151	
138	*Sparus auratus*	19	175	47
139	*Sphaeroides maculatus*	20	62	43
140	*Stenotomus chrysops*	20	174	2
141	*Tautoga onitis*	20	62	2
142	*Tautogolabrus adspersus*	21	120	44
143		26	192	
144	*Tinca tinca (Cyprinus tinca)*	20	104	57
	Cephalochordata[4]			
145	*Branchiostoma lanceo-*	16	35	86
146	*latum (Amphioxus*	20	45	86
147	*lanceolatus)*	25	149	65
	Thaliacea			
148	*Cyclosalpa pinnata (Sal-*	16	8.0	86
149	*pa pinnata)*	20	12.0	
150	*Salpa maxima africana*	25	23.0	65
151	*Thetys vagina (Salpa*	16	2.0	86
152	*tilesii)*	20	2.8	
	Ascidiacea			
153	*Ascidia mentula*	25	4.8	65
	Echinodermata			
	Ophiuroidea			
154	*Ophioderma longicauda*	25	8	22
155		25	32	65
	Asteroidea			
156	*Asterias rubens*[5]	15	21	11
157	*A. rubens*[6]	15	24	11
158	*Leptasterias pusilla*	14	28	42
159		16	40	
160		18	47	
	Echinoidea			
161	*Paracentrotus lividus (Strongylocentrotus lividus)*	25	15	65
162	*Strongylocentrotus pur-*	5	8[7], 19[8]	36
163	*puratus*	10	8[7], 21[8]	
164		15	13[7], 29[8]	
165		20	26[7], 44[8]	
	Holothuroidea			
166	*Holothuria impatiens*	25	17	65
167	*H. stellati*	25	4	65
	Arthropoda			
	Crustacea			
168	*Asellus* sp.	17	348	31
169	*A. aquaticus*	10	700	39
170	*Astacus astacus (A. fluviatilis)*	15	30	57
171	*A. leptodactylus*	20	70	94
172	*Austropotamobius torrentium (Astacus torrentium)*	20	100	93
173	*Callianassa subterranea*	15	930	65
174	*Carcinus maenus*	15	625	65
175	*Dromia vulgaris*	15	3000	65
176	*Emerita talpoida*	10	90	31
177		20	240	
178		30	0	
179	*Eriphia spinifrons*	15	1828	65
180	*Galathea squamifera*	15	215	65
181	*Hemigrapsus nudus*	10	32	30
182		20	70	
183		30	42	
184	*H. oregonensis*	10	44	30
185		20	62	
186		30	38	
187	*Homarus americanus*	15	507	15
188	*Ilia nucleus*	15	253	65
189	*Maja verrucosa*	15	1460	65
190	*Ocypode quadrata (O. albicans)*	26	139	37
191	*Orchomenella chilensis*	0	118	1

[2] For small fish. [3] For large fish. [4] Subphylum. [5] Baltic Sea. [6] North Sea. [7] Acclimated to 14-19°C. [8] Acclimated to 5°C.

continued

66. OXYGEN CONSUMPTION: ANIMALS

Part II. Lower Chordates and Other Metazoa

	Class & Species (Synonym)	Temp °C	Rate	Reference
192		2	141	
193		4	124	
194		6	147	
195		8	159	
196		10	231	
197		12	177	
198	*Orconectes immunis*	16	109	92
199		24	124	
200		30	129	
201		35	126	
202	*O. nais*	16	116	92
203		24	123	
204		30	126	
205		35	102	
206	*Pachygrapsus crassipes*	10	13	71
207		15	22	
208		20	38	
209	*P. marmoratus*	15	1137	65
210	*Paguristes maculata*	15	1600	65
211	*Palaemon serratus*	16	106	22
212	*P. squilla*	19	128	47
213	*Palinurus vulgaris*	15	12,874	65
214	*Pandalina brevirostris*	15	20	38
215	*Pandalus montagui*	15	289	38
216	*Pilumnus hirtellus*	15	160	65
217	*Pugettia producta*	15	100	90
218	*Sesarma cinereum*	7.5	23	79
219		13.2	62	
220		19.4	103	
221		26.4	197	
222	*Sicyonia carinata (S. sculpta)*	15	443	65
223	*Spirontocaris liljeborgi (S. securifrons)*	15	349	38
224	*Talorchestia longicornis*	10	120	31
225	*(T. megalophthalma)*	17	180	31
226		20	240	31
227		30	360	31
228		40	300	31
229		20	246	32
230	*Thoralus cranchi (Spirontocaris cranchi)*	15	6	38
231	*Trichodactylus petropolitanus*	20	0.19[9]	83
232		20	0.80[10]	
233		20	0.25[11]	
234	*Uca minax*	7	10	85
235		17	20.5	
236		28	71.1	
237	*U. pugilator*	7	18.7	85
238		17	43.4	
239		28	80	
240	*U. pugnax*	7	19.7	85
241		17	44	85
242		28	95.2	85
243		39	196	85
244		7.5	22	79
245		13.2	69	79
246		19.4	90	79
247		26.4	139	79
248	*U. rapax*	7	21.1	85
249		17	61.0	
250		28	99.8	
251		39	168	
	Insecta			
252	*Aedes aegypti*, ♂	26	2330	63
253	♀	26	4200	
	Anopheles quadrimaculatus			
254	♂	26	2300	63
255	♀	26	2840	
256	*Apis mellifera*, hive bee	20	17,466	68
257	True flight	20	87,000	48
258	*Blatta orientalis (Periplaneta orientalis)*	20	277	87
259		25	450	25
260	*Culex* sp.	20	575	34
261	*C. pipiens*, ♂	26	3430	63
262	♀	26	2580	
263	*Drosophila* sp.	20	1560	19
264	True flight	20	21,800	
265	*D. repleta*	20	1680	20
266	True flight	20	21,000	
267	*Formica* sp.	20	532	76
268	*Geotrupes* sp.	21	447	76
269	*Limnephilus vittatus*	10	500	39
270	*Melanotus communis*	10	600	31
271		20	1800	
272		21	1920	
273		27	2400	
274		30	4200	
275		40	15,000	
276	*Melolontha* sp.	20	960	6
277	*Musca domestica*	20	2000	31
278		30	5400	
279		40	9000	
280	*Phaenicia sericata (Lucilia sericata)*, true flight	20	95,600	26
281	*Popilius disjunctus (Passalus cornutus)*	17	30	31
282	*Vanessa* sp.	20	600	54
283	True flight	20	100,000	
284	*Zootermopsis angusticollis*	20	400	24
285	*Z. nevadensis*	20	423	23

[9] Normal fed. [10] Starved. [11] Dry weight.

continued

Part II. Lower Chordates and Other Metazoa

	Class & Species (Synonym)	Temp °C	Rate	Reference
	Onychophora			
286	*Epiperipatus brasiliensis*	25	230	66
287	*Peripatus accacioi*	10	37	61
288		20	92	
289		30	226	
	Annelida			
	Oligochaeta			
290	*Allolobophora caliginosa (Lumbricus communis)*	21.5	206	52
291	*Glossoscolex* sp., small	25	109	62
292	large	25	38	
293	*Limnodrilus claparedianus*	18.5	496	51
294	*L. hoffmeisteri*	25	1010[9]	60
295	*Lumbricus* sp.	18.5	64	55,56
296		20	170	82
297	*L. terrestris*	20.5	138	52
298	*(L. herculeus)*	10	45	46
	Pheretima hawayana			62
299	Small	25	271	
300	Large	25	60	
301	*Pontoscolex* sp., small	25	272	62
302	large	25	145	
303	*Tubifex* sp.	25	200	16
304	*T. tubifex*	18.7	408	51
	Polychaeta			
305	*Arenicola* sp.	12	30	14
306	*Chaetopterus variopedapus (C. pergamentaceus)*	15	8	15
307	*Glycera siphonostoma*	25	15	18
308	*Nereis virens*	15	26	15
309	*Sabella penicillus (S. pa-*	10	62	35
310	*vonina)*	17	43	
311	*Spirographis spallanzanii*	25	135	59
	Sipunculoidea			
312	*Sipunculus nudus*	16	50	22
	Mollusca			
	Cephalopoda			
313	*Eledone moschata*	16	181	22
314		25	28	65
315	*Octopus vulgaris*	16	47-87	47
316		20	117	86
317		25	68-102	65
318	*Sepia officinalis*	15	320	65
	Bivalvia			
319	*Mytilus* sp.	20	22	54
320		22.3	55	17
321	*M. edulis*	14	13	47
322	*M. galloprovincialis*	25	18	65
	Gastropoda			
323	*Aplysia fasciata (A. limacina)*	16	30	22
324	*Australorbis glabratus*	10	16.5	88
325		30	133	
326	*Bithynia leachi*	10	85	9
327		15	127	
328	*Deroceras reticulatum (Limax agrestis)*	20	350	82
329	*Helix pomatia*	20	94	87
330	*Hermissenda crassicornis*	12	95	42
331		14	130	
332	*Limax flavus*	0	47	75
333		10	100	
334		20	185	
335		30	225	
336	*Littorina littorea*	−10	0.2	49
337		0	20	
338		10	70	
339		20	145	
340		30	70	
341	*Lymnaea stagnalis*	10	36.7	88
342		20	123	
343	*Myxas glutinosa*	10	72	9
344		15	120	
345		20	160	
346	*Physa fontinalis*	10	125	9
347		15	200	
348		20	300	
349	*Pleurobranchaea meckelii*	25	36	65
350	*Pterotrachea coronata*	16	7.8	86
351		20	11.0	
352	*Tethys leporina*	16	12	86
353		20	15	
354	*Valvata piscinalis*	15	190	9
355		20	284	
	Ctenophora			
	Nuda			
356	*Beroe ovata*	16	5.0	86
357	*Cestum veneris*	16	2.6	86
358		25	25.0	65
	Cnidaria			
	Anthozoa			
359	*Anemonia sulcata*	18	13.4	18
	Scyphozoa			
360	*Aurelia aurita*	13	3.4	81
361		17	5.0	
362	*Rhizostoma pulmo*	16	7.2	86
	Hydrozoa			
363	*Carmarina hastata*	16	6.0	86
364		20	8.0	86
365		25	2.0	65
	Porifera			
	Demospongiae			
366	*Suberites massa*	22.4	24.1	70

[9] Normal fed.

Contributor: Flemister, Launce J.

continued

66. OXYGEN CONSUMPTION: ANIMALS

Part II. Lower Chordates and Other Metazoa

References

[1] Armitage, K. B. 1962. Biol. Bull. 123:225.
[2] Baldwin, F. M. 1924. Proc. Iowa Acad. Sci. 30:173.
[3] Barlow, G. W. 1961. Biol. Bull. 121:209.
[4] Bartholomew, G. A., and V. A. Tucker. 1963. Physiol. Zool. 36:199.
[5] Bartholomew, G. A., and V. A. Tucker. 1964. Ibid. 37:341.
[6] Battelli, F., and L. Stern. 1913. Biochem. Z. 56:50.
[7] Baumert, W. 1855. Chemische Untersuchungen über die Respiration des Schlammpeizers, Breslau Univ., Poland.
[8] Benedict, F. G. 1932. Carnegie Inst. Wash. Publ. 425.
[9] Berg, K., and K. W. Ockelmann. 1959. J. Exptl. Biol. 36:690.
[10] Blazka, P. 1958. Physiol. Zool. 31:117.
[11] Bock, K. J., and C. Schlieper. 1953. Kiel. Meeresforsch. 9:201.
[12] Bohr, C. 1899. Skand. Arch. Physiol. 10:74.
[13] Bohr, C. 1903. Ibid. 15:23.
[14] Borden, M. A. 1931. J. Marine Biol. Assoc. U.K. 17:709.
[15] Bosworth, M. W., et al. 1936. J. Cellular Comp. Physiol. 9:77.
[16] Brazda, P. 1939. Proc. Soc. Exptl. Biol. Med. 42:734.
[17] Bruce, R. 1926. Biochem. J. 20:829.
[18] Buddenbrock, W. von. 1938. Z. Vergleich. Physiol. 26:303.
[19] Chadwick, L. E. 1947. Biol. Bull. 93:229.
[20] Chadwick, L. E., and D. Gilmour. 1940. Physiol. Zool. 13:398.
[21] Clausen, H. J. 1936. J. Cellular Comp. Physiol. 8:367.
[22] Cohnheim, O. 1912. Z. Physiol. Chem. 76:298.
[23] Cook, S. F. 1932. Biol. Bull. 63:246.
[24] Cook, S. F., and R. E. Smith. 1942. J. Cellular Comp. Physiol. 19:211.
[25] Davis, J. G., and W. K. Slater. 1928. Biochem. J. 22:331.
[26] Davis, R. A., and G. Fraenkel. 1940. J. Exptl. Biol. 17:402.
[27] Dawson, W. R. 1960. Physiol. Zool. 33:87.
[28] Dawson, W. R., and G. A. Bartholomew. 1956. Ibid. 29:40.
[29] Dawson, W. R., and J. R. Templeton. 1963. Ibid. 36:219.
[30] Dehnel, P. A. 1960. Biol. Bull. 118:215.
[31] Edwards, G. A. 1946. J. Cellular Comp. Physiol. 27:53.
[32] Edwards, G. A., and L. Irving. 1943. Ibid. 21:183.
[33] Ege, R., and A. Krogh. 1914. Intern. Rev. Ges. Hydrobiol. Hydrog. 6:48.
[34] Ellinger, T. 1915. Intern. Z. Physik. Chem. Biol. 2:113.
[35] Ewer, R. F., and H. M. Fox. 1940. Proc. Roy. Soc. (London), B, 129:137.
[36] Farmanfarmaian, A., and A. C. Giese. 1963. Physiol. Zool. 36:237.
[37] Flemister, L. J., and S. C. Flemister. 1951. Biol. Bull. 101:259.
[38] Fox, H. M. 1936. Proc. Zool. Soc. London 106:945.
[39] Fox, H. M., and E. J. Baldes. 1935. J. Exptl. Biol. 12:174.
[40] Freeman, J. A. 1950. Biol. Bull. 99:416.
[41] Fry, F. E., and J. S. Hart. 1948. Ibid. 94:66.
[42] Fuhrman, G. J., and F. A. Fuhrman. 1959. J. Gen. Physiol. 42:715.
[43] Hall, F. G. 1931. Biol. Bull. 61:457.
[44] Haugaard, N., and L. Irving. 1943. J. Cellular Comp. Physiol. 21:19.
[45] Hill, A. V. 1911. J. Physiol. (London) 43:379.
[46] Johnson, M. L. 1942. J. Exptl. Biol. 18:266.
[47] Jolyet, L., and P. Regnard. 1877. Arch. Physiol. Normale Pathol., Ser. 2, 4:44, 584.
[48] Jongbloed, J., and C. A. G. Wiersma. 1934. Z. Vergleich. Physiol. 21:519.
[49] Kanwisher, J. 1959. Biol. Bull. 116:258.
[50] Knauthe, K. 1898. Arch. Ges. Physiol. 73:490.
[51] Koenen, M. L. 1951. Z. Vergleich. Physiol. 33:436.
[52] Konopacki, M. 1907. Mem. Acad. Polon. Sci., p. 357.
[53] Krehl, L., and F. Soetbeer. 1899. Arch. Ges. Physiol. 77:611.
[54] Krogh, A. 1941. The comparative physiology of respiratory mechanisms. Univ. Pennsylvania Press, Philadelphia.
[55] Lesser, E. J. 1908. Z. Biol. 50:421.
[56] Lesser, E. J. 1908. Ibid. 51:294.
[57] Lindstedt, P. 1914. Z. Fischerei 14:193.
[58] McCutcheon, F. H. 1943. Physiol. Zool. 16:255.
[59] Mendes, E. G. 1950. Pubbl. Staz. Zool. Napoli 22:349.
[60] Mendes, E. G., M. D. Gonzalez, and M. L. Coutinho. 1951. Univ. Sao Paulo Fac. Filosof. Cienc. Letras Zool. Bol. 16:289.
[61] Mendes, E. G., and P. Sawaya. 1957. Ciencia Cult. (Sao Paulo) 9:120.
[62] Mendes, E. G., and D. Valente. 1953. Univ. Sao Paulo Fac. Filosof. Cienc. Letras Zool. Bol. 18:91.
[63] Mercado, T. I., H. L. Trembley, and T. von Brand. 1956. Physiol. Comp. Oecol. 4:200.
[64] Moberly, W. R. 1963. Physiol. Zool. 36:152.
[65] Montuori, A. 1913. Arch. Ital. Biol. 59:213.
[66] Morrison, P. R. 1946. Biol. Bull. 91:181.
[67] Norris, W. E., P. A. Grandy, and W. K. Davis. 1963. Ibid. 125:523.
[68] Paron, M. 1909. Ann. Sci. Nat. Zool. 9:1.
[69] Potts, R. 1875. Landwirtsch. Vers. Sta. 18:81.
[70] Putter, A. 1914. Z. Allgem. Physiol. 16:65.
[71] Roberts, J. L. 1957. Physiol. Zool. 30:242.
[72] Sawaya, P. 1946. Univ. Sao Paulo Fac. Filosof. Cienc. Letras Zool. Bol. 11:255.
[73] Sawaya, P. 1946. Ibid. 11:333.
[74] Sawaya, P. 1947. Ibid. 12:43.
[75] Segal, E. 1961. Am. Zoologist 1:235.

continued

66. OXYGEN CONSUMPTION: ANIMALS

Part II. Lower Chordates and Other Metazoa

[76] Slowzoff, B. 1909. Biochem. Z. 19:497.
[77] Smith, H. W. 1935. J. Cellular Comp. Physiol. 6:43.
[78] Sumner, F. B., and U. N. Lanham. 1942. Biol. Bull. 82:313.
[79] Teal, J. M. 1959. Physiol. Zool. 32:1.
[80] Templeton, J. R. 1960. Ibid. 33:136.
[81] Thill, H. 1937. Z. Wiss. Zool. 150:51.
[82] Thunberg, T. 1905. Skand. Arch. Physiol. 17:133.
[83] Valente, D. 1945. Univ. Sao Paulo Fac. Filosof. Cienc. Letras Zool. Bol. 9:98.
[84] Vernberg, F. J. 1952. Physiol. Zool. 25:243.
[85] Vernberg, F. J. 1959. Biol. Bull. 117:163.
[86] Vernon, H. M. 1896. J. Physiol. (London) 19:18.
[87] Vernon, H. M. 1897. Ibid. 21:443.
[88] von Brand, T., and B. Mehlman. 1953. Biol. Bull. 104:301.
[89] Wells, N. A. 1935. Physiol. Zool. 8:196.
[90] Weymouth, F. W., et al. 1944. Ibid. 17:50.
[91] Whitford, W. G., and V. H. Hutchison. 1963. Biol. Bull. 124:344.
[92] Wiens, A. W., and K. B. Armitage. 1961. Physiol. Zool. 34:39.
[93] Wolsky, A. 1934. Ungar. Biol. Forsch. Arch. 7:116.
[94] Wolsky, A., and B. E. Holmes. 1933. Ibid. 6:123.

Part III. Roundworms, Flatworms, and Protozoa

Specification: G = in presence of glucose. **Rate:** Values are cubic millimeters oxygen per milligram dry substance per hour for mature animals, unless otherwise indicated.

	Class & Species (Synonym)	Specification	Temp °C	Rate	Reference
	Aschelminthes				
	Nematoda				
1	*Ascaridia galli*	....	37	2.5	40
	Ascaris lumbricoides	Egg			
2		0-2 days	30	0.38	33
3		10-20 days	30	0.80	33
4		45 days	30	0.15	33
5		Small	37	0.82[1]	21
6			39	0.42[1]	22
7		Large	37	0.33[1]	21
8		♂	37	0.59[1]	1
9		♀	37	0.32[1]	1,51
10	*Eustrongylides ignotus*	Larva	37	0.56[1]	52
11	*Gnathostoma spinigerum*	Larva	37	2.7	29
12		♂	37	3.4	
13		♀	37	7.9	
14	*Haemonchus contortus*	Egg[2]	30	9.7	40
15		Egg[3]	30	10.7	
16		Larva	30	12.6	
17	*Heterakis spumosa*	....	38	4.0	23
18	*Nematodirus* spp.	....	37	5.1	40
19	*Neoaplectana glaseri*	....	30	12.6	40
20	*Nippostrongylus brasiliensis*	....	37	7.6	39
21		Larva	25	2.4	60
22			30	4.0	60
23			35	8.0	60
24			38	10.0	60
25	*(N. muris)*	1 day	30	18.4	40
26		4 days	30	13.0	40
27		12 days	30	9.2	40
28			37	6.8	40
29	*Ostertagia circumcincta*	....	38	7.4	23
30	*Strongylus equinus*	....	38	3.3	23
31	*S. vulgaris*	....	38	3.6	23
32	*Syphacia obvelata*	....	38	4.4	23
33	*Tetrameres confusa*	....	.....	0.24	50
34	*Trichinella spiralis*	Larva	37.5	2.35	45
35		Larva; G	37.5	2.37	
	Platyhelminthes				
	Cestoda				
36	*Diphyllobothrium latum*	Plerocercoid; G	22	0.34-0.67	13
37		Proglottid	37	2.7	
38		Proglottid; G	37	15.0	
39	*Echinococcus granulosus*	Larval scolex	37	2.0	3
40	*Hymenolepis diminuta*	....	37	1.2	36
41		G	37	3.0	
42	*Moniezia expansa*	Head region; G	37.5	1.1	6
43		Mature proglottid; G	37.5	0.9	
44		Gravid proglottid; G	37.5	0.6	
45	*Taenia crassiceps*	Larva; G	37	1.3	46

[1] Calculated on dry matter percentage. [2] Morula. [3] Blastula.

continued

66. OXYGEN CONSUMPTION: ANIMALS

Part III. Roundworms, Flatworms, and Protozoa

	Class & Species (Synonym)	Specification	Temp °C	Rate	Reference
46	*T. taeniaeformis*	....	37	1.1	53
47		Larva from mouse	37	0.5	
48		Larva from rat	37	0.6	
	Trematoda				
49	*Clonorchis sinensis*	....	37	6.5	28
50	*Fasciola hepatica*	....	37.5	1.94	40
51	*Gastrothylax crumenifer*	....	37	0.3	15
52	*Gorgoderina attenuata*	....	21	0.40	16
53	*Gynaecotyla adunca*	....	23.6	0.13[4]	17
54		In air	30.4	0.29[4]	17
55		In 5% O_2	30.4	0.13[4]	18
56		In 100% O_2	30.4	0.10[4]	18
57	*G. adunca*[5]	Adult	6	0.26	49
58			18	1.32	
59			24	6.11	
60			36	6.62	
61			41	8.85	
62	*Himasthla quissetensis*[5]	Redia	6	0.09	48
63			18	0.12	
64			24	0.90	
65			36	1.62	
66			41	1.83	
67		Cercaria	6	0.10	
68			18	0.54	
69			24	0.83	
70			36	2.17	
71			41	2.71	
72	*Paragonimus westermani*	....	37.5	2.8	23
73	*Paramphistomum cervi*	....	38	0.03	23
74	*Pleurogonius malaclemys*[5]	Adult	6	0.37	49
75			18	1.48	
76			24	2.04	
77			36	5.33	
78	*Saccocoelium beauforti*[5]	Adult	6	0.30	49
79			18	1.28	
80			24	2.89	
81			36	3.20	
82	*Schistosoma japonicum*	Pairs	37.5	10.3	44
83	*S. mansoni*	Pairs	37.5	6.0	9
84		♂; G	37.5	9.1	9
85		♀; G	37.5	10.7	9
86		Pairs; G	37.5	8.7	9
87		Pairs, untreated hosts; G	.....	8.5	10
88		Pairs, treated hosts; G	.....	2.9	10
89	*Zoogonus lasius*[5]	Sporocyst	6	0.13	48
90			18	0.41	
91			24	0.42	
92			36	0.90	
93		Cercaria	6	0.39	
94			18	1.45	
95			24	1.56	
96			36	2.68	
	Turbellaria				
97	*Crenobia alpina (Planaria alpina)*	....	5	30	7
98			15	240	
99	*Dugesia gonocephala (P. gonocephala)*	....	5	40	7
100			15	170	
101	*D. tigrina (Euplanaria tigrina)*	Fed	20	1.4	42
102			25	2.2	
103			30	2.5	
104			35	2.6	
105		Starved	20	1.8	
106			25	2.0	
107			35	3.5	
	Protozoa				
	Ciliata				
108	*Balantidium coli*[6]	Culture; G	28	4.23	4
109			37	9.40	
110	*Bresslaua insidiatrix*[7]	No substrate	25	80-130	43
111	*Paramecium aurelia*[7]	No substrate	20	354	31
112			25	616	
113			30	831	
114			35	1512	
115	*P. aurelia*[6]	Preautogamous	26	1823	34
116		During autogamy	26	1544	
117		Postautogamous	26	5506	
118	*P. calkinsi*	Reactive for mating	25	250	8
119		Nonreactive for mating	25	450	
120	*P. caudatum*[7]	No substrate	25	3860	31
121			30	5379	
122			35	9700	
123	*Tetrahymena pyriformis*[7]	Cultures adapted to 10,20 & 30°C	20	9	19
124			20	15	19
125			20	28	19
126		Preadapted to G; no G	28	71	12

[4] Based on volume determinations. [5] Rate is mm^3 O_2/µg N/hr. [6] Rate is mm^3 O_2/1000 cells/hr. [7] Rate is mm^3 O_2/1,000,000 cells/hr.

continued

66. OXYGEN CONSUMPTION: ANIMALS

Part III. Roundworms, Flatworms, and Protozoa

	Class & Species (Synonym)	Specification	Temp °C	Rate	Reference
127		Preadapted to G; G	28	89	12
128		Not adapted to G; no G	28	57	12
129		Not adapted to G; G	28	60	12
	Sporozoa				
130	*Eimeria acervulina* [7/]	Young oocysts	30	3.5	61
131	*Haemogregarina boyli* [7/]	In erythrocytes	28	2.57 [8/]	24
132	*Plasmodium cathemerium*	25% grown; G	38	0.10	27
133		75% grown; G	38	0.25	
	Rhizopoda				
134	*Amoeba chaos chaos* [7/]	Fed	15	5040	30
135			20	7050	
136			25	9010	
137			30	13,244	
138			35	17,749	
	Mastigophora				
139	*Astasia longa* [7/]	Cultures incubated at 15, 20,25, & 30°C	15	18	32
140			20	22.7	
141			25	21.6	
142			30	47.2	
143	*Chilomonas paramecium* [7/]	Cultures adapted to 15,20, & 25°C	15	9	20
144			20	15	
145			25	28	
146	*Endotrypanum schaudinni* [7/]	Culture; G	30	0.47	62
147	*Leishmania brasiliensis* [7/]	Culture; G	28	0.42	11,54
148			32	0.32	
149			37	0.65	
150	*L. donovani* [7/]	Culture; G	25	0.44	2,11, 14, 54
151			28	0.18	
152			32	0.27	
153			37	0.38	
154	*L. enrietti* [7/]	Culture; G	30	0.24	62
155	*L. tropica* [7/]	Culture; G	28	0.39	2,11, 54
156			32	0.31	
157			37	0.45	
158	*Leptomonas ctenocephali*	Culture; G	28	0.27 [9/]	26
159	*Noctiluca miliaris* [6/]	....	29	43.5-204.3	35
160	*Strigomonas fasciculata*	Culture; G	28	0.37 [9/]	26
161	*S. oncopelti*	Culture; G	28	0.41 [9/]	26
162	*Trichomonas hepatica*	Culture; G	38	6.00	59
163	*T. vaginalis*	Culture	38	0.96	37
164		Culture; G	38	2.69	
165	*Tritrichomonas foetus (Trichomonas foetus)*	Culture; G	28	2.15	38
166	*Trypanosoma congolense* [7/]	Bloodstream form; G	37	1.36	5
167		Culture; G	30	0.38	56
168	*T. cruzi* [7/]	Culture; G	28	0.25	11,54, 55
169			32	0.43	
170			37	0.33	
171	*T. equiperdum* [7/]	Bloodstream form; G	37	1.49	47
172	*T. gambiense* [7/]	Bloodstream form; G	37	1.61	58
173		Culture; G	28	0.14	54,57
174			30	0.38	54,57
175			37	0.21	54,57
	T. lewisi [7/]	Bloodstream form; G			25
176		8 days old; in serum	37	1.65	
177		14 days old; in serum	37	2.59	
178	*T. rangeli* [7/]	Culture; G	30	0.21	41

[6/] Rate is mm^3 O_2/1000 cells/hr. [7/] Rate is mm^3 O_2/1,000,000 cells/hr. [8/] Calculated as rate of infected erythrocytes minus rate of noninfected erythrocytes. [9/] Calculated from dry weight.

Contributors: (a) von Brand, Theodor, (b) Vernberg, Winona B.

References

[1] Adam, W. 1932. Z. Vergleich. Physiol. 16:229.

[2] Adler, S., and R. Ashbel. 1934. Arch. Zool. Ital. 20: 521.

[3] Agosin, M. 1959. Biologica (Santiago) 27:3.

[4] Agosin, M., and T. von Brand. 1953. J. Infect. Diseases 93:101.

[5] Agosin, M., and T. von Brand. 1954. Exptl. Parasitol. 3:517.

[6] Alt, H. L., and O. A. Tischer. 1931. Proc. Soc. Exptl. Biol. Med. 29:222.

[7] Bläsing, I. 1953. Zool. Jahrb. Abt. Allgem. Zool. Physiol. Tiere 64:112.

[8] Boell, E. J., and L. L. Woodruff. 1941. J. Exptl. Zool. 87:385.

[9] Bueding, E. 1950. J. Gen. Physiol. 33:475.

[10] Bueding, E., et al. 1953. Brit. J. Pharmacol. 8:15.

[11] Chang, S. L. 1948. J. Infect. Diseases 82:109.

[12] Conner, R. L., and S. G. Cline. 1967. J. Protozool. 14:22.

[13] Friedheim, E. A. H., and J. G. Baer. 1933. Biochem. Z. 265:329.

[14] Fulton, J. D., and L. P. Joyner. 1949. Trans. Roy. Soc. Trop. Med. Hyg. 43:273.

[15] Goil, M. M. 1958. Z. Parasitenk. 18:435.

continued

66. OXYGEN CONSUMPTION: ANIMALS

Part III. Roundworms, Flatworms, and Protozoa

[16] Goodchild, C. 1954. J. Parasitol. 40:591.
[17] Hunter, W. S., and W. B. Vernberg. 1955. Exptl. Parasitol. 4:54.
[18] Hunter, W. S., and W. B. Vernberg. 1955. Ibid. 4: 427.
[19] James, T. W., and C. P. Read. 1957. Exptl. Cell Res. 13:510.
[20] Johnson, B. F. 1962. Ibid. 28:419.
[21] Krueger, F. 1936. Zool. Jahrb. Abt. Allgem. Zool. Physiol. Tiere 57:1.
[22] Laser, H. 1944. Biochem. J. 38:333.
[23] Lazarus, M. 1950. Australian J. Sci. Res., B, 3:245.
[24] Lehmann, D. L. 1964. Parasitology 54:117.
[25] Lincicome, D. R., and A. A. Warsi. 1966. Comp. Biochem. Physiol. 17:421.
[26] Lwoff, A. 1934. Zentr. Bakteriol. Parasitenk., I, 130:498.
[27] Maier, J., and L. T. Coggeshall. 1941. J. Infect. Diseases 69:87.
[28] Nagamoto, T., and K. Okabe. 1959. Kurume Igakkai Zasshi 22:3757.
[29] Oba, N. 1959. Ibid. 22:2988.
[30] Pace, D. M., and W. H. Belda. 1944. Biol. Bull. 86: 146.
[31] Pace, D. M., and K. K. Kimura. 1944. J. Cellular Comp. Physiol. 24:173.
[32] Padilla, G. M., and T. W. James. 1960. Exptl. Cell Res. 20:401.
[33] Passey, R., and D. Fairbairn. 1955. Can. J. Biochem. Physiol. 33:1033.
[34] Pringle, C. R., and J. M. Stewart. 1961. Experientia 17:73.
[35] Rajagopal, P. K. 1962. Proc. Indian Acad. Sci., B, 55:76.
[36] Read, C. P. 1956. Exptl. Parasitol. 5:325.
[37] Read, C. P., and A. Rothman. 1955. Am. J. Hyg. 61:249.
[38] Riedmuller, L. 1936. Zentr. Bakteriol. Parasitenk., I, 137:428.
[39] Roberts, L. S., and D. Fairbairn. 1965. J. Parasitol. 51:129.
[40] Rogers, W. P. 1948. Parasitology 39:105.
[41] Rudin de Monge, E., and R. Zeledon. 1965. Proc. Congr. Centroam. Microbiol., 1st, San Jose, Costa Rica, p. 85.
[42] Sawaya, P., and M. D. Ungaretti. 1948. Univ. Sao Paulo Fac. Filosof. Cienc. Letras Zool. Bol. 13:330.
[43] Scholander, P. F., C. L. Claff, and S. L. Sveinsson. 1952. Biol. Bull. 102:178.
[44] Shimomura, M. 1959. Kurume Igakkai Zasshi 22: 2435.
[45] Stannard, J. N., O. R. McCoy, and W. B. Latchford. 1938. Am. J. Hyg. 27:666.
[46] Taylor, A. E. R., M. McCabe, and I. S. Longmuir. 1966. Exptl. Parasitol. 19:269.
[47] Thurston, J. P. 1958. Parasitology 48:165.
[48] Vernberg, W. B. 1961. Exptl. Parasitol. 11:270.
[49] Vernberg, W. B., and W. S. Hunter. 1961. Ibid. 11: 34.
[50] Villela, G. G., and L. P. Ribeiro. 1955. Anais Acad. Brasil. Cienc. 27:87.
[51] von Brand, T. 1934. Z. Vergleich. Physiol. 21:220.
[52] von Brand, T. 1942. Biol. Bull. 82:1.
[53] von Brand, T., and I. B. R. Bowman. 1961. Exptl. Parasitol. 11:276.
[54] von Brand, T., and E. M. Johnson. 1947. J. Cellular Comp. Physiol. 29:33.
[55] von Brand, T., E. M. Johnson, and C. W. Rees. 1946. J. Gen. Physiol. 30:163.
[56] von Brand, T., and E. J. Tobie. 1959. J. Parasitol. 45:204.
[57] von Brand, T., E. J. Tobie, and B. Mehlman. 1950. J. Cellular Comp. Physiol. 35:273.
[58] von Brand, T., E. C. Weinbach, and E. J. Tobie. 1955. Ibid. 45:421.
[59] Willems, R., L. Massart, and G. Peeters. 1942. Naturwissenschaften 30:169.
[60] Wilson, P. A. G. 1965. Exptl. Parasitol. 17:318.
[61] Wilson, P. A. G., and D. Fairbairn. 1961. J. Protozool. 8:40.
[62] Zeledon, R. 1960. Ibid. 7:146.

67. CORRELATION OF OXYGEN CONSUMPTION WITH BODY SIZE: INVERTEBRATES

The relation of oxygen consumption to body weight is expressed in the general formula $M = bW^a$ (or in logarithmic transformation, $\log M = a \log W + \log b$), where M = metabolism, W = weight, a = weight exponent (allometric constant or regression coefficient in statistical treatment of the data), and b = the intercept of the line in the log–log plot (indicating M at weight 1). Values are for data on intraspecific comparison; for interspecific comparison, the value for the allometric exponent = 0.738 [26].

	Class & Species (Synonym)	Temp °C	Weight	*b*	*a*	Remarks	Reference
	Echinodermata						
	Asteroidea						
1	*Asterias rubens*	15	4.7-35.0 g	0.191 ml/g/hr	0.32	....	33
	Arthropoda						
	Crustacea						
2	*Armadillidium pallasi*	20	30-130 mg	0.487 µl/mg/hr	0.67	....	46

continued

67. CORRELATION OF OXYGEN CONSUMPTION WITH BODY SIZE: INVERTEBRATES

	Class & Species (Synonym)	Temp °C	Weight	b	a	Remarks	Reference
3	*Artemia salina*	25	0.03-0.4 mg[1]	1.06 µl/0.1 mg[1]	0.883	♂; seawater	24
4				1.02 µl/0.1 mg[1]	0.624	♂; 14% salinity	
5		25	0.03-0.4 mg[1]	1.37 µl/0.1 mg[1]	0.604	♀; seawater	23
6				0.955 µl/0.1 mg[1]	0.721	♀; 14% salinity	
7	*Asellus aquaticus*	23	4-60 mg	0.748 µl/mg/hr	0.65	....	66
8		20	0.6-35 mg	0.290 µl/mg/hr	0.719	....	18
9		10	2.5-40 mg	0.210 µl/mg/hr	0.679	....	18
10	*A. intermedius*	20	4.8-32 mg	0.580 µl/mg/hr	0.632	....	18
11		10	7-52 mg	0.675 µl/mg/hr	0.490	....	
12	*Astacus astacus*	14	17.6-51.4 g	0.118 ml/g/hr	0.67	....	29
13	*A. leptodactylus (Potamobius leptodactylus)*	20	16.3-63.7 g	0.070 ml/g/hr	1.00	....	68
14	*Austropotamobius torrentium (P. torrentium)*	20	7.9-31.7 g	0.120 ml/g/hr	1.00	....	67
15	*Calanus finmarchicus*	10	12.6-28 mg	0.680 µl/mg/hr	0.775	♀, ripe	41
16				0.815 µl/mg/hr	0.775	♀, unripe	
17	*Cambarellus shufeldtii*	28.5	0.12-0.31 g	0.166 ml/g/hr	0.814	♂	22
18			0.10-0.38 g	0.178 ml/g/hr	0.852	♀	
19	*Carcinus maenas*	24.5	1.65-47.0 g	0.162 ml/g/hr	0.75	....	45
20	*Emerita talpoida*	16	0.3-0.8 g	0.066 ml/g/hr	0.245	....	15
21	*Eriphia spinifrons*	24.5	0.45-96 g	0.395 ml/g/hr	0.58	....	45
22	*Eurytium limosum*	20	0.1-10 g	0.062 ml/g/hr	0.765	....	56
23	*Hemigrapsus nudus*	10	0.3-5 g	0.040 ml/g/hr	0.480	25% salinity; 20°C[2]	12
24				0.056 ml/g/hr	0.383	25% salinity; 10°C[2]	
25				0.049 ml/g/hr	0.349	75% salinity; 20°C[2]	
26				0.061 ml/g/hr	0.559	75% salinity; 10°C[2]	
27	*H. oregonensis*	15	0.5-5 g	0.114 ml/g/hr	0.355	8 hr daily illumination	11
28				0.087 ml/g/hr	0.355	16 hr daily illumination	
29				0.079 ml/g/hr	0.528	Total darkness	
30		10	0.3-5 g	0.047 ml/g/hr	0.589	25% salinity; 20°C[2]	12
31				0.062 ml/g/hr	0.315	25% salinity; 10°C[2]	
32				0.037 ml/g/hr	0.667	75% salinity; 20°C[2]	
33				0.053 ml/g/hr	0.409	75% salinity; 10°C[2]	
34	*Ligia oceanica*	25	42 mg-1.027 g	0.350 µl/mg/hr; 0.185 ml/g/hr	0.726	....	20
35	*Maja verrucosa*	24.5	2.0-43.0 g	0.135 ml/g/hr	1.00	....	45
36	*Metapenaeus monoceros*	31	2-6 g	0.074 ml/g/hr	0.930	Marine, 100% seawater	48
37			2.5-5.5 g	0.112 ml/g/hr	0.730	Brackish, 100% seawater	
38	*Orchomenella chilensis*	12	11-250 mg	1.635 µl/mg/hr	0.497	....	2
39		8	11-250 mg	1.020 µl/mg/hr	0.604	....	
40	*Orconectes immunis*	30	1.5-11.8 g	0.132 ml/g/hr	0.772	....	63
41		24	1.5-11.8 g	0.119 ml/g/hr	0.688	....	
42		16	1.5-11.8 g	0.118 ml/g/hr	0.311	....	
43	*O. nais*	30	1.5-12 g	0.147 ml/g/hr	0.560	....	63
44		24	1.5-12 g	0.119 ml/g/hr	0.631	....	
45		16	1.5-12 g	0.130 ml/g/hr	0.097	....	
46	*Pachygrapsus crassipes*	23.5	3.02-32.9 g	0.145 ml/g/hr	0.730	Adaptation temp, 16°C	49
47		16	3.02-39.7 g	0.076 ml/g/hr	0.664	Adaptation temp, 16°C	
48		8.5	3.05-36.2 g	0.036 ml/g/hr	0.665	Adaptation temp, 16°C	
49	*Penaeus japonicus*	22.6	3.1-16.1 g	0.629 ml/g/hr	0.711	Actively swimming	19
50	*Porcellio scaber*	20	65.5-110 mg	0.226 µl/mg/hr	0.784	Autumn-winter	64
51			42-89 mg	0.117 µl/mg/hr	1.00	Spring-summer	
52	*Procambarus alleni*	25	5 mg-13 g	0.115 ml/g/hr	0.760	....	10
53	*Pugettia producta*	15	1.64-329 g	0.166 ml/g/hr	0.802	....	27
54	*Rivulogammarus pulex*	19	0.78-3.45 mg[3]	3.640 µl/mg/hr	1.117	♂	44
55			0.76-2.17 mg[3]	6.255 µl/mg/hr	0.858	♀	
56	*Sesarma reticulatum*	20	0.2-1 g	0.086 ml/g/hr	0.653	....	56

[1] Dry weight. [2] Acclimation temperature. [3] Reduced weight.

continued

67. CORRELATION OF OXYGEN CONSUMPTION WITH BODY SIZE: INVERTEBRATES

	Class & Species (Synonym)	Temp °C	Weight	*b*	*a*	Remarks	Reference
57	*Talitrus sylvaticus*	25	2-48 mg	0.533 µl/mg/hr	0.836	....	6
58	*Talorchestia longicornis*	22	0.11-0.24 g	0.099 ml/g/hr	0.475	Summer	16
59	*(T. megalophthalma)*	12	0.11-0.24 g	0.008 ml/g/hr	0.540	Summer	
60		22	0.14-0.29 g	0.045 ml/g/hr	0.00	Winter	
61		12	0.14-0.29 g	0.004 ml/g/hr	0.325	Winter	
62	*Uca minax*	20	0.02-5 g	0.240 ml/g/hr	0.710	....	56
63	*U. pugilator*	20	5 mg-2.5 g	0.185 ml/g/hr	0.773	....	56
64	*U. pugnax*	28	0.48-3.49 g	0.126 ml/g/hr	0.627	North Carolina	57
65		23	0.09-5.6 g	0.109 ml/g/hr	0.695	North Carolina	55
66		14	0.07-4.7 g	0.045 ml/g/hr	0.731	North Carolina	55
67		24	0.1-4.3 g	0.140 ml/g/hr	0.679	New York	55
68		14	0.02-4.1 g	0.091 ml/g/hr	0.833	New York	55
69		20	0.05-2 g	0.112 ml/g/hr	0.681	Georgia, salt marsh	56
70	*U. rapax*	28	0.6-13.67 g	0.137 ml/g/hr	0.657	Jamaica	57
71		27	0.15-5.12 g	0.136 ml/g/hr	0.790	Florida	
	Insecta						
72	*Acheta domesticus*	20	0.08-68 mg	0.624 µl/mg/hr	1.00	Larva	36
73	*(Gryllus domesticus)*		68-543 mg	0.416 µl/mg/hr	1.00	Imago	
74	*Aeshna cyanea (Aeschna cyanea)*	16	100-787 mg	0.110 µl/mg/hr	0.99	Larva	3
75	*Apis mellifera*	32	7.5-432 mg	3.02 µl/mg/hr	0.443	♂, larva	1
76			8-153 mg	3.79 µl/mg/hr	0.700	Worker larva	
77	*Calopteryx virgo*	16	13-1213 mg	0.118 µl/mg/hr	0.97	Larva	3
78	*Chironomus riparius*	20	2-12 mg	4.44 µl/mg/hr	0.855	Larva	17
79		10	2-12 mg	1.85 µl/mg/hr	0.839	Larva	
80	*Coenagrion puella (Agrion puella)*	16	7.1-42.8 mg	0.250 µl/mg/hr	0.905	Larva	3
81	*Drosophila melanogaster*	26	0.72-2.15 mg	2.08 µl/mg/hr	0.772	Prepupa, diploid, triploid	21
82	*Enallagma cyathigerum*	16	7.4-32.4 mg	0.325 µl/mg/hr	0.95	Larva	3
83	*Formica polyctena*	32	80-300 mg	0.430 µl/mg/hr	1.00	Pupa	53
84		24	100-300 mg	0.182 µl/mg/hr	1.045	Pupa	
85		16	60-400 mg	0.127 µl/mg/hr	0.945	Pupa	
86	*Hydropsyche* sp.	16	1.3-45.6 mg	0.500 µl/mg/hr	0.77	Larva	3
87	*Locusta migratoria*	28	34-72.5 mg	0.806 µl/mg/hr	0.969	♀, 2nd instar	7
88			82-230 mg	0.452 µl/mg/hr	1.110	♀, 3rd instar	
89			642-1760 mg	33.1 µl/mg/hr; 0.762 ml/g/hr	0.454	♀, 5th instar	
90	*Nemobius sylvestris*	20	1.2-80.8 mg	0.496 µl/mg/hr	1.00	....	36
91	*Nymphalis io (Vanessa io)*	23	4.4-382.7 mg	0.416 µl/mg/hr	1.07	....	32
92	*N. urtica (V. urtica)*	23	3.1-272 mg	1.000 µl/mg/hr	0.93	....	32
93			6.4-296.3 mg	0.617 µl/mg/hr	1.04	....	
94	*Oncopeltus fasciatus*	20	0.2-80 mg	1.320 µl/mg/hr	0.82	....	14
95	*Periplaneta americana*	20	0.45-1.0 g	0.093 ml/g/hr	0.602	Nymph, adaptation temp, 26°C	13
96			0.37-1.1 g	0.145 ml/g/hr	0.456	Nymph, adaptation temp, 10°C	
97			0.8-1.1 g	0.135 ml/g/hr	0.541	Adult, adaptation temp, 26°C	
98			0.70-1.0 g	0.191 ml/g/hr	0.487	Adult, adaptation temp, 10°C	
99	*Perla burmeisteriana (P. abdominalis)*	16	6.9-331 mg	0.500 µl/mg/hr	0.808	Larva	3
100	*Schistocerca gregaria*	32	1.60-2.02 g	0.680 ml/g/hr[4]	1.279	♂	25
101	*Sialis lutaria (S. flavilatera)*	16	14.2-69.6 mg	0.320 µl/mg/hr	0.77	Larva	3
102	*Tenebrio molitor*	23	3.2-237 mg	1.180 µl/mg/hr	0.90	....	32
103		21	40-140 mg	0.765 µl/mg/hr	0.78	Starved 24 hr	59
104		20	20-220 mg	0.564 µl/mg/hr	0.95	Well-fed	59
105	*Tenebroides mauritanicus*	25	39.7-56.4 mg	16.90 µl/mg/hr	0.111	Larva	5
	Onychophora						
106	*Peripatus accacioi (P. acacioi)*	20	175-484 mg	0.223 µl/mg/hr	0.932	....	42

[4] CO_2 output.

continued

67. CORRELATION OF OXYGEN CONSUMPTION WITH BODY SIZE: INVERTEBRATES

	Class & Species (Synonym)	Temp °C	Weight	b	a	Remarks	Reference
	Annelida						
	Hirudinea						
107	*Erpobdella octoculata*	20	12-104 mg	0.263 µl/mg/hr	1.060	....	40
108	*E. testacea*	20	6-37 mg	0.740 µl/mg/hr	0.810	....	40
109	*Glossiphonia complanata*	20	4-94 mg	0.790 µl/mg/hr	0.715	....	40
110	*Haemopis sanguisuga*	19	0.6-2.5 g	0.049 ml/g/hr	0.692	....	54
111	*Helobdella stagnalis*	20	2-6 mg	0.770 µl/mg/hr	0.810	....	40
112	*Hirudo medicinalis*	19	0.5-6 g	0.046 ml/g/hr	0.677	....	54
113	*Piscicola geometra*	20	2-22 mg	1.705 µl/mg/hr	0.695	....	40
	Oligochaeta						
114	*Eisenia foetida*	15	13-850 mg	0.448 µl/mg/hr	0.67	....	35
115	*Glossoscolex* sp.	25	6.67-18.68 g	0.088 ml/g/hr	0.827	Well-fed	43
116			2.51-18.45 g	0.078 ml/g/hr	0.910	Starved 24 hr	
117	*Lumbricus* sp.	20	0.2-2.5 g	0.077 ml/g/hr	1.00	....	46
118	*Megaloscolex mauritii*	30	0.13-2.2 g	0.145 ml/g/hr	0.843	Summer	51
119		20	0.15-2.3 g	0.099 ml/g/hr	0.745	Summer	
120		30	0.2-3.2 g	0.200 ml/g/hr	0.435	Winter	52
121		20	0.2-3.2 g	0.140 ml/g/hr	0.515	Winter	
122	*Pheretima hawayana*	25	567-2017 mg	0.162 ml/g/hr	0.588	Well-fed	43
123			651-2766 mg	0.174 ml/g/hr	0.415	Starved 24 hr	
124	*Pontoscolex* sp.	25	360-1056 mg	1.580 µl/mg/hr; 0.064 ml/g/hr	0.700	Well-fed	43
125			381-900 mg	3.900 µl/mg/hr; 0.166 ml/g/hr	0.544	Starved 24 hr	
	Polychaeta						
126	*Arenicola marina*	20	2.37-18.76 g	0.058 ml/g/hr	0.740	Spring	38
127		10	2.37-18.76 g	0.036 ml/g/hr	0.750	Spring	
128		20	0.38-13.29 g	0.070 ml/g/hr	0.710	Autumn	
129		10	0.38-13.29 g	0.042 ml/g/hr	0.810	Autumn	
130	*Schizobranchia insignis*	12.5	460-2100 mg	0.142 ml/g/hr	0.366	Normal	8
131			460-2100 mg	0.054 ml/g/hr	0.372	Forced withdrawal[5]	
	Mollusca						
	Bivalvia						
132	*Anodonta cygnea*	20	0.061-117 g	0.053 ml/g/hr	0.93	....	61
133	*Dreissena polymorpha*	20	6.8 mg-5.24 g	0.084 µl/mg/hr; 0.118 ml/g/hr	1.05	....	61
134	*Musculium lacustre*	20	4.1-63 mg	0.036 µl/mg/hr	0.94	....	61
135	*Mytilus edulis*	16	106-1681 mg[1]	0.648 µl/mg/hr[1]	0.676	....	50
136		15	0.058-13.9 g	0.069-0.105 ml/g/hr	0.92	Flesh weight, spring	37
137			0.11-23.1 g	0.043-0.064 ml/g/hr	0.70-0.88	Flesh weight, summer	
138			0.211-18.98 g	0.061 ml/g/hr	0.73	Flesh weight, autumn	
139			0.18-11.04 g	0.070 ml/g/hr	0.83	Flesh weight, winter	
140	*Unio pictorum*	20	8.17-20.8 mg	0.037 ml/g/hr	1.10	....	61
	Gastropoda						
141	*Acroloxus lacustris*	18	2-10 mg	0.500 µl/mg/hr	0.67	May-June	4
142			3-6 mg	0.315 µl/mg/hr	0.70	September-October	
143	*Ancylus fluviatilis*	18	12-22 mg	0.475 µl/mg/hr	0.80	June	4
144			9-60 mg	0.515 µl/mg/hr	0.73	August	
145			8.4-42 mg	0.550 µl/mg/hr	0.75	October	
146			5.2-20 mg	0.325 µl/mg/hr	0.70	December	
147	*Arion ater*	20	0.317-16.2 g	0.112 ml/g/hr	0.90	....	61
148	*A. hortensis*	20	17.2-265 mg	0.465 µl/mg/hr	0.77	....	61

[1] Dry weight. [5] Within the tube.

continued

67. CORRELATION OF OXYGEN CONSUMPTION WITH BODY SIZE: INVERTEBRATES

	Class & Species (Synonym)	Temp °C	Weight	b	a	Remarks	Reference
149	*Australorbis glabratus*	28	0.07-15 mg	0.510 µl/mg/hr	0.800	Young	47
150			13-158 mg	0.725 µl/mg/hr	0.784	Juvenile, adult	
151	*A. tenagophilus*	20	8.5-189 mg	0.335 µl/mg/hr	0.60	....	61
152	*Bithynia leachi*	18	6-16 mg	0.330 µl/mg/hr	0.740	....	4
153	*B. tentaculata*	18	22-170 mg	0.230 µl/mg/hr	0.810	June	4
154				0.200 µl/mg/hr	0.80	October	
155	*Cepaea nemoralis*	20	0.217-2.49 g	0.097 ml/g/hr	0.73	....	61
156	*Deroceras agreste*	23.3	22-1600 mg	0.129 µl/mg/hr; 0.147 ml/g/hr	1.02	....	31
157		20	4.6-415 mg	0.463 µl/mg/hr	0.84	....	61
158	*Helicella candicans*	23.3	22-443 mg	0.143 µl/mg/hr	1.05	....	31
159	*Helix pomatia*	20	0.134-39.5 g	0.138 ml/g/hr	0.71	Inactive	61
160			0.32-20.0 g	0.221 ml/g/hr	0.80	Fully active	
161	*Lymnaea auricularia*	18	120-1000 mg	0.752 µl/mg/hr	0.72	....	4
162	*L. ovata*	20	2.5-545 mg	0.436 µl/mg/hr	0.71	....	61
163	*L. palustris*	18	62-210 mg	0.660 µl/mg/hr	0.76	June	4
164			37-170 mg	2.050 µl/mg/hr	0.45	August	
165	*L. peregra*	18	45-200 mg	0.300 µl/mg/hr	0.94	June	4
166			18-130 mg	1.400 µl/mg/hr	0.59	August	
167	*L. stagnalis*	23	10^{-3}-0.85 µg[1]	6.5 mµl/µg[1]	0.77	Larva	28
168			0.85-2 µg[1]	11.0 mµl/µg[1]	0.52	Embryo, onset of heart activity	
169		20	0.14-1.70 g	0.53 ml/g/hr	0.75	....	59
170		20	7.3 mg-2.64 g	0.57 ml/g/hr	0.70	....	61
171			0.16-1.4 g	0.109 ml/g/hr	0.76	Fully active	
172	*Melanoides tuberculata*	20	2.4-463 mg	0.472 µl/mg/hr	0.65	Active	61
173	*Myxas glutinosa*	18	95-570 mg	0.590 µl/mg/hr	0.75	....	4
174	*Oncomelania nosophora*	30	7.66-30.27 mg	0.351 µl/mg/hr	0.728	....	69
175	*Patella vulgata*	15	2-15 g	0.085 ml/g/hr	0.722	Low level shore	9
176				0.080 ml/g/hr	0.673	High level shore	
177		5	2-15 g	0.041 ml/g/hr	0.673	Low level shore	
178				0.038 ml/g/hr	0.722	High level shore	
179	*Physa acuta*	20	4-126 mg	0.438 µl/mg/hr	0.69	....	61
180	*P. fontinalis*	18	12-100 mg	0.290 µl/mg/hr	1.00	....	4
181	*Planorbis* sp.	23	30-300 mg	0.259 µl/mg/hr	0.76	....	59
182	*P. corneus*	20	0.192-3.52 g	0.047 ml/g/hr	0.63	....	61
183	*Potamopyrgus jenkinsi*	19	1.6-6 mg	0.235 µl/mg/hr	0.725	Freshwater	39
184			2.6-10 mg	0.330 µl/mg/hr	0.70	Brackish water	
185	*Theodoxus fluviatilis*	19	12.5-31 mg	0.625 µl/mg/hr	0.730	Fresh & brackish water	39
186	*Valvata piscinalis*	18	8-34 mg	0.295 µl/mg/hr	0.890	....	4
187	*Zebrina detrita*	23.3	50-839 mg	0.018 µl/mg/hr	1.09	Total weight	31
188			18-600 mg	0.145 µl/mg/hr	0.983	Weight minus shell	30
	Aschelminthes						
	Nematoda						
189	*Ascaris lumbricoides*	37	0.32-10.0 g	0.130 ml/g/hr	~0.67	....	34
190	*Enoplus communis*	20	1-100 µg	0.100 µl/mg/hr	~0.67	After molting	65
	Platyhelminthes						
	Cestoda						
191	*Taenia taeniaeformis*	37	66-331 mg/liter[6]	0.228 µl/liter[6]	0.90	Larva, aerobic	60
192			112-318 mg/liter[6]	1.655 µl/liter[6]	0.67	Larva, anaerobic	
193			251-1820 mg/liter[6]	1.501 µl/liter[6]	0.76	Adult, aerobic	
194			224-2630 mg/liter[6]	1.615 µl/liter[6]	0.84	Adult, anaerobic	
	Trematoda						
195	*Gynaecotyla adunca*	30	0.09-0.33 µg body N	0.0098 µl/µg body N	0.612	....	58

[1] Dry weight. [6] Of specimen.

continued

67. CORRELATION OF OXYGEN CONSUMPTION WITH BODY SIZE: INVERTEBRATES

	Class & Species (Synonym)	Temp °C	Weight	*b*	*a*	Remarks	Reference
	Turbellaria						
196	*Crenobia alpina*	14.5	2.8-14 mg	0.262 µl/mg/hr	0.70	....	62
197		7	1.6-14.3 mg	0.167 µl/mg/hr	0.70	....	
198	*Dugesia gonocephala (Planaria gonocephala)*	20	4-65 mg	0.353 µl/mg/hr	0.80	....	59
199	*D. polychroa (P. polychroa)*	14.5	3.5-16.9 mg	0.137 µl/mg/hr	0.87	....	62

Contributors: Locker, A., and von Bertalanffy, Ludwig.

References

[1] Allen, M. D. 1959. J. Econ. Entomol. 52:399.
[2] Armitage, K. B. 1962. Biol. Bull. 123:225.
[3] Balke, E. 1957. Z. Vergleich. Physiol. 40:415.
[4] Berg, K., and K. W. Ockelmann. 1959. J. Exptl. Biol. 36:690.
[5] Bond, E. J. 1956. Can. J. Zool. 34:405.
[6] Clark, D. P. 1958. Biol. Bull. 108:253.
[7] Clarke, K. U. 1957. J. Exptl. Biol. 34:29.
[8] Dales, R. P. 1961. Biol. Bull. 121:82.
[9] Davies, P. S. 1965. Nature 205:924.
[10] Davison, J. 1956. Biol. Bull. 110:264.
[11] Dehnel, P. A. 1958. Nature 181:1415.
[12] Dehnel, P. A. 1960. Biol. Bull. 118:215.
[13] Dehnel, P. A., and E. Segal. 1956. Ibid. 111:53.
[14] Edwards, G. A. 1953. In K. D. Roeder, ed. Insect physiology. J. Wiley, New York. pp. 106-107.
[15] Edwards, G. A., and L. Irving. 1943. J. Cellular Comp. Physiol. 21:169.
[16] Edwards, G. A., and L. Irving. 1943. Ibid. 21:183.
[17] Edwards, R. W. 1958. J. Exptl. Biol. 35:383.
[18] Edwards, R. W., and M. A. Learner. 1960. Ibid. 37:706.
[19] Egusa, S. 1961. Bull. Japan. Soc. Sci. Fisheries 27:650.
[20] Ellenby, C. 1951. J. Exptl. Biol. 28:492.
[21] Ellenby, C. 1953. Ibid. 30:475.
[22] Fingerman, M. 1955. Tulane Studies Zool. 3:103.
[23] Gilchrist, B. M. 1956. Hydrobiologia 8:54.
[24] Gilchrist, B. M. 1958. Ibid. 12:27.
[25] Hamilton, A. G. 1958. Proc. Intern. Congr. Entomol., 10th, Montreal, 1956, 2:343.
[26] Hemmingsen, A. M. 1960. Rept. Steno Mem. Hosp. Nord. Insulin Lab. 9(2):1.
[27] Heymouth, F. W., et al. 1944. Physiol. Zool. 17:50.
[28] Horstmann, H. J. 1958. Z. Vergleich. Physiol. 41:390.
[29] Kalmus, H. 1930. Ibid. 12:725.
[30] Kienle, M. L. 1957. Ibid. 40:440.
[31] Kienle, M. L., and W. Ludwig. 1956. Ibid. 39:102.
[32] Kittel, A. 1941. Ibid. 28:533.
[33] Koller, G., and H. Meyer. 1933. Biol. Zentr. 53:655.
[34] Krüger, F. 1940. Z. Wiss. Zool. 152:547.
[35] Krüger, F. 1952. Z. Vergleich. Physiol. 34:1.
[36] Krüger, F. 1958. Biol. Zentr. 77:581.
[37] Krüger, F. 1960. Helgolaender Wiss. Meeresuntersuch. 7:125.
[38] Krüger, F. 1964. Ibid. 10:38.
[39] Lumbye, J. 1958. Hydrobiologia 10:245.
[40] Mann, K. H. 1956. J. Exptl. Biol. 33:615.
[41] Marshall, S. M., and A. P. Orr. 1958. J. Marine Biol. Assoc. U.K. 37:459.
[42] Mendes, E. G., and P. Sawayana. 1958. Rev. Brasil. Biol. 18:129.
[43] Mendes, E. G., and D. Valente. 1953. Bol. Fac. Cienc. Sao Paulo Univ. Zool. 18:91.
[44] Micherdzinski, W. 1958. Folia Biol. (Warsaw) 6:145.
[45] Montuori, A. 1913. Arch. Ital. Biol. 59:213.
[46] Müller, I. 1943. Biol. Zentr. 63:446.
[47] Perlowagora-Szumlewicz, A., and T. von Brand. 1958. J. Wash. Acad. Sci. 48:38.
[48] Rao, K. P. 1958. J. Exptl. Biol. 35:307.
[49] Roberts, J. L. 1957. Physiol. Zool. 30:232.
[50] Rotthauwe, H. W. 1958. Veroeffentl. Inst. Meeresforsch. Bremerhaven 5:143.
[51] Saroja, K. 1959. Proc. Indian Acad. Sci., B, 49:183.
[52] Saroja, K. 1961. Nature 190:930.
[53] Schmidt, G. H. 1966. Helgolaender Wiss. Meeresuntersuch. 14:369.
[54] Schweer, M. 1959. Z. Vergleich. Physiol. 42:20.
[55] Tashian, R. E. 1956. Zoologica 41:39.
[56] Teal, J. M. 1959. Physiol. Zool. 32:1.
[57] Vernberg, F. J. 1959. Biol. Bull. 117:163.
[58] Vernberg, W. B., and W. Hunter. 1959. Exptl. Parasitol. 8:76.
[59] von Bertalanffy, L., and I. Müller. 1943. Riv. Biol. (Perugia) 35:48.
[60] von Brand, T., and D. W. Alling. 1962. Comp. Biochem. Physiol. 5:141.
[61] Wesemeier, H. 1960. Z. Vergleich. Physiol. 43:1.
[62] Whitney, R. J. 1942. J. Exptl. Biol. 19:168.
[63] Wiens, A. W., and K. B. Armitage. 1961. Physiol. Zool. 34:39.
[64] Wieser, W. 1962. Z. Vergleich. Physiol. 45:247.
[65] Wieser, W., and J. Kanwisher. 1960. Ibid. 43:29.
[66] Will, A. 1952. Ibid. 34:20.
[67] Wolsky, A. 1934. Arb. Ungar. Biol. Forsch. Inst. 7:116.
[68] Wolsky, A., and B. E. Holmes. 1933. Ibid. 6:123.
[69] Yanagisawa, T., and Y. Komiya. 1961. Japan. J. Med. Sci. Biol. 14:69.

68. METABOLIC RATES: SOIL ORGANISMS

Populations in Temperate Grasslands: Values are typical estimates of normal populations of whole systematic groups. Many of the groups would not be found in some types of grasslands, and no group would be found with other groups in the indicated amounts in the same place. **Individual Organisms in the Laboratory:** Values are specific laboratory measurements for a particular organism.

	Systematic Group & Species	Populations in Temperate Grasslands/m²			Individual Organisms in the Laboratory				Reference
		No. of Organisms	Weight g	Metabolism[1] kcal/yr	Weight mg	Temp °C	Oxygen Uptake $mm^3 \times hr^{-1}$	Metabolism[2] g-cal/day/g	
	Acari								
1	Oribatei	2×10^5	2.0	30					9
2	*Achipteria* sp.				0.1	16.0	18×10^{-3}	23	1
3	Parasitidae	5×10^3	1.0	64					11
4	*Pergamasus crassipes*				0.2	16.0	0.5	282	11
5	Araneae	600	6.0	34					4
6	*Lycosa* sp.				15.1	13.0	6.9	70	11
7	Opiliones	40	0.4	5					11
8	*Platybunus triangularis*				18.0	19.0	10.5	53	10
9	Isopoda	500	5	38					11
10	*Oniscus asellus*				23	19.0	9	34	10
11	Diptera	500	1.0	0.2					12
12	*Tipula* sp.[3]				275	13.0	60	33	2
13	Coleoptera	300	3.8	0.8					12
14	*Carabus nemoralis*				645	13.0	160	38	2
15	Collembola	5×10^4	5.0	38					11
16	*Onychiurus procampatus*				0.1	15.0	32×10^{-3}	41	5
17	Myriapoda	500	12.5	96					10
18	*Julus* sp.				25	19.0	10	36	10
	Oligochaeta								
19	Enchytraeidae	5.0×10^4	10	140					13
20	*Fridericia* sp.				0.14	16.0	0.117	95	13
21	Lumbricidae	1.0×10^3	120	180					2
22	*Lumbricus terrestris*				5000	16.0	300	7	8
23	Mollusca	50	10	62					14
24	*Helix aspersa*				1500	28.0	1000	29	15
25	Nematoda	2.0×10^7	18	282					13
26	*Plectus* sp.				1×10^{-3}	16.0	1.2×10^{-3}	135	12
27	Protozoa[4]	3.0×10^8	38	250					3,13
28	*Amoeba chaos chaos*				5×10^{-2}	22.5	1×10^{-2}	14	7
29	Fungi[4]	4.0×10^9	400	....[5]					3
30	*Mycoderma* sp.				1×10^{-7}	20.0	5×10^{-6}	161	6
31	Bacteria[4]	2.5×10^{13}	1000	....[5]					3
32	*Sarcina lutea*				1×10^{-9}	20.5	7×10^{-9}	539	6

[1] Daily metabolism values at 16°C multiplied by 212 to correct for annual temperature cycle in Northern Europe [13]. [2] Oxygen uptake in ml/day × 4.7, assuming a respiratory quotient of 0.82, except for bacteria (R.Q. = 0.7); Krogh's formula used for further correction for temperature to a standard value of 16°C [2]. [3] Larva. [4] Values for microorganisms are only available per gram of soil; therefore population estimates on a square-meter basis are obtained by multiplying the number of organisms per gram of soil by 10^4, in the case of protozoa, and by the number of organisms per gram of soil for the whole soil profile, in the case of fungi and bacteria. [5] Owing to suppression of microbial metabolism under field conditions, no estimates are possible for fungi and bacteria, but since total soil metabolism approximates 5000 kcal/yr, the difference between this value and the total due to the fauna gives only approximate metabolism for fungi plus bacteria.

Contributor: Macfadyen, Amyan

continued

68. METABOLIC RATES: SOIL ORGANISMS

References

[1] Berthet, P. 1964. Mem. Inst. Roy. Sci. Nat. Belg. 152.

[2] Bornebusch, C. H. 1930. The fauna of forest soil. Nielsen and Lydiche, Copenhagen.

[3] Burges, N. A. 1958. Microorganisms in the soil. Hutchinson Univ. Library, London.

[4] Duffey, E. 1962. J. Animal Ecol. 31:571.

[5] Healey, I. N. 1968. In K. Petrusewicz, ed. Secondary productivity of terrestrial ecosystems. I. B. P., Warsaw.

[6] Hemmingsen, A. M. 1950. Rept. Steno Mem. Hosp. Nord. Insulin Lab. 4:1.

[7] Holter, H. 1943. Compt. Rend. Trav. Lab. Carlsberg, Ser. Chim., 24:399.

[8] Konopaki, M. 1907. Bull. Intern. Acad. Sci. Cracovie, Cl. Sci. Math. Nat., p. 357.

[9] Macfadyen, A. 1952. J. Animal Ecol. 21:87.

[10] Macfadyen, A. 1961. J. Exptl. Biol. 38:323.

[11] Macfadyen, A. Unpublished. Univ. College of Swansea, Wales, 1966.

[12] Nielsen, C. O. 1949. Natura Jutlandica 2:1.

[13] Nielsen, C. O. 1961. Oikos 12:17.

[14] Stöckli, A. 1945. Schweiz. Landwirtsch. Monatsh. 24:3.

[15] Vernon, H. M. 1896. J. Physiol. (London) 19:18.

69. OXYGEN UPTAKE OF ORGANS IN SITU: MAMMALS

± = standard error.

Part I. Heart

Coronary Blood Flow: determined by N_2O method, unless otherwise stated.

	Animal	No. of Observations	No. of Subjects	Arterial Pressure mm Hg	Heart Rate beats/min	Cardiac Output ml/min [Cardiac Index ml/min/m²]	Left Ventricular Coronary Blood Flow ml/min·100 g	Left Ventricular O_2 Uptake ml/min·100 g	Experimental Conditions	Reference
1	Man	4	4	92	....	4582	65	7.8	Unanesthetized subjects	3
2		18	18	....	....	....	77	9.4	Unanesthetized subjects	2
3		19	19	92 ± 2.6	....	[3600 ± 170]	81 ± 2.4	9.0 ± 0.28	Unanesthetized subjects	9
4		9	9	92	77	[3220]	82	8.5	♂ subjects, fasting, at rest	13
5		13	13	90	83	[4000]	96	10.3	♀ subjects; no premedication	15
6		30	30	93	79	[3850]	85	9.65	15♂ and 15♀; no medication, except pentobarbital for 2 subjects	14
7		8	8	97	....	6011	103	10.5	Subjects sedated with Nembutal or Demerol	10
8	Dog	27	14	119	116	3144	133 ± 35	15.7 ± 3.5	Unanesthetized trained subjects	17
9		7	4	105	77	2398 1/	50	6.6	Unanesthetized trained subjects; coronary flow measured by implanted electromagnetic flowmeter on circumflex or main left coronary; output measure by flowmeter on ascending aorta	7
10		12	12	145 ± 3.7	158 ± 5	[4500 ± 200]	147 ± 11	19.1 ± 2.1	Nembutal anesthesia	6
11		7	7	133	163	3601	74	9.8	Pentobarbital anesthesia	4
12		9	9	95 ± 13	92 ± 19	2500 ± 500	81 ± 14	9.4 ± 2.6	Morphine & pentobarbital anesthesia	12
13		25	25	116 ± 2.6	69 ± 5.6	[2260]	66 ± 5	8.96 ± 0.8	Morphine-chloralose anesthesia	16
14		10	10	116 ± 17	87 ± 12	2300 ± 800	90 ± 16	10.9 ± 1.9	Morphine-Dial-urethan anesthesia	15
15		11	11	101	74	2850	85	9.3	Morphine & pentobarbital sodium with Dial-urethan	18
16		129	14	80	129	1049	....	6.92	Open chest, under pentobarbital; right heart bypass; coronary flow measured in pulmonary artery by graduated cylinder	5

1/ 5 observations in 2 experiments.

continued

69. OXYGEN UPTAKE OF ORGANS IN SITU: MAMMALS

Part I. Heart

	Animal	No. of Observations	No. of Subjects	Arterial Pressure mm Hg	Heart Rate beats/min	Cardiac Output ml/min [Cardiac Index ml/min/m²]	Left Ventricular Coronary Blood Flow ml/min·100 g	Left Ventricular O_2 Uptake ml/min·100 g	Experimental Conditions	Reference
17		37	37	103	141	1039[2]	65[3]	6.23[3]	Open chest, under Nembutal; right heart bypass; coronary flow measured in pulmonary artery with rotameter	11
18		5	5	97	....	1208[2]	143[3]	17.18[3]	Open chest, under pentobarbital; right heart bypass; coronary flow measured in pulmonary artery with rotameter	1
19				79	....	1208[2]	98[3]	12.47[3]		
20				122	....	1208[2]	141[3]	17.34[3]		
21		23	23	118	....	1720	64[3]	8.83[3]	Closed chest, under morphine; heparinized; coronary sinus blood flow measured with modified Morawitz cannula introduced through external jugular (assumed to represent 60% of total flow)	8

[2] Per 100 g heart weight. [3] Value for whole heart.

Contributor: Badeer, Henry S.

References

[1] Alella, A., et al. 1955. Am. J. Physiol. 183:570.
[2] Bing, R. J. 1951. Bull. N.Y. Acad. Med. 27:407.
[3] Bing, R. J., et al. 1949. Am. Heart J. 38:1.
[4] Eckenhoff, J. E., et al. 1948. Am. J. Physiol. 152: 545.
[5] Feinberg, H., L. N. Katz, and E. Boyd. 1962. Ibid. 202:45.
[6] Goodale, W. T., and D. B. Hackel. 1953. Circulation Res. 1:502.
[7] Gregg, D. E., E. M. Khouri, and C. R. Rayford. 1965. Ibid. 16:102.
[8] Harrison, T. R., B. Friedman, and H. Resnik, Jr. 1936. Arch. Internal Med. 57:927.
[9] Hellems, H. K., et al. 1957. Circulation 16:893.
[10] Leight, L., et al. 1956. Ibid. 14:90.
[11] Marchetti, G., M. Maccari, and L. Merlo. 1963. Cardiologia 42:1.
[12] Maxwell, G. M., et al. 1958. J. Clin. Invest. 37:1413.
[13] Regan, T. J., et al. 1961. Ibid. 40:624.
[14] Rowe, G. G., et al. 1959. Circulation Res. 7:728.
[15] Rowe, G. G., et al. 1964. Am. Heart J. 67:457.
[16] Scott, J. C., and T. A. Balourdas. 1959. Circulation Res. 7:162.
[17] Spencer, F. C., et al. 1950. Am. J. Physiol. 160:149.
[18] West, J. W., et al. 1959. Circulation Res. 7:476.

Part II. Other Organs

Organ Blood Flow: determined by N_2O method, unless otherwise stated.

	Animal	No. of Observations	No. of Subjects	Arterial Pressure mm Hg	Arterial O_2 Content vol %	A-V O_2 Difference vol %	Organ Blood Flow ml/min·100 g	Organ O_2 Uptake ml/min·100 g	Experimental Conditions	Reference
							Brain			
1	Man	13	13	86 ± 1.9	....	5.87 ± 0.3	67 ± 2.6	3.9 ± 0.22	Unanesthetized, normal subjects	41
2		11	11	86.5	19.44 ± 0.40	6.25 ± 0.40	55 ± 4	3.34 ± 0.23	Young adults, normal, resting; no premedication	32
3		30	30	95 ± 2	17.8 ± 0.4	6.4 ± 0.14	58 ± 1.2	3.7 ± 0.07	Unanesthetized, normal, resting subjects	6

continued

69. OXYGEN UPTAKE OF ORGANS IN SITU: MAMMALS

Part II. Other Organs

	Animal	No. of Observations	No. of Subjects	Arterial: Pressure mm Hg	Arterial: O_2 Content vol %	Organ: A-V O_2 Difference vol %	Organ: Blood Flow ml/min·100 g	Organ: O_2 Uptake ml/min·100 g	Experimental Conditions	Reference
4		9	9	98	....	7.28	49.3	3.43	Unanesthetized, normal ♂ subjects	35
5		34	14	86	....	6.3	54	3.3	Unanesthetized, healthy, young ♂ adults	23
6		31-33	20	83	....	6.02 ± 0.14	65 ± 2.1	3.8 ± 0.1	Normal ♂ subjects; supine position	39
7		8	8	80	18.5	6.4	56	3.5	Young ♂ adults; basal state	26
8		20	20	97.5	....	6.65	52 ± 1.9	3.4 ± 0.13	10♂ and 10♀; basal state; no premedication; cerebral blood flow measured by ^{85}Kr method	28
9		....	....	86	18.0	6.3	54	3.3	Normal pregnant ♀	33
10	Cat	6	6	....	15.4	5.6	68	3.6	Chloralose anesthesia; brain perfused with pump oxygenator, using defibrinated cat blood	10
11		6	6	....	....	....	>90	4.95	Ether & Dial anesthesia; isolated brain perfused with defibrinated ox blood; cerebral blood flow measured with graduated pipette	18
12	Dog	18	18	66	14.9	11.0	41	4.4	Pentobarbital anesthesia; cerebral blood flow measured by rotameter	20
13		4	4	....	....	....	49.1	7.18	Pentobarbital anesthesia; heparinized; cerebral blood flow measured by rotameter	38
14		88	34	....	....	4.8-11.8	....	7.7	Chloralose & urethan anesthesia; isolated brain perfused with blood from another dog; cerebral blood flow measured with graduated cylinder	16
15	Monkey 2-3 kg	17	17	....	....	....	....	5.9	Pentobarbital anesthesia	4
16	2-5 kg	22	22	115	....	8	40	4.0	Pentobarbital anesthesia	5
							Kidney			
17	Man	5	5	....	15.8	1.08	946 1/	10.3 1/	Unanesthetized, normal subjects; renal vein catheterized; renal blood flow measured by Fick method, using PAH	8
18		10	10	....	....	1.42	1155 1/	16.0 1/	Unanesthetized, normal subjects; renal vein catheterized; renal blood flow measured by Fick method, using PAH; all values corrected to surface area of 1.73 m^2	9
19		15	15	....	....	1.43 ± 0.10	1348 1/	6.24 ± 0.54	Unanesthetized, normal subjects; renal vein catheterized; renal blood flow measured by Fick method, using PAH; assumed that 300 g renal tissue = 1.73 m^2 of surface area	11
20	Dog	11	11	....	17.72	3.18	344	11.05	Unanesthetized; renal blood flow measured by cannula in inferior vena cava, with two balloons above & below renal vein	30
21		15	8	....	....	....	398	8.05	Unanesthetized; one kidney explanted for sampling renal venous blood; renal blood flow measured by Fick method, using urea	43
22		9	8	143	19.3	1.8	667	11.4	Nembutal anesthesia; renal blood flow measured by Fick method, using PAH	15
23		37	8	....	....	2.35	546	11.6	Nembutal anesthesia; renal blood flow measured by Fick method, using PAH	29
24		10	9	120	....	1.44	535	7.5	Morphine-inactin anesthesia; exposed kidney, with rotameter in renal vein	25
25		21	13	127	....	....	533	8.9	Morphine-inactin anesthesia; exposed kidney, with rotameter in renal vein	14
26		14	14	133	....	....	603	8.6		
27		19	19	115	....	2.04	294	5.7	Chloralose & numal or Nembutal anesthesia; 30-50% O_2 inhaled; renal blood flow measured with bubble flowmeter in renal vein	19

1/ Value for 2 kidneys.

continued

69. OXYGEN UPTAKE OF ORGANS IN SITU: MAMMALS

Part II. Other Organs

	Animal	No. of Observations	No. of Subjects	Arterial: Pressure mm Hg	Arterial: O_2 Content vol %	A-V O_2 Difference vol %	Organ: Blood Flow ml/min·100 g	Organ: O_2 Uptake ml/min·100 g	Experimental Conditions	Reference
	Skeletal Muscle									
28	Man	6	1	....	....	....	....	0.17	Resting, 11,000 g muscle mass; O_2 uptake of lower extremities determined by measuring O_2 uptake before and after excluding extremities by cuffs	1
29		9	1	....	....	....	....	11.2	Exercise, 1080 kg work/min	
30	Cat	....	....	....	....	....	6.0	0.3	Resting limb at body temp; Nembutal anesthesia; isolated hindlimb perfused by animal; venous outflow measured by modified Gaddum recorder; O_2 uptake measured by Fick method	27
31		13	12	....	....	....	10.0	0.45	Resting muscle, 20 g muscle mass; chloroform-ether mixture & urethan; gastrocnemius outflow measured directly; sciatic nerve cut; O_2 uptake measured by Fick method	44
32		7	7	....	....	....	26.0	2.2	Stimulated once/sec; isometric force, 1.38 kg; chloralose anesthesia supplemented with urethan; gastrocnemius-soleus perfused by animal; arterial blood flow recorded photoelectrically; O_2 uptake measured by Fick method	45
33	Dog	20	20	>90	....	....	13.3	0.72	Resting muscle; pentobarbital anesthesia; gastrocnemius-plantaris venous outflow recorded with Gaddum-type flowmeter; O_2 uptake measured by Fick method	17
34		39	39	....	....	....	11.0	0.6	Resting muscle; Anesthetized with Nembutal or Dial-urethan; gastrocnemius-plantaris venous outflow measured with rotameter; O_2 uptake by Fick method	42
35		....	....	....	....	....	....	4.8	Sciatic nerve stimulated once/sec	
36		8	8	....	....	....	29.0	1.3	Resting muscle; Anesthetized with Pernocton-morphine; gastrocnemius venous outflow recorded with Rein's thermostromuhr; O_2 uptake by Fick method	34
37		6	6	....	....	....	91.0	12.5	Sciatic nerve stimulated 10 times/sec	
38		8	4	....	....	....	28.7	0.21	Resting muscles; Anesthetized with Nembutal or chloralose; femoral arterial blood flow recorded with rotameter after ligating other arteries to hindlimb; leg skinned and paw excluded; O_2 uptake by Fick method	12
39		8	4	....	....	....	44.4	1.29	Thigh muscles strongly stimulated 60-120 times/min	
40		12	5	....	....	....	9.3	0.59	Resting muscles, 89.6 g muscle mass; decerebrated; gastrocnemius & flexor digitorum sublimus perfused by animal; venous outflow measured by calibrated tube; O_2 uptake measured by Fick method	21

continued

69. OXYGEN UPTAKE OF ORGANS IN SITU: MAMMALS

Part II. Other Organs

	Animal	No. of Observations	No. of Subjects	Arterial: Pressure mm Hg	Arterial: O_2 Content vol %	Organ: A-V O_2 Difference vol %	Organ: Blood Flow ml/min·100 g	Organ: O_2 Uptake ml/min·100 g	Experimental Conditions	Reference
	Liver & Organs Drained by Portal Vein									
41	Cat	5	5	....	....	....	24.3[2]; 15.1[3]	3.5[4]; 1.5[5]	Subjects fasting for 18 hr; chloroform-ether mixture & urethan anesthesia; portal vein blood flow measured by cannulation; hepatic venous blood flow by direct measurement; O_2 uptake measured by Fick method	3
42	Dog	6	4	....	16.3[6]	....	15.4[2]; 70.4[3]	4.23[4]	Unanesthetized fasting subjects; direct measurement of hepatic venous blood flow with special cannula having balloons; same after occlusion of hepatic arteries; O_2 uptake measured by Fick method	7
43	17-29 kg	9	9	....	18.07[7]	....	175[2,8]; 309[3,8]	24.15[4,8]; 19[5,8]	Nembutal anesthesia; hepatic arterial & portal vein blood flow measured by bristle flowmeters; O_2 uptake measured by Fick method	40
	Intestine									
44	Dog	11	5	112	16.9	4.9	23.4	1.18	Pentobarbital anesthesia; segment of intestine isolated, denervated, and venous outflow measured with graduated cylinder; O_2 uptake measured by Fick method	22
	Uterus									
45	Man	4	4	81	....	....	9.7	0.98	24-48 hr postpartum; uterine vein cannulated or catheterized	2
	Mammary Gland									
46	Goat	Variable	13	....	....	3.7	28.0	1.31	Nonpregnant (46-49: Unanesthetized subjects; arterial inflow measured by dye-dilution curves or venous outflow by thermo-dilution; O_2 uptake by Fick method)	31
47				....	....	3.9	26.0	1.09	Pregnant	
48				....	....	4.6	31.5	1.42	Lactating, <50 ml/day per 100 g gland	
49				....	....	4.88	47.0	2.34	Lactating, >50 ml/day per 100 g gland	
50		3	3	....	....	....	14.4	0.51	Pregnant, 2-6 days before parturition; udder wt, 1.90 kg (50-51: Unanesthetized subjects; blood flow measured by N_2O method; O_2 uptake by Fick method)	37
51		13	7	....	....	....	26.0	1.15	Lactating, 4.2 ml/hr per 100 g gland; udder wt, 1.75 kg	
	Thyroid									
52	Dog	....	13	115	....	....	355	9.27	Gland wt, 1.79 g; morphine-urethan & chloroform anesthesia; venous outflow measured directly; O_2 uptake measured by Fick method	24

2/ Hepatic artery. 3/ Portal vein. 4/ Liver. 5/ Portal organs. 6/ Portal vein O_2 content, 10.7 vol %; hepatic vein O_2 content, 6.67 vol %. 7/ Portal vein O_2 content, 11.57 vol %; hepatic vein O_2 content, 9.16 vol %. 8/ ml/min.

continued

69. OXYGEN UPTAKE OF ORGANS IN SITU: MAMMALS

Part II. Other Organs

	Animal	No. of Observations	No. of Subjects	Arterial: Pressure mm Hg	Arterial: O_2 Content vol %	A-V O_2 Difference vol %	Organ: Blood Flow ml/min·100 g	Organ: O_2 Uptake ml/min·100 g	Experimental Conditions	Reference
						Adrenal				
53	Cat	11	9	130	....	....	600-700	4.5	Chloroform-ether mixture with urethan anesthesia; abdominal viscera removed; venous outflow measured with graduated pipette; O_2 uptake measured by Fick method	36
54	Rabbit	4	3	....	....	....	....	4.4	Chloroform-ether mixture with urethan anesthesia; abdominal viscera removed; venous outflow measured with graduated pipette; O_2 uptake measured by Fick method	36
						Carotid Body				
55	Cat	10	2	130	....	0.15[9]	2000	....	Gland wt, 2 mg; Nembutal anesthesia; superior cervical & nodose ganglia removed; blood flow measured by bubble method	13
56		6	2	83[10]	....	2.0	450	9.0		

[9] Within error of method. [10] Blood pressure reduced and held constant by compensatory bottle.

Contributor: Badeer, Henry S.

References

[1] Asmussen, E., et al. 1939. Skand. Arch. Physiol. 82: 212.

[2] Assali, N. S., et al. 1953. Am. J. Obstet. Gynecol. 66:248.

[3] Barcroft, J., and L. E. Shore. 1912-13. J. Physiol. (London) 45:296.

[4] Bering, E. A., Jr. 1961. Am. J. Physiol. 200:417.

[5] Bering, E. A., Jr., et al. 1956. Surg. Gynecol. Obstet. 102:134.

[6] Bernsmeier, A., and K. Siemons. 1953-54. Arch. Ges. Physiol. 258:149.

[7] Blalock, A., and M. F. Mason. 1936. Am. J. Physiol. 117:328.

[8] Bradley, S. E., and M. H. Halperin. 1948. J. Clin. Invest. 27:635.

[9] Cargill, W. H., and J. B. Hickam. 1949. Ibid. 28:526.

[10] Chute, A. L., and D. H. Smyth. 1939. Quart. J. Exptl. Physiol. 29:379.

[11] Clark, J. K., and H. G. Barker. 1951. J. Clin. Invest. 30:745.

[12] Coffman, J. D. 1963. Am. J. Physiol. 205:365.

[13] Daly, M. DeB., et al. 1954. J. Physiol. (London) 125:67.

[14] Deetjen, P., and K. Kramer. 1961. Arch. Ges. Physiol. 273:636.

[15] Dole, V. P., et al. 1946. Am. J. Physiol. 145:337.

[16] Edmunds, L. H., Jr., and J. Folkman. 1961. J. Surg. Res. 1:201.

[17] Fales, J. T., et al. 1962. Am. J. Physiol. 203:470.

[18] Geiger, A., and J. Magnes. 1947. Ibid. 149:517.

[19] Grupp, G., et al. 1958. Arch. Ges. Physiol. 267:401.

[20] Halley, M. M., K. Reemtsma, and O. Creech, Jr. 1958. J. Thoracic Surg. 36:506.

[21] Himwich, H. E., and W. B. Castle. 1927-28. Am. J. Physiol. 83:92.

[22] Johnson, P. C. 1960. Ibid. 199:311.

[23] Kety, S. S., and C. F. Schmidt. 1948. J. Clin. Invest. 27:476.

[24] Knowlton, F. P., et al. 1922. Am. J. Physiol. 59:466.

[25] Kramer, K., and P. Deetjen. 1960. Arch. Ges. Physiol. 271:782.

[26] Lambertsen, C. J., et al. 1953. J. Appl. Physiol. 5: 471.

[27] Landis, E. M., and J. R. Pappenheimer. 1963. In W. F. Hamilton and P. Dow, ed. Handbook of physiology. American Physiological Society, Washington, D.C. sect. 2, v. 2, p. 1022.

[28] Lassen, N. A., and O. Munck. 1955. Acta Physiol. Scand. 33:30.

[29] Lassen, N. A., et al. 1961. Ibid. 51:371.

[30] Levy, S. E., and A. Blalock. 1938. Am. J. Physiol. 122:609.

[31] Linzell, J. L. 1960. J. Physiol. (London) 153:492.

[32] Mangold, R., et al. 1955. J. Clin. Invest. 34:1092.

[33] McCall, M. L. 1953. Am. J. Obstet. Gynecol. 66: 1015.

[34] Mercker, H., et al. 1949. Arch. Ges. Physiol. 251:73.

[35] Munck, O., and N. A. Lassen. 1957. Circulation Res. 5:163.

[36] Neuman, K. O. 1912-13. J. Physiol. (London) 45: 188.

[37] Reynolds, M. 1967. Am. J. Physiol. 212:707.

continued

69. OXYGEN UPTAKE OF ORGANS IN SITU: MAMMALS

Part II. Other Organs

[38] Rosomoff, H. L., and D. A. Holaday. 1954. Ibid. 179:85.

[39] Scheinberg, P., and E. A. Stead, Jr. 1949. J. Clin. Invest. 28:1163.

[40] Selkurt, E. E., and G. A. Brecher. 1956. Circulation Res. 4:693.

[41] Sokoloff, L., et al. 1957-58. Ann. N.Y. Acad. Sci. 66:468.

[42] Stainsby, W. N., and A. B. Otis. 1964. Am. J. Physiol. 206:858.

[43] Van Slyke, D. D., et al. 1934. Ibid. 109:336.

[44] Verzar, F. 1912. J. Physiol. (London) 44:243.

[45] Wright, D. L., and R. R. Sonnenschein. 1965. Am. J. Physiol. 208:782.

70. OXYGEN CONSUMPTION: ANIMAL TISSUES

Medium: K-R-P = Krebs-Ringer phosphate. Q_{O_2} (oxidation quotient): Values are mm^3 oxygen consumed per mg dry weight of tissue per hour, unless otherwise indicated. Fresh tissue was immersed in a buffered medium (phosphate or bicarbonate) in a closed chamber containing oxygen at 1 atmosphere pressure and usually maintained at 37°C (some determinations at 37.5° and 38°C). The decrease in amount of gaseous oxygen was measured as it was used by the tissue. As the rate of oxidation is limited by the amount of oxidizable nutrient available to the tissue, glucose or other nutrient was added when necessary to the medium. Values in parentheses are ranges, estimate "c" (*see* Introduction).

	Animal	Tissue	Medium	Q_{O_2}	Reference
		Hematopoietic & Associated Tissue			
1	Man	Aorta	Krebs phosphate	0.26	86
2				0.44 ± 0.24	101
3			Krebs phosphate, glucose	0.10	87
4		Erythrocytes	Ringer glucose	0.045	142
5		Leukocytes	Heparinized plasma	6.9	64
6			Serum	2.6	16
7			Serum, glucose	0.092[1]	115
8		Lymph nodes	Ringer glucose	(3.8-5.9)	152,192,201
9		Thrombocytes	Citrated plasma glucose	(6.2-8.4)	48,59,64
10			Hanks' solution, glucose	14.5 ± 4.8[2]	79
11			Hanks' solution, glycerol	21.4 ± 5.0[2]	79
12		Tonsil	Ringer glucose	5.1	201
13	Dog	Thrombocytes	Citrated plasma glucose	5.1	48
14	Guinea pig	Leukocytes	K-R-P	4.1	81
15			K-R-P, glucose	2.5	81
16		Phagocytosis	K-R-P, glucose	11.2	81
17		Spleen	Saline	8.3	42
18	Horse	Erythrocytes	Ringer glucose	0.06	84
19	Rabbit	Aortic arch: intima	K-R-P	8.83[3]	198
20		remainder	K-R-P	7.25[3]	198
21		Thoracic aorta: intima	K-R-P	7.93[3]	198
22		remainder	K-R-P	3.35[3]	198
		Abdominal aorta			
23		Intima	K-R-P	8.82[3]	198
24		Remainder	K-R-P	4.66[3]	198
25		Bone marrow	Ringer bicarbonate, glucose, pH 6.4	2.8[4]	17
26			pH 7.2	3.7[4]	17
27			pH 7.6	2.6[4]	17
28		Erythroid cells	Serum	ca. 9	193
29		Myeloid cells	Serum	ca. 6	193
30		Erythrocytes	Saline	0.008	115
31			Serum	0.10	125
32		Leukocytes: exudate	Citrated Ringer's solution	(4.0-4.6)	54,109
33			Serum	7.0	109
34		Reticulocytes	Ringer glucose	0.25	142,143
35			Serum	1.75	203

[1] $\mu M\ O_2$/10 million leukocytes/hr. [2] $m\mu M\ O_2/10^9$ platelets/min. [3] $\mu M\ O_2$/g wet wt/hr. [4] mm^3 O_2/mg cell protein/hr.

continued

70. OXYGEN CONSUMPTION: ANIMAL TISSUES

	Animal	Tissue	Medium	Q_{O_2}	Reference
36	Rat	Aorta	Krebs-Ringer solution, glucose	1.03	89
37		Thoracic aorta	Modified K-R-P	29 ± 0.7[5/]	139
38		Bone marrow	Neutralized serum	7.4[6/]	13
39		All cells	Normal serum	42.0[6/]	93
40		Nucleated cells	Normal serum	71.5[6/]	93
41		Erythrocytes	Ringer glucose	0.038	6
42			Saline, phosphate	0.045 ± 0.006	178
43		Leukocytes	Serum	(9.0-9.2)	58,59
44		Lymph nodes	Ringer glucose	4.4	8
45			K-R-P	0.87[7/]	7
46		Spleen	Ringer glucose	(7.2-12.9)	6,37,38,123, 196
47			Serum	12.5	58
48			K-R-P	1.42[7/]	7
49			Ringer phosphate, glucose	6.3	140
50		Thrombocytes	Serum	6.0	58
51		Thymus	Ringer glucose	(5.5-5.8)	8,192
52			Krebs-Ringer glucose	1.09[7/]	7
53			Ringer phosphate, glucose	8.8	140
54	100 g	Thymus	Ca-free K-R-P, glucose	0.76[7/]	18
55	400 g	Thymus	Ca-free K-R-P, glucose	0.40[7/]	18
56	Diestrus	Aorta	K-R-P	2.2 ± 0.1	110
57	Proestrus	Aorta	K-R-P	1.0 ± 0.1	110
58	Estrus	Aorta	K-R-P	0.9 ± 0.08	110
59	Metestrus	Aorta	K-R-P	1.3 ± 0.1	110
	Chick embryo				
60	3 days	Erythrocytes	Ringer phosphate, glucose	0.47[8/]	129
61	6 days	Erythrocytes	Ringer phosphate, glucose	0.14[8/]	129
62	9 days	Erythrocytes	Ringer phosphate, glucose	0.044[8/]	129
63	Chicken	Erythrocytes	Saline, Ringer glucose	0.14	50,142,143
64			Serum	(0.58-1.79)	158
65			K-R-P	0.17	153
66	Goose	Leukocytes	Citrated plasma glucose	4.4	54
67	Turtle	Erythrocytes	Saline	0.05	142,143
68	Bullfrog	Erythrocytes	Saline, phosphate	0.102 ± 0.004	113
	Epithelial & Associated Tissue				
69	Man	Gastric mucosa	Ringer glucose	9.6	152
70		Gingiva	Ringer phosphate	(1.26-1.90)	63,111,112, 159,162, 187
71		Rectum	Krebs-Ringer solution	3.3 ± 0.54	108
72		Sigmoid colon	Krebs-Ringer solution	3.6 ± 1.27	108
73		Stomach	Krebs-Ringer solution	3.1 ± 0.37	108
74		Ear epidermis	Ringer glucose	(0.52-2.11)	131
75		Synovial membrane	K-R-P	4.2[6/]	179
76	Fetus	Skin	Ringer phosphate	1.8	9
77	0-20 yr	Gingiva	K-R-P	(1.64-0.16)	186
78	21-40 yr	Gingiva	K-R-P	1.39 ± 0.14	186
79	41-60 yr	Gingiva	K-R-P	1.26 ± 0.12	186
80	Adult	Skin	Ringer glucose	2.1(0.5-2.8)	52
81	Cattle	Ear	K-R-P	2.5	62
82	Guinea pig	Skin	Ringer glucose	3.0	201
83		Ear	Serum, K-R-P, glucose, streptomycin	1.05	34
84		Epidermis	Serum, K-R-P, glucose, streptomycin	5.29	35
85		Dermis	Serum, K-R-P, glucose, streptomycin	2.21	35
86	Hamster	Cheek pouch mucosa	....	3.29	3
87		Epithelium	....	6.67	3
88		Subepithelial tissue	....	2.95	3

[5/] μl O_2/100 mg wet wt/hr. [6/] mm^3 O_2/mg N/hr. [7/] mm^3 O_2/mg wet wt/hr. [8/] mm^3 O_2/million cells/hr.

continued

70. OXYGEN CONSUMPTION: ANIMAL TISSUES

	Animal	Tissue	Medium	Q_{O_2}	Reference
89		Duodenum	Phosphate saline	22.7	200
90		Upper jejunum	Phosphate saline	14.3	200
91	Mouse	Skin, back	Tyrode's solution	1.24 ± 0.05	53
92		epidermis	Tyrode's solution	2.13 ± 0.29	53
93		dermis	Tyrode's solution	1.33 ± 0.31	53
94		ear	Tyrode's solution	2.28 ± 0.14	53
95		epidermis	Tyrode's solution	4.98 ± 0.38	53
96			Serum, K-R-P, glucose, streptomycin	2.95	35
97		dermis	Tyrode's solution	2.86 ± 0.40	53
98			Serum, K-R-P, glucose, streptomycin	1.40	35
99	Newborn	Skin	Ringer glucose	6.1	107
100	Adult	Skin	K-R-P	(1.24-2.47)[9]	40
101	Rabbit	Cartilage, costal	K-R-P	0.41	100
102		Cornea	No suspending medium	0.864	94
103		Epithelium	No suspending medium	6.25	94
104		Stroma	No suspending medium	0.231	94
105		Dermis	Krebs phosphate	0.27 ± 0.2	157
106		Mucosa, colonic	Ringer glucose, serum	11.1	152
107		uterine	Serum	6.1	11
	Rat	Adipose tissue			
108		Brown fat	Ringer phosphate	0.419[7]	21
109		White fat	Ringer phosphate	0.049[7]	21
110		Retroperitoneal fat body	Ringer phosphate	7.9[3]	71
		Connective tissue cells			
111		Heart	Krebs phosphate	0.85[10]	70
112		Peritoneum: macrophages	Ringer phosphate	0.053 ± 0.0021[10]	29
113			Ringer phosphate, glucose	0.047 ± 0.0030[10]	29
114			Ringer phosphate, succinate	0.050 ± 0.0022[10]	29
115		Lens	....	(0.63-0.85)[11]	168
116		Duodenum	Phosphate saline	23.0	200
117			K-R-P, glucose	3.6	151
118		Upper jejunum	Phosphate saline	21.5	200
119		Lower ileum	Phosphate saline	13.5	200
120		Mucosa, gastric	Ringer glucose	7.2	6
121		intestinal	Ringer glucose	(9.4-23.3)	192,196
122		duodenal	Ringer glucose	8.8	39
123		jejunal	Ringer glucose	15.6	39
124		ileal	Ringer glucose	5.3	39
125		colonic	Ringer glucose	(3.4-14.6)	39,152
126		Ear, epidermis	Serum, K-R-P, glucose, streptomycin	3.69	35
127		dermis	Serum, K-R-P, glucose, streptomycin	0.90	35
128	Newborn	Skin	Ringer glucose	3.5	107
129	10-36 days	Skin	Ringer glucose	(3.6-4.9)	2
130	79 days	Skin	Ringer glucose	(1.8-2.0)	1,2
131	12 wk	Skin	K-R-P	0.28	133
132	65 wk	Skin	K-R-P	0.09	133
133	Frog	Gastric mucosa	Modified Krebs' solution	3.11	186
134		Skin	Ringer phosphate, 24.8°C	0.96	4
			Glandular Tissue		
135	Man	Kidney cortex	Krebs' solution, phosphate	4.65 ± 3.0	101
136		Salivary gland	Ringer glucose	6.2	152
137		Liver	Krebs phosphate	6.35 ± 2.9	101
138	Cat	Pancreas	Ringer glucose	6.0	36
139	Cattle, ♂	Thyroid	Ringer phosphate	3.5	197
140	♀	Thyroid	Ringer phosphate	3.8	197
141		Liver	Ringer glucose	2.6	88

[3] μM O_2/g wet wt/hr. [7] mm^3 O_2/mg wet wt/hr. [9] Varies with phase of hair cycle. [10] μM O_2/million cells/hr. [11] μl O_2/whole lens/hr.

continued

70. OXYGEN CONSUMPTION: ANIMAL TISSUES

	Animal	Tissue	Medium	Q_{O_2}	Reference
142	calf	Thryoid	Ringer glucose	2.6	5
143			Ringer phosphate	2.8	197
144	steer	Thyroid	Ringer phosphate	3.1	197
145	beef	Adrenals: cortex	Potassium phosphate, KCl, $MgCl_2$, adenylic acid	1.1	170
146		medulla	Potassium phosphate, KCl, $MgCl_2$, adenylic acid	0.6	170
147	Dog	Pancreas	Ringer phosphate	3.2	192
148		Thyroid	Ringer glucose	2.0	5
149			Serum	9.1	174
150		Liver	Ringer glucose	6.0	90
151	Guinea pig	Adrenals: cortex	K-R-P, glucose	3.4	163,164
152			Potassium phosphate, KCl, $MgCl_2$, adenylic acid, citrate	6.0	170
153		medulla	Serum	6.0	58
154			Potassium phosphate, KCl, $MgCl_2$, adenylic acid, citrate	0.8	170
155		Pancreas	Saline	2.9	42
156		Salivary gland	Saline	5.0	42
157		Liver	Saline	8.1	42
158			Ringer's solution	5.0	116
159		Fatty	Ringer's solution	7.4	116
160	8 wk	Kidney	K-R-P, glucose homogenates	4.06	141
161		Liver	K-R-P	1.14	141
162	50-52 wk	Kidney	K-R-P, glucose homogenates	1.42	141
163		Liver	K-R-P	1.11	141
164	100 wk	Kidney	K-R-P, glucose homogenates	1.15	141
165		Liver	K-R-P	0.97	141
166	Horse	Liver	Ringer glucose	2.1	88
167	Mouse	Adrenals	Serum	6.0	58
168		Kidney	K-R-P	10.1(8.4-11.1)	165
169		Pituitary	Serum	8.0	58
170		Liver	Ringer's solution	(8.8-13.8)	31,99
171			Ringer phosphate	3	104
172			K-R-P	5.44	105
173	Rabbit	Kidney cortex	Robinson's medium	11.1 ± 0.3	199
174		Slices	Special medium	6.1 ± 0.5	25
175		Suspension of tubules	Special medium	8.0 ± 0.6	25
176		Pancreas	Ringer glucose	4.6	192
177		Thyroid	Ringer glucose, serum	11.7	152
178		Liver	Ringer glucose	(4.2-7.7)	41,88
179	Rat	Adrenals	Serum	10.0	58
180			Potassium phosphate, KCl, $MgCl_2$, potassium adenylate	1.1	169
181		Kidney	Ringer phosphate	16.3	134
182			K-R-P	3.72 [7]	7
183			Modified K-R-P	234 ± 11.0 [5]	139
184			K-R-P, dextrose	1.90 ± 0.07	106
185		Cortex	Ringer phosphate, glucose	22.2	140
186			K-R-P, glucose	11.61	154
187		Medulla	Ringer phosphate, glucose	19.9	140
188		Pancreas	Ringer glucose	5.2	8
189			Saline	3.7	42
190			K-R-P	1.04 [7]	7
191		Pituitary: anterior lobe	Ringer glucose	5.9	148
192			K-R-P	5.43	147
193		posterior lobe	Ringer glucose	6.6	148
194			K-R-P	5.42	147

[5] μl O_2/100 mg wet wt/hr. [7] mm^3 O_2/mg wet wt/hr.

continued

	Animal	Tissue	Medium	Q_{O_2}	Reference
195		Salivary gland	Ringer glucose	(9.7-24.2)	8,152
196			K-R-P	2.31 [7]	7
197		Thyroid	Ringer glucose	(12.5-13.0)	192
198		Liver	Ringer's solution	(7.0-10.2)	37,117,119
199			Ringer glucose	(6.5-11.6)	31,38,47,66, 88,117-119, 152,192
200			K-R-P	6.5	43
201			Modified K-R-P	159 ± 11.8 [5]	139
202			K-R-P, glucose	(4.12-7.99)	75,154
203			K-R-P, dextrose	0.98 ± 0.01	106
204			K-R-P, glucose	1.34	85
205		Regenerating	Ringer phosphate, glucose	10.0	140
206	Fetus	Liver	Serum, Ringer glucose	7.1	152
207	3-21 days	Liver	Ringer glucose	13.2	72
208	10 g	Liver	K-R-P	11.0	188
209	300 g	Liver	K-R-P	8.0	188
210	Young	Pituitary	Serum	12.0	58
211	Castrate	Liver	K-R-P	5.2	43
212	At room temp	Liver	Locke's solution	11.32	28
213	Cold-adapted	Liver	Locke's solution	19.25	28
214	Sheep	Liver	Ringer glucose	2.5	88
215	Swine	Thyroid	Ringer glucose	2.1	5
	Chick embryo				
216	6 days	Liver	Ringer glucose	7.5	26
217	12 days	Liver	Ringer glucose	4.5	26
218	20 days	Liver	Ringer glucose	1.5	26
219	Chicken, ♀	Liver	Serum	14.5	177
220	Pigeon	Pancreas	Saline	8.7	42
221			Ringer phosphate, glucose	4.8	140
222	Arctic cod	Liver	Ringer phosphate, 25°C	0.859 [7]	136
223	Golden orfe	Liver	Ringer phosphate, 25°C	0.792 [7]	136
224	Menhaden	Liver	Phosphate buffer, 30°C	11.08 [12]	183
225	Scup	Liver	Phosphate buffer, 30°C	14.87 [12]	183
226	Toadfish	Liver	Phosphate buffer, 30°C	4.42 [12]	183
			Lung		
227	Man, embryo	Lung	Ringer glucose	3.7	90
228	adult	Lung	K-R-P, glucose	2.05 ± 0.208; 2.10 ± 0.283	173
229	Cat	Lung	Ringer glucose	3.9	167
230	Guinea pig	Lung	Ringer glucose	6.1	167
231			Saline	7.4	42
232	Mouse	Lung	Ringer glucose	7.1	122
233	Rabbit	Lung	Ringer glucose	6.7	167
234	Rat, embryo	Lung	Serum	10.0	58
235	10 g	Lung	K-R-P	9.0	188
236	400 g	Lung	K-R-P	6.0	188
237	adult	Lung	Ringer glucose	(4.4-7.8)	98,167
238			Saline	7.9	42
239	Pigeon	Lung	Ringer glucose	3.6	167
			Muscle		
240	Man	Heart	Krebs phosphate	10.42 ± 5.9	101
241			Krebs-Henseleit saline	2.5	24
242		Atrium	Krebs-Ringer solution, glucose	2.6	33
243			Krebs-Ringer solution, succinate	8.2	33
244		Skeletal muscle	Modified Hollinger technique	0.24 [13]	120

[5] µl O_2/100 mg wet wt/hr. [7] mm^3 O_2/mg wet wt/hr. [12] µl O_2/g wet wt/min. [13] ml O_2/100 ml/min.

continued

	Animal	Tissue	Medium	Q_{O_2}	Reference
245		Smooth muscle: stomach	Ringer glucose	1.3	152
246		uterus	Ringer glucose	0.6	152
247	Cat	Heart	Ringer glucose	0.68[14]	166
248			Ringer phosphate	1.30[14]	145
249			K-R-P	3.31 ± 0.53	12
250			K-R-P, fructose	3.20 ± 0.28	12
251			K-R-P, glucose	3.47 ± 0.53	12
252		Skeletal muscle: papilla	Locke's solution, glucose	3.60	102
253		Smooth muscle: intestine	Ringer glucose	1.4	166
254	Cattle, beef	Heart: atrium	Wollenberger's medium	1.46[14]	124
255		ventricle	Wollenberger's medium	1.48[14]	124
256	Dog	Heart	Ringer glucose	0.94[14]	166
257	Young	Heart	Ringer glucose	4.2	5
258		Skeletal muscle: diaphragm	Ringer glucose	1.9	5
259	Guinea pig	Smooth muscle: seminal vesicles	Ringer glucose	1.7	103
260	Castrate	Smooth muscle: seminal vesicles	Ringer glucose	1.4	103
261	Mouse	Heart	Ringer phosphate	(2-2.5)	104
262	Rabbit	Skeletal muscle: diaphragm	Ringer glucose	2.4	5
263		Smooth muscle: intestine	Ringer glucose	2.6	152
264	Rat	Heart	Ringer glucose	(3.8-10.4)	6,51
265			Krebs-Henseleit phosphate	2.25 ± 0.08	175
266			K-R-P	2.7	134
267			K-R-P, dextrose	0.61 ± 0.04	106
268		Atrium	Ringer phosphate, glucose	8.8	182
269		Ventricle	Ringer phosphate, glucose	9.5	182
270		Skeletal muscle	Ringer glucose	(2.3-3.1)	6,51
271		Diaphragm	Serum	5.9	176
272			Ringer-Locke solution	0.97[14]	20
273			Ringer phosphate	3.4	134
274			K-R-P	6.3	43
275			Modified K-R-P, glucose	9.99 ± 0.94	49
276			Saline, Ringer's solution	(4.1-5.9)	6,42,61,118, 176
277		Levator ani	K-R-P	3.50	43
278		Smooth muscle: stomach	Ringer glucose	3.5	6
279		intestine	Ringer glucose	6.3	39
280			Saline	7.1	42
281		jejunum	Ringer-Locke's solution	1.26[14]	20
282	10 g	Heart	K-R-P	12.0	188
283	100 g	Skeletal muscle: diaphragm	K-R-P	15.0	188
284	300 g	Skeletal muscle: diaphragm	K-R-P	4.4	188
285	400 g	Heart	K-R-P	6.9	188
286	Diestrus	Skeletal muscle: diaphragm	K-R-P	3.2 ± 0.2	111
287	Proestrus	Skeletal muscle: diaphragm	K-R-P	3.1 ± 0.4	111
288	Estrus	Skeletal muscle: diaphragm	K-R-P	3.4 ± 0.3	111
289	Metestrus	Skeletal muscle: diaphragm	K-R-P	3.1 ± 0.2	111
290	Castrate	Skeletal muscle: diaphragm	K-R-P	5.9	43
291	Chicken	Heart	Saline, phosphate	6.0 ± 0.3	127
292	Pigeon	Skeletal muscle	Saline	2.1	42
293	Frog	Skeletal muscle, resting	Ringer glucose	(0.18-0.24)	60,117,118, 128,156
294		electrical stimulation	Ringer's solution	(0.79-4.24)	60,128
295		Smooth muscle: intestine	Ringer glucose	0.28	117
296	Menhaden	Skeletal muscle	Phosphate buffer, 30°C	1.024[12]	183

[12] μl O_2/g wet wt/min. [14] μl O_2/mg wet wt/hr.

continued

	Animal	Tissue	Medium	Q_{O_2}	Reference
297	Scup	Skeletal muscle	Phosphate buffer, 30°C	0.41[12]	183
298	Toadfish	Skeletal muscle	Phosphate buffer, 30°C	0.727[12]	183
			Nervous Tissue		
299	Man	Brain	....	3.3[15]	195
300		Cerebral cortex	Ringer's solution	1.09[14]	44
301			Ringer glucose	(6.0-10.3)	45
302	Cat	Brain	K-R-P, dextrose	0.86 ± 0.05	106
303		Cerebral cortex	Ringer glucose	(8.5-12.2)	32,45
304		Medulla	Ringer glucose	3.5	32
305		Spinal cord	Ringer glucose	1.3	32
306	1 wk	Spinal cord	Phosphate saline, glucose	3.24[16]	73,74
307	3 wk	Spinal cord	Phosphate saline, glucose	3.72[16]	73,74
308	Adult	Spinal cord	Phosphate saline, glucose	2.00[16]	73,74
309	Cattle	Retina	Ringer phosphate, glucose	10.2	140
310	Ox		Ringer glucose	10.7	67
311	Dog	Brain	K-R-P, dextrose	0.70 ± 0.19	106
312		Cerebral cortex	Ringer glucose	6.7	74
313		Retina	Ringer glucose	20.8	161
314		Tooth germ: enamel pulp	K-R-P	2.63 ± 0.76	155
315		dental papilla	K-R-P	3.56 ± 1.07	155
316	1 wk	Cerebral cortex	Phosphate saline, glucose	2.44[16]	73,74
317		Cerebellum	Phosphate saline, glucose	3.16[16]	73,74
318		Medulla	Phosphate saline, glucose	3.84[16]	73,74
319		Thalamus	Phosphate saline, glucose	3.04[16]	73,74
320	5-7 wk	Cerebral cortex	Phosphate saline, glucose	4.84[16]	73,74
321		Cerebellum	Phosphate saline, glucose	3.80[16]	73,74
322		Medulla	Phosphate saline, glucose	3.40[16]	73,74
323		Thalamus	Phosphate saline, glucose	4.94[16]	73,74
324	Adult	Cerebellum	Phosphate saline, glucose	4.28[16]	73,74
325		Medulla	Phosphate saline, glucose	2.76[16]	73,74
326		Thalamus	Phosphate saline, glucose	4.04[16]	73,74
327	Guinea pig	Brain	K-R-P, dextrose	0.97 ± 0.15	106
328		Cerebral cortex	Medium not defined	60 ± 1.9[3]	160
329			Phosphate buffer	53[3]	193,194
330			Saline	6.9	196
331			Saline glucose	11.7	42
332			Saline phosphate, glucose	530[17]	114
333			Saline, glucose, phosphate	620[17]	114
334	Monkey	Cerebral cortex	Ringer glucose	(7.4-11.8)	45
335	Mouse	Brain	K-R-P, dextrose	1.79 ± 0.09	106
336		Cerebral cortex	Ringer's solution	11.0	130
337	Rabbit	Brain	K-R-P, dextrose	0.74 ± 0.02	106
338		Cerebral cortex	Phosphate buffer	24.0[3]	193,194
339			Ringer glucose	(7.3-10.4)	37,41,92
340		Retina	Ringer phosphate, glucose	10.9	80
341	Alloxan diabetes	Retina	Ringer phosphate	8.7	80
342	Rat	Brain	Ringer phosphate	5.4	65
343			K-R-P	1.30[14]	7
344			K-R-P, glucose, 37°C	25.03[15]	82
345			42°C	32.44[15]	82
346			K-R-P, dextrose	1.37 ± 0.11	106
347		Cerebral cortex	K-R-P	10.40	137
348			K-R-P, glucose	8.57	75
349			Saline, glucose, phosphate	570[17]	114
350			Ringer phosphate, glucose	(10.5-12.7)	10,22
351			Ringer phosphate, glucose, 0.1 *M* KCl	(19.8-22.3)	10,22
352			Ca-free Ringer phosphate, glucose	15.0	22

[3] μM O_2/g wet wt/hr. [12] μl O_2/g wet wt/min. [14] μl O_2/mg wet wt/hr. [15] μl O_2/100 g/min. [16] Per mg dry weight value; obtained by multiplying author's data for fresh weight by 4, since nerve tissue contains approximately 75% water. [17] μl molecular O_2/g dry wt/hr.

continued

70. OXYGEN CONSUMPTION: ANIMAL TISSUES

	Animal	Tissue	Medium	Q_{O_2}	Reference
353		Hypothalamus	Ringer glucose	10.4	148
354		Anterior	K-R-P	7.53	147
355		Posterior	K-R-P	7.92	147
356		Spinal cord	Ringer phosphate, glucose	6.6	77
357		Retina	Ringer glucose	(22.0-32)	37,46,99, 126,146,192
358	5 days	Cerebral cortex	Ringer glucose	6.2	27
359		Medulla	Ringer glucose	3.4	27
360	30 days, castrate	Brain	Ringer phosphate	7.3	65
361	50 days	Cerebral cortex	Ringer glucose	14.7	27
362		Medulla	Ringer glucose	9.0	27
363	Adult	Cerebral cortex	Ringer glucose	(8.5-17.1)	27,37,38,45, 47,107, 117,192
364		Medulla	Ringer glucose	(2.5-4.9)	27,117
365	Sheep	Retina	Krebs-Ringer solution, glucose, pH 5	0.74	150
366			pH 6	3.67	150
367			pH 7	7.47	150
368	Swine	Retina	Ringer glucose	17.7	99
369	Fetus, 29-60 days	Cerebral cortex	Ringer's solution	5.5	55
370	99 days	Cerebral cortex	Ringer's solution	6.5	55
371	Birth to adult	Cerebral cortex	Ringer's solution	8.5	55
372	Chick embryo	Brain	Serum	25	191
373	Pigeon	Cerebral cortex	Saline glucose	14.6	42
374	Frog	Hippocampus	Ringer's solution	2.4	135
375		Spinal cord	Ringer glucose	2.3	107
376		Retina	Ringer glucose	3.5	126
377	Arctic cod	Brain, minced	Ringer phosphate, 25°C	1.65[14]	136
378	Flounder	Brain	Phosphate buffer, 30°C	6.96[12]	184
379	Golden orfe	Brain, minced	Ringer phosphate, 25°C	1.37[14]	136
380	Goldfish	Brain, brei	Phosphate, 27°C	11.9[14]	57
381	Menhaden	Brain	Phosphate buffer, 30°C	13.04[12]	183
382	Mullet	Brain	Phosphate buffer, 30°C	13.52[12]	184
383	Pinfish	Brain	Phosphate buffer, 30°C	9.30[12]	184
384	Scup	Brain	Phosphate buffer, 30°C	10.51[12]	183
385	Spot	Brain	Phosphate buffer, 30°C	7.78[12]	184
386	Toadfish	Brain	Phosphate buffer, 30°C	6.78[12]	183
			Reproductive Tissue		
387	Man	Uterus: endometrium	Saline, glucose	2.3[3]	69
388		Proliferative, early	Krebs-Ringer glucose	3.24	172
389		late	Krebs-Ringer glucose	4.40	172
390		Secretory, early	Krebs-Ringer glucose	3.87	172
391		late	Krebs-Ringer glucose	4.88	172
392	1-5 days	Uterus: endometrium	Potassium pyruvate, glucose	1.97	68
393	6-10 days	Uterus: endometrium	Potassium pyruvate, glucose	3.49	68
394	18 days	Uterus: endometrium	Potassium pyruvate, glucose	2.68	68
395	Menopausal	Uterus: endometrium	Potassium pyruvate, glucose	1.28	68
396	Cattle	Spermatozoa	Ringer phosphate	6.6	97
397			Horse serum	11.2	144
398			Horse serum, glucose	12.8	144
399			Whole serum	90	19
400		Epididymal	Ringer phosphate	2.6	95
401	Guinea pig	Seminal vesicles	Ringer's solution	4.6[18]	78
402			Ringer glucose	6.1	103
403		Spermatozoa	Serum	18.4	144
404			Ringer phosphate	8.0	144
405	Castrate	Seminal vesicles	Ringer glucose	2.8	103

[3] μM O_2/g wet wt/hr. [12] μl O_2/g wet wt/min. [14] μl O_2/mg wet wt/hr. [18] μl O_2/mg N_2/hr.

continued

	Animal	Tissue	Medium	Q_{O_2}	Reference
406	Mouse	Ovary	Serum	9.0	58
407	Rabbit	Spermatozoa, ejaculated	Ringer phosphate	4.4	96
408		Testis	Ringer glucose	7.7	41
409	Rat	Ovary	Ringer glucose	5.7	8
410			K-R-P	1.14[7]	7
411		Prostate	Ringer glucose	7.6	8
412			K-R-P	1.52[7]	7
413		Seminal vesicles	....	2.7	138
414			K-R-P	0.77[7]	7
415		Spermatozoa, ejaculated	Serum	7.7	58
416		Testis	Serum	11.0	58
417			Ringer glucose	(7.5-14.3)	6,37,38,42, 47,192,196
418			K-R-P	2.5	134
419		Uterus	....	5.1	149
420			K-R-P	0.73[7]	7
421	♂, 15-25 wk	Mammary gland	Ringer phosphate	3.4	180
422	>50 wk	Mammary gland	Ringer phosphate	1.9	180
423	♀	Mammary gland	Ringer phosphate, glucose	3.7	181
424	Virgin	Mammary gland	Ringer, bicarbonate, glucose	20.0[18]	76
425	15-25 wk	Mammary gland	Ringer phosphate	2.9	180
426	>50 wk	Mammary gland	Ringer phosphate	2.2	180
427	Breeder	Mammary gland	Ringer phosphate	4.0	180
428	Pregnancy	Mammary gland	Ringer phosphate, glucose	10.2	181
429	Termination	Mammary gland	Ringer glucose	1.3	56
430	Parturition	Mammary gland	Ringer's solution, bicarbonate, glucose	52[18]	76
431	Lactation	Mammary gland	Ringer phosphate, glucose	10.1	181
432	4th day	Mammary gland	Ringer's solution, bicarbonate, glucose	100.0[18]	76
433	15th-22nd day	Mammary gland	Ringer glucose	10.0	56
434	24th day	Mammary gland	Ringer's solution, bicarbonate, glucose	70.0[18]	76
	Weaning				
435	2 days after	Mammary gland	Ringer glucose	5.5	56
436	7 days after	Mammary gland	Ringer phosphate, glucose	5.1	181
437	Castrate	Mammary gland	Ringer phosphate, glucose	3.9	181
438		Uterus	Ringer glucose	5.3	149
439		Uterus	Ringer's solution	5.2	149
440	+ estrogen	Uterus	Ringer's solution	7.9	149
441	Sheep	Spermatozoa, ejaculated	Ringer phosphate	9.0	96
442	Chicken	Spermatozoa, ejaculated	Serum	2.8	96
			Placental Tissue		
443	Man	Decidua	Serum	2.5	11
444		Placenta, 7 wk	Salt solution, pyruvate, glucose	3.1	185
445		30 wk	Salt solution, pyruvate, glucose	2.2	185
446	Mouse	Placenta, 0.4 mg	Serum	7.5	58
447		10.9-13.7 mg	Serum	6.4	58
448	Rabbit	Placenta, fetal side	Serum	5.3	11
449		uterine side	Serum	3.4	11
450	Rat	Chorion	Ringer glucose	13.5	99
451		Placenta	Horse serum	3.9	11
452		20 days	Ringer's solution	7.3	123
453	Chicken	Allantois	Ringer glucose	22.3	99
454		Chorioallantois	Ringer glucose	10.4	23
455		Chorioallantois & yolk sac	Krebs saline phosphate	5.6	121
			Benign & Hyperplastic Tissue		
456	Man	Bladder papilloma	Ringer glucose	(8.5-13.0)	192
457		Colloid goiter, resting	Ringer glucose	(2.5-5.2)	152,189
458		hyperactive	Ringer glucose	12.3	189

[7] $mm^3\ O_2$/mg wet wt/hr. [18] $\mu l\ O_2$/mg N_2/hr.

continued

70. OXYGEN CONSUMPTION: ANIMAL TISSUES

	Animal	Tissue	Medium	Q_{O_2}	Reference
459		Hyperplastic tonsil	Ringer glucose	(6.6-14.7)	192
460		Nasal polyp	Ringer glucose	(4.2-5.9)	192
461		Skin wart	Ringer glucose	1.5	30
	Chicken, young	Heart fibroblasts[19]			
462		1 transfer	Serum glucose	22.5	191
463		3-8 transfers	Serum glucose	12.8	191
464		3000 transfers	Serum glucose	12.0	191
		Malignant Tissue			
	Man	Leukocytes, lymphatic leukemia			
465		Immature cells	Heparinized plasma	3.2[20]	64
466		Mature cells	Heparinized plasma	6.1[20]	64
467		Mixed cells	Heparinized plasma	2.6[20]	64
		Leukocytes, myelogenic leukemia			
468		Immature cells	Heparinized plasma	3.2[20]	64
469		Mature cells	Heparinized plasma	2.3[20]	64
470		Mixed cells	Heparinized plasma	2.2[20]	64
471		Various carcinomas	Ringer glucose	(2.0-7.9)	152,192
472	Mouse	Adenocarcinoma	Ringer glucose	(6.1-26)	123
473		Ascites cells (tumor)	K-R-P	324[21]	171
474		Ehrlich ascites carcinoma	Ringer phosphate	10.5	15
475		cells	Ringer phosphate	(11.8-14.0)	140
476			Ringer phosphate, glucose	(6.3-8.0)	14,140
477			Ringer phosphate, serum	16.2	15
478		Melanoma 591	Ringer phosphate, glucose	4.6	140
479		Sarcoma, A-274	K-R-P, glucose	4.58	16
480		Crocker	Ringer glucose	(9.7-14.8)	31,99
481		Various	Ringer glucose	(8.5-15.3)	31,99,152, 192
482	Rat	Flexner-Jobling sarcoma	Ringer's solution, Ringer glucose	(6.0-8.6)	107,119,123, 152,192
483		Jensen sarcoma, A-274	Ringer glucose	(9.2-14.4)	31,37,38, 132,196
484		Novikoff hepatoma	Ringer phosphate, glucose	7.0	140
485		Walker 256 carcinosarcoma	Ringer phosphate, glucose	5.4	140
486	Chicken	Rous sarcoma, A-274	Ringer glucose	(4.6-12.1)	30,38,190
487			Serum	6.0	91
488		Tumor, spontaneous	Ringer glucose	(7.3-8.8)	123
489	Unspecified	Earlis strain L cells	K-R-P, glucose	9.4	202
490		Ehrlich ascites cells, 5 X 10^7 cells/ml	K-R-P	8.1	83
491		Sarcoma 37 (solid)[22]	Ringer phosphate	9.8	140
492			Ringer phosphate, glucose	6.6	140

[19] In tissue culture. [20] μl O_2/mg wet wt. [21] μl O_2/ml/hr. [22] Grown in fertile chicken eggs.

Contributors: (a) Fitzgerald, Laurence R., (b) Quastel, J. H., (c) Vernberg, F. John, (d) Barker, S. B.

References

[1] Adams, P. D. 1936. J. Biol. Chem. 116:641.

[2] Adams, P. D. 1937. Arch. Dermatol. Syphilol. 36: 606.

[3] Araya, S., Y. Imagawa, and H. Shizuya. 1962. J. Dental Res. 41:732.

[4] Barch, S. H. 1953. Physiol. Zool. 26:223.

[5] Barker, S. B. Unpublished. Univ. Alabama Medical College, Birmingham, 1952.

[6] Barker, S. B., and H. M. Klitgaard. 1952. Am. J. Physiol. 170:81.

[7] Barker, S. B., and H. S. Schwartz. 1953. Proc. Soc. Exptl. Biol. Med. 83:500.

[8] Barker, S. B., and H. S. Schwartz. Unpublished. Univ. Alabama Medical College, Birmingham, 1952.

[9] Barron, E. S. G., J. Meyer, and Z. B. Miller. 1948. J. Invest. Dermatol. 11:97.

[10] Beer, C. T., and J. H. Quastel. 1958. Can. J. Biochem. Physiol. 36:531.

[11] Bell, W. B., J. Brooks, and M. Jowett. 1928. Cancer Res. 12:369.

continued

[12] Berg, W. von. 1962. Arch. Ges. Physiol. 274:480.
[13] Berwin, I., and A. S. Gordon. 1953. Am. J. Physiol. 173:184.
[14] Bickis, I. J., and J. H. Quastel. 1965. Nature 205:44.
[15] Bickis, I. J., J. H. Quastel, and S. I. Vas. 1959. Cancer Res. 19:602.
[16] Bird, R. M., J. A. Clements, and L. M. Becker. 1951. Cancer 4:1009.
[17] Bird, R. M., and J. D. Evans. 1949. J. Biol. Chem. 178:289.
[18] Birmingham, M. K., and M. Desbarats. 1952. Can. J. Med. Sci. 30:494.
[19] Bishop, M. W., and G. W. Salisbury. 1955. Am. J. Physiol. 180:107.
[20] Borrow, A., and J. R. Penney. 1951. Exptl. Cell. Res. 2:188.
[21] Breibart, S., and F. L. Engel. 1954. Endocrinology 55:70.
[22] Brossard, M., and J. H. Quastel. 1963. Can. J. Biochem. Physiol. 41:1243.
[23] Brown, B., and K. Odenheimer. 1953. Stanford Med. Bull. 11:218.
[24] Burdette, W. J. 1952. J. Lab. Clin. Med. 40:867.
[25] Burg, M. B., and J. Orloff. 1962. Am. J. Physiol. 203:327.
[26] Carroll, M. J. 1939. Arch. Exptl. Zellforsch. Gewebezucht. 22:592.
[27] Chester, A., and H. E. Himwich. 1944. Am. J. Physiol. 141:513.
[28] Clark, R. T., Jr., et al. 1954. Ibid. 177:207.
[29] Comolli, R. 1962. Nature 195:178.
[30] Crabtree, H. G. 1928. Biochem. J. 22:1289.
[31] Crabtree, H. G. 1929. Ibid. 23:536.
[32] Craig, F. N., and H. K. Beecher. 1943. J. Neurophysiol. 6:135.
[33] Crevasse, L., and M. W. Wheat, Jr. 1962. Circulation Res. 11:721.
[34] Cruickshank, C. N. D. 1954. Exptl. Cell Res. 7:374.
[35] Cruickshank, C. N. D., and J. R. Cooper. 1955. Ibid. 9:363.
[36] Deutsch, W., and H. S. Raper. 1936. J. Physiol. (London) 87:275.
[37] Dickens, F., and G. D. Greville. 1933. Biochem. J. 27:832.
[38] Dickens, F., and F. Simer. 1930. Ibid. 24:1301.
[39] Dickens, F., and H. Weil-Malherbe. 1941. Ibid. 35:7.
[40] Dushoff, I. M., et al. 1965. Am. J. Physiol. 209:231.
[41] Ebina, T. 1929. Tohoku J. Exptl. Med. 13:424.
[42] Edson, N. L., and L. F. Leloir. 1936. Biochem. J. 30:2319.
[43] Eisenberg, E., G. S. Gordan, and H. W. Elliott. 1949. Endocrinology 45:113.
[44] Elliott, H. W., and V. C. Sutherland. 1952. J. Cellular Comp. Physiol. 40:221.
[45] Elliott, K. A. C. 1948. J. Neurophysiol. 11:473.
[46] Elliott, K. A. C., and Z. Baker. 1935. Biochem. J. 29:2433.
[47] Elliott, K. A. C., M. E. Greig, and M. P. Benoy. 1937. Ibid. 31:1003.
[48] Endres, G., and F. Kubowitz. 1927. Biochem. Z. 191:395.
[49] Enerson, D. M., and H. M. Berman. 1966. Ann. Surg. 163:537.
[50] Engelhardt, W. A. 1932. Biochem. Z. 251:343.
[51] Field, J. 1948. Methods Med. Res. 1:289.
[52] Fitzgerald, L. R. 1957. Physiol. Rev. 37:325.
[53] Fitzgerald, L. R., and M. Klein. 1964. J. Invest. Dermatol. 42:209.
[54] Fleischmann, W., and F. Kubowitz. 1927. Biochem. Z. 181:395.
[55] Flexner, J. B., L. B. Flexner, and W. L. Strauss, Jr. 1941. J. Cellular Comp. Physiol. 18:355.
[56] Folley, S. J., and T. H. French. 1949. Biochem. J. 45:270.
[57] Freeman, J. A. 1950. Biol. Bull. 99:416.
[58] Fujita, A. 1928. Biochem. Z. 197:175.
[59] Fujita, A. 1928. Klin. Wochschr. 7:897.
[60] Gemmill, C. L. 1935. Am. J. Physiol. 112:294.
[61] Gemmill, C. L. 1941. Bull. Johns Hopkins Hosp. 68:329.
[62] Gilbert, D. 1962. J. Invest. Dermatol. 38:93.
[63] Glickman, I., S. Turesky, and R. Hill. 1949. J. Dental Res. 28:83.
[64] Glover, E. C., G. A. Daland, and H. L. Schmitz. 1930. Arch. Internal Med. 46:46.
[65] Gordan, G. S., R. C. Bentinck, and E. Eisenberg. 1951. Ann. N.Y. Acad. Sci. 54:575.
[66] Grassheim, K. 1926. Z. Klin. Med. 103:380.
[67] Greig, M. E., M. P. Munro, and K. A. C. Elliott. 1939. Biochem. J. 33:443.
[68] Hagerman, D. D., and C. A. Villee. 1953. Endocrinology 53:667.
[69] Hagerman, D. D., and C. A. Villee. 1953. J. Biol. Chem. 203:425.
[70] Harris, H. 1956. Brit. J. Exptl. Pathol. 37:512.
[71] Haugaard, N., and J. B. Marsh. 1952. J. Biol. Chem. 194:33.
[72] Hawkins, J. A. 1928. J. Gen. Physiol. 11:645.
[73] Himwich, H. E. 1951. Brain metabolism and cerebral disorders. Williams and Wilkins, Baltimore.
[74] Himwich, H. E., and J. F. Fazekas. 1941. Am. J. Physiol. 132:454.
[75] Hoexter, F. M. 1954. Endocrinology 54:1.
[76] Hoover, C. R., and C. W. Turner. 1954. Ibid. 54:666.
[77] Hudson, A. J., J. H. Quastel, and P. G. Scholefield. 1960. J. Neurochem. 5:177.
[78] Humphrey, G. F., and M. Robertson. 1953. Australian J. Exptl. Biol. Med. Sci. 30:131.
[79] Hussain, O. Z., and T. F. Newcomb. 1964. J. Appl. Physiol. 19:297.
[80] Illing, E. K., and C. H. Gray. 1951. Endocrinology 7:242.
[81] Iyer, G. Y. N., M. F. Islam, and J. H. Quastel. 1961. Nature 192:535.
[82] Jasper, R. L., and J. W. Archdeacon. 1951. Physiol. Zool. 24:163.
[83] Kalman, S. M., and E. R. Clewe. 1953. Stanford Med. Bull. 11:216.
[84] Kawashima, Y. 1925. J. Biochem. (Tokyo) 4:411.

continued

[85] Kayne, H. L., N. Taylor, and N. R. Alpert. 1964. Am. J. Physiol. 206:1091.
[86] Kirk, J. E., P. G. Effersøe, and S. P. Chiang. 1954. J. Gerontol. 9:10.
[87] Kirk, J. E., T. J. S. Laursen, and R. Schaus. 1955. Ibid. 10:178.
[88] Kleiber, M. 1941. Proc. Soc. Exptl. Biol. Med. 48: 419.
[89] Krantz, J. C., Jr., C. J. Carr, and M. J. Knapp. 1951. J. Pharmacol. Exptl. Therap. 102:258.
[90] Krebs, H. A. 1933. Handbuch Biochem. Menschen Tiere 1:863.
[91] Krebs, H. A., and F. Kubowitz. 1927. Biochem. Z. 189:194.
[92] Krebs, H. A., and H. Rosenhagen. 1931. Z. Ges. Neurol. Psychiat. 134:643.
[93] Landau, D., and A. S. Gordon. 1952. Endocrinology 51:157.
[94] Langham, M. 1952. J. Physiol. (London) 117:461.
[95] Lardy, H. A., R. G. Hansen, and P. H. Phillips. 1945. Arch. Biochem. 6:41.
[96] Lardy, H. A., and P. H. Phillips. 1943. Am. J. Physiol. 138:741.
[97] Lardy, H. A., and P. H. Phillips. 1943. J. Biol. Chem. 148:333.
[98] Laser, H. 1932. Biochem. Z. 248:9.
[99] Laser, H. 1937. Biochem. J. 31:1671.
[100] Laskin, D. M., and B. G. Sarnat. 1953. Surg. Gynecol. Obstet. 96:493.
[101] Laursen, T. J. S., and R. S. Laursen. 1958. Am. J. Clin. Pathol. 30:237.
[102] Lee, K. S. 1953. J. Pharmacol. Exptl. Therap. 109: 304.
[103] Levey, H. A., and C. M. Szego. Unpublished. State Univ. New York, Dept. Physiology, Brooklyn, 1952.
[104] Lincicome, D. R., and J. I. Bruce. 1965. Exptl. Parasitol. 17:332.
[105] Lipsett, M. N., and F. J. Moore. 1951. J. Biol. Chem. 192:743.
[106] Livingston, A., C. H. Williams, and F. W. Barnes, Jr. 1962. Proc. Soc. Exptl. Biol. Med. 111:75.
[107] Loebel, R. O. 1925. Biochem. Z. 161:219.
[108] Macbeth, R. A., and J. G. Bekesi. 1962. Cancer Res. 22:244.
[109] MacLeod, J., and C. P. Rhoads. 1939. Proc. Soc. Exptl. Biol. Med. 41:268.
[110] Malinou, S. 1964. Circulation Res. 14:364.
[111] Manhold, J. H., and A. R. Volpe. 1963. J. Dental Res. 42:103.
[112] Manhold, J. H., Jr., T. E. Bolden, and S. Katz. 1960. Ibid. 39:746.
[113] Martin, W. S., R. C. Grubbs, and M. A. Lessler. 1956. Am. J. Physiol. 187:505.
[114] McIlwain, H. 1951. Biochem. J. 50:132.
[115] McKinney, G. R., et al. 1953. J. Appl. Physiol. 5: 335.
[116] Meier, R., and E. Thoenes. 1933. Arch. Exptl. Pathol. Pharmakol. 169:655.
[117] Meyerhof, O., and K. Lohmann. 1926. Biochem. Z. 171:381, 421.
[118] Meyerhof, O., K. Lohmann, and R. Meier. 1925. Ibid. 157:459.
[119] Minami, S. 1923. Ibid. 142:334.
[120] Mottram, R. F. 1955. J. Physiol. (London) 128: 268.
[121] Moulder, J. W., and E. Weiss. 1951. J. Infect. Diseases 88:68.
[122] Moulder, J. W., and E. Weiss. 1951. Ibid. 88:77.
[123] Murphy, J. B., and J. A. Hawkins. 1925. J. Gen. Physiol. 8:115.
[124] Murray, J. B. 1954. Am. J. Physiol. 177:463.
[125] Negelein, E. 1925. Biochem. Z. 158:121.
[126] Negelein, E. 1925. Ibid. 165:122.
[127] Newcomer, W. S., and P. A. Barrett. 1960. Endocrinology 66:409.
[128] Ochoa, S. 1930. Biochem. Z. 227:116.
[129] O'Connor, R. J. 1951. Brit. J. Exptl. Pathol. 32: 336.
[130] Ogata, Y. 1932. Japan. J. Med. Sci., III, 2:131.
[131] Ohara, K. 1951. Japan. J. Physiol. 2:1.
[132] Okamoto, Y. 1925. Biochem. Z. 160:52.
[133] Patnaik, B. K., and M. S. Kanungo. 1966. Biochem. J. 98:374.
[134] Paul, H. E., M. F. Paul, and F. Kopko. 1952. Proc. Soc. Exptl. Biol. Med. 79:555.
[135] Pearce, J., and R. W. Gerard. 1942. Am. J. Physiol. 136:49.
[136] Peiss, C. N., and J. Field. 1950. Biol. Bull. 99:213.
[137] Peiss, C. N., and J. Field. 1952. Arch. Biochem. Biophys. 36:276.
[138] Porter, J. C., and R. M. Melampy. 1952. Endocrinology 51:412.
[139] Priest, R. E. 1963. Am. J. Physiol. 205:1200.
[140] Quastel, J. H., and I. J. Bickis. 1959. Nature 183: 281.
[141] Rafsky, H. A., B. Newman, and A. Horonick. 1952. J. Gerontol. 7:38.
[142] Ramsay, R., and C. O. Warren, Jr. 1930. Quart. J. Exptl. Physiol. 20:213.
[143] Ramsay, R., and C. O. Warren, Jr. 1932. Ibid. 22: 49.
[144] Redenz, E. 1933. Biochem. Z. 257:234.
[145] Reilly, J. 1953. Arch. Biochem. Biophys. 43:25.
[146] Robbie, W. A., and P. J. Leinfelder. 1949. Am. J. Ophthalmol. 32:208.
[147] Roberts, S., and M. R. Keller. 1953. Arch. Biochem. Biophys. 44:9.
[148] Roberts, S., and M. Rock. Unpublished. Univ. California Medical School, Los Angeles, 1952.
[149] Roberts, S., and C. M. Szego. 1953. J. Biol. Chem. 201:21.
[150] Röe, O. 1954. Acta Ophthalmol. 32:181.
[151] Rose, R. L., and J. W. Archdeacon. 1953. Trans. Kentucky Acad. Sci. 14:17.
[152] Rosenthal, O., and A. Lasnitzki. 1928. Biochem. Z. 196:340.
[153] Rubinstein, D., and O. F. Denstedt. 1953. J. Biol. Chem. 204:623.
[154] Russell, R. L., and B. A. Westfall. 1954. Am. J. Physiol. 176:468.

continued

70. OXYGEN CONSUMPTION: ANIMAL TISSUES

[155] Sasaki, S. 1959. J. Biochem. (Tokyo) 46:269.

[156] Saslow, G. 1937. J. Cellular Comp. Physiol. 10:385.

[157] Scarpelli, D. G., R. A. Knouff, and C. A. Angerer. 1953. Proc. Soc. Exptl. Biol. Med. 84:94.

[158] Schlayer, C. 1937. Biochem. Z. 293:94.

[159] Schrader, H. K., and R. Schrader. 1957. Helv. Odontol. Acta 1:13.

[160] Schwartz, A. 1962. Biochem. Pharmacol. 11:389.

[161] Sellei, C., P. Weinstein, and J. Jany. 1932. Biochem. Z. 247:146.

[162] Senter, A. D., J. J. Eiler, and K. H. Lee. 1959. Proc. Soc. Exptl. Biol. Med. 100:323.

[163] Sharma, S. K., R. M. Johnstone, and J. H. Quastel. 1963. Can. J. Biochem. Physiol. 41:597.

[164] Sharma, S. K., R. M. Johnstone, and J. H. Quastel. 1964. Biochem. J. 92:564.

[165] Sherman, J. K. 1964. Anat. Record 149:591.

[166] Shorr, E. 1939. Cold Spring Harbor Symp. Quant. Biol. 7:323.

[167] Simon, F. P., A. M. Potts, and R. W. Gerard. 1947. J. Biol. Chem. 167:303.

[168] Sippel, T. O. 1962. Invest. Ophthalmol. 1:385.

[169] Sourkes, T. L., and P. Heneage. 1951. Endocrinology 49:601.

[170] Sourkes, T. L., and P. Heneage. 1952. Ibid. 50:73.

[171] South, F. E., Jr., and S. F. Cook. 1954. J. Gen. Physiol. 37:335.

[172] Stuermer, V. M., and R. J. Stein. 1952. Am. J. Obstet. Gynecol. 63:359.

[173] Strauss, B. 1964. J. Appl. Physiol. 19:503.

[174] Sturn, A. 1930. Z. Ges. Exptl. Med. 74:555.

[175] Szekeres, L., G. Lenard, and J. Soti. 1958. Arch. Intern. Pharmacodyn. 115:141.

[176] Takane, R. 1926. Biochem. Z. 171:403.

[177] Tanyia, C. 1927. Ibid. 189:175.

[178] Taylor, D. W., and R. Wiseman. 1962. Nature 196: 1102.

[179] Thomas, D. P., and J. T. Dingle. 1955. Brit. J. Exptl. Pathol. 36:195.

[180] Tuba, J., and M. S. Fraser. 1952. Can. J. Med. Sci. 30:14.

[181] Tuba, J., H. E. Rawlinson, and L. G. Shaw. 1950. Can. J. Res., E, 28:217.

[182] Ulbrick, W. C., and W. V. Whitehorn. 1952. Am. J. Physiol. 171:407.

[183] Vernberg, F. J. 1954. Biol. Bull. 106:360.

[184] Vernberg, F. J., and I. E. Gray. 1953. Ibid. 104: 445.

[185] Villee, C. A. 1953. J. Biol. Chem. 205:113.

[186] Villegas, L., and R. Durbin. 1960. Biochim. Biophys. Acta 44:612.

[187] Volpe, A. R., J. H. Manhold, and B. S. Manhold. 1962. J. Dental Res. 41:1060.

[188] von Bertalanffy, L., and W. J. Pirozynski. 1953. Biol. Bull. 105:240.

[189] Walthard, B. 1931. Z. Ges. Exptl. Med. 79:451.

[190] Warburg, O. 1925. Biochem. Z. 160:307.

[191] Warburg, O., and F. Kubowitz. 1927. Ibid. 189: 242.

[192] Warburg, O., K. Posener, and E. Negelein. 1924. Ibid. 152:309.

[193] Warren, C. O. 1940. Am. J. Physiol. 131:176.

[194] Webb, J. L., and K. A. Elliott. 1951. J. Pharmacol. Exptl. Therap. 103:24.

[195] Wechsler, R. L., R. R. Dripps, and S. S. Kety. 1951. Anesthesiology 12:308.

[196] Weil-Malherbe, H. 1938. Biochem. J. 32:2257.

[197] Weiss, B. 1951. J. Biol. Chem. 193:509.

[198] Whereat, A. F. 1961. Circulation Res. 9:571.

[199] Whittam, R., and J. S. Willis. 1963. J. Physiol. (London) 168:158.

[200] Wilson, T. H., and G. Wiseman. 1954. Ibid. 123: 126.

[201] Wohlgemuth, J., and E. Klopstock. 1926. Biochem. Z. 175:202.

[202] Woodward, G. E., and M. T. Hudson. 1954. Cancer Res. 14:599.

[203] Wright, G. P. 1930. J. Gen. Physiol. 14:179, 201.

71. OXYGEN CONSUMPTION: FETAL TISSUES

Values should be considered representative, as rarely are enough data presented to justify statistical treatment, and rarely is independent confirmatory information available. Unless otherwise specified, values are for a single intact embryo.

	Species (Synonym)	Method	Medium [Weight]	Age [Stage]	μl O_2/hr [μl O_2/g/hr]	Reference
1	*Cavia porcellus*	Blood-flow & blood-gas measurements	[5.5 g wet wt]	....	4500 [810]	7
2			[16 g wet wt]	....	12,000 [756]	
3			[23.8 g wet wt]	....	6000 [252]	
4			[35.8 g wet wt]	....	23,000 [643]	
5			[39 g wet wt]	....	15,000 [385]	
6			[61.5 g wet wt]	....	27,000 [440]	

continued

71. OXYGEN CONSUMPTION: FETAL TISSUES

	Species (Synonym)	Method	Medium [Weight]	Age [Stage]	µl O_2/hr [µl O_2/g/hr]	Reference
7	*Ovis aries*	Blood-flow & blood-gas analysis	[250 g wet wt]	78 days	120,000 [474]	3
8			[570 g wet wt]	95 days	426,000 [750]	
9			[920 g wet wt]	99 days	378,000 [408]	
10			[960 g wet wt]	106 days	552,000 [576]	
11			[1050 g wet wt]	108 days	498,000 [474]	
12			[1200 g wet wt]	111 days	276,000 [228]	
13			[1000 g wet wt]	112 days	252,000 [252]	
14			[2040 g wet wt]	123 days	558,000 [234]	
15			[3000 g wet wt]	126 days	738,000 [246]	
16			[2850 g wet wt]	127 days	672,000 [234]	
17			[2850 g wet wt]	130 days	726,000 [252]	
18			[2810 g wet wt]	136 days	864,000 [396]	
19			[3850 g wet wt]	137 days	1,200,000 [312]	
20			[3650 g wet wt]	138 days	930,000 [252]	
21			[4100 g wet wt]	141 days	1,320,000 [324]	
22			[3500 g wet wt]	144 days	840,000 [240]	
23			[2800 g wet wt]	152 days	984,000 [258]	
24	*Rattus* sp.	....	Krebs solution	12 days	47	16
25				13 days	65	
26				14 days	145	
27				15 days	113	
28				16 days	154	
29		Cartesian diver technique	0.8% NaCl, phosphate buffer, pH 7.4	[Follicular ovum]	0.00111	6
30				[1-2 cells]	0.00072	
31				[3-4 cells]	0.00080	
32				[8-16 cells]	0.00094	
33				8 days	0.01	5
34				10 days	0.2	
		Warburg manometric technique	Serum, 0.025 *M* bicarbonate buffer, 0.2% glucose			18
35			[0.90 mg dry wt[1]]	....	12	
36			[0.90 mg dry wt[2]]	....	10.5	
37			[1.00 mg dry wt[1]]	....	14.6	
38			[1.00 mg dry wt[2]]	....	13.6	
39			[1.10 mg dry wt[1]]	....	11.7	
40			[1.10 mg dry wt[2]]	....	11.6	
41			[2.40 mg dry wt]	....	36.7	
42			[3.10 mg dry wt[1]]	....	38.7	
43			[3.10 mg dry wt[2]]	....	41.2	
44			Ringer phosphate, pH 7.4 [8.0 mg dry wt]	13 days	55	15
45	*Gallus domesticus*	Warburg manometric technique	Ringer phosphate, pH 7.2	16 hr	4.75	20
46				16.25 hr	4.73	
47				25.25 hr	6.91	
48				48 hr	14.5	
49				72.5 hr	24.1	
50			Ringer phosphate, glucose, pH 7.2	16 hr	7.12	20
51				16.25 hr	5.57	
52				25.25 hr	8.32	
53				48 hr	19.0	
54				72.5 hr	27.4	
			Intact egg in air & isolated tissues in Ringer phosphate, pH 7.4			17
55			[562 mg wet wt]	6 days	595 [1226]	
56			[901 mg wet wt]	7 days	869 [1076]	
57			[1488 mg wet wt]	8 days	1357 [1021]	
58			[2068 mg wet wt]	9 days	2090 [1050]	

[1] Membranes intact. [2] Membranes destroyed.

continued

	Species (Synonym)	Method	Medium [Weight]	Age [Stage]	$\mu l\ O_2/hr$ [$\mu l\ O_2/g/hr$]	Reference
59			[3168 mg wet wt]	10 days	2719 [949]	
60			[4304 mg wet wt]	11 days	4050 [1015]	
61			[6100 mg wet wt]	12 days	5460 [992]	
62			[8555 mg wet wt]	13 days	8262 [1055]	
63			[11,838 mg wet wt]	14 days	10,783 [1023]	
64			[14,320 mg wet wt]	15 days	13,293 [1030]	
65			[17,570 mg wet wt]	16 days	15,600 [990]	
66			[21,870 mg wet wt]	17 days	18,450 [920]	
67			[24,210 mg wet wt]	18 days	19,100 [850]	
68			[28,270 mg wet wt]	19 days	20,900 [765]	
69	*Coluber constrictor*	Warburg manometric technique, 23.9°C	....	1 day	210 [3500]	10
70				2 days	162	
71				3 days	185 [1610]	
72				4 days	120	
73				5 days	135	
74				6 days	225	
75				7 days	194	
76				8 days	198 [635]	
77				9 days	236	
78				10 days	223	
79				12 days	305 [468]	
80				13 days	282	
81				15 days	162	
82				17 days	234	
83				18 days	272 [310]	
84				20 days	253	
85				22 days	256	
86				23 days	252	
87				24 days	277 [233]	
88				25 days	300	
89				26 days	282	
90				27 days	334 [226]	
91				28 days	318	
92				30 days	337	
93				31 days	356 [200]	
94				33 days	334	
95				34 days	350 [192]	
96				36 days	365	
97				38 days	378	
98				39 days	426	
99				41 days	478	
100				43 days	500 [177]	
101				44 days	552	
102				46 days	531	
103				48 days	575	
104				50 days	722	
105				51 days	656 [175]	
106				53 days	813	
107				55 days	873	
108				56 days	970	
109				58 days	962 [175]	
110				59 days	1021	
111				61 days	1021	
112				62 days	1227 [175]	
113				64 days	1080	
114				67 days	1026 [125]	

continued

	Species (Synonym)	Method	Medium [Weight]	Age [Stage]	µl O_2/hr [µl O_2/g/hr]	Reference
115	*Ambystoma maculatum*[3]	Warburg manometric technique	Aquarium water	1 day [7-8]	0.54	21
116				1 day [8-9]	0.34	
117				2 days [15-16]	0.43	
118				3 days [18-19]	0.55	
119				3-4 days [29-31]	0.65	
120				4 days [32]	0.73	
121				5 days [33-34]	1.28	
122				6 days [37-38]	1.70	
123				7 days [39-40]	2.11	
124				8 days [41]	2.36	
125				9 days [42[4]]	2.69	
126				10 days [43]	3.64	
127				11 days [44]	4.53	
128				12 days [45]	5.46	
129				14 days [46[5]]	6.03	
130				15 days [46]	6.10	
131				17 days	5.47	
132				18 days	5.80	
133				19 days	6.10	
134				20 days	6.48	
135				21 days	5.65	
136				22 days	5.97	
137				23 days	5.88	
138				24 days	6.21	
139				25 days	6.48	
140				26 days	6.57	
141				27 days	7.08	
142				28 days	7.55	
143				29 days	8.27	
144				30 days	9.41	
145				31 days	10.48	
146				32 days	11.42	
147				33 days	11.15	
148				34 days	12.52	
149				35 days	13.46	
150				36 days	12.88	
151				37 days	13.40	
152				38 days	13.20	
153				39 days	15.36	
154				40 days	17.19	
155				41 days	18.22	
156				42 days	18.98	
157				43 days	19.18	
158				44 days	18.20	
159				45 days	20.82	
160				53 days	38.30	
161				58 days	41.50	
162				60 days	64.00	
163				66 days	45.20	
164				68 days	28.00	
165				73 days	63.10	
166				80 days	107.40	
167				85 days[6]	118.70	
168				105 days	107.30	
169				115 days	118.20	

[3] Stages are Harrison development stages. [4] Hatching. [5] Feeding begins. [6] Metamorphosis.

continued

71. OXYGEN CONSUMPTION: FETAL TISSUES

	Species (Synonym)	Method	Medium [Weight]	Age [Stage]	$\mu l\ O_2/hr$ [$\mu l\ O_2/g/hr$]	Reference
	(A. punctatum)	Modified Thunberg differential respirometer	Tap water or spring water			13
170			[2.67 mg dry wt]	[7,8,9]	0.180	
171			[3.18 mg dry wt [7]]	[10,11]	0.265 [7]	
172			[2.86 mg dry wt]	[12,13]	0.283	
173			[2.97 mg dry wt]	[14]	0.343	
174			[2.81 mg dry wt]	[15]	0.342	
175			[3.08 mg dry wt]	[16]	0.392	
176			[2.63 mg dry wt]	[17]	0.362	
177			[3.28 mg dry wt]	[18]	0.430	
178			[3.26 mg dry wt]	[19]	0.490	
179			[2.13 mg dry wt]	[20]	0.343	
180			[3.08 mg dry wt]	[21,22]	0.482	
181			[3.01 mg dry wt]	[23]	0.482	
182			[2.93 mg dry wt]	[24]	0.472	
183			[3.28 mg dry wt]	[25,26]	0.553	
184			[2.99 mg dry wt]	[27]	0.622	
185			[2.18 mg dry wt]	[28,29]	0.491	
186			[3.30 mg dry wt]	[30]	0.885	
187			[3.02 mg dry wt]	[31]	0.911	
188			[3.31 mg dry wt]	[33,34]	0.947	
189			[2.99 mg dry wt]	[35,36]	1.070	
190			[3.19 mg dry wt]	[37,38]	1.553	
191			[2.30 mg dry wt]	[39]	1.883	
192			[2.47 mg dry wt]	[40]	2.458	
193			[2.31 mg dry wt]	[41,42]	3.710	
194			[2.27 mg dry wt]	[43,44]	3.705	
195			[1.80 mg dry wt]	[45,46]	2.742	
196			[2.24 mg dry wt]	[14-16 mm [8]]	3.516	
197			[4.38 mg dry wt]	[17-21 mm [8]]	6.597	
198			[7.80 mg dry wt]	[22-27 mm [8]]	9.422	
199			[26.01 mg dry wt]	[28-36 mm [8]]	26.33	
200			[70.29 mg dry wt]	[37-48 mm [8]]	59.62	
	A. tigrinum [3]	Modified Thunberg differential respirometer	Tap water or spring water			13
201			[2.48 mg dry wt]	[10]	0.393	
202			[2.93 mg dry wt]	[11]	0.491	
203			[2.93 mg dry wt]	[12]	0.516	
204			[2.25 mg dry wt]	[13]	0.464	
205			[2.90 mg dry wt]	[14,15]	0.661	
206			[2.60 mg dry wt]	[16,17]	0.591	
207			[3.28 mg dry wt]	[18,19]	0.692	
208			[1.97 mg dry wt]	[20,21]	0.471	
209			[2.23 mg dry wt]	[22,23]	0.627	
210			[2.03 mg dry wt]	[24,25]	0.685	
211			[2.72 mg dry wt]	[26,27]	0.907	
212			[2.83 mg dry wt]	[28,29]	0.964	
213			[2.56 mg dry wt]	[30,31]	0.961	
214			[2.85 mg dry wt]	[32,33]	1.285	
215			[2.82 mg dry wt]	[34,35]	1.316	
216			[2.62 mg dry wt]	[36]	1.366	
217			[2.19 mg dry wt]	[37]	1.313	
218			[2.82 mg dry wt]	[38]	2.605	
219			[2.31 mg dry wt]	[39]	2.319	
220			[2.49 mg dry wt]	[40]	2.585	
221			[1.78 mg dry wt]	[41,42]	2.389	
222			[1.78 mg dry wt]	[43]	3.262	
223			[1.43 mg dry wt]	[44]	4.058	
224			[2.74 mg dry wt]	[45]	9.113	
225			[1.43 mg dry wt]	[46]	3.167	

[3] Stages are Harrison development stages. [7] Average for more than one weight of embryo. [8] Larva.

continued

71. OXYGEN CONSUMPTION: FETAL TISSUES

	Species (Synonym)	Method	Medium [Weight]	Age [Stage]	$\mu l\ O_2/hr$ [$\mu l\ O_2/g/hr$]	Reference
226			[2.20 mg dry wt]	[14-21 mm[8]]	4.974	
227			[15.81 mg dry wt]	[22-37 mm[8]]	28.86	
228			[53.40 mg dry wt]	[38-54 mm[8]]	67.37	
229			[148.3 mg dry wt]	[55-72 mm[8]]	136.4	
230			[317.6 mg dry wt]	[73-93 mm[8]]	213.8	
231			[346.6 mg dry wt]	[82-85 mm[8]]	298.3	
232	*Pelobates fuscus*	....	Aquarium water	1 hr	0.093	9
233	*(Rana fusca)*			2 hr	0.126	
234				3-4 hr	0.164	
235				[Morula]	0.098-0.120	8
236				[Blastula]	0.146	
237				[Gastrula]	0.184-0.213	
238				[Neurula]	0.334	
239				[Tadpole]	1.167	
240	*Rana pipiens*[9]	....	Spring water or 10% Ringer's solution	2.5-3.5 hr	0.050	2
241				3-4 hr	0.054	
242				3.5-4.5 hr	0.059	
243				4-5 hr	0.052	
244				5-6 hr	0.061	
245				6-7 hr	0.057	
246				6.5-7.5 hr	0.058	
247	*R. pipiens*[10]	....	Aquarium water	[3; early cleavage]	0.052	4
248				[3; 2 cells]	0.049-0.056	
249				[6+; 16-32 cells]	0.080	
250				[7+; cleavage]	0.105	
251				[10; beginning gastrula]	0.173	
252				[10+]	0.136	
253				[11+; middle gastrula]	0.147	
254				[12; late gastrula]	0.195-0.250	
255				[13; neural plate]	0.220-0.320	
256				[14; neural fold]	0.240-0.270	
257				[15; neurula]	0.280-0.290	
258				[16+; gill plate]	0.330-0.490	
259	*R. pipiens*[3]	Warburg manometric technique	Aquarium water	0 day [0]	0.06	21
260				1 day [1]	0.08-0.10	
261				1 day [2-3]	0.07	
262				1 day [3]	0.12	
263				1 day [4-5]	0.06	
264				1 day [5-6]	0.10	
265				1 day [7]	0.08	
266				1 day [7-8]	0.09	
267				1 day [8]	0.23	
268				1 day [10]	0.39	
269				2 days [11]	0.56	
270				2 days [12-13]	0.70	
271				2 days [18-19]	0.88	
272				3 days [25-28]	0.98	
273				3 days [29-33[4]]	1.22	
274				3 days [35]	1.61	
275				4 days [37]	1.93	
276				5 days[5]	3.26	
277				6 days	4.49	
278				7 days	7.27	
279				8 days	6.95	
280				9 days	5.83	
281				10 days	4.59	
282				11 days	4.64	

3/ Stages are Harrison development stages. 4/ Hatching. 5/ Feeding begins. 8/ Larva. 9/ Values are for fertilized ova, and ages are hours after fertilization. 10/ Stages are Shumway development stages.

continued

71. OXYGEN CONSUMPTION: FETAL TISSUES

	Species (Synonym)	Method	Medium [Weight]	Age [Stage]	µl O_2/hr [µl O_2/g/hr]	Reference
283				12 days	5.03	
284				13 days	4.33	
285				14 days	6.27	
286				15 days	5.92	
287				17 days	6.34	
288				18 days	7.52	
289				19 days	7.85	
290				20 days	12.04	
291				21 days	12.23	
292				22 days	12.02	
293				23 days	14.21	
294				24 days	13.96	
295				26 days	14.73	
296				27 days	18.31	
297				28 days	16.98	
298				29 days	23.49	
299				30 days	18.40	
300				31 days	19.94	
301				32 days	21.75	
302				33 days	18.09	
303				34 days	17.34	
304				35 days	17.22	
305				36 days	19.99	
306				37 days	19.81	
307				38 days	19.12	
308				39 days	18.85	
309				40 days	18.18	
310				41 days	22.49	
311				42 days	20.72	
312				43 days	18.58	
313				44 days	25.00	
314				45 days	18.13	
315				47 days	22.99	
316				48 days	27.13	
317				49 days	25.09	
318				50 days	35.46	
319				51 days	27.29	
320				52 days	32.57	
321				53 days	31.10	
322				54 days	41.15	
323				55 days	34.25	
324				60 days	43.8	
325				67 days	52.2	
326				72 days	63.1	
327				73 days	38.1	
328				74 days	115.6	
329				78 days	85.4	
330				81 days	192.8	
331				83 days	79.0	
332				85 days	69.6	
333				86 days	85.3	
334				90 days[6]	95.2	
335				100 days[6]	127.4	
336				110 days	176.1	

[6] Metamorphosis.

continued

71. OXYGEN CONSUMPTION: FETAL TISSUES

	Species (Synonym)	Method	Medium [Weight]	Age [Stage]	$\mu l\ O_2/hr$ [$\mu l\ O_2/g/hr$]	Reference
337	*Siredon mexicanum*	Warburg manometric	....	8 hr [Blastula]	0.168	11
338	*(Ambystoma mex-*	technique, 22.6°C		16 hr [Early gastrula]	0.193	
339	*icanum)*			24 hr [Late gastrula]	0.248	
340				32 hr [Early neurula]	0.286	
341				40 hr [Late neurula]	0.305	
342				48 hr [Early tail bud]	0.325	
343				56 hr [Late tail bud]	0.363	
344				65 hr	0.425	
345				75 hr	0.550	
346				90 hr	0.818	
347				100 hr	0.970	
348				115 hr	1.365	
349				140 hr	2.10	
350				165 hr	2.71	
351				190 hr	3.30	
352				220 hr	3.95	
353	*Triturus torosus*[3]	....	Aquarium water	1 day [1-3]	0.49	21
354				1 day [3-6]	0.25	
355				2 days [7-8]	0.20	
356				3 days [9]	0.39	
357				3 days [10]	0.31	
358				3 days [11]	0.46	
359				3 days [12]	0.39	
360				5 days [15]	0.43	
361				5 days [17]	0.60	
362				5 days [19]	0.54	
363				5 days [20]	0.67	
364				6 days [22]	0.57	
365				7 days [23]	0.68	
366				9 days [29]	0.44	
367				14 days [35]	1.04	
368				18 days [37]	1.20	
369				19 days [38]	1.49	
370				20 days [39[4]]	2.40	
371				21 days [40]	2.39	
372				24 days [43]	2.90	
373				25 days [44[5]]	3.40	
374				30 days	3.23	
375				55 days	43.79	
376				65 days	21.38	
377				75 days	53.27	
378				90 days	56.31	
379				95 days[6]	52.30	
380				100 days[6]	72.24	
381				105 days[6]	68.52	
382				110 days[6]	91.65	
383				115 days	57.62	
384				120 days	60.90	
385				135 days	60.30	
386	*Fundulus hetero-*	....	Seawater	1-1.5 hr	0.029-0.036	19
387	*clitus*			1.5-2 hr	0.026-0.033	
388				2-2.5 hr	0.023-0.037	
389				2.5-3 hr	0.022-0.035	
390				3-3.5 hr	0.028-0.038	
391				3.5-4 hr	0.025-0.037	
392				4-4.5 hr	0.022-0.044	
393				4.5-5 hr	0.027-0.054	
394				5-5.5 hr	0.026-0.040	

[3] Stages are Harrison development stages. [4] Hatching. [5] Feeding begins. [6] Metamorphosis.

continued

71. OXYGEN CONSUMPTION: FETAL TISSUES

	Species (Synonym)	Method	Medium [Weight]	Age [Stage]	µl O_2/hr [µl O_2/g/hr]	Reference
395				4-6 hr [2-4 cells]	0.04	14
396				6-8 hr [32 cells]	0.03	
397				9-11 hr [Small disc]	0.02	
398				9-11 hr [Many cells]	0.04	
399				22-24 hr [Large disc]	0.05	
400				26-29 hr	0.06	
401				30-32 hr	0.07	
402				34-37 hr 11/	0.07	
403				2 days	0.07	
404				2.5 days	0.07	
405				3 days	0.05	
406				3.5 days 12/	0.12	
407				4 days	0.09	
408				4.5 days	0.09	
409				5.5 days	0.08	
410				6 days	0.07	
411			Water-saturated air	1 day	0.03	1
412				2 days	0.09	
413				3 days	0.16	
414				4 days	0.21	
415				5 days	0.20	
416				6 days	0.26	
417				7 days	0.35	
418				8 days	0.40	
419				9 days	0.48	
420				10 days	0.43	
421				11 days	0.41	
422				12 days 4/	0.44	
423	*Salmo salar*	....	10% seawater [Wet wt]	19 days	[136.5]	12
424				21 days	[137.5]	
425				24 days	[131.5]	
426				26 days	[136.5]	
427				30 days	[151.0]	
428				32 days	[146.0]	
429				35 days	[156.0]	
430				37 days	[137.0]	
431				39 days	[149.0]	
432				45 days	[145.0]	
433				50 days	[152.0]	

4/ Hatching. 11/ Embryo with eyes. 12/ Circulation established.

Contributors: (a) Fitzgerald, Laurence R., (b) Clark, Hugh.

References

[1] Amberson, W. R., and P. B. Armstrong. 1933. J. Cellular Comp. Physiol. 2:381.
[2] Atlas, M. 1938. Physiol. Zool. 11:278.
[3] Barcroft, J. 1947. Researches on prenatal life. C. C. Thomas, Springfield, Ill.
[4] Barth, L. G. 1946. J. Exptl. Zool. 103:463.
[5] Boell, E. J., and J. S. Nicholas. 1939. Science 90: 411.
[6] Boell, E. J., and J. S. Nicholas. 1948. J. Exptl. Zool. 109:267.
[7] Bohr, C. 1900. Skand. Arch. Physiol. 10:413.
[8] Brachet, J. 1934. Arch. Biol. (Paris) 45:611.
[9] Brachet, J. 1935. Ibid. 46:1.
[10] Clark, H. 1953. J. Exptl. Biol. 30:502.
[11] Fisher, F. G., and H. Hartwig. 1938. Biol. Zentr. 58: 567.
[12] Hayes, F. A., I. R. Wilmot, and D. A. Livingstone. 1951. J. Exptl. Zool. 116:377.
[13] Hopkins, H. S., and S. W. Handford. 1943. Ibid. 93: 403.
[14] Hyman, L. H. 1921. Biol. Bull. 40:32.
[15] Kleiber, M., H. H. Cole, and A. H. Smith. 1943. J. Cellular Comp. Physiol. 22:167.
[16] Mislivechkova, A. 1954. Cesk. Morfol. 2:118.
[17] Needham, J. 1932. Proc. Roy. Soc. (London), B, 110:46.
[18] Negelein, E. 1930. In O. Warburg, ed. The metabolism of tumors. Constable, London.
[19] Philips, F. S. 1940. Biol. Bull. 78:256.
[20] Philips, F. S. 1941. J. Exptl. Zool. 86:257.
[21] Wills, I. A. 1936. Ibid. 73:481.

72. OXYGEN CONSUMPTION: INVERTEBRATE TISSUES

Q_{O_2} (oxidation quotient): Values are for endogenous respiration, and are microliters oxygen consumed per hour per milligram wet weight (unbracketed figures) or dry weight (bracketed figures). For information on the effects of various substrates and other factors on oxygen consumption, and for data on additional species, consult reference 5.

	Class & Species (Synonym)	Method	Tissue	No. of Specimens	Temp °C	Q_{O_2}	Remarks	Reference
	Echinodermata							
	Holothuroidea							
1	*Isostichopus badionotus (Stichopus mobii)*	Warburg	Intestine	12	25	[0.7]		49
2			Branchial tree	11	25	[0.6]		
	Arthropoda							
	Merostomata							
3	*Limulus polyphemus*	Warburg	Cardiac ganglion		25	0.104-0.114	Mean resting values from 3 experiments; 100 mg wet wt tissue (>5 ganglia pooled)	13
4			Claw nerve		24	0.082		8
5		Differential volumeter	Muscle		24	0.036		56
6			Forebrain		24	0.134		56
7			Optic nerve, pieces	5♂	16	0.018-0.032		23
8				2♂	28	0.050-0.076		
9				2♂	31	0.082-0.118		
10			Axon of optic nerve, pieces	8 adult ♂	24	0.086-0.110		56
11			Sheath of optic nerve, pieces	8 adult ♂	24	0.031-0.036		56
12			Retina		20	0.129		56
13			Foregut		24	0.123		56
14			Heart, slices		28	[2.1]	Gas phase: O_2	2
	Crustacea							
15	*Astacus* sp.	Warburg; also differential manometer	Nerve, unstimulated	1	16	[0.77]	2.72 mg dry wt tissue; in Ringer's solution, freezing point = −0.8°C	42
16	*Callinectes ornatus*	Warburg	Midgut gland		28	0.565 [2.22]	Freshly captured specimens from Florida. Gas phase: air.	24
17	*C. sapidus*	Warburg	Midgut gland	48	27	0.734		60
18			Gill	40	27	0.351		60
19			Gill, pieces	5	20	[2.36]	Gas phase: air	39
20		Fenn, modified	Nerve, 1st walking leg	11	20	0.156	Mean value for 11 leg nerves	38
21			Claw nerve	11	20	0.105	34 mg wet wt tissue; mean value for 20 claw nerves	38
22				11	26	0.136	36 mg wet wt tissue; mean value for 19 claw nerves	38
23	Intermolt	Warburg	Gill	10	25-27	[3.042]	Marine specimens. Gas phase: air.	35
24				10	25-27	[3.738]	Brackish-water specimens. Gas phase: air.	35
25	*Carcinus maenas (Carcinides maenas)*	Warburg	Muscle, homogenate		20-25	0.010	With eyestalks	52
26			Gill	19	24	[2.61]	In artificial seawater (salinity = 32°/oo)	47

continued

	Class & Species (Synonym)	Method	Tissue	No. of Specimens	Temp °C	Q_{O_2}	Remarks	Reference
27				8	24	[3.91]	In brackish water (salinity = 15°/oo)	47
28				6	24	[4.55]	In NaCl solution	47
29	*Carcinus mediterraneas*, intermolt	Warburg	Gill	16	25-27	[3.516]	Gas phase: air	35
30	*Cardisoma guanhumi*	Warburg	Midgut gland		28	0.162 [0.55]	Freshly captured specimens from Florida. Gas phase: air.	24
31			Gill		27	[3.93]	Specimens from Florida in 25% seawater. Gas phase: air.	48
32						[4.33]	Specimens from Florida in 75% seawater. Gas phase: air.	48
33						[2.50]	Specimens from Florida in 100% seawater. Gas phase: air.	48
34	*Clibanarius vittatus*	Warburg	Midgut gland	22	27	0.622		60
35	*(C. vittatius)*		Gill	17	27	0.325		60
36	*Eurytium limosum*	Warburg	Midgut gland		28	0.227 [0.67]	Freshly captured specimens from Florida. Gas phase: air.	24
	Gecarcinus lateralis							58
37	Intermolt	Warburg	Integumentary tissues	8♂	25	[0.53]		
38	Premolt	Warburg	Integumentary tissues	11♂	25	[0.85]		
39	*Hemigrapsus nudus*, intermolt	Warburg	Gill	50♂	20	0.110	50-70 mg tissues from 2.4-g crabs. Gas phase: O_2.	14
40				50♂	20	0.165	50-70 mg tissue from 12.5-g crabs. Gas phase: O_2.	14
41	*Homarus americanus*	Warburg	Ventral ganglionated nerve cord		24	0.123		8
42			All peripheral leg nerves		24	0.081		
43			Nerves of walking legs		24	0.071		
44			Claw nerves		24	0.086		
45	*Libinia dubia*	Warburg	Midgut gland	20	27	0.346		60
46			Gill	21	27	0.214		
47	*L. emarginata*	Thunberg, modified	Claw nerve	8	23	0.116	70 mg wet wt tissue (nerves of 4 specimens pooled); in seawater containing approx 12 mM K^+	55
48	Intermolt	Warburg	Gill	2	25-27	[2.648]	Gas phase: air	35
49	*Maja* sp.	Warburg; also differential manometer	Leg nerve, unstimulated	4	16		12.93 mg dry wt tissue; in artificial seawater with urea & bicarbonate	42
50	*M. verrucosa*, intermolt	Warburg	Gill	7	25-27	[2.200]	Gas phase: air	35
51	*Menippe mercenaria*	Warburg	Midgut gland	33	27	0.623		60
52			Gill	32	27	0.329		

continued

72. OXYGEN CONSUMPTION: INVERTEBRATE TISSUES

	Class & Species (Synonym)	Method	Tissue	No. of Specimens	Temp °C	Q_{O_2}	Remarks	Reference
53	*Ocypode quadrata*	Warburg	Midgut gland	32	27	0.772		60
54	*(O. albicans)*		Gill	25	27	0.914		
55	*Orconectes propinquus*	Warburg	Carpus of 3rd maxilliped		25	0.030	15.2 mg tissue. Gas phase: air.	59
	O. virilis						Dry wt is lipid-free. Gas phase: air.	41
56	Soft-shelled stage; A 1/		Midgut gland, fragments		25	[4.33]		
57	Partially hardened; B_2-C_1 1/		Midgut gland, fragments		25	[4.39]		
58	Early intermolt; C_1-C_2 1/		Midgut gland, fragments		25	[3.81]		
59	Intermolt; C_3-C_4 1/		Midgut gland, fragments		25	[2.41 2/; 2.92 3/]		
60	Early premolt; D_1 1/		Midgut gland, fragments		25	[2.12 2/; 2.77 3/]		
61	Middle & late premolt; D_2-D_4 1/		Midgut gland, fragments		25	[3.45 2/; 2.74 3/]		
62	*Pachygrapsus crassipes*	Scholander-Wennesland microrespirometer	Leg muscle, teased	14 adult ♂	20	0.0475 4/	293 mg wet wt tissue	50
63				19 adult ♂	20	0.0500 5/	291 mg wet wt tissue	50
64				17 adult ♂	20	0.0270 6/	297 mg wet wt tissue	50
65			Brain	6 adult ♂	20	0.268 4/	13.4 mg wet wt tissue (3 brains pooled)	50
66				6 adult ♂	20	0.258 5/	13.5 mg wet wt tissue (3 brains pooled)	50
67				7 adult ♂	20	0.242 6/	12.5 mg wet wt tissue (3 brains pooled)	50
68	*Palaemon squilla (Leander adspersus)*	Warburg	Muscle, homogenate		20-25	0.005	With eyestalks	52
69	*Pandalus borealis*		Dorsal extensor abdominal muscle		6	0.038	Specimens from Kristineberg, Sweden	17
70					10	0.065		
71	*P. montagui*		Dorsal extensor abdominal muscle		6	0.040	Specimens from Kristineberg, Sweden	17
72					10	0.070		
73					10	0.077	Specimens from Plymouth, England	17
74					16	0.094		
75	*Panopeus herbstii*	Warburg	Midgut gland	32	27	0.536		60
76					28	0.216 [0.81]	Freshly captured specimens from Florida. Gas phase: air.	24
77			Gill	32	27	0.319		60
78	*Panulirus argus*	Warburg	Leg muscle	2	25	[1.0]		49
79			Leg nerve	5	25	[1.1]		
80			Midgut gland	4	25	[3.0]		
81	*Pugettia producta*	Warburg	Midgut gland, slices	61	15	[1.73]		4
82	*Sesarma cinereum*	Warburg	Midgut gland	14	27	0.357		60
83	*(S. cinerea)*		Gill	10	27	0.911		
84	*Uca minax*	Warburg	Midgut gland	41	27	0.383		60
85			Gill	33	27	0.373		
86	*U. mordax*	Warburg	Midgut gland		28	0.303 [1.31]	Freshly captured specimens from Florida. Gas phase: air.	24

1/ Drach stage. 2/ Pre-June. 3/ Summer. 4/ Specimens acclimated to 8.5°C. 5/ Specimens acclimated to 16.0°C. 6/ Specimens acclimated to 23.5°C.

continued

	Class & Species (Synonym)	Method	Tissue	No. of Specimens	Temp °C	Q_{O_2}	Remarks	Reference
87	*U. pugilator*	Warburg	Midgut gland	34	27	0.360		60
88					28	0.312 [1.28]	Freshly captured specimens from Florida. Gas phase: air.	24
89			Gill	27	27	0.550		60
90		Cartesian diver respirometer	Muscle		10	[0.092]7/	Specimens from Beaufort, North Carolina	63
91					35	[0.204]8/		
92			Brain (supraesophageal ganglion)		5	[0.238]7/; [0.209]8/		
93					10	[0.316]8/		
94					20	[0.718]7/		
95			Heart		5	[0.232]7/		
96					10	[0.304]7/; [0.321]8/		
97					15	[0.393]7/; [0.292]8/		
98					20	[0.772]8/		
99					25	[0.825]7/		
100	*U. pugnax*	Warburg	Midgut gland		15	0.160 7/; 0.185 8/	Specimens from Beaufort, North Carolina, in spring	62
101					30	0.582 7/; 0.662 8/		
102					36	0.810 7/; 0.879 8/		
103			Gill		15	0.192 7/; 0.267 8/	Specimens from Beaufort, North Carolina, in spring. Gas phase: air.	62
104					30	0.650 7/; 0.914 8/		
105					36	0.764 7/; 0.868 8/		
106		Cartesian diver respirometer	Muscle		5	[0.090]8/	Specimens from Beaufort, North Carolina	63
107					10	[0.058]7/		
108					20	[0.171]7/; [0.189]8/		
109					30	[0.222]8/		
110					35	[0.502]8/		
111			Brain (supraesophageal ganglion)		5	[0.345]7/; [0.306]8/		
112					10	[0.515]7/; [0.427]8/		
113					15	[0.564]7/		
114					20	[0.968]7/		
115			Heart		5	[0.402]7/; [0.307]8/		
116					10	[0.517]7/; [0.442]8/		
117					15	[0.610]7/; [0.565]8/		
118					25	[1.077]7/; [0.825]8/		
119					35	[1.053]7/		

7/ Specimens warm-acclimated. 8/ Specimens cold-acclimated.

continued

	Class & Species (Synonym)	Method	Tissue	No. of Specimens	Temp °C	Q_{O_2}	Remarks	Reference
120	*U. rapax*	Warburg	Midgut gland		15	0.159[7]; 0.189[8]	Specimens from Jamaica	62
121					30	0.476[7]; 0.598[8]		
122					36	0.793[7]; 0.768[8]		
123					28	0.435 [1.86]	Freshly captured specimens from Florida. Gas phase: air.	24
124			Gill		15	0.193[7]; 0.318[8]	Specimens from Jamaica	62
125					30	0.673[7]; 0.690[8]		
126					36	1.183[7]; 0.963[8]		
127		Cartesian diver respirometer	Muscle		5	[0.058][8]	Specimens from Puerto Rico	61, 63
128					15	[0.109][8]		
129					20	[0.104][8]		
130					30	[0.312][8]		
131					35	[0.427][8]		
132					15	[0.068][8]	Specimens from Salvador, Brazil	61, 63
133					20	[0.162][8]		
134					30	[0.181][8]		
135					35	[0.267][8]		
136			Brain (supraesophageal ganglion)		5	[0.207][7]; [0.241][8]	Specimens from Puerto Rico	61, 63
137					10	[0.399][7]; [0.462][8]		
138					15	[0.798][7]		
139					20	[0.737][7]		
140					25	[0.893][7]; [0.611][8]		
141					30	[1.022][8]		
142					10	[0.255][8]	Specimens from Salvador, Brazil	61
143					15	[0.508][7]		
144					25	[0.668][7]; [0.785][8]		
145					30	[0.744][8]		
146			Heart		5	[0.229][7]; [0.246][8]	Specimens from Puerto Rico	63
147					10	[0.342][7]; [0.320][8]		
148					25	[0.536][8]		
149					35	[0.752][7]		
150	*U. uruguayensis*	Cartesian diver respirometer	Muscle		15	[0.062][7]	Specimens from Santos, Brazil	61
151					35	[0.277][7]; [0.264][8]		
152					15	[0.085][7]	Specimens from Florianopolis, Brazil	61
153					35	[0.138][7]; [0.189][8]		
154			Brain (supraesophageal ganglion)		5	[0.191][8]	Specimens from Santos, Brazil	61
155					15	[0.509][8]		
156					20	[0.646][8]		
157					35	[1.641][7]		

[7] Specimens warm-acclimated. [8] Specimens cold-acclimated.

continued

	Class & Species (Synonym)	Method	Tissue	No. of Speci-mens	Temp °C	Q_{O_2}	Remarks	Ref-er-ence
158					5	[0.290][8]	Specimens from Florianopolis, Brazil	61
159					15	[0.723][8]		
160					20	[0.856][8]		
161					35	[1.023][7]		
	Insecta							
162	*Antheraea polyphemus (Telea polyphemus)*	Warburg	Wing	3♀ pupae	25	[3.2]		57
163	*Belostoma* spp.	Volumetric microrespirometer	Flight muscle, teased	3 adults	25	1.16 [4.23]	10-20 mg wet wt tissue; in Wilder & Smith saline	46
164			Leg muscle (coxal levator), teased	3 adults	25	0.308 [1.43]		
165	*Carpocapsa pomonella (Cydia pomonella)*	Warburg	Fat body	5♂ larvae	20	[0.544]	Based on total dry wt	22
166				7♀ larvae	20	[0.607]		
167			Muscle	5♂ larvae	20	[0.785]		22
168				7♀ larvae	20	[0.972]		
169	*Hyalophora cecropia (Platysamia cecropia)*	Warburg	Wing	4♀ pupae	25	[5.1]	Pupae in diapause	57
170	*Hydrophilus ater*	Volumetric microrespirometer	Flight muscle, teased	6 adults	25	1.91 [5.71]	10-20 mg wet wt tissue; in Wilder & Smith saline	46
171			Leg muscle (coxal levator), teased	6 adults	25	0.416 [1.91]		
172	*Leucophaea maderae*	Warburg	Thoracic muscle, teased	11♂	26	[3.25]	Approx 150 mg wet wt tissue; in Belar's solution	51
173				10♀	26	[3.35]		
174	*Periplaneta americana*	Warburg	Prothorax	4 adults	25	0.88	Same 4 adults	36
175			Mesothorax	4 adults	25	0.80		
176			Metathorax	4 adults	25	0.54		
177			Abdomen	4 adults	25	0.61		
178			Leg muscle, teased	10 adult ♂	25	[5.04]	Approx 200 mg wet wt tissue; in Belar-phosphate buffer	3
179				16 adult ♀	25	[2.62]		
180		Volumetric microrespirometer	Flight muscle, teased	3 adult ♂	25	1.88 [7.30]	10-20 mg wet wt tissue; in Wilder & Smith saline	46
181				3 adult ♀	25	1.21 [4.54]		
182			Leg muscle (coxal levator), teased	5 adult ♂	25	1.55 [6.2]		
183				3 adult ♀	25	1.04 [4.41]		
184	*Schistocerca infumata*	Volumetric microrespirometer	Flight muscle, teased	4 adults	25	1.67	10-20 mg wet wt tissue; in Wilder & Smith saline	46
185			Leg muscle (coxal levator), teased	3 adults	25	1.22		
186	*Tachycines asynamorus (Diestrammena japanica)*	Warburg	Femur, intact	6	25	0.16	Gas phase: air	36
				Annelida				
	Oligochaeta							
187	*Eisenia foetida*[9]	Warburg	Body wall, minced			0.23-0.48	100 mg wet wt tissue; assays on groups of segments	44
188			Body wall, homogenate			0.026-0.076	200 mg wet wt tissue; assays on groups of segments	44

[7] Specimens warm-acclimated. [8] Specimens cold-acclimated. [9] Clitellate worms.

continued

	Class & Species (Synonym)	Method	Tissue	No. of Specimens	Temp °C	Q_{O_2}	Remarks	Reference
189			Viscera, minced			0.01-0.12	100 mg wet wt tissue; assays on groups of segments	44
190			Viscera, homogenate			0.025-0.046	200 mg wet wt tissue; assays on groups of segments	44
191	*Lumbricus terrestris*	Barcroft	Body wall, slices	32	15-18	[0.632]	2.5- to 5-g specimens; 83 mg dry wt tissue; in mixture of 20% O_2 & 80% N_2 gas	31
192				32	15-18	[0.685]	2.5- to 5-g specimens; 83 mg dry wt tissue; in mixture of 20% O_2, 20% CO_2, & 60% N_2 gas	31
	Polychaeta							
193	*Sabella penicillus (S. pavonina)*	Micro-Winkler	Isolated crown	21	17	0.167 [1.152]		16
	Mollusca							
	Cephalopoda							
194	*Eledone* sp.	Warburg; also differential manometer	Mantle nerve & stellate ganglion, unstimulated	3	16	[0.63]	9.8 mg dry wt tissue; in artificial seawater with urea & bicarbonate	42
195	*Loligo pealeii*	Warburg	Eye, retina	3	25	[1.1]		49
196			"cornea"	4	25	[0.4]		
197			lens	2	25	[0.002]		
198			Gill	5	25	[1.8]		
199		Continuous flow respirometer (O_2 cathode)	Stellar nerve, giant axons only		16	0.068	Mean value from 8 nerves	12
200			Stellar nerve, giant axons + accompanying small nerve fibers		16	0.074	Mean value from 5 nerves	12
201		Microvolumeter	Giant nerve fiber, entire		15	0.106-0.112		11, 54
202			Giant nerve fiber, isolated sheath		15	0.125-0.200		
203	*Octopus* sp.	Warburg; also differential manometer	Mantle nerve, unstimulated	1	16	[0.28]	24.5 mg dry wt tissue; in artificial seawater lacking urea & bicarbonate	42
204	*O. macropus*	Warburg	Salivary gland, slices		24	[0.88]	Frozen tissue used. Gas phase: 95% N_2 & 5% O_2.	19
205	*O. vulgaris*	Warburg	Mantle muscle		24	[0.42]	Gas phase: air	19
206			Optic ganglion		24	[1.86]		
207			Midgut gland		24	[0.67]		
208			Salivary gland		24	[0.83]		
209			Branchial gland		24	[1.13]		
210			Gill		24	[1.64]		
211			Branchial heart		24	[1.78]		
212			Central heart		24	[1.57]		
213			Kidney		24	[2.07]		
214	*Sepia officinalis*	Warburg	Nerve	4	20-22	[0.63]	50- to 100-mg wet wt tissue; in seawater	7

continued

	Class & Species (Synonym)	Method	Tissue	No. of Specimens	Temp °C	Q_{O_2}	Remarks	Reference
	Bivalvia							
215	*Anodonta cellensis (A. celensis)*	Polarograph	Posterior adductor muscle, strips			0.070[10]; 0.067[11]	Yellow portion of muscle	6
216						0.073[10]; 0.080[11]	White portion of muscle	6
217	*Corbicula sandai*	Warburg	Mantle		25	0.162	100 mg tissue. Gas phase: 95% N_2, 5% O_2.	25
218			Gill		25	0.248		
219	*Crassostrea angulata (Gryphaea angulata)*	Warburg	Mantle, whole	7	28	[0.89]	100 mg wet wt tissue	9
220			pieces	8	28	[0.98]		
221			Muscle, whole	7	28	[0.15]	120 mg wet wt tissue	9
222			pieces	8	28	[0.26]		
223			Midgut gland, pieces	8	28	[1.96]	60 mg wet wt tissue	9
224			Gill, whole	7	28	[1.76]	80 mg wet wt tissue	9
225			pieces	8	28	[1.86]		
226	*C. gigas (Ostrea gigas)*	Warburg	Mantle		25	0.29	2-yr specimens, 11 cm long; 50-100 mg wet wt tissue. Gas phase: air.	33
227			Gill		25	0.53		
228			Heart		25	0.39		
229		Micro-Winkler	Gill		25	0.86-1.44	500 mg wet wt tissue; in seawater	45
	C. virginica (Ostrea virginica)	Warburg	Mantle				Florida oysters	30
230			Marginal zone		18-21	0.13		
231			Pallial zone		18-21	0.15		
232			Central zone		18-21	0.12		
233			Strips		26	0.156	180-220 mg wet wt tissue	40
234		Thunberg	Adductor muscle, pieces	5	28	0.0480	Specimens 6.8-13.5 cm long; gray portion of muscle, 269 mg wet wt	27
235				5	28	0.0372	Specimens 6.8-13.5 cm long; white portion of muscle, 228 mg wet wt	27
236	*Cristaria plicata*	Warburg	Mantle, edge	6	25	[0.7]	4- to 6-yr specimens	26
237			lobe	6	25	[0.5]		
238			Adductor muscle, striated & smooth	4	25	[0.14]		
239			Gill	10	25	[1.8]		
240			Heart	5	25	[0.8]		
241	*Hyriopsis schlegelii*	Warburg	Mantle, edge	8	25	[0.6]	4- to 6-yr specimens	26
242			lobe	8	25	[0.5]		
243			Adductor muscle, striated & smooth	6	25	[0.19]		
244			Gill	24	25	[1.3]		
245			Heart	10	25	[0.8]		
246	*Isognomon alata (Pedalion alata)*	Warburg	Gill	6	25	[1.3]		49
247	*Mercenaria mercenaria (Venus mercenaria)*	Differential volumeter (modified Thunberg)	Mantle, pieces	8	20	[0.771]	Central portion of mantle, 20 mg dry wt; in seawater (specific gravity, 1.025)	28
248			Adductor muscle, pieces	3	20	[0.0712]	Red portion of muscle, 100 mg dry wt; in seawater (specific gravity, 1.025)	28

[10] Winter. [11] Spring.

continued

	Class & Species (Synonym)	Method	Tissue	No. of Speci-mens	Temp °C	Q_{O_2}	Remarks	Ref-er-ence
249			Gill pieces	21	20	[1.225]	25 mg dry wt tissue; in seawater (specific gravity, 1.025); respiratory quotient, 0.90	28
250	*Mytilus* sp.	Winkler	Gill	5-6	17	[1.26-1.73]	67-90 mg dry wt tissue; in seawater (salinity = $15^{0}/_{00}$)	53
251	*M. crassitesta*	Warburg	Gill		25	0.26	Specimens 8 cm long; 50-100 mg wet wt tissue. Gas phase: air.	33
252	*M. edulis*	Warburg	Retractor muscle of foot	9	7.5	0.018 [0.11]	In buffered artificial seawater	20
253				13	15	0.037 [0.22]		
254				13	25	0.040 [0.24]		
255		Winkler	Gill	11	19	[1.92]	Specimens 5.7-7.0 cm long; in artificial seawater (salinity = $15^{0}/_{00}$)	47
256	*M. galloprovincialis*	Warburg	Heart, ventricle		23	[1.18]	In seawater	7
257	*Noetia ponderosa* (*Arca ponderosa*)	Thunberg microrespirometer	Posterior adductor muscle, pieces	7	28	0.0312	Specimens 5.0-6.9 cm long; red portion of muscle, 278 mg wet wt	27
258				7	28	0.0179	Specimens 5.0-6.9 cm long; white portion of muscle, 285 mg wet wt	27
259	*Ostrea circumpicta*	Micro-Winkler	Heart, ventricle, resting		24	0.061	Specimens 15 cm long; 92 mg wet wt tissue	43
260	*Pecten irradians*	Thunberg microrespirometer	Adductor muscle, pieces	12	28	0.0767	Specimens 5.0-8.2 cm long; gray portion of muscle, 282 mg dry wt	27
261				12	28	0.0424	Specimens 5.0-8.2 cm long; white portion of muscle, 269 mg dry wt	27
262	*Pinctada martensii*	Warburg	Epithelium adhering to inner surface of shell	5	25	[0.17] 12/	2-yr specimens	32
263			Epithelium of middle part of mantle edge	5	25	[0.4] 12/	2-yr specimens	32
264			Mantle		25	0.15	Specimens 6 cm long; 50-100 mg wet wt tissue. Gas phase: air.	33
265			Mantle, pallial margin	7	25	[0.9] 12/	2-yr specimens	32
266			Foot muscle	4	25	[0.6] 12/	2-yr specimens	32
267			Adductor muscle	5	25	[0.15] 12/	2-yr specimens	32
268			Midgut gland	6	25	[0.8] 12/	2-yr specimens	32
269					25	0.27	Specimens 6 cm long; 50-100 mg wet wt tissue. Gas phase: air.	33
270			Gill	10	25	[2.1] 12/	2-yr specimens	32
271					25	0.48	Specimens 6 cm long; 50-100 mg wet wt tissue. Gas phase: air.	33
272			Gonad	6	25	[0.6] 12/	2-yr specimens	32

12/ Latter half of June.

continued

	Class & Species (Synonym)	Method	Tissue	No. of Specimens	Temp °C	Q_{O_2}	Remarks	Reference
273	*Pinna muricata*	Thunberg microrespirometer	Pedal retractor muscle, pieces	4	28	0.0371	Specimens 16.5-28.2 cm long; 258 mg wet wt tissue	27
274			Posterior adductor muscle, pieces	6	28	0.0507	Specimens 14.2-28.8 cm long; gray portion of muscle, 273 mg wet wt	27
275				6	28	0.0413	Specimens 14.2-28.8 cm long; white portion of muscle, 276 mg wet wt	27
276	*Saxostrea commercialis*	Warburg	Adductor muscle, homogenate		37	[≯0.21]	2- to 3-yr specimens; 600 mg tissue. Homogenization, 1.5 min at 37°C.	29
	Gastropoda							
277	*Aplysia* sp.	Warburg; also differential manometer	Nerve, unstimulated		16	[0.52]	22.9 mg dry wt tissue; in artificial seawater with urea & bicarbonate	42
278		Warburg	Gizzard, slices		25	[0.33]	Frozen tissue used	18
279	*Helix aspersa*	Warburg	Heart		23	[1.00]	1.50 mg dry wt tissue; in isotonic chloride solution	7
280	*H. pisana*	Warburg	Heart		23	[1.75]	0.50 mg dry wt tissue; in isotonic chloride solution	7
281	*H. pomatia*	Warburg	Mantle, slices	24	28	[1.76]	In Baldwin's phosphate solution	34
282			Body wall, slices	24	28	[0.78]		
283			Forefoot, slices	17	28	[0.81]		
284			Middle foot, slices	12	28	[0.67]		
285			Rear foot, slices	13	28	[0.79]		
286			Columella muscle, slices	24	28	[1.80]		
287			Cerebral ganglion, slices	20	28	[4.00]		
288			Pedal ganglion, slices	18	28	[2.89]		
289			Gut buccal mass, slices	24	28	[1.37]		
290			Esophagus, slices	24	28	[2.68]		
291			Midgut, slices	24	28	[2.56]		
292			Midgut gland, slices	23	28	[2.78]	In Baldwin's phosphate solution	34
293				92	28	[2.93]	In Baldwin's phosphate solution	1
294			Heart		23	[0.85]	3.50 mg dry wt tissue; in isotonic chloride solution	7
295			Kidney, slices	27	28	[2.24]	In Baldwin's phosphate solution	34
296			Female duct, slices	24	28	[1.03]		
297			Albuminous gland, slices	22	28	[1.20]		
298			Dart sac, slices	22	28	[0.66]		
299	*H. vermiculata*	Warburg	Heart		23	[1.36]	0.92 mg dry wt tissue; in isotonic chloride solution	7
	Aschelminthes							
	Nematoda							
300	*Ascaris lumbricoides*	Warburg	Muscle, homogenate		39	[1.3]		37

continued

	Class & Species (Synonym)	Method	Tissue	No. of Speci-mens	Temp °C	Q_{O_2}	Remarks	Ref-er-ence
301			Muscle, particulate fraction		25	0.0718	Undialyzed supernatant of perienteric fluid added. Gas phase: O_2.	10
302	*Parascaris equorum (Ascaris megalocephala)*	Warburg	Muscle of body wall, cell suspension		39	6.0	In physiological saline. Gas phase: air.	15
303					39	2.3	In distilled water. Gas phase: air.	15
				Cnidaria				
	Anthozoa							
304	*Condylactis gigantea*	Warburg	Tentacles	3	25	[0.8]		49
305	*Gorgonia flabellum*	Warburg	Branches, cell suspension	2	25	[2.2]	Dry wt tissue minus skeletal material	49
306	*Plexaura flexuosa*	Warburg	Slices	13	25	[3.0]	Dry wt tissue minus skeletal material	49
	Scyphozoa							
307	*Cassiopeia frondosa*	Warburg	Umbrella	18	25	[0.7]		49
308			Tentacles	10	25	[0.6]		
309	*Pelagia noctiluca (P. cyanella)*	Warburg	Umbrella	2	25	[0.8]		49
	Hydrozoa							
310	*Physalia physalis (P. pelagica)*	Warburg	Tentacles	3	25	[1.7]		49
				Porifera				
	Demospongiae							
311	*Cinachyra cavernosa*	Warburg	Slices	3	25	[0.6]	Dry wt tissue minus skeletal material	49
312	*Dysidea crawshayi*	Warburg	Slices	2	25	[0.6]	Dry wt tissue minus skeletal material	49
313	*Geodia gibberosa*	Warburg	Slices	1	25	[0.6]	Dry wt tissue minus skeletal material	49
314	*Ircinia fasciculata*	Warburg	Slices	5	25	[1.6]	Dry wt tissue minus skeletal material	49
315	*Lissodendoryx isodictyalis*	Warburg	Slices	4	25	[1.4]	Dry wt tissue minus skeletal material	49
316	*Microciona prolifera*	Warburg	Finger-like projections, apical portions, slices	1	37	0.115	Approx 200 mg tissue	21
317	*Pseudaxinella rosacea (Axinella rosacea)*	Warburg	Slices	2	25	[0.7]	Dry wt tissue minus skeletal material	49
318	*Spheciospongia* sp.	Warburg	Slices	1	25	[0.4]	Dry wt tissue minus skeletal material	49
319	*Tedania ignis*	Warburg	Slices	6	25	[2.9]	Dry wt tissue minus skeletal material	49
320	*Terpios fugax*	Warburg	Slices	1	25	[0.6]	Dry wt tissue minus skeletal material	49
321	*Tethya aurantia*	Warburg	Slices	1	25	[0.5]	Dry wt tissue minus skeletal material	49

Contributors: Bliss, Dorothy E., and Skinner, Dorothy M.

continued

References

[1] Baldwin, E. 1938. Biochem. J. 32:1225.
[2] Barron, E. S. G. 1958. Perspectives Marine Biol. Symp. Scripps Inst. Oceanog., 1956, p. 211.
[3] Barron, E. S. G., and T. N. Tahmisian. 1948. J. Cellular Comp. Physiol. 32:57.
[4] Belding, H. S., et al. 1942. Physiol. Zool. 15:75.
[5] Bliss, D. E., and D. M. Skinner. 1963. Tissue respiration in invertebrates. American Museum of Natural History, New York.
[6] Brecht, K., G. Utz, and E. Lutz. 1955. Arch. Ges. Physiol. 260:524.
[7] Cardot, H., S. Faure, and A. Arvanitaki. 1950. J. Physiol. (Paris) 42:849.
[8] Chang, T. H. 1931. Proc. Soc. Exptl. Biol. Med. 28: 954.
[9] Chapheau, M. 1932. Bull. Sta. Biol. Arcachon 29:85.
[10] Chin, C.-H., and E. Bueding. 1954. Biochim. Biophys. Acta 13:331.
[11] Coelho, R. R. Unpublished. Massachusetts Institute of Technology, Biology Dept., Cambridge, 1963.
[12] Connelly, C. M. 1952. Biol. Bull. 103:315.
[13] Dann, M., and E. M. Gardner. 1930. Proc. Soc. Exptl. Biol. Med. 28:200.
[14] Dehnel, P. A., and D. A. McCaughran. 1964. Comp. Biochem. Physiol. 13:233.
[15] Durrani, M. Z. 1958. Pakistan J. Sci. Res. 10:129.
[16] Fox, H. M. 1938. Proc. Roy. Soc. (London), B, 125: 554.
[17] Fox, H. M., and C. A. Wingfield. 1937. Nature 139: 369.
[18] Ghiretti, F., A. Ghiretti-Magaldi, and L. Tosi. 1959. J. Gen. Physiol. 42:1185.
[19] Ghiretti-Magaldi, A., A. Giuditta, and F. Ghiretti. 1958. J. Cellular Comp. Physiol. 52:389.
[20] Glaister, D., and M. Kerly. 1936. J. Physiol. (London) 87:56.
[21] Gordon, E. E., M. Spiegel, and C. A. Villee. 1955. J. Cellular Comp. Physiol. 45:479.
[22] Graham, K. 1946. Trans. Roy. Soc. Can., Ser. 3, Sect. V, 40:41.
[23] Guttman, R. 1935. Biol. Bull. 69:356.
[24] Herreid, C. F., and J. L. Smothers. 1967. Comp. Biochem. Physiol. 20:333.
[25] Higashi, S. 1961. Bull. Japan. Soc. Sci. Fisheries 27: 282.
[26] Higashi, S., and K. Kawai. 1959. Ibid. 25:222.
[27] Hopkins, H. S. 1930. J. Exptl. Zool. 56:209.
[28] Hopkins, H. S. 1946. Ibid. 102:143.
[29] Humphrey, G. F. 1946. Australian J. Exptl. Biol. Med. Sci. 24:261.
[30] Jodrey, L. H., and K. M. Wilbur. 1955. Biol. Bull. 108:346.
[31] Johnson, M. L. 1942. J. Exptl. Biol. 18:266.
[32] Kawai, K. 1957. Bull. Japan. Soc. Sci. Fisheries 22: 626.
[33] Kawai, K. 1959. Biol. Bull. 117:125.
[34] Kerkut, G. A., and M. S. Laverack. 1957. J. Exptl. Biol. 34:97.
[35] King, E. N. 1965. Comp. Biochem. Physiol. 15:93.
[36] Kubista, V. 1956. Vestn. Cesk. Zool. Spolecnosti 20: 188.
[37] Laser, H. 1944. Biochem. J. 38:333.
[38] Lindeman, V. F. 1939. Physiol. Zool. 12:214.
[39] Mantel, L. H. 1967. Comp. Biochem. Physiol. 20: 743.
[40] Maroney, S. P., Jr., A. A. Barber, and K. M. Wilbur. 1957. Biol. Bull. 112:92.
[41] McWhinnie, M. A., and J. J. Kirchenberg. 1962. Comp. Biochem. Physiol. 6:117.
[42] Meyerhof, O., and W. Schulz. 1929. Biochem. Z. 206:158.
[43] Nomura, S. 1950. Sci. Rept. Tohoku Univ., Ser. 4, 18:279.
[44] O'Brien, B. R. A. 1957. Australian J. Exptl. Biol. Med. Sci. 35:83.
[45] Okamura, N. 1959. Sci. Rept. Tohoku Univ., Ser. 4, 25:91.
[46] Perez-Gonzalez, M. D., and G. A. Edwards. 1954. Univ. Sao Paulo Fac. Filosof. Cienc. Letras Zool. Bol. 19:373.
[47] Pieh, S. 1936. Zool. Jahrb. Abt. Allgem. Zool. Physiol. Tiere 56:129.
[48] Quinn, D. J., and C. E. Lane. 1967. Biol. Bull. 133: 245.
[49] Robbie, W. A. 1949. J. Gen. Physiol. 32:655.
[50] Roberts, J. L. 1957. Physiol. Zool. 30:242.
[51] Samuels, A. 1956. Biol. Bull. 110:179.
[52] Scheer, B. T., C. W. Schwabe, and M. A. R. Scheer. 1952. Physiol. Comp. Oecol. 2:327.
[53] Schlieper, C. 1931. Biol. Zentr. 51:401.
[54] Schmitt, F. O., and N. Geschwind. 1957. Progr. Biophys. Biophys. Chem. 8:165.
[55] Shanes, A. M., and H. S. Hopkins. 1948. J. Neurophysiol. 11:331.
[56] Shapiro, H. 1937. J. Cellular Comp. Physiol. 9:381.
[57] Shappirio, D. G., and W. R. Harvey. 1965. J. Insect Physiol. 11:305.
[58] Skinner, D. M. 1962. Biol. Bull. 123:635.
[59] Stevenson, J. R., and R. P. Schneider. 1962. J. Exptl. Zool. 150:17.
[60] Vernberg, F. J. 1956. Physiol. Zool. 29:227.
[61] Vernberg, F. J., and W. B. Vernberg. 1966. Comp. Biochem. Physiol. 19:489.
[62] Vernberg, F. J., and W. B. Vernberg. 1966. J. Elisha Mitchell Sci. Soc. 82:30.
[63] Vernberg, W. B., and F. J. Vernberg. 1966. Comp. Biochem. Physiol. 17:363.

DIAGRAM FOR TABLE 73

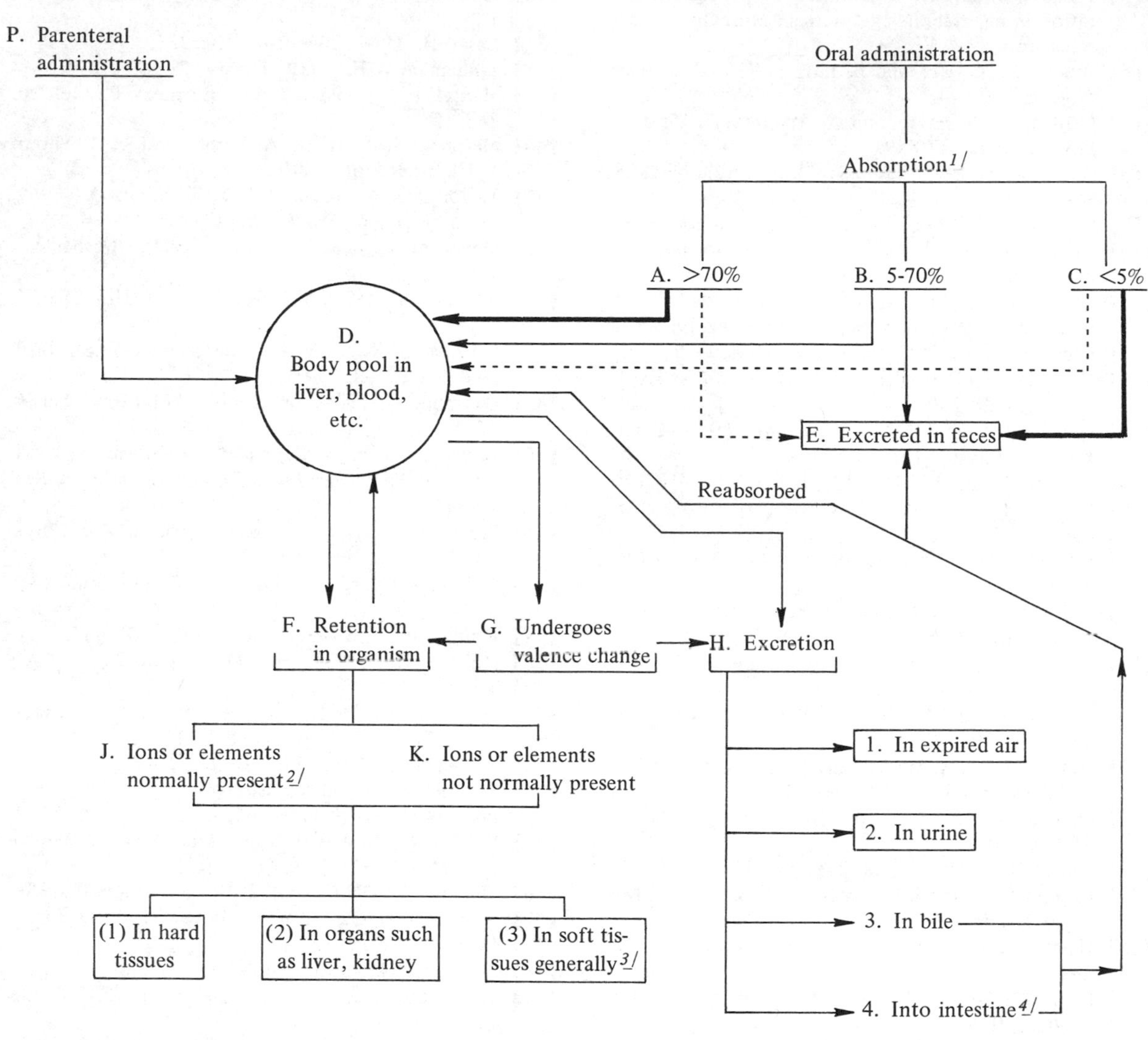

1/ Percent absorption of ions from oral administration has in some cases been rather arbitrarily classified, since the extent of absorption may depend on the amount administered and on the presence or absence of food residues in the digestive tract. 2/ Some trace elements with no known function also included. 3/ Primarily muscle, skin, and extracellular fluids. 4/ Other than in the bile, or by a route not definitely established.

VII. METABOLIC PATHWAYS

73. PATHWAYS OF MINERAL METABOLISM: LABORATORY MAMMALS

The course, or courses, of the various ions during metabolism can be located in the diagram *(at left)* by tracing the combination of letters or numbers accompanying each ion (Pathways columns *below*). Data present a consensus from the findings of various investigators regarding a variety of mammalian species. The ions were administered in the form of simple soluble compounds or metallic oxides, unless otherwise specified. Underscoring indicates that the data were obtained at least in part from studies using radioactive isotopes. Different isotopes of the same element may show different tissue predilections, but there is usually no difference in their absorption or route of excretion. **Other Known Pathways** are listed, insofar as possible, in order of decreasing importance. *Symbol:* $^{+}$ indicates valence state to which data applied.

	Ions	Principal Oral Pathways[1]	Other Known Pathways	Reference
	Cations[2]			
1	Actinium	CE	PDFK(1, 2)	14
2	Aluminum	CE	PDH2, PDH3, PDFJ(2, 3)	50,108,110
3	Americium	CE	PDH4, PDFK(2, 1), PDH2	105,116,121
4	Antimony $^{3+}$	BE, BDH2	BDFK(2, 3), BDH4	40,43,50,110
5	Arsenic $^{3+}$	BE, BDH2	BDFK(3, 2), BDH4	22,43,67,71,110
6	Barium	BE, BDH4	BDFK(1), BDH2(tr)	16,46,83,110,121
7	Beryllium	CE	PDFK(1, 2), PDH2, PDH4	100,110
8	Bismuth $^{3+}$	CE	PDFK(2, 3), PDH2, PDH4	43,50,70,110
9	Cadmium	CE	PDFK(2, 1, 3)[3], PDH4, PDH2	7,27,30,50,93,110,129
10	Calcium	BE, BDFJ(1)	BDH4, BDH3, BDH2, BDFJ(3)	4,26,50,89,109,115,121,122,129,130
11	Cerium[4]	CE	PDFK(2, 1), PDH3, PDH2	2,30,31,50,58,74,112,121
12	Cesium	ADH2	ADH3, ADH4, ADFJ(3)	38,46,65,85-88,107,110,121
13	Chromium $^{3+}$	CE	PDH2, PDH4, PDFK(2, 1)[3]	30,32,54,63,125
14	Cobalt $^{2+}$	BE, BDH2	BDH3, BDH4, BDFJ(2)	8,23,26,50,69,110,129
15	Copper $^{2+}$	BE, BDH3	BDH2, BDFJ(2)	26,50,75,90,110,129
16	Curium	CE	PDFK(2, 1), PDH4, PDH2	103,116,121
17	Dysprosium[4]	CE	PDFK(1), PDH2, PDH3, PDH4	31,45
18	Erbium[4]	CE	PDFK(1, 2), PDH3, PDH2, PDH4	31,45
19	Europium[4]	CE	PDH3, PDH2, PDFK(1, 2)	31,45
20	Francium	Probably ADH2[5]	PDFK(2, 3)	91
21	Gadolinium[4]	CE	PDH2, PDH3, PDFK(1, 2)	31,45
22	Gallium	CE	PDH2, PDFK(1, 2), PDH4	29,66,110
23	Germanium	ADH2	ADH4, ADFK(2)	110
24	Gold	CE	PDFK(2), PDH2, PDH4	43,50,94,110
25	Hafnium[4]	CE	PDFK(2, 1), PDH2, PDH4	45,59,110
26	Holmium[4]	CE	PDFK(2, 1), PDH3, PDH4	31,45,74
27	Indium	CE	PDFK(3, 1, 2), PDH4, PDH2	30,49
28	Iridium	CE	PDH2, PDH4, PDFK(3, 2, 1)	30
29	Iron	BE	PDH4, PDFJ(2, 1)	26,50,62,76,95,110,129,130
30	Lanthanum[4]	CE	PDFK(2, 1), PDH3, PDH2	19,30,31,45,46,50,113,121
31	Lead $^{2+}$	BE	BDFK(2, 1), BDH2	1,13,30,43,44,50,70,99,110
32	Lithium	ADH2	ADH4, ADFJ(3, 2)	37,44,98,110
33	Lutetium[4]	CE	PDFK(1, 2), PDH2, PDH4	31,45,74
34	Magnesium	BE, BDH2	BDH3, BDFJ(1, 3)	3,12,17,18,43,50,108,110,129
35	Manganese $^{2+}$	CE	PDH3, PDH4, PDFJ(2, 3)	11,26,35,50,77,78,110
36	Mercury $^{2+}$	BE, BDH2	BDFK(2, 1, 3), BDH4, BDH3	6,30,43,50,110
37	Neodymium[4]	CE	PDFK(2, 1), PDH3, PDH2	30,31,45,48,50,68
38	Neptunium	CE	PDFK(1)	46,116

1/ Ions when given parenterally may be assumed to follow the same pathways. 2/ Because of inadequate information no pathways have been listed for berkelium, californium, einsteinium, fermium, and mendelevium. 3/ Especially testis. 4/ Usually administered as a soluble complex. 5/ As judged from the position of the element in the periodic table, or on solubility at neutral pH values, or both.

continued

	Ion	Principal Oral Pathways[1]	Other Known Pathways	Reference
39	Nickel $^{2+}$	BE, BDH2	BDH4, BDFJ(2)	8,44,50,110,117,127,129
40	Niobium[4]	CE	PDH2, PDH4, PDFK(1, 2, 3)	19,30,46,96,121
41	Palladium	Probably CE[5]	PDH2, PDH4, PDFK(2)	30,50,81
42	Platinum	CE	PDH2, PDH4, PDFK(2, 3, 1)	30,50
43	Plutonium	CE	PDFK(1, 2), PDH4, PDH2	15,36,46,74,101,106,116,121,128
44	Polonium	CE	PDFK(2, 1), PDH4, PDH2	34,56,114,121
45	Potassium	ADH2	ADFJ(3, 2), ADH3, ADH4	25,26,50,85,87,110,122
46	Praseodymium	CE	PDFK(2, 3), PDH3, PDH2	31,45,46,50
47	Promethium	CE	PDFK(2, 1), PDH3, PDH2	31,45,46,121
48	Protactinium	Probably CE[5]	PDFK(1)	105
49	Radium	BE, BDFK(1, 2)	BDH4, BDH2	34,57,89,110,115,121
50	Radium D	Probably BE[5]	PDH2, PDH4, PDFK(1)	13,84
51	Rhodium	CE	PDFK(3, 2, 1), PDH2, PDH4	30
52	Rubidium	ADH2	ADFJ(2, 3), ADH3, ADH4	82,85,110
53	Ruthenium	CE	PDH2, PDH4, PDFK(3, 1, 2)	30,119-121
54	Samarium[4]	CE	PDFK(2, 1), PDH3, PDH2	30,45,50
55	Scandium	Probably CE[5]	PDFJ(2, 3, 1), PDH2	5,45
56	Selenium	ADH2	ADFK(2, 3), ADH4, ADGH1	39,52,79,80,110
57	Silver	CE	PDH3, PDFJ(2, 3), PDH2	43,50,104,110,129
58	Sodium	ADH2	ADFJ(3, 1, 2), ADH3, ADH4	26,50,108,110
59	Strontium	BE, BDFK(1)	BDH2, BDH4, BDH3	4,46,57,89,109,110,121
60	Tantalum	CE	PDH2, PDH4, PDFK(2, 1, 3)	30,31
61	Technetium	Probably CE[5]	PDH2, PDH4, PDFK(3, 2, 1)	30
62	Tellurium $^{4+}$	BE, BDGH2	BDGH3, BDGFK(2), BDGH1	46,110,121
63	Terbium[4]	CE	PDFK(1, 2), PDH2, PDH3, PDH4	31,45,74
64	Thallium	BE	BDFK(1, 2, 3), BDH2, BDH4	50,72,110
65	Thorium	CE	PDFK(2, 1), PDH4, PDH2, PDH3	46,102,110,121
66	Thulium[4]	CE	PDFK(1, 2), PDH2, PDH3, PDH4	31,45,74
67	Tin $^{2+}$	BE, BDH2	BDFJ(3, 2), BDH4, BDH3	50,110,129
68	Tin $^{4+}$	BE, BDH2	BDH4, BDFJ(1, 3, 2)	30
69	Titanium	Probably CE[5]	CDFJ(2), CDH2	110,111
70	Uranium $^{4+}$	Probably CE[5]	PDFK(2)	121
71	Uranium $^{6+}$	BE, BDH2	BDFK(1, 2)	28,50,110,121
72	Ytterbium[4]	CE	PDFK(1, 2), PDH2, PDH3, PDH4	31,45,74
73	Yttrium	CE	PDFK(1, 2), PDH2, PDH4	19,24,31,41,46,58,74,101,121,128
74	Zinc	CE	CDH4, CDFJ(2, 1, 3)[3], CDH2	10,42,50,78,92,97,121-124,129
75	Zirconium	CE	PDFK(1, 3)	19,46,96,121
	Anions[6]			
76	Astatide	Probably A[5]	PDFK(3), PDH2, PDH4	47
77	Bicarbonate	ADH2	ADH1, ADH3, ADH4, ADFJ	110
78	Borate	ADH2	....	50,110
79	Bromate	ADH2	ADG(to bromide)	51,110
80	Bromide	ADH2	ADH3, ADH4, ADFJ	20,51,110
81	Chlorate	ADH2	....	51,94
82	Chloride	ADH2	ADH3, ADH4, ADFJ	51,108,110
83	Chromate	BDH2	BDH4, BDGH2, BDGH4, BDGFK(2)	50,73,110,125
84	Cyanide	ADH2	ADH1, ADG(to SCN)	110
85	Ferrocyanide	ADH2	....	60,61,110
86	Fluoride	BDH2	BDFJ(1, 3), BDH4	43,78,108,110
87	Hypophosphite	ADH2	....	110
88	Iodate	ADG(to iodide)	ADH2	110
89	Iodide	ADH2	ADFJ(3, 2), ADH3	43,51,110

[1] Ions may be assumed to follow the same pathways when given parenterally. [3] Especially testis. [4] Usually administered as a soluble complex. [5] As judged from the position of the element in the periodic table, or on solubility at neutral pH values, or both. [6] Because of inadequate information, no pathways have been listed for cyanate, ferricyanide, and periodate.

continued

73. PATHWAYS OF MINERAL METABOLISM: LABORATORY MAMMALS

	Ion	Principal Oral Pathways[1/]	Other Known Pathways	Reference
90	Molybdate	BDH2	BDFJ(2, 3), BDH3	10,21,31,44,50,110,118,121
91	Nitrate	ADH2	ADH3, ADH4, ADFK	51,110
92	Nitrite	ADG(to nitrate)	....	110
93	Osmate	....	PDH2, PDH4, PDFK(3, 2, 1)	30
94	Oxalate	ADH2	....	110
95	Perchlorate	ADH2	....	51
96	Permanganate	CE(reduced to MnO_2)	....	51
97	Perrhenate	CE	PDH2, PDFK(3)[7/], PDH4	30,55
98	Phosphate	BE, BDH2	BDFJ(1, 2, 3), BDH3, BDH4	26,43,110
99	Silicate	BE, BDH2	BDFJ(2)	44,53,108,110,111
100	Sulfate	BE, BDH2	BDH3, BDH4, BDG	26,33,51,64,110
101	Sulfide	ADG(to sulfate)	ADH1	110
102	Thiocyanate	ADH2	ADH3, ADFJ, ADGH2	110
103	Thiosulfate	BE	BDH2, BDGH2(to sulfate), BDFJ	51,110
104	Tungstate	BE, BDH2	BDFK(3, 1, 2), BDH4	31,50,126
105	Vanadate	BE	BDH2, BDH3	9,50,110

[1/] Ions may be assumed to follow the same pathways when given parenterally. [7/] Especially skin.

Contributor: McChesney, E. W.

References

[1] Adam, K. R., and M. Weatherall. 1954. J. Pharm. Pharmacol. 6:403.
[2] Aeberhardt, A., et al. 1962. Intern. J. Radiation Biol. 5:217.
[3] Aikawa, J. K., et al. 1959. Am. J. Physiol. 197:99.
[4] Bauer, G. C. H., et al. 1955. Acta Physiol. Scand. 35:56.
[5] Beck, G. 1948. Mikrochem. Ver. Mikrochim. Acta 34:62.
[6] Berlin, M., and S. Ullberg. 1963. Arch. Environ. Health 6:589.
[7] Berlin, M., and S. Ullberg. 1963. Ibid. 7:686.
[8] Bertrand, G., and M. Macheboeuf. 1925. Bull. Soc. Chim. France, Ser. 4, 37:934.
[9] Boyd, T. C., and N. K. De. 1933. Indian J. Med. Res. 20:789.
[10] Bruner, H. D. 1955. Am. J. Physiol. 183:600.
[11] Bruner, H. D., et al. 1953. Federation Proc. 12:305.
[12] Burch, G. E., et al. 1965. Proc. Soc. Exptl. Biol. Med. 118:581.
[13] Calhoun, J. A., et al. 1954. Arch. Ind. Hyg. Occupational Med. 9:9.
[14] Campbell, J. E., et al. 1956. Radiation Res. 4:294.
[15] Carritt, J., et al. 1947. J. Biol. Chem. 171:273.
[16] Castagnou, R., et al. Compt. Rend. 244:2996.
[17] Chutkow, J. G. 1964. J. Lab. Clin. Med. 63:80.
[18] Chutkow, J. G. 1965. Ibid. 65:912.
[19] Cochran, K. W., et al. 1950. Arch. Ind. Hyg. Occupational Med. 1:637.
[20] Cole, B. T., and H. Patrick. 1958. Arch. Biochem. Biophys. 74:357.
[21] Comar, C. L., et al. 1949. J. Biol. Chem. 180:913.
[22] Cremia, A. 1955. Arch. Intern. Pharmacodyn. 103:57.
[23] Cuthbertson, W. F. J., et al. 1950. Brit. J. Nutr. 4:42.
[24] Daigneault, E. A. 1963. Toxicol. Appl. Pharmacol. 5:331.
[25] Danowski, T. S., and J. R. Elkinton. 1951. Pharmacol. Rev. 3:42.
[26] Davis, G. K., and J. K. Loosli. 1954. Ann. Rev. Biochem. 23:459.
[27] Decker, C. F., et al. 1957. Arch. Biochem. Biophys. 66:140.
[28] Dounce, A. L. 1949. In C. Voegtlin and H. C. Hodge, ed. Natl. Nucl. Energy Ser. VI-1(2):951.
[29] Dudley, H. C., and H. H. Marrer, Jr. 1952. J. Pharmacol. Exptl. Therap. 106:129.
[30] Durbin, P. W., K. G. Scott, and J. G. Hamilton. 1957. Univ. Calif. (Berkeley) Publ. Pharmacol. 3(1):1.
[31] Durbin, P. W., et al. 1956. Proc. Soc. Expt. Biol. Med. 91:78.
[32] Edstrom, R. 1959. Acta Psychiat. Neurol. Scand. 34:26.
[33] Everett, N. B., and B. S. Simmons. 1952. Arch. Biochem. Biophys. 35:152.
[34] Fink, R. M., ed. 1950. Natl. Nucl. Energy Ser. VI-3.
[35] Fore, H. H., and R. A. Morton. 1952. Biochem. J. 51:600.
[36] Foreman, J. 1953. J. Am. Pharm. Assoc. Sci. Ed. 42:629.
[37] Fox, H. M., and H. Ramage. 1931. Proc. Roy. Soc. (London), B, 108:157.
[38] Furchner, J. E., et al. 1964. Proc. Soc. Exptl. Biol. Med. 116:375.
[39] Ganther, H. E. 1965. World Rev. Nutr. Dietet. 5:338.
[40] Gellhorn, A., et al. 1946. J. Pharmacol. Exptl. Therap. 87:169.
[41] Gensicke, F., et al. 1963. Fortschr. Gebiete Roentgenstrahlen Nuklearmed. 98:338.
[42] Gilbert, I. G. F., and D. M. Taylor. 1956. Biochim. Biophys. Acta 21:545.
[43] Goodman, L. S., and A. Gilman. 1965. The pharmacological basis of therapeutics. Ed. 3. Macmillan, New York.
[44] Guelbenzu, M. D., et al. 1951. Rev. Espan. Fisiol. 7:63.
[45] Haley, T. J. 1965. J. Pharm. Sci. 54:667.
[46] Hamilton, J. G. 1950. New Engl. J. Med. 240:863.
[47] Hamilton, J. G., et al. 1953. Univ. Calif. (Berkeley) Publ. Pharmacol. 2:283.
[48] Hara, R. 1949. Bull. Chem. Soc. Japan 22:179, 194,225.

continued

[49] Harrold, G. C., et al. 1943. J. Ind. Hyg. Toxicol. 25:233.
[50] Heffter, A., ed. 1927-35. Handbuch der experimentellen Pharmakologie. J. Springer, Berlin. Bd. 3.
[51] Heffter, A., ed. 1950. Ibid. Bd. 10.
[52] Hirooka, T., and J. T. Galambos. 1966. Proc. Soc. Exptl. Biol. Med. 121:743.
[53] Holt, P. F., et al. 1951. Biochem. J. 48:xliv.
[54] Hopkins, L. L., Jr. 1965. Am. J. Physiol. 209:731.
[55] Hurd, L. C., et al. 1933. Proc. Soc. Exptl. Biol. Med. 30:926.
[56] Hursh, J. B. 1951. J. Pharmacol. Exptl. Therap. 103:450.
[57] Hursh, J. B., et al. 1960. Am. J. Physiol. 199:513.
[58] Jowsey, J., et al. 1958. Radiation Res. 8:490.
[59] Kittle, C. F., et al. 1951. Proc. Soc. Exptl. Biol. Med. 76:278.
[60] Kleeman, C. R., and F. H. Epstein. 1956. Ibid. 93: 228.
[61] Kleeman, C. R., et al. 1955. Am. J. Physiol. 182: 548.
[62] Konitzer, K., and K. Michalke. 1965. Acta Biol. Med. Ger. 14:489.
[63] Kraintz, L., and R. V. Talmage. 1952. Proc. Soc. Exptl. Biol. Med. 81:490.
[64] Kulwich, R., et al. 1957. J. Nutr. 61:113.
[65] Kurlyandskaya, E. B., et al. 1953. Chem. Abstr. 52:3078.
[66] Lang, F. R. 1951. Ann. Internal Med. 35:1237.
[67] Lang, H., Jr., et al. 1950. Univ. Calif. (Berkeley) Publ. Pharmacol. 2:263.
[68] Lass, A., et al. 1955. Klin. Wochschr. 33:959.
[69] Lee, C. C. 1953. Federation Proc. 12:84.
[70] Lomholt, S. 1924. Biochem. J. 18:693.
[71] Lowry, O. H., et al. 1942. J. Pharmacol. Exptl. Therap. 76:221.
[72] Lund, A. 1956. Acta Pharmacol. Toxicol. 12:251.
[73] MacKenzie, R. D., et al. 1959. Arch. Biochem. Biophys. 79:200.
[74] Magnusson, G. 1963. Acta Pharmacol. Toxicol. 20(Suppl. 3):25.
[75] Mahoney, J. P., et al. 1955. J. Lab. Clin. Med. 46: 702.
[76] Maynard, L. A., and S. E. Smith. 1947. Ann. Rev. Biochem. 16:273.
[77] Maynard, L. S., and G. C. Cotzias. 1955. J. Biol. Chem. 214:489.
[78] McClure, F. J. 1949. Ann. Rev. Biochem. 18:335.
[79] McConnell, K. P., and R. G. Martin. 1952. J. Biol. Chem. 194:183.
[80] McConnell, K. P., and O. W. Portman. 1952. Ibid. 195:277.
[81] Meek, S. F., et al. 1943. Ind. Med. 12:447.
[82] Mendel, L. B., and O. E. Closson. 1906. Am. J. Physiol. 16:152.
[83] Mendel, L. B., and D. F. Sicher. 1906. Ibid. 16:147.
[84] Miwa, M., and H. Yamashita. 1938. Gann 32:395.
[85] Mraz, F. R., and H. Patrick. 1957. Proc. Soc. Exptl. Biol. Med. 94:409.
[86] Mraz, F. R., and H. Patrick. 1957. Arch. Biochem. Biophys. 71:121.
[87] Mraz, F. R., and H. Patrick. 1957. J. Nutr. 61:535.
[88] Mraz, F. R., et al. 1957. Arch. Biochem. Biophys. 66:177.
[89] Norris, W. P., and W. Kisieleski. 1948. Cold Spring Harbor Symp. Quant. Biol. 13:164.
[90] Owen, C. A., Jr. 1964. Am. J. Physiol. 207:446.
[91] Perey, M., and A. Chevallier. 1951. Compt. Rend. Soc. Biol. 145:1205.
[92] Perrault, M., and F. Chain. 1958. Presse Med. 66: 1394.
[93] Princi, F., and E. F. Geever. 1950. Arch. Ind. Hyg. Occupational Med. 1:651.
[94] Rosenfeld, G. 1954. Arch. Biochem. Biophys. 48: 84.
[95] Santos Freire, C. A. 1963. Folha Med. (Rio de Janeiro) 47:35.
[96] Sastry, V. V., et al. 1963. Federation Proc. 22:540.
[97] Scandellari, C., and N. Conte. 1963. Acta Isotopica 3:71.
[98] Schou, M. 1957. Pharmacol. Rev. 9:17.
[99] Schubert, J., and M. R. White. 1952. J. Lab. Clin. Med. 39:260.
[100] Schubert, J., M. R. White, and A. Lindenbaum. 1952. J. Biol. Chem. 196:279.
[101] Schubert, J., et al. 1950. Ibid. 182:635.
[102] Scott, J. K., W. F. Neuman, and J. F. Bonner. 1952. J. Pharmacol. Exptl. Therap. 106:286.
[103] Scott, K. G., D. J. Axelrod, and J. G. Hamilton. 1949. J. Biol. Chem. 177:325.
[104] Scott, K. G., and J. G. Hamilton. 1950. Univ. Calif. (Berkeley) Publ. Pharmacol. 2:241.
[105] Scott, K. G., et al. 1948. J. Biol. Chem. 175:691.
[106] Scott, K. G., et al. 1948. Ibid. 176:283.
[107] Shapiro, R. 1956. Acta Radiol. 46:635.
[108] Shohl, A. T. 1939. Mineral metabolism. Reinhold, New York.
[109] Singer, L., et al. 1957. Arch. Biochem. Biophys. 66:404.
[110] Sollman, T. 1957. A manual of pharmacology. Ed. 8. W. B. Saunders, Philadelphia.
[111] Sorovka, V. R. 1965. Arkh. Patol. 27:58.
[112] Spode, E., and F. Gensicke. 1958. Naturwissenschaften 45:117.
[113] Spode, E., and F. Gensicke. 1958. Ibid. 45:135.
[114] Stannard, J. N., and F. A. Smith. 1957. U.S. At. Energy Comm. UR-287.
[115] Stover, B. J., et al. 1957. Proc. Soc. Exptl. Biol. Med. 94:269.
[116] Taylor, D. M. 1963. Brit. J. Radiol. 37:95.
[117] Tedeschi, R. E., and F. W. Sunderman. 1957. Arch. Ind. Hyg. Occupational Med. 16:486.
[118] Ter Meulen, H. 1931. Rec. Trav. Chim. 50:491.
[119] Thompson, R. C., and O. L. Hollis. 1956. U.S. At. Energy Comm. HW-45546.
[120] Thompson, R. C., et al. 1958. Am. J. Roentgenol. Radium Therapy Nucl. Med. 79:1026.
[121] Tregubenko, I. P. 1961. Chem. Abstr. 55:1922.
[122] Underwood, E. J. 1959. Ann. Rev. Biochem. 28: 499.
[123] Vallee, B. L. 1959. Physiol. Rev. 39:443.
[124] Vallee, B. L., and R. G. Fluharty. 1947. J. Clin. Invest. 26:1199.
[125] Visek, W. J., et al. 1953. Proc. Soc. Exptl. Biol. Med. 84:610.
[126] Wase, A. W. 1956. Arch. Biochem. Biophys. 61: 272.
[127] Wase, A. W., et al. 1954. Ibid. 51:1.
[128] White, M. R., and J. Schubert. 1952. J. Pharmacol. Exptl. Therap. 104:317.
[129] Widdowson, E. M., and R. A. McCance. 1944. Proc. Nutr. Soc. (Engl. Scot.) 1:220.
[130] Widdowson, E. M., et al. 1951. Clin. Sci. 10:113.

74. PATHWAYS OF LIPID METABOLISM

Pathways are based on studies confined chiefly to mammals. *Abbreviations:* CoA = coenzyme A; ADP = adenosine diphosphate; ATP = adenosine triphosphate; NAD^+ = nicotinamide adenine dinucleotide; NADPH = nicotinamide adenine dinucleotide phosphate (reduced form).

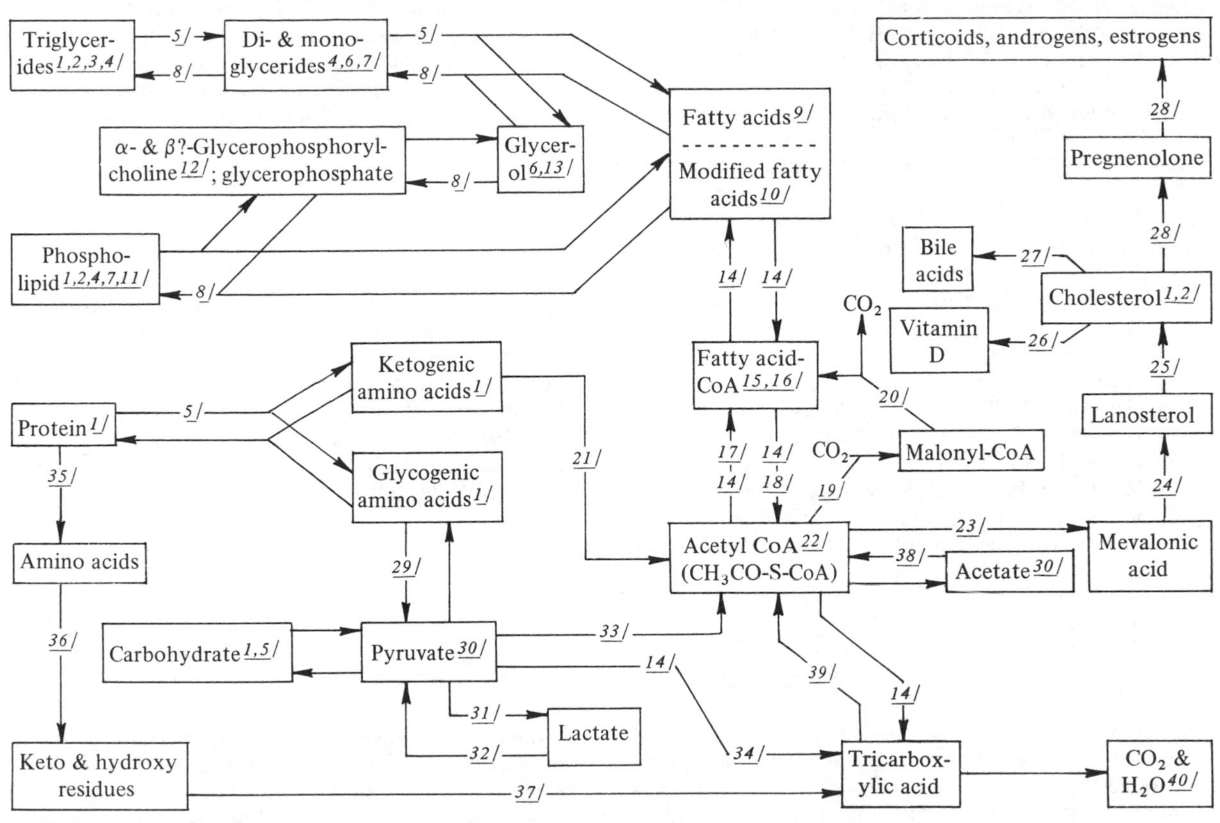

1/ In intestinal lumen, blood, liver, adipose tissue, and other tissues. 2/ In chyle. 3/ Absorption by intestinal mucosa questionable. 4/ Formed in intestinal mucosa, or absorbed from lumen; pass into chyle. Short chains possibly also pass into portal blood. 5/ Digestion in intestinal lumen. Hydrolysis in adipose tissue is under hormonal control. 6/ Probably transitory in tissues. 7/ Some absorption by intestinal mucosa. 8/ In intestinal mucosa, liver, adipose tissue, and other tissues. 9/ Occur free (ionized) in intestinal lumen, blood, and liver, but certain unsaturated fatty acids must be obtained from the diet. Free existence in chyle questionable; probably transitory if free existence occurs in other tissues. 10/ In liver, carbon chains are lengthened or shortened (*see* footnote 18), and H is added to C_{2-10}, or removed creating double bonds. 11/ Chiefly lecithin, cephalins (phosphatides of ethanolamine, serine, inositol, acetal, polyglyceride), and some sphingomyelin. 12/ In intestinal mucosa, liver (?), and other tissues (?). Split to choline, glycerol, and phosphoric acid. 13/ In intestinal lumen; absorbed by intestinal mucosa and resynthesized into glycerides, including phospholipids. Metabolized to pyruvate. Also liberated from triglycerides in adipose tissue. 14/ In liver, adipose tissue, and other tissues. Carnitine acts as a carrier of activated acetyl groups across the mitochondrial membrane. Fatty acids are synthesized extramitochondrially and oxidized intramitochondrially. 15/ Fatty acid ester of CoA (i.e., acyl CoA ester) is formed by ATP-dependent acylation of CoA, or by transfer of CoA from succinyl- or other CoA ester. 16/ CoA = pantetheine (pantoic acid + β-alanine + thioethanolamine) + ADP, with a third PO_4 at the ribose; forms fatty acid thiol esters via the SH in thioethanolamine. 17/ Reverse of β-oxidation (*see* footnote 18); NADPH required; mitochondrial pathway. 18/ Fatty acyl CoA is shortened 2 carbons at a time by β-oxidation and removal of acetyl CoA units, the precursor β-keto acid reacting with CoASH. 19/ Biotin-dependent carboxylation to malonyl CoA. The acetyl group attached to CoA is first transferred to an acyl carrier protein (ACPSH). All intermediates between acetyl ACP and fatty acid ACP are assumed to exist as ACPSH derivatives rather than as CoASH derivatives. 20/ 7 acetyl → 7 malonyl, then 1 acetyl + 7 malonyl → 1 palmityl CoA; NADPH required; extramitochondrial pathway. 21/ Tyrosine, leucine, and isoleucine also converted directly to acetoacetate. 22/ Acetic acid ester of CoA known also as S-acetyl CoA, active acetyl. 23/ Through intermediates--acetoacetyl CoA, β-hydroxy-β-methyl-glutaryl CoA, and mevaldic acid. 24/ Through intermediates: farnesyl and squalene. 25/ Several pathways available involving early or late reduction of the side chain and the formation of Δ^7 & Δ^8 isomers. 26/ Requires light. 27/ In liver by introduction of side chain and ring hydroxyl groups, and by shortening of the side chain. 28/ Adrenal gland.

continued

29/ Aspartate enters tricarboxylic acid cycle not via pyruvate, but by conversion directly to oxalacetate. 30/ Occurs in blood, liver, muscle, and other tissues. 31/ Occurs in muscle, especially in exercise, the lactate diffusing into the bloodstream. 32/ Occurs in liver, muscle, brain, and other tissues. 33/ Diphosphothiamine (cocarboxylase), lipoic acid, Mg^{2+}, and NAD^+ required. 34/ Pyruvate + $CO_2 \rightarrow$ oxalacetate and malate components of tricarboxylic acid cycle. Oxalacetate condenses with acetyl CoA to form citrate. This removal of acetyl CoA by oxalacetate (i.e., by pyruvate), occurring when acetyl CoA is being formed in active fat catabolism, may explain antiketogenic action of carbohydrate (and protein). 35/ Release of amino acids. 36/ Deamination and modification of amino acids. 37/ Entrance into the tricarboxylic acid cycle as malic, fumaric, α-ketoglutaric acids, etc. 38/ ATP-dependent reaction with CoA. 39/ Formation of acetyl CoA from citrate by the citrate cleavage enzyme (the "backward reaction"). 40/ And energy liberation.

Contributors: (a) Bonner, James, (b) Flock, Eunice V., (c) Van Bruggen, John T.

General References

[1] Bloor, W. R. 1943. Biochemistry of the fatty acids. Reinhold, New York.

[2] Bressler, R., R. Katz, and B. Wittels. 1965. Ann. N.Y. Acad. Sci. 131:207.

[3] Conn, E. C., and P. Stumpf. 1963. Outlines of biochemistry. J. Wiley, New York.

[4] Cornforth, J. W. 1959. J. Lipid Res. 1:3.

[5] Isselbacher, J. L. 1965. Federation Proc. 24:16.

[6] Lynen, F. 1961. Ibid. 20:941.

[7] Martin, D. B., and P. R. Vagelos. 1965. In A. E. Renold and G. F. Cahill, Jr., ed. Handbook of physiology. American Physiological Society, Washington, D.C. sect. 5, p. 211.

[8] Masoro, E. J. 1962. J. Lipid Res. 3:149.

[9] Mead, J. F. 1961. Federation Proc. 20:952.

[10] Nowinski, W. W., ed. 1960. Fundamental aspects of normal and malignant growth. American Elsevier, New York.

[11] Rizack, M. A. 1965. Ann. N.Y. Acad. Sci. 131:250.

[12] Senior, J. R. 1964. J. Lipid Res. 5:495.

[13] Wakil, S. J. 1961. Ibid. 2:1.

[14] West, E. S., et al. 1966. Textbook of biochemistry. Ed. 4. Macmillan, New York.

75. PATHWAYS OF CARBOHYDRATE METABOLISM

The conversion of stored or ingested carbohydrate to pyruvate releases stored energy by means of anaerobic oxidation (glycolysis). Released energy is partly dissipated as heat and partly stored (temporarily) in the labile energy pool as high-energy phosphate ($\sim PO_4$) by combination of $\sim PO_4$ with continuously available ADP to form ATP. In the conversion of 1 mole of glucose (180 g), or of other monosaccharides, to 2 moles of pyruvate (174 g), 2 moles of ATP are converted to ADP and 4 moles of ATP are formed from ADP, making a net gain of 2 moles of ATP, or approximately 14 kilocalories of readily available energy. If glucose-6-PO_4 has come from the metabolic breakdown of glycogen, the cost is only 1 mole of ATP, making a net gain of 3 moles of ATP (approximately 21 kilocalories). The ATP is an immediate source of energy, the utilization of which (e.g., for muscular activity) is independent of oxygen supply. Aerobic oxidation of the reduced coenzymes formed in glycolysis and in the tricarboxylic acid cycle yields considerable amounts of energy. The reactions may be summarized as follows: glucose + 2 ATP → 2 pyruvate + 8 ATP; 2 pyruvate → 2 acetyl CoA + 6 ATP; 2 acetyl CoA → 4 CO_2 + 4 H_2O + 24 ATP; a total of 38 ATP. The complete oxidation of glucose to CO_2 and water releases 685.5 kilocalories of energy. The ADP system traps 266 (38 × 7) kilocalories of this energy, resulting in a possible storage of 39% (266/685) of the energy in the form of ATP. *Abbreviations:* CoA = coenzyme A; ADP = adenosine 5′-diphosphate; ATP = adenosine 5′-triphosphate; NAD^+ (NADH) = nicotinamide adenine dinucleotide (reduced form); UDP = uridine diphosphate; UTP = uridine triphosphate.

ENZYME KEY

1.1.1.1 = alcohol dehydrogenase	2.7.1.6 = galactokinase	4.1.1.1 = pyruvate decarboxylase
1.1.1.27 = lactate dehydrogenase	2.7.1.7 = mannokinase	4.1.2.13 = fructosediphosphate aldolase
1.1.99.5 = glycerolphosphate dehydrogenase	2.7.1.11 = phosphofructokinase	4.2.1.11 = phosphopyruvate hydratase
1.2.1.12 = glyceraldehydephosphate dehydrogenase	2.7.2.3 = phosphoglycerate kinase	5.1.3.2 = UDP glucose epimerase
2.4.1.1 = glycogen phosphorylase	2.7.5.1 = phosphoglucomutase	5.3.1.1 = triosephosphate isomerase
2.4.1.21 = UDP glucose-starch glucosyltransferase	2.7.5.3 = phosphoglyceromutase	5.3.1.8 = mannosephosphate isomerase
2.7.1.1 = hexokinase	2.7.7.9 = UDP glucose pyrophosphorylase	5.3.1.9 = glucosephosphate isomerase
2.7.1.4 = fructokinase	3.1.3.11 = hexosediphosphatase	
	3.2.1.1 = α-amylase	

continued

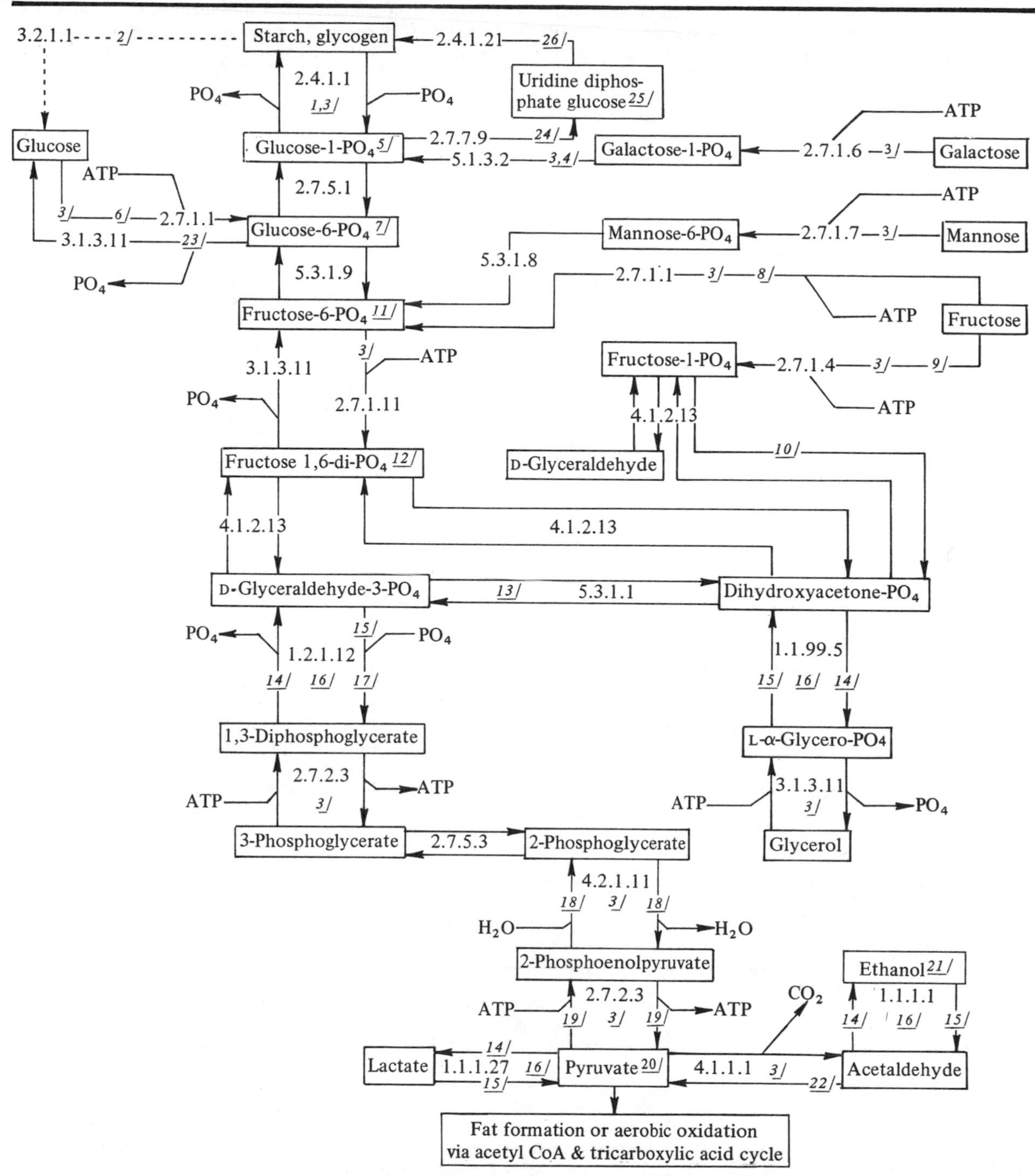

1/ Adenylic acid and PO_4 required for activity in either direction. 2/ Digestion; glycogen and/or starch are hydrolyzed to glucose in intestinal lumen. 3/ Mg^{++} required for this reaction. 4/ UDP-glucose required as coenzyme. 5/ Cori ester. 6/ Hexokinase reaction assumed to be inhibited by growth hormone plus adrenal cortex hormone; inhibition by these substances is blocked by insulin, thus favoring conversion of glucose to glucose-6-phosphate. 7/ Robison ester. 8/ In all tissues. 9/ In liver and muscle. 10/ Liver aldolase also degrades fructose-1-PO_4. 11/ Neuberg ester. 12/ Hardin-Young ester. 13/ This reaction (to left) causes each step in the conversion to pyruvate to be doubled quantitatively; thus 1 mole of glucose gives rise to 2 moles of pyruvate. 14/ Hydrogen enters into the reaction. 15/ Hydrogen atoms released. 16/ NAD^+ acts as acceptor of released hydrogen atoms, becoming NADH in oxidative direction of the reaction. NADH gives up hydrogen atoms and becomes NAD^+ in reverse direction. Hydrogen atoms accepted by NAD^+ are passed on in turn to flavoprotein, cytochrome *c*, cytochrome oxidase, and molecular O_2. If molecular O_2 is not sufficiently available, hydrogen atoms may be passed from NADH to pyruvate-forming lactate. 17/ Inhibited by iodoacetate. 18/ Inhibited by fluoride. 19/ K^+ also required. 20/ Pyruvate, followed by conversion to lactate when oxygen supply is

continued

75. PATHWAYS OF CARBOHYDRATE METABOLISM

deficient (*see* footnote 15), ends glycolysis in animal tissues. If oxygen is available, pyruvate is oxidized via the tricarboxylic acid cycle. 21/ End of fermentation of plant tissue. 22/ Thiamine pyrophosphate required as coenzyme. 23/ The reaction, glycogen to glucose-6-PO_4 to blood glucose, takes place in liver only; conversion of glucose to glucose-6-PO_4 to glycogen takes place in liver, muscle, and other tissues. 24/ UTP enters the reaction; pyrophosphate is eliminated. 25/ In plants, ADP-glucose is more efficiently utilized for starch synthesis than UDP-glucose. 26/ UDP is eliminated from the reaction.

Contributors: (a) Bonner, James, and Shih, Thomas Y., (b) Bishop, David W., (c) Van Bruggen, John T.

General References

[1] Axelrod, B. 1961. In D. M. Greenberg, ed. Metabolic pathways. Ed. 2. Academic Press, New York. v. 1, pp. 97-124 & 205-243.

[2] Baldwin, E. 1957. Dynamic aspects of biochemistry. Ed. 3. Cambridge Univ. Press, New York.

[3] Bonner, J., and J. Varner, ed. 1965. Plant biochemistry. Academic Press, New York.

[4] Cori, G. T., et al. 1951. Biochim. Biophys. Acta 7:304.

[5] Dickens, F. 1951. In J. B. Sumner and K. Myrbäck, ed. The enzymes. Academic Press, New York. v. 2, p. 624.

[6] Lardy, H. A., ed. 1949. Respiratory enzymes. Rev. ed. Burgess, Minneapolis.

[7] Krebs, H. A. 1949. Advan. Enzymol. 3:191.

[8] Mahler, H. R., and E. H. Cordes. 1966. Biological chemistry. Harper, New York.

[9] Sumner, J. B., and G. F. Somers. 1953. Chemistry and methods of enzymes. Ed. 3. Academic Press, New York.

[10] Umbreit, W. W. 1952. Metabolic maps. Burgess, Minneapolis.

[11] Werkman, C. H., and F. Schlenk. 1951. In C. H. Werkman and P. W. Wilson, ed. Bacterial physiology. Academic Press, New York. p. 281.

[12] West, E. S., et al. 1966. Textbook of biochemistry. Ed. 4. Macmillan, New York.

76. PATHWAYS OF AMINO ACID METABOLISM

The deamination of most amino acids in many systems involves transdeamination, i.e., transamination of the amino acid with an α-keto acid, usually α-ketoglutarate, to yield the respective α-keto acid analogue and glutamate. Through the action of glutamate dehydrogenase, glutamate is oxidatively deaminated to yield ammonia and regenerate α-ketoglutarate. A reversal of the transdeamination process leads to the formation of many amino acids from their respective α-keto acids and ammonia. Certain amino acids, e.g., serine, cysteine, threonine, or histidine, may undergo nonoxidative deamination. In certain systems, D- or L-amino acid oxidases are involved in deamination reactions. Ammonia may be converted either to glutamine or asparagine, or to carbamylphosphate which is utilized for pyrimidine biosynthesis or for urea production. The carbon chains of the amino acids are metabolized by pathways leading to intermediates in carbohydrate or lipid metabolism. The reactions leading to the formation of the compounds listed in the two middle columns are not included; only the reactions involved in further metabolism are shown in the pathways column. Cofactors for the various reactions have been omitted. *Abbreviations:* CoA = coenzyme A; ADP = adenosine diphosphate; AMP = adenosine phosphate; ATP = adenosine triphosphate; IMP = inosine phosphate; P_i = inorganic orthophosphate; PP_i = inorganic pyrophosphate.

	Amino Acid	Product of Oxidative Deamination or Transamination	Product of Decarboxylation	Pathways and Products of Metabolism
1	L-Alanine	Pyruvic acid		
2	L-Arginine	α-Keto-δ-guanidovaleric acid	Agmatine	Arginine → ornithine + urea; arginine → citrulline + NH_3; arginine + glycine ⟷ guanidoacetic acid + ornithine
3	L-Asparagine	α-Ketosuccinamic acid		Asparagine ⇌ aspartic acid + NH_3; α-ketosuccinamic acid → NH_3 + oxaloacetic acid
4	L-Aspartic acid	Oxaloacetic acid	α-Alanine	Aspartic acid + carbamylphosphate → P_i + carbamylaspartic acid → → → pyrimidines; aspartic acid ⟷ fumaric acid + NH_3; aspartic acid → aspartic semialdehyde → homoserine → (i) threonine, (ii) methionine, or (iii) lysine; aspartic acid → nitrogen of purine ring (*see* purine metabolism); aspartic acid + IMP → adenylosuccinate → AMP + fumarate. *See also* asparagine.
5	L-Citrulline	α-Keto-δ-carbamidovaleric acid		Citrulline + aspartic acid → argininosuccinic acid ⟷ arginine + fumaric acid; citrulline + P_i ⟷ ornithine + carbamylphosphate; carbamylphosphate + ADP ⟷ CO_2 + NH_3 + ATP
6	L-Cysteine and L-cystine	β-Mercaptopyruvic acid		Cysteine → H_2S + NH_3 + pyruvic acid; β-mercaptopyruvic acid → pyruvic acid + S; cysteine → cysteine sulfinic acid 1/ → (i) cysteic acid → CO_2 + taurine, (ii) CO_2 + hypotaurine, or (iii) via transamination → β-sulfinylpyruvate → pyruvate + SO_3^{2-}; 2 cysteine ⟷ cystine. *See also* methionine for biosynthesis of cysteine.
7	L-Glutamic acid	α-Ketoglutaric acid	γ-Aminobutyric acid	Glutamic acid ⟷ glutamic semialdehyde ⟷ (i) ornithine or (ii) → Δ'-pyrroline-5-carboxylate ⟷ proline; glutamic acid → *N*-acetylglutamic acid ⟷ *N*-acetylglutamic semialdehyde ⟷ *N*-acetylornithine → ornithine. *See also* glutamine, histidine.

1/ Desulfination pathway for cysteine sulfinic acid → alanine + SO_2.

continued

	Amino Acid	Product of Oxidative Deamination or Transamination	Product of Decarboxylation	Pathways and Products of Metabolism
8	L-Glutamine	α-Ketoglutaramic acid		α-Ketoglutaramic acid → NH_3 + α-ketoglutarate; glutamine ⇌ NH_3 + glutamic acid; glutamine + 5′-phospho-α-D-ribosylpyrophosphate → glutamate + 5′-phospho-β-D-ribosylamine → → 5′-phosphoribosyl-*N*-formylglycineamide + glutamine → glutamate + 5′-phosphoribosyl-*N*-formylglycineamidine → → → purines; glutamine + xanthylic acid → guanylic acid + glutamate; glutamine + fructose-6-phosphate → glucosamine-6-phosphate + glutamate. *See also* histidine.
9	Glycine	Glyoxylic acid	5,10-Methylene tetrahydrofolate + NH_3 + 2H	Glyoxylate → formate + CO_2; glycine + 5,10-methylene tetrahydrofolate ⟷ serine + tetrahydrofolate; glycine + succinyl CoA → δ-aminolevulinate → → → porphyrins; glycine + 5′-phospho-β-D-ribosylamine → 5-phosphoribosylglycineamide → → purines; glycine → glycocholic acid; glycine → hippuric acid. *See also* serine, threonine, arginine.
10	L-Histidine	β-Imidazolepyruvic acid	Histamine	Histidine → NH_3 + urocanic acid → imidazolone propionate → *N*-formiminoglutamate → glutamate + 5-formimino tetrahydrofolate; histidine → (i) anserine, or (ii) carnosine; histamine → imidazoleacetic acid → (i) imidazoleacetic acid ribonucleoside or (ii) NH_3 + formylaspartic acid; histamine → methylhistamine; ATP + 5-phosphoribosyl-l-phosphate → phosphoribosyl-ATP → phosphoribosyl-AMP + glutamine → 5-amino-1-ribosyl-4-imidazolecarboxamide-5′-phosphate + imidazoleglycerol phosphate → histidinol phosphate → histidinol → histidine
11	Hydroxyproline	α-Keto-2-hydroxy-δ-aminovaleric acid		Hydroxyproline → Δ'-pyrroline-3-hydroxy-5-carboxylate → γ-hydroxyglutamate ⟷ α-keto-2-hydroxyglutarate ⟷ pyruvate + glyoxylate. *See also* proline.
12	L-Isoleucine	α-Keto-β-methylvaleric acid	2-Methylbutylamine	α-Keto-β-methylvaleric acid → CO_2 + α-methylbutyryl CoA ⟷ tiglyl CoA ⟷ α-methyl-β-hydroxybutyryl CoA ⟷ α-methylacetoacetyl CoA ⟷ acetyl CoA + propionyl CoA; pyruvate + α-ketobutyrate *(see* threonine) → CO_2 + α-aceto-α-hydroxybutyrate → α-β-dihydroxy-β-methylvalerate ⟷ α-keto-β-methylvalerate ⟷ isoleucine
13	L-Leucine	α-Ketoisocaproic acid	3-Methylbutylamine	α-Ketoisocaproic acid → CO_2 + isovaleryl CoA ⟷ β-methylcrotonyl CoA + CO_2 ⟷ β-methylglutaconyl CoA ⟷ β-hydroxy-β-methylglutaryl CoA → (i) acetoacetic acid + acetyl CoA, or (ii) → → → cholesterol; α-ketoisovaleric acid *(see* valine) + acetyl CoA → β-carboxy-β-hydroxyisocaproic acid → α-hydroxy-β-carboxyisocaproic acid → α-keto-β-carboxyisocaproic acid ⟷ α-ketoisocaproic acid ⟷ leucine
14	L-Lysine	α-Keto-ε-aminocaproic acid	Cadaverine	α-Keto-ε-aminocaproic acid → Δ'-dehydropipecolate → L-pipecolate → Δ^6-dehydropipecolate → α-aminoadipate semialdehyde ⟷ α-aminoadipic acid ⟷ α-ketoadipic acid → glutaryl CoA → glutaconyl CoA → crotonyl CoA (fatty acid degradation); aspartic semialdehyde + pyruvate → → → diaminopimelic acid → lysine; α-ketoglutarate + acetyl CoA → → → → α-ketoadipic acid → α-aminoadipic acid → → saccharopine → lysine + α-ketoglutarate
15	L-Methionine	α-Keto-γ-methiolbutyric acid		Methionine + ATP → PP_i + P_i + *S*-adenosylmethionine (active methyl donor); *S*-adenosylmethionine + guanidoacetate *(see* arginine) → creatine + *S*-adenosylhomocysteine; *S*-adenosylhomocysteine → adenosine + homocysteine; homocysteine + serine → cystathionine → cysteine + homoserine; homoserine → α-ketobutyrate + NH_3; α-ketobutyrate → CO_2 + propionyl CoA → methylmalonyl CoA → succinyl CoA; homoserine (*see* aspartic acid) + cysteine → cystathionine → serine + homocysteine; homocysteine + one C donor → methionine; homocysteine → (i) homocysteic acid or (ii) NH_3 + H_2S + α-ketobutyrate
16	L-Ornithine	Glutamic semialdehyde, or α-keto-δ-aminovaleric acid	Putrescine	Ornithine ⟷ proline; ornithine ⟷ glutamic semialdehyde ⟷ glutamate; ornithine + carbamylphosphate → citrulline. *See also* citrulline, glutamic acid.
17	L-Phenylalanine	Phenylpyruvic acid	Phenylethylamine	Phenylalanine → tyrosine; phenylpyruvic acid → (i) phenyllactic acid or (ii) CO_2 + phenylacetic acid; phosphoenolpyruvate + erythrose-4-phosphate → 3-deoxy-D-arabino-heptulosonic acid-7-phosphate → → → 5-dehydroquinate → 5-dehydroshikimate → shikimate → shikimate-5-phosphate → → → prephenate → (i) phenylpyruvate → phenylalanine or (ii) → *p*-hydroxyphenylpyruvate → tyrosine. *See also* tyrosine.
18	L-Proline	Glutamic semialdehyde or α-keto-δ-aminovaleric acid	----	Proline ⟷ glutamate; proline ⟷ ornithine; proline → hydroxyproline. *See also* glutamic acid, ornithine.
19	L-Serine	β-Hydroxypyruvic acid		Serine → pyruvate + NH_3; hydroxypyruvate ⟷ D-glycerate ⇌ (i) 2-phosphoglycerate or (ii) 3-phosphoglycerate; 3-phosphoglycerate ⟷ β-phosphohydroxypyruvate ⟷ phosphoserine → serine; phosphatidyl ethanolamine + serine → ethanolamine + phosphatidyl serine; phosphatidyl serine → CO_2 + phosphatidyl ethanolamine; palmitaldehyde + serine → dihydrosphingosine. *See also* glycine, methionine, tryptophan.

continued

76. PATHWAYS OF AMINO ACID METABOLISM

	Amino Acid	Product of Oxidative Deamination or Transamination	Product of Decarboxylation	Pathways and Products of Metabolism
20	L-Threonine	α-Keto-β-hydroxybutyric acid		Threonine → NH_3 + α-ketobutyrate; α-ketobutyrate → CO_2 + propionyl CoA → methylmalonyl CoA → succinyl CoA; threonine → (i) glycine + acetaldehyde or (ii) CO_2 + aminoacetone. *See also* aspartic acid.
21	L-Tryptophan	β-Indolepyruvic acid	Tryptamine	Tryptophan → *N*-formylkynurenine → formate + kynurenine → 3-hydroxykynurenine → alanine + 3-hydroxyanthranilate → α-amino-β-carboxymuconate semialdehyde → CO_2 + α-aminomuconate semialdehyde → α-aminomuconate → α-ketoadipate (*see* lysine for further degradation); tryptophan → 5-hydroxytryptophan → CO_2 + 5-hydroxytryptamine (serotonin) → 5-hydroxyindoleacetic acid; indole-3-glycerol phosphate + serine → tryptophan
22	L-Tyrosine	*p*-Hydroxyphenylpyruvic acid	Tyramine	*p*-Hydroxyphenylpyruvic acid → CO_2 + homogentisic acid → maleylacetoacetic acid → fumarylacetoacetic acid → fumarate + acetoacetate; tyrosine → 3,4-dihydroxyphenylalanine → CO_2 + 3,4-dihydroxyphenylethylamine → noradrenalin → adrenalin. *See also* phenylalanine.
23	L-Valine	α-Ketoisovaleric acid	2-Methylpropylamine	α-Ketoisovaleric acid → CO_2 + isobutyryl CoA ⟷ methacrylyl CoA ⟷ β-hydroxybutyryl CoA → β-hydroxyisobutyrate ⟷ methylmalonic semialdehyde → (i) β-aminoisobutyric acid or (ii) methylmalonyl CoA (?); 2 pyruvic acid → α-acetolactate → α,β-dihydroxyisovaleric acid → α-ketoisovaleric acid ⟷ valine

Contributors: (a) Sallach, H. J., (b) Meister, Alton, (c) Elwyn, David H.

General References

[1] Greenberg, D. M., ed. 1961. Metabolic pathways. Academic Press, New York. v. 2.

[2] Meister, A. 1965. Biochemistry of the amino acids. Ed. 2. Academic Press, New York.

77. PATHWAYS OF NUCLEOPROTEIN CATABOLISM

Nucleoproteins are composed of basic proteins (histones or protamines) associated with nucleic acid in a salt linkage broken by salts, acids and bases. Catabolism may be initiated in the alimentary canal or in the tissues. Nucleic acids are composed of many nucleotide units joined by sugar-phosphate linkages. The nucleotides shown below are obtained by enzymatic hydrolysis of nucleic acids, although several may be obtained from other sources. Each nucleotide is composed of a purine or pyrimidine base linked to a pentose sugar, which in turn is linked to phosphate. In catabolism, nucleic acids are degraded to nucleotides which are dephosphorylated to yield inorganic phosphate plus a nucleoside; nucleosides are cleaved to yield the free base plus, usually, ribose- or deoxyribose-1-phosphate. In some instances, nucleotides and free bases are interconverted through the action of pyrophosphorylase enzymes. Nucleosides and free bases are absorbed from the intestine; there is little intestinal absorption of nucleotides. *Abbreviations:* DNA = deoxyribonucleic acid; RNA = ribonucleic acid.

ENZYME KEY

1.2.3.2 = xanthine oxidase
1.2.99.1 = uracil dehydrogenase
1.3.1.2 = dihydro-uracil dehydrogenase ($NADP^+$)
1.4.3.2 = L-amino acid oxidase
1.4.3.4 = monoamine oxidase
1.7.3.3 = urate oxidase
2.4.2.3 = uridine phosphorylase
2.4.2.4 = thymidine phosphorylase
2.6.1.– = aminotransferases
2.6.1.? = uncharacterized aminotransferase
2.6.1.18 = β-alanine aminotransferase
2.7.7.16 = ribonuclease(s)
3.1.3.1 = alkaline phosphatase
3.1.4.5 = deoxyribonuclease(s)
3.2.2.1 = nucleosidase
3.4.4.– = proteases
3.5.1.6 = β-ureidopropionase
3.5.2.1 = barbiturase
3.5.2.2 = dihydropyrimidinase
3.5.2.5 = allantoinase
3.5.3.1 = arginase
3.5.3.4 = allantoicase
3.5.4.1 = cytosine deaminase
3.5.4.2 = adenine deaminase
3.5.4.3 = guanine deaminase
3.5.4.4 = adenosine deaminase
3.5.4.5 = cytidine deaminase
3.5.4.6 = adenosine phosphate deaminase
4.1.1.– = amino acid decarboxylases

continued

77. PATHWAYS OF NUCLEOPROTEIN CATABOLISM

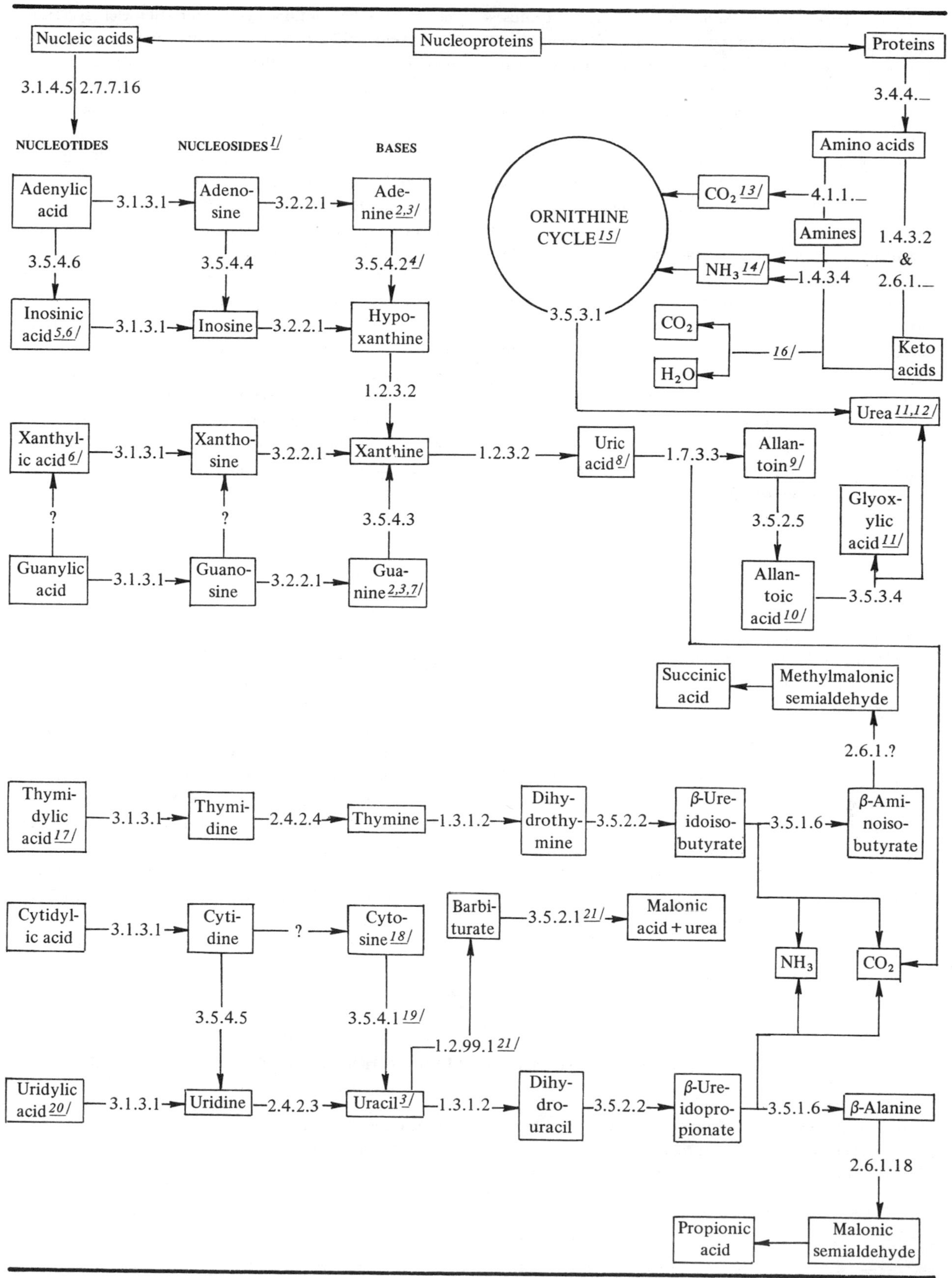

continued

77. PATHWAYS OF NUCLEOPROTEIN CATABOLISM

1/ Purine nucleosides are split into purines and pentoses by purine nucleosidase present in tissues. 2/ Adenine and guanine are the major purines occurring in nucleic acids. 3/ Mammals do not require but can synthesize exogenous purines or pyrimidines from products of protein metabolism. 4/ The route adenine → hypoxanthine is of no importance in animals. Adenine deaminase is not found to any extent in mammals. 5/ In the biosynthesis of nucleotides, inosinic acid is the precursor of adenylic and guanylic acids; in uricotelic species, a portion of inosinic acid is a direct precursor of uric acid. 6/ Important in metabolism, but does not occur in nucleic acid. 7/ Excreted by swine and spider. 8/ Excreted by primates, some reptiles, and some insects as the end product of purine catabolism; excreted by birds as the end product of protein, purine, and pyrimidine catabolism; no urea formation by birds. 9/ Excreted by mammals other than primates, by gastropods, and some insects. 10/ Excreted by some teleosts. 11/ Excreted by most fishes, amphibians, and freshwater lamellibranchs. 12/ Excreted by mammals as the end product of amino acid metabolism; excreted by some animals as the end product of purine and pyrimidine metabolism. 13/ May enter into metabolic processes, into the ornithine cycle (Krebs-Henseleit cycle), and be incorporated into and excreted as urea, or be excreted as CO_2. 14/ NH_3, as in the case of CO_2, is also used to synthesize many tissue constituents; hence, it may enter into metabolic processes, be built into amino acids, incorporated into urea and excreted, or excreted as NH_3 across the kidney tubule. 15/ Urea formation in mammalian liver occurs via the ornithine cycle; ornithine → citrulline → arginine succinate → arginine → ornithine. CO_2 and NH_3 enter the cycle via carbamylphosphate at ornithine; NH_3 enters the cycle via aspartic acid at citrulline. Arginine succinate is split into arginine and fumaric acid; arginine is then converted to ornithine with the release of urea. 16/ Via the tricarboxylic acid cycle. In the course of amino acid metabolism, prior to entry into the tricarboxylic acid cycle, sulfur-containing amino acids lose their sulfur, usually in the form of SO_4. 17/ Occurs in DNA. 18/ Cytosine is converted to uracil at the nucleotide stage. Free cytosine is excreted unchanged. 19/ In yeasts and *Escherichia coli.* 20/ Occurs in RNA. 21/ In *Corynebacterium, Mycobacterium,* and U-i soil bacterium.

Contributors: (a) Barrett, Harold W., (b) Brown, George B., (c) Zbarsky, S. H.

General References

[1] Boyer, P. D., H. Lardy, and K. Myrbäck, ed. 1959-63. The enzymes. Ed. 2. Academic Press, New York. v. 1-8.

[2] Davidson, J. N. 1965. Biochemistry of the nucleic acids. Ed. 5. Methuen, London.

[3] Davidson, J. N., and W. E. Cohn, ed. 1959-66. Progress in nucleic acid research. Academic Press, New York. v. 1-8.

[4] Fruton, J. S., and S. Simmonds. 1958. General biochemistry. Ed. 2. J. Wiley, New York.

[5] Greenberg, D. M. 1961. Metabolic pathways. Academic Press, New York. v. 2.

[6] Laskowski, M. 1951. In J. B. Sumner and K. Myrbäck, ed. The enzymes. Academic Press, New York. v. 1, pt. 1, pp. 946-948.

[7] Long, C., ed. 1961. Biochemists' handbook. Van Nostrand, Princeton, N.J.

[8] Mahler, H. R., and E. H. Cordes. 1966. Biological chemistry. Harper and Row, New York.

[9] West, E. S., et al. 1966. Textbook of biochemistry. Ed. 4. Macmillan, New York.

[10] White, A., P. Handler, and E. L. Smith. 1964. Principles of biochemistry. Ed. 3. McGraw-Hill, New York.

78. METABOLIC INTERRELATIONSHIPS: LIPIDS, CARBOHYDRATES, AND PROTEINS

Amino acids (shown in broken-line boxes) are liberated through the hydrolysis of proteins by proteases and peptidases. In the biosynthesis of proteins from activated amino acids, aminoacyl adenosine 5′-phosphate is transferred to aminoacyl ribonucleic acid.

continued

78. METABOLIC INTERRELATIONSHIPS: LIPIDS, CARBOHYDRATES, AND PROTEINS

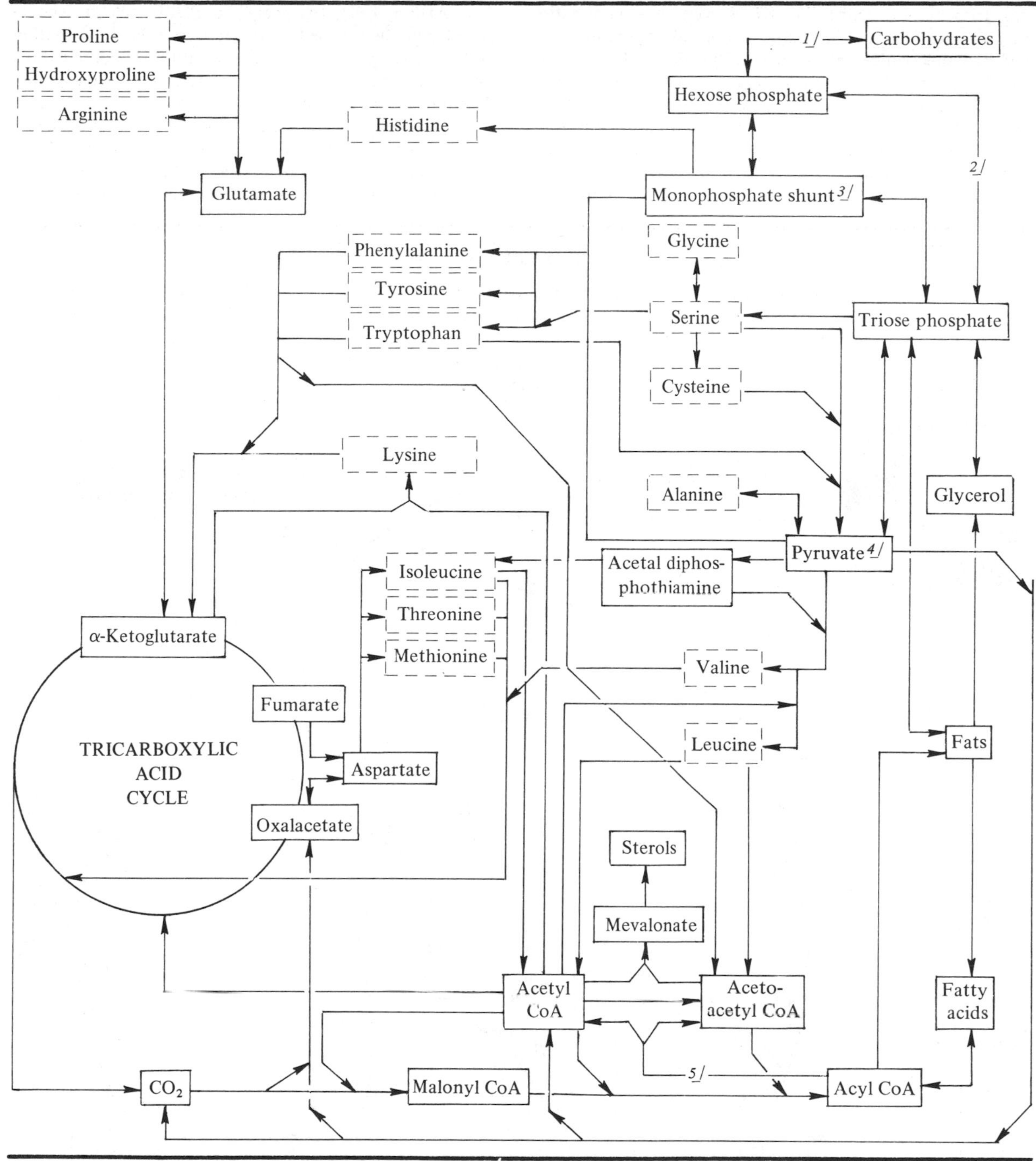

1/ Phosphorylation of hexose units in stored polysaccharides by phosphorylase and phosphate; phosphorylation of hexoses by hexokinase and adenosine 5′-triphosphate. 2/ Glycolysis. 3/ Erythrose phosphate, heptulose phosphate, and pentose phosphate. 4/ Hydroxypyruvate, phosphoenolpyruvate, and pyruvate. 5/ β-Oxidation.

Contributor: Koft, Bernard W.

General References

[1] Cohen, G. N. 1967. Biosynthesis of small molecules. Harper and Row, New York.

[2] Harper, H. A. 1967. Review of physiological chemistry. Ed. 11. Lange, Los Altos, Calif.

[3] Mahler, H. R., and E. H. Cordes. 1966. Biological chemistry. Harper and Row, New York.

[4] West, E. S., et al. 1966. Textbook of biochemistry. Ed. 4. Macmillan, New York.

[5] White, H., P. Handler, and E. L. Smith. 1964. Principles of biochemistry. Ed. 3. McGraw-Hill, New York.

79. TRICARBOXYLIC ACID CYCLE

The tricarboxylic acid cycle (Krebs cycle) is a major pathway for the final aerobic oxidation of carbohydrates, fats, and proteins, which are channeled into the cycle via their two key metabolites, pyruvate and acetyl CoA (active acetate). Each "revolution" of the cycle oxidizes acetate to CO_2 and H_2O. One mole (59 g) of acetate thus oxidized releases approximately 200 kilocalories of energy. A portion of the released energy (approximately 144 kilocalories) enters the phosphate pool as ATP. Twelve moles of ATP are formed from ADP and PO_4 (by energizing PO_4 to $\sim PO_4$). The remainder of the released energy appears as heat. Oxidation of 1 mole (87 g) of pyruvate, via acetyl CoA, contributes a total of 14 moles of ATP to the energy pool. Heavy lines show main sequence of reactions. *Abbreviations:* CoA = coenzyme A; ADP = adenosine diphosphate; ATP = adenosine triphosphate; NAD^+(NADH) = nicotinamide adenine dinucleotide (reduced form); $NADP^+$(NADPH) = nicotinamide adenine dinucleotide phosphate (reduced form).

ENZYME KEY

1.1.1.37 = malate dehydrogenase
1.1.1.40 = malate dehydrogenase (decarboxylating) ($NADP^+$)
1.1.1.42 = isocitrate dehydrogenase
1.2.4.1 = pyruvate dehydrogenase
1.2.4.2 = oxoglutarate dehydrogenase
1.3.99.1 = succinate dehydrogenase
2.6.1.1 = aspartate aminotransferase
4.1.1.3 = oxaloacetate decarboxylase
4.1.3.1 = isocitrate lyase
4.1.3.2 = malate synthetase
4.1.3.7 = citrate synthetase
4.2.1.2 = fumarate hydratase
4.2.1.3 = aconitate hydratase

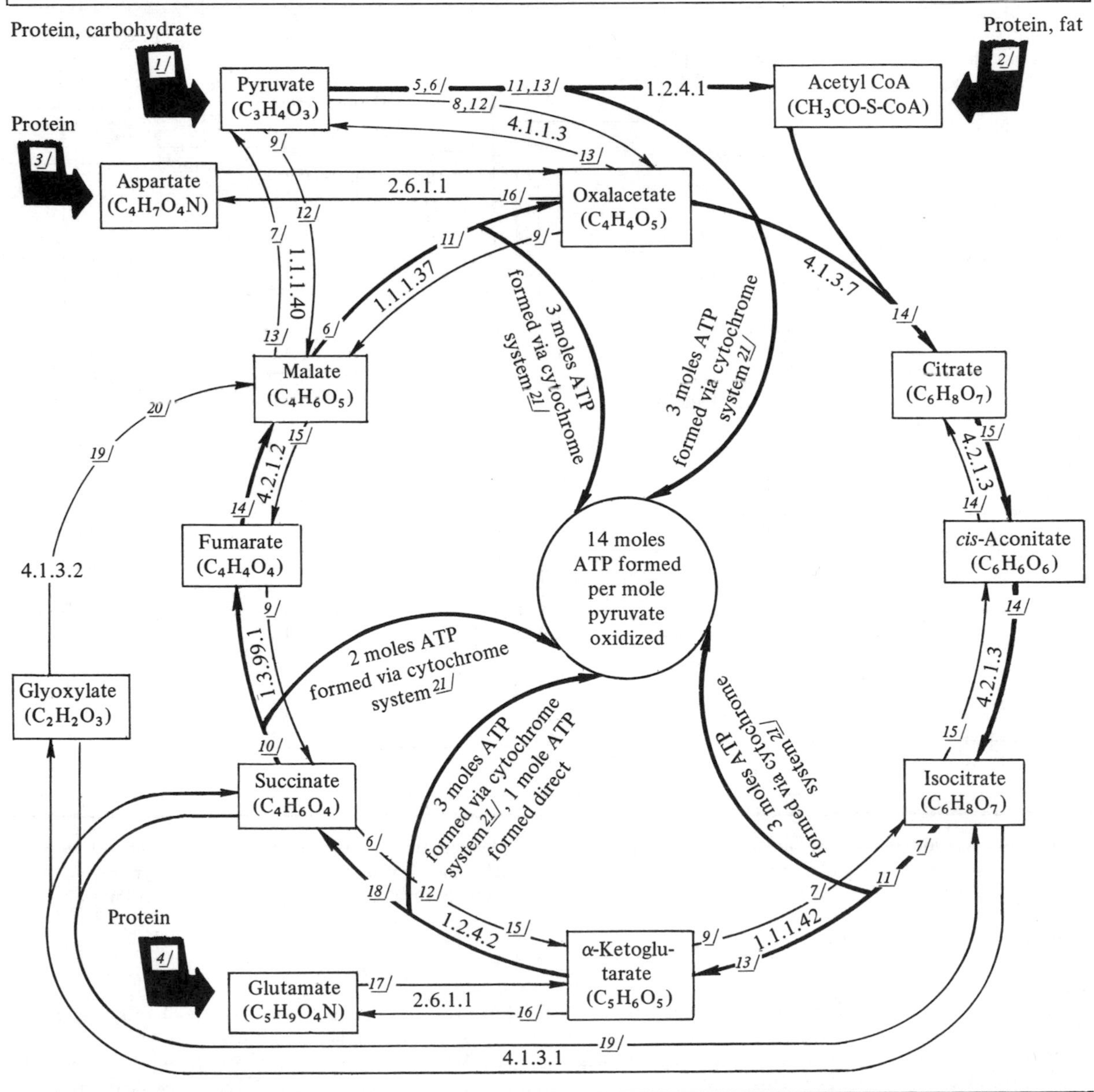

continued

79. TRICARBOXYLIC ACID CYCLE

1/ Glucogenic amino acid precursors for pyruvate are alanine, glycine, serine, threonine, methionine, cysteine, and valine. 2/ Ketogenic amino acid precursors for acetyl CoA are leucine, isoleucine, phenylalanine, and tyrosine. 3/ Aspartic acid occurs as a component of protein. 4/ Glutamic acid occurs as a component of protein, or may be formed from arginine, proline, hydroxyproline, histidine, ornithine. 5/ CoA (ATP-pantoyl-β-alanyl-thioethanolamine) and α-lipoic acid required. 6/ In the oxidative direction, NAD^+ acts as hydrogen acceptor; in the reverse direction, NADH is hydrogen donor. 7/ In the oxidative direction, $NADP^+$ acts as hydrogen acceptor; in the reverse direction, NADPH is hydrogen donor. 8/ Biotin required as coenzyme for carboxylation. 9/ 2 moles of hydrogen enter into the reaction. 10/ 2 moles of hydrogen released and their electrons transferred to cytochrome. 11/ Hydrogen atoms transferred to NAD^+ or to $NADP^+$, and pass in turn to flavoprotein, cytochrome *c*, cytochrome oxidase, and finally combine with molecular oxygen. For each mole of hydrogen thus passed and finally oxidized, 1.5 moles of ATP are formed by the addition of energized phosphate ($\sim PO_4$) to ADP. 12/ CO_2 enters into the reaction. 13/ CO_2 released. 14/ H_2O enters into the reaction. 15/ H_2O released. 16/ NH_3 enters into the reaction by transamination. 17/ NH_3 transferred from glutamate by transamination, then enters into the tricarboxylic acid cycle via α-ketoglutarate. 18/ Footnotes 5, 6, 11, and 13 apply to this reaction. 19/ Cysteine and Mg^{++} required. 20/ Acetyl CoA enters the reaction. 21/ For details, *see* Table 80 on the cytochrome system.

Contributors: (a) Bonner, James F., and Shih, Thomas Y., (b) Bishop, David W.

General References

[1] Artom, C. 1953. Ann. Rev. Biochem. 22:211.
[2] Baldwin, E. 1957. Dynamic aspects of biochemistry. Ed. 3. Cambridge Univ. Press, New York. p. 415.
[3] Black, K. 1952. Ann. Rev. Biochem. 21:273.
[4] Dickens, F. 1951. In J. B. Sumner and K. Myrbäck, ed. The enzymes. Academic Press, New York. v. 2, pt. 1, pp. 624-683.
[5] Evans, E. A., Jr. 1944. Ann. Rev. Biochem. 13:187.
[6] Frazer, A. C. 1952. Ibid. 21:245.
[7] Fruton, J. S., and S. Simmonds. 1958. General biochemistry. Ed. 2. J. Wiley, New York.
[8] Greenberg, D. M. 1960-61. Metabolic pathways. Academic Press, New York.
[9] Krebs, H. A. 1943. Advan. Enzymol. 3:191.
[10] Ochoa, S. 1951. Physiol. Rev. 31:56.
[11] Ochoa, S., and J. R. Stern. 1952. Ann. Rev. Biochem. 21:547.
[12] Potter, V. R., and C. Heidelberger. 1950. Physiol. Rev. 30:487.
[13] Umbreit, W. W. 1952. Metabolic maps. Burgess, Minneapolis. v. 1, pp. 90-112.
[14] Umbreit, W. W. 1960. Ibid. v. 2.
[15] West, E. S., et al. 1966. Textbook of biochemistry. Ed. 4. Macmillan, New York.
[16] White, A., P. Handler, and E. L. Smith. 1964. Principles of biochemistry. Ed. 3. McGraw-Hill, New York.

80. CYTOCHROME SYSTEM

The cytochromes (iron-containing compounds) in association with certain enzymes comprise the cytochrome system. The system operates as the final pathway by which an intermediate metabolite (substrate), under the influence of its specific dehydrogenase, releases hydrogen to the first member in a series of carriers for ultimate combination with oxygen to form water. Each step in the process involves both oxidation and reduction: the system oxidizes the hydrogen of the substrate by removing electrons from it, thereby producing oxidized substrate and hydrogen ions. In the process, the system itself is reduced and is finally oxidized by molecular oxygen. For each gram of hydrogen thus passed through NADH and finally oxidized, enough energy is produced to form 1.5 moles of adenosine triphosphate from adenosine diphosphate and PO_4. *Abbreviations:* NAD^+ (NADH) = nicotinamide adenine dinucleotide (reduced form).

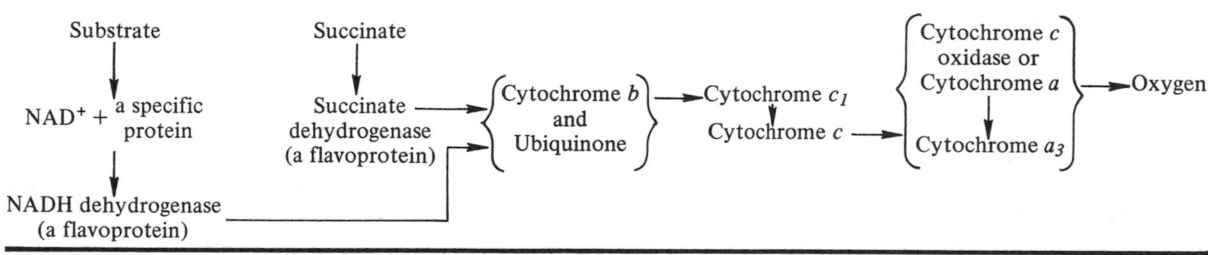

Contributor: Wainio, Walter W.

General References

[1] Chance, B. 1961. In J. E. Falk, ed. Haematin enzymes. Pergamon Press, Oxford. p. 597.
[2] Green, D. E., and S. Fleischer. 1963. Biochim. Biophys. Acta 70:554.
[3] Okunuki, K., et al. 1958. Proc. Intern. Symp. Enzyme Chem., Tokyo-Kyoto, 1957, p. 264.
[4] Slater, E. C. 1958. Advan. Enzymol. 20:147.
[5] Slater, E. C. 1961. In J. E. Falk, ed. Haematin Enzymes. Pergamon Press, Oxford. p. 575.

81. PATHWAYS OF ENERGY METABOLISM IN MUSCLE

Excitation through membrane depolarization leads to the release of Ca^{2+} from intracellular stores located in the sarcoplasmic reticulum. Ca^{2+} promotes the interaction of actin and myosin, leading to the hydrolysis of ATP. The ADP formed is first of all rephosphorylated by creatine phosphate. Concomitantly there is stimulation of phosphorylase and phosphofructokinase, leading to formation of ATP. The mechanism of this stimulation is not quite clear, and Ca^{2+} may play a role. Neurohormonal and hormonal control of enzymes is indicated. Under aerobic conditions the excitation of pyruvate leads to formation of more ATP, by phosphorylation of 6 moles of ADP per mole of O_2. The energy of ATP breakdown is used for performing mechanical work. Shortening of the muscle without load apparently is not coupled to breakdown of high-energy phosphate. *Abbreviations:* ADP = adenosine diphosphate; AMP = adenosine phosphate; ATP = adenosine triphosphate; CoA = coenzyme A; GTP = guanosine triphosphate; P_i = inorganic orthophosphate; PP_i = inorganic pyrophosphate; UTP = uridine triphosphate.

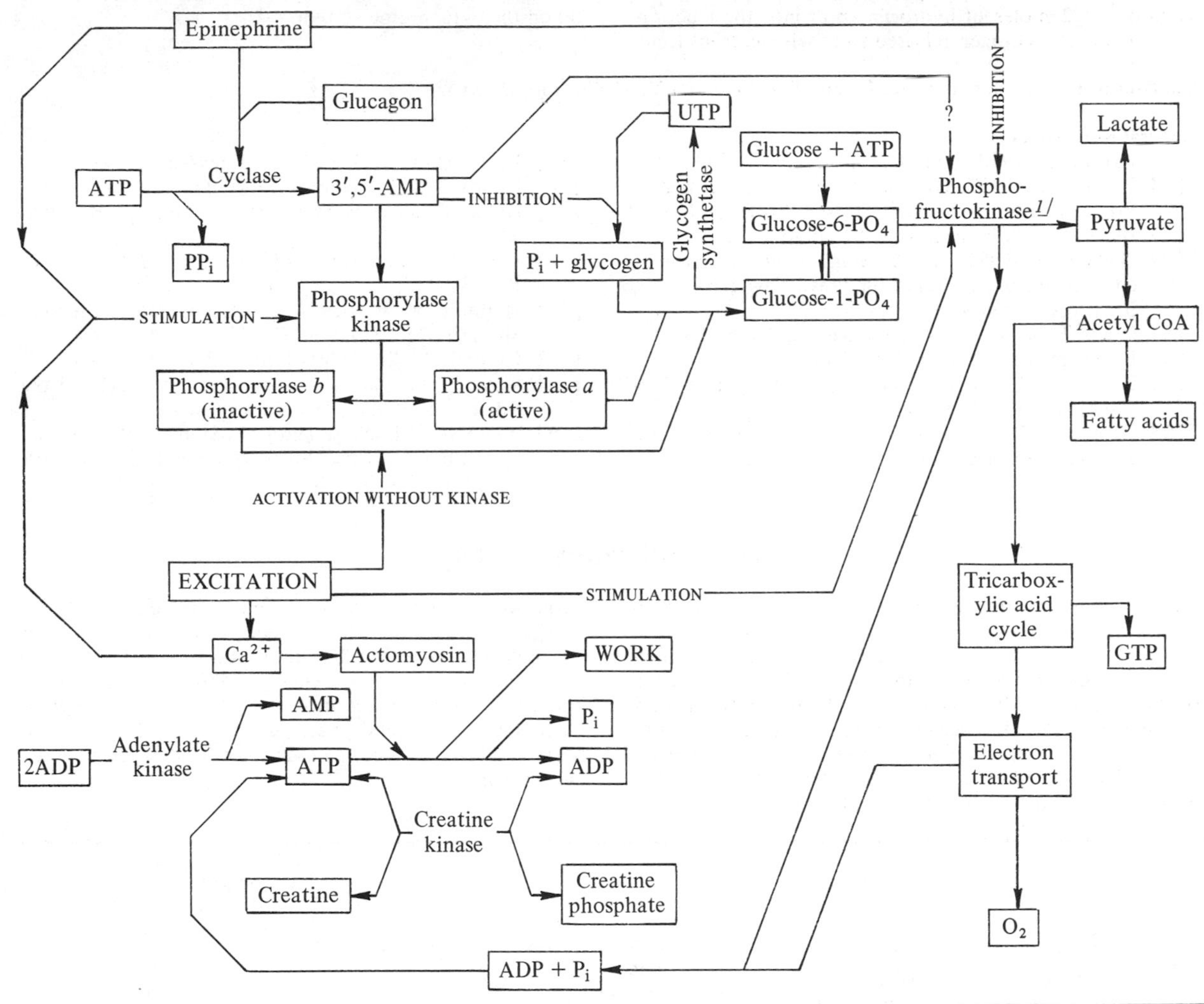

1/ This enzyme, one of several involved in the breakdown of glucose-6-phosphate to pyruvate, is essential in the regulation of glycolysis [4,7,8].

Contributor: Gergely, J.

General References

[1] Davies, R. E., M. J. Kushmerick, and R. E. Larson. 1967. Nature 214:148.

[2] Gergely, J. 1964. In J. N. Walton, ed. Diseases of voluntary muscle. Little, Brown; Boston.

[3] Gergely, J., ed. 1964. Biochemistry of muscle contraction. Little, Brown; Boston.

[4] Helmreich, E., and F. C. Cori. 1965. Advan. Enzyme Regulation 3:91.

[5] Hungarian Academy of Science. 1967. Symp. Muscle, Budapest, 1966.

[6] Huxley, A. F., and H. E. Huxley. 1964. Proc. Roy. Soc. (London), B, 160:433.

[7] Larner, J. 1966. Trans. N.Y. Acad. Sci., II, 29:192.

[8] Leloir, L. F., C. E. Cardini, and E. Cabib. 1960. In M. Florkin and H. S. Mason, ed. Comparative biochemistry. Academic Press, New York. v. 2, p. 97.

[9] Paul, W. M., et al., ed. 1965. Muscle. Pergamon Press, New York.

[10] Weber, A. 1965. Current Topics Bioenerget. 3:91.

82. PATHWAYS OF PHOTOSYNTHESIS: CARBON DIOXIDE REDUCTION CYCLE

According to current evidence, photosynthetic carbon dioxide reduction follows the same general pathways in all plants. The first reaction results in formation of two molecules of phosphoglycerate from carbon dioxide and ribulose diphosphate. Phosphoglycerate is then reduced via the reverse of glycolysis (indicated by light arrows) to supply hexose phosphates for synthesis of sucrose and polysaccharides. A portion of the intermediate compounds goes through the sequence of reactions shown in the diagram, leading to regeneration of the carbon dioxide acceptor, ribulose diphosphate. Heavy arrows indicate directions of material transfer during steady-state photosynthesis. Light arrows indicate some reverse reactions, and some reactions of glycolysis and the oxidative pentose phosphate cycle.

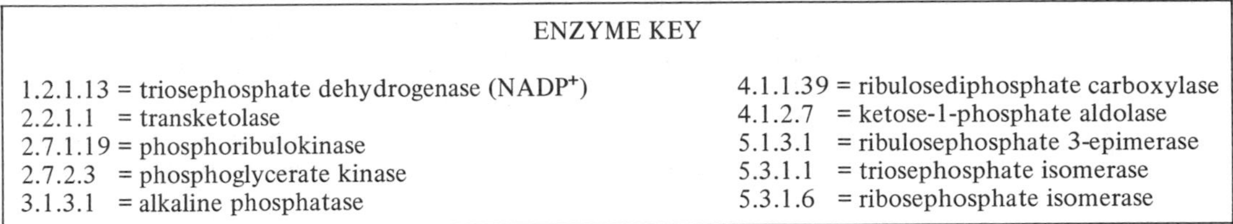

ENZYME KEY

1.2.1.13 = triosephosphate dehydrogenase ($NADP^+$)
2.2.1.1 = transketolase
2.7.1.19 = phosphoribulokinase
2.7.2.3 = phosphoglycerate kinase
3.1.3.1 = alkaline phosphatase
4.1.1.39 = ribulosediphosphate carboxylase
4.1.2.7 = ketose-1-phosphate aldolase
5.1.3.1 = ribulosephosphate 3-epimerase
5.3.1.1 = triosephosphate isomerase
5.3.1.6 = ribosephosphate isomerase

CO_2
Ribulose-1,5-diphosphate (5 carbons)
4.1.1.39 — 1/
2/ 1.2.1.13 & 2.7.2.3
3-Phosphoglycerate (3 carbons)
Glyceraldehyde-3-phosphate (3 carbons)
5.3.1.1 — 3/
Dihydroxyacetone-3-phosphate (3 carbons)
4.1.2.7 4/
12/
Fructose-1,6-diphosphate (6 carbons)
3.1.3.1 5/
2.7.1.19
2.2.1.1
Xylulose-5-phosphate (5 carbons) + Erythrose-4-phosphate (4 carbons)
6/
Fructose-6-phosphate (6 carbons)
5.1.3.1 10/
Dihydroxyacetone-3-phosphate (3 carbons)
Glucose-6-phosphate (6 carbons)
Ribulose-5-phosphate (5 carbons)
4.1.2.7 7/
Sedoheptulose-1,7-diphosphate (7 carbons)
6-Phosphogluconic acid (6 carbons)
11/
3.1.3.1 8/
5.3.1.6
Sedoheptulose-7-phosphate (7 carbons)
Glyceraldehyde-3-phosphate (3 carbons)
Ribose-5-phosphate (5 carbons)
2.2.1.1 9/
CO_2

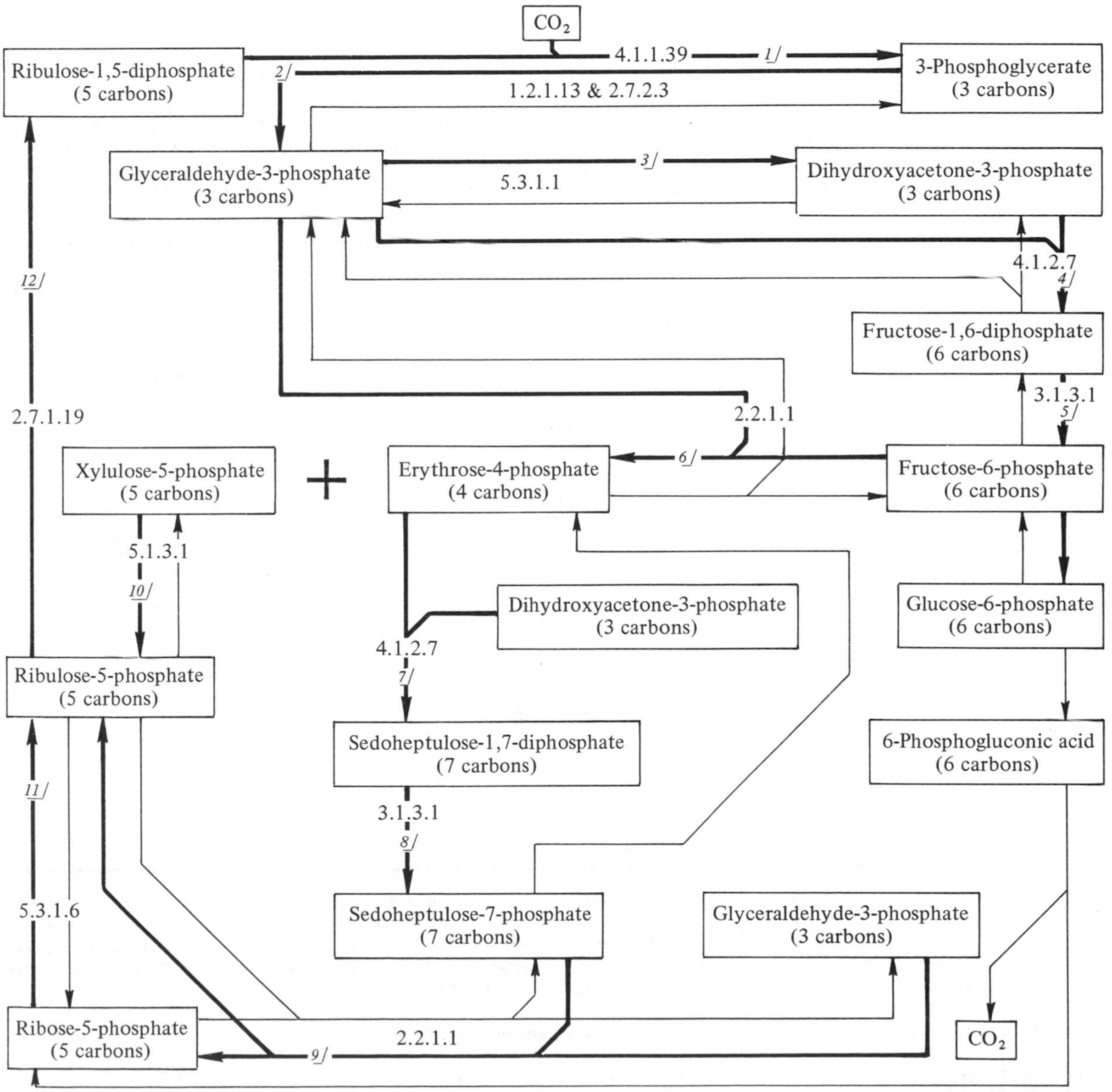

1/ Ribulose diphosphate adds CO_2 at carbon-2 and splits hydrolytically to give 2 molecules of 3-phosphoglycerate. 2/ The carboxyl group is reduced to an aldehyde group with the aid of adenosine triphosphate (ATP) and reduced nicotinamide adenine dinucleotide phosphate (NADPH). 3/ Isomerization involves transfer of 2 hydrogen atoms from

continued

82. PATHWAYS OF PHOTOSYNTHESIS: CARBON DIOXIDE REDUCTION CYCLE

carbon-2 to carbon-1. 4/ Aldol condensation of carbon-1 of glyceraldehyde-3-PO_4 with carbon-1 of dihydroxyacetone-3-PO_4. 5/ Removal of the phosphate ester group from carbon-1 by hydrolysis. 6/ 2 hydrogen atoms plus the glycolyl group (carbon-1,2) of fructose transferred to glyceraldehyde-PO_4 to form xylulose-5-PO_4, leaving erythrose-PO_4. 7/ Aldol condensation of carbon-1 of erythrose-4-PO_4 with carbon-1 of dihydroxyacetone-3-PO_4 obtained from step 3. 8/ Hydrolysis of the phosphate ester group on carbon-1 to give inorganic phosphate. 9/ Transfer of the glycolyl group (carbon-1,2) of sedoheptulose-7-PO_4 to carbon-1 of glyceraldehyde-3-PO_4 to give ribulose-5-PO_4, leaving ribose-5-PO_4. 10/ Epimerization of carbon-3 of ketopentose. Xylulose-5-PO_4 isomerizes to ribulose-5-PO_4 with phosphoketopentose epimerase. 11/ Isomerization of aldose to ketose by the transfer of 2 hydrogen atoms. 12/ Phosphorylation of carbon-1 by reaction with ATP.

Contributors: (a) Bassham, James A., (b) Calvin, Melvin, (c) Benson, Andrew A.

General References

[1] Bassham, J. A., and M. Calvin. 1957. The path of carbon in photosynthesis. Prentice-Hall, Englewood Cliffs, N.J.

[2] Calvin, M., and J. A. Bassham. 1962. The photosynthesis of carbon compounds. W. A. Benjamin, New York.

83. PATHWAYS OF SUCROSE SYNTHESIS: INTERMEDIATES

Sucrose, common to all green plants, is the first free sugar formed by a series of steps involving phosphorylated intermediates. Photosynthesis supplies reduced pyridine nucleotides and adenosine triphosphate (ATP). Phosphoglycerate, provided by the photosynthetic carboxylation reaction, is reduced and condensed to form hexose molecules. Energy required to produce sucrose from hexose phosphates comes largely from high-energy uridine triphosphate (UTP) which becomes uridine diphosphate glucose (UDP-glucose) for condensation with fructose phosphate.

ENZYME KEY

2.4.1.13 = UDP glucose-fructose glucosyltransferase
2.4.1.14 = UDP glucose-fructose-phosphate glucosyltransferase
2.7.5.1 = phosphoglucomutase
2.7.7.12 = hexose-1-phosphate uridylyltransferase
3.1.3.1 = alkaline phosphatase
5.3.1.9 = glucosephosphate isomerase

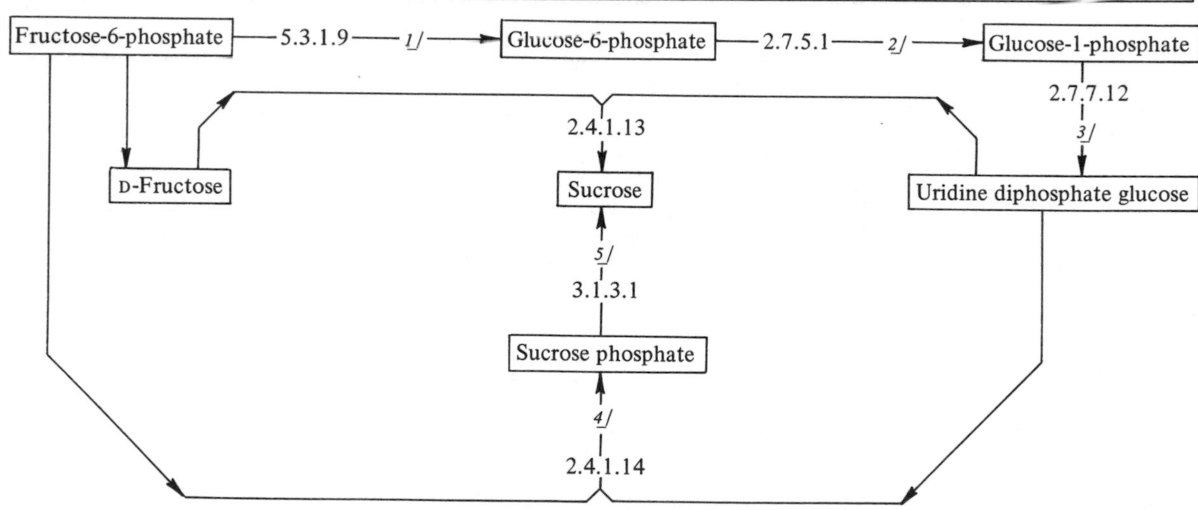

1/ Hydrogen atom on carbon-1 shifts to carbon-2, forming the epimer, glucose-6-phosphate; furanose ring structure is changed to pyranose. 2/ Phosphate group on carbon-6 is transferred to carbon-1 through the required coenzyme intermediate, glucose-1,6-diphosphate; Mg^{2+} is required. 3/ UTP reacts with glucose-1-phosphate to form pyrophosphate and UDP-glucose. 4/ Fructose-6-phosphate and UDP-glucose react to give UDP and an unstable sucrose phosphate. 5/ Hydrolysis occurs to give free sucrose and orthophosphate.

Contributors: (a) Bassham, James A., (b) Calvin, Melvin, (c) Benson, Andrew A.

General References

[1] Bassham, J. A., and M. Calvin. 1957. The path of carbon in photosynthesis. Prentice-Hall, Englewood Cliffs, N.J.

[2] Calvin, M., and J. A. Bassham. 1962. The photosynthesis of carbon compounds. W. A. Benjamin, New York.

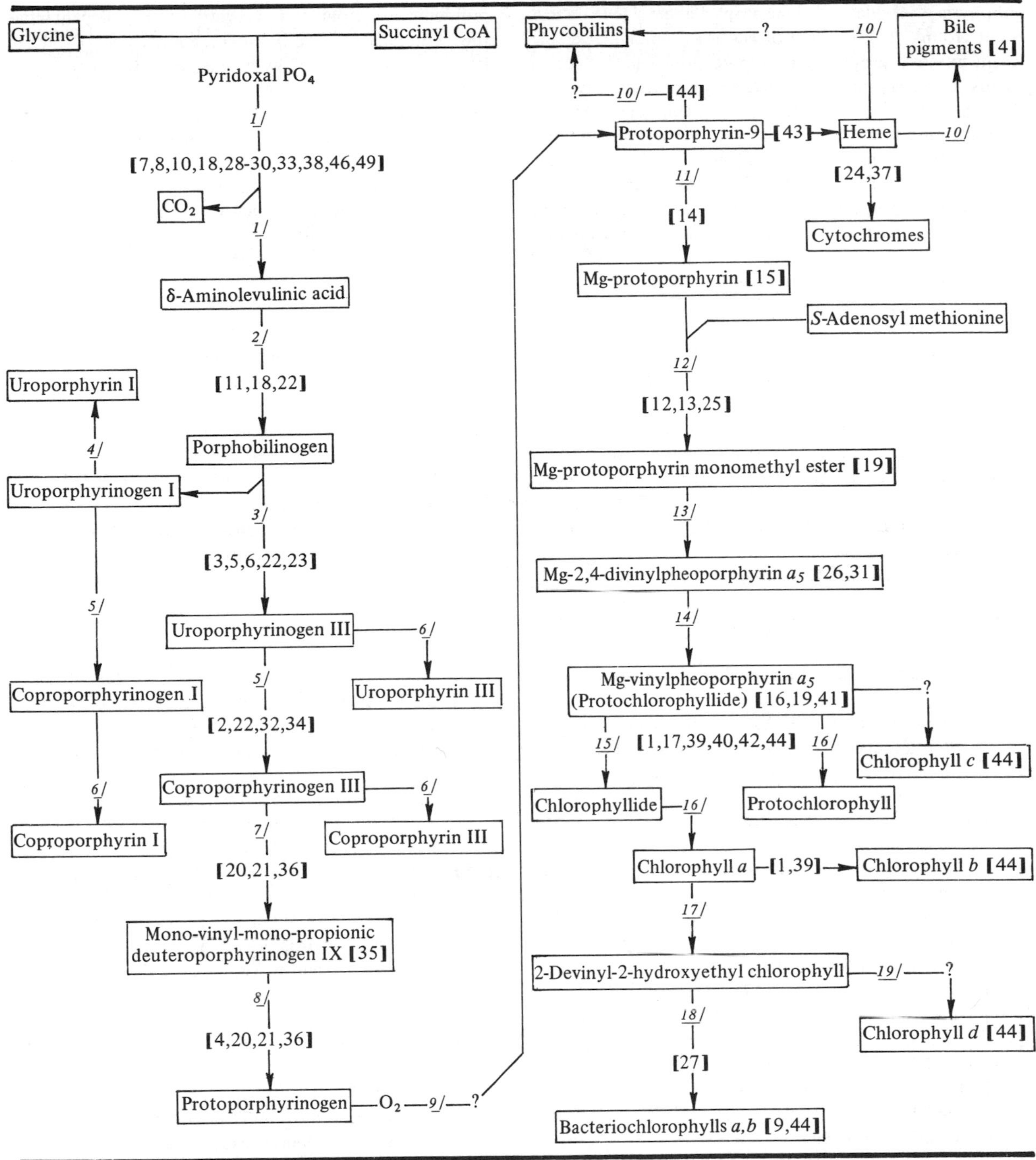

1/ Condensation of glycine with succinyl CoA on the pyridoxal-phosphate enzyme, δ-aminolevulinic acid synthetase. An unstable intermediate, δ-amino-α-ketoadipate [33], may first be formed which decarboxylates spontaneously to δ-aminolevulinate. 2/ 2 molecules of δ-aminolevulinate are condensed with the splitting of 2 molecules of water by the dehydrase enzyme, forming the pyrrole, porphobilinogen. 3/ 4 molecules of porphobilinogen are condensed by the sequential action of 2 enzymes, the deaminase (uroporphyrinogen I synthetase) and the isomerase (uroporphyrinogen III cosynthetase), forming a reduced porphyrin, uroporphyrinogen III. 4/ Produced by autoxidation in *Chlorella* cell preparations by heating to 55°C for 30 minutes. This inactivates the isomerase enzyme, forming urogen I which autoxidizes to uroporphyrin I. 5/ Decarboxylation of uroporphyrinogen to coproporphyrinogen. 6/ Autoxidation products found with broken *Chlorella* or *Rhodopseudomonas spheroides* cells, lysed erythrocytes, or in congenital

continued

porphyria. 7/ Oxidation of one propionic acid side chain to a vinyl group. 8/ Oxidation of another propionic acid side chain to vinyl, producing protoporphyrinogen. 9/ Spontaneous (or enzymatic?) oxidation to protoporphyrin-9. 10/ Open-chain tetrapyrroles. 11/ Magnesium protoporphyrin found in a *Chlorella* mutant. 12/ Found in a *Chlorella* mutant, etiolated barley, and *Rhodopseudomonas spheroides*. 13/ Found in *Rhodopseudomonas spheroides* treated with 8-hydroxyquinoline, and in cucurbid seed coats. 14/ 2 or 3 postulated steps, including oxidation of a propionic acid group and cyclization to a cyclopentanone ring. Found in a *Chlorella* mutant, etiolated beans and barley. 15/ Addition of 2 hydrogens, one *cis* and the other *trans* to the β,β' positions of pyrrole ring D. 16/ Esterification of propionic acid group with phytol, the C-20 alcohol. 17/ Found in *Rhodopseudomonas spheroides* grown in 8-hydroxyquinoline. 18/ Oxidation of hydroxyethyl side chain to acetyl on ring A, and reduction of pyrrole ring B at the β,β' positions. 19/ 2-Devinyl-2-formyl chlorophyll *a*.

Contributors: Nadler, Kenneth, and Granick, S.

Specific References

[1] Boardman, N. K. 1966. In L. P. Vernon and G. R. Seely, ed. The chlorophylls. Academic Press, New York. p. 437.

[2] Bogorad, L. 1955. Science 121:878.

[3] Bogorad, L. 1962. Methods Enzymol. 5:885.

[4] Bogorad, L., and S. Granick. 1953. J. Biol. Chem. 202:793.

[5] Bogorad, L., and S. Granick. 1953. Proc. Natl. Acad. Sci. U.S. 39:1176.

[6] Booj, H. L., and C. Rimington. 1957. Biochem. J. 65(1):4P.

[7] Burnham, B. F. 1962. Biochem. Biophys. Res. Commun. 7:351.

[8] Burnham, B. F., and J. Lascelles. 1963. Biochem. J. 87:462.

[9] Eimhjellen, K. E., O. Aasmundrud, and A. Jensen. 1963. Biochem. Biophys. Res. Commun. 10:232.

[10] Gibson, K. D., W. G. Laver, and A. Neuberger. 1958. Biochem. J. 70:71.

[11] Gibson, K. D., A. Neuberger, and J. J. Scott. 1955. Ibid. 61:618.

[12] Gibson, K. D., A. Neuberger, and G. H. Tait. 1962. Ibid. 83:550.

[13] Gibson, K. D., A. Neuberger, and G. H. Tait. 1963. Ibid. 88:325.

[14] Granick, S. 1948. J. Biol. Chem. 172:717.

[15] Granick, S. 1948. Ibid. 175:333.

[16] Granick, S. 1950. Ibid. 183:713.

[17] Granick, S. 1951. Ann. Rev. Plant Physiol. 2:115.

[18] Granick, S. 1958. J. Biol. Chem. 232:1101.

[19] Granick, S. 1959. Plant Physiol. 34:xviii.

[20] Granick, S., and D. Mauzerall. 1958. Ann. N.Y. Acad. Sci. 75:115.

[21] Granick, S., and D. Mauzerall. 1958. Federation Proc. 17:233.

[22] Granick, S., and D. Mauzerall. 1958. J. Biol. Chem. 232:1119.

[23] Heath, H., and D. S. Hoare. 1959. Biochem. J. 72:14.

[24] Jensen, J. 1957. J. Bacteriol. 73:324.

[25] Jones, O. T. G. 1963. Biochem. J. 86:429.

[26] Jones, O. T. G. 1963. Ibid. 89:182.

[27] Jones, O. T. G. 1964. Ibid. 91:572.

[28] Kilkuchi, G., D. Shemin, and B. J. Bachmann. 1958. Biochim. Biophys. Acta 28:219.

[29] Kikuchi, G., et al. 1958. J. Biol. Chem. 233:1214.

[30] Lascelles, J. 1957. Biochem. J. 66:65.

[31] Lascelles, J. 1966. Ibid. 100:175.

[32] Mauzerall, D., and S. Granick. 1958. Ibid. 232:1141.

[33] Neuberger, A. 1961. Biochem. J. 78:1.

[34] Neve, R. A., R. F. Labbe, and R. S. Aldrich. 1956. J. Am. Chem. Soc. 78:691.

[35] Porra, R. J., and J. E. Falk. 1964. Biochem. J. 90:69.

[36] Sano, S., and S. Granick. 1961. J. Biol. Chem. 236:1173.

[37] Sano, S., and K. Tanaka. 1964. Ibid. 239:3109.

[38] Schulman, M. P., and D. A. Richert. 1957. Ibid. 226:181.

[39] Shlyk, A. A., et al. 1963. Photochem. Photobiol. 2:129.

[40] Smith, J. H. C. 1960. In M. B. Allen, ed. Comparative biochemistry of photoreactive systems. Academic Press, New York. pp. 257-277.

[41] Stanier, R. Y., and J. H. C. Smith. 1959. Carnegie Inst. Wash. Yearbook 58:336.

[42] Vlasenok, L. I., L. I. Fradkin, and A. A. Shlyk. 1965. Photochem. Photobiol. 4:385.

[43] White, D. C., and S. Granick. 1963. J. Bacteriol. 85:842.

General References

[44] Goodwin, T. W., ed. 1965. Chemistry and biochemistry of plant pigments. Academic Press, New York. pp. 3, 29, & 175.

[45] Granick, S. 1966. In T. W. Goodwin, ed. The biochemistry of chloroplasts. Academic Press, New York. v. 2, p. 373.

[46] Granick, S., and R. D. Levere. 1964. Progr. Hematol. 4:1.

[47] Lascelles, J. 1964. Tetrapyrrole biosynthesis and its regulation. W. A. Benjamin, New York.

[48] Marks, G. S. 1966. Botan. Rev. 32:56.

[49] Shemin, D. 1955. Ciba Found. Symp. Porphyrin Biosyn. Metab., p. 4.

[50] Vernon, L. P., and G. R. Seely, ed. 1966. The chlorophylls. Academic Press, New York.

85. PATHWAYS OF BIOSYNTHESIS: WATER-SOLUBLE VITAMINS

Part I. Thiamine

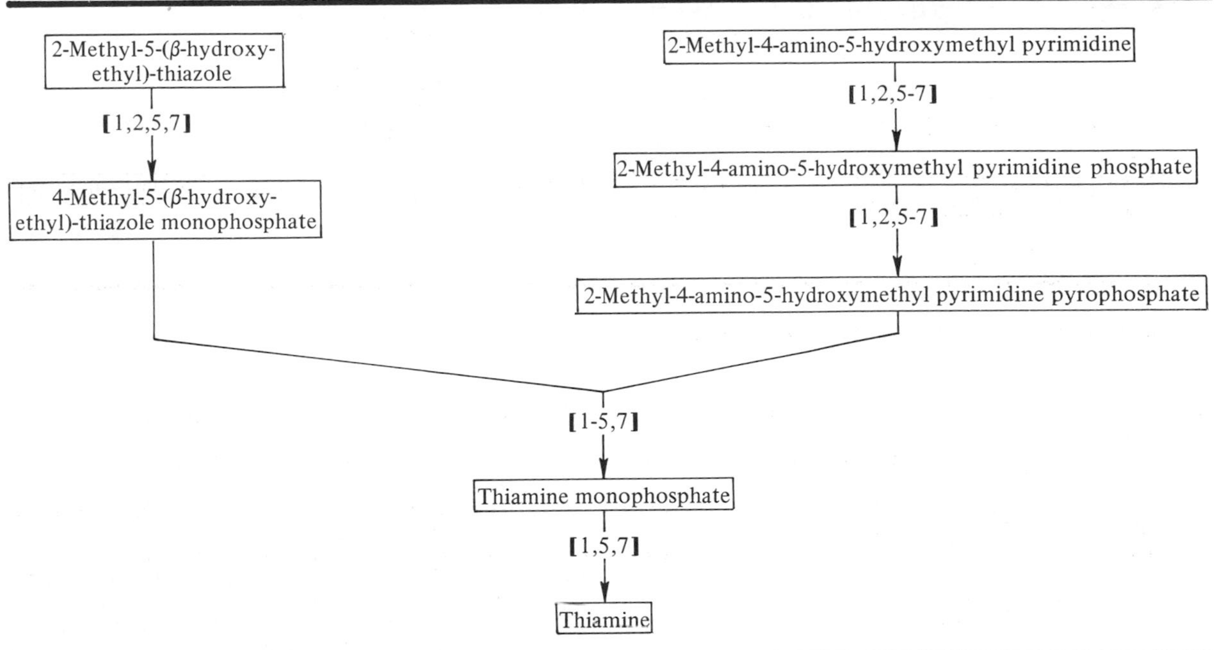

Contributors: Storvick, Clara A., and Fincke, Margaret L.

References

[1] Brown, G. M., and J. J. Reynolds. 1963. Ann. Rev. Biochem. 32:437.

[2] Camiener, G. W., and G. M. Brown. 1960. J. Biol. Chem. 235:2404, 2411.

[3] Leder, I. G. 1959. Biochem. Biophys. Res. Commun. 1:63.

[4] Leder, I. G. 1961. J. Biol. Chem. 236:3066.

[5] Lewin, L. M. 1963. Georgetown Med. Bull. 17:101.

[6] Lewin, L. M., and G. M. Brown. 1961. J. Biol. Chem. 236:2768.

[7] Nose, Y., et al. 1961. J. Vitaminol. (Kyoto) 7:98.

Part II. Riboflavin

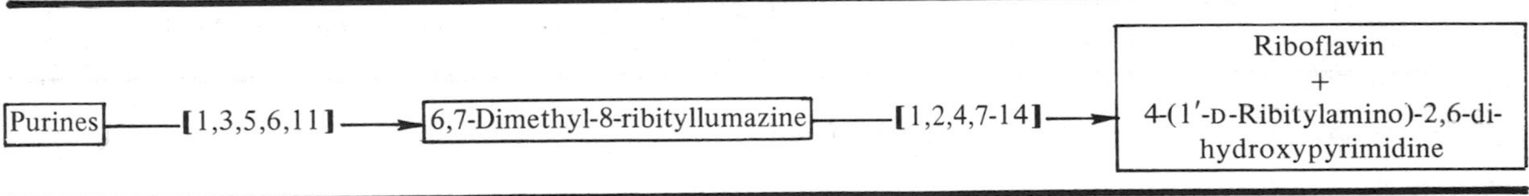

Contributors: Storvick, Clara A., and Fincke, Margaret L.

References

[1] Goodwin, T. W. 1963. The biosynthesis of vitamins and related compounds. Academic Press, New York. pp. 24-68.

[2] Harvey, R. A., and G. W. E. Plaut. 1966. J. Biol. Chem. 241:2120.

[3] Howells, D. J., and G. W. E. Plaut. 1965. Biochem. J. 94:755.

[4] Katagiri, H., I. Takeda, and K. Imai. 1958. J. Vitaminol. (Kyoto) 4:211,278,285.

[5] Kuwada, S., et al. 1958. Ibid. 4:217.

[6] McNutt, W. S. 1961. J. Am. Chem. Soc. 83:2303.

[7] Mitsuda, H., F. Kawai, and S. Moritaka. 1961. J. Vitaminol. (Kyoto) 7:128.

[8] Mitsuda, H., Y. Suzuki, and F. Kawai. 1963. Ibid. 9:121.

[9] Mitsuda, H., et al. 1961. Ibid. 7:247.

[10] Mitsuda, H., et al. 1963. Ibid. 8:178.

[11] Plaut, G. W. E. 1961. Ann. Rev. Biochem. 30:409.

[12] Plaut, G. W. E. 1963. J. Biol. Chem. 238:2225.

[13] Wacker, H., et al. 1964. Ibid. 239:3493.

[14] Winestock, C. H., T. Aogaichi, and G. W. E. Plaut. 1963. Ibid. 238:2866.

continued

Part III. Biotin

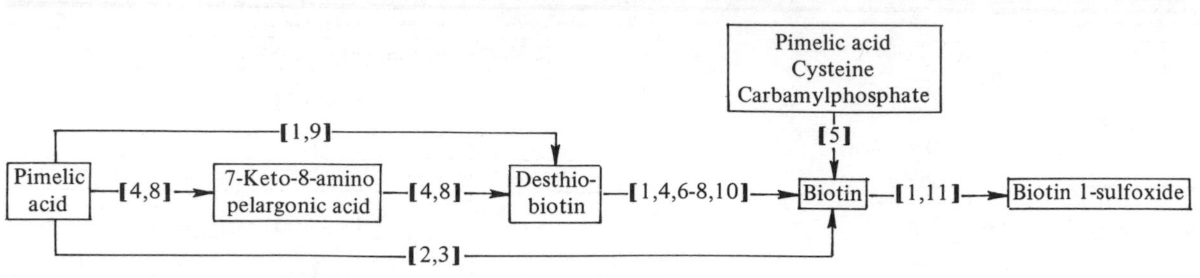

Contributors: Storvick, Clara A., and Fincke, Margaret L.

References

[1] Eisenberg, M. A. 1962. Biochem. Biophys. Res. Commun. 8:437.
[2] Elford, H. L., and L. D. Wright. 1962. Federation Proc. 21:467.
[3] Elford, H. L., and L. D. Wright. 1963. Biochem. Biophys. Res. Commun. 10:373.
[4] Iwahara, S., et al. 1966. Agr. Biol. Chem. (Tokyo) 30:304.
[5] Lezius, A., E. Ringlemann, and F. Lynen. 1963. Biochem. Z. 336:510.
[6] Niimura, T., T. Suzuki, and Y. Sahashi. 1964. J. Vitaminol. (Kyoto) 10:218.
[7] Niimura, T., T. Suzuki, and Y. Sahashi. 1964. Ibid. 10:224.
[8] Okumura, S., et al. 1962. Nippon Nogei Kagaku Kaishi 36:599, 605.
[9] Tatum, E. L. 1945. J. Biol. Chem. 160:455.
[10] Tepper, J. P., D. B. McCormick, and L. D. Wright. 1966. Ibid. 241:5734.
[11] Wright, L. D., E. L. Cresson, and C. A. Driscoll. 1955. Proc. Soc. Exptl. Biol. Med. 89:234.

Part IV. Nicotinic Acid

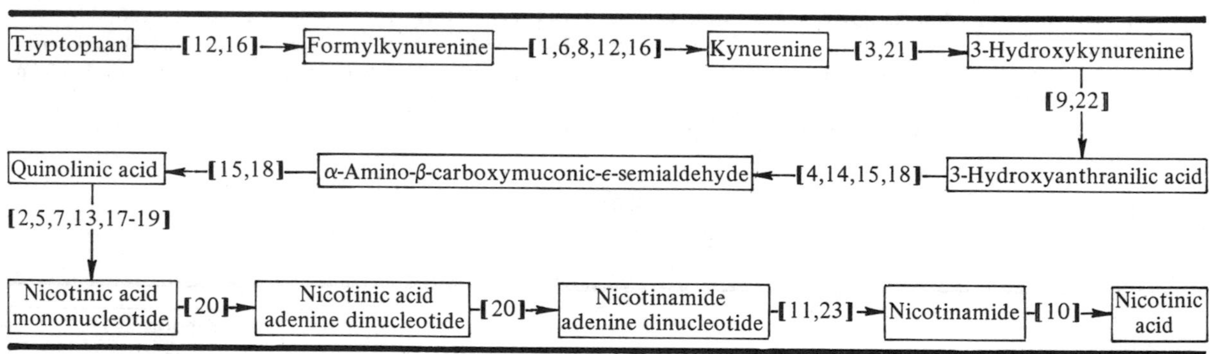

Contributors: Storvick, Clara A., and Fincke, Margaret L.

References

[1] Ahmad, F., and A. G. Moat. 1966. J. Biol. Chem. 241:775.
[2] Andreoli, A. J., et al. 1963. Biochem. Biophys. Res. Commun. 12:92.
[3] DeCastro, F. T., J. M. Price, and R. R. Brown. 1956. J. Am. Chem. Soc. 78:2904.
[4] Decker, R. H., et al. 1961. J. Biol. Chem. 236:3076.
[5] Gholson, J. K., et al. 1964. Ibid. 239:1208.
[6] Glassman, E. 1956. Genetics 41:566.
[7] Hadwiger, L. A., et al. 1963. Biochem. Biophys. Res. Commun. 13:466.
[8] Jakoby, W. B. 1954. J. Biol. Chem. 207:657.
[9] Jakoby, W. B., and D. M. Bonner. 1953. Ibid. 205:699.
[10] Joshi, J. G., and P. Handler. 1962. Ibid. 237:929.
[11] Kaplan, N. O., S. P. Colowick, and A. Nason. 1951. Ibid. 191:473.
[12] Knox, W. E., and A. H. Mehler. 1950. Ibid. 187:419.
[13] Konno, K., et al. 1965. Am. Rev. Respirat. Diseases 91:383.
[14] Kuss, E. 1966. Z. Physiol. Chem. 345:195.
[15] Mehler, A. H. 1956. J. Biol. Chem. 218:241.
[16] Mehler, A. H., and W. E. Knox. 1950. Ibid. 187:431.
[17] Nakamura, S., et al. 1963. Biochem. Biophys. Res. Commun. 13:285.
[18] Nishizuka, Y., and O. Hayaishi. 1963. J. Biol. Chem. 238:3369.
[19] Packman, P. M., and W. B. Jakoby. 1965. Biochem. Biophys. Res. Commun. 18:710.
[20] Preiss, J., and P. Handler. 1958. J. Biol. Chem. 233:493.
[21] Saito, I., O. Hayaishi, and S. Rothberg. 1957. Ibid. 229:921.
[22] Weiss, O., and H. Fuchs. 1950. Experientia 6:472.
[23] Zatman, L. J., N. O. Kaplan, and S. P. Colowick. 1953. J. Biol. Chem. 200:197.

continued

85. PATHWAYS OF BIOSYNTHESIS: WATER-SOLUBLE VITAMINS

Part V. Pantothenic Acid

Abbreviations: CoA = coenzyme A; AMP = adenosine phosphate; PP_i = inorganic pyrophosphate.

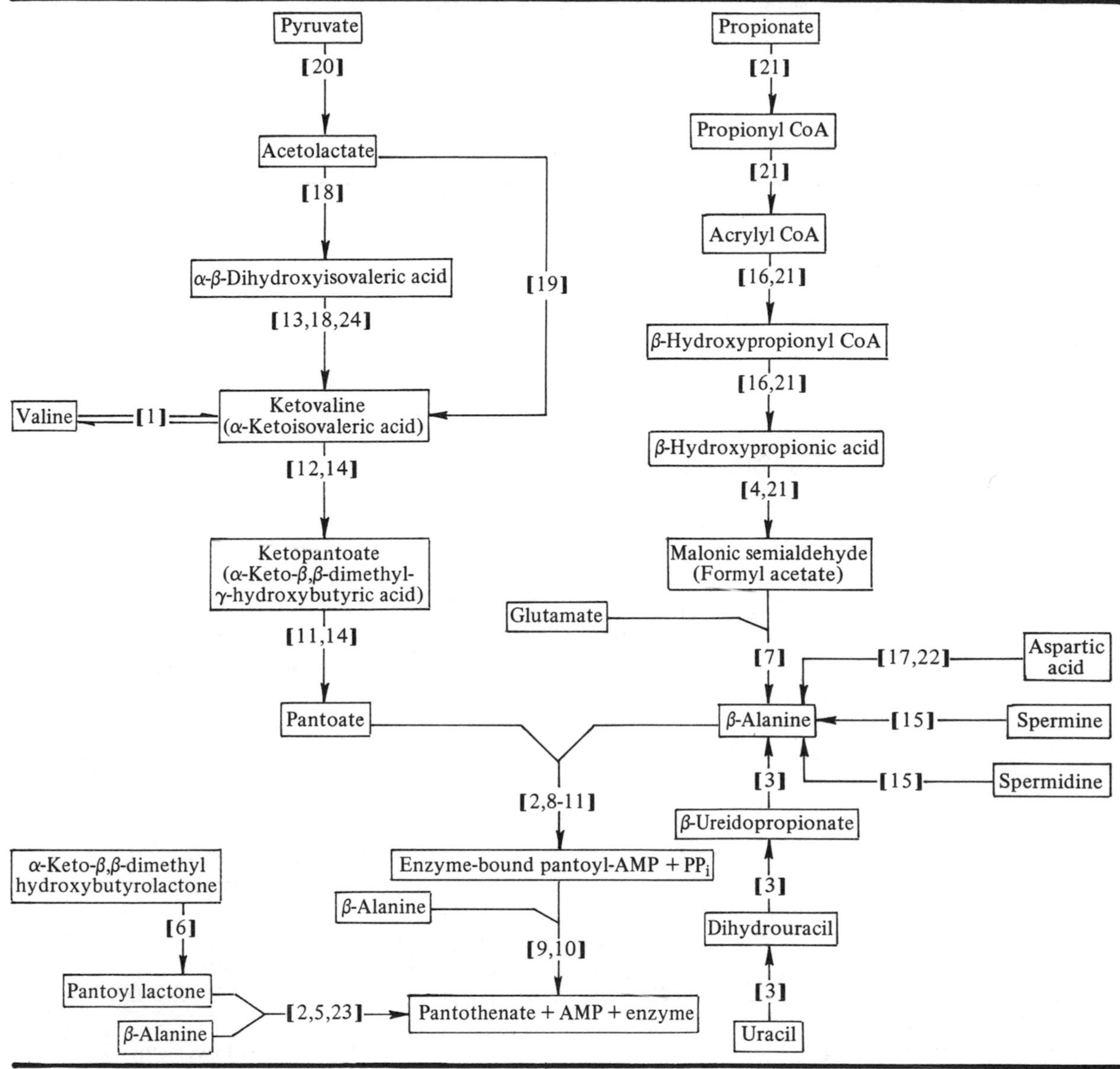

Contributors: Storvick, Clara A., and Fincke, Margaret L.

References

[1] Adelberg, E. A., and H. E. Umbarger. 1953. J. Biol. Chem. 205:475.
[2] Altenbern, R. A., and H. S. Ginoza. 1954. J. Bacteriol. 68:570.
[3] Campbell, L. 1957. Ibid. 73:225.
[4] Den, H., W. G. Robinson, and M. J. Coon. 1959. J. Biol. Chem. 234:1666.
[5] Ginoza, H. S., and R. A. Altenbern. 1955. Arch. Biochem. Biophys. 56:537.
[6] Kuhn, R., and T. Wieland. 1942. Ber. Deut. Chem. Ges. 75:121.
[7] Kupiecki, F. P., and M. J. Coon. 1957. J. Biol. Chem. 229:743.
[8] Maas, W. K. 1952. Ibid. 198:23.
[9] Maas, W. K. 1954. Federation Proc. 13:256.
[10] Maas, W. K. 1956. Ibid. 15:305.
[11] Maas, W. K., and B. D. Davis. 1950. J. Bacteriol. 60:733.
[12] McIntosh, E. N., M. Purko, and W. A. Wood. 1957. J. Biol. Chem. 228:499.
[13] Myers, J. W., and E. A. Adelberg. 1954. Proc. Natl. Acad. Sci. U.S. 40:493.
[14] Purko, M., W. O. Nelson, and W. A. Wood. 1954. J. Biol. Chem. 207:51.
[15] Razin, S., U. Bachrach, and I. Gery. 1958. Nature 181:700.
[16] Redina, G., and M. J. Coon. 1957. J. Biol. Chem. 225:523.
[17] Roberts, E., and H. M. Bregoff. 1953. Ibid. 201: 393.
[18] Strassman, M., J. B. Shatton, and S. Weinhause. 1960. Ibid. 235:700.

continued

Part V. Pantothenic Acid

[19] Strassman, M., et al. 1958. J. Am. Chem. Soc. 80: 1771.

[20] Umbarger, H. E., B. Brown, and E. J. Eyring. 1957. J. Am. Chem. Soc. 79:2980.

[21] Vagelos, P. R., and J. M. Earl. 1959. J. Biol. Chem. 234:2272.

[22] Virtanen, A. I., and T. Laine. 1937. Enzymologia 3:266.

[23] Wagner, R. P., and B. M. Guirard. 1948. Proc. Natl. Acad. Sci. U.S. 34:398.

[24] Wixom, R. L., J. B. Shatton, and M. Strassman. 1960. J. Biol. Chem. 235:128.

Part VI. Folic Acid

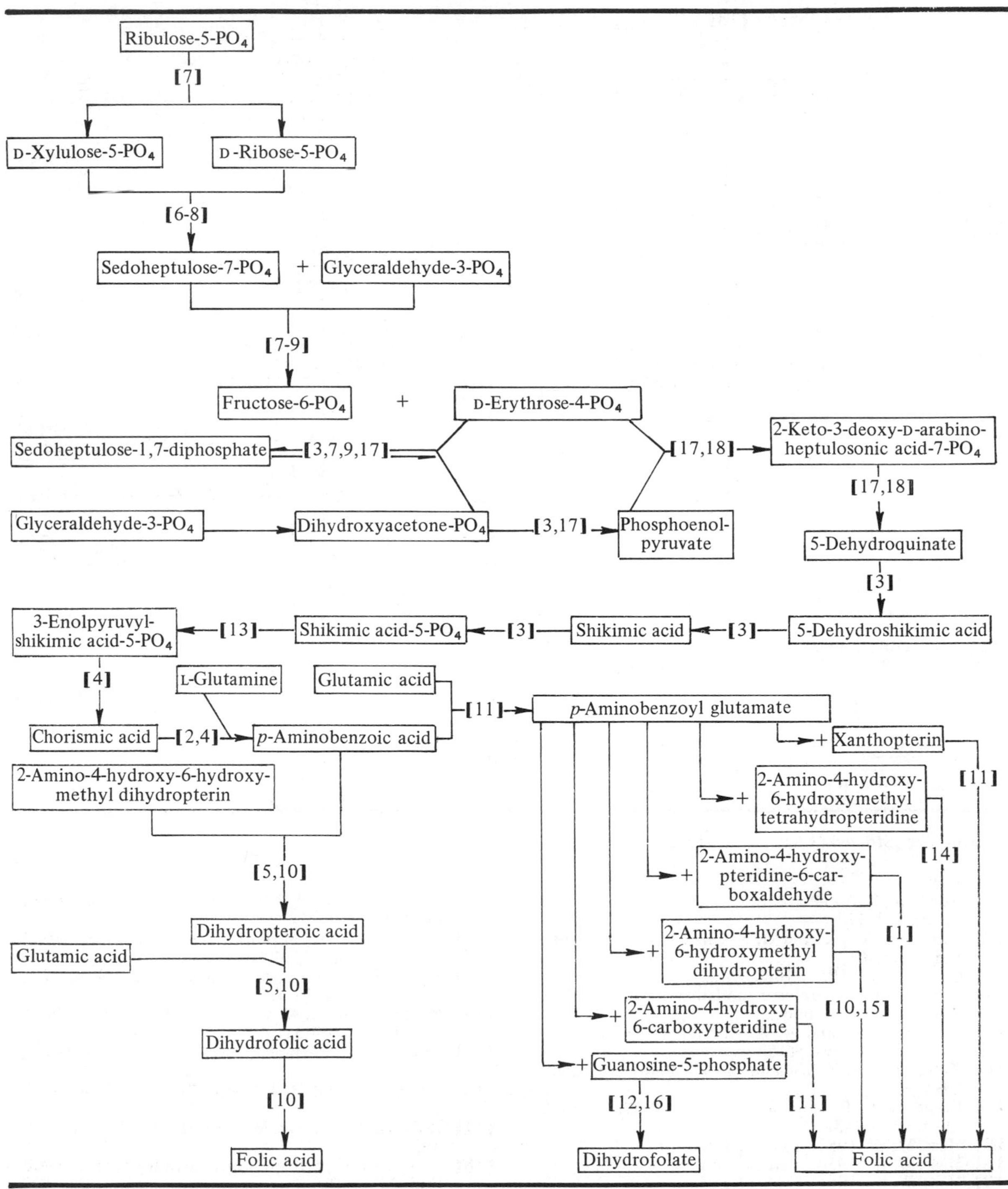

continued

85. PATHWAYS OF BIOSYNTHESIS: WATER-SOLUBLE VITAMINS

Part VI. Folic Acid

Contributors: Storvick, Clara A., and Fincke, Margaret L.

References

[1] Brown, G. M. 1959. Federation Proc. 18:19.
[2] Cox, G. B., and F. Gibson. 1964. Biochim. Biophys. Acta 93:204.
[3] Davis, B. D. 1955. Harvey Lectures Ser. 50:230.
[4] Gibson, F., M. Gibson, and G. B. Cox. 1964. Biochim. Biophys. Acta 82:637.
[5] Griffin, M. J., and G. M. Brown. 1964. J. Biol. Chem. 239:310.
[6] Gunsalus, I. C., B. L. Horecker, and W. A. Wood. 1955. Bacteriol. Rev. 19:79.
[7] Horecker, B. L. 1962. Ciba Lectures Microbial Biochem. 6.
[8] Horecker, B. L., and P. Z. Smyrniotis. 1955. J. Biol. Chem. 212:811.
[9] Horecker, B. L., et al. 1955. Ibid. 212:827.
[10] Jaenicke, L., and Ph. C. Chan. 1960. Angew. Chem. 72:752.
[11] Katenuma, N., T. Shoda, and H. Noda. 1957. J. Vitaminol. (Kyoto) 3:77.
[12] Reynolds, J. J., and G. M. Brown. 1964. J. Biol. Chem. 239:317.
[13] Rivera, A., Jr., and P. R. Srinivasan. 1963. Biochemistry 2:1063.
[14] Shiota, T. 1959. Arch. Biochem. Biophys. 80:155.
[15] Shiota, T., and M. N. Disraely. 1961. Biochim. Biophys. Acta 52:467.
[16] Shiota, T., and M. P. Palumbo. 1965. J. Biol. Chem. 240:4449.
[17] Srinivasan, P. R., M. Katagiri, and D. B. Sprinson. 1959. Ibid. 234:713.
[18] Srinivasan, P. R., and D. B. Sprinson. 1959. Ibid. 234:716.

Part VII. Inositol

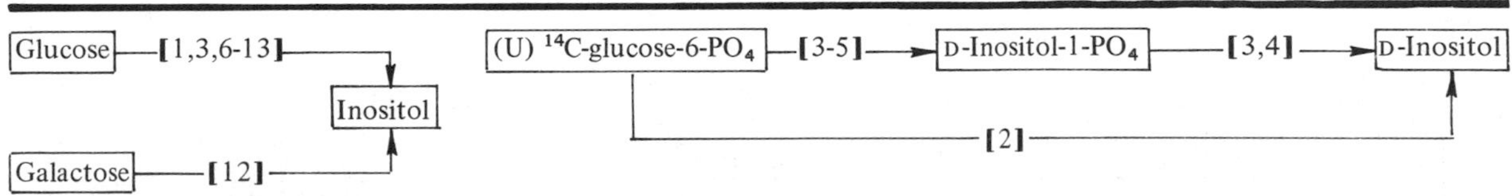

Contributors: Storvick, Clara A., and Fincke, Margaret L.

References

[1] Chen, I. W., and F. C. Charalampous. 1963. Biochem. Biophys. Res. Commun. 12:62.
[2] Chen, I. W., and F. C. Charalampous. 1965. J. Biol. Chem. 240:3507.
[3] Chen, I. W., and F. C. Charalampous. 1966. Ibid. 241:2194.
[4] Chen, I. W., and F. C. Charalampous. 1966. Arch. Biochem. Biophys. 117:154.
[5] Chen, I. W., and F. C. Charalampous. 1967. Biochim. Biophys. Acta 136:568.
[6] Daughaday, W. H., J. Larner, and C. Hartnett. 1955. J. Biol. Chem. 212:869.
[7] Eisenberg, F., Jr., and A. H. Bolden. 1963. Biochem. Biophys. Res. Commun. 12:72.
[8] Freinkel, N., and R. M. C. Dawson. 1961. Biochem. J. 81:250.
[9] Halliday, J. W., and L. Anderson. 1955. J. Biol. Chem. 217:797.
[10] Hauser, G. 1963. Biochim. Biophys. Acta 70:278.
[11] Hauser, G., and V. N. Finellis. 1963. Federation Proc. 22:655.
[12] Imai, Y. 1963. J. Biochem. (Tokyo) 53:50.
[13] Loewus, F. A., and S. Kelly. 1962. Biochem. Biophys. Res. Commun. 7:204.

Part VIII. Choline

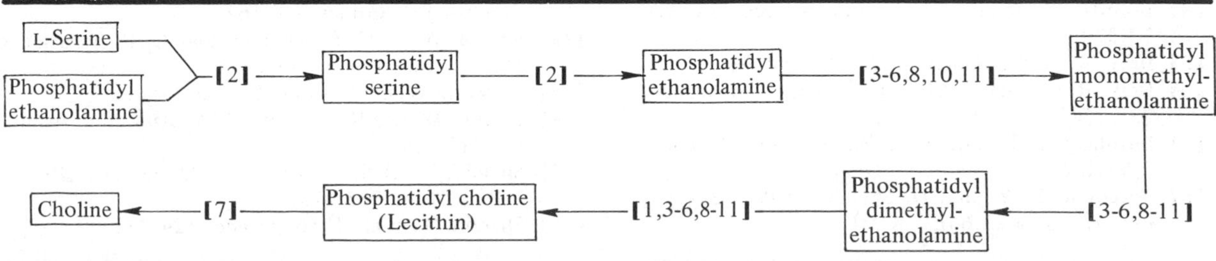

continued

85. PATHWAYS OF BIOSYNTHESIS: WATER-SOLUBLE VITAMINS

Part VIII. Choline

Contributors: Storvick, Clara A., and Fincke, Margaret L.

References

[1] Artom, C., and H. B. Lofland. 1960. Biochem. Biophys. Res. Commun. 3:244.
[2] Borkenhagen, L., E. P. Kennedy, and L. Fielding. 1961. J. Biol. Chem. 236:PC28.
[3] Bremer, J., P. H. Figard, and D. M. Greenberg. 1960. Biochim. Biophys. Acta 43:477.
[4] Bremer, J., and D. M. Greenberg. 1960. Ibid. 37:173.
[5] Gibson, K. D., J. D. Wilson, and S. Udenfriend. 1961. J. Biol. Chem. 236:673.
[6] Kaneshiro, T., and J. H. Law. 1964. Ibid. 239:1705.
[7] Kates, M. 1956. Can. J. Biochem. Physiol. 34:967.
[8] Lust, G., and L. J. Daniel. 1966. Arch. Biochem. Biophys. 113:603.
[9] Rehbinder, D., and D. M. Greenberg. 1965. Ibid. 109:110.
[10] Scarborough, G. A., and J. F. Nyc. 1967. J. Biol. Chem. 242:238.
[11] Wilson, J. D., K. D. Gibson, and S. Udenfriend. 1960. Ibid. 235:3213.

Part IX. Vitamin B_{12}

Abbreviation: CoA = coenzyme A.

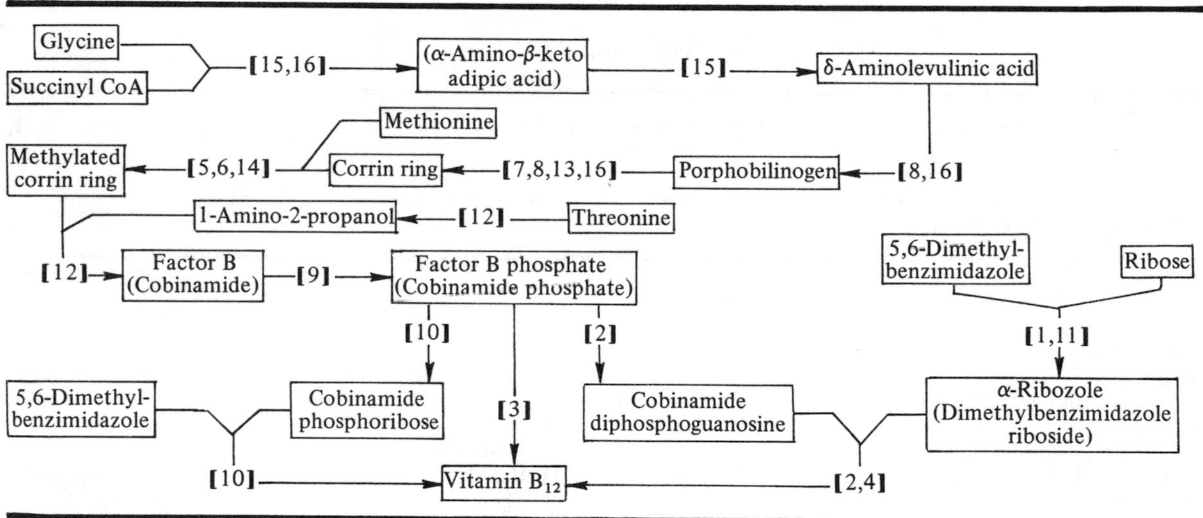

Contributors: Storvick, Clara A., and Fincke, Margaret L.

References

[1] Barbieri, P., et al. 1962. Biochim. Biophys. Acta 57: 599.
[2] Barchielli, R., et al. 1960. Biochem. J. 74:382.
[3] Bernhauer, K., and F. Wagner. 1962. Biochem. Z. 335:325.
[4] Boretti, G., et al. 1960. Biochim. Biophys. Acta 37:379.
[5] Bray, R., and D. Shemin. 1958. Ibid. 30:647.
[6] Bray, R. C., and D. Shemin. 1963. J. Biol. Chem. 238:1501.
[7] Burnham, B. F., and R. A. Plane. 1966. Biochem. J. 98:13c.
[8] Corcoran, J. W., and D. Shemin. 1957. Biochim. Biophys. Acta 25:661.
[9] Dellweg, H., E. Becher, and K. Bernhauer. 1956. Biochem. Z. 327:422.
[10] Dellweg, H., and K. Bernhauer. 1957. Arch. Biochem. Biophys. 69:74.
[11] Friedmann, H. C., and D. L. Harris. 1962. Biochem. Biophys. Res. Commun. 8:164.
[12] Krasna, A. I., C. Rosenblum, and D. B. Sprinson. 1957. J. Biol. Chem. 225:745.
[13] Schwartz, S., et al. 1959. Science 129:40.
[14] Shemin, D., and R. C. Bray. 1964. Ann. N.Y. Acad. Sci. 112:615.
[15] Shemin, D., C. S. Russell, and T. Abramsky. 1955. J. Biol. Chem. 215:613.
[16] Shemin, D., et al. 1956. Science 124:272.

continued

85. PATHWAYS OF BIOSYNTHESIS: WATER-SOLUBLE VITAMINS

Part X. Ascorbic Acid

Abbreviation: UDP = uridine diphosphate

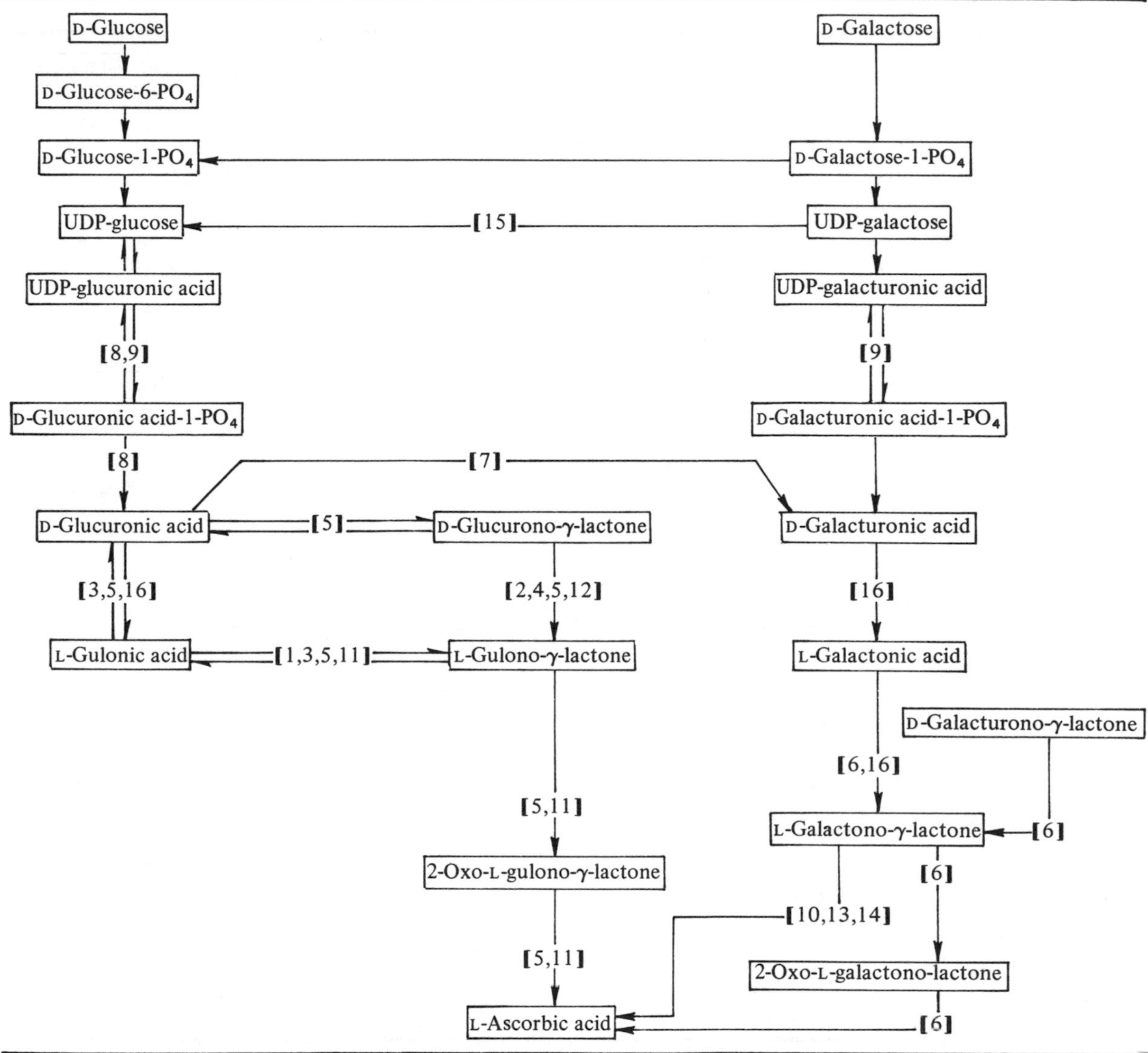

Contributors: Storvick, Clara A., and Fincke, Margaret L.

References

[1] Bublitz, C., and A. L. Lehninger. 1959. Federation Proc. 18:519.

[2] Burns, J. J. 1957. Nature 180:553.

[3] Burns, J. J. 1959. Am. J. Med. 26:740.

[4] Burns, J. J., and C. Evans. 1956. J. Biol. Chem. 223:897.

[5] Chatterjee, I. B., et al. 1960. Biochem. J. 74:193.

[6] Chatterjee, I. B., et al. 1961. Ann. N.Y. Acad. Sci. 92:36.

[7] Deuel, H., and E. Stutz. 1958. Advan. Enzymol. 20:341.

[8] Evans, C., et al. 1959. Federation Proc. 18:223.

[9] Feingold, D. S., E. F. Neufeld, and W. Z. Hassid. 1958. Arch. Biochem. Biophys. 78:401.

[10] Isherwood, F. A., Y. T. Chen, and L. W. Mapson. 1953. Nature 171:348.

[11] Kanfer, J., J. J. Burns, and G. Ashwell. 1959. Biochim. Biophys. Acta 31:556.

[12] Mano, Y., et al. 1959. Ibid. 34:563.

[13] Mapson, L. W., and F. A. Isherwood. 1956. Biochem. J. 64:13.

[14] Mapson, L. W., F. A. Isherwood, and Y. T. Chen. 1954. Ibid. 56:21.

[15] Strominger, J. L., et al. 1954. J. Am. Chem. Soc. 76:6411.

[16] ul Hassan, M., and A. L. Lehninger. 1956. J. Biol. Chem. 223:123.

86. PATHWAYS OF BIOSYNTHESIS: FAT-SOLUBLE VITAMINS

Part I. Carotene

Abbreviation: CoA = coenzyme A.

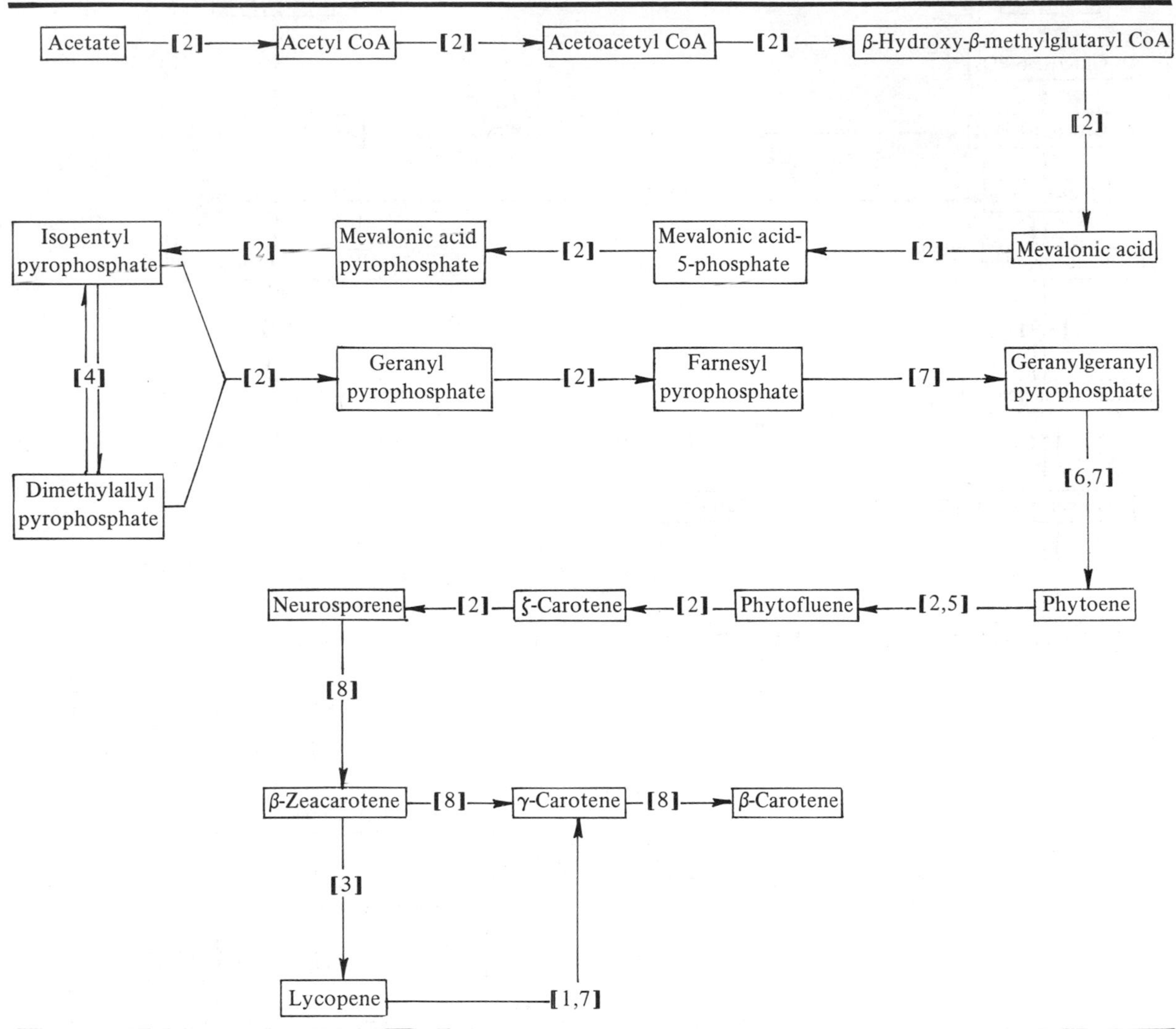

Contributors: Storvick, Clara A., and Fincke, Margaret L.

References

[1] Decker, K., and H. Uehleke. 1966. Z. Physiol. Chem. 323:61.

[2] Goodwin, T. W. 1965. In J. P. Pridham and T. Swain. ed. Biosynthetic pathways in higher plants. Academic Press, New York. pp. 37-55.

[3] Goodwin, T. W., and R. J. Williams. 1966. Proc. Roy. Soc. (London), B, 163:515.

[4] Olson, J. A. 1964. J. Lipid Res. 5:281.

[5] Porter, J. W., and D. G. Anderson. 1962. Arch. Biochem. Biophys. 97:520.

[6] Rilling, H. C. 1962. Biochim. Biophys. Acta 65:156.

[7] Wells, L. W., W. J. Schelble, and J. W. Porter. 1964. Federation Proc. 23:426.

[8] Williams, R. J. H., et al. 1967. Biochem. J. 104:767.

continued

86. PATHWAYS OF BIOSYNTHESIS: FAT-SOLUBLE VITAMINS

Part II. Vitamin A

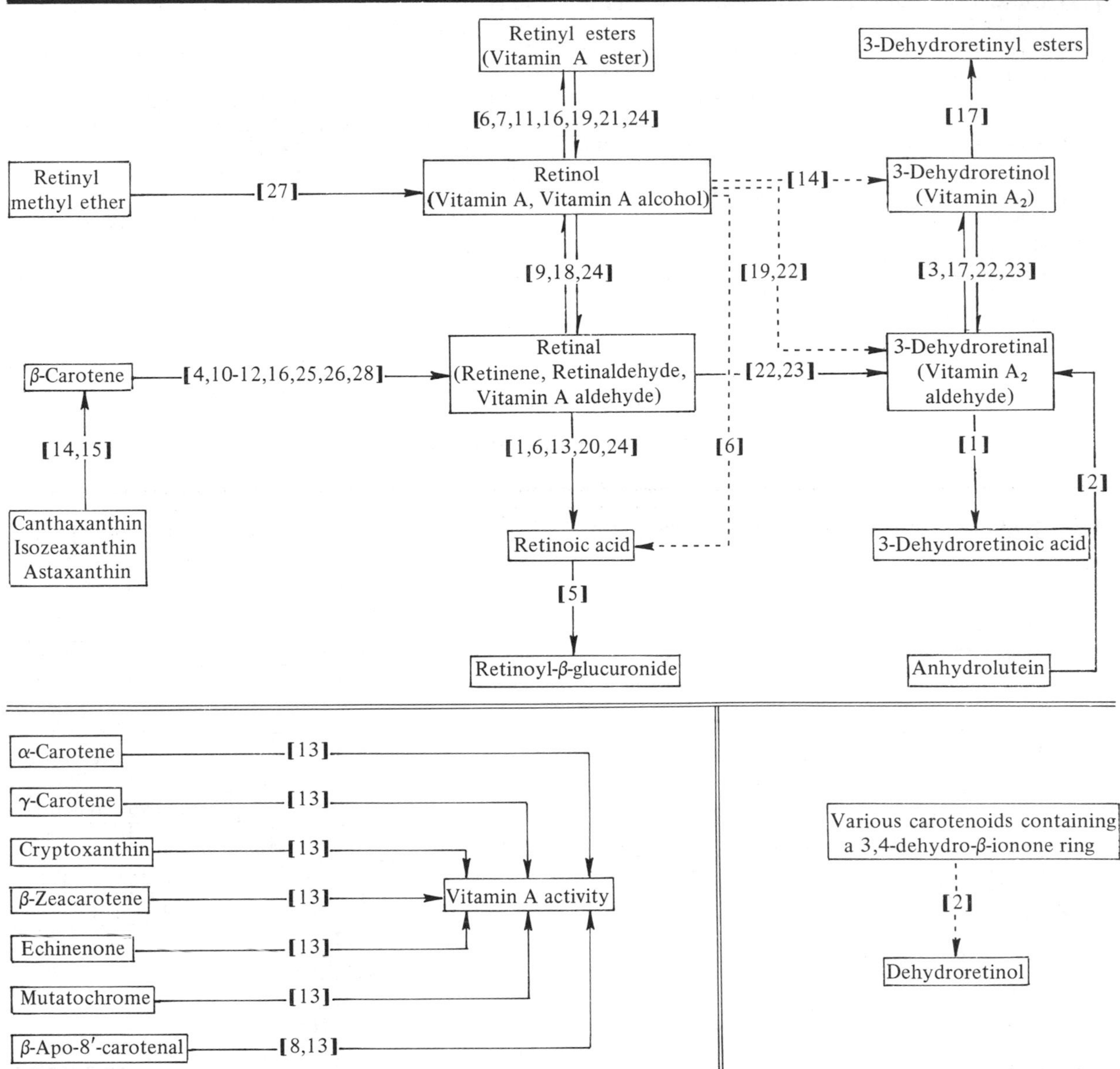

Contributors: Storvick, Clara A., and Fincke, Margaret L.

References

[1] Banji, M. S., et al. 1962. Nature 196:672.

[2] Budowski, P., and J. Gross. 1965. Ibid. 206:1254.

[3] Cama, H. R., et al. 1952. Biochem. J. 52:542.

[4] Crain, F. S., F. J. Lotspeich, and R. F. Krause. 1965. Proc. Soc. Exptl. Biol. Med. 119:606.

[5] Dunagin, P. L., R. D. Zachman, and J. A. Olson. 1966. Biochim. Biophys. Acta 124:71.

[6] Emerick, R. S., M. Zile, and H. F. De Luca. 1967. Biochem. J. 102:606.

[7] Futterman, S., and J. S. Andrews. 1964. J. Biol. Chem. 239:4077.

[8] Glover, J. 1960. Ann. Rept. Progr. Chem. (Chem. Soc. London) 56:331.

[9] Glover, J., T. W. Goodwin, and R. A. Morton. 1948. Biochem. J. 43:109.

[10] Goodman, D. S., et al. 1965. J. Clin. Invest. 44:1054.

[11] Goodman, D. S., and H. S. Huang. 1965. Science 149:879.

[12] Goodman, D. S., H. S. Huang, and T. Shiratori. 1966. J. Biol. Chem. 241:1929.

[13] Goodwin, T. W. 1963. The biosynthesis of vitamins and related compounds. Academic Press, New York. pp. 270-319.

[14] Grangaud, R., et al. 1957. Bull. Soc. Chim. Biol. 39:1271.

continued

Part II. Vitamin A

[15] Gross, J. A., and P. Budowski. 1966. Biochem. J. 101:747.
[16] Huang, H. S., and D. S. Goodman. 1965. J. Biol. Chem. 240:2839.
[17] John, K. V., M. R. Lakshmanan, and H. R. Cama. 1966. Biochem. J. 99:312.
[18] Koen, A. L., and C. R. Shaw. 1966. Biochim. Biophys. Acta 128:48.
[19] Mahadevan, S., N. I. Ayoub, and O. A. Roels. 1966. J. Biol. Chem. 241:57.
[20] Mahadevan, S., S. K. Murthy, and J. Ganguly. 1962. Biochem. J. 85:326.
[21] Mahadevan, S., P. Seshadri Sastry, and J. Ganguly. 1963. Ibid. 88:531.
[22] Morton, R. A., M. K. Salah, and A. L. Stubbs. 1957. Nature 159:744.
[23] Naito, K., and F. H. Wilt. 1962. J. Biol. Chem. 237:3060.
[24] Olson, J. A. 1964. J. Lipid Res. 5:281.
[25] Olson, J. A., and O. Hayaishi. 1965. Proc. Natl. Acad. Sci. U.S. 54:1364.
[26] Olson, J. A., and J. S. Herron. 1961. J. Biol. Chem. 236:349.
[27] Thompson, J. N., and G. A. J. Pitt. 1963. Biochim. Biophys. Acta 78:753.
[28] Zachman, R. D., and J. A. Olson. 1963. J. Biol. Chem. 238:541.

Part III. Vitamin D

Abbreviation: CoA = coenzyme A.

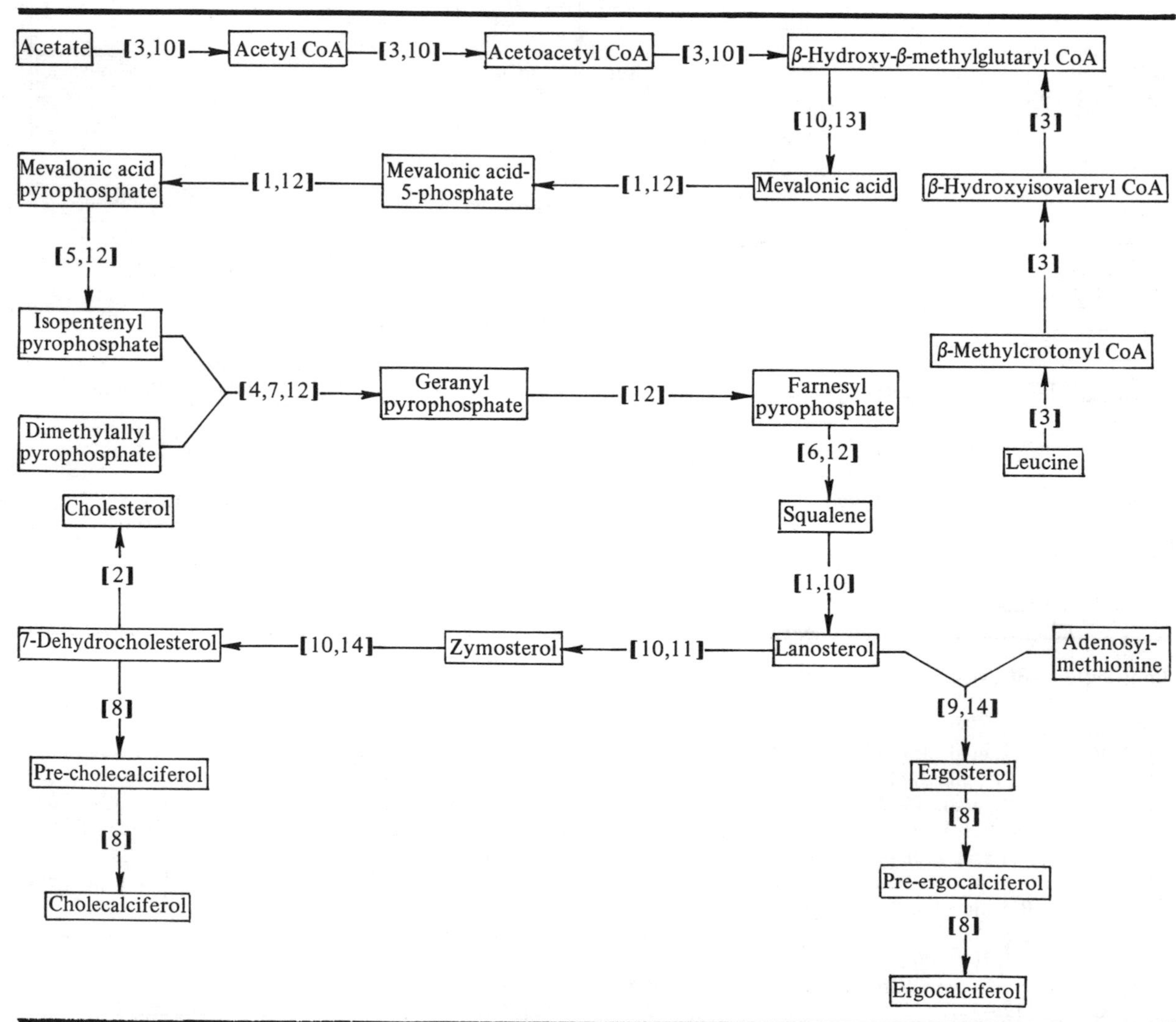

continued

86. PATHWAYS OF BIOSYNTHESIS: FAT-SOLUBLE VITAMINS

Part III. Vitamin D

Contributors: Storvick, Clara A., and Fincke, Margaret L.

References

[1] Bloch, K. 1959. Ciba Found. Symp. Biosyn. Terpenes Sterols, p. 4.
[2] Clayton, R. B. 1965. Quart. Rev. (London) 19:168.
[3] Coon, M. J., et al. 1959. Ciba Found. Symp. Biosyn. Terpenes Sterols, p. 62.
[4] Cornforth, J. W., et al. 1966. J. Biol. Chem. 241: 3970.
[5] Cornforth, J. W., et al. 1966. Proc. Roy. Soc. (London), B, 163:436.
[6] Cornforth, J. W., et al. 1966. Ibid., B, 163:492.
[7] Donninger, C., and G. Popjak. 1966. Ibid., B, 163: 465.
[8] Havinga, E., R. J. de Kock, and M. P. Rappoldt. 1960. Tetrahedron 11:276.
[9] Katsuki, H., and K. Bloch. 1967. J. Biol. Chem. 242:222.
[10] Olson, J. A. 1965. Ergeb. Physiol. Biol. Chem. Exptl. Pharmakol. 56:173.
[11] Olson, J. A., M. Lindberg, and K. Bloch. 1957. J. Biol. Chem. 226:941.
[12] Popjak, G., and J. W. Cornforth. 1966. Biochem. J. 101:553.
[13] Rudney, H. 1959. Ciba Found. Symp. Biosyn. Terpenes Sterols, p. 75.
[14] Turner, J. R., and L. W. Parks. 1965. Biochim. Biophys. Acta 98:394.

Part IV. Vitamin K

Abbreviation: CoA = coenzyme A.

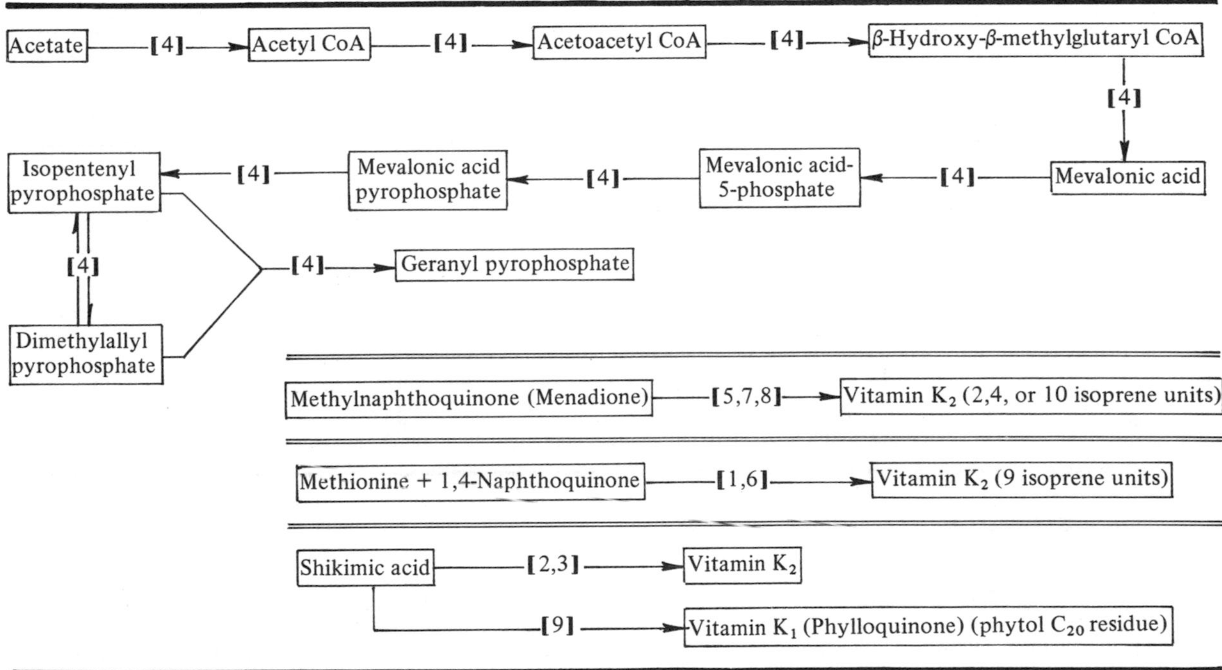

Contributors: Storvick, Clara A., and Fincke, Margaret L.

References

[1] Azerad, R., R. Bleiler-Hill, and E. Lederer. 1965. Biochem. Biophys. Res. Commun. 19:194.
[2] Cox, G. B., and F. Gibson. 1964. Biochim. Biophys. Acta 93:204.
[3] Cox, G. B., and F. Gibson. 1966. Biochem. J. 100:1.
[4] Goodwin, T. W. 1965. In J. P. Pridham and T. Swain, ed. Biosynthetic pathways in higher plants. Academic Press, New York. pp. 324-326.
[5] Martius, C., and H. O. Esser. 1958. Biochem. Z. 331:1.
[6] Martius, C., and W. Leuzinger. 1964. Ibid. 340:304.
[7] Martius, C., E. G. Semadeni, and C. Alvino. 1960. Ibid. 342:492.
[8] Schiefer, H. G., and C. Martius. 1960. Ibid. 333: 454.
[9] Whitance, G. R., D. R. T. Threlfell, and T. W. Goodwin. 1966. Biochem. Biophys. Res. Commun. 23: 849.

continued

86. PATHWAYS OF BIOSYNTHESIS: FAT-SOLUBLE VITAMINS

Part V. Essential Fatty Acids

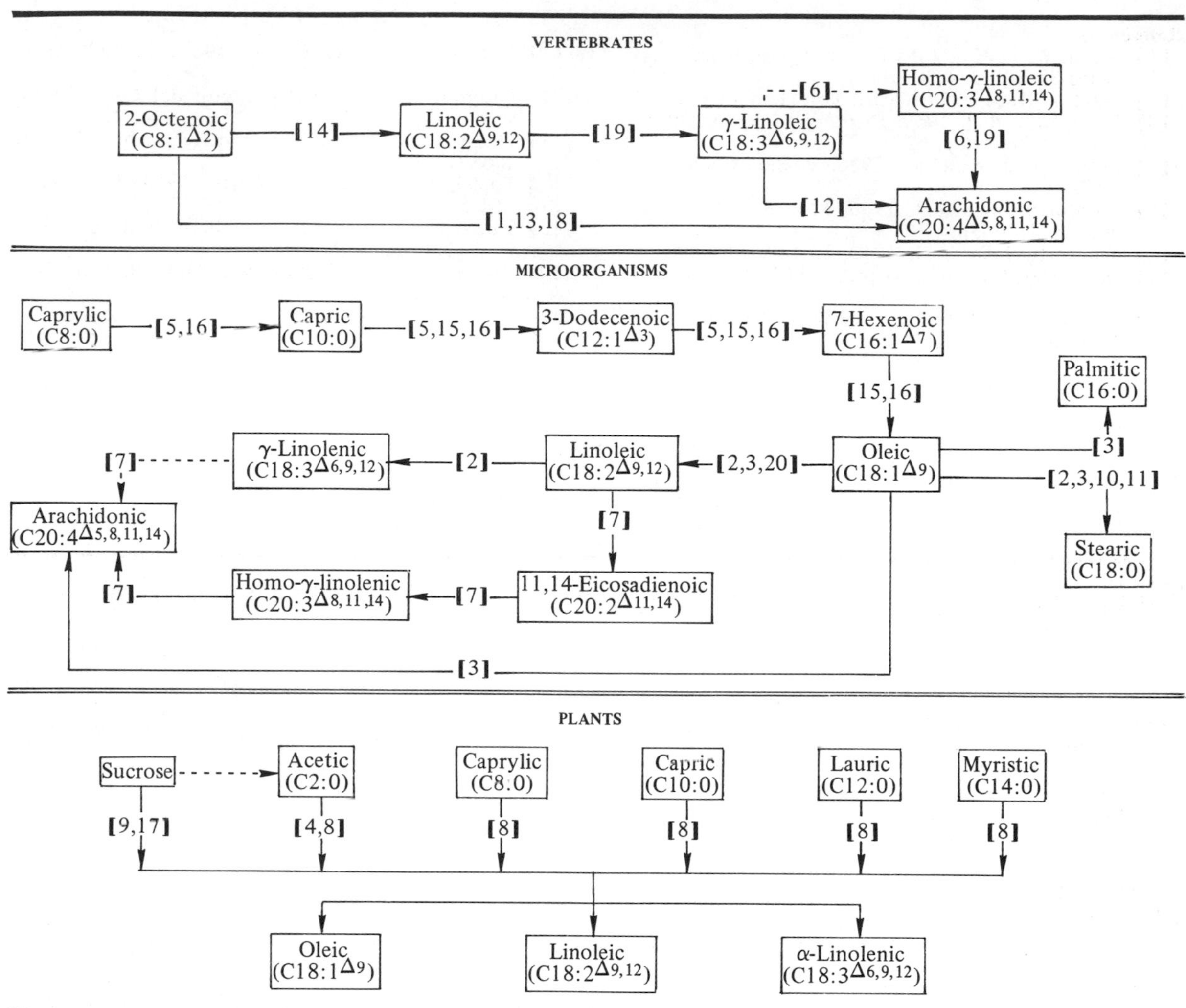

Contributors: Storvick, Clara A., and Fincke, Margaret L.

References

[1] Davis, J. T., and J. G. Coniglio. 1966. J. Biol. Chem. 241:610.

[2] Erwin, J., and K. Bloch. 1963. Ibid. 238:1618.

[3] Erwin, J., D. Hulanicka, and K. Bloch. 1964. Comp. Biochem. Physiol. 12:191.

[4] Gibble, W. P., and E. B. Kurtz, Jr. 1956. Arch. Biochem. Biophys. 64:1.

[5] Goldfine, H., and K. Bloch. 1961. J. Biol. Chem. 236:2596.

[6] Howton, D. R., and J. F. Mead. 1960. Ibid. 235: 3385.

[7] Hulanicka, D., J. Erwin, and K. Bloch. 1964. Ibid. 239:2778.

[8] James, A. T. 1963. Biochim. Biophys. Acta 70:9.

[9] Leegwater, D. C., et al. 1962. Can. J. Biochem. Physiol. 40:847.

[10] Lennarz, W. J., G. Scheuerbrandt, and K. Bloch. 1962. J. Biol. Chem. 237:664.

[11] Marsh, J. B., and A. T. James. 1962. Biochim. Biophys. Acta 60:320.

[12] Mead, J. F., and D. R. Howton. 1957. J. Biol. Chem. 229:575.

[13] Mohrhauer, H., and R. T. Holman. 1963. J. Lipid Res. 4:346.

[14] Reiser, R., N. L. Murtz, and H. Rakoff. 1962. Ibid. 3:56.

[15] Scheuerbrandt, G., and K. Bloch. 1962. J. Biol. Chem. 237:2064.

[16] Scheuerbrandt, G., et al. 1961. Ibid. 236:PC70.

[17] Simmons, R. O., and F. W. Quackenbush. 1954. J. Am. Oil Chem. Soc. 31:441.

[18] Steinberg, G., et al. 1956. J. Biol. Chem. 220:257.

[19] Stoffel, W. 1961. Biochem. Biophys. Res. Commun. 6:270.

[20] Yuan, C., and K. Bloch. 1961. J. Biol. Chem. 236: 1277.

Part I. Pathways

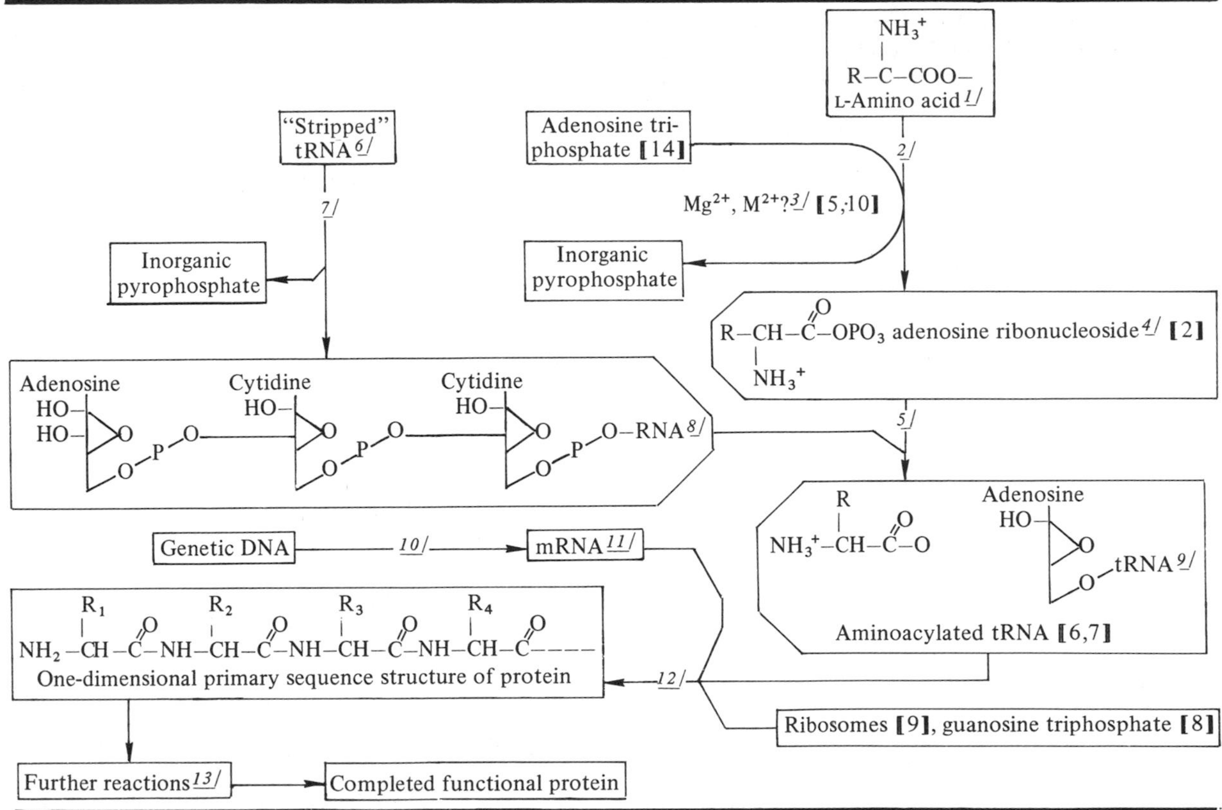

1/ 20 different L-α-amino acids. 2/ 20 different aminoacyl transfer RNA (tRNA) ligases in each species; perhaps additional enzymes are specific for individual organs and organelles. 3/ Unpublished observations from University of New Mexico School of Medicine biochemistry laboratory and other laboratories indicate the participation of a polyvalent metal in this reaction. 4/ 20 different aminoacyl adenylates tightly bound to the ligase enzyme. 5/ Aminoacyl adenylate, and same aminoacyl ligases as in reaction indicated by footnote 2 [1,4]. 6/ Source unknown, molecular weight about 30,000. 7/ Adenosine triphosphate and unisolated enzymes of cytidine triphosphate [15]. 8/ Transfer ribonucleic acids (tRNA's) are specific for 20 different amino acids, with possibly as many as 5 different tRNA's specific for a single amino acid [13]. For the structure of phenylalanine tRNA, and for references to work on alanine tRNA by R. W. Holley et al., and on serine tRNA by H. Zachau et al., consult reference 13. 9/ With anti-codons. 10/ DNA-dependent RNA polymerase and riboside triphosphates. 11/ Messenger RNA (mRNA) containing triplet nucleotide codons [11]; presently suspected codon triplets and experimental techniques are summarized in reference 11. 12/ Association of triplet codons of mRNA with triplet anti-codons of tRNA and 2 enzyme fractions [3,12]. 13/ Hydroxylation of proline in protocollagen, formation of α-helix or other stable conformations, formation of disulfide or other bridges, and partial hydrolysis of zymogens.

Contributor: Loftfield, Robert B.

References

[1] Berg, P., and E. J. Offengand. 1958. Proc. Natl. Acad. Sci. U.S. 44:78.

[2] DeMoss, J. A., S. M. Genuth, and G. D. Novelli. 1956. Ibid. 42:325.

[3] Fessenden, J. M., and K. Moldave. 1962. Biochemistry 1:485.

[4] Hecht, L. I., M. L. Stephenson, and P. C. Zamecnik. 1959. Proc. Natl. Acad. Sci. U.S. 45:505.

[5] Hoagland, M. B., E. B. Keller, and P. C. Zamecnik. 1956. J. Biol. Chem. 218:345.

[6] Hoagland, M. B., P. C. Zamecnik, and M. L. Stephenson. 1957. Biochim. Biophys. Acta 24:215.

[7] Holley, R. W. 1957. J. Am. Chem. Soc. 79:658.

[8] Littlefield, J. W., and E. B. Keller. 1957. J. Biol. Chem. 224:13.

[9] Littlefield, J. W., et al. 1955. Ibid. 217:111.

[10] Loftfield, R. B., and E. A. Eigner. 1965. Federation Proc. 24:216.

[11] Marshall, R. E., C. T. Caskey, and M. Nirenberg. 1967. Science 155:820.

[12] Nathans, D., and F. Lipmann. 1960. Biochim. Biophys. Acta 43:126.

[13] RajBhandary, U. L., et al. 1967. Proc. Natl. Acad. Sci. U.S. 57:751.

[14] Zamecnik, P. C., and E. B. Keller. 1954. J. Biol. Chem. 209:337.

[15] Zamecnik, P. C., M. L. Stephenson, and L. I. Hecht. 1958. Proc. Natl. Acad. Sci. U.S. 44:73.

continued

87. PROTEIN BIOSYNTHESIS

Part II. RNA Codons

Nucleotide sequences of RNA codons were determined by stimulating the binding of *Escherichia coli* aminoacyl-tRNA to *E. coli* ribosomes with trinucleoside diphosphate templates. Internal phosphates of trinucleoside diphosphates (XpYpZ) are 3′,5′-phosphodiester linkages. The first purine-pyrimidine base of each triplet is occupied by a nucleoside with a free 5′-terminal hydroxide; the third base is occupied by a nucleotide with free 2′- and 3′-terminal hydroxide groups.

Codon	Amino acid	Codon	Amino acid	Codon	Amino acid	Codon	Amino acid
UUU	Phe	UCU	Ser	UAU	Tyr	UGU	Cys
UUC		UCC		UAC		UGC	
UUA	Leu	UCA		UAA 3/	Ochre	UGA 4/	?
UUG		UCG		UAG 3/	Amber	UGG	Trp
CUU	Leu	CCU	Pro	CAU	His	CGU	Arg
CUC		CCC		CAC		CGC	
CUA		CCA		CAA	Gln	CGA	
CUG		CCG		CAG		CGG	
AUU	Ile	ACU	Thr	AAU	Asn	AGU	Ser
AUC		ACC		AAC		AGC	
AUA		ACA		AAA	Lys	AGA	Arg
AUG	Met_F 1/, $_M$ 2/	ACG		AAG		AGG	
GUU	Val	GCU	Ala	GAU	Asp	GGU	Gly
GUC		GCC		GAC		GGC	
GUA		GCA		GAA	Glu	GGA	
GUG	Met_F 1/	GCG		GAG		GGG	

1/ Met_F corresponds to *N*-formyl-methionyl-$tRNA_F$, an initiator of protein synthesis. *N*-Formyl-Met-$tRNA_F$ binds to a different ribosomal site than Met-$tRNA_M$'s; hence GUG corresponds to different amino acids at different ribosomal sites. 2/ Met_M corresponds to methionyl-$tRNA_M$, which responds to noninitiator methionyl-codons. 3/ Terminator codons. 4/ Status is uncertain; possibly UGA corresponds to "stop" or "terminate."

Contributor: Nirenberg, Marshall W.

References: [1] Khorana, H. G., et al. 1966. Cold Spring Harbor Symp. Quant. Biol. 31:39. [2] Nirenberg, M. W., et al. 1966. Ibid. 31:11.

88. PATHWAYS OF POLYNUCLEOTIDE BIOSYNTHESIS

Part I. Purines

Abbreviations: ADP = adenosine 5′-diphosphate; AMP = adenosine 5′-monophosphate; ATP = adenosine 5′-triphosphate; Asp = aspartic acid (aspartate); Gln = glutamine; Glu = glutamic acid (glutamate); Gly = glycine; GDP = guanosine 5′-diphosphate; GTP = guanosine 5′-triphosphate; NAD^+ and NADH = nicotinamide adenine dinucleotide (oxidized and reduced forms, respectively); $NADP^+$ and NADPH = nicotinamide adenine dinucleotide phosphate (oxidized and reduced forms, respectively); P_i = inorganic orthophosphate; PP_i = inorganic pyrophosphate; THF = tetrahydrofolic acid coenzyme.

continued

88. PATHWAYS OF POLYNUCLEOTIDE BIOSYNTHESIS

Part I. Purines

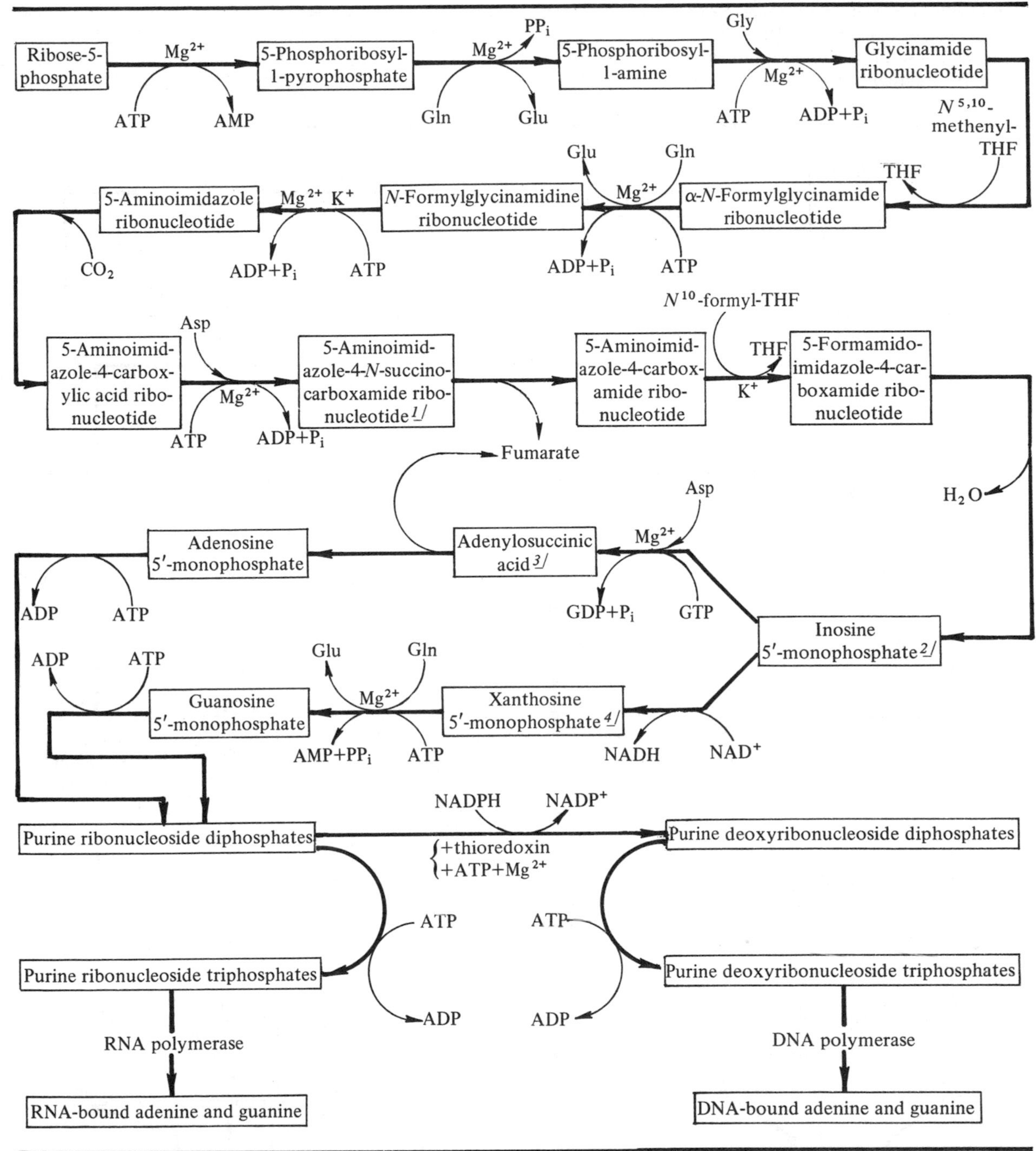

1/ Succinylaminoimidazole carboxamide ribonucleotide. 2/ Inosinic acid or inosinate. 3/ Adenylosuccinate. 4/ Xanthylic acid.

Contributor: Lansford, Edwin M., Jr.

General References

[1] Hartman, S. C. 1967. In R. J. Williams and E. Lansford, Jr., ed. The encyclopedia of biochemistry. Reinhold, New York. pp. 705-708.

[2] Mahler, H. R., and E. H. Cordes. 1966. Biological chemistry. Harper and Row, New York. pp. 714-751.

[3] White, A., P. Handler, and E. L. Smith. 1964. Principles of biochemistry. Ed. 3. McGraw-Hill, New York. pp. 558-583.

continued

88. PATHWAYS OF POLYNUCLEOTIDE BIOSYNTHESIS

Part II. Pyrimidines

Abbreviations: ADP = adenosine 5′-diphosphate; ATP = adenosine 5′-triphosphate; DHF = dihydrofolic acid coenzyme; THF = tetrahydrofolic acid coenzyme; Gln = L-glutamine; Glu = glutamic acid (glutamate); NAD^+ and NADH = nicotinamide adenine dinucleotide (oxidized and reduced forms, respectively); $NADP^+$ and NADPH = nicotinamide adenine dinucleotide phosphate (oxidized and reduced forms, respectively); P_i = inorganic orthophosphate; PP_i = inorganic pyrophosphate; PRPP = 5-phosphoribosyl-1-pyrophosphate.

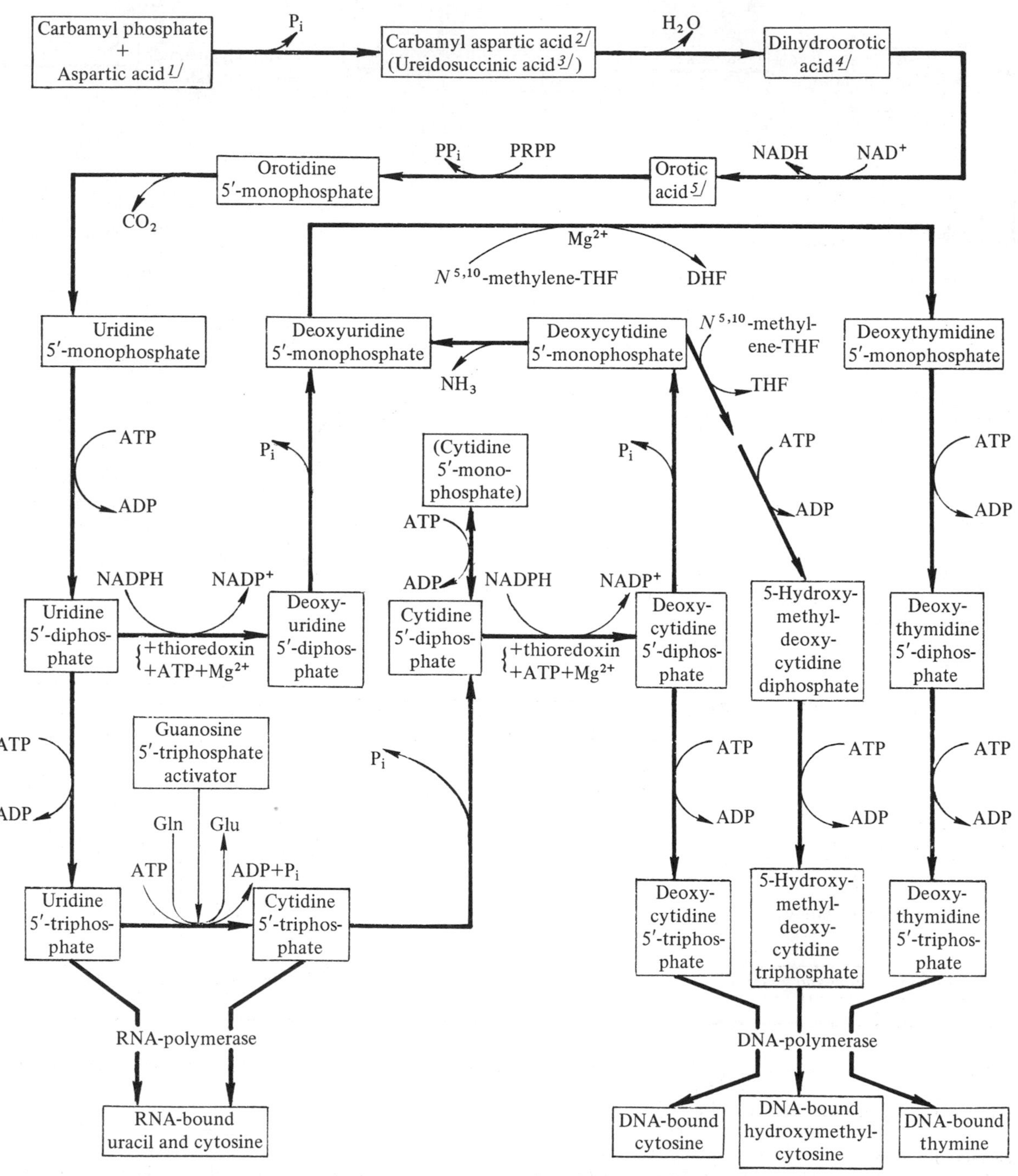

1/ Aspartate. 2/ Carbamyl aspartate. 3/ Ureidosuccinate. 4/ Dihydroorotate. 5/ Orotate.

Contributor: Lansford, Edwin M., Jr.

continued

88. PATHWAYS OF POLYNUCLEOTIDE BIOSYNTHESIS

Part II. Pyrimidines

General References

[1] Hurlbert, R. B. 1967. In R. J. Williams and E. Lansford, Jr., ed. The encyclopedia of biochemistry. Reinhold, New York. pp. 713-715.

[2] Mahler, H. R., and E. H. Cordes. 1966. Biological chemistry. Harper and Row, New York. pp. 714-751.

[3] White, A., P. Handler, and E. L. Smith. 1964. Principles of biochemistry. Ed. 3. McGraw-Hill, New York. pp. 558-583.

89. PATHWAYS OF CHOLESTEROL BIOSYNTHESIS

The biosynthesis of cholesterol may be divided into two parts (as indicated by the broken line). Part one consists of a series of 11 steps, from acetate to the straight-chain C_{30} compound squalene. The second part involves the folding of squalene into the steroid lanosterol, which is converted progressively into C_{29}, C_{28}, and C_{27} sterols, and finally to cholesterol. The biosynthetic pathway from lanosterol to cholesterol is not simple and fixed; in the present representation, a likely pathway is shown. *Abbreviations:* CoA = coenzyme A; ATP = adenosine triphosphate; NADH = nicotinamide adenine dinucleotide (reduced form); NADPH = nicotinamide adenine dinucleotide phosphate (reduced form).

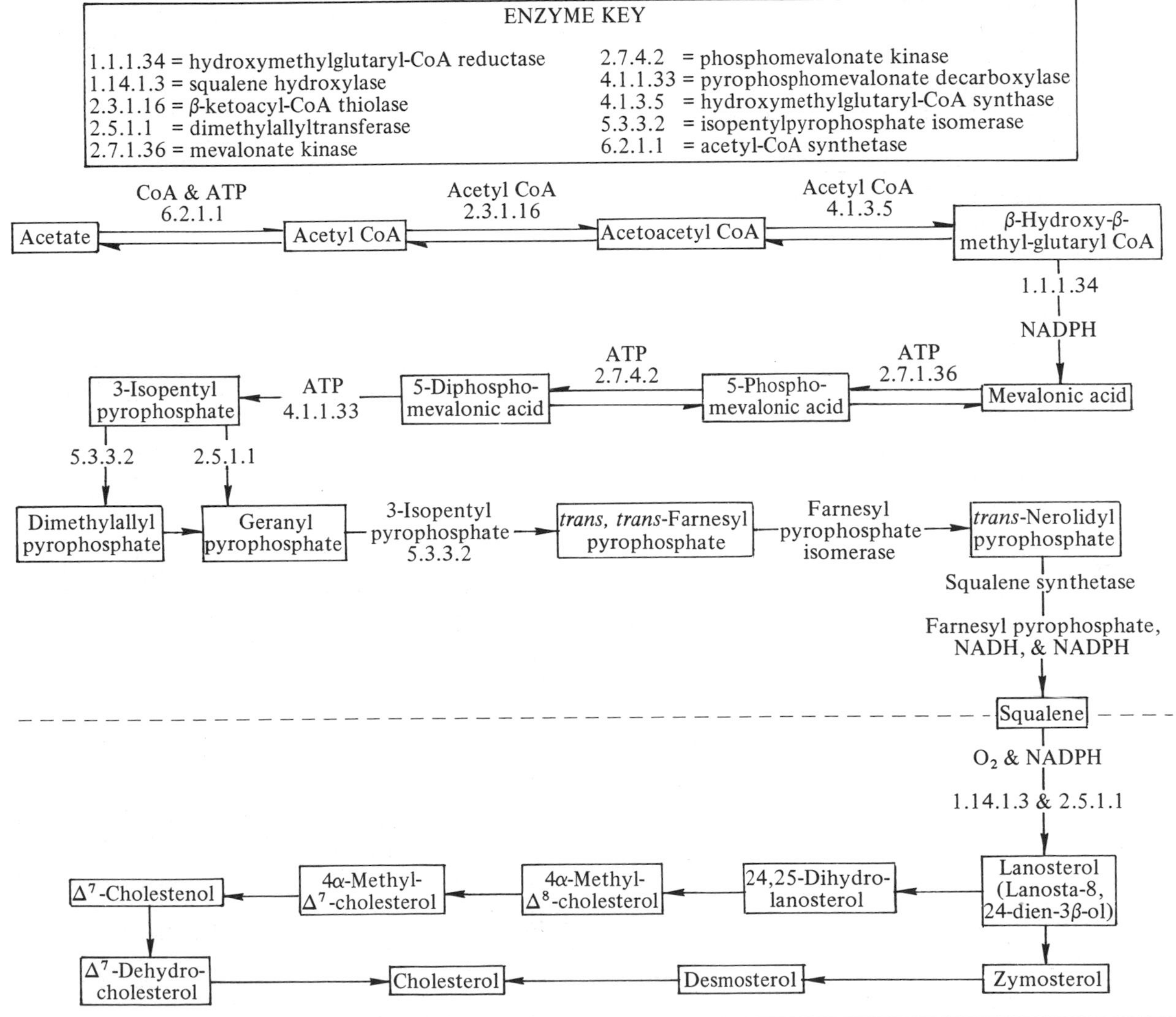

Contributor: Dorfman, Ralph I.

Reference: Olson, J. A. 1965. Ergeb. Physiol. Biol. Chem. Exptl. Pharmakol. 56:173.

90. PATHWAYS OF STEROID HORMONE BIOSYNTHESIS

Abbreviation: NADPH = nicotinamide adenine dinucleotide phosphate (reduced form).

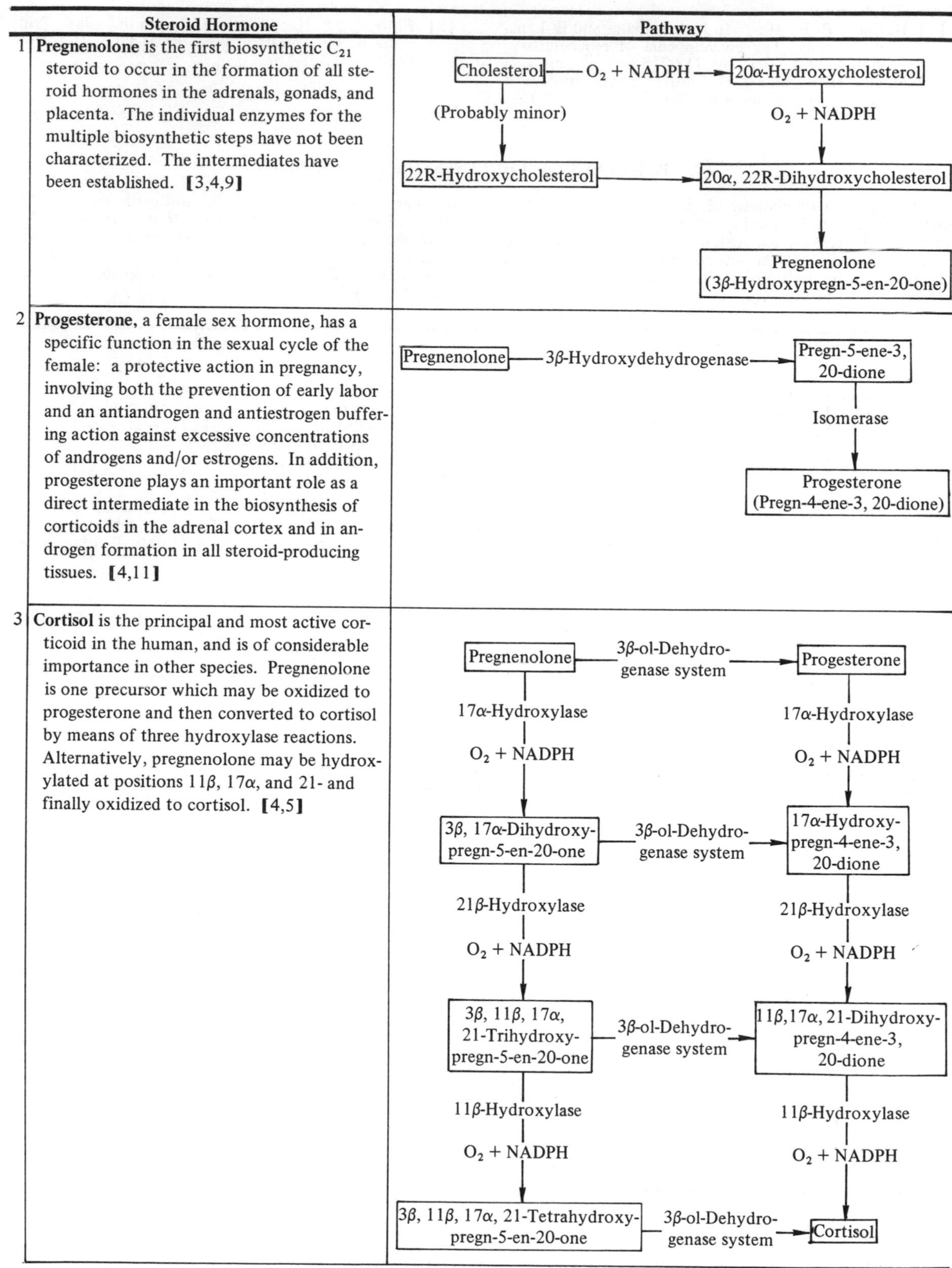

	Steroid Hormone	Pathway
1	**Pregnenolone** is the first biosynthetic C_{21} steroid to occur in the formation of all steroid hormones in the adrenals, gonads, and placenta. The individual enzymes for the multiple biosynthetic steps have not been characterized. The intermediates have been established. [3,4,9]	Cholesterol — O_2 + NADPH → 20α-Hydroxycholesterol Cholesterol — (Probably minor) → 22R-Hydroxycholesterol 20α-Hydroxycholesterol — O_2 + NADPH → 20α, 22R-Dihydroxycholesterol 22R-Hydroxycholesterol → 20α, 22R-Dihydroxycholesterol 20α, 22R-Dihydroxycholesterol → Pregnenolone (3β-Hydroxypregn-5-en-20-one)
2	**Progesterone,** a female sex hormone, has a specific function in the sexual cycle of the female: a protective action in pregnancy, involving both the prevention of early labor and an antiandrogen and antiestrogen buffering action against excessive concentrations of androgens and/or estrogens. In addition, progesterone plays an important role as a direct intermediate in the biosynthesis of corticoids in the adrenal cortex and in androgen formation in all steroid-producing tissues. [4,11]	Pregnenolone — 3β-Hydroxydehydrogenase → Pregn-5-ene-3, 20-dione Pregn-5-ene-3, 20-dione — Isomerase → Progesterone (Pregn-4-ene-3, 20-dione)
3	**Cortisol** is the principal and most active corticoid in the human, and is of considerable importance in other species. Pregnenolone is one precursor which may be oxidized to progesterone and then converted to cortisol by means of three hydroxylase reactions. Alternatively, pregnenolone may be hydroxylated at positions 11β, 17α, and 21- and finally oxidized to cortisol. [4,5]	Pregnenolone — 3β-ol-Dehydrogenase system → Progesterone Pregnenolone — 17α-Hydroxylase, O_2 + NADPH → 3β, 17α-Dihydroxy-pregn-5-en-20-one Progesterone — 17α-Hydroxylase, O_2 + NADPH → 17α-Hydroxy-pregn-4-ene-3, 20-dione 3β, 17α-Dihydroxy-pregn-5-en-20-one — 3β-ol-Dehydrogenase system → 17α-Hydroxy-pregn-4-ene-3, 20-dione 3β, 17α-Dihydroxy-pregn-5-en-20-one — 21β-Hydroxylase, O_2 + NADPH → 3β, 11β, 17α, 21-Trihydroxy-pregn-5-en-20-one 17α-Hydroxy-pregn-4-ene-3, 20-dione — 21β-Hydroxylase, O_2 + NADPH → 11β,17α, 21-Dihydroxy-pregn-4-ene-3, 20-dione 3β, 11β, 17α, 21-Trihydroxy-pregn-5-en-20-one — 3β-ol-Dehydrogenase system → 11β,17α, 21-Dihydroxy-pregn-4-ene-3, 20-dione 3β, 11β, 17α, 21-Trihydroxy-pregn-5-en-20-one — 11β-Hydroxylase, O_2 + NADPH → 3β, 11β, 17α, 21-Tetrahydroxy-pregn-5-en-20-one 11β,17α, 21-Dihydroxy-pregn-4-ene-3, 20-dione — 11β-Hydroxylase, O_2 + NADPH → Cortisol 3β, 11β, 17α, 21-Tetrahydroxy-pregn-5-en-20-one — 3β-ol-Dehydrogenase system → Cortisol

continued

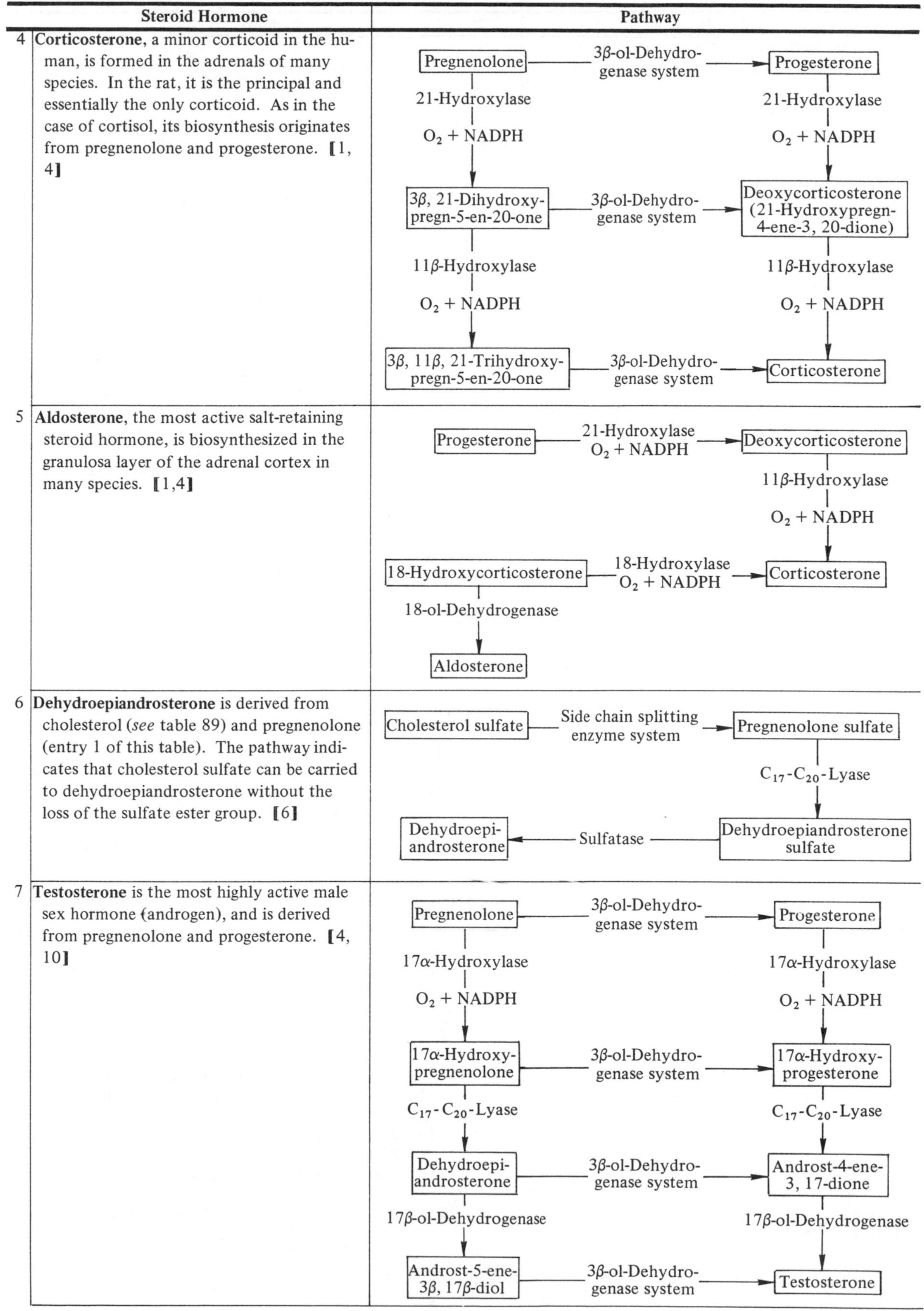

	Steroid Hormone	Pathway
4	**Corticosterone,** a minor corticoid in the human, is formed in the adrenals of many species. In the rat, it is the principal and essentially the only corticoid. As in the case of cortisol, its biosynthesis originates from pregnenolone and progesterone. [1, 4]	Pregnenolone → 3β-ol-Dehydrogenase system → Progesterone Pregnenolone → 21-Hydroxylase, O_2 + NADPH → 3β, 21-Dihydroxypregn-5-en-20-one Progesterone → 21-Hydroxylase, O_2 + NADPH → Deoxycorticosterone (21-Hydroxypregn-4-ene-3, 20-dione) 3β, 21-Dihydroxypregn-5-en-20-one → 3β-ol-Dehydrogenase system → Deoxycorticosterone (21-Hydroxypregn-4-ene-3, 20-dione) 3β, 21-Dihydroxypregn-5-en-20-one → 11β-Hydroxylase, O_2 + NADPH → 3β, 11β, 21-Trihydroxypregn-5-en-20-one Deoxycorticosterone → 11β-Hydroxylase, O_2 + NADPH → Corticosterone 3β, 11β, 21-Trihydroxypregn-5-en-20-one → 3β-ol-Dehydrogenase system → Corticosterone
5	**Aldosterone,** the most active salt-retaining steroid hormone, is biosynthesized in the granulosa layer of the adrenal cortex in many species. [1,4]	Progesterone → 21-Hydroxylase, O_2 + NADPH → Deoxycorticosterone Deoxycorticosterone → 11β-Hydroxylase, O_2 + NADPH → Corticosterone Corticosterone → 18-Hydroxylase, O_2 + NADPH → 18-Hydroxycorticosterone 18-Hydroxycorticosterone → 18-ol-Dehydrogenase → Aldosterone
6	**Dehydroepiandrosterone** is derived from cholesterol (*see* table 89) and pregnenolone (entry 1 of this table). The pathway indicates that cholesterol sulfate can be carried to dehydroepiandrosterone without the loss of the sulfate ester group. [6]	Cholesterol sulfate → Side chain splitting enzyme system → Pregnenolone sulfate Pregnenolone sulfate → C_{17}-C_{20}-Lyase → Dehydroepiandrosterone sulfate Dehydroepiandrosterone sulfate → Sulfatase → Dehydroepiandrosterone
7	**Testosterone** is the most highly active male sex hormone (androgen), and is derived from pregnenolone and progesterone. [4, 10]	Pregnenolone → 3β-ol-Dehydrogenase system → Progesterone Pregnenolone → 17α-Hydroxylase, O_2 + NADPH → 17α-Hydroxypregnenolone Progesterone → 17α-Hydroxylase, O_2 + NADPH → 17α-Hydroxyprogesterone 17α-Hydroxypregnenolone → 3β-ol-Dehydrogenase system → 17α-Hydroxyprogesterone 17α-Hydroxypregnenolone → C_{17}-C_{20}-Lyase → Dehydroepiandrosterone 17α-Hydroxyprogesterone → C_{17}-C_{20}-Lyase → Androst-4-ene-3, 17-dione Dehydroepiandrosterone → 3β-ol-Dehydrogenase system → Androst-4-ene-3, 17-dione Dehydroepiandrosterone → 17β-ol-Dehydrogenase → Androst-5-ene-3β, 17β-diol Androst-4-ene-3, 17-dione → 17β-ol-Dehydrogenase → Testosterone Androst-5-ene-3β, 17β-diol → 3β-ol-Dehydrogenase system → Testosterone

continued

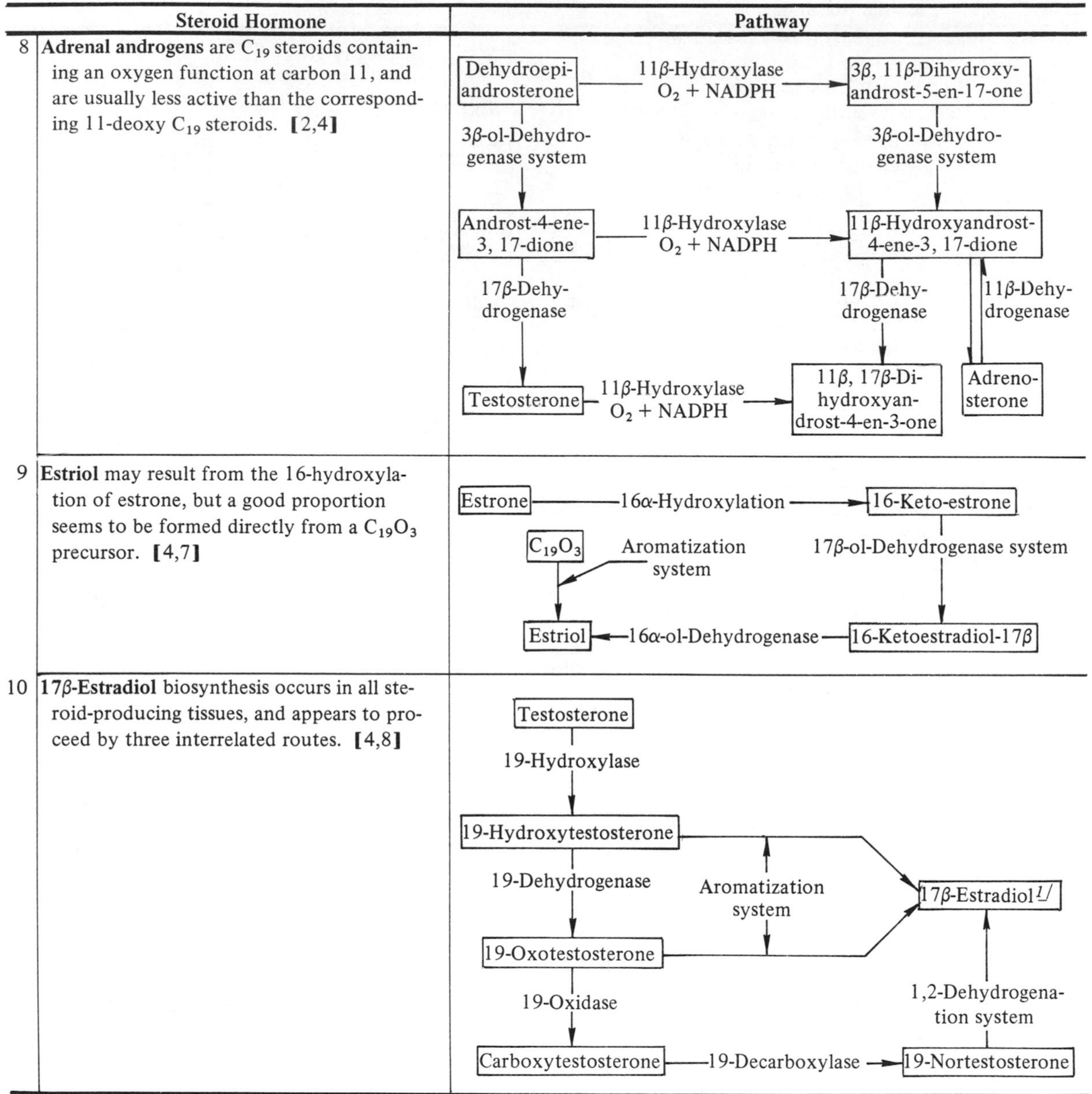

	Steroid Hormone	Pathway
8	**Adrenal androgens** are C_{19} steroids containing an oxygen function at carbon 11, and are usually less active than the corresponding 11-deoxy C_{19} steroids. [2,4]	Dehydroepiandrosterone → 11β-Hydroxylase, O_2 + NADPH → 3β, 11β-Dihydroxyandrost-5-en-17-one Dehydroepiandrosterone → 3β-ol-Dehydrogenase system → Androst-4-ene-3, 17-dione 3β, 11β-Dihydroxyandrost-5-en-17-one → 3β-ol-Dehydrogenase system → 11β-Hydroxyandrost-4-ene-3, 17-dione Androst-4-ene-3, 17-dione → 11β-Hydroxylase, O_2 + NADPH → 11β-Hydroxyandrost-4-ene-3, 17-dione Androst-4-ene-3, 17-dione → 17β-Dehydrogenase → Testosterone 11β-Hydroxyandrost-4-ene-3, 17-dione → 17β-Dehydrogenase → 11β, 17β-Dihydroxyandrost-4-en-3-one 11β-Hydroxyandrost-4-ene-3, 17-dione ⇄ 11β-Dehydrogenase ⇄ Adrenosterone Testosterone → 11β-Hydroxylase, O_2 + NADPH → 11β, 17β-Dihydroxyandrost-4-en-3-one
9	**Estriol** may result from the 16-hydroxylation of estrone, but a good proportion seems to be formed directly from a $C_{19}O_3$ precursor. [4,7]	Estrone → 16α-Hydroxylation → 16-Keto-estrone 16-Keto-estrone → 17β-ol-Dehydrogenase system → 16-Ketoestradiol-17β 16-Ketoestradiol-17β → 16α-ol-Dehydrogenase → Estriol $C_{19}O_3$ → Aromatization system → Estriol
10	**17β-Estradiol** biosynthesis occurs in all steroid-producing tissues, and appears to proceed by three interrelated routes. [4,8]	Testosterone → 19-Hydroxylase → 19-Hydroxytestosterone 19-Hydroxytestosterone → 19-Dehydrogenase → 19-Oxotestosterone 19-Oxotestosterone → 19-Oxidase → Carboxytestosterone Carboxytestosterone → 19-Decarboxylase → 19-Nortestosterone 19-Nortestosterone → 1,2-Dehydrogenation system → 17β-Estradiol[1/] 19-Hydroxytestosterone, 19-Oxotestosterone → Aromatization system → 17β-Estradiol[1/]

[1/] Estrone biosynthesis proceeds by the same routes except that the 17-keto group replaces the 17β-hydroxyl group.

Contributor: Dorfman, Ralph I.

References

[1] Ayres, P. J., et al. 1960. Acta Endocrinol. 33:37.
[2] Bloch, E., A. I. Cohen, and J. Furth. 1960. J. Natl. Cancer Inst. 24:97.
[3] Chaudhuri, A. C., et al. 1962. J. Biol. Chem. 237:703.
[4] Dorfman, R. I., and F. Ungar. 1965. Metabolism of steroid hormones. Academic Press, New York.
[5] Levy, H., and S. Kushinsky. 1955. Arch. Biochem. Biophys. 55:290.
[6] Roberts, K. D., et al. 1964. Biochemistry 3:1983.
[7] Ryan, K. J. 1958. Biochim. Biophys. Acta 27:658.
[8] Ryan, K. J. 1963. Intern. Congr. Biochem., 5th, Moscow, 1961, Reprint 61.
[9] Shimizu, K., R. I. Dorfman, and M. Gut. 1962. J. Biol. Chem. 237:699.
[10] Slaunwhite, W. R., Jr., and L. T. Samuels. 1961. Ibid. 236:695.
[11] Solomon, S., R. Vande Wiele, and S. Lieberman. 1956. J. Am. Chem. Soc. 78:5453.

91. HORMONES AFFECTING METABOLISM

Data are for man, unless otherwise specified. Hormones of the gastrointestinal tract are not included, since they apparently have little effect on metabolism in other tissues. *Symbols:* ↑ = increased; ↓ = decreased.

	Hormone (Synonym)	Principal Functions & Effects	Effects of Deficiency (−) & Excess (+)	Secretion Inhibitors (I) & Stimulators (S)	Reference
	Adenohypophysis				
1	Adrenocorticotropin (ACTH)	**Decreases:** ascorbic acid & cholesterol in adrenal cortex; renal transport of P, urate; urea production from exogenous amino acids; liver degradation of corticosteroids **Increases:** secretion of adrenocortical hormones; oxidative phosphorylation; lipolysis in adipose tissue; fatty acid transport & oxidation; protein synthesis; iodine uptake by thyroid; synthesis of cyclic AMP, activating phosphorylase *a* & increasing NADPH in adrenal cortex	(−): atrophy & hyposecretion of adrenal cortex, especially fasciculata; ↓ 17-hydroxy- & 17-ketosteroids in blood, urine. Fasting hypoglycemia & ↑ insulin sensitivity. (+): hypertrophy & hypersecretion of fasciculata, reticularis; ↑ output of 17-hydroxy- & 17-ketosteroids	**(I):** ↑ blood concentration of glucocorticoids; "negative feedback" or servomechanism **(S):** corticotropin-releasing factor of neurohypophysis; stimulation of median eminence; psychic trauma, acting through hypothalamus; ↓ level of circulating glucocorticoids, mainly, cortisol	16,18
2	Follicle-stimulating hormone (FSH)	Stimulates growth & maturation of ovarian follicles[1] **Increases:** spermatogenesis; growth of seminiferous tubules; testosterone secretion; Sertoli cell hormone secretion in testis; incorporation of α-aminoisobutyric acid into proteins of ovaries (rat)	(−): atrophy or immaturity of gonads; no maturation of ova, sperm; obesity; ↓ libido, potency, hair growth; ↓ blood levels of estrogen (+): hypertrophy of secondary sex organs; ↑ growth & maturation of numerous follicles; ↑ estrogen secretion (FSH + LH)	**(I):** ↑ blood level of circulating estrogens **(S):** low blood levels of estrogens or possibly androgens; castration; menopause; hypothalamus-neurohypophysis stimulation	1,11, 14, 16, 18
3	Growth hormone (GH; somatotropin; STH)	**Decreases:** blood amino acid & glucose levels after short-time administration; urinary excretion of inorganic ions **Increases:** skeletal & soft tissue growth; protein anabolism; fibroblastic activity; swelling of mitochondria in liver (rat); activity or synthesis of RNA polymerase; transport of neutral amino acids into tissues; erythropoiesis; renal function; tubular reabsorption of sulfate (dog); blood glucose levels after prolonged administration	(−): dwarfism and/or infantilism, delayed closure of epiphyses; ↑ sensitivity to insulin (+): gigantism (prepubertal), acromegaly (postpubertal); hypertrophy of viscera; diabetes mellitus; hyperglycemia. ↑ liver glycogenolysis, lipolysis, fatty acid oxidation.	**(I):** large doses of estrogens or androgens **(S):** unknown	1,5,8, 10
4	Luteinizing hormone (LH; interstitial-cell-stimulating hormone; ICSH)	Stimulates spermatogenesis **Increases** (♂): secretion of testosterone by Leydig cells in testis **Increases** (♀): ovulation, with synergistic action of FSH; estrogen & progesterone production by corpus luteum	(−): estrogen or androgen secretion inhibited. Atrophy of interstitial tissue in ovary or testis; lack of ovulation, luteinization. (+): ↑ estrogen (with FSH) or androgen secretion. Hypertrophy of Leydig cells; precocious ovulation & luteinization of prepared follicles.	**(I):** high blood levels of gonadal hormones **(S):** low blood levels of gonadal hormones; hypothalamus-adenohypophyseal axis	1,18
5	Lactogenic hormone (LTH; luteotropin; prolactin)	**Increases:** milk secretion & ejection by mammary glands prepared by estrogen & progesterone; nidation of zygote; protein anabolism (some species); growth & secretion of crop gland (pigeon)	(−): lactation failure; progesterone deficiency; possible abortion (+): precocious lactation of functional mammary glands	**(I):** inhibition of oxytocin release; nervous inhibition **(S):** Oxytocin, in turn stimulated by suckling	1,7, 18, 20

[1] Minute amounts of luteinizing hormone also required.

continued

91. HORMONES AFFECTING METABOLISM

	Hormone (Synonym)	Principal Functions & Effects	Effects of Deficiency (−) & Excess (+)	Secretion Inhibitors (I) & Stimulators (S)	Reference
6	Thyrotropic hormone (TSH)	Stimulates coupling of diiodotyrosine to form thyroxine **Increases:** synthesis & mobilization of thyroid hormones; serum protein-bound iodine; thyroid RNA & protein; proteolytic activity; oxidase granules; O_2 consumption by thyroid cells; entry of glucose into cells; entry of I^- into thyroid cells; rate of glucose oxidation by hexose monophosphate, glycolytic & tricarboxylic pathways, without ↑ $NADP^+$	(−): ↓ synthesis of thyroid hormones; low serum protein-bound iodine; ↓ I^- uptake by thyroid. Normal or ↑ thyroid iodine. (+): ↑ synthesis of thyroid hormones, serum protein-bound iodine, I^- uptake by thyroid, basal metabolic rate. ↓ thyroid iodine, blood cholesterol. Exophthalmos[2]; goiter.	**(I):** ↑ circulating thyroid hormones; high environmental temperature; inhibition of hypothalamus **(S):** ↓ circulating thyroid hormones; low environmental temperature; stimulation of hypothalamus	1,7, 15, 18
			Neurohypophysis		
7	Oxytocin (Pitocin)	Facilitates sperm movement up fallopian tube; stimulates release of lactogenic hormone **Increases:** uterine muscle contraction--may initiate labor; permeability of myometrial cell membrane to K^+, thus decreasing membrane potential & excitability threshold[3]	(−): delayed, weak uterine contractions (pre- or postpartum); ↓ milk secretion & ejection (+): rapid, forceful uterine contractions; danger of abortion during pregnancy; excessive milk secretion	**(I):** no known specific inhibitors **(S):** suckling, by neural stimuli through hypothalamus; vaginal stimulation	1,7,8, 20
8	Vasopressin (Antidiuretic hormone; ADH)	**Increases:** water reabsorption in renal tubules, by ↑ cell membrane permeability in distal tubules; excretion of Na^+, Cl^-, urea; blood pressure by arteriole constriction	(−): polyuria (diabetes insipidus); polydipsia; ↓ NaCl & urea excretion (+): oliguria; water retention (intoxication); Na^+ loss resulting from ↑ Na^+ excretion in urine. ↑ blood pressure; smooth muscle contraction.	**(I):** ↓ blood plasma osmotic pressure, extracellular fluid volume **(S):** ↑ osmotic pressure of blood, stimulating osmoreceptors in diencephalon; ↓ volume of extracellular fluid (e.g., hemorrhage) stimulating volume ("stretch") receptors; neurogenic stimuli[4], through hypothalamus. Drugs, e.g., morphine, nicotine, anesthetics.	1,7,8, 20
			Pars Intermedia		
9	Melanocyte-stimulating hormones (α-MSH; β-MSH; melanotropins)	Rapidly (within a few minutes) expand chromatophores, causing pigment granules to disperse and color skin (either in vivo or in vitro). Not species-specific; MSH from animals expand melanocytes in human skin. Increase during most of pregnancy. Expand chromatophores, contract guanophores (anuran larvae). Adipokinetic effect.	(−): chromatophore contraction & guanophore expansion. Complete lack causes permanent blanching of skin. (+): hyperglycemia; darkening of skin. Potentiated or supplemented by ACTH.	**(I):** corticoids(?); may be a feedback mechanism **(S):** ACTH(?); central nervous system	1,7,9
			Pineal Body		
10	Adrenoglomerulotropin (GTH)	Stimulates aldosterone secretion, possibly from ACTH-dependent precursors along a branch in synthetic chain	(−): ↓ aldosterone secretion, resulting in loss of Na^+ from body (+): ↑ aldosterone secretion	Unknown	1,7, 15

[2] May be caused by a separate factor. [3] Action involves -S-S- ⟷2-SH. [4] Emotional states, such as pain and fear.

continued

91. HORMONES AFFECTING METABOLISM

	Hormone (Synonym)	Principal Functions & Effects	Effects of Deficiency (−) & Excess (+)	Secretion Inhibitors (I) & Stimulators (S)	Reference
11	Melatonin	Blanches skin (amphibians, fishes). Antagonistic to MSH. **Decreases:** ovarian weight, estrus (rat); pineal weight, uptake of ^3H-melatonin (rat), on exposure to light **Increases:** estrus (rat), on exposure to light	(−): darkening of skin of animals with expandable melanocytes. ↑ estrus, ovarian weight. ↑ gametogenesis. Precocious puberty(?). (+): blanching of skin; ↓ or delayed estrus, ↓ ovarian weight. ↓ or delayed gametogenesis. Erythema or punched-out ulcer (man).	**(I):** level of circulating melatonin(?); light **(S):** dark(?); ↓ concentration of circulating melatonin	1,7,9
			Thyroid		
12	Thyroxine ("T_4") & 3,5,3′-triiodothyronine ("T_3")[5]	Stimulate growth, maturation, neuromuscular function, skin development, hematopoiesis, spermato- & oogenesis, lactation, absorption through intestinal wall. In large amounts, "uncouple" phosphorylation from oxidation in mitochondria. **Decrease:** TSH secretion **Increase:** rate of O_2 uptake without ↑ P uptake; rate of protein synthesis in cells, possibly by increasing mRNA synthesis; rate of CHO, lipid, protein, H_2O, & mineral metabolism	(−): in adults, myxedema with ↓ mental processes, dry & brittle hair, edema of face, thick tongue & speech, goiter; ↓ circulation, respiration, cardiac output, intestinal absorption. In children, cretinism, dwarfism; delayed maturation, calcification, epiphyseal closure & growth; incomplete differentiation or metamorphosis; mental retardation; ↑ serum cholesterol. (+): excessive acceleration of maturation, growth, basal metabolic rate, metamorphosis. Thyrotoxicosis (toxic goiter or Grave's disease); exophthalmos. Mitochondrial swelling; lymphocytosis. ↓ serum cholesterol; ↑ protein-bound iodine, butanol-extractable iodine.	**(I):** severe stress[6]; ↑ intake of I^- or antithyroid drugs, e.g., thiouracil, thiourea, thiocyanate; ↑ plasma levels of thyroid hormones **(S):** chronic stress (exposure to cold); TSH	1,7-9, 15, 17, 20
			Parathyroids		
13	Parathyroid hormone (PTH; parathormone)	Regulates distal renal tubule excretion of K^+, $HPO_4{}^{2-}$, $H_2PO_4{}^-$. Controls Ca & PO_4 levels in blood serum by mineral exchange between blood and bone, and PO_4 excretion by kidney. Stimulates osteoclastic activity. **Increases:** renal tubule reabsorption of Ca^{2+}; intestinal absorption of Ca^{2+}; Ca^{2+} in urine as plasma Ca^{2+} concentration in urine rises; citrate in plasma, kidney, bone; rate of collagen synthesis in bone; mitochondrial uptake of $HPO_4{}^{2-}$, K^+, Mg^{2+}; release of Ca^{2+}, H^+	(−): hypocalcemia; tetany; convulsive seizures; hypersensitivity of autonomic nervous system. Chronic mental sluggishness. Spotty alopecia. (+): hypercalcemia, renal calculi. ↓ serum phosphate (↑ renal $HPO_4{}^{2-}$ excretion); ↑ serum alkaline phosphatase activity. Depolymerization of skeletal mucopolysaccharides.	**(I):** ↓ serum $HPO_4{}^{2-}$ (?); ↑ serum Ca^{2+} **(S):** ↑ serum $HPO_4{}^{2-}$; ↓ serum Ca^{2+}	1,2,7, 8, 12, 15, 20, 21
14	Calcitonin (Thyrocalcitonin)[7]	**Decreases:** Ca^{2+} in blood serum, possibly by stimulating osteoblasts and inhibiting osteoclasts	(−): ↑ Ca^{2+} in blood serum; symptoms of hyperparathyroidism (+): ↓ Ca^{2+} in blood serum; symptoms of hypoparathyroidism	**(I):** ↓ serum Ca^{2+}; feedback mechanism opposite to that of parathyroid hormone **(S):** ↑ serum Ca^{2+}	1,2, 7-9, 20, 21

[5] "T_3" is usually 5-10 times more potent than "T_4." [6] Emotional or physical stress (such as fear, rage, hemorrhage, and inflammation) inhibits secretion usually for the first 24-48 hours. [7] Source uncertain; may be parathyroids or thyroid.

continued

91. HORMONES AFFECTING METABOLISM

	Hormone (Synonym)	Principal Functions & Effects	Effects of Deficiency (−) & Excess (+)	Secretion Inhibitors (I) & Stimulators (S)	Reference
			Adrenal Cortex		
15	Aldosterone	**Increases:** K^+ excretion & Na^+ reabsorption in renal tubules, sweat & salivary glands; absorption of Na^+ by intestinal mucosa[8]; reabsorption of H_2O in distal tubules accompanied by reabsorption of Na^+ Salt-retaining potency: 20->100 times that of deoxycorticosterone, 40-1000 times that of glucocorticoids	(−): excessive loss of Na^+ in urine; dehydration & ↓ plasma Na^+. ↑ plasma K^+, resulting in cardiac arrhythmia & heart block. (+): ↑ plasma Na^+, extracellular fluid volume. ↓ plasma K^+, resulting in muscle spasms, polyuria, polydipsia, alkalosis, hypertension. Congestive heart failure.	(I): ↓ plasma K^+; ↑ plasma Na^+; hemodilution (S): ↑ plasma K^+; ↓ plasma Na^+; hemoconcentration. Renin-angiotensin system (angiotensin II). ACTH[9]; glomerulotropin.	1,4,7, 19, 20
16	Cortisol (Hydrocortisone) & cortisone[10]	Administration is followed by lymphocytopenia, eosinopenia, neutrophilia. Cortisol is antiallergic & anti-inflammatory; inhibits fibroblasts, migration & vascular margination of leukocytes, prevents ↑ capillary permeability in inflamed area. **Decrease:** incorporation of proline-^{14}C & hydroxyproline-^{14}C into chick embryos; purine nucleotide & protein synthesis in lymphoid tissue; oxidation, lipogenesis, extrahepatic synthesis of protein; extrahepatic synthesis of acid-sulfated mucopolysaccharides **Increase:** deamination of amino acids to glucose; activities of liver & kidney glucose-6-phosphatase, glycogen synthetase, phosphoenolpyruvate carboxykinase in liver, & aminopeptidase in muscle; activities of liver tryptophan pyrrolase & tyrosine α-ketoglutarate transaminase, thereby increasing synthesis of proteins from amino acids; alkaline phosphatase activity in liver; arginase in liver & kidney	(−): asthenia; hemoconcentration; chronic Addison's disease; ↓ blood glucose, liver glycogen, body weight, blood pressure, stress resistance. Delayed or minimal secondary sex characteristics. ↑ K^+/Na^+ ratio in serum. Emaciation, vomiting, diarrhea; acute Waterhouse-Friderichsen syndrome. (+): Cushing's syndrome. Excess lipogenesis, with obesity; negative N balance; hyperglycemia unless insulin also high; osteoporosis; wasting of muscle; alkalosis; ↑ gastric acidity; adrenogenital syndrome; hypertension. Inhibits inflammatory repair of wounds & antibody formation.	(I): ↓ACTH; ↑ plasma glucocorticoids (S): ACTH[11]; ↓ plasma glucocorticoids (negative feedback)	1,3,4, 6-8, 13-15, 20
			Adrenal Medulla		
17	Epinephrine & norepinephrine	**Decreases** (norepinephrine): cardiac output. Does not stimulate central nervous system, increase O_2 consumption, or cause eosinopenia. Moderate hyperglycemia after administration. **Increases** (norepinephrine): blood pressure by vasoconstriction, basal metabolic rate **Increases** (epinephrine): cardiac output, basal metabolic rate. Dilates bronchi, & blood vessels in liver, muscle; inhibits intestinal motility; stimulates central nervous system. Administration is followed by neutrophilia, eosinopenia, marked hyperglycemia.	(−): no clinical syndrome (+): pheochromocytoma; marked hypertension, pigmentation, tachycardia, headache, nausea, blanching of skin, sweating; ↑ nonesterified fatty acids	(I): unknown (S): splanchnic (sympathetic) nervous system; neurohumor	1,7, 14-16, 18, 20

[8] Probable mechanism is the binding of aldosterone to receptor sites in tubule cells, inducing a DNA-dependent synthesis of RNA, thereby stimulating synthesis of proteins which facilitates transport of Na^+ through cell membrane. [9] Stimulates secretion indirectly by steroidogenesis. [10] Principal glucocorticoids in man. [11] Stimulates fasciculata and reticularis of adrenal cortex.

continued

	Hormone (Synonym)	Principal Functions & Effects	Effects of Deficiency (−) & Excess (+)	Secretion Inhibitors (I) & Stimulators (S)	Reference
		Ovaries			
18	Estradiol-17β	Estrogenic; affects endometrial proliferation, development & maintenance of vaginal mucosa, cornification of superficial layer. Stimulates transhydrogenases in human placenta. Slows growth of skeleton; promotes closure of epiphysis; moderately stimulates calcification of bones. Antagonizes androgen effects. Potentially carcinogenic. **Decreases:** erythrocyte uptake of P; plasma cholesterol; β-lipoproteins **Increases:** mammary gland duct development; uterine motility, fallopian tube growth; growth of axillary & pubic hair (♀, human), down (♀, bird); growth of all female secondary sex organs; tissue growth, cell division; uterine uptake of H_2O, Na^+, K^+, glucose; endometrial alkaline phosphatase & glycogen; vaginal glycogen; anabolism of proteins in uterus by stimulation of RNA polymerase & serine aldolase synthesis	(−): immaturity or atrophy of accessory sex organs. Lack of secondary sex characteristics & female behavior patterns. ↓ mammary gland development. Delayed epiphyseal closure; continued growth of long bones. Osteoporosis. (+): precocious maturity; hypertrophy of accessory sex organs, mammary glands; estrus changes; cystic hyperplasia of endometrium; blocking of ovulation. Skeletal growth deceleration; premature closing of epiphyses; excessive calcification of tissues, if parathyroids are normal.	(I): ↑ blood level of estradiol, which inhibits FSH production (S): combined FSH and LH; cyclic changes in blood levels with estrus or menstrual periods	1,7,8, 15, 18, 20
19	Progesterone	Luteinizing. Affects preparation of endometrium for implantation of zygote. Antagonistic to aldosterone, promoting excretion of Na^+, Cl^-, H_2O. Stimulates protein catabolism, galactose oxidation. **Decreases:** uterine contractions; alkaline phosphatase in uterus **Increases:** growth of lining epithelial cells in estrogen-primed endometrium, with ↑ glycogen, mucin, fat; mammary gland lobule development; estrogen metabolism & excretion; basal metabolic rate; body temperature	(−): lack of normal cyclic changes & of endometrial development for implantation & gestation; danger of abortion (+): Pregestational changes; pregnancy prolongation; inhibition of uterine growth, especially endometrium. ↑ Na^+ & K^+ excretion, catabolism.	(I): degeneration of corpus luteum in estrus & menstrual cycles; ↓ LH secretion (S): LH; LH plus LTH (mouse, rat)	1,7, 15, 20
20	Relaxin[12]	Effects relaxation of pubic ligament and separation of symphysis pubis, chiefly during last stages of pregnancy (most mammals). After presensitization with estrogen, connective tissues of symphysis become more vascular, collagen fibers are dissolved, and mucopolysaccharides are depolymerized, rendering the ligament more flexible. Inhibits rhythmic uterine contractions (rat) & uterine motility; effects softening & relaxation of uterine cervix after pretreatment with estrogen, & water imbibition by myometrium (rat). Synergistic with estrogen & progesterone in mammary development (rat).	Not definitely known	(I): ↓ progesterone levels at term (S): progesterone; deoxycorticosterone; pregnenolone	1,7, 20

[12] Produced during pregnancy by ovaries, placenta, and uterus.

continued

91. HORMONES AFFECTING METABOLISM

	Hormone (Synonym)	Principal Functions & Effects	Effects of Deficiency (−) & Excess (+)	Secretion Inhibitors (I) & Stimulators (S)	Reference
			Placenta		
21	Chorionic gonadotropin	Actions similar to those of LH & LTH. Synergistic with hypophyseal gonadotropins. Maintains corpus luteum during pregnancy. Stimulates luteal production of progesterone until placenta attains full function; stimulates premature descent of testes in immature primates. High titer in urine one month after first missed menstrual period is basis for pregnancy tests, e.g., Ascheim-Zondek. **Increases,** by injection: follicle maturation & ovum release in nongravid females; androgen secretion by Leydig cells of testis	(−): corpus luteum degeneration, with ↓ progesterone secretion; danger of abortion (+): unknown. May be related to toxemias of pregnancy.	**(I)**: female sex steroids, notably progesterone **(S)**: enzyme systems of developing placenta. Specific stimulant unknown.	1,7, 15, 20
			Testes		
22	Testosterone	Androgenic. Inhibits growth of thymus, adrenals; little effect on weight of heart, urinary bladder. Produces positive balances of N, Ca, K, S, P. **Decreases**: folliculoid & luteoid activity (immature ♀); amino acid catabolism; creatinuria; Na^+ & Cl^-excretion; alkaline phosphatase in kidney **Increases**: development of male secondary sex organs & sex characteristics; libido; basal metabolic rate; protein anabolism, probably by DNA-based stimulation of mRNA synthesis; amino acid transport in skeletal muscle; amino acid incorporation, D-amino acid oxidase activity, arginase, acid phosphatase, & β-glucuronidase in kidney cortex; renal transport of Na^+, K^+; synthesis rate of fatty acids, citrate, fructose in seminal vesicles; respiration rate of seminal vesicles, prostate	(−): immaturity or atrophy of accessory sex organs; lack of secondary sex characteristics, ♂ behavior patterns. Poor muscle development & function; delayed closure of epiphyses. ↓ excretion of 17-ketosteroids in urine. Functional decrease with age, inducing ♂ climacteric characterized by "hot flashes," vasomotor & neurologic disturbances similar to those in menopause. Deficiency effects more pronounced before puberty than after. (+): precocious sex development; hypertrophy of ♂ accessory sex organs. ↑ muscle mass; ↑ skeletal growth until closure of epiphyses. ↑ excretion of 17-ketosteroids in urine. ↓ scalp hair(?); ↑ hirsutism.	**(I)**: panhypopituitarism (↓ LH & FSH secretion) **(S)**: LH; FSH	1,4,7, 8, 11, 15, 20
23	Sertoli cell hormone (SCH)	Secretion of steroid(s) necessary for spermatogenesis	Unknown	**(I)**: Unknown **(S)**: FSH	11
			Pancreas		
24	Insulin	Regulates CHO & fatty acid metabolism; promotes uptake of glucose by cells, oxidation of CHO; activates ribosomes(?), glycogen synthetase Stimulates hexokinases; phosphorylases; lipogenesis; transport & oxidation of lipids, amino acid transport into cells; synthesis of protein, mucopolysaccharides **Decreases**: gluconeogenesis; ketogenesis; lipolysis in adipose tissue; free sulfhydryl content of muscles **Increases**: sugar transfer through cell membrane; transport of α-aminoisobutyric acid, K^+-Rb^+ through cell membrane; peptide bond synthesis; adenine incorporation into RNA of mammary tissue; hydrolysis of glycerol phosphate, thereby increasing triglyceride synthesis; incorporation of sulfate into chondroitin sulfate	(−): diabetes mellitus (hyperglycemia; glycosuria; ketonuria; ↓ weight & blood volume; negative N balance). Delayed wound-healing; gangrene. Dwarfism; ↓ response to growth hormone. ↓ HPO_4^{2-} uptake by cells; ↓ ATP; ↑ glycogenesis, lipogenesis, proteogenesis. (+): hyperinsulinism (hypoglycemia; convulsions; nausea; muscular weakness; anxiety; confusion). ↑ food intake; ↑ fat & protein deposition. Hypermotility & hypersecretion of stomach.	**(I)**: low blood glucose. Antagonized by growth hormone, glucosteroids (corticoids), epinephrine, thyroxine, glucagon. **(S)**: ↑ blood glucose; ↑ growth hormone; ↑ ACTH, thyroxine, estrogens. Vagus stimulation.	1,7,8, 14, 15, 18, 20, 22

continued

91. HORMONES AFFECTING METABOLISM

	Hormone (Synonym)	Principal Functions & Effects	Effects of Deficiency (−) & Excess (+)	Secretion Inhibitors (I) & Stimulators (S)	Reference
25	Glucagon	Antagonistic to insulin; inhibits synthesis of fatty acids from precursors; promotes glycogenesis in liver but not muscle. Promotes glycogenolysis in liver by stimulating synthesis of cyclic AMP, which mediates: conversion of phosphorylase *b* to *a*, release of nonesterified fatty acids from adipose tissue by glucagon & epinephrine, ↑ protein catabolism (↑ urine levels of creatinine & urea), stimulatory effect of epinephrine on cerebral cortex, ↑ force of heart beat (inotropic effect) by glucagon & epinephrine. **Decreases**: protein synthesis in liver **Increases**: blood glucose level; O_2 consumption by tissues; ion excretion by kidneys; gluconeogenesis from amino acids; conversion of acetate to ketone bodies	(−): hypoglycemia; symptoms of hyperinsulinism (+): ↑ N excretion; negative N balance. ↓ plasma amino acids. ↓ volume & acidity of gastric juice; ↓ gastrointestinal motility & pancreatic secretion; permanent diabetes by destruction of β-cells of pancreatic islets.	(I): high levels of blood glucose 13/ (S): low levels of blood glucose	1,4,7, 8, 14, 15, 18, 20

13/ Glucagon and insulin regulate blood glucose levels by opposite feedback mechanisms, involving liver glycogen as the storage form.

Contributor: Pritham, Gordon H.

References

[1] Cantarow, A., and B. Schepartz. 1967. Biochemistry. Ed. 4. W. B. Saunders, Philadelphia. pp. 677-757.

[2] Copp, D. H. 1964. Recent Progr. Hormone Res. 20:59.

[3] DeVenuto, F., and R. J. G. Lange. 1967. Proc. Soc. Exptl. Biol. Med. 124:793.

[4] Eisenstein, A. B., ed. 1964. The biochemical aspects of hormone action. Little, Brown; Boston.

[5] Frohman, L. A., M. H. MacGillivray, and T. Aceto, Jr. 1967. J. Clin. Endocrinol. Metab. 27(4):561.

[6] Gould, B. S., and G. Manner. 1967. Biochim. Biophys. Acta 138:189 (Chem. Abstr. 66:11258p).

[7] Grollman, A. 1964. Clinical endocrinology. J. B. Lippincott, Philadelphia.

[8] Karlson, P., ed. 1965. Mechanisms of hormone action. Academic Press, New York.

[9] Karlson, P., and C. E. Sekeris. 1966. Acta Endocrinol. 53:505.

[10] Korner, A. 1965. Recent Progr. Hormone Res. 21:205.

[11] Lacy, D. 1967. Endeavour 26(97):101.

[12] Laitinen, O. 1967. Endocrinology 80:815.

[13] Landau, B. R. 1965. Vitamins Hormones 23:2.

[14] Larner, J. 1966. Trans. N.Y. Acad. Sci., II, 29(2): 192.

[15] Litwack, G., and D. Kritchevsky, ed. 1964. Actions of hormones on molecular processes. J. Wiley, New York.

[16] Malmejac, J. 1964. Physiol. Rev. 44:186.

[17] Pastan, I. 1966. Ann. Rev. Biochem. 35:370.

[18] Pincus, G., K. V. Thimann, and E. B. Astwood, ed. 1964. The hormones. Academic Press, New York. v. 5.

[19] Sharp, G. W. G., and A. Leaf. 1966. Physiol. Rev. 46(4):593.

[20] Turner, C. D. 1966. General endocrinology. W. B. Saunders, Philadelphia.

[21] Wallach, S., et al. 1967. Endocrinology 80:61.

[22] Wayne, R., and J. M. Barry. 1967. Biochim. Biophys. Acta 138:195 (Chem. Abstr. 66:11257g).

92. METABOLIC ERRORS OF GENETIC ORIGIN: MAN

Part I. Metabolites in Plasma and Urine

	Disease	Inheritance	Enzyme Deficiency	Metabolite	Metabolite Level: In plasma, mg/100 ml		In Urine, mg/24 hr		Treatment	Reference
					Abnormal	Control	Abnormal	Control		
1	Branched-chain ketoaciduria (Maple syrup urine disease)	Single autosomal recessive	α-Ketoisocaproic acid decarboxylating enzyme	Branched-chain keto acids	12.3	0.5	65	-	Diet low in leucine, isoleucine, & valine	3,14, 15
2				Leucine	14-52	1.5-3	25	3-11		
3				Isoleucine	2.2-18	0.8-1.5	....	....		
4				Valine	14-24	2-3	....	....		

continued

92. METABOLIC ERRORS OF GENETIC ORIGIN: MAN

Part I. Metabolites in Plasma and Urine

	Disease	Inheritance	Enzyme Deficiency	Metabolite	Metabolite Level: In Plasma, mg/100 ml: Abnormal	In Plasma, mg/100 ml: Control	In Urine, mg/24 hr[1]: Abnormal	In Urine, mg/24 hr[1]: Control	Treatment	Reference
5	Galactosemia	Single autosomal recessive	Galactose-1-phosphate uridyl transferase	Galactose	7-59	4-11[2]	Increased or decreased	Decreased	Galactose-free diet	8,9, 15
6	Histidinemia	Probably single autosomal recessive	Histidine α-deaminase (histidase)	Histidine	5-17.3	1-1.5	112-850	10-200	Low protein diet could be tried, but may not be necessary	3,6, 15, 16
7	Homocystinuria	Single autosomal recessive	Cystathionine synthase	Homocystine	0-2	0	7.2-80	0	Normal or low methionine diet, with added cystine and cystathionine, should be tried	2,4, 12, 15, 17
8				Methionine	0.4-22	<0.7	....	....		
9	Hyperglycinemia	Probably single autosomal recessive	Glycine transhydroxymethylase	Glycine	5.7-70	1.5-2.3	34-860	12-107	Low protein diet	5,15
10				Oxalic acid	....	....	3.4-11.7	2.1-25.5		
11	With hypooxaluria	Not known	Glycine oxidase?	Glycine	6.9-9.3	1.5-2.3	1040-3290	12-107	Not known	5
12				Oxalic acid	....	....	0.4-2.4	2.1-25.5		
13	Phenylketonuria	Single autosomal recessive	Phenylalanine hydroxylase	Phenylalanine	15-72	1.1 ± 0.68	10-53 mg/ 100 ml	0-18 mg/ 100 ml	Diet low in phenylalanine	1,7, 10, 11, 13, 15, 18, 19
14				Phenylpyruvic acid	0.16-1.05	Decreased	300-2000	Decreased		
15				*o*-Hydroxyphenylacetic acid	0.12-0.60	Decreased	0.10-0.40 g/g creatinine	1 mg/g creatinine		
16				Tyrosine	1.42 ± 0.36	1.7 ± 0.2	....	....		
17				Phenyllactic acid	....	....	290-1060	Decreased		
18				Phenylacetylglutamine	....	....	300-2400	200-500		

1/ Unless otherwise indicated. 2/ For heterozygotes.

Contributors: Waisman, Harry A., and Brown, Eleanor S.

References

[1] Berry, H. K., B. Umbarger, and B. Livingston. 1963. J. Pediat. 63:954.

[2] Brenton, D. P., et al. 1966. Quart. J. Med., N.S.35: 325.

[3] Carver, M. J., and R. Paska. 1961. Clin. Chim. Acta 6:721.

[4] Finkelstein, J. D., et al. 1964. Science 146:785.

[5] Gerritsen, T., E. Kaveggia, and H. A. Waisman. 1965. Pediatrics 36:882.

[6] Ghadimi, H., M. W. Partington, and A. Hunter. 1962. Ibid. 29:714.

[7] Gjessing, L. R. 1966. Symp. Tyrosinosis, Oslo, p. 55.

[8] Hsia, D. Y.-Y., I. Huang, and S. G. Driscoll. 1958. Nature 182:1389.

[9] Hugh-Jones, K., A. L. Newcomb, and D. Y.-Y. Hsia. 1960. Arch. Disease Childhood 35:521.

[10] Jervis, G. A. 1950. Proc. Soc. Exptl. Biol. Med. 75: 83.

[11] Jervis, G. A., and E. J. Drejza. 1966. Clin. Chim. Acta 13:435.

[12] Mudd, S. H., et al. 1964. Science 143:1443.

[13] Partington, M. W., and E. J. M. Lewis. 1963. J. Pediat. 62:348.

[14] Patrick, A. D. 1961. Arch. Disease Childhood 36: 269.

[15] Stanbury, J. B., J. B. Wyngaarden, and D. S. Fredrickson, ed. 1966. The metabolic basis of inherited disease. Ed. 2. McGraw-Hill, New York.

[16] Waisman, H. A. 1967. Am. J. Diseases Children 113:93.

[17] Waisman, H. A. 1967. Ibid. 113:101.

[18] Wang, H. L., N. E. Morton, and H. A. Waisman. 1961. Am. J. Human Genet. 13:255.

[19] Wright, S. W., and G. Tarjan. 1957. Am. J. Diseases Children 93:405.

continued

92. METABOLIC ERRORS OF GENETIC ORIGIN: MAN

Part II. Diseases Caused by Inborn Errors

	General Type	Specific Disease	Reference
1	Disorders of carbohydrate metabolism	Diabetes mellitus	3
2		Familial lactic acidosis	2,4
3		Fructose intolerance	3
4		Fructosuria	3
5		Glycogen deposition	3
6		Hyperoxaluria	3
7		Pentosuria	3
8		Renal glycosuria	3
9	Disorders of amino acid metabolism	Albinism	3
10		Alcaptonuria	3
11		Argininosuccinicaciduria	2
12		Ataxia telangiectasia	2
13		Blue diaper syndrome	4
14		Branched chain ketoaciduria	3
15		Citrullinemia	2
16		Cystathioninuria	3
17		Cystinuria	3
18		Dopa-uria	2
19		Familial dysautonomia	2
20		Formiminotransferase deficiency	2
21		Goiter	3
22		Hartnup disease	3
23		Histidinemia	3
24		Homocystinuria	3
25		3-Hydroxykynureninuria	2
26		Hydroxyprolinemia	2
27		Hyperammonemia	2
28		Hyperglycinemia	3
29		With hypooxaluria	4
30		Hyperlysinemia	4
31		Hypersarcosinemia	2
32		Hyperserotoninemia	2
33		Hypervalinemia	2,4
34		Hypoglycemia, leucine induced	1
35		Imidazole aminoaciduria	2
36		Indolylacroyl glycinuria	2
37		Joseph's syndrome	2
38		Methionine malabsorption	2
39		Oculo-cerebro-renal syndrome	2
40		Osteopathy, peptiduria, & mental retardation	2
41		Phenylketonuria	3
42		Prolinemias	2
43		Pyridoxine dependency	2
44		Tryptophanuria	2
45		Tyrosinemia	3
46	Disorders of lipid metabolism	Familial hyperlipoproteinemia	3
47		α-β-Lipoproteinemia	3
48		Lipidosis, cerebroside	3
49		ganglioside	3
50		glycolipid	3
51		sphingomyelin	3
52		sulfatide	3
53		Tangier disease	3
54	Disorders of steroid metabolism	Adrenogenital syndromes	3,4
55	Disorders of purine & pyrimidine metabolism	Gout	3
56		Hyperuricemia	4
57		Orotic aciduria	3
58		Xanthinuria	3
59	Disorders of metal metabolism	Hemochromatosis	3
60		Wilson's disease	3
61	Disorders of porphyrin & heme metabolism	Hyperbilirubinemia	3
62		Porphyrias	3
63	Diseases of connective tissue, muscle, or bone	Central core disease & nemaline myopathy	3
64		Hurler syndrome	3
65		Hypophosphatasia	3
66		Muscular dystrophies	3
67		Periodic paralysis	3
68		Pseudohypoparathyroidism & pseudo-pseudohypoparathyroidism	3
69		Systemic amyloidoses	3
70	Disorders of blood & blood forming tissues	Disorders of hemostasis (classical hemophilia, etc.)	3
71		Elliptocytosis	1,3
72		Glucose-6-phosphate dehydrogenase deficiency	3
73		Hemoglobinopathies & thallassemia	3
74		Hemolytic anemia	3
75		Hereditary spherocytosis	3
76		Methemoglobinemias	3
77		Pyruvate kinase deficiency	3
78	Disorders of epithelial transport	Cystic fibrosis	3
79		Fanconi syndrome	3
80		Renal tubular acidosis	3
81		Vasopressin-resistant diabetes insipidus	3
82		Vitamin D-resistant rickets with hypophosphatemia	3
83	Deficiency of circulating enzymes or plasma proteins	Acatalasia	3
84		Agammaglobulinemia	3
85		Pseudocholinesterase deficiency	3

Contributors: Waisman, Harry A., and Brown, Eleanor S.

References

[1] Hsia, D. Y.-Y. 1966. Ann. N.Y. Acad. Sci. 134:946.

[2] O'Brien, D. 1965. U.S. Dept. Health Educ. Welfare Childrens Bur. Publ. 429.

[3] Stanbury, J. B., J. B. Wyngaarden, and D. S. Fredrickson, ed. 1966. The metabolic basis of inherited disease. Ed. 2. McGraw-Hill, New York.

[4] Waisman, H. A. 1966. Pediat. Clin. N. Am. 13:469.

93. BIOCIDES

Part I. Antibiotics

Route: iv = intravenous; ip = intraperitoneal; sc = subcutaneous.

	Common Name (Synonym) [Empirical Formula]	Mode of Action	Organisms Affected	Acute Toxicity: Animal	Acute Toxicity: Route	Acute Toxicity: LD_{50} mg/kg[1]	Reference
1	Actinomycin D (Actinomycin C_1) [$C_{60}H_{76}N_{12}O_{15}$]	Selectively inhibits RNA synthesis; binds to guanine residues in DNA but not in RNA. Formation of a stable actinomycin-DNA complex inhibits DNA-dependent RNA synthesis by RNA polymerase.	Gram-positive microorganisms (e. g., *Lactobacillus, Streptococcus).* Highly toxic to both normal & neoplastic mammalian cells.	Mouse	iv	0.67-0.74	9-11,22
2	Amphotericin B [$C_{46}H_{73}NO_{20}$]	Increases cell permeability by binding to sterols in membranes of sensitive cells, thus permitting potassium & other essential metabolites to leak out, causing cellular death. Fungistatic or fungicidal, depending on concentration & time of contact.	Strains of *Leishmania brasiliensis & L. donovani;* many yeasts & fungi, including those responsible for many systemic fungal infections of man	Dog	Oral	>500	7,14, 17,23, 24,26
3				Mouse	ip	1640	
4					iv	4.5	
5					Oral	>8000	
6				Rat	Oral	>1000	
7	Ampicillin (α-Aminobenzyl penicillin) [$C_{16}H_{19}N_3O_4S$]	Inhibits synthesis of bacterial cell walls	*Aerobacter, Diplococcus, Escherichia, Haemophilus, Neisseria, Proteus, Salmonella, Shigella, Staphylococcus, Streptococcus*	Mouse	iv	Nontoxic[2]	11,20, 27
8				Mouse, rat	Oral & sc	Nontoxic[3]	
9	Bacitracin A [$C_{66}H_{103}N_{17}O_{16}S$]	Disrupts structure and/or function of bacterial cell walls	*Actinomyces, Clostridium, Corynebacterium, Diplococcus, Haemophilus, Neisseria, Staphylococcus, Streptococcus, Treponema*	......	......	....	11,33
10	Benzylpenicillin (Penicillin G) [$C_{16}H_{18}N_2O_4S$]	Inhibits cell wall formation, probably by inhibiting peptidoglycan transpeptidase, which is responsible for the cross-linking reaction in murein synthesis; bactericidal	Gram-positive bacteria; *Haemophilus & Neisseria* spp.	Mouse	iv	1800	2,11, 23,25-27,29, 32-34
11					ip	3880	
12					Oral	12,750	
13					sc	6000	
14	Cephalothin [$C_{16}H_{17}N_2O_6S_2$]	Inhibits cell wall formation, probably by inhibiting peptidoglycan transpeptidase, which is responsible for the cross-linking reaction in murein synthesis; bactericidal	Penicillinase-producing staphylococci, β-hemolytic streptococci, pneumococci, & sensitive strains of certain gram-negative bacteria (e. g., *Escherichia coli, Haemophilus influenzae, Klebsiella* sp., *Paracolobactrum* sp., *Proteus mirabilis)*	Mouse	ip	>7000	1,8,11, 30
15					iv	5000	
16					Oral	>10,000	
17				Rat	ip	6300	
18					iv	>4000	
19					Oral	>10,000	
20					sc	7500	
21	Chloramphenicol [$C_{11}H_{12}N_5O_2Cl_2$]	Inhibits protein synthesis; binds to the 50S ribosome subunit, thus inhibiting reactions following formation of amino-acyl-sRNA and before formation of the complete polypeptide chain on the ribosome; bacteriostatic	Large viruses, rickettsiae; many species of gram-positive & gram-negative bacteria; blue-green algae	Mouse	ip	1320	4,10, 11,23, 26,27, 29
22					iv	100-200	
23					Oral	2640	
24					sc	2300-2585	
25				Rabbit	iv	117	
26				Rat	iv	175-278	

1/ Unless otherwise specified. 2/ No lethal effect from 2 g/kg. 3/ No observable toxic effects from single doses up to 5 g/kg.

continued

93. BIOCIDES

Part I. Antibiotics

Line	Common Name (Synonym) [Empirical Formula]	Mode of Action	Organisms Affected	Acute Toxicity: Animal	Acute Toxicity: Route	Acute Toxicity: LD_{50} mg/kg[1/]	Reference
27 28 29 30	Chlortetracycline [$C_{22}H_{23}N_2O_8Cl$]	Tetracyclines inhibit protein synthesis at a stage preceding peptide bond formation on the ribosome	*Amoeba* spp.; lymphogranuloma-psittacosis group, *Rickettsia; Aerobacter, Bacillus, Borrelia, Brucella, Clostridium, Corynebacterium, Diplococcus, Escherichia, Haemophilus, Leptospira, Mycobacterium, Mycoplasma, Neisseria, Pasteurella, Proteus, Pseudomonas, Salmonella, Shigella, Staphylococcus, Streptococcus, Treponema*	Mouse Rat 	iv Oral iv Oral	134 1500 118 3000	10,11, 27,29
31 32 33 34	Colistin [$C_{45}H_{85}N_{13}O_{10}$]	Disorganizes the cell membrane, causing leakage of intracellular materials & subsequent death. Bacteriostatic or bactericidal, depending on concentration & time of contact.	Bacteriostatic & bactericidal against a wide spectrum of gram-negative bacteria; less active against gram-positive bacteria & fungi. Colistin & polymyxin are the most active inhibitors of *Pseudomonas.*	Mouse	ip iv Oral sc	126-220 220-400 767-2000 138-220	23,27, 36
35 36	Dihydrostreptomycin [$C_{21}H_{41}N_7O_{12}$]	Inhibits protein synthesis, probably by inhibiting the proper function of 30S ribosomes	*Actinobacillus, Brucella, Diplococcus, Erysipelothrix, Escherichia, Haemophilus, Mycobacterium, Mycoplasma, Neisseria, Nocardia, Pasteurella, Proteus, Salmonella, Shigella, Staphylococcus, Streptococcus, Vibrio*	Mouse	iv Oral	ca. 200 9000	11,29, 31
37 38 39 40 41 42 43	Erythromycin (Erythromycin A) [$C_{37}H_{67}NO_{13}$]	Interferes with transfer of amino acids from aminoacyl-sRNA to proteins on the ribosomes. Bacteriostatic or bactericidal, depending on nature of the organism & drug concentration.	Most gram-positive bacteria. Rickettsiales, certain large viruses, *Haemophilus,* & *Neisseria* are sensitive; also some strains of *Bordetella, Brucella, Listeria, Mycoplasma, Pasteurella,* & *Treponema.*	Mouse Rat 	ip iv Oral sc iv Oral sc	490 426 2927 1849 209 >2000 1442	10,11, 27,29, 31,35
44 45 46 47 48 49 50	Griseofulvin [$C_{17}H_{17}O_6Cl$]	Causes morphological distortions, and may therefore be an inhibitor of cell wall synthesis. Tests on several fungi show nucleus as possible target site. Fungistatic.	Fungistatic against some species of *Epidermophyton, Microsporum,* & *Trichophyton*	Mouse Rat 	ip iv Oral sc ip iv Oral	1550 280 >5000 >12,000 5000 Nontoxic[4/] 10,000	3,11, 12,14, 23,27, 28,31
51 52 53 54	Lincomycin [$C_{18}H_{34}N_2O_6S$]	Inhibits protein synthesis; binds to the 50S ribosome	Most gram-positive bacteria; *Leptospira pomona*	Mouse Rat	ip Oral sc Oral	1000 >2000 >800 >4000	6,13, 19,21
55 56	Novobiocin [$C_{31}H_{36}N_2O_{11}$]	Directly inhibits DNA synthesis; indirectly interferes with protein synthesis & cell wall permeability	*Bacillus, Corynebacterium, Diplococcus, Haemophilus, Listeria, Neisseria, Nocardia, Staphylococcus, Streptococcus*	Mouse	iv Oral	407 962->1000	10,27, 29,31
57 58 59 60 61	Nystatin [$C_{47}H_{75}NO_{18}$]	Binds to sterols in the cell membrane, causing leakage of potassium & other cell constituents. Fungistatic or fungicidal, depending on concentration & time of contact.	Many yeasts & fungi, including those responsible for many systemic infections in man	Mouse Rat 	ip Oral sc ip Oral	30,000-50,000 units/kg >12.5 × 10^6 units/kg 120 85,000-93,000 units/kg >8.34 × 10^6 units/kg	11,14, 15,17, 23,24, 26,27, 29

[1/] Unless otherwise specified. [4/] Rats have survived an intravenous dose of 200 mg/kg.

continued

Part I. Antibiotics

	Common Name (Synonym) [Empirical Formula]	Mode of Action	Organisms Affected	Acute Toxicity			Reference
				Animal	Route	LD_{50} mg/kg[1]	
62	Polymyxin B $[C_{56}H_{104}N_{16}O_{14}Cl_5]$	Affects organization & function of bacterial cell membranes	*Aerobacter, Brucella, Escherichia, Haemophilus, Pasteurella, Pseudomonas, Salmonella, Shigella, Vibrio*	Mouse	iv	6-9	11,27, 29
63	Streptomycin $[C_{21}H_{39}N_7O_{12}]$	Inhibits protein synthesis by binding to the ribosome. Bacteriostatic or bactericidal, depending on concentration.	Rickettsiae & some larger viruses; many species of gram-positive & gram-negative bacteria, including spirochetes	Mouse	ip	610	2,5,11, 23,26
64					iv	85	
65					Oral	15,550	
66					sc	500	
67	Tetracycline $[C_{22}H_{24}N_2O_8]$	Tetracyclines inhibit protein synthesis by interfering with formation of the necessary complex among ribosome, mRNA & aminoacyl-sRNA	Rickettsiae & some larger viruses; many species of gram-positive & gram-negative bacteria, including spirochetes	Mouse	ip	200-300[5]	16,18, 23,27
68					iv	150-170[5]	
69					Oral	>3000[5]	

[1] Unless otherwise specified. [5] Tetracycline hydrochloride.

Contributors: (a) Meyers, Edward, (b) Gale, George O., and Jukes, Thomas H.

References

[1] American Medical Association. 1967. New drugs evaluated by A.M.A. Council on Drugs. Chicago. p. 53.

[2] Bacharach, A. L., et al. 1959. J. Pharm. Pharmacol. 11:737.

[3] Bent, K. J., and R. H. Moore. 1966. Symp. Soc. Gen. Microbiol. 16:82.

[4] Brock, T. D. 1961. Bacteriol. Rev. 25:32.

[5] Brock, T. D. 1966. Symp. Soc. Gen. Microbiol. 16:131.

[6] Chang, F. N., C. J. Sih, and B. Weisblum. 1966. Proc. Natl. Acad. Sci. U.S. 55:431.

[7] Cope, A. C., et al. 1966. J. Am. Chem. Soc. 88:4228.

[8] Flynn, E. H. 1966. Antimicrobial Agents Chemotherapy, p. 715.

[9] Foley, G. E. 1955-56. Antibiot. Ann., p. 432.

[10] Goldberg, I. H. 1965. Am. J. Med. 39:722.

[11] Goodman, L. S., and A. Gilman, ed. 1965. The pharmacological basis of therapeutics. Ed. 3. Macmillan, New York.

[12] Grove, J. F. 1963. Quart. Rev. (London) 17:1.

[13] Herr, R. R., and M. E. Bergy. 1962. Antimicrobial Agents Chemotherapy, p. 560.

[14] Hildick-Smith, G., H. Blank, and I. Sarkany. 1964. Fungus diseases and their treatment. Little, Brown; Boston.

[15] Ikeda, M., M. Suzuki, and C. Djerassi. 1967. Tetrahedron Letters (38):3745.

[16] Kaul, P. N. 1961. Hindustan Antibiot. Bull. 4:59.

[17] Lampen, J. O. 1966. Symp. Soc. Gen. Microbiol. 16:111.

[18] Laskin, A. I. 1967. In D. Gottlieb and P. D. Shaw, ed. Antibiotics. J. Springer, New York. v. 1, p. 331.

[19] Lewis, C., H. W. Clapp, and J. E. Grady. 1962. Antimicrobial Agents Chemotherapy, p. 570.

[20] Lynn, B. 1965. Antibiot. Chemotherapia 13:125.

[21] Magerlein, B. J., R. D. Birkenmeyer, and F. Kagan. 1966. Antimicrobial Agents Chemotherapy, p. 727.

[22] Manaker, R. A., et al. 1954-55. Antibiot. Ann., p. 853.

[23] Newton, B. A. 1965. Ann. Rev. Microbiol. 19:209.

[24] Oroshnik, W., and A. D. Mebane. 1963. Fortschr. Chem. Org. Naturstoffe 21:17.

[25] Park, J. T. 1966. Symp. Soc. Gen. Microbiol. 16:70.

[26] Porter, J. N. 1964. In P. L. Altman and D. S. Dittmer, ed. Biology data book. Federation of American Societies for Experimental Biology, Washington, D.C.

[27] Schnitzer, R. J., and F. Hawking, ed. 1964. Exptl. Chemotherapy 3.

[28] Sharpe, H. M., and E. G. Tomick. 1960. Toxicol. Appl. Pharmacol. 2:44.

[29] Spector, W. S., ed. 1957. Handbook of toxicology. W. B. Saunders, Philadelphia. v. 2.

[30] Spencer, J. L., et al. 1966. Antimicrobial Agents Chemotherapy, p. 573.

[31] Stecher, P. G., et al., ed. 1960. The Merck index. Ed. 7. Merck, Rahway, N.J.

[32] Stewart, G. T. 1965. The penicillin group of drugs. Elsevier, New York.

[33] Strominger, J. L., and D. J. Tipper. 1965. Am. J. Med. 39:708.

[34] Strominger, J. L., et al. 1967. Federation Proc. 26:9.

[35] Taubman, S. B., et al. 1963. Antimicrobial Agents Chemotherapy, p. 395.

[36] Vogler, K., and R. O. Studer. 1966. Experientia 22: 345.

continued

Part II. Insecticides

Route: iv = intravenous; pc = percutaneous; ip = intraperitoneal; IAM = insecticide added to medium. Values in parentheses are ranges, estimate "c" (*see* Introduction).

	Common Name (Synonym) [Chemical Name]	Mode of Action	Organisms Affected	Acute Toxicity: Animal	Route	LD_{50}	Reference
1	Aldrin	Contact &	Most insects	Dog	Oral	65-95 mg/kg	1,2,15
2	[1,2,3,4,10,10-Hexachloro-1,4,4a,	stomach		Guinea pig	Oral	33 mg/kg	1,2,15
3	5,8,8a-hexahydro-*endo*-1,4-*exo*-	toxicant		Mouse	Oral	44 mg/kg	1,2,15
4	5,8-dimethanonaphthalene]			Rabbit	Oral	50-80 mg/kg	1,2,15,19
5				Rat, ♂	Oral	38-54 mg/kg	1,2,5,11, 15,19
6				♀	iv	18 mg/kg	2,15
7					Oral	46-67 mg/kg	1,2,5,11, 15,19
8	Allethrin	Neurotoxin	Selected insects	Rat, ♀	Oral	680 mg/kg	8,13,14
9	[Allylrethronyl *d,l-cis-trans*-chry-			Housefly[1], ♀	Topical	8.0 mg/kg	12-14
10	santhemate]			Mosquito[2], larva	IAM	0.14 ppm	12-14
11	Azinphosmethyl	Anticholin-	Most animals	Rat, ♀	Oral	11 mg/kg	8,13,14
12	[*O,O*-Dimethyl-*S*-4-oxo-1,2,3-ben-	esterase		Housefly[1], ♀	Topical	2.7 mg/kg	12-14
13	zotriazin-3-(4*H*)ylmethyl phos- phorodithioate]			Mosquito[2], larva	IAM	0.025 ppm	12-14
14	Carbaryl	Anticholin-	Insects & other	Rat, ♂	Oral	850 mg/kg	8,13,14
15	[1-Naphthyl-*N*-methylcarbamate]	esterase	invertebrates	Housefly[1], ♀	Topical	900 mg/kg	12-14
16				Mosquito[2], larva	IAM	1.0 ppm	12-14
17	Chlordane	Contact &	Insects, espe-	Goat	Oral	180 mg/kg	15,25
18	(Octa-Klor; Octachlorodihydro-	stomach	cially locusts,	Mouse	Oral	430 mg/kg	15,22
19	dicyclopentadiene; Toxichlor)	toxicant;	grasshoppers,	Rat	Oral	335-430 mg/kg	5,15
20	[1,2,4,5,6,7,8,8-Octachloro-2,3,3a,	marked	crickets, soil	Sheep	Oral	500-1000 mg/kg	15,25
21	4,7,7a-hexahydro-4,7-methano- indene]	residual toxicity	insects, cock- roaches, flies, ants, insects predatory on cotton	Chick	Oral	220-230 mg/kg	15,21
22	Chlorobenzilate	Direct con-	Mites	Mouse	Oral	4850 mg/kg	6,7,15
23	[Ethyl 4,4′-dichlorobenzilate]	tact ac-				729 mg/kg[3]	9,15
24		tion for		Rat	Oral	3100 mg/kg	6,7,15
25		some acar-				702 mg/kg[3]	9,15
26		ians, resid- ual action for others; low insecticidal power				735(682-792) mg/kg[4]	9,15
27	DDT	Peripheral	Wide range of	Cat	Oral	400-600 mg/kg[5]	13-15
28	(Chlorophenothane; Dicophane;	neurotox-	insects &	Dog	iv	ca. 50 mg/kg	13-15
29	Neocid; Zeidane)	in	other arthro-	Guinea pig	Oral	400 mg/kg	13-15
30	[1,1,1-Trichloro-2,2-*bis*(*p*-chloro-		pods	Horse	Oral	300 mg/kg	13-15
31	phenyl)ethane]			Monkey	Oral	200 mg/kg	13-15
32				Mouse	Oral	150-400 mg/kg[5]	13-15
33				Rabbit	Oral	250-400 mg/kg[5]	13-15
34				Rat	iv	40-60 mg/kg	13-15
35					Oral	150-420 mg/kg[5]	13-15
36				♀	Oral	118 mg/kg	8,13,14
37				Housefly[1], ♀	Topical	2.0 mg/kg	12-14
38				Mosquito[2], larva	IAM	0.007 ppm	12-14
39	Diazinon	Anticholin-	Most animals	Rat, ♀	Oral	76 mg/kg	8,13,14
40	[*O,O*-Diethyl-*O*-(2-isopropyl-6-	esterase		Housefly[1], ♀	Topical	2.85 mg/kg	12-14
41	methyl-4-pyrimidyl) phospho- rothionate]			Mosquito[2], larva	IAM	0.086 ppm	12-14

1/ *Musca domestica.* 2/ *Culex pipiens quinquefasciatus (C. fatigans),* southern house mosquito. 3/ Technical product used. 4/ 25% xylene emulsion used. 5/ LD_{50} dose varies with sex and type of vehicle used; young animals are especially susceptible.

continued

93. BIOCIDES

Part II. Insecticides

	Common Name (Synonym) [Chemical Name]	Mode of Action	Organisms Affected	Acute Toxicity			Reference
				Animal	Route	LD$_{50}$	
42	Dieldrin	Central	Household &	Dog	Oral	56-80 mg/kg	1,2,13,14
43	[1,2,3,4,10,10-Hexachloro-6,7-	neuro-	agricultural	Guinea pig	Oral	49 mg/kg	1,2,13,14
44	epoxy-1,4,4a,5,6,7,8,8a-octahy-	toxin	insects, grass-	Mouse	Oral	38 mg/kg	1,2,13,14
45	dro-*endo*-1,4-*exo*-5,8-dimethano-		hoppers, lo-	Rabbit	Oral	45-50 mg/kg	1,2,13,14
46	naphthalene]		custs, crick-	Rat	Oral	38-87 mg/kg	1,2,13,14
47			ets, cotton		pc	60-90 mg/kg	2,13,14
48			insects, soil-	♀	Oral	46 mg/kg	8,13,14
49			inhabiting in-	Sheep	Oral	50-75 mg/kg	1,2,13,14
50			sects	Housefly[1], ♀	Topical	0.95 mg/kg	12-14
51				Mosquito[2], larva	IAM	0.0078 ppm	12-14
52	Dilan[6]	May be	Insects, espe-	Mouse	ip	600 mg/kg	15
53	(Bulan plus Prolan)	similar to	cially potato		Oral	ca. 1100 mg/kg	
54	[2-Nitro-1,1-*bis*(*p*-chlorophenyl) butane plus 2-nitro-1,1-*bis*(*p*-chlorophenyl)propane]	DDT & methoxy- chlor	leafhopper, Mexican bean beetle & other bean insects	Rat	Oral	300 mg/kg[7]; 4000 mg/kg[8]	
55	Endrin	Contact &	Insects, espe-	Guinea pig	Oral	ca. 16-36 mg/kg	15,20
56	[1,2,3,4,10,10-Hexachloro-6,7-	stomach	cially Orthop-	Monkey	Oral	ca. 3 mg/kg	15,20
57	epoxy-1,4,4a,5,6,7,8,8a-octahy-	toxicant;	tera, cotton	Rabbit, ♀	Oral	7-10 mg/kg	15,20
58	dro-*endo*-1,4-*endo*-5,8-dimethano-	may have	plant insects,	Rat, ♂, young	Oral	28.8 mg/kg	15,20
59	naphthalene]	delayed	flies & other	adult	Oral	40-43.4 mg/kg	15,18,20
60		neurotox-	household	♀, young	Oral	16.8 mg/kg	15,20
61		ic action	insects	adult	Oral	7.3 mg/kg	15,20
62	Fenitrothion	Anticholin-	Selected insects	Rat, ♀	Oral	500 mg/kg	8,13,14
63	[*O,O*-Dimethyl-*O*-3-methyl-4-nitro-	esterase		Housefly[1], ♀	Topical	2.2 mg/kg	12-14
64	phenyl phosphorothionate]			Mosquito[2], larva	IAM	0.0056 ppm	12-14
65	Heptachlor	Central	Cotton insects,	Guinea pig	Oral	116 mg/kg	13-15
66	[1,4,5,6,7,8,8-Heptachloro-3a,4,7,	neuro-	grasshoppers,	Mouse	Oral	68 mg/kg	13-15
67	7a-tetrahydro-4,7-methanoin- dene]	toxin	soil insects, onion thrips,	Rat	pc	195-250 mg/kg	5,13,14, 24
68			alfalfa weevil	♂	Oral	60-169 mg/kg	13-15,24
69				♀	Oral	162 mg/kg	8,13,14
70				Chick	Oral	63 mg/kg	13,14,16
71				Housefly[1], ♀	Topical	2.25 mg/kg	12-14
72				Mosquito[2], larva	IAM	0.0056 ppm	12-14
73	Isodrin [1,2,3,4,10,10-Hexachloro-1,4,4a,	Neurotox- ic, with	Many insects, especially	Rat, ♂, weanling	Oral	27.8(23.3-33.3) mg/kg	15
74	5,8,8a-hexahydro-1,4-*endo,endo*- 5,8-dimethanonaphthalene]	delayed action	Orthoptera, cotton insects,	6 mo	Oral	42.1(35.9-49.4) mg/kg	
75			household in- sects, soil in-	♀, weanling	Oral	16.4(12.6-21.5) mg/kg	
76			sects	6 mo	Oral	11.7(10.2-13.5) mg/kg	
77	Kelthane	....	Mites	Rat, ♂	Oral	809 mg/kg	17
78	[1,1-*bis*(*p*-Chlorophenyl)-2,2,2- trichloroethanol]			♀	Oral	684 mg/kg	
79	Lindane	Central	Insects	Dog	iv	7.5 mg/kg[9]	13-15
80	(Gamma-BHC; Gammexane;	neuro-			Oral	40-200 mg/kg[9]	13-15
81	Gamma-HCH)	toxin		Guinea pig	Oral	100-127 mg/kg	13-15
82	[γ-1,2,3,4,5,6-Hexachlorocyclo-			Mouse	Oral	86 mg/kg	13-15
83	hexane]			Rabbit	Oral	60-200 mg/kg	10,11,13-15

[1] *Musca domestica.* [2] *Culex pipiens quinquefasciatus (C. fatigans),* southern house mosquito. [6] Mixture of two nitroalkyl DDT analogues. [7] Bulan. [8] Prolan. [9] Lethal dose.

continued

93. BIOCIDES

Part II. Insecticides

	Common Name (Synonym) [Chemical Name]	Mode of Action	Organisms Affected	Acute Toxicity			Reference
				Animal	Route	LD_{50}	
84				Rat	ip	35-85 mg/kg	13-15
85					Oral	125-230 mg/kg	3,10,11, 13-15,23
86				♀	Oral	91 mg/kg	8,13,14
87				Housefly1/, ♀	Topical	0.9 mg/kg	12-14
88				Mosquito2/, larva	IAM	0.025 ppm	12-14
89	Malathion	Anticholinesterase	Selected insects	Rat, ♀	Oral	1000 mg/kg	8,13,14
90	[*O,O*-Dimethyl *S*-(1,2-dicarbethoxyethyl) phosphorodithioate]			Housefly1/, ♀	Topical	27.5 mg/kg	12-14
91				Mosquito2/, larva	IAM	0.081 ppm	12-14
92	Methoxychlor	Peripheral neurotoxin	Most insects	Rat, ♀	Oral	6000 mg/kg	8,13,14
93	[2,2-*bis*(*p*-Methoxyphenyl)-1,1,1-trichloroethane]			Housefly1/, ♀	Topical	9.0 mg/kg	12-14
94				Mosquito2/, larva	IAM	0.067 ppm	12-14
95	Parathion	Anticholinesterase	Most animals	Rat, ♀	Oral	3.6 mg/kg	8,13,14
96	[*O,O*-Diethyl *O*-*p*-nitrophenyl phosphorothioate]			Housefly1/, ♀	Topical	0.85 mg/kg	12-14
97				Mosquito2/, larva	IAM	0.0032 ppm	12-14
98	Perthane [1,1-Dichloro-2,2-*bis*(*p*-ethylphenyl)ethane]	....	Many insects	Rat	Oral	9.34 g/kg	4
99	Phthalthrin	Neurotoxin	Selected insects	Rat, ♀	Oral	>20,000 mg/kg	8,13,14
100	[3,4,5,6-Tetrahydrophthalimidomethyl *d,l-cis, trans*-chrysanthemate]			Housefly1/, ♀	Topical	1.95 mg/kg	12-14
101				Mosquito2/, larva	IAM	0.062 ppm	12-14
102	Propoxure	Anticholinesterase	Insects & other invertebrates	Rat, ♀	Oral	104 mg/kg	8,13,14
103	[2-Isopropoxyphenyl-*N*-methylcarbamate]			Housefly1/, ♀	Topical	21.5 mg/kg	12-14
104				Mosquito2/, larva	IAM	0.33 ppm	12-14
105	Toxaphene10/	Contact & stomach toxicant. Neurotoxic symptoms after direct application are manifested following a latent period.	Agricultural insects, soil insects, orthopteran pests, household insects, insects on livestock, certain phytophagous acarians	Guinea pig	Oral	69 mg/kg	15
106				Mouse	Oral	112 mg/kg	
107				Rat	Oral	ca. 69 mg/kg	

1/ *Musca domestica.* 2/ *Culex pipiens quinquefasciatus (C. fatigans),* southern house mosquito. 10/ Chlorinated camphene containing 67-69% chlorine.

Contributors: (a) Fitzhugh, O. G., (b) Metcalf, Robert L.

References

[1] Borgmann, A. R., et al. Unpublished. Univ. Cincinnati, Kettering Laboratory, 1952.

[2] Council of Europe, Working Party on Poisonous Substances in Agriculture. 1962. Agricultural pesticides. Strasbourg, France.

[3] Dallemagne, M. J., and E. Philippot. 1948. Arch. Intern. Pharmacodyn. 76:274.

[4] Finnegan, J. K., et al. 1955. Ibid. 103:404.

[5] Gaines, T. B. 1960. Toxicol. Appl. Pharmacol. 2:88.

[6] Gasser, R. 1952. Congr. Intern. Phytopharm., Compt. Rend., 3e, Paris, p. 357.

[7] Gasser, R. 1952. Experientia 8:65.

[8] Hayes, W. H., Jr. 1963. Clinical handbook on economic poisons. U.S. Dept. of Health, Education, and Welfare, Public Health Service, Washington, D.C.

[9] Horn, J. J., R. B. Bruce, and O. E. Paynter. 1955. J. Agr. Food Chem. 3:752.

[10] Lehman, A. J. 1948. Assoc. Food Drug Officials U.S. Quart. Bull. 12:82.

[11] Lehman, A. J. 1951. Ibid. 15:122.

[12] Metcalf, R. L. 1957. World Health Organ Insecticide Mimeo. Doc. 71.

[13] Metcalf, R. L. 1966. Kirk-Othmer Encycl. Chem. Technol., 2nd Ed., 2:677.

[14] Metcalf, R. L., C. L. Metcalf, and W. P. Flint. 1962. Destructive and useful insects. Ed. 4. McGraw-Hill, New York.

[15] Negherbon, W. O. 1959. Handbook of toxicology. W. B. Saunders, Philadelphia.

[16] Sherman, M., and E. Ross. 1961. Toxicol. Appl. Pharmacol. 3:521.

[17] Smith, R. B., Jr., et al. 1959. Ibid. 1:119.

[18] Street, J. C., et al. 1957. Proc. Ann. Meeting Western Sect. Am. Soc. Animal Prod. 8(46):1.

continued

Part II. Insecticides

[19] Treon, J. F., and F. P. Cleveland. 1955. J. Agr. Food Chem. 3:402.
[20] Treon, J. F., F. P. Cleveland, and J. Cappel. 1955. Ibid. 3:842.
[21] Turner, H. F., and W. G. Eden. 1952. J. Econ. Entomol. 45:130.
[22] U.S. Food and Drug Administration. 1947. U.S. Food Drug Admin. Quart. Rept. 3.
[23] U.S. Public Health Service, National Communicable Disease Center. 1956. Clinical memoranda on economic poisons. Atlanta, Ga.
[24] Velsicol Corporation. 1965. In Food Agr. Organ. U.N. Meeting Rept. PL-10.
[25] Welch, H. 1948. J. Econ. Entomol. 41:36.

Part III. Nematocides

Route: Resp = respiratory (inhalation of vapor).

	Common Name (Synonym) [Chemical Name]	Mode of Action	Organisms Affected	Acute Toxicity			Reference
				Animal	Route	LD_{50}	
1	Dasanit	Contact	Soil insects, nematodes	Rat, white	Dermal	3-30 mg/kg	1-3
2	(B-25141; Bay 25141)				Oral	2-11 mg/kg	
	[*O,O*-Diethyl *O-p*-(methylsulfinyl)phenyl phosphorothioate]						
3	DD Mixture	Fumigant	Nematodes	Rat, white	Dermal	2100 mg/kg	3,7
4	(Vidden D)				Oral	140 mg/kg	
5	[1,3-Dichloropropene plus 1,2-dichloropropane]				Resp	500 ppm	
6	Dowfume MC-2 (Bedfume; Pestmaster) [Methyl bromide]	Fumigant	Soil insects, nematodes, fungi, weed seeds	Rat, white	Resp[1/]	200 ppm	3,7
7	Dowfume W-85	Fumigant	Nematodes	Rat, white	Oral	108-170 mg/kg	3,7
8	(Soilfume) [Ethylene dibromide]				Resp	200 ppm	
9	Larvacide (Picfume) [Chloropicrin]	Fumigant	Soil insects, nematodes, fungi, weed seeds	Rat, white	Resp[1/]	20 ppm	3,7
10	Mylone [3,5-Dimethyl-1,3,5,2H-tetrahydrothiadiazine-2-thione]	Fumigant	Soil insects, nematodes, fungi, weed seeds	Rat, white	Oral	500 mg/kg	4,7
11	Nemagon	Fumigant	Nematodes	Rabbit	Dermal	1420 mg/kg	3,7
12	(Fumazone)			Rat, white	Oral	173 mg/kg	
13	[1,2-Dibromo-3-chloropropane]				Resp	100 ppm	
14	Sarolex	Contact	Soil insects, nematodes	Rat, white	Dermal	379-1107 mg/kg	3,9
15	[*O,O*-Diethyl *O*-(2-isoprophyl-4-methyl-6-pyrimidinyl) phosphorothioate]				Oral	66-600 mg/kg	
16	Telone	Fumigant	Nematodes	Rat, white	Oral	250-500 mg/kg	7
17	[Mixture of dichloropropenes]				Resp	500 ppm	3,7
18	Vapam	Fumigant	Soil insects, nematodes, fungi, weed seeds	Rabbit	Dermal	800 mg/kg	3,7
19	[Sodium *N*-methyldithiocarbamate dihydrate]			Rat, white	Oral	820 mg/kg	
20	Vorlex [Methyl isothiocyanate plus chlorinated C_3 hydrocarbons]	Fumigant	Soil insects, nematodes, fungi, weed seeds	Rat, white	Oral	100 mg/kg	3,7
21	Zinophos	Contact	Soil insects, nematodes	Rat, white	Dermal	8-15 mg/kg	3,5, 6,8
22	(Cynem) [*O,O*-Diethyl *O*-2-parazinyl phosphorothioate]				Oral	9-16 mg/kg	

1/ Values for oral and dermal toxicity are absent because the volatility of the nematocide makes ingestion or contact with the skin for any length of time difficult.

continued

93. BIOCIDES

Part III. Nematocides

Contributor: Smart, Grover C., Jr.

References

[1] Bell, A. A., and L. R. Krusberg. 1964. Plant Disease Reptr. 48(9):721.

[2] Brodie, B. B., and G. W. Burton. 1967. Ibid. 51(7): 562.

[3] Kenaga, E. E. 1966. Bull. Entomol. Soc. Am. 12(2): 161.

[4] Kerr, S. H., and J. E. Brogdon. 1960. Florida Univ. Agr. Ext. Serv. Gainesville) Entomol. Mimeo. 10.

[5] Locascio, S. J., G. C. Smart, Jr., and M. E. Marvel. 1967. Proc. Florida State Hort. Soc. 79:170.

[6] Miller, H. N., and V. G. Perry. 1965. Plant Disease Reptr. 49(1):51.

[7] Rhoades, H. L., J. A. Winchester, and A. J. Overman. 1966. Florida Univ. Agr. Expt. Sta. (Gainesville) Bull. 707.

[8] Smart, G. C., Jr., and V. G. Perry. 1966. Bull. Florida Turf Grass Assoc. 13(1):2.

[9] Streu, H. T., and L. M. Vasvary. 1966. Bull. New Jersey Acad. Sci. 11(1):17.

Part IV. Fungicides

	Common Name [Chemical Name]	Mode of Action	Organisms Affected	Toxicity: Animal	Toxicity: Oral LD_{50}	Toxicity: No-Effect Level[1] ppm	Reference
1	Captan [*N*-(Trichloromethylthio)-4-cyclohexene-1,2-dicarboximide]	Reacts mainly with thiols; affects many metabolic processes involving sulfhydryl enzymes & coenzymes. May be fungistatic with lower dosages; fungicidal with higher dosages or prolonged exposure.	Toxic to most fungi	Dog	Nontoxic[2]	4000	9-11, 14
2				Rat	9000 mg/kg	1000	
3	Cycloheximide [β-[2-(3,5-Dimethyl-2-oxocyclohexyl)-2-hydroxyethyl] glutarimide]	Inhibits incorporation of leucine into ribosomal protein in a cell-free system; does not interfere with activation of amino acids or their transfer to soluble RNA. Resistance is determined by ribosomes, not by supernatant enzymes.	Certain protozoa & yeasts; *Ceratocystis fagacearum; Higginsia hiemalis* (cherry leaf spot); *Ustilago tritici*[3]; some turf diseases	Guinea pig	65 mg/kg	....	4,5, 16, 17
4				Monkey	60 mg/kg	....	
5				Mouse	133 mg/kg	....	
6				Rat	2.5 mg/kg	....	
7	Dexon [*p*-Dimethylaminobenzenediazo-sodium sulfonate]	Unknown	Soil fungi of the class Phycomycetes	Guinea pig, ♂	150 mg/kg	....	2
8				Rat, ♀	60 mg/kg	....	
9				weanling[4]	....	80	
10	Dichlone [2,3-Dichloro-1,4-naphthoquinone]	Inactivates enzymes with functional sulfhydryl or amino groups. Toxicity results from concomitant inhibition of phosphorylation, certain dehydrogenases, carboxylases, & coenzyme A.	Soil fungi; *Venturia inaequalis* (apple scab)	Dog	....	500[5]	9,15
11				Rat	1.3 mg/kg	1580[5]	
12	Dodine [*n*-Dodecylguanidine acetate]	Mechanism of action unknown, but surfactant properties & highly basic nature of the guanidine moiety are implicated. In solution at pH 5.6, dodine acetate, as the positively charged dodine cation, reacts rapidly with the surface carboxyl & phosphate groups of the spores. Enzyme inhibition at the cytoplasmic membrane or at the intracellular reaction (rather than physical disorganization of the membrane) may explain the toxicity of Dodine.	In vivo: *Fusicladium cerasi* (peach scab), *F. effusum* (pecan scale), *Higginsia hiemalis* (cherry leaf spot), *Venturia inaequalis* (apple scab). In vitro: many other fungi.	Dog	....	>50-<200	9,18, 19
13				Rabbit[6]	....	....	
14				Rat, ♂	750 mg/kg	200	

[1] After chronic feeding. [2] No evidence of chronic toxicity to subjects fed 300 mg technical Captan/kg/day for 66 weeks; skin may become irritated. [3] Highly specific fungicide; inhibits some organisms with 0.1-1.0 ppm, but does not inhibit others with 100 ppm or more. [4] ♂♀, fed 16 weeks. [5] Minimal-effect level. [6] Severe skin irritation.

continued

93. BIOCIDES

Part IV. Fungicides

	Common Name [Chemical Name]	Mode of Action	Organisms Affected	Toxicity: Animal	Toxicity: Oral LD_{50}	Toxicity: No-Effect Level[1/] ppm	Reference
15	Dyrene [2,4-Dichloro-6-*o*-chloroanilino-*s*-triazine]	Mechanism of action has not been clarified	*Alternaria solani* & *Phytophthora infestans* (potato pathogens); *Fusarium* spp.; *Helminthosporium* spp. (causing diseases of turf)	Dog	7.1 g/kg	5,000->10,000	1,9
16				Rat	2.7 g/kg	5000	
17	Ferbam [Ferric dimethyldithiocarbamate]	Inhibits urease, pancreatic & malt amylases, polyphenol oxidases. A dithiocarbamate-metal-protein complex may be formed through either sulfhydryl or carboxyl groups of the protein, or through both groups.	Many fungi[7/]	Rat	>17 g/kg	250	9,13, 15
18	Glyodin [2-Heptadecylglyoxalidine acetate]	Unknown	In vivo: *Venturia inaequalis* (apple scab) & other fruit-infecting pathogens.	Dog	....	210[8/]	9
19				Guinea pig	....	450[8/]	
20				Rat	1300 mg/kg[9/]	270[8/]	
21			In vitro: many fungi.		3800 mg/kg[10/]		
22	Karathane [2-(1-Methylheptyl)-4,6-dinitrophenyl crotonate]	Unknown; may be attributed to the phenolic portion of the molecule	Acarians; fungi causing powdery mildew.	Dog	....	50[11/]	7,8, 12
23			In vitro: many fungi affected by 0.01% concentration.	Rat, ♂	980 mg/kg	....	
24				♀	1190 mg/kg	....	
25				Duck, Pekin[12/]	....	....	
26	Maneb [Manganous ethylenebis-[dithiocarbamate]]	Action mechanism only partially known. Inhibits metabolism but not synthesis of citrate, apparently through inhibition of aconitase; no detectable effect on other enzymes of the tricarboxylic acid cycle at minimum lethal doses.	In vivo: foliage fungal pathogens, e. g., *Phytophthora infestans* (potato late blight), *Peronospora cubensis* (downy mildew of muskmelon), *Alternaria* spp. (causing leaf spot on many plants)	Dog	....	80	9,13, 15
27				Rat	6750 mg/kg	25	
28	PCNB [Pentachloronitrobenzene]	Unknown	*Rhizoctonia solani*	Rat	>12 g/kg	2500[13/]	12
29	Scutl [Phenylmercuric acetate]	Low concentrations of phenylmercuric salts react with both amino- & sulfhydryl-dependent enzymes; higher concentrations react with other kinds of proteins. Reactions involving organometallic compounds are usually reversible in the presence of another thiol such as cysteine or glutathione.	In vitro: bacteria, fungi, algae	Rat[14/]	37 mg/kg	....	6,13
30	[Sodium *o*-phenylphenate]	Unknown	In vitro: fungi causing postharvest diseases of citrus fruits	Dog	....	20,000	9
31				Rat	2700 mg/kg	2000	

1/ After chronic feeding. 7/ Insolubility of Ferbam limits use for in vitro studies. 8/ 2-Heptadecylimidazoline. 9/ Heptadecylimidazoline component. 10/ 2-Heptadecyl-1-(hydroxyethyl imidazoline) component. 11/ Caused no weight loss after one-year feeding. 12/ 25 ppm produced cataracts. 13/ Rats survived after two-year feeding. 14/ Subjects fed diets as low as 0.5 ppm had renal lesions. [3]

Contributor: Mitchell, J. E.

References

[1] Burchfield, H. P. 1957. Contrib. Boyce Thompson Inst. 19:169.

[2] Chemagro Corporation. 1968. Dexon technical sheet. Kansas City, Mo.

[3] Fitzhugh, O. G., et al. 1950. Arch. Ind. Hyg. Occupational Med. 2:433.

[4] Ford, J. H., et al. 1958. Plant Disease Reptr. 42:680.

continued

Part IV. Fungicides

[5] Greig, M. E., et al. 1959. Toxicol. Appl. Pharmacol. 1:599.
[6] Hunter, D., et al. 1940. Quart. J. Med. 9:193.
[7] Kirby, A. H. M., et al. 1958. Nature 182:1445.
[8] Larson, F. S., et al. 1959. Arch. Intern. Pharmacodyn. 119:31.
[9] Lehman, A. J. 1965. Summaries of pesticide toxicity. Association of Food and Drug Officials, Topeka, Kansas. pp. 93-111.
[10] Leukens, R. J. 1959. Phytopathology 49:339.
[11] Leukens, R. J., and H. D. Sisler. 1958. Ibid. 48:235.
[12] Martin, H. 1961. Can. Dept. Agr. Publ. 1093.
[13] Owens, R. G. 1963. Ann. Rev. Phytopathol. 1:77.
[14] Owens, R. G., and G. Blaac. 1960. Contrib. Boyce Thompson Inst. 20:475.
[15] Owens, R. G., and H. M. Novotny. 1958. Ibid. 19:463.
[16] Siegel, M. R., and H. D. Sisler. 1965. Biochim. Biophys. Acta 103:558.
[17] Siegel, M. R., et al. 1966. Biochem. Pharmacol. 15: 1213.
[18] Somers, E., and D. J. Fisher. 1967. J. Gen. Microbiol. 48:147.
[19] Somers, E., and R. J. Pring. 1966. Ann. Appl. Biol. 58:457.

Part V. Herbicides

Each major herbicide group is represented in the data by a compound having a mode of action typical for the group. Differences in absorption and translocation in organisms do exist, however. Some responses are mediated mainly by physiological concentrations, others only by herbicidal concentrations. The metabolic alterations and other anomalous plant responses described do not necessarily have physiological significance as a site of primary or secondary herbicidal action. LD_{50} values for acute oral toxicity are for rats, unless otherwise indicated [9, 31, 62].

	Common Name [Chemical Name]	Oral LD_{50} mg/kg	Mode of Action	Organisms Affected	Reference
1	Amitrole [3-Amino-1, 2,4-triazole]	1100-2500	Inhibits plastid development. Interferes with purine metabolism, as evidenced by altered biosynthesis of histidine & riboflavin, and by impeded incorporation of phosphate during nucleic acid synthesis. Inhibits activity of catalase, fatty acid peroxidase, & certain other enzymes. Forms complexes with glycine, serine, alanine, glucose, & other natural constituents, and is rapidly transformed into many metabolites of varying phytotoxicity.	Various microorganisms & higher plants	3,8,18, 22,24, 39,57, 58,70, 82
2			Competitively inhibits activity of imidazoleglycerol phosphate dehydratase, an enzyme of histidine biosynthesis	*Salmonella typhimurium*	59
3				*Saccharomyces cerevisiae*	69
4				*Chlorella vulgaris, Prototheca zopfii*	95
5			Competitively inhibits DNA & RNA synthesis; blocks cell division; enhances respiration	*Chlorella pyrenoidosa*	51
6			Stimulates phosphatase activity, depending on presence of NH_4SCN & pH level	*Onopordum acanthium*	80
7			Readily metabolized and converted into sucrose, glucose, fructose, & other compounds in fruit of plant, but forms relatively stable complexes with such compounds in vegetative parts	*Phaseolus vulgaris*	94
8			Enhances incorporation of serine into soluble protein, and results in other changes in amino acid content	*Phaseolus vulgaris*	16
9				*Sorghum halepense, Zea mays*	77
10			Inhibits chloroplastic ribosome formation; causes misshapen & reduced numbers of plastids in seedlings	*Triticum aestivum*[1]	13,102
11			Induces marked increases in 4 anthocyanidins	*Triticum aestivum*[1]	12
12	Atrazine [2-Chloro-4-ethylamino-6-isopropylamino-*s*-triazine]	2000-3080[2]	Strongly inhibits Hill reaction[3] & subsequent sucrose formation; probably forms hydrogen bonds with protein of an enzyme involved in the oxidation of water; inhibits oxidation of α-ketoglutarate & succinate by mitochondria; reduces transpiration. Plant resistance is related to extent of metabolism, although susceptible plants can degrade Atrazine via the 2-hydroxy analogue & other metabolites. The heterocyclic nucleus may be broken by a phenol oxidase system.	Various green algae & higher plants	8,14, 18,24, 58,81, 82

[1] Synonym: *Triticum vulgare.* [2] For mouse, 1750 mg/kg. [3] The oxygen-liberating pathway in photosynthesis.

continued

Part V. Herbicides

	Common Name [Chemical Name]	Oral LD_{50} mg/kg	Mode of Action	Organisms Affected	Reference
13			Usually causes increased percentage of protein, nonprotein, & nitrate nitrogen in resistant corn & other species. However, susceptibility may be related to percentage of nonprotein & ammonia nitrogen.	*Arachis hypogaea, Avena sativa, Glycine max, Gossypium hirsutum, Phaseolus vulgaris, Sorghum halepense, S. vulgare*	28,49
14				*Zea mays*	26,35
15			Increases content of free amino acids, particularly the more basic ones, e. g., asparagine	*Avena sativa*	43
16			In citrus, decreases catalase activity and increases peroxidase activity. In corn, significantly decreases catalase activity in a susceptible line, and increases catalase activity in a resistant line.	*Citrus aurantium, C. limetioides*	47
17				*Zea mays*	29
18			Inhibits respiration & photosynthesis. In barnyard grass, induces swelling of the fret system and subsequent swelling & disruption of granal disks. In raspberry leaves, reduces chlorophyll-*a* & -*b* content; blocks Hill reaction[3].	*Echinochloa* sp.	53
19				*Rubus* sp.	40
20				*Triticum* sp.[4]	73
21			Degraded by *N*-dealkylation in species studied to a less toxic metabolite. Corn & wheat, which contain benzoxazinone, also metabolize Atrazine by hydrolysis to the nontoxic 2-hydroxy analogue. The cyclic hydroxamate has been isolated from corn seedlings, and readily degrades several 2-chlorotriazines.	*Glycine max, Pisum sativum, Sorghum vulgare, Triticum aestivum*[1]	93
22				*Zea mays*	38
23	Bromacil [5-Bromo-3-*sec*-butyl-6-methyluracil]	5200	Strongly inhibits Hill reaction[3] in isolated chloroplasts & whole leaves. In soybean, which is sensitive, decreases sucrose & alanine, and increases malic, aspartic, & glutamic acids.	*Euglena gracilis, Chlorella pyrenoidosa, Spinacia* sp.	60
24				*Brassica rapa*	82
25				*Glycine max, Gossypium hirsutum, Zea mays*	23
26			Causes depletion of total reducing sugars	*Agropyron repens*	98
27			Inhibits growth of tobacco callus tissue cultured in dark, suggesting interference with mechanism other than photosynthesis	*Nicotiana tabacum*	64
28	2,4-D [2,4-Dichlorophenoxyacetic acid]	375-500	Induces changes in composition of carbohydrates, lipids, organic acids, alkaloids, steroids, aromatics, vitamins, pigments, minerals, & in hormone balance. Enhances growth of excised tissue, and increases both mRNA & ribosomal RNA synthesis & subsequent protein synthesis. Physically adsorbed to cytoplasmic proteins & other cellular constituents. Maintains protein retention in leaves. Uncouples oxidative phosphorylation mediated by mitochondria, and enhances respiration via the pentose phosphate cycle by inhibiting the action of certain glycolytic pathway enzymes. Affects activity of many enzymes, including ascorbic acid oxidase, catalase, indoleacetic acid oxidase, phosphatase, polyphenol oxidase, pectin methylesterase, ribonuclease, & monodehydroascorbic acid reductase. Induces chlorosis, with any effect on photosynthesis probably indirect. Decreases amino & amide nitrogen. May have metal chelating properties. The side chain of 2,4-D is readily decarboxylated, but a plant's ability to so metabolize the compound is not completely related to the plant's susceptibility.	Many animals & plants	3,8,18,24,39,58,82,86
29			Inhibits succinate & α-ketoglutarate oxidase system & Mg-activated adenosinetriphosphatase in liver mitochondria. Degree of inhibition highly dependent on 2,4-D formulation.	*Lepomis macrochirus*	54
30			Principal metabolite formed is 2,4-dichloro-5-hydroxyphenoxyacetic acid. A minor melabolite, the 2,5-dichloro-4-hydroxy analogue, is also formed, but apparently is not involved in the synthetic pathway of the principal metabolite.	*Aspergillus niger*	33

[1] Synonym: *Triticum vulgare*. [3] The oxygen-liberating pathway in photosynthesis. [4] Millet.

continued

Part V. Herbicides

	Common Name [Chemical Name]	Oral LD_{50} mg/kg	Mode of Action	Organisms Affected	Reference
31			Stimulates ^{32}P uptake by bean seedlings, but retards ^{32}P accumulation into newly synthesized nucleic acids of peanut cotyledon slices. Also inhibits ^{32}P & ^{86}Rb uptake by cocklebur, although the ions (& photosynthate) accumulate in areas of maximum swelling.	*Arachis hypogaea*	21
32				*Phaseolus vulgaris*	32
33				*Xanthium* sp.	20
34			Residues in peel apparently exist as insoluble conjugation products with pectin	*Citrus sinensis*	78
35			Stimulates ethylene evolution in soybean hypocotyls, and is accompanied by swelling & increased RNA, DNA, & protein. 2,4,5-T(2,4,5-trichlorophenoxyacetic acid) also enhances ethylene production in fig fruits & leaves.	*Ficus carica*	74
36				*Glycine max*	61
37			Enhances activity of invertase, hydrolase, & pectin methylesterase in tissue	*Helianthus tuberosus*	36,72
38			Induced repression of plants grown in dark; repression cannot be explained in terms of interference with endogenous auxin catabolism by auxin-oxidases	*Hordeum hexastichum*, *Triticum aestivum* 5/	37
39			Reduces rutin content in tomato leaves	*Lycopersicon esculentum*	101
40			Apparently inhibits cocarboxylase, or probably α-lipoic acid metabolism, but not coenzyme A. Prevents production of certain amino acids from glucose, and the incorporation of others into protein of root tips. In roots, induces synthesis of new cytoplasmic proteins which are not complexes with the herbicide.	*Pisum sativum*	67,68, 83
41			In root segments, growth inhibition is independent of metabolic processes involving conjugation with aspartic acid or decarboxylation. Site of inhibition may be external to cytoplasm, e. g., cell wall or cytoplasmic membrane.	*Pisum sativum*	4
42	Dalapon [2,2-Dichloropropionic acid]	6590-9330 6/	Not readily degraded in plants, but may be metabolized by various microorganisms. Interferes with pantothenic acid metabolism, competitively inhibiting the enzyme which forms pantothenic acid from β-alanine & pantoic acid. The protective effect of pantothenate against Dalapon-induced growth inhibition is small in lower plants, and even less in higher plants. Induces breakdown of proteins to amino acids & NH_3. Inhibits uptake & esterification of phosphate. Inhibits growing points of shoots more than roots, and causes reduced deposition of leaf surface wax. Subsequent increased wettability increases plant's susceptibility to secondary herbicides. Reduction of meristematic activity may be the principal factor responsible for overall cellular growth inhibition.	Various microorganisms & higher plants	8,24, 58,87
43			Concentration of 10^{-4} *M* inhibits anthocyanin synthesis but does not appreciably affect growth	Many plants	6,48, 90
44			Inhibits conversion of ketopantoate to pantoate, and formation of pantothenate from pantoate	*Escherichia coli* 7/	56
45			Reduces content of pectic substances at least 50 days after treatment	*Beta vulgaris*	2
46			Alters metabolism of Johnson grass to favor sucrose production at the expense of glucose. Apparently does not alter glucose metabolism in barley, but may cause partial blocks at the beginning of the glycolytic pathway, and subsequently in the tricarboxylic acid cycle.	*Hordeum vulgare*, *Sorghum halepense*	63,76
47			In germinating seedlings, increases fumarate & one unidentified organic acid, and decreases succinate, malate, aconitate, & citrate. In older plants, markedly increases malate, aconitate, & citrate.	*Triticum aestivum* 1/	85

1/ Synonym: *Triticum vulgare*. 5/ Synonym: *Triticum sativum*. 6/ For rabbit, 3860 mg/kg. 7/ Ketopantoate-requiring mutant.

continued

Part V. Herbicides

	Common Name [Chemical Name]	Oral LD_{50} mg/kg	Mode of Action	Organisms Affected	Reference
48	Diuron [3-(3,4-Dichlorophenyl)-1,1-dimethylurea]	3400	Strongly inhibits Hill reaction[3]. Inhibits cytochrome reductions, interfering with water participation in noncyclic photosynthetic electron flow. Further impedes the azide-insensitive ground respiration mediated by cytochrome b_3, but does not affect azide-sensitive anion respiration. These inhibitions are reflected by reduced formation of carbohydrates & dry matter. Inhibits photophosphorylation only at concentrations 50-100 times those required for inhibition of the Hill reaction. Diuron may form one of several types of conjugates in plants.	Various green algae & higher plants	3,8,14, 24,39, 50,58, 82
49			Toxic to certain species of fungi	*Colletotrichum lindemuthianum, Rhizoctonia solani, Rhizopus nigricans, Septoria apii*	30
50			In green algae, concentration of 2×10^{-7} *M* causes prolonged inhibition of photosynthesis.	*Scenedesmus* sp.	88
51			In dodder, Diuron blocks photosynthesis, but has no effect on twining.	*Cuscuta indecora*	71
52			In leaves of soybean, a susceptible plant, Diuron is metabolized mainly to phytotoxic 1-(3,4-dichlorophenyl)-3-methylurea. In leaves of cotton plant, which is tolerant, Diuron is metabolized mainly to nonphytotoxic 1-(3,4-dichlorophenyl) urea.	*Glycine max, Gossypium* sp.	96
53			Has some cytokinin activity	*Nicotiana tabacum*	17
54			Suppresses total leaf ketoses & sucrose; alters activity of maltase, hexokinase, glucose-6-phosphatase, fructose-6-phosphatase, glucose oxidase, transaminase, L-amino acid oxidase, & catalase	*Saccharum officinarum*	1
55			Alters translocation pattern of ^{32}P	*Sorghum halepense*	15
56	DNBP [4,6-Dinitro-*o-sec*-butylphenol]	40-60	Causes uncoupling of oxidative phosphorylation, possibly by acting on membranes of organelles in which phosphorylation occurs. Inhibits incorporation of ^{32}P into adenosine triphosphate and stimulates oxygen utilization. Inhibits incorporation of leucine into protein, and adenosine triphosphate into nuclear, mitochondrial, ribosomal, & soluble RNA.	Various mammalian tissues & plants	8,82, 103
57	EPTC [Ethyl *N,N*-dipropylthiocarbamate]	1630[8]	A mitotic poison when applied to soil, mainly inhibiting cell division in root meristems. At high concentrations, inhibits oxidative phosphorylation in cucumber mitochondria. May slightly inhibit acetate uptake without affecting its metabolism. Inhibits surface wax formation on developing cabbage leaves.	Various higher plants	8,58, 82
58			Causes a delayed inhibition of CO_2 absorption in seedlings	*Pinus resinosa*	91
59	MSMA [Monosodium acid methanearsonate]	625-1800	Alters the translocation pattern of ^{32}P, when applied as $H_3{}^{32}PO_4$ to a single leaf	*Sorghum halepense*	15
60			Other arsenic compounds[9]: Sodium arsenite affects root protoplasm (modifies osmotic properties); has upset normal mitosis in roots of vetch; inhibits respiration & growth, and conversion of reducing sugars to noncarbohydrates; may combine with an enzyme dependent on free sulfhydryl groups. Sodium arsenate uncouples oxidative phosphorylation and stimulates respiration	Various higher plants	8,100
61			Arsenite is 10 times more toxic than arsenate in inhibiting corn seed germination. Trivalent arsenic reacts with sulfhydryl groups in cysteine, glutathione, & various sulfhydryl-containing enzymes. Pentavalent arsenic, having chemical & physical resemblance to phosphate, may inhibit sucrose synthesis via glucose-1-phosphate	*Zea mays* & other plants	89

[3] The oxygen-liberating pathway in photosynthesis. [8] For mouse, 3160 mg/kg. [9] Little information exists about the metabolism of MSMA.

continued

Part V. Herbicides

	Common Name [Chemical Name]	Oral LD_{50} mg/kg	Mode of Action	Organisms Affected	Reference
62	Picloram [4-Amino-3,5 5,6-trichloropicolinic acid]	8200[10]	Inhibits oxidation of α-ketoglutarate & succinate by mitochondria; induces greatly enhanced RNA & DNA synthesis in *Cucumis sativus* & *Glycine max* seedlings, which are susceptible, but not in *Hordeum vulgare* & *Triticum aestivum*[1] seedlings, which are resistant	Various higher plants	82
63			50 ppm does not reduce fungal growth. Picloram is degraded by the fungus, but less effectively than 2,4-D is degraded.	*Aspergillus niger*	5
64			Inhibits photosynthesis & subsequent translocation of assimilates to roots of woody legumes	*Acacia farnesiana, Prosopis juliflora*	44
65			Substitutes for indoleacetic & naphthaleneacetic acids, and for 2,4-D as an auxin source for callus growth. Strong auxinic effect on extension of root, stem, & coleoptile sections.	*Avena sativa, Pisum sativum, Triticum aestivum*[1]	65
66				*Nicotiana tabacum, Psoralea bituminosa, Salvia mellifera*	46
67			Increases proteolytic activity in cotyledons	*Cucurbita maxima*	7
68			Very slowly metabolized by plants and decomposed by soil microorganisms	*Gossypium* sp.	79
69			Inhibits nicotinamide adenine dinucleotide nucleotide-linked dehydrogenase systems	*Prosopis juliflora*	25
70	Propanil [3′,4′-Dichloropropionanilide]	1300-1384	Inhibits Hill reaction[3] of isolated chloroplasts (*see* Diuron). Affects phosphate uptake more than oxygen utilization in soybean mitochondria; inhibits leucine incorporation into protein, and adenosine triphosphate incorporation into nuclear, mitochondrial, ribosomal, & soluble RNA of excised soybean hypocotyls.	*Glycine max* & other plants	58,82
71			Hydrolyzed to 3,4-dichloroaniline by leaves of rice, which is resistant, but not by leaves of barnyard grass, which is sensitive.	*Echinochloa crusgalli, Oryza sativa*	75,104
72			The Propanil molecule is cleaved by rice & pea, and the propionic acid moiety is catabolized; the dichloroaniline moiety & its complexes remain.	*Pisum sativum*	97
73			Concentrations inhibiting growth of excised root tips stimulate respiration without influencing respiratory quotient, and increase protein & nonprotein nitrogen & nucleic acid content. No metaphase or anaphase stages in nuclear division were observed.	*Zea mays*	10
74	2,3,6-TBA [2,3,6-Trichlorobenzoic acid]	705-1500	A strong auxin which resists biological breakdown in the plant. Causes chlorosis & disorganization of cellular extension. Inhibits bud growth & normal geotropic & phototropic responses. Stimulates rate of apparent $^{14}CO_2$ fixation, possibly by induction of a higher incidence of open stomata; also, the proportion of ^{14}C is increased in serine & glycine, but reduced in sucrose, implying a possible inhibition of purine synthesis. Inhibits uptake and disturbs metabolism of acetate. Probably affects most enzymes adversely, but promotes enzymatically-catalyzed formation of indoleacetic acid-aspartate, α-naphthaleneacetic acid-aspartate and benzyl-aspartate in excised pea tissue.	Various higher plants	8,18,24, 58,82
75			May become bound to bovine serum albumin	*Bos* sp.	19
76			Recovered from excreta following feeding: mouse, 2.7%; rabbit, 17.6%. Present at harvest in wheat seeds & straw after earlier application at recommended rates to either soil or foliage.	*Mus* sp., *Oryctolagus* sp., *Triticum aestivum*[1]	11
77			Inhibits biosynthesis of pantothenate, in the conversion of ketopantoate to pantoate; inhibition probably has little or no physiological significance	*Escherichia coli*, various strains	55

[1] Synonym: *Triticum vulgare*. [3] The oxygen-liberating pathway in photosynthesis. [10] For mouse, 2000-4000 mg/kg.

continued

93. BIOCIDES

Part V. Herbicides

	Common Name [Chemical Name]	Oral LD_{50} mg/kg	Mode of Action	Organisms Affected	Reference
78			Inhibits normal basipetal transport of indoleacetic acid-2-^{14}C in epicotyl sections	*Phaseolus vulgaris*	66
79	Trifluralin [α,α,α-Trifluoro-2,6-dinitro-*N,N*-dipropyl-*p*-toluidine]	5000-5400	Of 16 Trifluralin analogues, those with CF_3 in the 4-position were more active as preemergence treatments, and those with CH_3 in the 4-position were more active as postemergence treatments. In both series, preemergence toxicity decreased when the amino substituents contained more than 6 carbons.	Many crop plants & weeds	42
80			Several fungi tested, but only *Aspergillus niger* appears able to metabolize Trifluralin to its monopropyl analogue	*Aspergillus niger, Fusarium* sp., *Sclerotium rolfsii, Trichoderma* sp.	41
81			Increases carbohydrate & nucleic acid content in peanuts & sweet potatoes. These plants degrade Trifluralin-^{14}C, and $^{14}CO_2$ is evolved. At least 5 active compounds were observed, suggesting the formation of new plant constituents or degradation intermediates of Trifluralin.	*Arachis hypogaea, Ipomoea batatas*	27,52
82			Concentration of 0.5-1.0 ppm inhibits elongation of roots & coleoptiles, but does not affect formation of seminal roots or oxygen uptake of excised roots	*Avena* sp.	34
83			Besides Trifluralin, major metablic product found in treated plants is α,α,α-trifluoro-2,6-dinitro-*N*-propyl-*p*-toluidine	*Daucus carota*	45
84			Inhibits cell division in meristematic root tissue; probably acts as a mitotic poison	*Glycine max*	99
85			Concentration of 10^{-4} *M* inhibits mitochondrial respiration and oxidative phosphorylation approx 25% in sorghum (susceptible) and corn (less susceptible). Inhibits oxidative phosphorylation much less than oxygen uptake in soybean (resistant).	*Glycine max, Sorghum vulgare, Zea mays*	84
86			In seedlings, induces swelling of root tips & first internodes; in root tips, decreases DNA, total RNA & protein; in shoots, increases DNA & protein, but does not change total RNA	*Zea mays*	92

Contributor: Hull, Herbert M.

References

[1] Alexander, A. G., and J. Gonzalez Ibanez. 1964. J. Agr. Univ. Puerto Rico 48:284.

[2] Alley, H. P., D. W. Bohmont, and H. M. Hepworth. 1961. J. Am. Soc. Sugar Beet Technologists 11:365.

[3] Andreae, W. A. 1963. Metab. Inhibitors: Comprehensive Treatise 2:243.

[4] Andreae, W. A. 1967. Can. J. Botany 45:737.

[5] Arnold, W. R., P. W. Santelmann, and J. Q. Lynd. 1966. Weeds 14:89.

[6] Asen, S., L. L. Jansen, and J. L. Hilton. 1963. Nature 198:185.

[7] Ashton, F. M., and D. Penner. 1966. Abstr. Weed Soc. Am., p. 48.

[8] Audus, L. J., ed. 1964. The physiology and biochemistry of herbicides. Academic Press, New York.

[9] Bailey, G. W., and J. L. White. 1965. Residue Rev. 10:97.

[10] Baker, J. B., H. Webert, and T. D. Pizzolato. 1966. Plant Physiol. 41(Suppl.):vii.

[11] Balayannis, P. G., M. S. Smith, and R. L. Wain. 1965. Ann. Appl. Biol. 55:149.

[12] Bartels, P. G., and F. T. Wolf. 1967. Biochim. Biophys. Acta 136:166.

[13] Bartels, P. G., et al. 1967. Plant Physiol. 42:736.

[14] Black, C. C., Jr., and L. Myers. 1966. Weeds 14:331.

[15] Boyd, F. M., and D. E. Bayer. 1966. Abstr. Weed Soc. Am., p. 63.

[16] Brown, J. C., and M. C. Carter. 1967. Ibid., p. 61.

[17] Bruce, M. I., and J. A. Zwar. 1966. Proc. Roy. Soc. (London), B, 165:245.

[18] Bruinsma, J. 1965. Residue Rev. 10:1.

[19] Camper, N. D., and D. E. Moreland. 1966. Abstr. Weed Soc. Am., p. 32.

[20] Cardenas, J., F. W. Slife, and J. B. Hanson. 1966. Ibid., p. 43.

[21] Carpenter, W. J. G., and J. H. Cherry. 1966. Plant Physiol. 41:919.

continued

Part V . Herbicides

[22] Castelfranco, P., and M. S. Brown. 1963. Weeds 11: 116.

[23] Couch, R. W., and D. E. Davis. 1966. Ibid. 14:251.

[24] Crafts, A. S. 1961. The chemistry and mode of action of herbicides. Interscience, New York.

[25] Davis, F. S., and R. H. Priest. 1966. Abstr. Weed Soc. Am., p. 48.

[26] Doll, J. D., and W. F. Meggitt. 1967. Ibid., p. 9.

[27] Dukes, I. E., and P. K. Biswas. 1967. Ibid., p. 59.

[28] Eastin, E. F., and D. E. Davis. 1967. Weeds 15:306.

[29] Eastin, E. F., R. D. Palmer, and C. O. Grogan. 1964. Ibid. 12:64.

[30] Ebner, L. 1965. Z. Pflanzenkrankh. Pflanzenschutz 72:344.

[31] Edson, E. F., D. M. Sanderson, and D. N. Noakes. 1966. World Rev. Pest Control 5:143.

[32] Etter, H. M. 1967. Can. J. Botany 45:535.

[33] Faulkner, J. K., and D. Woodcock. 1964. Nature 203:865.

[34] Feeny, R. W. 1966. Proc. Northeastern Weed Control Conf., p. 595.

[35] Fink, R. J., and O. H. Fletchall. 1967. Weeds 15: 272.

[36] Flood, A. E., P. P. Rutherford, and E. W. Weston. 1967. Nature 214:1049.

[37] Fooz, G. de, T. Gaspar, and M. Bouillenne-Walrand. 1966. Weed Res. 6:359.

[38] Foy, C. L. 1967. Plant Physiol. 42:S-51.

[39] Freed, V. H., and M. L. Montgomery. 1963. Residue Rev. 3:1.

[40] Freeman, J. A., A. J. Renney, and H. Driediger. 1966. Can. J. Plant Sci. 46:454.

[41] Funderburk, H. H., Jr., et al. 1967. Proc. Southern Weed Conf., p. 389.

[42] Gentner, W. A. 1966. Weeds 14:176.

[43] Glabiszewski, J. 1966. Pamietnik Pulawski 21:233.

[44] Glenn, R. K., and O. A. Leonard. 1967. Res. Progr. Rept. Western Weed Control Conf., p. 24.

[45] Golab, T., et al. 1966. Abstr. Weed Soc. Am., p. 40.

[46] Goodin, J. R., and F. L. A. Becher. 1967. Plant Physiol. 42:S-23.

[47] Goren, R., and S. P. Monselise. 1966. Weeds 14:141.

[48] Gowing, D. P., and A. H. Lange. 1962. Proc. Am. Soc. Hort. Sci. 80:645.

[49] Gramlich, J. V., and D. E. Davis. 1967. Weeds 15: 157.

[50] Gromet-Elhanan, Z., and M. Avron. 1965. Plant Physiol. 40:1053.

[51] Guerin-Dumartrait, E. 1966. Physiol. Vegetale 4:135.

[52] Hamilton, W., Jr., and P. K. Biswas. 1967. Abstr. Weed Soc. Am., p. 62.

[53] Hill, E. R., E. C. Putala, and J. Vengris. 1967. Ibid., p. 47.

[54] Hiltibran, R. C. 1966. Ibid., p. 91.

[55] Hilton, J. L. 1965. Weeds 13:267.

[56] Hilton, J. L. 1966. Ibid. 14:174.

[57] Hilton, J. L. 1966. Isotopes Weed Res., Proc. Symp., Vienna, 1965, p. 71.

[58] Hilton, J. L., L. L. Jansen, and H. M. Hull. 1963. Ann. Rev. Plant Physiol. 14:358.

[59] Hilton, J. L., P. C. Kearney, and B. N. Ames. 1965. Arch. Biochem. Biophys. 112:544.

[60] Hoffman, C. E., J. W. McGahen, and P. B. Sweetser. 1964. Nature 202:577.

[61] Holm, R. E., and F. B. Abeles. 1967. Plant Physiol. 42:S-30.

[62] Hull, H. M., et al., ed. 1967. Herbicide handbook of the Weed Society of America. W. F. Humphrey Press, Geneva, N.Y.

[63] Jain, M. L., E. B. Kurtz, Jr., and K. C. Hamilton. 1966. Weeds 14:259.

[64] Jordan, L. S., et al. 1966. Ibid. 14:134.

[65] Kefford, N. P., and O. H. Caso. 1966. Botan. Gaz. 127:159.

[66] Keitt, G. W., Jr., and R. A. Baker. 1966. Plant Physiol. 41:1561.

[67] Kim, W. K., and R. G. S. Bidwell. 1967. Can. J. Botany 45:1751.

[68] Kim, W. K., and R. G. S. Bidwell. 1967. Ibid. 45: 1789.

[69] Klopotowski, T., and A. Wiater. 1965. Arch. Biochem. Biophys. 112:562.

[70] Kröller, E. 1966. Residue Rev. 12:162.

[71] Lane, H. C., J. E. Baker, and L. L. Danielson. 1965. Weeds 13:371.

[72] Macey, M. J. K. 1965. Physiol. Plantarum 18:368.

[73] Mashtakov, S. M., and R. A. Prokhorchik. 1963. Dokl. Akad. Nauk Belorussk. SSR 7:418.

[74] Maxie, E. C., and J. C. Crane. 1967. Science 155: 1548.

[75] McRae, D. H., R. Y. Yih, and H. F. Wilson. 1964. Abstr. Weed Soc. Am., p. 87.

[76] McWhorter, C. G. 1961. Weeds 9:563.

[77] McWhorter, C. G., and J. L. Hilton. 1967. Physiol. Plantarum 20:30.

[78] Meagher, W. R. 1966. J. Agr. Food Chem. 14:599.

[79] Meikle, R. A., E. A. Williams, and C. T. Redemann. 1966. Ibid. 14:384.

[80] Michael, P. W. 1967. Weed Res. 7:145.

[81] Montgomery, M. L., and V. H. Freed, 1964. J. Agr. Food Chem. 12:11.

[82] Moreland, D. E. 1967. Ann. Rev. Plant Physiol. 18:365.

[83] Morris, R. O. 1966. Biochim. Biophys. Acta 127: 273.

[84] Negi, N. S., et al. 1967. Abstr. Weed Soc. Am., p. 58.

[85] Oyolu, C., and R. C. Huffaker. 1964. Crop Sci. 4:95.

[86] Penner, D., and F. M. Ashton. 1966. Residue Rev. 14:39.

[87] Prasad, R., and G. E. Blackman. 1965. J. Exptl. Botany 16:545.

[88] Rensen, J. J. S. van, and P. A. van Steekelenburg. 1965. Mededel. Landbouwhogeschool Wageningen 13:8.

[89] Rogers, B. J. 1959. Proc. North Central Western Can. Weed Control Conf., p. 20.

[90] Rogers, B. J. 1963. Plant Physiol. 38(Suppl.):Liv.

[91] Sasaki, S., and T. T. Kozlowski. 1967. Can. J. Botany 45:961.

continued

Part V. Herbicides

[92] Schultz, D. P., and H. H. Funderburk, Jr. 1967. Plant Physiol. 42:S-50.
[93] Shimabukuro, R. H. 1967. Ibid. 42:1269.
[94] Shimabukuro, R. H., and A. J. Linck. 1965. Physiol. Plantarum 18:532.
[95] Siegel, J. N., and A. C. Gentile. 1966. Plant Physiol. 41:670.
[96] Smith, J. W., and T. J. Sheets. 1966. Abstr. Weed Soc. Am., p. 39.
[97] Still, G. G., and R. E. Kadunce. 1967. Ibid., p. 64.
[98] Swann, C. W., and K. P. Buchholtz. 1966. Weeds 14:103.
[99] Talbert, R. E. 1965. Proc. Southern Weed Conf., p. 652.
[100] Ter Welle, H. F., and E. C. Slater. 1967. Biochim. Biophys. Acta 143:1.
[101] van Bragt, J., L. M. Rohrbaugh, and S. H. Wender. 1965. Phytochemistry 4:963.
[102] Weier, T. E., and A. A. Imam. 1965. Am. J. Botany 52:631.
[103] Wojtaszek, T. 1966. Weeds 14:125.
[104] Yamada, N., and H. Makamura. 1963. Nippon Sakumotsu Gakkai Kiji 32:69.

VIII. PLANT METABOLISM

94. NITROGEN FIXATION

Part I. Symbiotic Associations

The effectiveness of a symbiotic relationship of endophytes with host plants determines whether nitrogen fixation occurs and how much nitrogen is fixed by the endophyte. Other factors influencing the amount of nitrogen fixation are soil and climate conditions, and individual crop handling. Values for legumes are averages; other values are the exact quantities of nitrogen fixed by the species indicated in footnotes 2-5. Unless otherwise specified, values are for nitrogen fixation occurring in root nodules.

	Endophyte	Host Plant	N_2 Fixed kg/ha	Reference
	Leguminous Plants			
1	*Rhizobium* spp.	*Lespedeza* spp.	96	14
2		*Vigna sinensis*	101	14
3		Mixed legumes	121	14,19
4	*R. japonicum*	*Glycine max*	68	14,19
5	*R. leguminosarum*	*Pisum sativum*	82	14
6	*R. lupini*	*Lupinus angustifolium*	168	14
7	*R. meliloti*	*Medicago sativa*	179	14,19
8	*R. phaseoli*	*Phaseolus vulgaris*	45	14
9	*R. trifolii*	*Trifolium pratense*	121	14,19
10		*T. repens*	131	14,19
	Nonleguminous Plants			
11	Actinomycete[1/]	*Alnus* spp.	62; 167[2/]	1,3,5,8,10, 12,15,17,19
12		*Casuarina* spp.	58[3/]	1,8,10,13,19
13		*Ceanothus* spp.	....	1,8,10,19
14		*Cercocarpus* spp.	....	19,21
15		*Comptonia* spp.	....	19,24
16		*Coriaria* spp.	....	1,2,8,10,16, 19
17		*Discaria* spp.	....	1,10,19
18		*Dryas* spp.	....	11
19		*Elaeagnus* spp.	....	1,8,10,19
20		*Hippophae* spp.	58[4/]	1,8,10,19,20
21		*Myrica* spp.	9[5/]	1,8,10,19
22		*Purshia* spp.	....	19,22
23		*Shepherdia* spp.	....	1,8,10,19
24	*Anabaena* or	*Ceratozamia* spp.	....	9,19
25	*Nostoc*[6/]	*Cycas* spp.	....	19,23
26		*Encephalartos* spp.	....	9,19,23
27		*Macrozamia* spp.	....	7,19,23
28		*Stangeria* spp.	....	19,23
29	*Klebsiella*	*Psychotria* spp.[7/]	....	18,19
30	Phycomycete[1/]	*Podocarpus* spp.	....	4,6,9,19

1/ Nodule endophyte has not been isolated or identified with certainty. 2/ Values are for *Alnus crispa.* 3/ Value is for *Casuarina equisetifolia.* 4/ Value is for *Hippophae rhamnoides.* 5/ Value is for *Myrica gale.* 6/ Not a strict symbiont, since endophyte continues to fix nitrogen when isolated from host plant. 7/ Leaf nodules; nitrogen fixation in leaf nodules has been demonstrated satisfactorily only in one species of *Psychotria.*

Contributor: Stewart, William D. P.

References

[1] Allen, E. K., and O. N. Allen. 1965. Proc. Ann. Biol. Colloq. 25:77.

[2] Allen, J. D., et al. 1966. New Zealand J. Botany 4: 57.

[3] Becking, J. H. 1965. Nature 207:885.

[4] Becking, J. H. 1965. Plant Soil 23:213.

[5] Becking, J. H., et al. 1964. Antonie van Leeuwenhoek J. Microbiol. Serol. 30:343.

[6] Bergersen, F. J., and A. B. Costin. 1964. Australian J. Biol. Sci. 17:44.

[7] Bergersen, F. J., et al. 1965. Ibid. 18:1135.

[8] Bond, G. 1958. Nottingham Univ. Easter School Agr. Sci. 5:216.

[9] Bond, G. 1959. Advan. Sci. 60:382.

[10] Bond, G. 1963. Symp. Soc. Gen. Microbiol. 13:72.

[11] Bond, G. Unpublished. Univ. Glasgow, Dept. Botany, Scotland, 1967.

[12] Crocker, R. L., and J. Major. 1955. J. Ecol. 43:427.

[13] Dommergues, Y. 1963. Agrochimica 7:335.

[14] Erdman, L. W. 1948. U.S. Dept. Agr. Farmers Bull. 2003.

[15] Gardner, I. C. 1965. Arch. Mikrobiol. 51:365.

[16] Harris, G. P., and T. M. Morrison. 1958. Nature 182:1812.

[17] Lawrence, D. B. 1958. Am. Scientist 46:89.

[18] Silver, W. S., et al. 1963. Nature 199:396.

[19] Stewart, W. D. P. 1966. Nitrogen fixation in plants. Athlone Press, London.

continued

Part I. Symbiotic Associations

[20] Stewart, W. D. P., and M. C. Pearson. 1967. Plant Soil 26(2): 348.
[21] Vlamis, J., et al. 1964. J. Range Mgt. 17:73.
[22] Wagle, R. F., and J. Vlamis. 1961. Ecology 42:745.
[23] Watanabe, A., and T. Kiyohara. 1963. In Japanese Society of Plant Physiologists, ed. Studies on microalgae and photosynthetic bacteria. Tokyo Univ. Press, Tokyo. pp. 189-198.
[24] Ziegler, H., and R. Hüser. 1963. Nature 199:508.

Part II. Free-living, Nitrogen-fixing Microorganisms

Nourishment: Hetero = heterotrophic; Auto = autotrophic. *Abbreviation:* ATP = adenosine 5′-triphosphate.

	Genus[1]	Characteristics		Reference
		Oxygen	Nourishment	
	Bacteria			
1	*Achromobacter*[2]	Aerobic or anaerobic	Hetero	10,22,35
2	*Azotobacter*[3]	Aerobic	Hetero	7-10,35
3	*Bacillus*[4]	Anaerobic	Hetero	10,17,23,35
4	*Beijerinckia*	Aerobic	Hetero	3,4,10,35
5	*Chlorobium*	Anaerobic	Auto	20,35
6	*Chromatium*[5,6]	Anaerobic	Auto	2,6,10,35
7	*Clostridium*[7]	Anaerobic	Hetero	10,35
8	*Derxia*	Aerobic	Hetero	18,35
9	*Desulfovibrio*	Anaerobic	Hetero	31
10	*Klebsiella*	Anaerobic	Hetero	22,29
11	*Methanobacterium*	Anaerobic	Hetero	26,35
12	*Pseudomonas*	Aerobic or anaerobic	Hetero	1,13,38
13	*Rhodomicrobium*	Anaerobic	Hetero	21
14	*Rhodopseudomonas*	Anaerobic	Hetero	20,21
15	*Rhodospirillum*[8]	Anaerobic	Hetero	10,27,28,35
16	*Spirillum*	Aerobic	Hetero	5
	Blue-green Algae			
17	*Anabaena*[5,9]	Aerobic[10]	Auto[11]	11,12,35
18	*Anabaenopsis*	Aerobic	Auto	35
19	*Aulosira*	Aerobic	Auto	30,35
20	*Calothrix*	Aerobic	Auto	32-35,41
21	*Chlorogloea*[5,9]	Aerobic	Auto or hetero	14,15,35
22	*Cylindrospermum*	Aerobic	Auto	35
23	*Fischerella*	Aerobic	Auto	24,35
24	*Hapalosiphon*	Aerobic	Auto	35,36
25	*Mastigocladus*[5]	Aerobic	Auto	16,35
26	*Nostoc*[5]	Aerobic	Auto	35
27	*Scytonema*	Aerobic	Auto	19,35
28	*Stigonema*	Aerobic	Auto	35,37
29	*Tolypothrix*	Aerobic	Auto	35,39,40
30	*Westiellopsis*	Aerobic	Auto	25,35

[1] Not all strains fix nitrogen. [2] Nitrogen-fixing strains may be misidentified *Klebsiella* strains. [3] Uses either H_2 + hydrogenase + ATP + ferredoxin or ATP + $Na_2S_2O_4$ as additive supporting cell-free fixation. [4] Uses pyruvate as additive supporting cell-free fixation. [5] Requires no additive to support cell-free fixation. [6] H_2 stimulates in cell-free extracts. [7] Uses either pyruvate or H_2 + hydrogenase + ATP + ferredoxin as additive supporting cell-free fixation; α-ketobutyrate partially substitutes. [8] Uses either pyruvate or ATP + $Na_2S_2O_4$ as additive supporting cell-free fixation. [9] Pyruvate stimulates in cell-free extracts. [10] *Anabaena* may fix nitrogen anaerobically; may also fix nitrogen for a short time in the dark. [11] May grow heterotrophically in cycad root nodules.

Contributor: Stewart, William D. P.

References

[1] Anderson, G. R. 1955. J. Bacteriol. 70:129.
[2] Arnon, D. I., et al. 1960. Nature 190:601.
[3] Becking, J. H. 1961. Plant Soil 14:49.
[4] Becking, J. H. 1961. Ibid. 14:297.
[5] Becking, J. H. 1963. Antonie van Leeuwenhoek J. Microbiol. Serol. 29:326.
[6] Bennett, R., et al. 1964. Proc. Natl. Acad. Sci. U.S. 52:762.
[7] Bulen, W. A., et al. 1964. Biochem. Biophys. Res. Commun. 17:265.
[8] Bulen, W. A., et al. 1965. Proc. Natl. Acad. Sci. U.S. 53:532.
[9] Bulen, W. A., and J. R. Lecomte. 1966. Ibid. 56:987.
[10] Burris, R. H. 1966. Ann. Rev. Plant Physiol. 17:155.
[11] Cox, R. M. 1966. Arch. Mikrobiol. 53:263.
[12] Cox, R. M., et al. 1964. Biochim. Biophys. Acta 88: 208.
[13] Davis, J. B., et al. 1964. J. Bacteriol. 88:468.
[14] Fay, P. 1965. J. Gen. Microbiol. 39:11.
[15] Fay, P., and G. E. Fogg. 1962. Arch. Mikrobiol. 42: 310.

continued

94. NITROGEN FIXATION

Part II. Free-living, Nitrogen-fixing, Microorganisms

[16] Fogg, G. E. 1951. J. Exptl. Botany 2:117.
[17] Grau, F. H., and P. W. Wilson. 1963. J. Bacteriol. 85:446.
[18] Jensen, H. L., et al. 1960. Arch. Mikrobiol. 36:182.
[19] Laloraya, V. K., and A. K. Mitra. 1964. Current Sci. (India) 33:619.
[20] Lindstrom, E. S., et al. 1949. J. Bacteriol. 58:313.
[21] Lindstrom, E. S., et al. 1951. Ibid. 61:481.
[22] Mahl, M. C., et al. 1965. Ibid. 89:1482.
[23] Moore, A. W., and J. H. Becking. 1963. Nature 198: 915.
[24] Pankow, H. 1964. Naturwissenschaften 51:274.
[25] Pattnaik, H. 1966. Ann. Botany (London) 30:118.
[26] Pine, M. J., and H. A. Barker. 1954. J. Bacteriol. 68:589.
[27] Pratt, D. C., and A. W. Frenkel. 1959. Plant Physiol. 34:333.
[28] Schneider, K. C., et al. 1960. Proc. Natl. Acad. Sci. U.S. 46:726.
[29] Silver, W. S., et al. 1963. Nature 199:396.
[30] Singh, R. M. 1942. Indian J. Agr. Sci. 12:743.
[31] Sisler, F. D., and C. E. ZoBell. 1951. J. Bacteriol. 62:117.
[32] Stewart, W. D. P. 1962. Ann. Botany (London) 26: 439.
[33] Stewart, W. D. P. 1964. J. Gen. Microbiol. 36:333.
[34] Stewart, W. D. P. 1965. Ann. Botany (London) 29: 229.
[35] Stewart, W. D. P. 1966. Nitrogen fixation in plants. Athlone Press, London.
[36] Taha, M. S. 1964. Fiziol. Rast. 11:424.
[37] Venkataraman, G. S. 1961. Indian J. Agr. Sci. 31: 213.
[38] Voets, J. B., and J. Debacker. 1955. Naturwissenschaften 43:40.
[39] Watanabe, A. 1951. Arch. Biochem. Biophys. 34:50.
[40] Watanabe, A. 1961. Studies Tokugawa Inst. 9:162.
[41] Williams, A. E., and R. H. Burris. 1952. Am. J. Botany 39:340.

95. CARBON FIXATION AND SOLAR ENERGY BUDGET

Part I. Carbon Balance Computed as Carbon Dioxide

	Reservoir	CO_2 Total on Earth 10^{18} g	Units of Atmospheric CO_2	Reference
1	Atmosphere	2.41	1.0	3
	Ocean			
2	Living organic matter	0.03	0.01	1
3	Dead organic matter	10.0	4.2	2
4	Inorganic carbon	129.7	55.0	2
5	Total carbon in ocean	140.0	59.2	1,2
	Sediments			2
6	Carbonate in sediments	67,000	28,000	
7	Organic carbon in sediments	25,000	10,000	
8	Total carbon in sediments	92,000	38,000	
	Land			1
9	Living organic matter	0.4	0.17	
10	Dead organic matter	2.4	1.0	
11	Total carbon on land	2.8	1.17	

Contributor: Lemon, Edgar R.

References

[1] Leith, H. 1963. J. Geophys. Res. 68:3887.
[2] Revelle, R., and H. E. Suess. 1957. Tellus 9:18.
[3] Takahashi, T. 1961. J. Geophys. Res. 66:477.

Part II. Carbon Dioxide Exchange Processes

Values are estimated annual rates of some CO_2 exchange processes involving atmospheric and oceanic carbon dioxide. *Symbols:* + = CO_2 produced; − = CO_2 consumed.

	Process	Total Area km^2	CO_2 10^{18} g	Reference
1	Consumption of fossil fuels	....	+0.0091	1
2	Photosynthesis in ocean	361×10^6	−0.46 ± 0.20	1
3	Photosynthesis on land	149×10^6	−0.073 ± 0.018	1
4	Forest	44×10^6	−0.036 ± 0.006	2,3
5	Cultivated land	27×10^6	−0.013 ± 0.002	2,3
6	Grassland	31×10^6	−0.004 ± 0.002	2,3
7	Desert	47×10^6	−0.001 ± 0.0006	2,3
8	Animal respiration	....	+0.004	2
9	Soil respiration	....	+0.028	2

Contributor: Lemon, Edgar R.

References

[1] Hutchinson, G. E. 1954. In G. Kuiper, ed. The earth as a planet. Univ. Chicago Press, Chicago. pp. 371-427.
[2] Leith, H. 1963. J. Geophys. Res. 68:3887.
[3] Rabinowitch, E. I. 1945. Photosynthesis. Interscience, New York. v. 1, p. 6.

continued

95. CARBON FIXATION AND SOLAR ENERGY BUDGET

Part III. Net Photosynthesis and Energy Utilization

	Species (Synonym)	Location	Harvest Period days	Dry Matter Produced 10^6 g/ha	CO_2 Stored[1] 10^6 g/ha	Energy Stored[1] 10^6 kcal/ha	Incident Light Energy[2] 10^8 kcal/ha	Photo-synthetic Efficiency %	Ref-er-ence
	Mass Algae Culture								
1	*Chlorella*	Japan	1	0.20	0.30	0.80	0.18	4.5	12
	Trees								
2	*Elaeis guineensis*	Nigeria	27	2.32	3.5	9.4	4.9	1.9	11
3			365	19.5[3]	29	78	60	1.4	11
4	*Fagus sylvatica*	Denmark	164	13.3	20.0	53.2	21.5[4]	2.5	8
5	*Pinus sylvestris*	England	360	21.7	32.3	86.8	39.3[4]	2.2	8
	Agricultural Crops								
6	*Beta vulgaris*	England	10	3.2	4.8	12.8	1.2	10.5	14
7			112	16.5	25	66	13.4	4.9	10
8		Holland	76	12	18	48	9.6	5.1	7
9			136	12.7	19	51	19	2.7	7
10	*Brassica oleracea*	England	1	0.21	0.31	0.84	0.13	6.5	3
11	*Hordeum vulgare*	England	1	0.23[3]	0.35	0.92	0.21	4.3	4
12	*Oryza sativa*	Japan	1	0.55[3]	0.83	2.2	0.22	10.0	3
13			150	11.8[3]	17.7	47	21.5	2.2	8
14	*Pennisetum glaucum (P. typhoideum)*	Australia	15	8.1[3]	12.2	32.4	3.4	9.5	2
15	*Saccharum officinarum*	Hawaii	100	37[3]	56	148	17.5	8.5	5
16			360	72	108	288	91	3.2	6
17		Java	360	30.6[3]	47.5	122	63.7	1.9	8
18	*Sorghum vulgare*	California	35	17.9[3]	27	71.4	10.6	6.7	9
19	*Trifolium subterraneum*	Australia	14	3.2[3]	4.8	12.8	4.1	3.1	3
20	*Zea mays*	California	12	6.2	9.3	25.0	3.9	6.4	15
21		New York	66	19.8	30	80.5	12.1	6.7	1
22		Ohio	89	20.5[3]	31	82	22	3.7	13
23	Mixed grass sward[5]	Holland	1	0.32[3]	0.48	1.3	0.22	6.0	3
24			1	0.32[3]	0.48	1.3	0.17	7.6	3

[1] Assuming 1 g dry matter produced = 1.5 g CO_2 stored = 4000 cal energy stored. [2] Assuming incident light energy = 0.44 incident solar radiation. [3] Roots not included. [4] Estimated. [5] Mixture consists of *Festuca elatior (F. pratensis), Lolium perenne, Phleum pratense, Poa pratensis,* and *P. trivialis.*

Contributor: Lemon, Edgar R.

References

[1] Allen, L. H., C. S. Yocum, and E. R. Lemon. 1964. Agron. J. 56:253.

[2] Begg, J. E. 1965. Nature 205:1025.

[3] Black, J. N. 1963. Australian J. Agr. Res. 14:20.

[4] Blackman, G. E., and J. N. Black. 1959. Ann. Botany (London), N.S. 23:131.

[5] Borden, R. J. 1942. Hawaiian Planters Record 46: 191.

[6] Burr, J. O., et al. 1957. Ann. Rev. Plant Physiol. 8: 275.

[7] Gaastra, P. 1958. Mededel. Landbouwhogeschool Wageningen 58(4):1.

[8] Hellmers, H. 1964. Quart. Rev. Biol. 39:249.

[9] Loomis, R. S., and W. A. Williams. 1963. Crop Sci. 3:67.

[10] Monteith, J. L. 1966. Exptl. Agr. 2:1.

[11] Rees, A. R. 1962. Nature 195:1118.

[12] Tamiya, H. 1957. Ann. Rev. Plant Physiol. 8:309.

[13] Transeau, E. N. 1926. Ohio J. Sci. 26:1.

[14] Watson, D. J. 1958. Ann. Botany (London), N.S. 22:37.

[15] Williams, W. A., R. S. Loomis, and C. R. Lepley. 1965. Crop Sci. 5:211.

96. LIGHT INTENSITY AND RATE OF PHOTOSYNTHESIS

	Species (Synonym)	Concentration of Sample [Amount Tested]	Method [CO_2 in Air]	Temp °C	Type of Illumination	Light Intensity erg/cm² × sec [1]	Rate of Gas Exchange	Reference
	Bacteriophyta							
1	*Chlorobium thiosulfatophilum*	2.5 mg wet wt/ml [3.0 ml]	Manometric	....	Tungsten lamp	0.2	25 µl CO_2/hr	13
2						0.4	60 µl CO_2/hr	
3						0.6	80 µl CO_2/hr	
	Algae							
4	*Ankistrodesmus braunii*	[10 mm³ cells]	Manometric	25	Presumed to be tungsten lamp	6 × 10^3	18 mm O_2/mm³ cells/hr	11
5						3 × 10^3	12 mm O_2/mm³ cells/hr	
6						1.5 × 10^3	6.4 mm O_2/mm³ cells/hr	
7	*Chlamydomonas reinhardii* [2]	[0.2 mg chlorophyll]	Manometric	15	....	6.4 × 10^6	750 µl O_2/hr/mg chlorophyll	14
8	*Chlorella ellipsoidea*	0.192 mg dry wt/ml [20 ml]	Manometric	25	Tungsten lamp	1.15 × 10^3	1.92 × 10^{-4} µM O_2/mg × sec	22
9						2.41 × 10^3	3.89 × 10^{-4} µM O_2/mg × sec	
10						5.30 × 10^3	7.55 × 10^{-4} µM O_2/mg × sec	
11						1.04 × 10^4	1.17 × 10^{-3} µM O_2/mg × sec	
12						2.41 × 10^4	1.50 × 10^{-3} µM O_2/mg × sec	
13						3.84 × 10^4	1.54 × 10^{-3} µM O_2/mg × sec	
14						Saturation	1.63 × 10^{-3} µM O_2/mg × sec	
15	*C. pyrenoidosa*, strain 3	[14 µl cells]	Platinum electrode	22-25	Tungsten lamp	Saturation	20-60 µl O_2/µl cells/hr	1
16					482 nm	1700	6.4 µl O_2/µl cells/hr	
17						170	4.7 µl O_2/µl cells/hr	
18					696 nm	2000	3.5 µl O_2/µl cells/hr	
19						300	0.5 µl O_2/µl cells/hr	
20					482 + 696 nm	1700 + 300	13.3 µl O_2/µl cells/hr	
21						170 + 2000	4.1 µl O_2/µl cells/hr	
22	*C. saccharophila*	....	[Carbonate buffer 9]	22.4	....	2480 ft-c	452.3 mm³ O_2/100 million cells/hr	30
23	*C. vulgaris*	1.15 × 10^7 cells/ml [2.4 × 10^8 cells]	Manometric	23-25	Tungsten lamp	8.37 × 10^2	0.75 µl O_2/min	6
24						2.39 × 10^3	1.80 µl O_2/min	
25						5.98 × 10^3	3.70-3.77 µl O_2/min	
26						3.29 × 10^4	4.74-6.06 µl O_2/min	
27	*C. vulgaris viridis*	10 µl cells/ml	[Carbonate buffer 9]	22.4	....	2480 ft-c	194.7 mm³ O_2/100 million cells/hr	30
28		[2.0 ml]	Manometric	29.8	Na-vapor lamp	1.45 × 10^4	175 µl CO_2/hr	27
29	*Cladophora glomerata*	....	....	17	....	....	0.3 M CO_2/10 µ³/hr	25
30	*Nostoc muscorum*	....	[Carbonate buffer 9]	25	....	1000 ft-c	13.2 ml O_2/ml packed cells/hr	4
31	*Scenedesmus*, D_3	[25 µl cells]	Manometric	25	....	25 × 10^3	12.0 µl CO_2/µl cells/hr	3
32						18 × 10^3	10.2 µl CO_2/µl cells/hr	
33						10 × 10^3	8.4 µl CO_2/µl cells/hr	
	Bryophyta							
34	*Hylocomium proliferum*	....	....	......	....	93-186 ft-c	1.25-3 mg CO_2/g dry wt/hr	9
35	*Sphagnum girgensohnii*	....	....	......	....	110-260 ft-c	2.75 mg CO_2/g dry wt/hr	9

1/ Unless otherwise specified. 2/ Wild type.

continued

	Species (Synonym)	Concentration of Sample [Amount Tested]	Method [CO_2 in Air]	Temp °C	Type of Illumination	Light Intensity erg/cm² × sec 1/	Rate of Gas Exchange 3/	Reference
	Spermatophyta							
	Gymnospermae							
36	*Picea pungens*	....	[Natural]	24	....	2200 ft-c	0.03 mg CO_2/100 leaves/hr	7
37	*Pinus taeda*	....	[Natural]	30	....	2000 ft-c	2[3.9] mg CO_2/dm²/hr	12
	Angiospermae							
38	*Citrus limon*	....	[1.5%]	......	....	1300 ft-c	3-5 ml O_2/dm²/hr	28
39	*C. sinensis*	....	[1.5%]	......	....	1300 ft-c	4-6 ml O_2/dm²/hr	28
40	*Cornus florida*	....	[Natural]	30	....	2000 ft-c	2[3.06] mg CO_2/dm²/hr	12
41	*Cucurbita pepo*	....	....	......	....	....	0.68 g/m² increase in dry wt/hr	20
42	*Helianthus annuus*	....	[5%]	......	....	4460 ft-c	[80] mg CO_2/dm²/hr	29
43	*Hordeum vulgare*	....	[Natural]	Nat 4/	....	500 ft-c	9-16 mg CO_2/dm²/hr	8
44	*Lycopersicon esculentum*	....	....	......	....	....	16.5-18.6 mg CO_2/dm²/hr	17
45	*Malus sylvestris*	....	[Natural]	Nat 4/	Natural	....	6.6 mg CO_2/dm²/hr	10
46	*Medicago sativa*	[560 g]	CGA 5/	15.6	Sunlight	2.02 × 10⁵	18 g CO_2/80 min	24
47						3.37 × 10⁵	28 g CO_2/80 min	
48		[665 g]	CGA 5/	29.7	Sunlight	5.73 × 10⁵	39 g CO_2/80 min	
49		....	[Natural]	Nat 4/	Noon sun	....	0.75[1.042] g/6 × 6 ft plot/hr	23
50	*Oryza sativa*	....	[Natural]	31	....	1.74 cal/cm/min	9-20 mg CO_2/m²/hr	18
51	*Phaseolus vulgaris*	....	[Natural]	25	....	1400 ft-c	5.8-16.6 mg CO_2/dm²/hr	2
52	*Pisum sativum*	[Whole leaf]	$NaHC^{14}O_3$	13.5	White light	2.4 × 10⁷	0.63-1.12 μM CO_2 fixed/hr/mg chlorophyll	21
53	*Prunus laurocerasus*	....	[Natural]	29.5	Noon sun	....	23.2 mg CO_2/dm²/hr	16
54	*P. persica*	....	[Natural]	Nat 4/	Natural	....	0.146-0.18 g/m² increase in dry wt/hr	19
55	*Quercus falcata (Q. rubra)*	....	[Natural]	30	....	2000 ft-c	5[6.04] mg CO_2/dm²/hr	12
56	*Rheum rhaponticum*	....	....	......	....	....	0.65 g/m² increase in dry wt/hr	20
57	*Solanum tuberosum*	....	[Natural]	Nat 4/	....	>5000 ft-c	16-20 mg CO_2/dm²/hr	5
58	*Spinacia* sp.	[Whole leaf]	$C^{14}O_2$	20	Reflector flood lamps	3.4 × 10⁴	16.4-30.7 μM CO_2 fixed/hr/mg chlorophyll	15
59	*Zea mays*	[Whole leaf]	CGA 5/	18-34	Sunlight	3.02 × 10⁴	0.4-2.3 g CO_2/m² × hr	26
60						1.21 × 10⁵	1.74 g CO_2/m² × hr	
61						1.51 × 10⁵	0.9-3.3 g CO_2/m² × hr	
62		....	[Natural]	Nat 4/	Full sun	....	1.8 g CO_2/m² leaf/hr	

1/ Unless otherwise specified. 3/ Values in brackets are maximum rates. 4/ Nat = under natural conditions. 5/ Chemical gas analysis.

Contributors: Vishniac, Wolf, and Weiss, Margaret L.

References

[1] Bannister, T. T., and M. J. Vrooman. 1964. Plant Physiol. 39:622.

[2] Bing, A. Unpublished. Cornell Univ. Ornamentals Research Laboratory, N.Y., 1953.

[3] Bishop, N. I. 1962. Biochim. Biophys. Acta 57:186.

[4] Brown, T. E. 1954. Ph.D. Thesis. Ohio State Univ., Columbus.

[5] Chapman, H. W. 1951. Am. Potato J. 28(5):602.

[6] Craig, F. N., and S. F. Trelease. 1937. Am. J. Botany 24:232.

[7] Freeland, R. O. 1952. Plant Physiol. 27(4):685.

[8] Gregory, F. G., and F. J. Richards. 1929. Ann. Botany (London) 43:119.

[9] Harder, R. 1930. Planta 11:263.

continued

96. LIGHT INTENSITY AND RATE OF PHOTOSYNTHESIS

[10] Heinicke, A. J., and M. B. Hoffman. 1933. Cornell Univ. Agr. Expt. Sta. Bull. 577.
[11] Kessler, E. 1955. Arch. Biochem. Biophys. 59:527.
[12] Kramer, P. J., and J. P. Decker. 1944. Plant Physiol. 19(2):350.
[13] Larsen, H., C. S. Yocum, and C. B. van Niel. 1952. J. Gen. Physiol. 36:161.
[14] Levine, R. P. 1960. Proc. Natl. Acad. Sci. U.S. 46: 972.
[15] Losada, M., A. V. Trebst, and D. I. Arnon. 1960. J. Biol. Chem. 235:832.
[16] Matthaei, G. L. C. 1905. Phil. Trans. Roy. Soc. London, B, 197:47.
[17] Mitchell, J. W. 1936. Botan. Gaz. 98:87.
[18] Noguti, Y. 1941. Japan. J. Botany 11(2):167.
[19] Pickett, W. F., A. S. Fish, and W. S. Shan. 1951. Proc. Am. Soc. Hort. Sci. 57:111.
[20] Sachs, J. 1884. Arb. Botan. Inst. Wuerzburg 3:1.
[21] Smillie, R. M., and R. C. Fuller. 1959. Plant Physiol. 34:651.
[22] Tamiya, H. 1949. Studies Tokugawa Inst. 6(2).
[23] Thomas, M. D., and G. R. Hill. 1937. Plant Physiol. 12:285.
[24] Thomas, M. D., and G. R. Hill. 1949. In J. Franck and W. E. Loomis, ed. Photosynthesis in plants. Iowa State College Press, Ames. pp. 19-52.
[25] Verduin, J. 1952. Am. J. Botany 39(3):157.
[26] Verduin, J., and W. E. Loomis. 1944. Plant Physiol. 19:278.
[27] Wassink, E. C., et al. 1938. Enzymologia 5:100.
[28] Wedding, R. T., L. A. Riehl, and W. H. Rhoads. 1952. Plant Physiol. 27(2):269.
[29] Willstätter, R., and A. Stoll. 1918. Untersuchungen über die Assimilation der Kohlensäure. J. Springer, Berlin.
[30] Winokur, M. 1948. Am. J. Botany 35(5):207.

97. PHOTOCHEMICAL CONTROL MECHANISMS OF HIGHER PLANTS

	Photoreaction	Chemical or Physical Change	Product	Photoreceptor	Action Spectra Maxima nm	Reference
1	Chlorophyll synthesis	Addition of 2 hydrogens to ring IV of protochlorophyllide *a* or protochlorophyll *a*	Chlorophyllide *a* or chlorophyll *a*	Protochlorophyllide *a* or protochlorophyll *a*	445; 640	1,9
2	Phototropism	Indole-3-acetic acid distribution	Unknown	Unknown (carotenoid or flavin?)	370; 425; 445; 474	2
3	Chloroplast movement	Chloroplast distribution	....	Unknown	Red; blue	10
4	Protoplasmic streaming	Protoplasmic viscosity	....	Unknown	430; 470; 490	10
5	Phytochrome regulated reactions 1/	Phytochrome $_{red}$ $\overset{h\nu\,2/}{\rightleftharpoons}$ phytochrome $_{far\text{-}red}$	Unknown	Bilitriene-type bile pigment	660; 725	4,6,8, 12
6	High-energy regulated reactions 3/	Unknown	Unknown	Unknown (chlorophyll or phytochrome?)	440-470; 600-725	3,5,7, 11

1/ Partial list: seed germination, seedling growth, anthocyanin synthesis, chloroplast development, photoperiodism, chromosome response, heterotrophic growth, leaf abscission, bulb formation, floral initiation and development, sex expression, geotropic response. 2/ h = Planck's constant (6.626×10^{-27} erg-sec), and ν = frequency of the radiation expressed in sec^{-1}. 3/ Partial list: flavonoid synthesis, hypocotyl lengthening, lettuce plumular hook opening, hair formation, leaf enlargement.

Contributor: Siegelman, H. W.

References

[1] Boardman, N. K. 1966. In L. P. Vernon and G. R. Seely, ed. The chlorophylls. Academic Press, New York. pp. 437-479.
[2] Briggs, W. R. 1964. In A. C. Giese, ed. Photophysiology. Academic Press, New York. v. 1, pp. 223-271.
[3] Downs, R. J., et al. 1965. Nature 205:909.
[4] Hendricks, S. B., and H. A. Borthwick. 1965. In T. A. Goodwin, ed. Chemistry and biochemistry of plant pigments. Academic Press, London. pp. 405-436.
[5] Mohr, H. 1964. Biol. Rev. 39:87.
[6] Mohr, H. 1966. Z. Pflanzenphysiol. 54:63.
[7] Siegelman, H. W. 1964. In J. B. Harborne, ed. Biochemistry of phenolic compounds. Academic Press, London. pp. 437-456.
[8] Siegelman, H. W., B. C. Turner, and S. B. Hendricks. 1966. Plant physiol. 41:1289.
[9] Smith, J. H. C., and S. French. 1963. Ann. Rev. Plant Physiol. 14:181.

continued

97. PHOTOCHEMICAL CONTROL MECHANISMS OF HIGHER PLANTS

[10] Virgin, H. I. 1964. In A. C. Giese, ed. Photophysiology. Academic Press, New York. v. 1, pp. 273-303.

[11] Wagner, E., and H. Mohr. 1966. Photochem. Photobiol. 5:397.

[12] Withrow, R. B. 1959. Publ. Am. Assoc. Advan. Sci. 55:439.

98. RESPIRATION RATES: BACTERIA

Rate of respiration differs with the strain of bacteria, cultural conditions, age of cells, origin of inoculum, nature of solution used for washing, and composition of the respiratory system. Data are for bacterial suspensions in the presence of glucose, and in most instances have not been corrected for endogenous respiration.

	Species (Synonym)	Temp °C	Culture Age hr	Q_{O_2} µl/mg dry wt/hr	Reference
1	*Aerobacter aerogenes*	30	....	122[1]	7
2		30	48	50	1,2
3		36	17	47	1,2
4	*Azotobacter chroococcum*	22	36	2,000-10,000[2]	15
	Bacillus cereus				
5	Short	30	....	21[1]	7
6		30	18	42-86	16
7	Filamentous	30	18	3-49	16
8	*B. subtilis*	37	6-8	170	9
9	Spores	32	98-147	10	6
10	*Corynebacterium* sp.	30	48-96	67	14
11	*Diplococcus pneumoniae*, serotype 1	37	18	27	3
12	*Escherichia coli*	30	....	67.7[1]	7
13		32	20	272	1
14		40	20	200	13
15	*Lactobacillus bulgaricus*	37	8	34	24
16		45	8	55	24
17	*Leuconostoc citrovorum*	38	16	8	4
18	*Micrococcus aurantiacus*	35	30-34	14	17
19	*M. cinnabareus*	35	30-34	36	17
20	*M. flavus*	35	30-34	8	17
21	*M. freudenreichii*	35	30-34	20	17
22	*M. luteus*	35	30-34	15	17
23	*Mycobacterium* sp.[3]	38	84	22	8
24	Leprous[4]	38	84	8	8
25	*M. avium (M. tuberculosis,* avian)	37	84	1	18
26	*M. phlei*	38	84	28	8
27	*M. ranae*	38	84	32	8
28	*M. smegmatis*	38	84	23	8
29	*(M. butyricum)*	38	84	13	8
30	*M. stercoris*	38	84	15	8
31	*M. tuberculosis (M. tuberculosis,* human)	38	252	4	8
32	*Pseudomonas fluorescens*	26	20	58	21
33	*P. natriegens*	30	....	268	5
34	Psychrophilic species	30	14	127	20
35	*Rhizobium leguminosarum*	30	....	33[1]	7
36	*Staphylococcus epidermi-*	30[5]	8	66	11
37	*dis*	30[6]	8	67	12
	Streptococcus faecalis				
38	B33A	38	18	106	22
39	10Cl	37	15	57-80	19
40	Lancefield D	37	12-15	7	10
41	*S. pyogenes*	37.5	4	57-63	23
42	*S. thermophilus*	37	8	4-9	24
43		50	8	5-10	24

[1] Assuming 10% nitrogen. [2] Values may be 10 times too high. [3] Karlinski. [4] Kedrowsky. [5] Cells grown aerobically at 37°C. If grown anaerobically for 16 hours, Q_{O_2} = 7; if anaerobically plus heme, Q_{O_2} = 42. [6] Cells grown aerobically at 37°C. If grown anaerobically for 16 hours, Q_{O_2} = 10; if heme added after growth, Q_{O_2} = 13, if during growth, Q_{O_2} = 37.

Contributor: Umbreit, Wayne W.

References

[1] Ajl, S. J. 1950. J. Bacteriol. 59:499.

[2] Ajl, S. J., and T. O. Wong. 1951. Ibid. 61:379.

[3] Bernheim, F., and M. L. Bernheim. 1943. Ibid. 46: 225.

[4] Chang, S. C., M. Silverman, and J. C. Keresztesy. 1951. Ibid. 62:753.

[5] Cho, H. W., and R. G. Eagon. 1967. Ibid. 93:866.

[6] Crook, P. G. 1952. Ibid. 63:193.

[7] Dietrich, S. M. C., and R. H. Burris. 1967. Ibid. 93: 1467.

[8] Edson, N. L., and G. J. Hunter. 1943. Biochem. J. 37:563.

[9] Gary, N. D., and R. C. Bard. 1952. J. Bacteriol. 64: 501.

[10] Gunsalus, I. C., and W. W. Umbreit. 1945. Ibid. 49: 347.

[11] Jacobs, N. J., and S. F. Conti. 1965. Ibid. 89:675.

[12] Jacobs, N. J., E. R. Maclosky, and S. F. Conti. 1967. Ibid. 93:278.

[13] Krebs, H. A. 1937. Biochem. J. 31:2095.

[14] Levine, S., and L. O. Krampitz. 1952. J. Bacteriol. 64:645.

[15] Meyerhof, O., and D. Burk. 1928. Z. Physiol. Chem. 139:117.

continued

[16] Nickerson, W. J., and F. J. Sherman. 1952. J. Bacteriol. 64:667.
[17] Nunheimer, T. D., and F. W. Fabian. 1942. Ibid. 44:215.
[18] Oginsky, E. L., P. H. Smith, and M. Solotorovsky. 1950. Ibid. 59:29.
[19] O'Kane, D. J. 1950. Ibid. 60:449.
[20] Purohit, K., and J. L. Stokes. 1967. Ibid. 93:199.
[21] Sebek, O. K., and C. I. Randles. 1952. Ibid. 63:693.
[22] Seeley, H. W., and P. J. Van Demark. 1951. Ibid. 61:27.
[23] Sevag, M. G., and M. Shelburne. 1942. Ibid. 43:411.
[24] Stein, R. M., and W. L. Frazier. 1941. Ibid. 42:501.

99. RESPIRATION RATES: SLIME MOLDS AND FUNGI

Method: Mano = manometric; Chem = chemical; Volu = volumetric. **Substrate:** Endo = endogenous; Org = organic compounds; CHO = carbohydrates; Nat = natural; Com = complex substrates. Q_{CO_2}: Values in boldface are for anaerobic CO_2 production; all other values are for aerobic CO_2 production.

	Species (Synonym)	Material [Method]	Substrate	Specification	Temp °C	Respiration Rate µl/mg dry wt/hr[1/] $Q_{O_2}[Q_{CO_2}]$	Respiratory Quotient CO_2/O_2	Reference
				Myxomycetes				
1	*Physarum polycephalum*	Plasmodium [Mano]	Endo	50 mg/vessel	22	1.4[2/][1.0[2/]; **0.24**[2/]]	0.75-0.85	4
2				PO_4 buffer, pH 6.0; 0 days	25	1.08[2/][**0.11**[2/]]	0.83	42
				Phycomycetes				
3	*Albugo candida (Cystopus candidus)*	Mycelia [Chem]	Nat	Host *(Isatis djurjaedae)*	....	....	0.93	40
4				Host + fungus	....	....	0.95	
5	*Allomyces arbuscula*	Washed mycelia [Mano]	Endo	Control & starved	28	1.5 & 17.9	....	27
6			Org	+0.1 M glutamate	20	0.84	....	48
7	*Leptomitus lacteus*	Pellets [Mano]	Endo	Starved; 0 hr	20	20	....	46
8				4 hr	20	15	....	
9				8 hr	20	10	....	
10			Org	Endogenous	20	....	0.98	46
11	*Mucor guilliermondii*	Mycelia [Mano]	Endo	Endogenous; mycelial phase	25	5.7-10.0[3.2; **7.1**]	....	29
12			CHO	Glucose; mycelial phase	25	5.6-21.4[10.7-42.3; **18.3-82.1**]	....	29
13		Cell suspension [Mano]	CHO	Glucose; yeast phase	25	7.8-39.0[21.9-118.0; **30.9-142.0**]	....	29
14		Mycelia + cell suspension [Mano]	CHO	Glucose; mixed phase	25	12.1-29.0[38.6-65.3; **52.3-78.7**]	....	29
15	*Phycomyces blakesleeanus*	Mycelia [Chem]	CHO	1.5 days	20	[27]	....	55
16				3.5 days	20	[13]	....	
17				7 days	20	[3]	....	
18	*Rhizopus sexualis*	Mycelia [Chem]	Org	52 hr	20	[25.7[3/]]	....	22
19	*Zygorhynchus moelleri*	Mycelia [Mano]	Endo	Endogenous; pH 3.6	25	6.3	....	35
20				5.0	25	8.6	....	
21				6.0	25	9.4	....	
22				6.8	25	6.4	....	
23				8.8	25	10.3	....	
24			CHO	Glucose; pH 3.6	25	33.6	....	35
25				5.0	25	40.0	....	
26				6.0	25	31.5	....	
27				6.8	25	26.4	....	
28				8.8	25	13.8	....	

1/ Unless otherwise indicated. 2/ µl/mg wet wt/hr. 3/ mg/g dry wt/hr.

continued

	Species (Synonym)	Material [Method]	Sub-strate	Specification	Temp °C	Respiration Rate μl/mg dry wt/hr[1] Q_{O_2}[Q_{CO_2}]	Respiratory Quotient CO_2/O_2	Ref-er-ence
				Ascomycetes				
29	*Ashbya gossy-*	Washed mycelia	Endo	Starved; 1 day	30	19	......	34
30	*pii*	[Mano]		2 days	30	11	......	
31				3 days	30	8	......	
32			CHO	Glucose; 1 day	30	32	......	34
33				2 days	30	20	......	
34				3 days	30	12	......	
35	*Chaetomium* sp.	Pellets [Chem]	CHO	......	23-25	......	1.22	7
36	*Cochliobolus*	Mycelia [Mano]	Endo	10 days	......	3.8	......	1
37	*miyabeanus*			15 days	......	4.3	......	
38				18 days	......	3.1	......	
39				35 days	......	1.5	......	
40				42 days	......	1.7	......	
41	*Erysiphe com-*	Mycelia [Chem]	Nat	Host *(Torilis nodosa)*	......	......	0.89	40
42	*munis*			Host + fungus	......	......	0.74	
43	*E. graminis tri-*	Growing culture	Nat	Normal wheat leaf	22	1.7[4][**1.8**[4]]	......	3
44	*tici*	[Mano]		Leaf + fungus	22	6.0[4][**2.7**[4]]	......	
45	*E. lamprocarpa*	Mycelia [Chem]	Nat	Host *(Prasium majus)*	......	......	0.82	40
46				Host + fungus	......	......	0.78	
47	*Melanospora destruens*	Mycelia [Mano]	CHO	Glucose	......	6	......	21
48	*Neurospora crassa*	Mycelia [Mano]	Org	Endogenous	30	11-38[**0.5**]	......	53
49	*N. tetrasperma*	Ascospores	Endo	Dormant	25	0.25-0.59[**<0.03**]	......	17
50		[Mano]		Activated by heat	25	4.5-10.9[**5.0-10.9**]	......	
51	*Saccharomyces*	Washed cell sus-	Endo	Endogenous; 24 hr	28	16	......	37
52	*acidifaciens*	pension		48 hr	28	7	......	
53	*(Zygosaccha-*	[Mano]		72 hr	28	7	......	
54	*romyces acid-*		CHO	Glucose; 24 hr	28	60	......	37
55	*ifaciens)*			48 hr	28	35	......	
56				72 hr	28	35	......	
	S. cerevisiae							
57	Baker's	Washed cell sus-	CHO	Endogenous	22-25	4.8[2]	......	25
58		pension [Mano]		Glucose	22-25	3.9[2]	......	
59	Brewer's	Washed cell sus-	CHO	Endogenous	22-25	4.2[2]	......	25
60		pension [Mano]		Glucose	22-25	19.5[2]	......	
61	R	Cell suspension [Mano]	CHO	No stored reserves	......	83-109[370-432; **278-299**]	......	28
62				Fat reserves	......	76[249; **322**]	......	
63				Glycogen reserves	......	0[63: **116**]	......	
64	U	Cell suspension [Mano]	CHO	No stored reserves	......	10-137[160-348; **276-284**]	......	28
65				Fat reserves	......	125[151; **261**]	......	
66				Glycogen reserves	......	47[82; **83**]	......	
67	*Saccharomyco-*	Cell suspension	CHO	Endogenous	30	38[**0.9**]	......	51
68	*des ludwigii*	[Mano]		Glucose	30	144[**375**]	......	
69	*Schizosaccha-*	Cell suspension	CHO	Endogenous	30	21[**0.1**]	......	51
70	*romyces oc-tosporus*	[Mano]		Glucose	30	90[**225**]	......	

[1] Unless otherwise indicated. [2] μl/mg wet wt/hr. [4] μl/cm^2 area/hr.

continued

	Species (Synonym)	Material [Method]	Substrate	Specification	Temp °C	Respiration Rate µl/mg dry wt/hr[1/] $Q_{O_2}[Q_{CO_2}]$	Respiratory Quotient CO_2/O_2	Reference
71	*S. pombe*	Cell suspension [Mano]	CHO	Endogenous	30	17.9[**0.4**]	....	51
72				Glucose	30	36.4[**22.0**]	....	
73	*Sclerotinia* sp.	Pellets [Chem]	CHO	....	23-25	....	1.15	7
74	*Sordaria* sp.	Pellets [Chem]	CHO	....	23-25	....	1.56	7
75	*S. fimicola*	Mycelia [Mano]	Endo	....	26	1.28	....	15
76	*Taphrina deformans*	Mycelia [Chem]	Nat	Host *(Prunus amygdalus*[5/]*)*	....	....	1.04	40
77				Host + fungus	....	....	0.84	
78	*Thermoascus aurantiacus*	Mycelia [Chem]	Com	....	27	....	0.91-0.94	41
79					45	....	1.04-1.07	
	Basidiomycetes							
80	*Agaricus campestris (Psalliota campestris)*	Sporophores [Mano]	Endo	....	28	....	1.07	44
81		Growing culture [Volu]	......	....	25	1.9-2.9[2.3-4.0]	0.70-0.90	10
82	*Auricularia mesenterica (Thelephora tremelloides)*	Mycelia [Chem]	......	....	....	....	0.5-0.6	8
83	*Boletus luridus*	Sporophores [Chem]	Endo	....	17	[1.5]	....	45
84	*Bovista tunicata*	Sporophores [Chem]	Endo	....	18	[1.07-1.78[2/]; **5.6-8.7**[2/]]	....	52
85	*Coprinus comatus*	Sporophores [Chem]	Endo	....	17	[2.7]	....	45
86	*Daedalea quercina*	Mycelia [Chem]	......	....	....	....	0.7-0.8	8
87	*Exidia glandulosa*	Mycelia [Chem]	......	....	....	....	0.7	8
88	*Flammulina velutipes (Agaricus velutipes; Collybia velutipes)*	Sporophores [Mano]	Endo	....	28	....	0.88	44
89	*Gymnopilus sapineus (Flammula sapinea)*	Sporophores [Chem]	Endo	....	20	0.66[2/]	....	52
90	*Lactarius serifluus*	Sporophores [Chem]	Endo	....	17	[2.7]	....	45
91	*Marasmius conigenus*	Sporophores [Chem]	Endo	....	17	[3.4]	....	45
92	*Melampsora pulcherrima (M. pulcherrinum)*	Mycelia [Chem]	Nat	Host *(Mercurialis annua*[6/]*)*	....	....	0.97	40
93				Host + fungus	....	....	0.96	
94	*Merulius lacrymans*	Sporophores [Chem]	Endo	....	17	[1.0]	....	45
95	*Naematoloma fasciculare (Agaricus fascicularis)*	Sporophores [Chem]	Endo	....	17	[0.73[2/]; **0.41**[2/]]	....	52
96	*Phragmidium rosaesempervirentis*	Mycelia [Chem]	Nat	Host *(Rosa sempervirens)*	....	....	0.92	40
97				Host + fungus	....	....	0.93	

[1/] Unless otherwise indicated. [2/] µl/mg wet wt/hr. [5/] Synonym: *Amygdalus communis.* [6/] Synonym: *Mercurialis ambigua.*

continued

99. RESPIRATION RATES: SLIME MOLDS AND FUNGI

	Species (Synonym)	Material [Method]	Substrate	Specification	Temp °C	Respiration Rate µl/mg dry wt/hr[1] Q_{O_2}[Q_{CO_2}]	Respiratory Quotient CO_2/O_2	Reference
98	*Polyporus fumosus (P. imberbis)*	Sporophores [Mano]	Endo	....	28	....	0.89	44
99	*P. squamosus*	Growing culture [Mano]	......	....	......	3.0	0.85	20
100		Sporophores [Chem]	Endo	....	17	[1.0]	....	45
101	*P. versicolor (Coriolus versicolor; Polystictus versicolor)*	Mycelia [Chem]	Com	....	17.5	[8.4[7]]	....	47
102					25.5	[12.2[7]]	....	
103					33.5	[14.6[7]]	....	
	Puccinia graminis	Urediospore [Mano]	Endo	PO_4 buffer, pH 6.5				49
104				Ungerminated	30	1.6[2][1.1[2]]	0.65	
105				Germinated	30	1.4[2][1.0[2]]	0.70	
106	*Stereum hirsutum*	Sporophores [Mano]	Endo	....	28	....	0.89	44
107	*Urocystis anemones*	Mycelia [Chem]	Nat	Host *(Ranunculus macrophyllus)*	......	....	0.80	40
108				Host + fungus	......	....	0.84	
109	*Ustilago avenae*	Pellets [Chem]	CHO	....	23-25	....	1.01	7
110	*U. sphaerogena*	Washed sporidia [Mano]	Endo	Endogenous	......	75	....	2
111			CHO	Sugars	......	375	....	2
				Fungi Imperfecti				
112	*Alternaria* sp.	Pellets [Chem]	CHO	Mutants or strains	23-25	....	1.26-1.31	7
113	*Aspergillus awamori (A. luchuensis)*	Conidia [Mano]	Endo	Endogenous; pH 4	30	2.0	....	31
114				6	30	2.3	....	
115				8	30	2.8	....	
116			CHO	Glucose; pH 4	30	9.6	....	31
117				6	30	9.7	....	
118				8	30	10.8	....	
119	*A. niger*	Mycelia [Chem]	Endo	Starved; 1 day	3-5	....	0.36	43
120					19-20	....	0.66	
121					35	....	1.06-1.19	
122				3 days	21	....	0.62	
123					36	....	0.87	
124				5 days	22	....	0.51	
125					36	....	0.57	
126			CHO	Glucose	22	....	1.00	43
127					36	....	1.32	
128			Endo	2 days	20	5.2	....	23
129				5 days	20	1.6	....	
130				9 days	20	0.6	....	
131			CHO	2 days	20	12.2	....	23
132				5 days	20	2.9	....	
133				9 days	20	1.1	....	
134	*A. oryzae*	Mycelia [Volu]	CHO	2 days	30	26	....	54
135				3 days	30	30	....	
136				6 days	30	20	....	
137	*Blastomyces brasiliensis*	Washed cell suspension [Mano]	CHO	Starved; mycelial phase	20	2.4	....	39
138				yeast phase	20	14.2	....	
139	*B. dermatitidis*	Washed cell suspension [Mano]	Endo	Starved	3	1.3	....	39
140					41	13.3	....	
141					45	10.3	....	

[1] Unless otherwise indicated. [2] µl/mg wet wt/hr. [7] µl/10^8 cells/hr.

continued

	Species (Synonym)	Material [Method]	Sub-strate	Specification	Temp °C	Respiration Rate µl/mg dry wt/hr[1] $Q_{O_2}[Q_{CO_2}]$	Respiratory Quotient CO_2/O_2	Reference
142		Mycelia, washed cell suspension [Mano]	CHO	Endogenous	37	16[8]	0.80	5
143				Glucose	37	23[8]	0.96	
144	*Botrytis cinerea*	Mycelia [Mano]	CHO	Starved; 2 days	26	3.0	1.5	16
145				4 days	26	2.0	1.5	
146				6 days	26	1.5	1.5	
147	*Brettanomyces* sp. (*B. claussenii)*	Cell suspension [Mano]	CHO	64 & 168 hr; grown aerobically	....	38 & 28	....	11
148				144 hr; grown anaerobically	....	10	....	
149	*Candida albicans*	Cell suspension [Mano]	Endo	Starved	30	5	....	36
150			CHO	Glucose	30	40	....	36
151	*Cephalotrichum* sp. (*Stysanus* sp.)	Pellets [Chem]	CHO	....	23-25	....	1.21	7
152	*Cladosporium* spp.	Pellets [Chem]	CHO	5 strains	23-25	....	1.10-1.28	7
153	*Clasterosporium* spp.	Pellets [Chem]	CHO	2 strains	23-25	....	1.30-1.74	7
154	*Eidamia catenulata*	Pellets [Chem]	CHO	....	23-25	....	1.69	7
155	*Epicoccum* spp.	Pellets [Chem]	CHO	2 species	23-25	....	1.16-1.64	7
156	*Epidermophyton floccosum*	Mycelia [Mano]	Endo	pH 3.0	....	3.0	....	38
157				5.0	....	0.8	....	
158				6.0	....	1.6	....	
159	*Fusarium* sp., H	Mycelia [Mano]	CHO	Endogenous	....	7.3[6.7]	0.95	18
160				Glucose	....	6.1[10.2]	1.75	
161	*F. graminearum*	Pellets [Mano]	CHO	Whole cells; endogenous	30	13.6	0.84	14
162				glucose	30	15.7	1.24	
163				Minced cells; endogenous	30	25.9	0.72	
164				glucose	30	28.0	1.11	
	F. tricothecioides	Homogenized mycelia [Mano]						
165		1 day old	Endo	Endogenous; 1 hr	30	40[31]	0.78	19
166				4 hr	30	13[11]	0.84	
167			CHO	Glucose; 1 hr	30	34[64]	1.85	19
168				4 hr	30	39[56]	1.55	
169		3 days old	Endo	Endogenous; 1 hr	30	14[14]	1.01	19
170				4 hr	30	13[12]	0.92	
171			CHO	Glucose; 1 hr	30	14[19]	1.36	19
172				4 hr	30	13[26]	1.97	
173	*Geotrichum candidum* (*Oidium lactis*)	Mycelia [Chem]	CHO	....	15	....	0.70	43
174					35	....	0.72	
175	*Gliocladium roseum*	Pellets [Chem]	CHO	....	23-25	....	1.44	6
176	*Helminthosporium gramineum*	Pellets [Chem]	CHO	....	23-25	....	1.31	7
177	*Heterosporium gracile*	Pellets [Chem]	CHO	....	23-25	....	1.09	7
178	*Memnoniella echinata*	Conidia [Mano]	CHO	Glucose; pH 4	30	2.6	....	31
179				6	30	3.1	....	
180				8	30	2.7	....	

[1] Unless otherwise indicated. [8] µl/10 µl tissue volume/hr.

continued

99. RESPIRATION RATES: SLIME MOLDS AND FUNGI

	Species (Synonym)	Material [Method]	Sub-strate	Specification	Temp °C	Respiration Rate µl/mg dry wt/hr[1] Q_{O_2}[Q_{CO_2}]	Respiratory Quotient CO_2/O_2	Ref-erence
181	*Microsporum canis*	Pellets [Mano]	......	Starved; 0 & 3 days	37.5	....	1.0 & 0.87	33
182	*Mycelium radicis atrovirens*	Washed pellets	Endo	Unstarved	25	21	....	56
183				Starved	25	1.9	....	
184			CHO	Glucose	25	8.7; 10.9	....	56
185	*Mycoderma vini*	Washed cell suspension [Mano]	......	....	10	25	....	9
186					37	20	....	
187	*Myrothecium verrucaria*	Washed, homogenized mycelia [Mano]	Com	4 hr	30	45	....	12
188				24 hr	30	108	....	
189				100 hr	30	22	....	
190		Conidia [Mano]	Endo	Endogenous; 1 & 3 hr	30	[1.9]	0.91 & 0.79	32
191			CHO	Glucose; 1 & 3 hr	30	[5.2]	1.15 & 1.24	32
192				Germinating spores; 0 hr	30	2	....	32
193				1 hr	30	65	....	
194				3 hr	30	75	....	
195				Glucose; pH 4	30	11.4	....	31
196				6	30	13.5	....	
197				8	30	23.6	....	
198	*Penicillium chrysogenum*	Pellets [Mano]	Com	2 days	23-24	17	....	26
199				3 days	23-24	29	....	
200				4 days	23-24	9	....	
201	*P. glaucum*	Mycelia [Chem]	Com	Endogenous	25	[6]	....	13
202				Exogenous	25	[28]	....	
203	*P. notatum*	Mycelia [Mano]	Endo	Starved; 0 day	20-24	6.5	....	57
204				1 day	20-24	1.7	....	
205			CHO	2 days	20-24	6	....	57
206				4 days	20-24	16	....	
207				7 days	20-24	2	....	
208		[Chem]	Com	4 days	24	[46]	....	24
209				8 days	24	[198]	....	
210				11 days	24	[152]	....	
211	*Racodium cellare*	Pellets [Chem]	CHO	....	23-25	....	1.03	7
212	*Scopulariopsis brevicaulis*	Pellets [Chem]	CHO	3 strains	23-25	....	1.20-1.33	6
213	*Sporotrichum bombycinum*	Pellets [Chem]	CHO	....	23-25	....	1.28	7
214	*Torula* sp.	Washed cell suspension [Mano]	CHO	± Glutathione, ± cysteine	30	28[9]	....	30
215	*Torulopsis utilis*	Cell suspension [Mano]	Endo	Nitrogen-starved	30	3.9[2] [3.8[2]]	0.97	50
216	*Trichoderma lignorum*	Pellets [Chem]	CHO	....	23-25	....	1.20	7
217	*Trichophyton gypseum*	Mycelia [Mano]	Endo	pH 4.6	....	1.06	....	38
218				7.0	....	1.73	....	
219				8.0	....	2.69	....	
220	*Trichothecium roseum (Cephalothecium roseum)*	Pellets [Chem]	CHO	....	23-25	....	1.19	7
221	*Verticillium cinnabarinus (Acrostalagmus cinnabarinus)*	Mycelia [Chem]	Org, CHO	....	15	....	1.02	43
222					35	....	0.96	

[1] Unless otherwise indicated. [2] µl/mg wet wt/hr.

continued

99. RESPIRATION RATES: SLIME MOLDS AND FUNGI

Contributors: (a) Darby, Richard T., and Mandels, Gabriel R., (b) Henderson, Lavaniel L., Sr.

References

[1] Akai, S., and S. Itoi. 1955. Kyoto Univ. Lab. Phytopathol. Contrib. 39.
[2] Allen, P. J. 1948. Am. J. Botany 35:799.
[3] Allen, P. J., and D. R. Goddard. 1938. Science 88: 192.
[4] Allen, P. J., and W. H. Price. 1950. Am. J. Botany 37:393.
[5] Bernheim, F. 1942. J. Bacteriol. 44:533.
[6] Birkinshaw, J. H., et al. 1931. Phil. Trans. Roy. Soc. London, B, 220:55.
[7] Birkinshaw, J. H., et al. 1931. Ibid. 220:99.
[8] Bonnier, G., and L. Mangin. 1884. Ann. Sci. Nat. Botan. Biol. Vegetale, Ser. 6, 17:210.
[9] Chauvet, J. 1943. Enzymologia 11:57.
[10] Chevillard, L., A. Meyer, and L. Plantefol. 1930. Ann. Physiol. Physicochim. Biol. 6:506.
[11] Cori, C. F. 1941. Biol. Symp. 5:131.
[12] Darby, R. T., and D. R. Goddard. 1950. Am. J. Botany 37:379.
[13] Diakonow, N. W. 1886. Ber. Deut. Botan. Ges. 4:1.
[14] Dorrell, W. W. 1948. Doctoral Thesis. Univ. Wisconsin, Madison.
[15] Edwards, G. A., C. B. Buell, and W. H. Weston. 1947. Am. J. Botany 34:551.
[16] Gentile, A. C. 1954. Plant Physiol. 29:257.
[17] Goddard, D. R. 1939. Cold Spring Harbor Symp. Quant. Biol. 7:362.
[18] Gould, B. S., and A. A. Tytell. 1940. Intern. Congr. Microbiol., 3rd, Rept. Proc., p. 230.
[19] Gould, B. S., and A. A. Tytell. 1941. J. Gen. Physiol. 24:655.
[20] Hammon, F. 1936. Ann. Physiol. Physicochim. Biol. 12:940.
[21] Hawker, L. E. 1950. Physiology of fungi. Univ. London Press, London.
[22] Hawker, L. E., and P. M. Hepden. 1962. Ann. Botany 26:619.
[23] Hee, A. 1927. Bull. Soc. Chim. Biol. 9:802.
[24] Hickenhull, D. J. 1946. Biochem. J. 40:337.
[25] Holtz, P., M. Exner, and H. J. Schumann. 1948. Arch. Exptl. Pathol. Pharmakol. 205:243.
[26] Koffler, H., et al. 1945. J. Bacteriol. 50:549.
[27] Leonard, W. R. 1949. J. Cellular Comp. Physiol. 34: 293.
[28] Lindegren, C. C. 1946. Arch. Biochem. 9:353.
[29] Lüers, H., E. Kühles, and H. Fink. 1930. Biochem. Z. 217:253.
[30] Machlis, S., and K. C. Blanchard. 1937. J. Cellular Comp. Physiol. 9:207.
[31] Mandels, G. R. Unpublished. U.S. Army Quartermaster Depot, Research and Development Laboratories, Philadelphia, 1953.
[32] Mandels, G. R., and A. B. Norton. 1948. Quartermaster Gen. Lab. Res. Rept., Microbiol. Ser. 11.
[33] Melton, F. M. 1951. J. Invest. Dermatol. 17:27.
[34] Mickelson, M. N. 1950. J. Bacteriol. 59:659.
[35] Moses, V. 1954. Biochem. J. 57:547.
[36] Nickerson, W. J. 1946. Am. J. Botany 33:831.
[37] Nickerson, W. J., and W. R. Carroll. 1943. J. Cellular Comp. Physiol. 22:21.
[38] Nickerson, W. J., and J. B. Chadwick. 1946. Arch. Biochem. 10:81.
[39] Nickerson, W. J., and G. A. Edwards. 1949. J. Gen. Physiol. 33:41.
[40] Nicolas, M. G. 1920. Compt. Rend. 170:750.
[41] Noack, K. 1920. Jahrb. Wiss. Botan. 59:413.
[42] Ohta, J. 1954. J. Biochem. (Tokyo) 39:489.
[43] Porievitch, K. 1805. Ann. Sci. Nat. Botan. Biol. Vegetale, Ser. 9, 1:1.
[44] Pringsheim, E. G. 1935. Jahrb. Wiss. Botan. 81:579.
[45] Richards, F. J. 1927. New Phytologist 26:187.
[46] Schade, A. L., and K. V. Thimann. 1940. Am. J. Botany 27:659.
[47] Scheffer, T. C. 1936. Plant Physiol. 11:535.
[48] Shoup, C. S., and F. T. Wolf. 1946. J. Cellular Comp. Physiol. 28:365.
[49] Shu, P., K. G. Tanner, and G. A. Ledingham. 1954. Can. J. Botany 32:16.
[50] Sperber, E. 1945. Arkiv Kemi Mineral. Geol. 21A(3): 1.
[51] Spiegelman, S., and M. Nozawa. 1945. Arch. Biochem. 6:303.
[52] Stich, C. 1891. Flora (Jena) 74:1.
[53] Strauss, B. S. 1952. Arch. Biochem. 36:33.
[54] Tamiya, H., and T. Hida. 1928-29. Acta Phytochim. (Japan) 4:343.
[55] Wassink, E. C. 1934. Rec. Trav. Botan. Neerl. 31: 583.
[56] Wiken, T., and H. Somm. 1952. Experientia 8:140.
[57] Wolf, F. T. 1947. Arch. Biochem. 13:83.

100. RESPIRATION RATES: LICHENS, ALGAE, AND BRYOPHYTES

Method: Mano = manometric; Chem = chemical; Cond = conductometric. Figures in parentheses are control or endogenous values.

	Division or Class, & Species	Method	Temp °C	Respiration Rate µl/100 mg dry wt/hr [1/]		Respiratory Quotient CO_2/O_2	Reference
				Q_{O_2}	Q_{CO_2}		
	Lichenes						
	Ascolichenes						
1	*Alectoria nigricans*	Mano	0	8	....	....	24
2			10	14	....	....	
3			30	33	....	....	

1/ Unless otherwise indicated.

continued

100. RESPIRATION RATES: LICHENS, ALGAE, AND BRYOPHYTES

	Division or Class, & Species	Method	Temp °C	Respiration Rate µl/100 mg dry wt/hr[1] Q_{O_2}	Q_{CO_2}	Respiratory Quotient CO_2/O_2	Reference
4	*Cetraria glauca*	Chem	0	...	10	...	26
5			20	...	31	...	
6			30	...	61	...	
7	*C. islandica*	Chem	0	...	2.5	...	26
8			20	...	13	...	
9			30	...	31	...	
10		Mano	0	8	...	...	24
11			10	19	...	...	
12			30	48	...	...	
13	*Cladonia rangiferina*	Mano	50	...	8	0.80	14
14	*C. sylvatica*	Mano	0	2.9	...	...	24
15			10	6.8	...	...	
16			30	24	...	...	
17	*Cornicularia divergens*	Mano	0	5	...	...	24
18			10	11	...	...	
19			30	40	...	...	
20	*Dactylina arctica*	Mano	0	7	...	...	24
21			10	14	...	...	
22			30	41	...	...	
23	*Evernia prunastri*	Chem	0	...	5	...	26
24			20	...	31	...	
25			30	...	66	...	
26		Mano	50	...	31	0.78	14
27			60	...	27	0.88	
28	*Lecanora haematomma & L. subfusca*	Mano	.....	...	...	0.80	14
29	*Lecidea superans*	Mano	.....	...	...	0.85	14
30	*Lobaria linita*	Mano	0	10	...	...	24
31			10	22	...	...	
32			30	72	...	...	
33	*L. pulmonaria*	Chem	27	...	1; 26[2]	...	27
34	*Omphalodiscus decussatus*	Mano	0	3.1	...	...	24
35			10	6.2	...	...	
36			30	27	...	...	
37	*Opegrapha notha*	Mano	.....	...	...	0.74	14
38	*Parmelia acetabulum*	Mano	.....	...	2.3	0.79	14
39	*P. nigrociliata*	Mano	0	4	...	...	24
40			10	13	...	...	
41			30	25	...	...	
42	*Peltigera aphthosa*	Mano	0	17	...	...	24
43			10	33	...	...	
44			30	90	...	...	
45	*P. canina*	Chem	20	...	15.3[3]	...	4
46	*P. subamericana*	Mano	0	5.7	...	...	24
47			10	19	...	...	
48			30	42	...	...	
49	*Pertusaria communis*	Mano	.....	...	...	0.84	14
50	*Physcia ciliaris*	Mano	45	...	14	0.80	14
51	*Ramalina farinacea*	Chem	0	...	5	...	26
52			20	...	41	...	
53			30	...	71	...	
54		Mano	50	...	19	0.77	14
55	*R. usnea*	Mano	0	3.5	...	...	24
56			10	7	...	...	
57			30	16	...	...	
58	*Solorina crocea*	Mano	0	10	...	...	24
59			10	24	...	...	
60			30	43	...	...	

[1] Unless otherwise indicated. [2] Effect of moisture. [3] µl/cm²/hr.

continued

100. RESPIRATION RATES: LICHENS, ALGAE, AND BRYOPHYTES

	Division or Class, & Species	Method	Temp °C	Respiration Rate µl/100 mg dry wt/hr[1]		Respiratory Quotient CO_2/O_2	Reference
				Q_{O_2}	Q_{CO_2}		
61	*Sticta weigelii*	Mano	0	6.7	...	...	24
62			10	14	...	...	
63			30	40	...	...	
64	*Teloschistes flavicans*	Mano	0	5	...	...	24
65			10	11	...	...	
66			30	24	...	...	
67	*Thamnolia vermicularis*	Mano	0	4.2	...	...	24
68			10	14	...	...	
69			30	28	...	...	
70	*Umbilicaria proboscidea*	Mano	0	3.5	...	...	24
71			10	6.5	...	...	
72			30	18	...	...	
73	*U. pustulata*	Chem	28	...	11; 22[2]	...	27
74	*Usnea dasypoga*	Cond	...	...	60; 90[2]	...	22
	Algae						
	Cyanophyta						
75	*Anabaena variabilis*[4]	Mano	25	170(840)	...	1.0(1.1)	18
76	*Anacystis nidulans*[4]	Mano	25	30(160)	...	0.9(1.0)	18
77			39	200(500)	...	1.1(1.1)	
78	*Nostoc muscorum*[4]	Mano	25	110(440)	...	...	18
	Chlorophyta						
79	*Chlorella pyrenoidosa*	Mano	3.5	200(150)	...	(0.98)	6
80			18	890(430)	...	(0.94)	6
81			20	1700	...	1.39	7
82	*Cladophora rupestris*	Chem	20	33	...	...	10
83	*Coelastrum proboscideum*	Mano	20	170	...	...	8
84	*Enteromorpha compressa*	Chem	20	...	27	3.6	23
85			20	67	...	...	10
86	*E. linza*	Chem	19	...	66	0.62	12
87	*Haematococcus pluvialis*	Mano	20	180	...	...	8,9
88	*Monostroma grevillei*	Chem	...	150	...	...	11
89	*Prasiola crispa*	Chem	18.5	1; 126[2]	...	...	5
90	*Spirogyra majuscula*	Chem	10.4	0.5[5,6]	...	...	3
91	*Stichococcus bacillaris*	Mano	20	140	...	...	8,9
92	*Taonia atomaria*	Chem	20	...	6.7; 20.0[7]	0.91; 3.10[7]	23
93	*Trebouxia* sp.	Chem	18.5	1.8; 30.0[2]	...	...	5
94	*Ulothrix flacca*	Chem	...	160	...	...	11
95	*Ulva lactuca*	Chem	12	56	...	0.95	15
96			18	...	50	0.67	12
97	*Urospora penicillioides*	Chem	...	160	...	...	11
98	*Valonia utricularis*	Chem	20	...	8.4	1.5; 5.7[7]	23
	Charophyta						
99	*Chara vulgaris*	Chem	18	...	1.5[5]	...	16
100	*Nitella flexilis*	Chem	18	...	1.6[5]	...	16
	Phaeophyta						
101	*Ascophyllum nodosum*	Mano	20	1.9[5]	...	0.80	19
102	*Chorda tomentosa*	Chem	9	74	...	...	12
103	*Chordaria flagelliformis*	Chem	...	130	...	...	11
104	*Cladostephus spongiosus*	Chem	20	39	...	...	10
105	*Cutleria multifida*	Chem	20	...	7.2; 17.0[7]	0.53; 2.10[7]	23
106	*Cystoseira barbata*	Chem	20	...	13; 17[7]	2.1; 4.0[7]	23
107	*Desmarestia aculeata*	Chem	14	24[5]	...	...	12
108			20	27	...	...	10
109	*Dictyota dichotoma*	Chem	20	...	9.4; 9.2[7]	0.98; 1.04[7]	23
110	*Ectocarpus siliculosus*	Chem	12	41[5]	...	...	12
111	*Fucus serratus*	Chem	17	19	...	0.99	15

[1] Unless otherwise indicated. [2] Effect of moisture. [4] After 24-hour dark starvation. [5] µl/100 mg wet wt/hr. [6] Effect of pH. [7] Effect of O_2.

continued

100. RESPIRATION RATES: LICHENS, ALGAE, AND BRYOPHYTES

	Division or Class, & Species	Method	Temp °C	Respiration Rate µl/100 mg dry wt/hr[1]		Respiratory Quotient CO_2/O_2	Reference
				Q_{O_2}	Q_{CO_2}		
112			18	...	18	0.54	12
113	*F. vesiculosus*	Chem	14	...	12.7[8]	...	2
114		Mano	18	5.1[5]	...	0.78	19
115	*Halidrys siliquosa*	Chem	.....	33	...	...	11
116	*Laminaria digitata*	Mano	5	...	0.9[3]	0.67	17
117	*L. saccharina*	Mano	5	...	2.1[3]	0.80	17
118	*Myelophycus caespitosus*	Mano	25	46	...	...	29
119	*Pogotrichum filiformis*	Chem	.....	210	...	...	11
120	*Pseudendoclonium brasiliense*	Mano	20	110	...	...	9
121	*Punctaria plantaginea*	Chem	.....	73	...	...	11
122	*Sargassum linifolium*	Chem	20	...	24	5.5	23
123	*Scytosiphon lomentarius*	Mano	25	150	...	...	29
	Rhodophyta						
124	*Batrachospermum moniliforme*	Chem	20	64	...	...	10
125	*Ceramium rubrum*	Chem	17	...	45	0.89	12
126	*Chondrus crispus*	Mano	23	2.8[5]	...	0.81	19
127	*Cryptonemia lomation*	Chem	20	...	7.5; 9.9[7]	2.4; 3.8[7]	23
128	*Cystoclonium purpurascens*	Chem	.....	65	...	...	11
129	*Delesseria alata*	Chem	20	41	...	...	10
130	*Dumontia filiformis*	Chem	.....	140	...	...	11
131	*Furcellaria fastigiata*	Chem	14	7	...	...	15
132			20	12	...	...	10
133	*Gelidium corneum*	Chem	20	...	13	3.26	23
134	*Gigartina teedii*	Chem	12	49	...	0.98	15
135	*Gloiopeltis complanata*	Mano	25	63	...	...	29
136	*Gracilaria compressa*	Chem	20	...	9	1.4	23
137	*Grateloupia proteus*	Chem	20	...	8.8	4.5	23
138	*Laurencia papillosa*	Chem	20	...	18	4.88	23
139	*Phyllophora nervosa*	Chem	20	...	4.6	1.56	23
140	*Plocamium coccineum*	Chem	20	21	...	...	10
141	*Polyides lumbricoides*	Chem	14	5	...	...	15
142	*Polysiphonia violacea*	Chem	11	...	107	1.02	12
143	*Porphyra laciniata*	Chem	17	39	...	...	15
144	*Rhodomela confervoides*[9]	Chem	.....	160	...	...	11
	Bryophyta						
	Hepaticae						
145	*Chiloscyphus fragilis*	Mano	25	60; 100[10]	...	...	28
146	*Frullania tamarisci*	......	.....	...	32; 47[11]	...	13
147	*Marchantia polymorpha*	Chem	20	...	0.6[3]	...	25
148	*Riccia fluitans*	Mano	25	250; 300[10]	...	...	28
	Musci						
149	*Fissidens taxifolius*	......	.....	...	30	...	13
150	*Fontinalis antipyretica*	Mano	25	70; 140[10]	...	...	28
151	*Hylocomium parietinum & H. proliferum*	Chem	0	...	15	...	25
152			20	...	46	...	
153			30	...	92	...	
154	*H. squarrosum*	Chem	5	...	15	...	25
155			20	...	61	...	
156			30	...	100	...	
157	*Hypnum cupressiforme*	Chem	18.5	2;30[2]	...	...	5
158	*H. triquetrum*	......	20	...	0.8; 30.0[2]	...	20
159		Mano	.....	0.5; 40.0[2]	...	...	21
160	*Mnium undulatum*	......	.....	...	7.5; 97.0[2]	...	13
161	*Orthotrichum affine*	Mano	55	...	12	0.70	14
162	*Polytrichum juniperinum*[12]	......	18	...	1.2[5]; 0.7[5,13]	1.00; 0.65[13]	1

[1] Unless otherwise indicated. [2] Effect of moisture. [3] µl/cm^2/hr. [5] µl/100 mg wet wt/hr. [7] Effect of O_2. [8] µg/100 g wet wt/hr. [9] Synonym: *R. subfusca.* [10] Effect of inhibitors. [11] Effect of light. [12] Shoots or tops only. [13] Effect of growth, development, or maturation.

continued

100. RESPIRATION RATES: LICHENS, ALGAE, AND BRYOPHYTES

	Division or Class, & Species	Method	Temp °C	Respiration Rate µl/100 mg dry wt/hr		Respiratory Quotient CO_2/O_2	Reference
				Q_{O_2}	Q_{CO_2}		
163	*Sphagnum girgensohnii*	Chem	5	....	20	....	25
164			20	....	71	....	
165			30	....	130	....	

Contributors: (a) Mandels, Gabriel R., and Darby, Richard T., (b) Myers, Jack, (c) Henderson, Lavaniel L., Sr.

References

[1] Bastit, E. 1891. Rev. Gen. Botan. 3:255.
[2] Bidwell, R. C. S. 1963. Can. J. Botany 41(1):155.
[3] Bode, H. R. 1925. Jahrb. Wiss. Botan. 65:352.
[4] Boysen-Jense, P., and D. Müller. 1929. Ibid. 70:503.
[5] Fraymouth, J. 1928. Ann. Botany (London) 42:75.
[6] French, C. S., H. I. Kohn, and P. S. Tang. 1934. J. Gen. Physiol. 18:193.
[7] Gaffron, H. 1939. Biol. Zentr. 59:288.
[8] Genevois, L. 1927. Biochem. Z. 186:461.
[9] Genevois, L. 1928. Rev. Gen. Botan. 40:654.
[10] Gessner, F. 1940. Jahrb. Wiss. Botan. 89:1.
[11] Harder, R. 1915. Ibid. 56:254.
[12] Hoffmann, C. 1929. Ibid. 71:214.
[13] Jönsson, B. 1894. Compt. Rend. 119:440.
[14] Jumelle, H. 1892. Rev. Gen. Botan. 4:49, 103, 159, 220, 259, 305.
[15] Kniep, H. 1914. Intern. Rev. Ges. Hydrobiol. Hydrog. 7:1.
[16] Kolkwitz, R. 1900. Wiss. Meeresuntersuch. Abt. Helgoland 4:31.
[17] Kraschennikoff, T. 1926. Compt. Rend. 182:939.
[18] Kratz, W. A., and J. Myers. 1955. Plant Physiol. 30: 275.
[19] Kylin, H. 1911. Arkiv Botan. 11:1.
[20] Mayer, A., and L. Plantefol. 1924. Compt. Rend. 178:1385.
[21] Mayer, A., and L. Plantefol. 1925. Ann. Physiol. Physicochim. Biol. 1:239.
[22] Neubauer, A. F. 1938. Beitr. Biol. Pflanz. 25:273.
[23] Pantanelli, E. 1914. Ber. Deut. Botan. Ges. 32:488.
[24] Scholander, P. F., et al. 1952. Am. J. Botany 39: 707.
[25] Stalfelt, M. G. 1937. Planta 27:30.
[26] Stalfelt, M. G. 1938. Ibid. 29:11.
[27] Stocker, O. 1927. Flora (Jena) 121:334.
[28] Usami, S. 1937. Acta Phytochim. (Japan) 9:287.
[29] Watanabe, A. 1937. Ibid. 9:235.

101. RESPIRATION RATES: VASCULAR PLANTS

Method: Mano = manometric; Chem = chemical; Cond = conductometric; Elec = electrode; Magn = paramagnetic oxygen analyzer; Gas = gas chromatography and electrical conductivity; Color = colorimetric; IR = infrared carbon dioxide analyzer. Figures in parentheses are control or endogenous values.

	Species (Synonym)	Condition or Plant Part	Method	Temp °C	Respiration Rate Q_{O_2} [Q_{CO_2}] µl/100 mg wet wt/hr 1/	Respiratory Quotient CO_2/O_2	Reference
	Seeds						
1	*Acacia melanoxylon*	Resting	Mano	....	[0.01 2/]	....	125
2	*Acer saccharum*	Resting	....	....	[14]	....	63
3	*Amaranthus retroflexus*	Moist	Mano	25	6.7	0.86	110
4	*Avena sativa*	Resting	Chem	37.8	[0.02 2/; 0.17 2,3/]	....	8
5	Sieges Hafer	Coleoptile, segment	Mano	30	47; 39 4/	....	20
6	*Cannabis sativa*	Resting	Mano	18	11	0.82	44
7		Germinating	Mano	18	105	0.66	
8	*Chenopodium album*	Moist	Mano	25	9.6	0.93	110
9	*Citrullus vulgaris*	Resting	Mano	28	....	0.90	103
10	*Cocos nucifera*	Embryo	Mano	30	400 2/; 50 2,5/	....	29
11		Hypocotyl	Mano	30	64 2/	....	
12		Endosperm	Mano	30	0 2/	....	

1/ Unless otherwise indicated. 2/ µl/100 mg dry wt/hr. 3/ Effect of moisture. 4/ Effect of substrate. 5/ Effect of development.

continued

101. RESPIRATION RATES: VASCULAR PLANTS

	Species (Synonym)	Condition or Plant Part	Method	Temp °C	Respiration Rate Q_{O_2} [Q_{CO_2}] μl/100 mg wet wt/hr[1]	Respiratory Quotient CO_2/O_2	Reference
13	*Cucurbita pepo,* Sutton's Long White Vegetable Marrow	Germinating	Chem	25	[10; 117[5]]	0.94; 0.62[5]	73
14	*Fagopyrum sagittatum (F. esculentum)*	Germinating	....	25	[41; 306[5]]	0.8; 1.0[5]	72
15	*Glycine max (G. soja, Soja max)*	Germinating	Mano	....	....	0.93; 0.87[6]	35
16	*Gossypium hirsutum,* Delfos-3506	Resting	Mano	26	[0.03[3]; 6.0[7]]	0.96[3]; 1.12[7]	65
17	*Helianthus annuus*	Resting	Mano	28	....	1.05	103
18	Simpson's Giant Yellow & Sutton's Giant Yellow	Germinating	Chem	25	[41; 407[5]]	0.85; 0.50[5]	73
19	*Hordeum vulgare*	Resting	Chem	37.8	[0.002[2]; 0.36[2,3]]	....	8
20	*Juglans regia*	Resting	Mano	28	....	0.52	103
21	*Juniperus virginiana*	Resting	Mano	25	[0.05]	0.76	98
22		Germinating	Mano	25	[6.6; 2.5[5]]	0.84; 0.97[5]	
23	*Lathyrus odoratus,* Maxima Alba	Moist	Mano	20	6.4[2]	....	42
24		Seedling	Mano	20	430[2]; 100[2,6]	....	
25	Whatjoy	Germinating	....	25	[46; 102[5]]	0.9; 0.98[5]	72
26	*Linum usitatissimum*	Resting	Chem	37.8	[0.03[2]; 1.5[2,3]]	....	8
27		Germinating	Mano	18	....	0.90; 0.35[6]	35
28	*Malus pumila (Pyrus malus),* Newton Pippin	Resting	....	19	[2.8[2]]	0.86	50
29	*Medicago sativa*	Resting	Mano	18	38	1.08	44
30		Germinating	Mano	18	106	0.86	
31	*Oryza sativa,* Oobe	Resting	Mano	....	0.03[2]	1.15	36
32		Moist	Mano	....	2.8[2]	1.96	
33		Germinating	Mano	....	4.9[2]	1.98	
34		Seedling	Mano	....	1.06[2]	1.00	
35	*Phaseolus vulgaris*	Germinating	....	....	[65]	....	74
36	*Pinus radiata (P. insignis)*	Resting	Mano	....	[0.0013[2]]	....	125
37	*Pisum sativum*	Resting	Mano	28	....	1.00	103
38		Intact	Chem	20	[15[8](35)]	4.9[8](1.1)	100
39	*Prunus amygdalus (Amygdalus communis)*	Germinating	Mano	....	....	0.7; 0.86[6]	35
40	*P. domestica,* Blue Gage	Moist	Mano	25	8.0	0.70	110
41	Burbank	Moist	Mano	25	4.7	0.91	
42	*P. persica*	Moist	Mano	25	5.8	0.68	110
43	*Raphanus sativus*	Resting	Mano	20	7.0	0.86	44
44		Germinating	Mano	20	1.03	0.58	
45	*Ricinus communis*	Resting	Mano	28	....	1.03	103
46		Germinating	Mano	....	....	0.70	86
47		Seedling	Mano	30	133	0.39	89
48		Seedling	Chem	17	[25]	....	115
49	*Rumex crispus*	Moist	Mano	25	6.7	1.16	110
50	*Secale cereale*	Resting	Chem	38	[0.002; 0.11[3]]	....	8
51		Seedling	Chem	18	[12]	....	115
52	*Sorghum vulgare*	Resting	Chem	37.8	[0.011[2]; 0.32[2,3]]	....	8
53	*Triticum aestivum*	Resting	Chem	38	[0.005[2]; 0.16[2,3]]	....	9
54		Germinating	Chem	38	[0.014[2]; 0.53[2,3]]	....	9
55		Seedling	Chem	18	[21]	....	115
56	*Tropaeolum majus,* Sutton's Tall Scarlet	Germinating	Chem	25	....	0.89; 0.68	117

[1] Unless otherwise indicated. [2] μl/100 mg dry wt/hr. [3] Effect of moisture., [5] Effect of development. [6] Effect of growth, development, or maturation. [7] Effect of storage or starvation. [8] Effect of O_2.

continued

101. RESPIRATION RATES: VASCULAR PLANTS

	Species (Synonym)	Condition or Plant Part	Method	Temp °C	Respiration Rate Q_{O_2} [Q_{CO_2}] μl/100 mg wet wt/hr[1]	Respiratory Quotient CO_2/O_2	Reference
57	*Vicia faba*	Resting	Mano	28	....	0.99	103
58		Seedling	Chem	20	[13]	....	115
59	Sutton's Broad Windsor	Germinating	Chem	25	....	1.23; 0.82	117
60	*Zea mays*	Seedling	Chem	18	15	....	115
61	Hopeland Sweet	Resting	Chem	22	[0.24[2]; 1.2[2,3]]	....	3
62	Sutton's Improved Japanese Striped	Germinating	....	25	[10; 127[5]]	0.75; 1.0[5]	72
			Roots				
63	*Allium cepa*	Segment	Mano	25	1390[2]; 1140[2,6]	0.99; 1.07	16
64	*Beta saccharifera*	Slice	Mano	15	1.8	....	79
65				25	6.0	....	
66	*B. vulgaris*	Intact	Chem	25	[0.9[8]; 0.6[7]]	0.8	26
67		Segment	Mano	25	70[2]; 180[2,7]; 110[2,7]	1.01; 0.85	116
68	*Bryonia dioica*	Intact	Mano	Room	[1.5]	0.90	91
69	*Chrysanthemum morifolium (C. sinense)*	Intact	Mano	28	....	0.93	103
70	*Dahlia* sp.	Intact	....	22	[0.9; 0.4[7]]	....	112
71	*Daucus carota*	Slice	Mano	12	4.0	....	79
72				25	10.5	....	
73	Red Core Chantenay	Intact	Chem	0.5	[0.44; 0.22[7]]	0.92; 1.16[7]	99
74				10	[1.5; 0.5[7]]	1.08; 1.01[7]	
75				24	[3.3; 1.5[7]]	1.10; 1.18[7]	
76	*Geranium robertianum*	Intact	Mano	Room	[10.3]	0.86	91
77	*Glycine max (G. soja, Soja max)*	Nodule	Mano	28	60-430[2]	1.0-2.0	2
78	*Gossypium roseum*	Intact	Chem	38	[380[2]; 73[2,6]]	....	58
79	*Hordeum vulgare*, Plumage Archer	Intact	Cond	20	[484[2]; 740[2,8]]	....	128
80	*Impatiens* sp.	Intact	Chem	38	[625[2]; 104[2,6]]	....	58
81	*Ipomoea batatas*	Segment	Mano	25	96	1.0	122
82	Triumph	Intact	Chem	15	[1.4]	....	62
83				25	[3.2]	....	
84				35	[5.6]	....	
85	*Lathyrus odoratus*	Excised	Mano	20	160[2]	....	42
86	*Lespedeza stipulacea*	Nodule	Mano	28	130[2]; 550[2]	0.94; 1.4	2
87	*Lycopersicon esculentum*, Bonny Best	Excised	Mano	25	600[2]; 800[2,9]	1.0	52
88	*Malus pumila (Pyrus malus)*	Intact	Chem	14	[26[2]]	0.73	124
89	*Melilotus alba*	Nodule	Mano	28	380[2]; 660[2]	0.95; 1.09	2
90	*Oryza sativa*	Intact	....	15-18	180[2]; 230[2,6]	....	68
91	*Pastinaca sativa*	Intact	Chem	1.5	[1.1]	....	3
92				22	[2.7]	....	
93	*Raphanus sativus*	Intact	Mano	28	....	0.99	103
94	*Taraxacum officinale*	Intact	Chem	....	[0.04[2]; 0.1[2,10]]	0.94; 1.24[10]	104
95	*Triticum aestivum (T. vulgare)*	Intact	Chem	20	25[2,11](10[2])	....	76
96	*Vicia faba*	Excised	Mano	26	....	1.46	107
97	*Vigna sinensis*	Nodule	Mano	28	71[2]; 580[2]	1.0; 1.1	2
			Stems				
98	*Acacia melanoxylon*	Intact	Mano	Room	[10.5]	0.82	91

1/ Unless otherwise indicated. 2/ μl/100 mg dry wt/hr. 3/ Effect of moisture. 5/ Effect of development. 6/ Effect of growth, development, or maturation. 7/ Effect of storage or starvation. 8/ Effect of O_2. 9/ Effect of organic acids or metabolic poisons. 10/ Effect of herbicides. 11/ Effect of inorganic nutrition, salts.

continued

101. RESPIRATION RATES: VASCULAR PLANTS

	Species (Synonym)	Condition or Plant Part	Method	Temp °C	Respiration Rate Q_{O_2} [Q_{CO_2}] µl/100 mg wet wt/hr[1]	Respiratory Quotient CO_2/O_2	Reference
99	*Acer rubrum*	Xylem	Mano	25	3.7; 2.3[6]	...	45
100		Cambium	Mano	25	22.4[6]	...	
101		Phloem	Mano	25	16.9[6]	...	
102	*Aesculus* sp.	Bud	...	20	[9.7]	...	110
103	*Asparagus officinalis*	Shoot	Chem	30	[915[2]; 254[2,7]]	...	13
104	Mary Washington	Intact	Chem	0.5	[3.0; 2.0[7]]	0.98; 0.95[7]	99
105				10	[9.7; 3.6[7]]	1.03; 0.86[7]	
106				24	[35.4; 13.2[7]]	1.04; 0.95[7]	
107	*Bryonia dioica*	Intact	Mano	Room	[8.5]	0.91	91
108	*Dahlia pinnata (D. variabilis)*	Bulb	Mano	25	...	0.99	103
109	*Elodea* sp.	Shoot	...	7	[15[2]]	...	106
110				15	[31[2]]	...	
111				25	[64[2]]	...	
112	*E. canadensis*	Shoot	Mano	20	90[2]	...	42
113	*Equisetum telmateia*	Shoot or top	Mano	20	[6]	0.78	81
114		Fruiting shoot or top	Mano	20	[100]	0.83	81
115		Intact	Mano	Room	[9.6]	0.80	91
116		Branchlet	Mano	Room	[19]	0.69	91
117	*Fagus sylvatica*	Intact	Mano	5	[0.07]	...	75
118				15	[0.15]	...	
119				20	[0.25]	...	
120	*Fraxinus nigra*	Xylem	Mano	25	[31.3; 1.4[6]]	...	45
121		Cambium	Mano	25	[22[6]]	...	
122		Phloem	Mano	25	[16.7[6]]	...	
123	*Geranium robertianum*	Intact	Mano	Room	[6.5]	0.94	91
124	*Gladiolus* sp.	Corm	Chem	23	[8.5[2]]	...	32
125	*Gossypium roseum*	Intact	Chem	38	[168[2]; 42[2,6]]	...	58
126	*Hedera helix*	Shoot	Mano	20	[23.6]	0.93	5
127	*Helianthus annuus,* Sutton's Giant	Shoot	Chem	5	[76[2]]	...	66
128	Yellow			10	[141[2]]	...	
129				25	[483[2]]	...	
130	*Impatiens* sp.	Intact	Chem	38	[270[2]; 59[2,6]]	...	58
131	*Ipomoea batatas*	Tuber	Chem	30	[1.4; 7.0[7]; 2.4[7]]	...	51
132	*Lathyrus odoratus*	Intact	Mano	20	160[2]	...	42
133		Shoot	Mano	20	350[2]	...	
134	*Lycopersicon esculentum*	Segment	Mano	28	420[2]; 350[2,11]	0.91; 0.95[11]	66
	Malus pumila (Pyrus malus)						31
135	Jonathan	Intact	Chem	6	[2.3; 4.6[12]]	...	
136	McIntosh	Intact	Chem	6	[1.7; 3.8[12]]	...	
137	*Nicotiana glauca* × *N. langsdorffi*	Callus	Mano	30	380[2,13,14]	1.0[13,14]	90
	Phaseolus vulgaris						
138	Black Valentine	Shoot	Chem	24	[190[2,10](150[2])]	...	25
139	California Red Kidney	Intact	Mano	30	28[2]; 710[2,10,14]	0.9; 1.1[10,14]	113
140	*Picea abies (P. excelsa)*	Shoot	Mano	19	25.0; 6.3[6]	...	5
141	*Pisum sativum,* Alaska	Segment	Mano	25	334[2,7](532[2])	0.98[7](1.07)	27
142	*Prunus laurocerasus*	Shoot	Chem	22.5	[14.4; 2.6[7]]	...	7
143	*Quercus coccifera*	Segment	Mano	21	[31; 11[6]]	0.91; 0.83[6]	92
144	*Ranunculus pseudofluitans*	Tip	Elec	10	41.2[2]	...	97
145				15	81.1[2]	...	
146				20	111.0[2]	...	

1/ Unless otherwise indicated. 2/ µl/100 mg dry wt/hr. 6/ Effect of growth, development, or maturation. 7/ Effect of storage or starvation. 10/ Effect of herbicides. 11/ Effect of inorganic nutrition, salts. 12/ Effect of precooling. 13/ Effect of pH. 14/ Effect of metabolic poisons.

continued

	Species (Synonym)	Condition or Plant Part	Method	Temp °C	Respiration Rate Q_{O_2} [Q_{CO_2}] µl/100 mg wet wt/hr[1/]	Respiratory Quotient CO_2/O_2	Reference
147	*Raphanus raphanistrum*	Intact	Mano	Room	[10.5]	0.87	91
148	*Ricinus communis*	Shoot	Mano	20	[19.2]	0.96	5
149	*Rumex pulcher*	Intact	Mano	Room	[11.8]	0.85	91
150	*Saccharum officinarum*	Intact	Chem	28	[27[2/]; 4[2,6/]]	...	53
151	Pindar	Intact	Chem	6	[0.14-0.27]	...	18
152				15	[0.36-0.72]	...	
153				35	[1.4-2.7]	...	
154				45	[1.6-3.1]	...	
155	*Salix herbacea*	Shoot	Chem	0	[2.5]	...	121
156				10	[9.1]	...	
157				20	[23.4]	...	
158	*Saxifraga oppositifolia*	Shoot	Chem	0	[0.87]	...	121
159				20	[7.1]	...	
160				40	[25]	...	
161	*Sedum acre*	Shoot	Mano	25	7.2; 7.1[15/]	0.96; 0.84[15/]	5
162	*S. reflexum*	Intact	Mano	23 & 31	[12.0; 8.7[15/]]	0.98; 0.88[15/]	5
	Solanum tuberosum						
163	Rural	Tuber	Chem	0.5	[0.07; 0.15[7/]]	0.45; 0.66[7/]	99
164				10	[0.2; 0.15[7/]]	0.86; 0.99[7/]	
165				24	[0.6; 0.3[7/]]	1.02; 0.75[7/]	
166	Russet Burbank	Tuber	Chem	2.5	[0.2]	...	3
167				22	[0.5]	...	
168		Tuber[16/]	Mano	25	3.3	...	80
169			Elec	0	0.28	...	
170				5	0.26	...	
171				14	1.5	...	
172				24	3.1	...	
173		Tuber[17/]	Mano	25	13.5	...	80
174			Elec	0	1.5	...	
175				5	2.6	...	
176				14	6.1	...	
177				24	12.5	...	
178	Sebago	Tuber	Chem	22	[7.3; 1.8[6/]]	...	39
179					[0.5; 1[7/]]	...	
180	*Syringa vulgaris*	Cambium	Mano	...	...	1.29; 1.38	107
181	*Taxus baccata*	Shoot	Mano	28	...	0.97	103
182	*Triticum aestivum (T. sativum)*	Shoot	Mano	8	[19]	1.03	5
183				13	[29]	0.98	
184	*Vicia faba*	Intact	Mano	Room	[6.2]	...	91
185		Shoot	Mano	21	[62.6]	0.90	
186		Shoot, etiolated	Mano	21	[48.8]	0.87	
187	*Zea mays*	Shoot	Mano	30	[760[2,15/]]	...	47
	Leaves						
188	*Acacia melanoxylon*	Tendril, phyllode, or cladode	Mano	Room	[11.9]	0.66	91
189	*Acer pseudoplatanus*	Intact	Chem	10	[33]	...	101
190	*Aesculus hippocastanum*	Intact	Mano	0	[6]	0.97	22
191				14	[25]	1.01	
192				25	[77]	0.98	

[1/] Unless otherwise indicated. [2/] µl/100 mg dry wt/hr. [6/] Effect of growth, development, or maturation. [7/] Effect of storage or starvation. [15/] Effect of light or photoperiod. [16/] Slices freshly cut. [17/] Slices aged 24 hours.

continued

101. RESPIRATION RATES: VASCULAR PLANTS

	Species (Synonym)	Condition or Plant Part	Method	Temp °C	Respiration Rate Q_{O_2} [Q_{CO_2}] µl/100 mg wet wt/hr[1/]	Respiratory Quotient CO_2/O_2	Reference
193	*Allium cepa,* Yellow Blade	Bulb	Chem	22	[2.1]	....	3
194	*Antirrhinum majus*	Intact	Mano	20	[16]	0.88	81
195	*Asparagus albus*	Tendril, phyl-lode, or cladode	Mano	Room	[22.3]	0.78	91
196	*Asplenium adiantum nigrum*	Frond	Mano	20	[13]	0.86	81
197		Frond with sori	Mano	20	[17]	1.01	81
198		Blade	Mano	Room	[13.4]	0.80	91
199		Petiole	Mano	Room	[8.3]	0.80	91
200	*Begonia tuberhybrida*	Intact	....	36	[13[18/]]	0.79	87
201	*Beta vulgaris*	Intact	Chem	27	[23]	....	84
202	*Betula nana*	Intact	Chem	10	[26]	....	121
203				20	[66]	....	
204	*Bryonia dioica*	Intact	Mano	20	[76; 11[6/]]	0.90; 0.60[6/]	92
205		Blade	Mano	Room	[13.2]	0.65	91
206		Petiole	Mano	Room	[9.4]	0.87	91
207		Tendril, phyl-lode, or cladode	Mano	Room	[11.3]	1.02	91
208	*Calonyction aculeatum (Ipomoea grandiflora)*	Intact	Mano	20	220[2/]	....	42
209	*Camellia sinensis (Thea sinensis)*	Segment	Mano	36	80; 46[7/]	1.27; 0.74[7/]	30
210			Chem	36	[16.4]	....	
211	*Castanea* sp.	Intact	Mano	25	....	1.02; 0.92[6/]	82
212	*Catalpa bignonioides*	Intact	Chem	14	[18-25]	....	101
213	*Citrus limon*	Intact	Mano	....	7.7-9.5[18/]	....	123
214	*C. sinensis,* Washington Navel	Intact	Mano	....	9.6-12.9[18/]	....	123
215	*Dryopteris austriaca*	Frond	Chem	10	[25]	....	60
216				30	[36]	....	
217				48	[122]	....	
218	*Elodea canadensis*	Intact	Mano, Chem	....	....	8.4	105
219	*Fagus sylvatica*	Intact	Chem	20	[1-5[18/]]	....	23
220	*Fragaria* sp.	Intact	Chem	24.5	[10[18/]; 5[6,18/]]	....	4
221	*Fraxinus excelsior*	Intact	Chem	20	[1[18/]; 6[15,18/]]	....	23
222	*Geranium robertianum*	Blade	Mano	Room	[13.9]	0.72	91
223		Petiole	Mano	Room	[4.4]	0.91	
224	*Gladiolus gandavensis*	Intact	Mano	24	[18]	0.64	81
225	*Gossypium roseum*	Intact	Chem	38	[224[2/]; 94[2,6/]]	....	58
226	*Hedera helix*	Intact	Mano	25	50; 80[6/]	....	11
227	*Helianthus annuus*	Intact	Chem	25	[9[18/]; 3[7,18/]]	....	114
228	*Hibiscus rosa-sinensis*	Intact	Chem	20	[1.3[18/]]	....	40
229	*Hordeum vulgare*	Intact	Chem	25	[76; 15[7/]]	1.2; 0.8[7/]	129
230	*Ilex aquifolium*	Intact	Mano	21	[12]	....	115
231	*Impatiens* sp.	Intact	Chem	38	[312[2/]; 120[2,6/]]	....	58
232	*Iris germanica*	Intact	Chem	22.5	[12; 13.6[7/]; 5[7/]]	....	6
233	*Lactuca sativa,* Imperial 44	Intact	Chem	0.5	[0.8; 0.35[7/]]	0.84; 0.98[7/]	98
234				10	[1.3; 0.73[7/]]	1.09; 0.93[7/]	
235				24	[3.3; 2.6[7/]]	1.12; 0.99[7/]	
236	*Lathyrus odoratus*	Intact	Mano	20	170[2/]	....	42
	Lycopersicon esculentum						
237	Bonny Best	Segment	Mano	28	390[2/]; 430[2,11/] [0.96; 0.91[11/]]	....	67

[1/] Unless otherwise indicated. [2/] µl/100 mg dry wt/hr. [6/] Effect of growth, development, or maturation. [7/] Effect of storage or starvation. [11/] Effect of inorganic nutrition, salts. [15/] Effect of light or photoperiod. [18/] µl/cm²/hr.

continued

101. RESPIRATION RATES: VASCULAR PLANTS

	Species (Synonym)	Condition or Plant Part	Method	Temp °C	Respiration Rate Q_{O_2} [Q_{CO_2}] µl/100 mg wet wt/hr[1]	Respiratory Quotient CO_2/O_2	Reference
238	John Baer	Segment	Mano	30	46[11]/(42)	1.13[11]/(1.28)	118
239	Michigan State Forcing	Intact	Mano	27	260[2]; 320[2,15]	...	34
240	*Malus pumila (Pyrus malus),* McIntosh	Intact	Chem	33	[8.6[18]; 43.0[3,18]]	...	108
241	*Nicotiana glauca × N. langsdorffi*	Segment	Mano	25	330[2]; 170[2,6]	1.27; 1.43[6]	90
242	*Oenothera biennis*	Blade	Mano	18	[24; 12[6]]	0.83; 0.70[6]	92
243	*Phaseolus vulgaris*	Intact	Mano	26	26-57	...	61
244	*Phleum pratense*	Intact	...	21-26	124[2]	...	68
245	*Phoenix dactylifera*	Intact	Chem	20	[4.5[18]]	...	40
246	*Phyllitis scolopendrium (Scolo-*	Frond	Mano	3	2.2	...	12
247	*pendrium scolopendrium)*			13	9.9	...	
248				22	17.5	...	
249				25	23; 130[6]; 40[6]	...	
250				30	31	...	
251	*Pinus pinea*	Intact	Mano	14	[6.9]	0.82	22
252				24	[12]	0.83	
253	*Pisum sativum,* Alaska	Intact	Mano	27	430[2]; 680[2,15]	...	34
254	*Polypodium vulgare*	Frond	Mano	20	[10]	0.92	81
255		Frond with sori	Mano	20	[19]	1.06	81
256		Frond	Chem	16	[250; 86[6]]	...	60
257	*Populus deltoides × P. nigra (P. canadensis)*	Intact	Chem	...	[19]	...	101
258	*Prunus amygdalus (Amygdalus communis)*	Intact	Mano	14	[29]	1.00	93
259	*P. laurocerasus*	Intact	Chem	22.5	[20; 3.4[7]; 13.6[7]]	...	7
260	*Pteridium aquilinum (Eupteris*	Frond	Mano	22	[19]	0.84	81
261	*aquilina)*	Frond with sori	Mano	22	[35]	1.01	
262	*Pteridium aquilinum (Eupteris*	Frond	Chem	10	[15]	...	60
263	*aquilina)*			30	[46]	...	
264				48	[168]	...	
265				15.5	[265; 66[6]]	...	
266	*Quercus coccifera*	Intact	Mano	21	[44; 13[6]]	0.87; 0.79[6]	92
267	*Raphanus raphanistrum*	Blade	Mano	Room	[13.3]	0.73	91
268		Petiole	Mano	Room	[6.2]	0.86	
269	*Rheum rhaponticum*	Segment	Mano	30	[29]	1.17	88
270	*Rhododendron fargesi*	Intact	Chem	22.5	[13.6; 5.1[7]]	...	6
271	*Rosa* sp.	Intact	Mano	14	[23]	0.93	93
272	*Rumex pulcher*	Blade	Mano	Room	[14.7]	0.76	91
273		Petiole	Mano	Room	[3.3]	0.80	
274	*Salix glauca*	Intact	Chem	0	[13]	...	121
275				10	[45]	...	
276				20	[78]	...	
277	*Saxifraga cernua*	Intact	Chem	0	[2.4]	...	121
278				10	[5.6]	...	
279				20	[17.8]	...	
280	*Secale cereale*	Intact	Mano	15	[26]	...	19
281				25	[44]	...	
282	*Sedum acre*	Intact	Mano	25	...	1.07	82
283	*Solanum tuberosum*	Intact	Chem	10	10	...	60
284				30	[41]	...	
285				48	[137]	...	

[1] Unless otherwise indicated. [2] µl/100 mg dry wt/hr. [3] Effect of moisture. [6] Effect of growth, development, or maturation. [7] Effect of storage or starvation. [11] Effect of inorganic nutrition, salts. [15] Effect of light or photoperiod. [18] $\mu l/cm^2/hr$.

continued

	Species (Synonym)	Condition or Plant Part	Method	Temp °C	Respiration Rate Q_{O_2} [Q_{CO_2}] µl/100 mg wet wt/hr[1]	Respiratory Quotient CO_2/O_2	Reference
286	*Sorghum vulgare*	Intact	Chem	....	[1.2[2]; 0.2[2,6]]	....	54
287	*Spinacia oleracea*	Intact	Chem	20	[4.7[8]/(7.2)]	0.87[8]/(0.82)	100
288		Segment	Mano	30	41[7]/(62)	1.0; 0.74[7]	21
289	*Syringa vulgaris*	Intact	Mano	18	[3.7]	0.98	22
290				24	[7.5]	0.94	
291				32	[28]	0.99	
292	*Taraxacum officinale*	Intact	Mano	19	[48.5]	0.95	70
293	*Taxus baccata*	Intact	Mano	16	[6]	0.86	22
294				34	[23]	0.80	
295				46	[55]	0.89	
296	*Tradescantia viridis*	Intact	Mano	29	....	1.01	103
297	*Triticum aestivum (T. sativum)*	Intact	Mano	25	[40.2]	0.97	91
298		Intact, etiolated	Mano	25	[37.5]	0.98	
299	*Tulipa* sp., Le Notre	Bulb	....	20	[4.6[2]; 2.8[2,7]; 8.6[2,7]]	1.2; 1.1[7]; 2.6[7]	1
300	*Ulmus glabra (U. montana)*	Intact	Chem	16	[24]	....	101
301	*Vicia faba*	Blade	Mano	Room	[11.1]	....	91
302		Petiole	Mano	Room	[4.1]	....	
303	*Vitis vinifera*	Blade	Chem	....	[81[2]]	....	85
304	*Yucca gloriosa*	Intact	Chem	22.5	[8.5; 3.3[7]]	....	6
305	*Zea mays*	Intact	Mano	26	[68.3]	0.99	91
306		Intact, etiolated	Mano	26	[54.1]	0.97	
			Flowers				
307	*Antirrhinum majus*	Petal	Mano	23	[82; 70[6]; 34[6]]	1.15; 1.13[6]; 1.00[6]	81
308		Stamen	Mano	24	[81; 106[6]; 76[6]]	....	
309	*Arum maculatum*	Spadix	Mano	30	1560[2]; 3180[2,6]; 780[2,6]	1.09; 0.87[6]	59
310	*Begonia rex*	Petal	Mano	20	[37]	....	81
311		Sepal	Mano	20	[39]	....	
312		Stamen	Mano	20	[43]	....	
313		Pistil	Mano	20	[31]	....	
314	*Camellia sinensis (Thea sinensis)*	Pollen	Mano	15	690[2]	1.18	94,95
315	*Cucumis sativus*	Pistil	Mano	22	[48; 43[6]; 29[6]]	....	81
316	*Dahlia pinnata (D. variabilis)*	Petal	Mano	28	....	0.94	103
317	*Gladiolus gandavensis*	Petal	Mano	24	[15]	0.72	81
318		Stamen	Mano	24	[27]	0.77	
319		Pistil	Mano	24	[71]	0.90	
320	*Helianthus annuus*	Inflorescence	Chem	10	[57[2]; 43[2,6]]	....	66
321	*Hibiscus rosa-sinensis*	Petal	Mano	26	[130; 86[6]; 38[6]]	1.06; 1.04[6]; 0.96[6]	81
322		Sepal	Mano	24	[75; 44[6]; 29[6]]	0.81; 0.90[6]; 0.94[6]	
323	*Lathyrus odoratus*	Petal	Mano	20	330[2]	....	42
324		Filament	Mano	20	160[2]	....	
325		Ovary	Mano	20	300[2]	....	
326		Ovule	Mano	20	420[2]	....	
327	*Lilium bulbiferum (L. croceum)*	Stamen	....	....	[56; 21[6]]	1.14; 0.98[6]	48
328		Pistil	....	....	[58; 19[6]]	1.06; 1.12[6]	
329	*Pinus densiflora*	Pollen	Mano	25	160[2]	....	94,95
330	*Rosa* sp.	Intact	Mano	28	....	1.04	81
331	*Syringa vulgaris*	Intact	....	20	[40]	....	110

[1] Unless otherwise indicated. [2] µl/100 mg dry wt/hr. [6] Effect of growth, development, or maturation. [7] Effect of storage or starvation. [8] Effect of O_2.

continued

	Species (Synonym)	Condition or Plant Part	Method	Temp °C	Respiration Rate Q_{O_2} [Q_{CO_2}] µl/100 mg wet wt/hr[1/]	Respiratory Quotient CO_2/O_2	Reference
332	*Tulipa gesneriana*	Intact	....	28	....	0.95	103
333		Pollen	Mano	20	300[2/]	....	94,95
334	*Yucca gloriosa*	Petal	Mano	24	[67; 41[6/]; 44[6/]]	0.91; 0.97[6/]; 1.07[6/]	81
335		Pistil	Mano	16	[24; 23[6/]; 22[6/]]	....	
			Fruits				
336	*Ananas comosus (A. sativus)*	Intact	Chem	......	3	1.2	71
337	*Bryonia dioica*	Intact	Chem	25	[64; 8.5[6/]]	....	119
338	*Capsicum frutescens,* Windsor A	Intact	Chem	0.5	[0.44; 0.29[7/]]	0.96[7/]	99
339				10	[1.2; 0.58[7/]]	1.27; 0.88[7/]	
340				24	[4.0; 1.4[7/]]	1.12; 0.88[7/]	
341	*(C. annuum),* California Wonder	Slices	Mano	25	8; 3[6/] [5; 2[6/]]	0.6	55
342	*Carica papaya,* Solo	Intact	Chem	4.4	[0.24]	....	64
343				10	[0.46]	....	
344				15.6	[0.83]	....	
345	*Citrus grandis,* Marsh	Intact	....	0	[0.1]	1.2	49
346				10	[0.4]	1.4	
347				21	[1.0]	1.1	
348				38	[2.5]	2.1	
349	*C. limon*	Intact	Magn	20	0.7; 0.14[7/]	....	130
350	Eureka	Intact	....	0	[0.15]	1.2	49
351				21	[1.1]	1.0	
352				38	[4.1]	1.4	
353	*C. sinensis,* Washington Navel	Intact	....	0	[0.15]	1.2	49
354				10	[0.8]	1.1	
355				21	[2.0]	1.1	
356	*Cocos nucifera*	Endocarp & nucellus	Mano	30	400[2/]; 0[2,6/]	....	29
357	*Cucumis melo*	Intact	Gas	20	[1.9; 4.3[7/]]	....	78
358				30	[4; 6.5[7/]]	....	
359	Cantaloupe	Intact	Color	20	[2.5; 1.3[6/]; 4.5[6/]]	....	83
360	*C. sativus,* Davis Perfect	Intact	Chem	0.5	[0.2; 0.08[7/]]	0.97; 0.88[7/]	99
361				10	[1.0; 0.4[7/]]	1.01; 1.10[7/]	
362				24	[2.3; 0.8[7/]]	1.01; 0.91[7/]	
363	*Fragaria* sp.	Intact	Chem	20	[3.3; 5.1[6/]]	0.84; 0.91[6/]	96
364	*Hedera helix*	Intact	Chem	20	[13; 50[6/]; 19[6/]]	....	120
365	*Helianthus annuus*	Intact	Mano	25	....	0.96	103
366	*Hibiscus esculentus*	Intact	Chem	30	[306[2/]; 104[2,7/]]	....	13
367	*Lycopersicon esculentum (Solanum lycopersicum)*	Intact	Mano	28	....	1.9	103
368	Marglobe	Intact	Chem	0.5	[0.36; 0.15[7/]]	1.11; 0.9[7/]	99
369				10	[0.77; 0.58[7/]]	1.39; 1.06[7/]	
370				24	[2.5; 1.6[7/]]	1.11; 1.13[7/]	
	Malus pumila (Pyrus malus)						
371	Cox's Orange	Intact	Chem	12	[0.6; 1.4[7/]]	....	57
372				15	[0.7; 1.6[7/]]	....	
373	Early Victoria	Intact	Chem	12	[2.8; 0.7[6/]; 1.0[6/]]	....	56
374	Jonathan	Intact	Mano	27	[2.4; 5.1[6/]; 0.6[6/]]	0.43; 0.91[6/]	109
375		Intact	Chem	20	[1.7; 0.8[6/]]	....	38

[1/] Unless otherwise indicated. [2/] µl/100 mg dry wt/hr. [6/] Effect of growth, development, or maturation. [7/] Effect of storage or starvation.

continued

	Species (Synonym)	Condition or Plant Part	Method	Temp °C	Respiration Rate Q_{O_2} [Q_{CO_2}] µl/100 mg wet wt/hr[1]	Respiratory Quotient CO_2/O_2	Reference
376	*Musa sapientum*	Intact	Chem	0	[0.4]	....	41
377				12.5	[0.9]	....	
378				20	[1.8]	....	
379				31	[3.1]	....	
380			Magn	15	1; 0[7]; 3.7[7]	....	130
381			IR	18	[1.0; 5.7[7]]	....	10
382		Slices	Mano	25	5.1; 5.8[7]; 1.9[7]	....	10
383	*Nicotiana tabacum*	Intact	Mano	28	....	0.94	103
384	*Persea americana (P. gratissima)*	Intact	Magn	15	2.5; 8.5[7]	....	15,130
385				20	2; 12[7]	....	15,130
386		Peel	Magn	20	12; 20[7]	....	14
387		Pulp	Magn	20	12; 20[7]	....	14
388	Fuerte	Intact	Chem	15	[5.8; 3.6[7]; 8.1[7]]	....	17,102
389	*Phaseolus vulgaris,* Tendergreen	Intact	Chem	0.5	[0.95; 0.65[7]]	0.94; 0.96[7]	99
390				10	[4.6; 2.0[7]]	1.08; 0.98[7]	
391				24	[16.4; 6.6[7]]	1.14; 1.00[7]	
392	*Pisum sativum,* Laxton Progress	Intact	Chem	0.5	[2.2; 1.4[7]]	1.07; 0.96[7]	99
393				10	[7.9; 3.1[7]]	1.13; 1.00[7]	
394				24	[20; 12[7]]	1.32; 1.06[7]	
395	*Prunus domestica,* Santa Rosa	Intact	Chem	4	[0.5]	....	28
396				18	[1.7; 3.6[7]]	....	
397	*P. persica,* Primrose	Intact	Chem	4	[0.4; 0.3[7]]	....	28
398				18	[1.4; 2.0[7]]	....	
399	*Pyrus communis,* Bartlett	Intact	Chem	18	[6.3; 1.0[6]; 1.2[6]]	....	37
400	*Quercus alba*	Intact	Mano	2.5	17[2]	0.16	24
401				10	16[2]	0.30	
402				30	21[2]	0.71	
403	*Ribes nigrum*	Intact	Chem	1.2	[0.5]	....	46
404				11.2	[1.5]	....	
405				30.9	[7.7]	....	
406	*R. rubrum*	Intact	Mano	28	....	1.4	103
407	Fay	Intact	Chem	1.8	[0.3]	....	46
408				11.8	[0.7]	....	
409				32.0	[3.2]	....	
410	*Ricinus communis*	Intact	Mano	28	....	1.07	103
411	*Rosa* sp.	Intact	Mano	28	....	0.86	103
412	*Secale cereale,* Abbruzzi	Intact	Mano	28	245[2]; 12[2,6]	....	111
413	*Triticum aestivum (T. vulgare),* Leapland	Intact	Mano	28	340[2]; 8[2,6]	....	111
414	*Vitis vinifera*	Intact	....	0	0.15 [0.14]	0.91	77
415				10	0.5 [0.5]	1.05	
416				21.1	1.4 [1.7]	1.20	
417				26.7	1.6 [2.0]	1.25	
418	*Zea mays,* Stowell's Evergreen	Intact	Chem	4.5	[3.5]	....	3
419	Sweet			28	[11-17]	....	
	Whole Plants						
420	*Berula erecta*	Intact	Elec	10	31.4[2]	....	97
421				15	49.5[2]	....	
422				20	64.3[2]	....	
423	*Betula nana*	Intact	Mano	16	[7.0[18]]	0.93	69

[1] Unless otherwise indicated. [2] µl/100 mg dry wt/hr. [6] Effect of growth, development, or maturation. [7] Effect of storage or starvation. [18] µl/cm²/hr.

continued

	Species (Synonym)	Condition or Plant Part	Method	Temp °C	Respiration Rate Q_{O_2} [Q_{CO_2}] µl/100 mg wet wt/hr 1/	Respiratory Quotient CO_2/O_2	Reference
424	*Gossypium roseum*	Intact	Chem	38	[198 2/; 65 2,6/]	....	58
425	*Helianthus annuus,* Sutton's Giant Yellow	Intact	Chem	10	[148 2/; 13 2,6/]	....	66
426	*Impatiens* sp.	Intact	Chem	38	[390 2/; 91 2,6/]	....	58
427	*Ipomoea batatas,* Big Stem Jersey	Intact	Mano	21	[1; 2 19/]	....	127
428	*Nicotiana tabacum,* Samsun	Intact	Chem	....	[(7.7) 20/; 10.0 21/]	....	43
429	*Ranunculus pseudofluitans*	Intact	Elec	20	100.0 2/	....	97
430	*Ricinus communis*	Intact	Mano	30	180	0.78	89
431	*Sedum hybridum*	Intact	....	26	....	0.37	110
432	*Solanum tuberosum,* Arran Comrade	Intact	Chem	19	[10.7 20/; 14.3 21/]	....	126
433	*Triticum aestivum,* Minhardi	Intact	Chem	2	[38 2/; 13 2,7/]	....	33

1/ Unless otherwise indicated. 2/ µl/100 mg dry wt/hr. 6/ Effect of growth, development, or maturation. 7/ Effect of storage or starvation. 19/ Effect of wounding. 20/ Healthy. 21/ Diseased.

Contributors: (a) Mandels, Gabriel R., and Darby, Richard T., (b) Forward, Dorothy F.

References

[1] Algera, L. 1936. Koninkl. Ned. Akad. Wetenschap. Proc., Sect. Sci., 39:846, 971, 1106.
[2] Allison, F. E., et al. 1940. Botan. Gaz. 101:513.
[3] Appleman, C. O., and R. G. Brown. 1946. Am. J. Botany 33:170.
[4] Arney, S. E. 1947. New Phytologist 46:68.
[5] Aubert, E. 1892. Rev. Gen. Botan. 4:421.
[6] Audus, L. J. 1939. New Phytologist 38:284.
[7] Audus, L. J. 1947. Ann. Botany (London), N.S. 11:165.
[8] Bailey, C. H. 1946. Plant Physiol. 15:257.
[9] Bailey, C. H., and A. M. Gurjar. 1920. J. Biol. Chem. 44:17.
[10] Baur, J. R., and M. Workman. 1964. Plant Physiol. 39:540.
[11] Beatty, A. V. 1946. Am. J. Botany 33:145.
[12] Belehradek, J., and M. Belehradkova. 1929. New Phytologist 28:313.
[13] Benoy, M. P. 1929. J. Agr. Res. 39:75.
[14] Ben-Yehoshua, S. 1964. Physiol. Plantarum 17:71.
[15] Ben-Yehoshua, S., R. N. Robertson, and J. B. Biale. 1963. Plant Physiol. 38:194.
[16] Berry, L. J. 1949. J. Cellular Comp. Physiol. 33:41.
[17] Biale, J. B. 1946. Am. J. Botany 33:363.
[18] Bieleski, R. L. 1958. Australian J. Biol. Sci. 11:315.
[19] Blanc, L. 1916. Rev. Gen. Botan. 28:65.
[20] Bonner, J. 1949. Am. J. Botany 36:429.
[21] Bonner, J., and S. G. Wildman. 1946. Arch. Biochem. 10:497.
[22] Bonnier, G., and L. Mangin. 1884. Ann. Sci. Nat. Zool., Ser. 6, 19:217.
[23] Boysen-Jensen, P., and D. Müller. 1929. Jahrb. Wiss. Botan. 70:503.
[24] Brown, J. W. 1939. Plant Physiol. 14:621.
[25] Brown, J. W. 1946. Botan. Gaz. 107:332.
[26] Choudhury, J. K. 1939. Proc. Roy. Soc. (London), B, 127:238.
[27] Christiansen, G. S., and K. V. Thimann. 1950. Arch. Biochem. 26:248.
[28] Claypool, L. L., and F. W. Allen. 1948. Proc. Am. Soc. Hort. Sci. 51:103.
[29] Cutter, V. M., Jr., K. S. Wilson, and J. F. Dube. 1952. Am. J. Botany 39:51.
[30] Deb, S. B., and E. A. Roberts. 1940. Biochem. J. 34:1507.
[31] DeLong, W. A., J. H. Beaumont, and J. J. Willaman. 1930. Plant Physiol. 15:509.
[32] Denny, F. E. 1939. Contrib. Boyce Thompson Inst. 10:453.
[33] Dexter, S. T. 1934. Plant Physiol. 9:831.
[34] Elliott, B. B., and A. C. Leopold. 1952. Ibid. 27:787.
[35] Ermakov, A. I., and N. N. Ivanov. 1931. Biochem. Z. 231:79.
[36] Erygin, P. S. 1936. Plant Physiol. 11:821.
[37] Ezell, B. D., and F. Gerhardt. 1938. J. Agr. Res. 56: 365.
[38] Ezell, B. D., and F. Gerhardt. 1942. Ibid. 65:453.
[39] Forward, D. F. 1953. Can. J. Botany 31:33.
[40] Gabrielsen, E. K. 1931. Planta 14:217.
[41] Gane, R. 1936. New Phytologist 35:383.
[42] Genevois, L. 1927. Biochem. Z. 191:147.
[43] Glasstone, V. F. 1942. Plant Physiol. 17:267.
[44] Godlewski, E. 1882. Jahrb. Wiss. Botan. 13:491.
[45] Goodwin, R. H., and D. R. Goddard. 1940. Am. J. Botany 27:234.
[46] Gore, H. C. 1911. U.S. Dept. Agr. Bur. Chem. Bull. 142.
[47] Groner, M. G. 1936. Am. J. Botany 23:381.
[48] Guilcher, J. M. 1937. Rev. Gen. Botan. 49:235.
[49] Haller, M. H., et al. 1945. J. Agr. Res. 71:327.

continued

[50] Harrington, G. T. 1923. Ibid. 23:117.
[51] Hasselbring, H., and L. A. Hawkins. 1913. Ibid. 5: 509.
[52] Henderson, J. H., and J. F. Stauffer. 1944. Am. J. Botany 31:528.
[53] Hes, J. W. 1949. Koninkl. Ned. Akad. Wetenschap. Proc., Sect. Sci., 52:915.
[54] Hover, J. M., and F. G. Gustafson. 1926. J. Gen. Physiol. 10:33.
[55] Howard, F. D., and M. Yamaguchi. 1957. Plant Physiol. 32:418.
[56] Hulme, A. C. 1951. J. Hort. Sci. 26:118.
[57] Hulme, A. C. 1954. Ibid. 29:142.
[58] Inamdar, R. S., S. B. Singh, and T. D. Pande. 1925. Ann. Botany (London) 39:281.
[59] James, W. D., and H. Beevers. 1950. New Phytologist 49:353.
[60] Johansson, N. 1926. Svensk Botan. Tidskr. 20:107.
[61] Johnson, C. M., and W. M. Hoskins. 1952. Plant Physiol. 27:507.
[62] Johnstone, G. R. 1925. Botan. Gaz. 80:145.
[63] Jones, H. A. 1920. Ibid. 69:127.
[64] Jones, W. W. 1942. Plant Physiol. 17:481.
[65] Karon, M. L., and A. M. Altschul. 1946. Ibid. 21: 506.
[66] Kidd, F., C. West, and G. E. Briggs. 1921. Proc. Roy. Soc. (London), B, 92:368.
[67] Klein, R. M. 1951. Arch. Biochem. 30:207.
[68] Kostytschev, S. 1927. Plant respiration. Blakiston, Philadelphia.
[69] Krascheninnikoff, T. 1926. Compt. Rend. 182:939.
[70] Kylin, H. 1911. Arkiv Botan. 11:1.
[71] Langworthy, C. F., R. D. Milner, and H. G. Barott. 1920. J. Biol. Chem. 41:LXIX.
[72] Leach, W. 1936. Proc. Roy. Soc. (London), B, 119: 507.
[73] Leach, W., and K. W. Dent. 1934. Ibid., B, 116:150.
[74] Lewin, M. 1905. Ber. Deut. Botan. Ges. 23:100.
[75] Löhr, E. 1957. Physiol. Plantarum 10:340.
[76] Lundegardh, H. 1950. Nature 165:513.
[77] Lutz, J. M. 1938. U.S. Dept. Agr. Tech. Bull. 606.
[78] Lyons, J. M., W. B. McGlasson, and H. K. Pratt. 1962. Plant Physiol. 37:31.
[79] MacDonald, I. R., and P. C. deKock. 1958. Ann. Botany (London), N.S. 22:429.
[80] MacDonald, I. R., and G. C. Laties. 1962. J. Exptl. Botany 13:435.
[81] Maige, G. 1911. Ann. Sci. Nat. Botan. Biol. Vegetale, Ser. 9, 14:1.
[82] Maquenne, L., and E. Demoussey. 1913. Compt. Rend. 156:278.
[83] McGlasson, W. B., and H. K. Pratt. 1964. Plant Physiol. 39:120.
[84] Meyer, A., and N. T. Deleano. 1911. Z. Botan. 3: 657.
[85] Meyer, A., and N. T. Deleano. 1913. Ibid. 5:209.
[86] Meyer, B. S., and D. S. Rader. 1936. Plant Physiol. 11:437.
[87] Miller, E. S., and G. O. Burr. 1935. Ibid. 10:93.
[88] Morrison, J. F. 1949. Australian J. Exptl. Biol. Med. Sci. 27:581.
[89] Murlin, J. R. 1933. J. Gen. Physiol. 17:283.
[90] Newcomb, E. H. 1950. Am. J. Botany 37:264.
[91] Nicolas, G. 1909. Ann. Sci. Nat. Botan. Biol. Vegetale, Ser. 9, 10:1.
[92] Nicolas, G. 1918. Rev. Gen. Botan. 30:209.
[93] Nicolas, G. 1919. Ibid. 31:161.
[94] Okunuki, K. 1937. Acta Phytochim. (Japan) 9: 267.
[95] Okunuki, K. 1939. Ibid. 11:27.
[96] Overholser, E. L., M. B. Hardy, and H. D. Locklin. 1931. Plant Physiol. 6:549.
[97] Owens, M., and P. J. Maris. 1964. Hydrobiologia 23:533.
[98] Pack, D. A. 1920. Botan. Gaz. 71:32.
[99] Platenius, H. 1942. Plant Physiol. 17:179.
[100] Platenius, H. 1943. Ibid. 18:671.
[101] Plester, W. 1912. Beitr. Biol. Pflanz. 11:249.
[102] Pratt, R., and J. B. Biale. 1944. Plant Physiol. 19: 519.
[103] Pringsheim, E. G. 1935. Jahrb. Wiss. Botan. 81:579.
[104] Rasmussen, L. W. 1947. Plant Physiol. 22:377.
[105] Ronkin, R. R., and S. C. Brooks. 1942. Science 95: 231.
[106] Rosenfels, R. S. 1935. Protoplasma 23:503.
[107] Ruhland, W., and K. Ramshorn. 1938. Planta 28: 471.
[108] Schneider, G. W., and N. F. Childers. 1941. Plant Physiol. 16:565.
[109] Shaw, S. T. 1942. Ibid. 17:80.
[110] Sherman, H. 1921. Botan. Gaz. 72:1.
[111] Shirk, H. G. 1942. Am. J. Botany 29:105.
[112] Smith, C. L. 1936. J. Agr. Res. 53:557.
[113] Smith, F. G. 1948. Plant Physiol. 23:70.
[114] Spoehr, H. A., and J. M. McGee. 1924. Am. J. Botany 11:493.
[115] Stich, C. 1891. Flora (Jena) 74:1.
[116] Stiles, W., and K. W. Dent. 1947. Ann. Botany (London), N.S. 11:1.
[117] Stiles, W., and W. Leach. 1933. Proc. Roy. Soc. (London), B, 113:405.
[118] Tsui, C. 1949. Nature 164:970.
[119] Ulrich, R. 1944. Bull. Soc. Botan. France 91:210.
[120] Ulrich, R. 1945. Ibid. 92:131.
[121] Wager, H. G. 1941. New Phytologist 40:1.
[122] Walter, E. M., and J. M. Nelson. 1945. Arch. Biochem. 6:131.
[123] Wedding, R. T., L. A. Riehl, and W. A. Rhoads. 1952. Plant Physiol. 27:269.
[124] White, D. G., and N. F. Childers. 1944. Ibid. 19: 699.
[125] White, J. 1909. Proc. Roy. Soc. (London), B, 81: 417.
[126] Whitehead, R. 1934. Ann. Appl. Biol. 21:48.
[127] Whiteman, T. M., and H. A. Schomer. 1945. Plant Physiol. 20:171.
[128] Woodford, E. K., and F. G. Gregory. 1948. Ann. Botany (London), N.S. 12:335.
[129] Yemm, E. W. 1935. Proc. Roy. Soc. (London), B, 117:504.
[130] Young, R. E., R. J. Romani, and J. B. Biale. 1962. Plant Physiol. 37:416.

IX. METABOLIC END PRODUCTS

102. EXCRETION PRODUCTS IN FECES: MAN

Values are based on "normal" dietary intake, including approximately 10 g nitrogen/day. In reducing values to mg/kg or µg/kg, a body weight of 70 kg was assumed, unless specific weight was reported in the literature. Values in parentheses are ranges, estimate "c" (*see* Introduction).

	Constituent (Synonym)	Amount Excreted per kg body wt per day	Reference
	General Chemical Constituents, mg		
1	Solids	394(140-560)	46
2	Water	(910-1820)	40
	Electrolytes, mg		
3	Aluminum	0.0006	26
4	Arsenic	0.033(0.001-0.116)	36
5	Calcium	(5-10)	16,38
6	Chlorine	(0.21-0.50)	4
7	Cobalt	(0.000002-0.000020)	20
8	Copper	0.027(0.023-0.037)	26
9	Iron	120(65-208)	9
10	Lead	0.0042	26
11	Magnesium	2.5(1.510-3.185)	29
12	Manganese	(0.018-0.120)	26,27
13	Mercury	0.00014	39
14	Nickel	(0.0012-0.0025)	27
15	Phosphorus, total	0.00986(0.00710-0.02000)	9
16	Potassium	6.7	7
17	Silver	0.0008	26
18	Sodium	1.7	7
19	Sulfur, total	2.0	7
20	Tin	(0.17-0.45)	7,26
21	Zinc	0.100(0.058-0.144)	41
	Vitamins & Related Compounds, µg		
22	Thiamine	7.80(0.67-18.00)	10
23	Riboflavin	14.7(8.0-23.0)	10
24	Nicotinic acid	52(12-124)	10
25	Biotin	1.90(0.63-6.64)	10
26	Pantothenic acid	31.40(3.85-63.40)	10
27	Folic acid	4.3(1.8-7.7)	10
28	*p*-Aminobenzoic acid	3.50(1.01-8.20)	10
29	Ascorbic acid	(60-70)	6
30	Vitamin E	308(226-391)	28
31	Xanthophyll	(8-100)	42
32	Xanthophyll + carotene	(20-600)	42
	Lipids & Miscellaneous Organic Acids, mg		
33	Fats, total	56(30-100)	46
34	Neutral	(10-45)	15
35	Unsaponifiable	33(22-38)[1]	45
36	Fatty acids, total	(41-92)	3,18,25
37	linoleic	(1.6-3.6)	18
38	oleic	(5-11)	18
39	palmitic	(13-30)	18
40	stearic	(14-33)	18
41	Soaps, total	53(40-66)[1]	45
42	*n*-dodecanoic	0.3[2]	34
43	*n*-tetradecanoic	1.9[2]	34
44	*n*-pentadecanoic	0.4[2]	34
45	*n*-hexadecanoic	38.8[2]	34
46	*n*-heptadecanoic	1.3[2]	34
47	*n*-octadecanoic	49.2[2]	34
48	$\Delta^{9,10}$-hexadecanoic	1.1[2]	34
49	$\Delta^{9,10}$-octadecanoic	7.0[2]	34
	Neutral steroids		
50	Total	(9-14)	2,12
51	Campesterol (24α-Methyl-cholest-5-en-3β-ol)	0.6	12
52	Cholesterol (cholest-5-en-3-α-ol)	1.4	12
53	Coprostanol (5β-cholestan-3β-ol)	6	12
54	Coprostanone (5β-cholestan-3-one)	0.6	12
55	β-Sitosterol (24β-ethyl-cholest-5-en-3β-ol)	0.6	12
56	Stigmasterol (24β-ethyl-cholest-5,22-dien-3β-ol)	2	12
57	Hydrocarbons	3.9(1.4-5.6)	2
58	Mono- & di-glycerides	1.2(0.4-1.7)	2
59	Triglycerides	3.9(1.4-5.6)	2
60	Long-chain alcohols	1.9(0.7-2.6)	2
61	Long-chain esters	1.9(0.7-2.6)	2
62	Phospholipids	2.3(0.8-3.4)	2
63	Bile acids, total	3.9(1.4-5.6)	3
64	individual[3]	Trace	5,8,11,13,19,23,24,32
65	Phenol, total	(0-3)	14

[1] At 8-12 years old. [2] Expressed as % of total fatty acids. [3] Includes lithocholic; 3β-hydroxy-5β-cholanoic; chenodeoxycholic; 3α,7α-dihydroxy-5β-cholanoic; 3α,7β-dihydroxy-5β-cholanoic; 3β,7α-dihydroxy-5β-cholanoic; deoxycholic; 3α,12β-dihydroxy-5β-cholanoic; 3β,12α-dihydroxy-5β-cholanoic; 3β,12β-dihydroxy-5β-cholanoic; cholic; 3α,7α,12α-trihydroxy-5α-cholanoic; 3α,7β,12α-trihydroxy-5β-cholanoic; 3β,7α,12α-trihydroxy-cholanoic; 3β,7β,12α-trihydroxy-cholanoic; 3-keto-5β-cholanoic; 3,12-diketo-5β-cholanoic; 3-keto-7α-hydroxy-5β-cholanoic; 3-keto-12α-hydroxy-5β-cholanoic; 3α-hydroxy-7-keto-5β-cholanoic; 3α-hydroxy-12-keto-5β-cholanoic; 3β-hydroxy-12-keto-5β-cholanoic; 3α,7α-dihydroxy-12-keto-5β-cholanoic; and 3α,12α-dihydroxy-7-keto-5β-cholanoic acids.

continued

102. EXCRETION PRODUCTS IN FECES: MAN

	Constituent (Synonym)	Amount Excreted per kg body wt per day	Reference
	Nitrogenous Substances, mg		
66	Imidazole derivatives	(0-0.2)	30
	Porphyrins		
67	Bilirubin	0.14	44
68	Coproporphyrin	(0.005-0.014)	35
69	Protoporphyrin	0.014	17
70	Urobilinogen + stercobilinogen	2	43,44
71	Uroporphyrin	(0.00014-0.00060)	35
72	Purine bases	(2-3)	31
73	Amino acids, arginine, total	3.8(2.9-5.0)	37
74	histidine, total	1.7(1.4-2.1)	37
75	isoleucine, total	4.3(3.3-5.5)	37
76	leucine, total	5.6(4.3-6.9)	37
77	lysine, total	5.7(4.5-6.9)	37
78	threonine, total	4.0(3.3-5.2)	37
79	valine, total	4.6(3.6-6.2)	37
80	Nitrogen, total	(11.4-36.0)	21
81	ammonia	(0.36-1.2)	33
	Enzymes		
82	Chymotrypsin	Consult references	1,22
83	Trypsin		1,22

Contributor: Van Pilsum, John F.

References

[1] Ammann, R., et al. 1964. Klin. Wochschr. 42:5333.
[2] Aylward, F., and P. A. Wills. 1962. Brit. J. Nutr. 16: 339.
[3] Aylward, F., and P. D. S. Wood. 1962. Ibid. 16:345.
[4] Cammidge, P. J. 1914. The faeces of children and adults. W. Wood, New York.
[5] Carey, J. B., and C. J. Watson. 1963. J. Biol. Chem. 216:847.
[6] Chinn, H., and C. J. Farmer. 1939. Proc. Soc. Exptl. Biol. Med. 41:561.
[7] Clark, G. W. 1926. Univ. Calif. (Berkeley) Publ. Physiol. 5(17):195.
[8] Danielsson, H., et al. 1963. J. Biol. Chem. 238:2299.
[9] Daum, K., et al. 1951. J. Am. Dietet. Assoc. 27: 475.
[10] Denko, C. W., et al. 1946. Arch. Biochem. 10:33.
[11] Eneroth, P., B. Gordon, and J. Sjövall. 1966. J. Lipid Res. 7:524.
[12] Eneroth, P., K. Hellström, and R. Ryhage. 1964. Ibid. 5:245.
[13] Eneroth, P., et al. 1966. Ibid. 7:511.
[14] Folin, O., and W. Denis. 1916. J. Biol. Chem. 26: 507.
[15] Fowweather, F. S. 1926. Brit. J. Exptl. Pathol. 7:15.
[16] Goiffon, R., B. Goiffon, and G. Fron. 1961. Gastroenterology 96:312.
[17] Goldberg, J. S. 1966. Calif. Med. 104:488.
[18] Gompertz, S. M., and H. G. Sammons. 1963. Clin. Chim. Acta 8:591.
[19] Hamilton, J. G. 1963. Arch. Biochem. Biophys. 101:7.
[20] Harp, M. J., and F. I. Scoular. 1952. J. Nutr. 47:67.
[21] Hawk, P. B., B. L. Oser, and W. H. Summerson. 1947. Practical physiological chemistry. Ed. 12. Blakiston, Philadelphia.
[22] Haverback, B. J., et al. 1963. Gastroenterology 44: 588.
[23] Heftmann, E., et al. 1959. Arch. Biochem. Biophys. 84:324.
[24] Jenke, M., and F. Bandow. 1937. Z. Physiol. Chem. 249:16.
[25] Jover, A., and R. S. Gordon, Jr. 1962. J. Lab. Clin. Med. 59:878.
[26] Kehoe, R. A., J. Cholak, and R. V. Story. 1940. J. Nutr. 19:579.
[27] Kent, N. L., and R. A. McCance. 1941. Biochem. J. 35:877.
[28] Klatskin, G., and D. W. Molander. 1952. J. Lab. Clin. Med. 39:802.
[29] Leichsenring, J. M., L. M. Norris, and S. A. Lamison. 1951. J. Nutr. 45:477.
[30] Loeper, M., A. Lesurl, and A. Thomas. 1934. Bull. Soc. Chim. Biol. 16:385.
[31] Mendel, L. B., and J. F. Lyman. 1910. J. Biol. Chem. 8:115.
[32] Norman, A., and R. H. Palmer. 1964. J. Lab. Clin. Med. 63:986.
[33] Robinson, C. S. 1922. J. Biol. Chem. 52:445.
[34] Sammons, H. G., and S. M. Wiggs. 1960. Clin. Chim. Acta 5:141.
[35] Schwartz, S., et al. 1960. Methods Biochem. Anal. 8.
[36] Schwarz, L., and W. Deckert. 1931. Arch. Hyg. Bakteriol. 106:346.
[37] Sheffner, A. L., J. B. Kirsner, and W. L. Palmer. 1948. J. Biol. Chem. 175:107.
[38] Shohl, A. T. 1939. Mineral metabolism. Reinhold, New York.
[39] Stock, A. 1940. Biochem. Z. 304:73.
[40] Sunderman, F. W., and F. Boerner. 1949. Normal values in clinical medicine. W. B. Saunders, Philadelphia.
[41] Tribble, H. M., and F. I. Scoular. 1954. J. Nutr. 52: 210.
[42] Wald, G., W. R. Carroll, and D. Sciarra. 1941. Science 94:95.
[43] Watson, C. J. 1937. Arch. Internal Med. 59:196.
[44] Watson, C. J. 1963. J. Clin. Pathol. 16:1.
[45] Williams, H. H., et al. 1943. J. Nutr. 25:379.
[46] Wollaeger, E. E., M. W. Comfort, and A. E. Osterberg. 1947. Gastroenterology 9:272.

103. EXCRETION PRODUCTS IN SEBUM

Part I. Man

Sebum, a thick semifluid substance, is composed of fat and epithelial debris from the cells of the malpighian layer of the skin. For determinations on hair, consult reference 9.

Values in parentheses are ranges, estimate "c" (*see* Introduction).

	Property or Constituent	Body Area	Value	Reference
	Physical Properties			
1	Melting point	Forearm	35.8°C	5-7
2	Specific gravity at 20°/4°C	Forehead	0.911	2
3	Surface tension	Forehead	24.89 dynes/cm	2
4	Viscosity at 30°C	Forehead	859.7 millipoises	2
	Chemical Constituents			
	Fatty acids			
5	Combined[1/]	Forearm	34.6(27.5-41.0) g/100 g	5-7
6		Scalp	28(21-39) g/100 g	1,3
7	Triglycerides	Forearm	32.5 g/100 g	5-7
8		Forehead	44 g/100 g	4
9	Waxes (including cholesterol esters)	Scalp	16 g/100 g	9
10	Free	Forearm	28.3(22.0-32.2) g/100 g	5-7,10
11		Forehead	38 g/100 g	4
12		Scalp	33 g/100 g	1,3
	Unsaponifiable matter			
13	Total	Forearm	30.1(25.1-35.9) g/100 g	5-7
14		Scalp	34(29-40) g/100 g	1,3
15	Aliphatic alcohols	Forearm	6.2(4.7-6.9) g/100 g	5-7
16		Scalp	9 g/100 g	1,3
17	Straight-chain	Forearm	2.4 g/100 g	5-7
18		Scalp	4.5 g/100 g	3
19	Branched-chain	Forearm	3.8 g/100 g	5-7
20		Scalp	0.9 g/100 g	3
21	Cholesterol	Forearm	4.1(2.7-6.9) g/100 g	5-7
22		Forehead	3.5 g/100 g	4
23		Scalp	3.5 g/100 g	1,3,8
24	Dihydrocholesterol	Forearm	0.1 g/100 g	5-7
25	Hydrocarbons	Forearm	8.1(5-20) g/100 g	5-7
26		Scalp	9 g/100 g	3
27	Phosphatides	Forehead	0.9 g/100 g	4
28	Squalene	Forearm	5.5(3.3-11.2) g/100 g	5-7
29		Scalp	7(4-10) g/100 g	1,8

[1/] As triglycerides, waxes, and other esters.

Contributor: Wheatley, Victor R.

References

[1] Bloom, R. E., S. Woods, and N. Nicolaides. 1955. J. Invest. Dermatol. 24:97.

[2] Butcher, E. O., and A. Coonin. 1949. Ibid. 12:249.

[3] Houghen, F. W. 1955. Biochem. J. 59:302.

[4] Kvorning, S. A. 1949. Acta Pharmacol. Toxicol. 5:383.

[5] MacKenna, R. M. B., V. R. Wheatley, and A. Wormall. 1950. J. Invest. Dermatol. 15:33.

[6] MacKenna, R. M. B., V. R. Wheatley, and A. Wormall. 1952. Biochem. J. 52:161.

[7] MacKenna, R. M. B., V. R. Wheatley, and A. Wormall. Unpublished. Medical College of St. Bartholomew's Hospital, London, 1955.

[8] Nicolaides, N., and S. Rothman. 1952. J. Invest. Dermatol. 19:389.

[9] Nicolaides, N., and S. Rothman. 1953. Ibid. 21:9.

[10] Weitkamp, A. W., A. M. Smiljanic, and S. Rothman. 1947. J. Am. Chem. Soc. 69:1936.

continued

103. EXCRETION PRODUCTS IN SEBUM

Part II. Vertebrates Other Than Man

Sebum is present in untreated skin, hair, or wool of mammals; in birds, it is present in the preen gland oil.

	Animal	Constituent	Value g/100 g	Reference
1	Camel	Isocholesterol[1/]	2.2	2
2	Goat	Isocholesterol[1/]	2.5	2
3	Guinea pig	Fatty acids, combined[2/]	49.3	7
4		free	6.0	7
		Unsaponifiable matter		
5		Total	44.8	7
6		Aliphatic alcohols	5.0	7
7		Straight-chain	0.1	7
8		Branched-chain	4.9	7
9		Aliphatic diols	11.2	7
10		Cholesterol	17.9	7
11		Lathosterol[3/]	1.8	7
12		Hydrocarbons	1.5	7
13	Llama	Isocholesterol[1/]	1.2	2
14	Mouse	Fatty acids, combined[2/]	36.7	7
15		free	7.5	7
		Unsaponifiable matter		
16		Total	54.6	7
17		Aliphatic alcohols	5.9	7
18		Straight-chain	0.1	7
19		Branched-chain	5.8	7
20		Aliphatic diols	27.5	7
21		Cholesterol	4.5	7
22		Lathosterol[3/]	8.1	7
23		Hydrocarbons	1.1	7
24	Ox	Fatty acids, combined[2/]	53.4	1
25		free	5.1	1
		Unsaponifiable matter		
26		Total	42.7	1
27		Cholesterol	14.4	1
28		Isocholesterol[1/]	<0.1	2
29	Rabbit	Fatty acids, combined[2/]	43.6	7
30		free	9.0	7
		Unsaponifiable matter		
31		Total	45.9	7
32		Aliphatic alcohols	31.5	7
33		Straight-chain	20.8	7
34		Branched-chain	10.7	7
35		Aliphatic diols	2.2	7
36		Cholesterol	3.5	7
37		Lathosterol[3/]	0.1	7
38		Hydrocarbons	3.4	7
39	Rat	Fatty acids, combined[2/]	51.4	7
40		free	7.4	7
		Unsaponifiable matter		
41		Total	41.4	7
42		Aliphatic alcohols	17.6	7
43		Straight-chain	4.5	7
44		Branched-chain	13.1	7
45		Aliphatic diols	2.9	7
46		Cholesterol	5.8	7
47		Lathosterol[3/]	4.4	7
48		Hydrocarbons	1.5	7
49	Sheep	Fatty acids, combined[2/]	44.0	4
50		free	11.0	4
		Unsaponifiable matter		
51		Total	46.1	4
52		Aliphatic alcohols	9.0	3
53		Straight-chain	1.5	3
54		Branched-chain	7.5	3
55		Aliphatic diols	2.5	3
56		Cholesterol	10.0	3
57		Dihydrocholesterol	2.5	3
58		Isocholesterol[1/]	12.5	3
59		Lathosterol[3/]	2.5	3
60		Hydrocarbons	<1	3
61	Duck	Fatty acids, combined[2/]	47.6	5,6
62		Aliphatic alcohols	48.0	5,6
63		Straight-chain	48.0	5,6
64		Branched-chain	0	5,6
65		Cholesterol	1.4	5,6
66	Goose	Fatty acids, combined[2/]	47.5	5,6
67		Aliphatic alcohols	48.0	5,6
68		Straight-chain	48.0	5,6
69		Branched-chain	0	5,6
70		Cholesterol	0.25	5,6

[1/] A mixture of lanosterol, dihydrolanosterol, agnosterol, and dihydroagnosterol. [2/] As triglycerides, waxes, and other esters. [3/] Cholest-7-en-3β-ol.

Contributor: Wheatley, Victor R.

References

[1] Koppenhoefer, R. M. 1936. J. Biol. Chem. 116:321.

[2] Lederer, E., and P. K. Tchen. 1945. Bull. Soc. Chim. Biol. 27:419.

[3] Truter, E. V. 1951. Quart. Rev. (London) 5:390.

[4] Weitkamp, A. W. 1945. J. Am. Chem. Soc. 67:447.

[5] Weitzel, G., A. M. Fretzdorff, and J. Wojahn. 1952. Z. Physiol. Chem. 291:46.

[6] Weitzel, G., and K. Lennert. 1951. Ibid. 288:251.

[7] Wheatley, V. R., and A. T. James. 1957. Biochem. J. 65:36.

104. EXCRETION PRODUCTS IN SWEAT: MAN

Eccrine sweat, a clear aqueous solution, is generally 99.0-99.5% water and 0.5-1.0% solids (the latter approximately half inorganic and half organic) [27]. Although much is known about the chemical composition of sweat secreted onto the skin surface, the concentration of solute in sweat as it is formed in the coil of the gland remains largely unknown [56]. Indications are that sweat in the secretory part of the gland is isotonic with plasma and that variable reabsorption occurs in the duct [19,57]. The physical-chemical processes which characterize the changes in sweat content while passing through the duct are currently being elaborated [20,23,41]. Quantitative studies of dissolved substances in sweat have been made by analysis of sweat samples collected from the skin, and in a few instances from the sweat pore or from micropunctures of the duct [52]; by analysis of sweat residues washed from the skin; and by estimation of sweat components in material balance studies [47]. Methods and techniques have been carefully evaluated by Robinson [47], who has also thoroughly reviewed the literature on the chemical composition of sweat [48]. For additional information, consult references 2, 17, 34, 35, 41, and 43. Values in parentheses are ranges, estimate "c" (*see* Introduction).

	Property or Constituent	Value	Reference
	Physical Properties & General Chemical Constituents		
1	Freezing point	(-0.09 to -0.69) °C	26
2	pH	(3.8-8.2)	26,49
3	Production rate, max.	(17.7-38.2) ml/min	36
4	Specific gravity	(1.001-1.006)	49
5	Solids, total	(1.174-1.597) %	42
6	Water	(99.0-99.5) %	49
	Electrolytes		
7	Calcium	(1.0-24) mg/100 ml	4,15,48
8	Chloride	(36-468) mg/100 ml	14,37, 62,63
9	Copper	0.006 mg/100 ml	40
10	Iodine	0.9(0.5-1.2) µg/100 ml	59
11	Iron	0.027(0.022-0.045) mg/100 ml	12,15, 16,33
12	Magnesium	(0.004-0.286) mg/100 ml	4,40
13	Manganese	0.006(0.003-0.007) mg/100 ml	40
14	Phosphorus	(0.009-0.043) mg/100 ml	15,40
15	Potassium	(21-126) mg/100 ml	5,22,25
16	Sodium	(24-312) mg/100 ml	8,10,14, 23,53
17	Sulfur	(0.7-7.4) mg/100 ml	60
18	Zinc	93 ± 26 µg/100 ml	46
19	Bicarbonate	(1.6-18.6) vol %	26
20	Sulfate	(4.0-6) mg/100 ml	26
	Vitamins & Related Compounds		
21	Thiamine	0.15(0-0.6) µg/100 ml	35,39
22	Riboflavin	(0-0.5) µg/100 ml	35,39
23	Nicotinic acid	(1.7-8.7) µg/100 ml	30
24	Vitamin B_6	(0.04-0.17) µg/100 ml	28
25	Pantothenic acid	(1.5-7.7) µg/100 ml	58
26	Folic acid	(0.53-0.88) µg/100 ml	31
27	*p*-Aminobenzoic acid	0.24(0.08-1.70) µg/100 ml	32
28	Inositol	21(15-36) µg/100 ml	32
29	Choline	7.1 µg/100 ml	29
30	Ascorbic acid	(0-0.6) mg/100 ml	35
31	Dehydroascorbic acid	70.5 µg/100 ml	55
	Carbohydrates & Organic Acids		
32	Sugar, as glucose	(0-3) mg/100 ml	23,48
33	Lactic acid	(285-336) mg/100 ml	3,11, 61,62
34	Phenol	(2-8) mg/100 ml	51
35	Pyruvic acid	(0.9-6.9) mg/100 ml	26
	Nitrogenous Substances		
36	Creatinine	(0.1-1.3) mg/100 ml	1,48
37	Histamine (base)	(10-20) µg/liter	21
38	Urea	(12-57) mg/100 ml	7,8,48, 54
39	Uric acid	0.16(0.07-0.25) mg/100 ml	50
	Amino acids		
40	Alanine	3.21 ± 0.72 mg/100 ml	13
41	Arginine	13.6(6.05-17.00) mg/100 ml	24
42	Aspartic acid	4.58 ± 0.76 mg/100 ml	13
43	Citrulline	6.99 ± 0.91 mg/100 ml	13
44	Glutamic acid	5.43 ± 0.69 mg/100 ml	13
45	Glycine	2.95 ± 0.74 mg/100 ml	13
46	Histidine	8(4.25-14.00) mg/100 ml	24
47	Isoleucine	2.27(1.63-3.73) mg/100 ml	24
48	Leucine	2.69(1.98-3.75) mg/100 ml	24
49	Lysine	2.26(1.96-3.38) mg/100 ml	24
50	Ornithine	2.03 ± 1.01 mg/100 ml	13
51	Phenylalanine	2.19(1.70-3.47) mg/100 ml	24
52	Threonine	5.38(2.13-8.18) mg/100 ml	24
53	Tryptophan	1.12(0.75-1.85) mg/100 ml	24
54	Tyrosine	3.15(1.32-5.45) mg/100 ml	24
55	Valine	2.96(2.40-4.35) mg/100 ml	24
	Nitrogen		
56	Total N	(21-50) mg/100 ml	18
57	Nonprotein N	(66-108) mg/100 ml	45
58	Amino acid N	(1.1-10.2) mg/100 ml	27
59	Ammonia N	(2.0-35) mg/100 ml	27,35
60	Urea N	(5-36) mg/100 ml	6,9,39
61	Uric acid N	(0-0.27) mg/100 ml	26
	Hormones, Enzymes, & Miscellaneous Organic Compounds		
62	Corticoids	(4-8) µg/100 ml	44
63	Alkaline phosphatase	(0.1-5.3) King-Armstrong units	38
64	Ketone bodies, total	(0.4-0.6) mM/liter	1

continued

104. EXCRETION PRODUCTS IN SWEAT: MAN

Contributors: (a) Randall, Walter C., (b) Levey, Stanley

References

[1] Adams, R., R. E. Johnson, and F. Sargent. 1958. Quart. J. Exptl. Physiol. 43:241.

[2] Adolph, E. F. 1947. Physiology of man in the desert. Interscience, New York.

[3] Astrand, I. 1963. Acta Physiol. Scand. 58:359.

[4] Bara, B. 1963. Polskie Arch. Med. Wewnetrznej 33:1125.

[5] Borchardt, W. 1926. Arch. Ges. Physiol. 214:169.

[6] Brusilow, S. W., and E. H. Gordes. 1964. J. Clin. Invest. 43:477.

[7] Brusilow, S. W., and E. H. Gordes. 1965. Am. J. Physiol. 209:1213.

[8] Bulmer, M. G. 1957. J. Physiol. (London) 137:261.

[9] Bulmer, M. G., and G. D. Forwell. 1956. Ibid. 132:115.

[10] Cage, G. W., and R. L. Dobson. 1965. J. Clin. Invest. 44:1270.

[11] Collins, K. J. 1962. J. Appl. Physiol. 17:99.

[12] Coltman, C. A., and N. J. Rowe. 1966. Am. J. Clin. Nutr. 18:270.

[13] Coltman, C. A., N. J. Rowe, and R. J. Atwell. 1966. Ibid. 18:373.

[14] Conn, J. W. 1949. Arch. Internal Med. 83:416.

[15] Consolazio, F. C., et al. 1962. J. Nutr. 78:78.

[16] Consolazio, F. C., et al. 1962. Ibid. 79:407.

[17] Dill, D. B. 1938. Life, heat, and altitude. Harvard Univ. Press, Cambridge.

[18] Dill, D. B., F. G. Hall, and H. T. Edwards. 1938. Am. J. Physiol. 123:412.

[19] Dobson, R. L. 1962. Advan. Biol. Skin 3:54.

[20] Dobson, R. L. 1965. Arch. Environ. Health 11:423.

[21] Garden, J. W. 1966. J. Appl. Physiol. 21:631.

[22] Gordon, R. S., and H. L. Andrews. 1966. Federation Proc. 25:1372.

[23] Gordon, R. S., and G. W. Cage. 1966. Lancet 1: 1246.

[24] Hier, S. W., T. Cronbleet, and O. Bergeim. 1946. J. Biol. Chem. 166:327.

[25] Isaksson, B., and B. Sjögren. 1963. Scand. J. Clin. Lab. Invest., Suppl. 69:108.

[26] Itoh, S. 1960. In H. Yoshimura, K. Ogata, and S. Itoh, ed. Essential problems in climatic physiology. Nankodo, Kyoto. pp. 3-25.

[27] Itoh, S., and T. Nakayama. 1952. Japan. J. Physiol. 2:248.

[28] Johnson, B. C., T. S. Hamilton, and H. H. Mitchell. 1945. J. Biol. Chem. 158:619.

[29] Johnson, B. C., T. S. Hamilton, and H. H. Mitchell. 1945. Ibid. 159:5.

[30] Johnson, B. C., T. S. Hamilton, and H. H. Mitchell. 1945. Ibid. 159:231.

[31] Johnson, B. C., T. S. Hamilton, and H. H. Mitchell. 1945. Ibid. 159:425.

[32] Johnson, B. C., H. H. Mitchell, and T. S. Hamilton. 1945. Ibid. 161:357.

[33] Johnson, F. A., T. J. McMillan, and E. R. Evans. 1950. J. Nutr. 42:285.

[34] Kuno, Y. 1934. Physiology of human perspiration. J. and A. Churchill, London.

[35] Kuno, Y. 1956. Human perspiration. C. C. Thomas, Springfield, Ill.

[36] Ladell, W. S. S. 1949. J. Physiol. (London) 108:440.

[37] Lieberman, J., and F. Kellogg. 1963. Am. J. Med. Sci. 246:261.

[38] Locwenthal, L. J. A., and W. M. Politzer. 1963. Nord. Med. 69:3.

[39] Mickelson, O., and A. Keys. 1943. J. Biol. Chem. 149:479.

[40] Mitchell, H. H., and T. S. Hamilton. 1949. Ibid. 178:345.

[41] Montagna, W. 1962. The structure and function of the skin. Academic Press, New York.

[42] Mosher, H. H. 1932. J. Biol. Chem. 99:78.

[43] Newburgh, L. H. 1949. Physiology of heat regulation. W. B. Saunders, Philadelphia.

[44] Nichols, J., and A. T. Miller. 1948. Proc. Soc. Exptl. Biol. Med. 69:448.

[45] Peters, J. P., and D. D. Van Slyke. 1946. Quantitative clinical chemistry. Williams and Wilkins, Baltimore. v. 1.

[46] Prasas, A. S., et al. 1963. J. Lab. Clin. Med. 62:84.

[47] Robinson, S., and A. H. Robinson. 1954. Methods Med. Res. 6:100.

[48] Robinson, S., and A. H. Robinson. 1954. Physiol. Rev. 34:221.

[49] Rothman, S. 1954. Physiology and biochemistry of the skin. Univ. Chicago Press, Chicago.

[50] Saiki, A. K., G. Olmanson, and G. A. Talbert. 1932. Am. J. Physiol. 100:328.

[51] Schultz, W. 1940. Arch. Dermatol. Syphilis 181: 471.

[52] Schulz, I., et al. 1966. Proc. Intern. Res. Conf. Pathogenesis Cystic Fibrosis, 3rd, Bethesda, Md., 1964, p. 136.

[53] Schwartz, I. L., and J. H. Thaysen. 1956. J. Clin. Invest. 35:114.

[54] Schwartz, I. L., J. H. Thaysen, and V. P. Dole. 1953. J. Exptl. Med. 97:429.

[55] Shields, J. B., et al. 1945. J. Biol. Chem. 161:351.

[56] Slegers, J. F. G. 1963. Dermatologica 127:242.

[57] Slegers, J. F. G. 1964. Arch. Ges. Physiol. 279:269.

[58] Spector, H., T. S. Hamilton, and H. H. Mitchell. 1945. J. Biol. Chem. 161:145.

[59] Spector, H., H. H. Mitchell, and T. S. Hamilton. 1945. Ibid. 161:137.

[60] Talbert, G. A., F. Stinchfield, and H. Staff. 1933. Am. J. Physiol. 106:488.

[61] Thurmon, F. M., and B. Ottenstein. 1952. J. Invest. Dermatol. 18:333.

[62] Van Heyningen, R., and J. S. Weiner. 1952. J. Physiol. (London) 116:395.

[63] Warwick, W. J., and L. Hansen. 1965. Pediatrics 36:261.

105. EXCRETION PRODUCTS IN URINE: VERTEBRATES

Part I. Man

Values are based on "normal" dietary intake, including approximately 10 g nitrogen/day. In reducing values to mg/kg or µg/kg, a body weight of 70 kg was assumed, unless specific weight was reported in the literature. Values in parentheses are ranges, estimate "c" (*see* Introduction).

	Constituent	Amount Excreted per kg body wt per day	Reference
	General Chemical Constituents, mg		
1	Solids	860(780-1000)	14,53,76,126
2	Solids, total nondialyzable	1.3	13
3	Water	20,000(7,000-42,000)	73
	Electrolytes, mg		
4	Aluminum	0.0011(0.0007-0.0016)	65
5	Arsenic	0.00033(0-0.00130)	148
6	Bromine	(0.012-0.110)	20
7	Calcium	3.3(0.6-8.3)	53
8	Chlorine	100(40-180)	53
9	Cobalt	0.00007(0.00005-0.00012)	51
10	Copper	0.0005(0.0003-0.0007)	100,137
11	Fluorine	0.022(0.007-0.100)1/	53,86
12	Iodine	(0.0001-0.0070)	16
13	Iron	0.007	37
14	Lead	0.00040(0.00016-0.00110)	65
15	Magnesium	1.35(0.42-2.40)	35,49
16	Manganese	(0.0001-0.0014)	65,66
17	Mercury	(0.000007-0.000010)	125
18	Nickel	(0.002-0.004)	66
19	Phosphorus, inorganic	12(10-15)	143
20	organic	0.131(0.089-0.187)	102
21	Potassium	34(16-56)	53
22	Selenium	0.0005(0-0.0020)	124
23	Silicon	0.13(0.06-0.20)	10
24	Sodium	60(25-94)	53
25	Sulfur, total	16.0(5.1-20.6)	40
26	ethereal	0.95(0.56-1.40)	40
27	inorganic	11.1(3.5-17.5)	40
28	neutral	1.90(1.05-2.60)	40
29	Tin	(0.00013-0.00025)	19,65
30	Zinc	0.018(0.011-0.033)	135
31	Bicarbonate	2.0(0.5-12.0)	44
	Vitamins & Related Compounds, µg		
32	Thiamine	3.0(0.6-6.0)	27
33	Riboflavin	12.4(2.0-24.0)	27,95
34	Nicotinic acid	3.4(2.0-20.0)	27,60
35	Trigonelline	(30-300)	98
36	Nicotinamide	20(10-50)	27,60
37	*N*-Methylnicotinamide	(40-600)	27,60
38	Vitamin B_6	(0.08-2.70)	58
39	Pyridoxal	1.0(0.7-5.3)	5
40	Pyridoxamine	1.6(0.4-3.0)	101
41	4-Pyridoxic acid	(9-160)	58,101
42	Biotin	0.5(0.2-1.0)	27
43	Pantothenic acid	45(16-100)	27
44	Folic acid	0.058(0.030-0.300)	27,105
45	Folinic acid2/	0.037(0.023-0.069)	105
46	*p*-Aminobenzoic acid	(2-3)	27
47	Inositol	200	61
48	Vitamin B_{12}	0.00044(0.00023-0.00079)	105
49	Choline	79(68-130)	59
50	Ascorbic acid	(100-400)	18
51	Dehydroascorbic acid	(190-290)	18

1/ Upper limit of range was obtained in an area of Texas where dental fluorosis is endemic. 2/ Citrovorum factor.

continued

Part I. Man

	Constituent	Amount Excreted per kg body wt per day	Reference
52	Dehydroascorbic acid + diketogulonic acid	230(0-1280)	41
53	Diketogulonic acid	(140-190)	18
54	Vitamins A, D, & K	(0-trace)	126
	Lipids & Carbohydrates, mg		
55	Cholesterol	(0-0.0714)	83
56	Sugars: arabinose	Trace[2]	134
57	deoxyribose	Trace[2]	134
58	galactose	Trace[2]	134
59	glucose	Trace[2]	134
60	lactose	Trace[2]	134
61	ribose	Trace[2]	134
62	ribulose	Trace[3]	42
63	xylose	Trace[3]	42
64	xylulose	Trace[3]	133
65	reducing substances	(7-21)	14
66	Acid mucopolysaccharides	(0.03-0.14)	70,130
	Nitrogenous Substances, mg		
67	Protein(s), total	(0.03-1.00)	106,113
68	antibody[4]	Consult references	88,127
69	glyco-	0.5	47
70	individual[5]	Traces	7,8,48,97
71	Acetic acid, 1-methyl-4-imidazole	Trace	67
72	Acetylkynurenine	0.03	15
73	Aminoacetone	(0.002-0.02)	116
74	*o*-Aminohippuric acid	0.06	15
75	4-Aminoimidazole-5-carboxamide	0.015	21,22
76	β-Aminoisobutyric acid	(0.0007-0.004)	45
77	δ-Aminolevulinic acid	(0.01-0.3)	116
78	Anthranilic acid	(0.002-0.009)	1
79	Carnosine + anserine	(0.045-0.14)	23
80	Creatine	0.8(0-2.0)	68,136
81	Creatinine	23(15-30)	136
82	*S*-(1,2-Dicarboxyethyl) cysteine	Trace	74
83	Ergothionine	(1.7-4.0)	94
84	Ethanolamine	(0.07-0.7)	80
85	Forminoglutamic acid	(0.7-1.5)	62
86	Guanidinoacetic acid	(0.2-0.5)	136
87	Hippuric acid	(7.0-18.0)	152
88	Histamine	(0.00025-0.001)	109
89	Hydroxyproline, containing glycopeptides	23	12
90	Imidazole derivatives	(2-3)	72
91	Indoleacetic acid	(0.02-0.06)	152
92	Indoxylsulfuric acid	1.0(0.5-2.0)	24,118
93	Kynurenic acid	0.03	15
94	Kynurenine	(0.023-0.078)	1
95	Methionine sulfoxide	(0-0.31)	17,154
96	*S*-Methylcysteine	0.021	131
97	1-Methylhistidine	Trace	128
98	3-Methylhistidine	Trace	128
99	*N*-Methyl-2-pyridone-5-carboxamide	0.24	15
100	Porphyrin derivatives: bilirubin	Trace	92
101	coproporphyrin I & III	(0.00024-0.00400)	107,117,147
102	porphobilinogen	(0.01-0.03)	91,116
103	urobilin & urobilinogen	(0.007-0.05)	75,146
104	uroporphyrin	(0.0001-0.0004)	117
105	Prolyl hydroxyproline	0.26	69

[2] Citrovorum factor. [3] Determined by chromatography. [4] Tetanus, poliomyelitis; γ-μA- and γ-μB-globulins. [5] Albumin; ceruloplasmin; fibrinogen; α_1-globulin; β_1-A-globulin; β_2-A-globulin; β_1-E-globulin; γ-globulin; γL-globulin; Ba-α_2-glycoprotein; Zn-α_2-glycoprotein; haptoglobulin; hemopexin; α_1-lipoprotein; α_2-macroglobulin; prealbumin; α_1-seromucoid; transferrin.

continued

105. EXCRETION PRODUCTS IN URINE: VERTEBRATES

Part I. Man

	Constituent	Amount Excreted per kg body wt per day	Reference
	Purine bases & derivatives		
106	Purine bases, total	(0.2-1.0)	53
107	Adenine	0.020(0.016-0.024)	149
108	Allantoin	0.17(0.14-0.21)	151
109	1,3-Dimethyluric acid	Trace	29
110	Guanine	0.006(0.003-0.009)	149
111	7-Methylguanine	0.09(0.08-0.11)	149
112	N^2-Methylguanine	0.007(0.006-0.009)	149
113	8-Hydroxy-7-methylguanine	0.020(0.016-0.030)	149
114	Hypoxanthine	0.14(0.08-0.19)	149
115	1-Methylhypoxanthine	0.006(0.003-0.010)	149
116	Pseudouridine	(0.7-1.3)	34
117	6-Succinopurine	0.014	150
118	Theophylline (1,3-dimethylxanthine)	Trace	29
119	Uric acid	2.0(0.8-3.0)	53
120	Xanthine	0.09(0.07-0.12)	149
121	Pyrrole-2-carboxylic acid	(0.0022-0.0055)	46
122	Serotonin	(0.00025-0.001)	63
123	Urea	(200-500)	53
124	Xanthurenic acid	0.02	3,15
125	*O*-Xylosyl-serine	0.014	131
126	Amino acids, total	(20-40)	17
127	free	(13-20)	17
128	Alanine, total	0.55	17
129	β-Alanine	(0.2-0.3)	23
130	Arginine, total	0.45(0.34-0.50)	136
131	free	0.16(0.07-0.30)	136
132	Asparagine	0.77	122
133	Aspartic acid, total	1.7(1.2-2.7)	153
134	free	0.04(0.01-0.07)	153
135	Citrulline	0.09(0-2.8)	154
136	Cystine, total	1.7(1.0-2.6)	132
137	free	1.3(0.6-1.9)	119
138	Glutamic acid, total	(3.7-5.0)	17,54
139	free	0.8(0-1.5)	17,54
140	Glycine, total	6.5	33
141	free	2.2	17
142	Histidine, total	2.7(1.0-5.0)	17,132,153
143	free	2.0(1.2-2.7)	17,153
144	Hydroxyproline, total	0.02	17,69
145	Isoleucine, total	0.2(0.1-0.3)	33,119,153
146	free	0.08(0.04-0.20)	33,119,153
147	Leucine, total	0.30(0.22-0.45)	33,119,153
148	free	0.13(0.05-0.17)	33,119,153
149	Lysine, total	0.80(0.48-1.70)	33,119,153
150	free	0.40(0.17-0.67)	33,54,119
151	Methionine, total	0.14(0.10-0.17)	33,119,153
152	free	0.05(0.03-0.10)	33,119,153
153	Ornithine	0.15	17
154	Phenylalanine, total	0.30(0.21-0.54)	17,33,153
155	free	0.17(0.09-0.23)	17,33,153
156	Proline, total	0.61(0.30-0.90)	153
157	free	0.12(0.03-0.20)	153
158	Serine, total	0.6(0.5-0.7)	17,144
159	free	0.3(0.2-0.5)	17,144
160	Taurine	(0.11-0.20)	154
161	Threonine, total	0.50(0.36-2.60)	17,33,119,144,153
162	free	0.25(0.11-0.35)	17,33,119,144,153
163	Tryptophan, total	0.40(0.23-0.70)	144,153
164	free	0.20(0.11-0.36)	144,153
165	Tyrosine, total	0.70(0.44-0.82)	132,144,153
166	free	0.20(0.15-0.30)	132,144,153
167	Valine, total	0.30(0.25-0.42)	33,119,144
168	free	0.09(0.04-0.18)	33,119,144

continued

105. EXCRETION PRODUCTS IN URINE: VERTEBRATES

Part I. Man

	Constituent	Amount Excreted per kg body wt per day	Reference
169	Nitrogen, total	(130-300)	53
170	amino acid	(3-6)	52
171	protein	(0.0046-0.0180)	145
172	ammonia	(3-13)	145
	Hormones, μg		
173	Adrenocorticotropin	Consult reference	110
174	Aldosterone, ♂	0.05(0.01-0.13)	138
175	♀	0.06(0.03-0.10)	138
176	Androgens, ♂, 3-5 yr	210	31
177	20-40 yr	260(200-330)	31
178	60+ yr	70(30-130)	31
179	♀, 3-5 yr	50	31
180	20-40 yr	200(180-210)	31
181	60+ yr	40(15-130)	31
182	Androsterone, ♂	50(35-60)	111
183	♀	60(50-80)	111
184	Erythropoietin	Consult references	38,78
185	Estradiol, ♀, follicular phase	0.03(0-0.05)	108
186	luteal phase	0.10(0.07-0.17)	108
187	postmenopause	0.01(0-0.09)	85
188	Estriol, ♀, follicular phase	0.1(0-0.3)	108
189	luteal phase	0.40(0.13-1.30)	108
190	postmenopause	0.05(0-0.18)	85
191	Estrone, ♀, follicular phase	0.08(0.06-0.12)	108
192	luteal phase	0.20(0.17-0.40)	108
193	postmenopause	0.03(0-0.12)	85
194	Etiocholanolone, ♂	60(40-70)	111
195	♀	50(30-60)	111
196	17-Hydroxysteroids, ♂	80(40-170)	103,104
197	♀	60(20-140)	103,104
198	Insulin	Consult references	79,90
199	17-Ketogenic adrenocorticoids, ♂	210(150-310)	30
200	♀	180(120-300)	30
201	α-Ketol steroids	260(130-470)	82
	17-Ketosteroids		
202	Total, ♂	180(110-220)	140
203	♀	110(70-200)	140
204	Conjugates: glucuronide fraction, total	(20-45)	115
205	androsterone	(6.2-22.0)	115
206	dehydroepiandrosterone	(0.4-1.1)	115
207	etiocholanolone	(12-32.0)	115
208	sulfate fraction, total	(8-21)	115
209	androsterone	(1.4-6.0)	115
210	dehydroepiandrosterone	(6-17)	115
211	etiocholanolone	(0.6-6.0)	115
212	Individual: 3α-hydroxy-5β-androstane-11,17-dione; ♂	8	36
213	♀	10	36
214	3α,11β-dihydroxy-5α-androstane-17-one; ♂	23	36
215	♀	20	36
216	3α,11β-dihydroxy-5β-androstane-17-one; ♂♀	8	36
217	Melanocyte-stimulating hormone	Consult reference	120
218	Parathyroid hormone	Consult reference	25
219	Pregnanediol, ♂	13(5-20)	71
220	♀, follicular phase	18(13-25)	71
221	luteal phase	55(30-70)	71
222	postmenopause	10(5-14)	71
223	Pregnanetriol, ♀, follicular phase	25	123
224	luteal phase	32	123
225	postmenopause	11	123
226	Testosterone, ♂	(0.25-1.00)	139
227	♀	(0.04-0.20)	139

continued

105. EXCRETION PRODUCTS IN URINE: VERTEBRATES

Part I. Man

	Constituent	Amount Excreted per kg body wt per day	Reference
228	Tetrahydrocortisol	24(8-50)	108
229	Tetrahydrocortisone	54(20-120)	108
230	Miscellaneous urinary steroids	Trace[3/]	32
	Enzymes		
231	Acid phosphatase	Consult references	2
232	Amylase, salivary & pancreatic		4,81
233	Cadaverinase		64
234	Cathepsin		89
235	Esterases		114
236	β-Glucuronidase		87
237	γ-Glutamyl transpeptidase		96
238	Histaminase		64
239	Lactic dehydrogenase		55
240	Lipase		93
241	Maltase		39
242	Ribonuclease		77
243	Urokinase		11
244	Uropepsinogen		57
	Miscellaneous Organic Compounds, mg		
245	Acetoacetic acid	0.04(0.03-0.06)	121
246	Acetone bodies, total	0.20(0.03-0.30)	121
247	Aconitic acid	Trace	50
248	Carbonic acid	2.7(2.1-3.3)	44
249	Citric acid	(3-20)	129
250	Formic acid	0.8(0.4-2.0)	6
251	Glucuronic acid	Trace[3/]	134
252	Glycolic acid	0.6	56
253	Glyoxylic acid	0.05	56
254	Lactic acid	3(2-5)	43
255	Oxalic acid	0.5(0.3-0.7)	53,56
256	Phenol, total	(0.2-0.6)	26
257	free	(0-0.05)	26
258	Phenolic derivatives: 3,4-dihydroxymandelic acid	0.005	28
259	dopamine	(0.0041-0.0063)	5,9
260	epinephrine	0.00014	84,142
261	homovanillic acid	(0.065-0.110)	112,152
262	3-hydroxyanthranilic acid	(0.008-0.04)	1
263	*p*-hydroxybenzylamine	0.002	63
264	5-hydroxyindoleacetic acid	(0.02-0.03)	152
265	3-hydroxykynurenine	0.075	15
266	*p*-hydroxyphenylacetic acid	(0.2-1.2)	152
267	metanephrine	(0.002-0.006)	63,84
268	3-methoxy-4-hydroxymandelic acid	0.053	142
269	3-methoxytyramine	(0-0.0005)	63
270	norepinephrine	0.001	84,142
271	normetanephrine	(0.0002-0.0005)	84
272	tryptamine	(0.0013-0.0028)	99
273	*m*-tyramine	(0.001-0.0025)	63
274	*p*-tyramine	(0.0005-0.0025)	63
275	vanillyl mandelic acid	0.05	28
276	other organic acids[6/]	Traces[3/]	21,22,141

[3/] Determined by chromatography. [6/] *p*-Hydroxybenzoic acid; 3-methoxy-4-hydroxybenzoic acid; 3-methoxy-4-hydroxycinnamic acid; *m*-hydroxyhippuric acid; *p*-hydroxyhippuric acid; *p*-hydroxymandelic acid; *m*-hydroxyphenylacetic acid; *o*-hydroxyphenylacetic acid; 3-methoxy-4-hydroxyphenylacetic acid; *m*-hydroxyphenyl-β-hydroxypropionic acid; *p*-octopamine; and *p*-sympatol.

Contributor: Van Pilsum, John F.

continued

105. EXCRETION PRODUCTS IN URINE: VERTEBRATES

Part I. Man

References

[1] Abul-Fadl, M. A. M., and A. S. Khalafallah. 1961. Brit. J. Cancer 15:479.
[2] Aoyama, S. 1961. Acta Schol. Med. Univ. Kioto 37:203.
[3] Austin, W. H., and S. C. Littlefield. 1966. J. Lab. Clin. Med. 67:516.
[4] Aw, S. E. 1966. Nature 209:298.
[5] Barbeau, A., and T. L. Sourkes. 1961. Rev. Can. Biol. 20:197.
[6] Benedict, E. M., and G. A. Harrop. 1922. J. Biol. Chem. 54:443.
[7] Berggard, I. 1961. Clin. Chim. Acta 6:413.
[8] Berggard, I., H. Cleve, and A. G. Bearn. 1964. Ibid. 10:1.
[9] Bishoff, F., and A. Torres. 1962. Clin. Chem. 8:370.
[10] Bloomfield, I. J., R. R. Sayers, and F. H. Goldman. 1932. Public Health Rept. (U.S.) 50:421.
[11] Boomgaard, J. B., et al. 1966. Clin. Chim. Acta 13: 484.
[12] Bourrillon, R., and J. L. Vernay. 1966. Biochim. Biophys. Acta 117(2):319.
[13] Boyce, W. H., et al. 1961. J. Clin. Invest. 40:1453.
[14] Bradley, S. E. 1945. Med. Clin. N. Am. 29:1314.
[15] Brown, R. R., M. J. Thornton, and J. M. Price. 1961. J. Clin. Invest. 40:617.
[16] Bruger, M., J. W. Hinton, and W. G. Lough. 1941. J. Lab. Clin. Med. 26:1942.
[17] Carsten, M. E. 1952. J. Am. Chem. Soc. 74:5954.
[18] Chen, S. D., and C. Shuck. 1951. J. Nutr. 23:111.
[19] Clark, G. W. 1926. Univ. Calif. (Berkeley) Publ. Physiol. 5(17):195.
[20] Conway, E. J., and J. C. Flood. 1936. Biochem. J. 30:716.
[21] Coward, R. F., and P. Smith. 1965. Clin. Chim. Acta 12:206.
[22] Coward, R. F., P. Smith, and O. S. Wilson. 1964. Ibid. 9:381.
[23] Crokaert, R. 1953. Ann. Soc. Roy. Sci. Med. Nat. Bruxelles 6:157.
[24] Curzon, G., and J. Walsh. 1962. Clin. Chim. Acta 7:657.
[25] Davies, B. M. A. 1958. J. Endocrinol. 16:369.
[26] Deichmann, W., and L. J. Schafer. 1942. Am. J. Clin. Pathol. 12:129.
[27] Denko, C. W., et al. 1946. Arch. Biochem. 10:33.
[28] DeQuattro, V., et al. 1964. J. Lab. Clin. Med. 63: 864.
[29] Dikstein, S., F. Bergman, and M. Chaimovitz. 1958. J. Biol. Chem. 230:203.
[30] Diszfalusy, E., et al. 1955. Acta Endocrinol. 18: 356.
[31] Dorfman, R. I., and R. A. Shipley. 1956. The androgens. J. Wiley, New York.
[32] Dorfman, R. I., and F. Ungar. 1965. Metabolism of steroid hormones. Academic Press, New York.
[33] Dunn, M. S., et al. 1947. Arch. Biochem. 13:207.
[34] Eisen, A. Z., S. Weissman, and M. Karow. 1962. J. Lab. Clin. Med. 59:620.
[35] Evans, R. A., and L. Watson. 1966. Lancet 1(7436): 522.
[36] Feher, T. 1966. Clin. Chim. Acta 14:91.
[37] Figueroa, W. G., et al. 1955. J. Lab. Clin. Med. 46: 534.
[38] Finn, P. H. 1965. Brit. Med. J. 1:697.
[39] Fleury, P. F., J. E. Courtois, and D. Ramon. 1951. Bull. Soc. Chim. Biol. 33:1762.
[40] Folin, O. 1905. Am. J. Physiol. 13:45.
[41] Freeman, J. T., R. Hafkesbring, and E. K. Caldwell. 1951. Gastroenterology 18:224.
[42] Futterman, S., and J. H. Roe. 1955. J. Biol. Chem. 215:257.
[43] Gambigliani-Zoccoli, A., et al. 1939. Z. Klin. Med. 135:457.
[44] Gamble, J. L. 1954. Chemical anatomy, physiology and pathology of extracellular fluid. Ed. 6. Harvard Univ. Press, Cambridge.
[45] Gerber, G. B., and G. Gerber. 1960. Clin. Chim. Acta 5:607.
[46] Gerber, G. B., et al. 1964. Ibid. 9:185.
[47] Gottschalk, A. 1966. Glycoproteins. Elsevier, Amsterdam.
[48] Grant, G. H. 1957. J. Clin. Pathol. 10:360.
[49] Gwens, M. H. 1918. J. Biol. Chem. 34:119.
[50] Halpern, M. N. 1960. Clin. Chim. Acta 5:264.
[51] Harp, M. J., and F. I. Scoular. 1952. J. Nutr. 47:67.
[52] Harrow, B., and A. Mazur. 1962. Testbook of biochemistry. Ed. 8. W. B. Saunders, Philadelphia.
[53] Hawk, P. B., B. L. Oser, and W. H. Summerson. 1947. Practical physiological chemistry. Ed. 12. Blakiston, Philadelphia.
[54] Hier, S. W. 1948. Trans. N.Y. Acad. Sci. 10:200.
[55] Hochella, N. J., and S. Weinhouse. 1965. Anal. Biochem. 13:322.
[56] Hockaday, T. D. R., et al. 1965. J. Lab. Clin. Med. 65:667.
[57] Hostrup, H., and P. Bastrup-Madsen. 1957. Acta Med. Scand. 158:193.
[58] Johnson, B. C., T. S. Hamilton, and H. H. Mitchell. 1945. J. Biol. Chem. 158:619.
[59] Johnson, B. C., T. S. Hamilton, and H. H. Mitchell. 1945. Ibid. 159:5.
[60] Johnson, B. C., T. S. Hamilton, and H. H. Mitchell. 1945. Ibid. 159:231.
[61] Johnson, B. C., H. H. Mitchell, and T. S. Hamilton. 1945. Ibid. 161:357.
[62] Johnson, J. M., J. H. Kemp, and E. D. Hibbard. 1965. Clin. Chim. Acta 12:440.
[63] Kakimoto, Y., and M. D. Armstrong. 1962. J. Biol. Chem. 237:208.
[64] Kapeller-Adler, R., and R. Renwick. 1956. Clin. Chim. Acta 1:197.
[65] Kehoe, R. A., J. Cholak, and R. V. Story. 1940. J. Nutr. 19:579.
[66] Kent, N. L., and R. A. McCance. 1941. Biochem. J. 35:877.
[67] Kerr, J. W. 1964. Brit. Med. J. 2:606.
[68] Kibrick, A. C. 1965. Clin. Chim. Acta 11:408.
[69] Kibrick, A. C., et al. 1964. Ibid. 10:344.
[70] King, J. S., Jr., M. L. Fielden, and W. H. Boyce. 1962. Ibid. 7:316.

continued

Part I. Man

[71] Klopper, A., E. A. Mitchie, and J. B. Brown. 1955. J. Endocrinol. 12:209.
[72] Koessler, K. K., and M. T. Hanke. 1924. J. Biol. Chem. 59:803.
[73] Kolmer, J. A., et al. 1951. Approved laboratory technique. Ed. 5. Appleton-Century-Crofts, New York.
[74] Kuwaki, T., and S. Mizuhara. 1966. Biochim. Biophys. Acta 115:491.
[75] Lemberg, R., and J. W. Legge. 1949. Hematin compounds and bile pigments. Interscience, New York.
[76] Levinson, S. A., and R. P. MacFate. 1961. Clinical laboratory diagnosis. Ed. 6. Lea and Febiger, Philadelphia.
[77] Levy, A. L., and A. Rottino. 1960. Clin. Chem. 6:43.
[78] Lewis, J. P., et al. 1964. Proc. Soc. Exptl. Biol. Med. 116:742.
[79] Lieberman, L. L. 1962. Clin. Chim. Acta 7:159.
[80] Luck, J. M., and A. Wilcox. 1953. J. Biol. Chem. 205:859.
[81] MacFate, R. P. 1961. Assoc. Clin. Scientists Proc. 2nd Appl. Seminar 2:14.
[82] Marks, L. J., J. H. Leftin, and P. Leonard. 1957. J. Clin. Endocrinol. Metab. 17:407.
[83] Mattice, M. R. 1936. Chemical procedures for clinical laboratories. Lea and Febiger, Philadelphia.
[84] Mattok, G. L., D. L. Wilson, and R. A. Heacock. 1966. Clin. Chim. Acta 14:99.
[85] McBride, J. M. 1957. J. Clin. Endocrinol. Metab. 17:1440.
[86] McClure, F. J. 1944. Public Health Rept. (U.S.) 59:1575.
[87] Melicow, M. M., A. C. Uson, and R. Lipton. 1961. J. Urol. 86:89.
[88] Merler, E., et al. 1963. J. Clin. Invest. 42:1340.
[89] Merten, R., and H. Wojta. 1954. Z. Ges. Exptl. Med. 123:315.
[90] Mirsky, I. A., et al. 1948. J. Clin. Invest. 27:515.
[91] Moore, D. J., and R. F. Labbe. 1964. Clin. Chem. 10:1105.
[92] Nauman, H. N. 1936. Biochem. J. 36:692.
[93] Nothmann, M. M., J. H. Pratt, and A. D. Callow. 1955. Arch. Internal. Med. 96:188.
[94] Ohara, M., et al. 1952. Japan. J. Med. Sci. Biol. 5:259.
[95] Oldham, H., B. B. Sheft, and T. Porter. 1950. J. Nutr. 41:231.
[96] Orlowski, M., and A. Szewczyquk. 1962. Clin. Chim. Acta 7:755.
[97] Patte, J. C., G. Baldassaire, and J. Loret. 1958. Rev. Franc. Etudes Clin. Biol. 3:960.
[98] Perlzweig, W. A., H. P. Sarett, and L. H. Margoles. 1942. J. Am. Med. Assoc. 118:28.
[99] Perry, T. L. 1962. Science 136:879.
[100] Plooij, M., et al. 1959. Ned. Tijdschr. Geneesk. 103:1528.
[101] Rabinowitz, J. C., and E. E. Snell. 1949. Proc. Soc. Exptl. Biol. Med. 70:235.
[102] Rae, J. J. 1937. Biochem. J. 31:1622.
[103] Reddy, W. J., D. Jenkins, and G. W. Thorn. 1952. Metab. Clin. Exptl. 1:511.
[104] Reddy, W. J., et al. 1956. J. Clin. Endocrinol. Metab. 16:380.
[105] Register, V. D., and H. P. Sarett. 1951. Proc. Soc. Exptl. Biol. Med. 77:837.
[106] Rigas, D. A., and C. G. Heller. 1951. J. Clin. Invest. 30:853.
[107] Rogers, C. J. 1964. Clin. Chem. 10:678.
[108] Romanoff, L. P., et al. 1957. J. Clin. Endocrinol. Metab. 17:777.
[109] Rose, B., et al. 1951. Proc. Clin. ACTH Conf., 2nd, 1:519.
[110] Rubin, B. L., R. I. Dorfman, and A. Dorfman. 1954. J. Clin. Endocrinol. Metab. 14:154.
[111] Rubin, B. L., R. I. Dorfman, and G. Pincus. 1954. Recent Progr. Hormone Res. 9:213.
[112] Ruthven, C. R. J., and M. Sandler. 1966. Clin. Chim. Acta 14:511.
[113] Saifer, A., and S. Gerstenfeld. 1964. Clin. Chem. 10:321.
[114] Saint-Cyr, C. de Vaux, G. Hermann, and N. Talal. 1963. Rev. Franc. Etudes Clin. Biol. 8:241.
[115] Sarfaty, G. A., and M. B. Summers. 1964. Clin. Chim. Acta 10:505.
[116] Schlenker, F. S., N. A. Taylor, and B. P. Kiehn. 1964. Am. J. Clin. Pathol. 42:349.
[117] Schwartz, S., et al. 1960. Methods Biochem. Anal. 8.
[118] Sharlit, H. 1938. Arch. Pediat. 55:277.
[119] Sheffner, A. L., J. B. Kirsner, and W. L. Palmer. 1948. J. Biol. Chem. 175:107.
[120] Shizume, K., W. Mori, and A. B. Lerner. 1962. Gen. Comp. Endocrinol., Suppl. 1:110.
[121] Stark, I. E., and M. Somogyi. 1943. J. Biol. Chem. 147:319.
[122] Stein, W. H. 1953. Ibid. 201:45.
[123] Stern, M. I. 1957. J. Endocrinol. 16:180.
[124] Sterner, J. H., and V. Lidfeldt. 1941. J. Pharmacol. Exptl. Therap. 73:205.
[125] Stock, A. 1940. Biochem. Z. 304:73.
[126] Sunderman, F. W., and F. Boerner. 1949. Normal values in clinical medicine. W. B. Saunders, Philadelphia.
[127] Takatsuki, K., and E. F. Osserman. 1964. J. Immunol. 92:100.
[128] Tallan, H. H., W. H. Stein, and S. Moore. 1954. J. Biol. Chem. 206:825.
[129] Taussky, H. H. 1949. Ibid. 181:195.
[130] Teller, W. M., et al. 1962. J. Lab. Clin. Med. 59:95.
[131] Tominaga, F., K. Oka, and H. Yoshida. 1965. J. Biochem. (Tokyo) 57(6):717.
[132] Tompsett, S. L., and J. Fitzpatrick. 1950. Brit. J. Exptl. Pathol. 31:70.
[133] Touster, O., R. M. Hutcheson, and V. H. Reynolds. 1954. J. Am. Chem. Soc. 76:5005.
[134] Tower, D. B., E. L. Peters, and M. A. Pogorelskin. 1956. Neurology 6:37.
[135] Tribble, H. M., and F. I. Scoular. 1954. J. Nutr. 52:210.

continued

105. EXCRETION PRODUCTS IN URINE: VERTEBRATES

Part I. Man

[136] Van Pilsum, J. F., et al. 1956. J. Biol. Chem. 222: 225.

[137] Van Ravesteyn, A. H. 1944. Acta Med. Scand. 118:163.

[138] Venning, E. H., I. Dyrenfurth, and C. J. P. Giroud. 1956. J. Clin. Endocrinol. Metab. 16:1326.

[139] Vestergaard, P., E. Raabo, and S. Vedso. 1966. Clin. Chim. Acta 14:540.

[140] Vestergaard, P., and J. F. Sayegh. 1966. Ibid. 14: 247.

[141] Von Studnitz, W., K. Engelman, and A. Sjoerdsma. 1964. Ibid. 9:224.

[142] Voorhess, M. L., and L. I. Gardner. 1962. J. Clin. Endocrinol. Metab. 22:126.

[143] Walker, B. S. 1931. J. Lab. Clin. Med. 17:347.

[144] Wallraff, E. B., G. C. Brodie, and A. L. Borden. 1950. J. Clin. Invest. 29:1542.

[145] Wang, C. C., et al. 1930. J. Nutr. 3:79.

[146] Watson, C. J. 1937. Arch. Internal Med. 59:196.

[147] Watson, C. J., et al. 1949. J. Clin. Invest. 28:447.

[148] Webster, S. H. 1941. Public Health Rept. (U.S.) 56:1953.

[149] Weissmann, B., P. A. Bromberg, and A. B. Gutman. 1957. J. Biol. Chem. 224:423.

[150] Weissmann, B., and A. B. Gutman. 1957. Ibid. 229:239.

[151] Wiechouski, W. 1909. Biochem. Z. 19:368.

[152] Williams, C. M., and C. C. Sweeley. 1961. J. Clin. Endocrinol. Metab. 21:1500.

[153] Woodson, H. W., et al. 1948. J. Biol. Chem. 172: 613.

[154] Young, M. K., et al. 1951. Texas Univ. Publ. 5109: 189.

Part II. Mammals Other Than Man

Values are mg/kg body wt/day, unless otherwise specified. In reducing values to mg/kg, the following body weights (in kilograms) were assumed unless a specific weight was recorded in the literature: cat, 2.5; cattle, 500; dog, 12; goat, 50; guinea pig, 0.5; horse, 630; monkey, 12; rabbit, 2.0; rat, 0.33; swine, 200. Values in parentheses are ranges, estimate "c" (*see* Introduction).

	Animal	Property or Constituent	Value	Reference
1	Cat	Freezing point depression	5.0°C	30
2		Specific gravity	1.030(1.020-1.040)	30
3		Volume	(10-20)[1]	47
4		Calcium	(0.20-0.45)	34
5		N^1-Methylnicotinamide	(0.030-0.200)	31
6		Allantoin	80	63
7		Creatinine	(12-20)	47
8		Histamine	(0.006-0.300)	2
9		Imidazole derivatives	(3-4)	57
10		Urea	(800-4000)	47
11		Uric acid	(0.2-13.0)	47
12		Nitrogen, total	(500-1100)	47
13		ammonia	60	35,47
14		Phenol	(8-25)	36
15	Cattle	Volume	(17-45)[1]	29
16		Calcium	(0.10-1.40)	39,48,49
17		Chlorine	140	59
18		Magnesium	(3-7)	12,39
19		Phosphorus, ♂	(5-13)	12,39
20		♀	(0.06-0.14)	12,39
21		Sulfur, ethereal	(1.6-7.0)[2]	17
22		inorganic	(0.2-5.0)[2]	17
23		neutral	(0.8-3.0)[2]	17
24		Sulfate, total	(3-15)[2]	17
25		Thiamine	0.010	106
26		Riboflavin	0.020	106
27		Nicotinic acid	(0.040-0.050)	106
28		Pantothenic acid	0.170	106
29		Ascorbic acid	(0.040-0.140)	110
30		Allantoin	(20-60)	56,63,83
31		Creatine	(1-2)	83
32		Creatinine	(15-20)	16,17,83
33		Hippuric acid	(50-200)	16,17,115
34		Purine bases	(0.2-3.0)	56,83
35		Urea	(50-60)	83
36		Uric acid	(1-4)	56,83
37		Nitrogen, total	(40-450)	17,56,83, 85
38		ammonia	(1-17)	56,83
39		Androgens, ♂	0.0070	53,62
40		Acetone bodies	(0.5-5.0)	17,61
41		Citric acid	(1-3)	12
42	Dog	Freezing point depression	(1.573-3.638)°C	30
43		Specific gravity	1.025(1.016-1.060)	30
44		Volume	(20-100)[1]	29
45		Calcium	(1-3)	104,117
46		Magnesium	(1.7-3.0)	43,45,104, 117
47		Phosphorus	(20-30)	43,45
48		Potassium	(40-100)	104,117

[1] ml/kg body wt/day. [2] After 24-hour fast.

continued

105. EXCRETION PRODUCTS IN URINE: VERTEBRATES

Part II. Mammals Other Than Man

	Animal	Property or Constituent	Value	Reference
49		Sulfur, total	(25-40)	113
50		ethereal	(1.3-3.5)	113
51		neutral	(5-10)	113
52		Sulfate, total	(30-50)	113
53		Riboflavin	(0.010-0.020)	97
54		Nicotinamide	(0.300-0.400)	31
55		N^1-Methylnicotinamide	(0.090-0.800)	31
56		Pantothenic acid	0.130	100
57		Choline	(0.200-0.500)	68
58		Allantoin	(35-45)	1,10,41,65
59		Creatine	(10-50)	50,83,113
60		Creatinine	(30-80)	16,50,113
61		Hippuric acid	34	25
62		Histamine	(0.010-0.300)	2,79
63		Urea	(300-500)	66,94
64		Uric acid	4.5	77
		Amino acids		
65		Arginine	(0.2-1.9)	109
66		Lysine	3.5	109
67		Ornithine	0.1	109
68		Nitrogen, total	(250-800)	6,43,45, 50,66
69		ammonia	(30-60)	6,50
70		Androgens	(0.010-0.030)	88
71		Formaldehydogenic steroids	0.010	20
72		17-Ketosteroids	(0.040-0.100)	88
73		Acetone bodies	(5-6)	69
74		Citric acid	(2-20)	13,81
75		Phenol	5	36
76	Goat	Specific gravity	1.030(1.015-1.045)	30
77		Volume	(10-40)[1]	29
78		Calcium	1	83
79		Phosphorus	1	83
80		Thiamine	0.006	71
81		Riboflavin	0.020	71
82		Nicotinic acid	(0.050-0.200)	90
83		N^1-Methylnicotinamide	(0.060-0.090)	90
84		Pantothenic acid	0.160	71
85		Allantoin	(30-70)	56,83
86		Creatine	(3-4)	83
87		Creatinine	10	83
88		Hippuric acid	(200-300)	83
89		Purine bases	(2-8)	56,83
90		Urea	230	83
91		Uric acid	(2-5)	56,83
92		Nitrogen, total	(120-400)	56,83
93		ammonia	(3-5)	83
94		Phenol	15	36
95	Guinea pig	Sulfur, neutral	(5-8)	16
96		Allantoin	50	80
97		Creatinine	30	16,101
98		Nitrogen, total	180	101
99		Phenol	24	2
100	Horse	Freezing point depression	(1.77-2.00)°C	30
101		Specific gravity	1.040(1.025-1.060)	30
102		Volume	(3-18)[1]	29
103		Riboflavin	0.002	95
104		Nicotinic acid	(0.002-0.007)	99,106
105		N^1-Methylnicotinamide	(0.003-0.020)	102
106		Ascorbic acid	0.090	110
107		Allantoin	(5-15)	56
108		Hippuric acid	100	51
109		Histamine	(0.0001-0.0030)	2
110		Purine bases	0.04	56
111		Uric acid	(1-2)	56
112		Nitrogen, total	(100-160)	56,86
113		Estrogens, ♂	(0.020-1.000)	28,67
114		♀	(0.200-0.400)	28,67
115	Monkey	Volume	(70-80)[1]	8
116		Calcium	15	8
117		Chlorine	100	8
118		Magnesium	5.2	8
119		Phosphorus	15	8
120		Potassium	200	8
121		Sulfur, ethereal	(3-4)	8
122		inorganic	12	8
123		neutral	(4-5)	8
124		Sulfate, total	(20-30)	8
125		Allantoin	(5-10)	26,65
126		Creatine	(0-14)	58,93
127		Creatinine	(20-60)	26,58,93
128		Hippuric acid	(4-5)	55
129		Purine bases	(5-6)	55,93
130		Urea	(200-700)	55,93
131		Uric acid	(1-2)	26,93
132		Nitrogen, total	(140-400)	8,55,93
133		ammonia	(2-10)	8,55,93
134		Androgens	0.010	112
135	Rabbit	Volume	(50-75)[1]	82
136		Calcium	(3-7)	111
137		Chlorine	(190-300)	82
138		Phosphorus	(10-60)	15,75,111
139		Sulfur, neutral	(4-10)	16
140		Nicotinic acid	(0.250-0.700)	31
141		Allantoin	(60-80)	26,63,65, 80
142		Coproporphyrin I & III	(0.003-0.012)	98
143		Creatine	(13-20)	82
144		Creatinine	(20-50)	11,16,18, 82,101
145		Hippuric acid	100	32
146		Histamine	(0.020-0.200)	2
147		Indoxylsulfuric acid	(0-trace)	3
148		Urea	(1200-1500)	52
149		Uric acid	(4-6)	42

[1] ml/kg body wt/day.

continued

105. EXCRETION PRODUCTS IN URINE: VERTEBRATES

Part II. Mammals Other Than Man

	Animal	Property or Constituent	Value	Reference
150		Nitrogen, total	(120-300)	75,101,111
151		ammonia	(3-5)	11
152		Androgens	(0.003-0.020)	22
153		17-Ketosteroids	(0.030-1.000)	21,22,24
154		Acetone bodies	(0.4-1.0)	5
155		3-Hydroxyanthranilic acid	0.039	103
156		Phenol	30	36
157	Rat	Volume	(150-300)[1]	46
158		Calcium	(3-9)	33,78
159		Chlorine	250	60,107
160		Phosphorus	30	94
161		Potassium	160	60,107
162		Sodium	110	60,107
163		Sulfur, neutral	(7-20)	16
164		Bicarbonate	6	60,107
165		Thiamine	(0.003-0.013)	96,116
166		Riboflavin	(0.040-0.080)	95,97
167		Nicotinic acid	(0.090-0.120)	54
168		Trigonelline	(0.300-0.700)	54
169		Nicotinamide	(0.200-0.700)	31
170		N^1-Methylnicotinamide	(0.900-5.000)	31
171		Pantothenic acid	(0.300-0.600)	74
172		Ascorbic acid	(1.0-6.0)	64,84
173		Allantoin	(100-600)	7,40,65
174		Ammonia	80	60,107
175		Creatine	(0-13)	19,108
176		Creatinine	(24-40)	7,16,38, 108
177		Histamine	(0.020-0.200)	2
178		Purines[3]	Traces	70
179		Urea	(1000-1600)	38,91
180		Uric acid	(8-12)	7,37,40
		Amino acids		
181		Arginine, total	2.7	4
182		free	1.3	4
183		Aspartic acid, free	0.29	4
184		Citrulline	(0.54-2.5)	92
185		Cystine, total	0.5	4
186		Glutamic acid	7.1	4
187		Glycine, total	6.9	4
188		Histidine, total	1.5	4
189		free	0.43	4
190		Isoleucine, total	2.2	4
191		free	0.43	4
192		Leucine, free	2.4	4
193		Lysine, total	4.6	4
194		free	1.0	4
195		Methionine, free	0.4	4
196		Phenylalanine, free	0.8	4
197		Taurine	(0.54-2.50)	92
198		Threonine, total	2.9	4
199		free	0.63	4
200		Tryptophan, free	0.47	4
201		Tyrosine, free	0.47	4
202		Valine, free	0.93	4
203		Nitrogen, total	(200-1000)	14,44,101
204		ammonia	(10-30)	38,46
205		Androgens	0.018	27
206		Acetic acid	30	60
207		*cis*-Aconitic acid	5	60
208		Citric + isocitric acid	25	60
209		Fumaric acid	6	60
210		α-Ketoglutaric acid	7	60
211		Lactic acid	3	60
212		Phenol	(6-60)	23
213		Succinic acid	4	60
214	Sheep	Specific gravity	1.030(1.015-1.045)	30
215		Volume	(10-40)[1]	29
216		Calcium	2	83
217		Phosphorus	0.2	83
218		Sulfur, total	10	114
219		ethereal	4	114
220		inorganic	5	114
221		neutral	5	114
222		Nicotinic acid	(0.080-0.130)	90
223		N^1-Methylnicotinamide	(0.018-0.060)	90
224		Choline	0.060	68
225		Reducing sugars	40	114
226		Protein, total	8	87
227		Allantoin	(20-50)	56,80,83
228		Creatine	(0-6)	83
229		Creatinine	10	83
230		Hippuric acid	(20-40)	83,89
231		Mucoprotein	4	87
232		Purine bases	(2-5)	56,83
233		Urea	210	83
234		Uric acid	(2-4)	56,83
235		Amino acids	3	114
236		Nitrogen, total	(120-350)	51,56,83
237		ammonia	(0-8)	51,83
238		Estrogens, ♀	(0.00005-0.00300)	9
239	Swine	Specific gravity	1.012(1.010-1.050)	30
240		Volume	(5-30)[1]	29
241		Sulfur, neutral	(1-3)	105
242		Ascorbic acid	0.160	110
243		Allantoin	(20-80)	56,63,80
244		Creatine	(15-25)	73
245		Creatinine	(20-90)	16,73,101
246		Purine bases	(3-4)	56
247		Urea	430	105
248		Uric acid	(1-2)	56
249		Nitrogen, total	(40-240)	72,76,101
250		Phenol	(1-3)	36

[1] ml/kg body wt/day. [3] Guanine; 1-methylguanine; 7-methylguanine; N^2-dimethylguanine; xanthine; hypoxanthine; 1-methylhypoxanthine.

Contributor: Van Pilsum, John F.

continued

105. EXCRETION PRODUCTS IN URINE: VERTEBRATES

Part II. Mammals Other Than Man

References

[1] Allan, F. W., and L. R. Carecedo. 1931. J. Biol. Chem. 93:293.
[2] Anrep, G. V., et al. 1944. J. Physiol. (London) 103: 155.
[3] Asayama, C. 1916. J. Am. Med. Assoc. 67:475.
[4] Bakerman, H. A., M. Silverman, and F. S. Daft. 1951. J. Biol. Chem. 188:117.
[5] Banerjee, S., and G. Bhattacharya. 1949. Ibid. 178:145.
[6] Bartlett, P. D., O. H. Gaebler, and A. Harmon 1949. Ibid. 180:1021.
[7] Bass, A. D., et al. 1950. Proc. Soc. Exptl. Biol. Med. 73:687.
[8] Baumann, L., and E. Oviatt. 1915. J. Biol. Chem. 22:43.
[9] Beck, A. B. 1950. Australian J. Agr. Res. 1:322.
[10] Beher, W. T., and O. H. Gaebler. 1950. J. Nutr. 41:447.
[11] Bernheim, F., M. L. C. Bernheim, and H. R. Higgens. 1945. Am. J. Physiol. 145:115.
[12] Blosser, T. H., and V. R. Smith. 1950. J. Dairy Sci. 33:329.
[13] Boothby, W. M., and M. Adams. 1934. Am. J. Physiol. 107:471
[14] Bothwell, J. W., and J. N. Williams, Jr. 1951. J. Nutr. 45:245.
[15] Brain, R. T., H. D. Kay, and P. G. Marshall. 1928. Biochem. J. 22:628.
[16] Brody, S., R. C. Procter, and U. S. Ashworth. 1934. Missouri Univ. Agr. Expt. Sta. Res. Bull. 214:34.
[17] Carpenter, T. A. 1927. Am. J. Physiol. 81:519.
[18] Cheetham, R. W. S., and H. Zwarenstein. 1938. Biochem. J. 32:871.
[19] Coffman, J. R., and F. C. Kock. 1939. Proc. Soc. Exptl. Biol. Med. 42:779.
[20] Corcoran, A. C., and I. H. Page. 1948. J. Lab. Clin. Med. 33:1326.
[21] Danford, P. A., and H. G. Danford. 1950. Endocrinology 47:139.
[22] Davis, C. T., C. R. Slater, and B. Krichesky. 1949. Ibid. 44:83.
[23] Deichmann, W., and L. J. Schafer. 1942. Am. J. Clin. Pathol. 12:129.
[24] DeKoning, K. B., and S. J. Glass. 1948. Proc. Soc. Exptl. Biol. Med. 68:320.
[25] Delprat, G. D., and G. H. Whipple. 1921. J. Biol. Chem. 49:229.
[26] Dinning, J. S., and P. L. Day. 1949. Ibid. 181:897.
[27] Dorfman, R. I. 1938. Ibid. 123:xxx.
[28] Dow, D. S., and C. E. Allen. 1949. Sci. Agr. 29:330.
[29] Dukes, H. H. 1947. The physiology of domestic animals, Ed. 6. Comstock, Ithaca.
[30] Ellenberger, W., and A. Scheunert. 1925. Lehrbuch der vergleichenden Physiologie der Haussaugetiere. Ed. 3. P. Parey, Berlin.
[31] Ellinger, P., and M. M. Abdel Kader. 1949. Biochem. J. 44:77.
[32] Epstein, A. A., and S. Bookman. 1912. J. Biol. Chem. 13:117.
[33] Fairhall, L. T. 1926. Ibid. 70:495.
[34] Fiske, C. H., and M. A. Logan. 1931. Ibid. 93:211.
[35] Folin, O., and R. D. Bell. 1917. Ibid. 29:329.
[36] Folin, O., and W. Denis. 1915. Ibid. 22:309.
[37] Folin, O., and W. Denis. 1916. Ibid. 26:497.
[38] Folin, O., and J. L. Morris. 1913. Ibid. 14:509.
[39] Forbes, E. B., R. B. French, and T. V. Letonoff. 1928. J. Nutr. 1:201.
[40] Friedman, M. 1948. Am. J. Physiol. 152:302.
[41] Friedman, M., and S. O. Byers. 1948. J. Biol. Chem. 175:727.
[42] Friedman, M., and S. O. Byers. 1950. Am. J. Physiol. 163:684.
[43] Givens, M. H., and L. B. Mendel. 1917. J. Biol. Chem. 31:421.
[44] Gordon, G. S., H. M. Evans, and M. E. Simpson. 1947. Endocrinology 40:375.
[45] Greenwald, I., and J. Gross. 1925. J. Biol. Chem. 66:201.
[46] Griffith, J. Q. 1949. The rat in laboratory investigation. Ed. 2. J. B. Lippincott, Philadelphia.
[47] Hammett, F. S. 1915. J. Biol. Chem. 22:551.
[48] Hansard, S. L., C. L. Comar, and M. P. Plumlee. 1952. J. Animal Sci. 11:524.
[49] Hart, E. B., et al. 1931. J. Dairy Sci. 14:307.
[50] Hawk, P. B. 1910. J. Biol. Chem. 8:465.
[51] Healy, D. J., J. F. Bullard, and H. D. Spears. 1928. J. Am. Vet. Med. Assoc. 73:87.
[52] Herrin, R. C. 1947. Am. J. Physiol. 149:492.
[53] Hooker, C. W. 1937. Endocrinology 21:655.
[54] Huff, J. W., and W. A. Perlzweig. 1942. J. Biol. Chem. 142:401.
[55] Hunter, A., and M. H. Givens. 1914. Ibid. 17:55.
[56] Hunter, A., and M. H. Givens. 1914. Ibid. 18:403.
[57] Hunter, G. 1925. Biochem. J. 19:34.
[58] Jailer, J. W. 1940. Am. J. Physiol. 130:503.
[59] Keitt, T. E. 1916. S. Carolina Agr. Expt. Sta. Ann. Rept. 29.
[60] Kesner, L., and E. Muntwyler. 1963. J. Lab. Clin. Med. 61:604.
[61] Knodt, C. B., J. C. Shaw, and G. C. White. 1942. J. Dairy Sci. 25:851.
[62] Kock, F. C. 1937. Physiol. Rev. 17:153.
[63] Kostyak, J. 1941. Koezl. Oesszehas. Elet. Kort. Koereb. (Budapest) 29:178.
[64] Langwill, K. E., C. G. King, and G. MacLeod. 1945. J. Nutr. 30:99.
[65] Larson, H. W. 1931. J. Biol. Chem. 94:727.
[66] Larson, P. S., and I. L. Chaikoff. 1937. J. Nutr. 13:287.
[67] Levin, L. 1949. J. Biol. Chem. 178:229.
[68] Luecke, R. W., and P. B. Pearson. 1945. Ibid. 158: 561.
[69] Maignon, F., and E. Kinthakis. 1928. Compt. Rend. 186:463.
[70] Mandel, L. R., P. R. Srinivasan, and E. Borek. 1966. Nature 209:586.
[71] Marsh, D. C., P. B. Pearson, and I. W. Rupel. 1947. J. Dairy Sci. 30:867.

continued

Part II. Mammals Other Than Man

[72] McCollum, E. V., and D. R. Hoagland. 1913. J. Biol. Chem. 16:299.
[73] McCollum, E. V., and H. Steenbock. 1912. Ibid. 13:209.
[74] McIlwain, H., and F. Hawking. 1943. Lancet 1: 449
[75] Mendel, L. B., and J. F. Lyman. 1910. J. Biol. Chem. 8:115.
[76] Miller, E. R. 1929. J. Am. Vet. Med. Assoc. 74: 376.
[77] Miller, G. E., L. S. Danzey, and J. H. Talbott. 1951. Am. J. Physiol. 164:155.
[78] Miller, H. G. 1929. J. Biol. Chem. 70:593.
[79] Misrahy, G., and S. Salams. 1947. Am. J. Physiol. 150:420.
[80] Miyahara, T. 1934. Sei-i-kwai Med. J. 53(8-9).
[81] Morendo, G. C., and L. Flore. 1949. Minerva Med. 39(2):149.
[82] Morgulis, S., and H. C. Spencer. 1936. J. Nutr. 12:191.
[83] Morris, S., and S. C. Ray. 1939. Biochem. J. 33: 1217.
[84] Musulin, R. R., et al. 1939. J. Biol. Chem. 129: 437.
[85] Nehring, K., U. Zelck, and R. Schiemann. 1965. Arch. Tierernaehr. 15:45.
[86] Nietsche, H. 1937. Biochem. Z. 294:174.
[87] Packett, L. V., and S. P. Coburn. 1965. Am. J. Vet. Res. 26:112.
[88] Paschkis, K. E., et al. 1943. Proc. Soc. Exptl. Biol. Med. 53:213.
[89] Pazur, J. H., and W. A. Delong. 1948. Sci. Agr. 28:39.
[90] Pearson, P. B., W. A. Perlzweig, and F. Rosen. 1949. Arch. Biochem. 22:191.
[91] Persike, E. C. 1948. Endocrinology 42:356.
[92] Reed, J. G. 1951. Texas Univ. Publ. 5109:139.
[93] Rheinberger, M. B. 1936. J. Biol. Chem. 115:343.
[94] Richet, C., Jr. 1929. J. Lab. Clin. Med. 15:9.
[95] Robinson, F. A. 1951. The vitamin B complex. J. Wiley, New York.
[96] Salcedo, J., Jr., et al. 1948. J. Nutr. 36:307.
[97] Sarett, H. P., J. R. Klein, and N. A. Perlzweig. 1942. Ibid. 24:295.
[98] Schwartz, S., and R. Zagaria. 1956. U.S. At. Energy Comm. TID-5220(2):185.
[99] Schweigert, B. S., P. B. Pearson, and M. C. Wilkening. 1947. Arch. Biochem. 12:139.
[100] Silber, R. H. 1944. J. Nutr. 27:425.
[101] Smuts, D. B. 1935. Ibid. 9:403.
[102] Spector, H., T. S. Hamilton, and H. H. Mitchell. 1945. J. Biol. Chem. 161:145.
[103] Spiera, H., and C. L. Christian. 1964. Proc. Soc. Exptl. Biol. Med. 116:944.
[104] Stehle, R. L. 1917. J. Biol. Chem. 31:461.
[105] Stekol, J. A. 1936. Ibid. 113:675.
[106] Terri, A. E., et al. 1950. Ibid. 182:509.
[107] Thompson, J. H., Y. H. Lee, and L. B. Campbell. 1966. Am. J. Vet. Res. 27:1093.
[108] Tidwell, H. C. 1946. Proc. Soc. Exptl. Biol. Med. 63:13.
[109] Treacher, R. J. 1964. Brit. Vet. J. 120:178.
[110] Ugolini, M. 1942. Biochim. Terap. Sper. 29:187.
[111] Underhill, F. P., and L. J. Bogert. 1916. J. Biol. Chem. 27:161.
[112] Valle, J. R., S. B. Henriques, and O. B. Henriques. 1947. Endocrinology 41:335.
[113] Vassel, B., R. Partridge, and M. L. Crossley. 1944. Arch. Biochem. 4:59.
[114] Walker, D. M., and G. J. Faichney. 1964. Brit. J. Nutr. 18:201.
[115] Warth, F. J., and N. C. Das Gupta. 1928. Biochem. J. 22:621.
[116] Wertz, A. W., P. S. van Horn, and L. E. Lloyd. 1951. J. Nutr. 43:181.
[117] Whelan, M. 1925. J. Biol. Chem. 63:585.

Part III. Chicken

All values are for urine collections of at least 24 hours from birds with either a colostomy or exteriorized ureters, plus a suitable collection device for the purpose of avoiding fecal contamination. Values in parentheses are ranges, estimate "c", unless otherwise indicated (*see* Introduction).

	Property or Constituent	Value	Remarks	Reference
1	Specific gravity	1.015	3 cocks; mean of 24 samples, supernatant fraction of urine	2
2	Volume	(25-90) ml/kg body wt/day	15 adult cocks and hens	2,4,6
3	Calcium	(0.06-0.16)[b] mg/kg body wt/day	4 hens consuming an average of 3 g Ca/day; body wt estimated as 2 kg; 7-day collection period	7
4	Phosphorus	(0.12-0.17)[b] mg/kg body wt/day	4 hens consuming an average of 0.57 g P/day; body wt estimated as 2 kg; 7-day collection period	7
	Nitrogen			
5	Endogenous urinary N	0.65 mg/g body wt$^{0.75}$/day	6 adult cocks; 14-day collections	1

continued

105. EXCRETION PRODUCTS IN URINE: VERTEBRATES

Part III. Chicken

	Property or Constituent	Value	Remarks	Reference
6	Total N	(40-1500) mg/kg body wt/day	Adult cocks or capons receiving 96-3300 mg N/bird/day	1
7	Amino acid N	(1.7-2.2) % of total N	Young and adult birds	10
8	Ammonia N	(8-15) % of total N		
9	Creatine + creatinine N	(0.2-8.0) % of total N		
10	Urea N	(5-10) % of total N		
11	Uric acid N	(60-80) % of total N		
12	Unaccounted for N	(1.2-2.8) % of total N		
13	Ornithuric acid	(68-163) μg/bird/day	6 adult hens receiving a purified diet; 48-hr collections	9
14	Estradiol-17β 1/	(1.9-3.0) μg/bird/day	Nonlaying hens; eight 24-hr collections	5
15		(2.5-4.2) μg/bird/day	Laying hens; eight 24-hr collections	
16	Estrone 2/	(0.2-7.5) μg/bird/day 3/	8 adult hens; several collections; lowest values were for nonlayers, highest at onset of lay	3,8

1/ 1,3,5(10)-estratriene-3,17β-diol. 2/ 1,3,5(10)-estratriene-3-ol-17-one. 3/ Values are uncorrected for methodological loss, which may be one-third of total value.

Contributor: Nesheim, M. C.

References

[1] Ariyoshi, S. 1957. Nogyo Gijutsu Kenkyusho Hokoku, G, 13:93.

[2] Ariyoshi, S., and H. Morimoto. 1956. Ibid., G, 12:37.

[3] Common, R. H., et al. 1965. Can. J. Biochem. Physiol. 45:539.

[4] Hart, W. M., and H. E. Essex. 1942. Am. J. Physiol. 136:657.

[5] Hertelendy, F., et al. 1965. Can. J. Biochem. Physiol. 43:1379.

[6] Hester, H. R., H. E. Essex, and F. C. Mann. 1940. Am. J. Physiol. 128:592.

[7] Hurwitz, S. 1961. Ph. D. Thesis. Rutgers Univ., New Brunswick, N.J.

[8] Mathur, R. S., P. A. Anastassiadis, and R. H. Common. 1966. Poultry Sci. 45:946.

[9] Nesheim, M. C., and J. D. Garlich. 1963. J. Nutr. 79:311.

[10] O'Dell, B. L., et al. 1960. Poultry Sci. 39:426.

106. URINE ELECTROLYTE EXCRETION RATE: VERTEBRATES

Values in parentheses are ranges, estimate "c" (*see* Introduction).

Part I. Terrestrial Mammals

	Animal	Water Excretion Rate	Electrolyte	Concentration mEq/liter	Excretion Rate mEq/day	Excretion Rate mEq/kg/day
1	Man	1400(500-3000) ml/day; 20(7-42) ml/kg/day [2,30,45]	Calcium	7.5(1.4-13.0) [4,5,14, 25,26,40]	8(2-18) [5,14,25,26,40]	0.14(0.08-0.23) [5,40]
2			Chloride	110(49-210) [4,14]	118(58-250) [3,14,30,40]	1.6(1.0-2.2) [3,40]
3			Magnesium	8.2(5.8-11.6) [34]	9(6-16) [14,25,40,47]	0.15(0.11-0.21) [40,47]
4			Potassium	50(27-119) [14,31]	64(53-91) [14,26,40]	1.1(0.8-1.2) [3,40]
5			Sodium	114(35-167) [4,14,31]	120(40-186) [14,26,40]	1.9(1.3-2.4) [14,26,40]
6			Ammonia 1/	27(20-50) [4,14,24,40]	38(30-70) [4,14,24,40]	0.7(0.4-1.5) [10,40]
7			Bicarbonate 2/	1.1(0-26) [14]	1.5(0-36) [14]	0.02(0-0.5) [14]
8			Phosphate	28(22-41) [14,34]	36(22-54) 3/ [3,14,34,40]	0.6(0.5-0.9) [3,34,40]
9			Sulfate	26(13-56) [14,18]	37(11-56) [14,18,40]	0.6(0.2-0.9) [14,18,40]

1/ Excretion rate is directly proportional to urinary pH. 2/ Excretion rate is dependent on urinary pH. No appreciable amount is excreted at pH 5.2; 1.5 mEq/day at pH 6.0; 6 mEq/day at pH 6.6; 14 mEq/day at pH 7.0; 36 mEq/day at pH 7.4. [14] 3/ Base equivalence assumed as 1.0.

continued

106. URINE ELECTROLYTE EXCRETION RATE: VERTEBRATES

Part I. Terrestrial Mammals

	Animal	Water Excretion Rate	Electrolyte	Concentration mEq/liter	Excretion Rate mEq/day	Excretion Rate mEq/kg/day
10	Cat	36 ml/day; 12 ml/kg/day [27]	Calcium	2.95 [27]	0.11 [27]	0.04 [27]
11			Magnesium	11.9 [27]	0.4 [27]	0.13 [27]
12			Phosphate	....	22 [9]	3.6 [9]
13	Cow	....	Calcium	....	18.0(4.5-74.3) [11]	0.04(0.01-0.14) [11]
14			Chloride	....	282(127-606) [11]	0.6(0.1-1.1) [11]
15			Magnesium	....	339(154-578) [11]	0.66(0.26-1.02) [11]
16			Potassium	....	2370(1650-2980) [11]	5(3-6) [11]
17			Sodium	....	360(89-475) [11]	0.7(0.2-1.1) [11]
18	Dog	420(122-2000) ml/day [13, 16,21,29,51, 52]; 20(5-55) ml/kg/day [13,21,29, 41,51]	Calcium	2.12(0.18-7.70) [52]	1.3(0.1-7.0) [1,52]	0.11(0.08-0.14) [1,52]
19			Chloride	76(0-289) [8,21,35,41, 51,52]	40(0-222) [8,21,28,41,51-53]	2.0(0-10.3) [21,27,41,51]
20			Magnesium	8.3(2.8-26.9) [41,52]	3.9(0.7-20.7) [41,52]	0.21(0.05-0.53) [27,41]
21			Potassium	84(18-234) [8,51,52]	31(3-128) [8,13,17,51,52]	1.0(0.1-2.4) [13,17,51]
22			Sodium	74(2-189) [8,21,41,52]	32(1-209) [8,16,21,41,52]	1.9(0.04-13) [8,16,21,41, 52]
23			Ammonia[1/]	69(4-190) [51]	25(2.9-82) [17,51]	1.2(0.2-3.7) [17,51]
24			Bicarbonate	39 [51,52]	18(0.01-71) [51-53]	1.3(0.05-3.2) [51]
25			Phosphate	(0-120) [51,52]	7(0-38)[3/] [27,33,51-53]	0.25(0-1.04) [27,33,51]
26			Sulfate	48(6-233) [41,52]	26(1-48) [15,17,41,52]	1.7(0.05-3.1) [15,17,41]
27	Rabbit	258(34-935) ml/day; 90(19-295) ml/kg/ day [12,27, 32,49,50]	Calcium	5.2(1.6-11.4) [27]	1.7(0.46-3.4) [27]	0.86(0.29-1.7) [27]
28			Chloride	41(3.4-94) [32]	3.6(0.8-9.8) [32]	0.5(0.1-1.4) [32]
29			Magnesium	8.5 [27]	2.7 [27]	1.47 [27]
30			Sodium	60 [32]	....	....
31			Phosphate	4.6(1.5-6.9) [27]	1.4(0.6-2.1) [27]	0.75(0.3-1.3) [27]
32	Rat	12(4.3-24.0) ml/ day [7,39,43]; 50(38-100) ml/kg/day [7, 22,39,43]	Calcium	....	0.09(0.02-0.16) [19,28,38]	0.26(0.08-0.46) [19,28,38]
33			Chloride	96 [6,42]	1.3(0.4-1.9) [28,37,46]	3.4(0.9-8.2) [23,28,37,44]
34			Magnesium	....	0.17(0.04-0.3) [19,37,38]	0.86 [19]
35			Potassium	230(190-260) [37]	0.9(0.4-1.9) [19,37,38,46, 48]	4.0(2.7-5.4) [19,37,38]
36			Sodium	90.4 [42]	1.4(0.2-1.9) [19,37,38,46, 48]	4.5(1.7-7.3) [19,38]
37			Ammonia[1/]	....	0.7 [39]	3.0 [38]
38			Phosphate	....	0.5(0.27-0.55) [20,28]	3.3(0.8-3.6) [20,28]
39			Sulfate	5.5 [37]	0.17(0.13-0.21) [36,37]	0.8 [37]

[1/] Excretion rate is directly proportional to urinary pH. [3/] Base equivalence assumed as 1.0.

Contributors: (a) Peschel, Ernst, (b) Booker, Walter M.

References

[1] Barbour, H. G., and J. E. Winter. 1931. J. Pharmacol. Exptl. Therap. 43:607.

[2] Barclay, J. A., et al. 1947. Am. J. Physiol. 148:327.

[3] Bassett, S. H., C. A. Elden, and W. S. McCann. 1932. J. Nutr. 5:1.

[4] Cantarow, A., and M. Trumper. 1962. Clinical biochemistry. Ed. 6. W. B. Saunders, Philadelphia.

[5] Carswell, H. E., and J. E. Winter. 1931. J. Biol. Chem. 93:411.

[6] Corey, E. L., and S. W. Britton. 1941. Am. J. Physiol. 133:511.

[7] Danford, P. A., and H. G. Danford. 1951. Ibid. 164:690.

[8] Davis, A. K., A. C. Bass, and R. R. Overman. 1951. Ibid. 166:493.

[9] Eggleton, M. G., and Y. A. Habib. 1949. J. Physiol. (London) 110:98.

[10] Farquharson, R. F., et al. 1931. J. Clin. Invest. 10: 221.

[11] Forbes, E. B., et al. 1922. J. Biol. Chem. 52:281.

[12] Forster, R. P. 1952. Am. J. Physiol. 168:666.

[13] Foulks, J., G. H. Mudge, and A. Gilman. 1952. Ibid. 168:642.

[14] Gamble, J. L. 1954. Chemical anatomy, physiology and pathology of extracellular fluid. Ed. 6. Harvard Univ. Press, Cambridge.

[15] Goudsmit, A., Jr., M. H. Power, and J. L. Bollman. 1939. Am. J. Physiol. 125:506.

[16] Green, D. M., and A. Farah. 1949. Ibid. 158:444.

[17] Harris, F. D., et al. 1952. Ibid. 168:20.

[18] Hayman, J. M., Jr., and S. M. Johnston. 1932. J. Clin. Invest. 11:607.

[19] Hegstedt, D. M., et al. 1951. Am. J. Physiol. 164: 695.

continued

106. URINE ELECTROLYTE EXCRETION RATE: VERTEBRATES

Part I. Terrestrial Mammals

[20] Kochakian, C. D., and A. R. Terepka. 1951. Ibid. 165:142.

[21] Kuschinsky, G., and H. Langecker. 1947. Arch. Exptl. Pathol. Pharmakol. 204:699.

[22] Kuschinsky, G., H. Langecker, and R. Hotovy. 1947. Ibid. 204:752.

[23] Langecker, H., and G. Kuschinsky. 1947. Ibid. 204: 738.

[24] Lotspeich, W. D., and R. F. Pitts. 1947. J. Biol. Chem. 168:611.

[25] McCance, R. A., and E. M. Widdowson. 1939. Biochem. J. 33:523.

[26] McKay, E. M., and A. M. Butler. 1935. J. Clin. Invest. 14:923.

[27] Mendel, L. B., and S. R. Benedict. 1909. Am. J. Physiol. 25:1.

[28] Miller, H. G. 1926. J. Biol. Chem. 70:593.

[29] Mulinos, M. G., C. L. Spingarn, and M. E. Lojkin. 1941. Am. J. Physiol. 135:102.

[30] Oser, B. L., ed. 1965. Hawk's Physiological chemistry. Ed. 14. McGraw-Hill, New York.

[31] Overman, R. R., and A. K. Davis. 1947. J. Biol. Chem. 168:641.

[32] Pickering, G. W., and M. Prinzmetal. 1940. J. Physiol. (London) 98:314.

[33] Pitts, R. F., and R. S. Alexander. 1944. Am. J. Physiol. 142:648.

[34] Renvall, G. 1904. Skand. Arch. Physiol. 15:94.

[35] Roemmelt, J. C., O. W. Sartorius, and R. F. Pitts. 1949. Am. J. Physiol. 159:124.

[36] Sandberg, M., and D. Perla. 1936. J. Biol. Chem. 113:35.

[37] Sandberg, M., D. Perla, and O. M. Holly. 1937. Endocrinology 21:346.

[38] Sandberg, M., D. Perla, and O. M. Holly. 1937. Ibid. 21:352.

[39] Sartorius, O. W., D. Calhoon, and R. F. Pitts. 1952. Ibid. 51:444.

[40] Sartorius, O. W., J. C. Roemmelt, and R. F. Pitts. 1949. J. Clin. Invest. 28:423.

[41] Schwartz, B. M., P. K. Smith, and A. W. Winkler. 1942. Am. J. Physiol. 137:658.

[42] Sellers, A. L., et al. 1951. Ibid. 166:619.

[43] Semple, R. E. 1952. Ibid. 168:55.

[44] Silvette, H. 1940. Ibid. 128:747.

[45] Smith, H. W. 1951. The kidney. Structure and function in health and disease. Oxford Univ. Press, New York.

[46] Stein, J. D., et al. 1952. Am. J. Physiol. 171:587.

[47] Tibbetts, D. M., and J. C. Aub. 1937. J. Clin. Invest. 16:491.

[48] Whitney, J. E., and L. L. Bennett. 1952. Endocrinology 50:657.

[49] Wilkinson, D. M., and R. A. McCance. 1940. Quart. J. Exptl. Physiol. 30:249.

[50] Wills, J. H., and E. Main. 1948. Am. J. Physiol. 154:220.

[51] Winkler, A. W., and P. K. Smith. 1942. Ibid. 138:94.

[52] Wolf, A. V., and S. M. Ball. 1949. Ibid. 158:205.

[53] Wolf, A. V., and S. M. Ball. 1950. Ibid. 160:353.

Part II. Aquatic and Semiaquatic Vertebrates

	Animal	Electrolyte	Excretion Rate	Reference
	Mammalia			
1	Seal[1]	Calcium	4.01 mM/liter	12
2		Chloride	289 mM/liter	
3		Magnesium	195 mM/liter	
4		Phosphate	(Trace-26.7) mM/liter	
5		Sulfate	766 mM/liter	
6	Whale	Calcium	2.7 mM/liter/day	6
7		Chloride	362 mM/liter/day	
8		Potassium	74 mM/liter/day	
9		Sodium	266 mM/liter/day	
	Amphibia			
10	Frog	Chloride	1.89 mM/liter/day	6
11		Potassium	0.95 mM/liter/day	
12		Sodium	2.44 mM/liter/day	
13		Phosphate	2.35 mM/liter/day	
	Pisces			
14	*Anguilla* sp.	Calcium	7.5 mM/liter/day	6
15		Chloride	>76 mM/liter	11
16		Potassium	5.7 mM/liter/day	6
17		Sodium	2.44 mM/liter/day	6
18	*Carassius auratus*	Chloride	(2.5-4.1) mM/liter	5
19	*Glyptocephalus*	Chloride	(0-48) mM/liter	8
20	sp.	Magnesium	(44-47) mM/liter	
21		Phosphate	(5-46) mM/liter	
22		Sulfate	(28-49) mM/liter	
23	*Limanda ferrugi-*	Chloride	70 mM/liter	8
24	*nea*	Magnesium	125 mM/liter	
25		Phosphate	75 mM/liter	
26		Sulfate	44 mM/liter	
27	*Lophius piscato-*	Chloride	(2-98) mM/liter	7,8
28	*rius*	Magnesium	(38-151) mM/liter	1,8

[1] *Phoca vitulina,* 40-lb female; values obtained 3-10 hours after feeding.

continued

106. URINE ELECTROLYTE EXCRETION RATE: VERTEBRATES

Part II. Aquatic and Semiaquatic Vertebrates

	Animal	Electrolyte	Excretion Rate	Reference
29		Phosphate	(1-17) mM/liter	8
30		Sulfate	(40-110) mM/liter	8
31	*Merluccius bilinearis*	Chloride	0	8
32		Magnesium	(19-127) mM/liter	
33		Phosphate	(65-92) mM/liter	
34		Sulfate	(20-86) mM/liter	
35	*Myoxocephalus octodecemspinosus*	Chloride	(0-29) mM/liter	2-4
36		Magnesium	(36-161) mM/liter	8
37		Phosphate	(50-155) mM/liter	8
38		Sulfate	(6-85) mM/liter	8
39	*M. scorpius*	Chloride	(0-124) mM/liter	3,8
40		Magnesium	(72-167) mM/liter	8
41		Phosphate	(64-158) mM/liter	8
42		Sulfate	(30-102) mM/liter	8
43	*Opsanus tau*	Chloride	>86 mM/liter	4
44	*Salmo gairdneri (S. irideus)*	Chloride	(1.9-11.8) mM/liter	5
	Chondrichthyes			
45	*Mustelus canis*	Chloride	262 mM/liter	10
46	*Pristis microdon*	Chloride	5.5 mM/liter	14
47	*Squalus acanthias*	Chloride	150 mM/liter/day	6
48		Phosphate	79 mM/liter/day	13
	Agnatha			
49	*Lampetra fluviatilis*	Chloride	0.7 mM/liter	15
50	*Petromyzon marinus*	Chloride	4.7 mM/liter	9

Contributor: Booker, Walter M.

References

[1] Brull, L., and Y. Cuypers. 1954. Arch. Intern. Physiol. 62:70.

[2] Clarke, R. W. 1934. J. Cellular Comp. Physiol. 5:73.

[3] Forster, R. P. 1953. Ibid. 42:487.

[4] Grafflin, A. L. 1931. Am. J. Physiol. 97:602.

[5] Krogh, A. 1937. Z. Vergleich. Physiol. 24:656.

[6] Krogh, A. 1939. Osmotic regulation in aquatic animals. Univ. Press, Cambridge, England.

[7] Marshall, E. K., Jr. 1930. Am. J. Physiol. 94:1.

[8] Pitts, R. F. 1934. J. Cellular Comp. Physiol. 4:389.

[9] Sawyer, W. H. Unpublished. New York Univ., College Medicine, New York, 1955.

[10] Scott, G. G. 1913. Ann. N.Y. Acad. Sci. 23:1.

[11] Smith, H. W. 1930. Am. J. Physiol. 93:480.

[12] Smith, H. W. 1935-36. J. Cellular Comp. Physiol. 7:465.

[13] Smith, H. W. 1939. Ibid. 14:95.

[14] Smith, H. W., and C. G. Smith. 1931. Am. J. Physiol. 98:279.

[15] Wikgren, B. 1953. Acta Zool. Fennica 71:1.

107. RENAL TUBULAR REABSORPTION OF ELECTROLYTES: MAN AND DOG

Values in parentheses are ranges, estimate "c" (*see* Introduction).

	Electrolyte	Plasma Concentration mM/liter	Reabsorption Rate mM/min	Reabsorption Rate mM/min/100 ml glomerular filtrate	Remarks	Reference
	Man					
1	Calcium	2.40(2.15-2.75)	0.135(0.069-0.179)[1/]	0.125(0.099-0.149)		6,8,27
2	Chloride	108.0(104.4-112.7)	13.49(10.00-18.57)	10.92(10.40-11.21)		19,22,26
3	Magnesium	0.92(0.76-1.20)	0.068(0.062-0.080)[2/]	0.0563(0.048-0.068)		2
4	Potassium	3.91(3.5-4.4)	0.529(0.516-0.543)[3/]	0.353(0.339-0.366)		22
5	Sodium	137.6(122.0-143.1)	16.33(12.2-22.8)	13.18(12.0-14.2)		13,22,26
6	Bicarbonate	24.1(23.6-28.0)	2.59(2.32-3.11)	2.42(2.41-2.80)		17,19,22
7	Phosphate	1.11(0.69-1.35)	0.117(0.048-0.152)[4/]	0.111(0.065-0.167)	Plasma concentration given as phosphorus	5,6,16,22, 23,25,27

[1/] Reabsorption calculated on the basis of 55% of plasma (or serum) Ca being filterable [10,21]. [2/] Based on 65% of magnesium being freely filterable. [3/] Considered to be "net" reabsorption, the resultant of proximal tubular reabsorption and distal tubular secretion. [4/] Maximal tubular rate of reabsorption (Tm) considered to be a fixed, reproducible reabsorptive capacity when load (plasma concentration × glomerular filtration rate) exceeds Tm by 1.5 times or more.

continued

107. RENAL TUBULAR REABSORPTION OF ELECTROLYTES: MAN AND DOG

	Electrolyte	Plasma Concentration mM/liter	Reabsorption Rate		Remarks	Reference
			mM/min	mM/min/100 ml glomerular filtrate		
	Dog					
8	Calcium	1.83(1.73-1.93)	0.073(0.072-0.074)[1]	0.110(0.10-0.12)		10,21
9	Chloride	112.3(110.0-118.6)	5.89(5.08-6.00)	11.23(11.0-11.8)	Some with NaCl loading	7
10		127.0(126-128)	7.70(6.2-10.2)	11.50(10.24-13.00)	Under conditions of acidosis and with NaCl loading	12
11	Potassium	4.23(3.90-5.29)	0.195(0.122-0.276)[3]	0.369(0.308-0.512)	10 experiments on 10 subjects under pentobarbital anesthesia	3,14,15
12	Sodium	145(134.3-150.5)	8.66(7.57-12.54)	14.48(13.44-15.25)	Anesthetized; no salt or water loading	4
13		145(131-155)	8.15(6.03-10.10)	13.80(12.4-14.4)	16 experiments on 3 trained unanesthetized subjects given orally 50 ml 0.9% saline/kg body wt	24
14		143(132-149)	6.07(4.38-9.00)	13.53(12.7-14.1)	9 experiments on subjects anesthetized with 125 mg chloralose/kg body wt	24
15		180(169-196)	7.29(4.42-10.20)	12.80(11.2-14.2)	Values obtained on same subjects used in collecting data for entry 14; given intravenous infusion of 5% NaCl	24
16	Bicarbonate	23.3(22.0-27.6)	1.264(1.18-1.47)	2.30(2.18-2.69)		20
17		41.6(29.4-51.5)	2.19(1.81-2.55)	2.46(2.27-2.64)	Elevated plasma bicarbonate levels from infusion of 3.2-6.8% bicarbonate at 10 ml/min	20
18	Phosphate	(3.0-17.3)[1,5]	0.10(0.05-0.14)	0.146(0.135-0.155)		1,9,10,18, 23
19	Sulfate	(2.2-20.0)[5]	0.075(0.05-0.10)[4]	0.135(0.080-0.205)		11

1/ Reabsorption calculated on the basis of 55% of plasma (or serum) Ca being filterable [10,21]. 3/ Considered to be "net" reabsorption, the resultant of proximal tubular reabsorption and distal tubular secretion. 4/ Maximal tubular rate of reabsorption (Tm) considered to be a fixed, reproducible reabsorptive capacity when load (plasma concentration X glomerular filtration rate) exceeds Tm by 1.5 times or more. 5/ Lower limit of range considered to be plasma concentration at which urinary excretion occurs, and above which Tm is reached.

Contributor: Selkurt, Ewald E.

References

[1] Ayer, J. L., W. A. Schiess, and R. F. Pitts. 1947. Am. J. Physiol. 151:168.

[2] Barker, E. S., J. R. Elkinton, and J. K. Clark. 1959. J. Clin. Invest. 38:1733.

[3] Berliner, R. W., T. J. Kennedy, Jr., and J. G. Hilton. 1950. Am. J. Physiol. 162:348.

[4] Blythe, W. B., and L. G. Welt. 1963. J. Clin. Invest. 42:1491.

[5] Corvilain, J., and M. Abramow. 1962. Ibid. 41:1230.

[6] Duarte, C. G., and J. H. Bland. 1965. Metab. Clin. Exptl. 14:203.

[7] Hare, R. S., K. Hare, and D. M. Phillips. 1943. Am. J. Physiol. 140:334.

[8] Hiatt, H. H., and D. D. Thompson. 1957. J. Clin. Invest. 36:557.

[9] Hogben, C. A. M., and J. L. Bollman. 1951. Am. J. Physiol. 164:670.

[10] Jahan, I., and R. F. Pitts. 1948. Ibid. 155:42.

[11] Lotspeich, W. D. 1947. Ibid. 151:311.

[12] Lotspeich, W. D., R. C. Swan, and R. F. Pitts. 1947. Ibid. 148:445.

[13] Mokotoff, R., G. Ross, and L. Leiter. 1948. J. Clin. Invest. 27:1.

[14] Mudge, G. H., J. Foulks, and A. Gilman. 1950. Am. J. Physiol. 161:159.

[15] Mudge, G. H., et al. 1950. Ibid. 161:151.

[16] Parsons, V., and J. Andersen. 1964. Clin. Sci. 27:313.

[17] Pitts, R. F. 1934. J. Cellular Comp. Physiol. 4:389.

[18] Pitts, R. F., and R. S. Alexander. 1944. Am. J. Physiol. 142-648.

[19] Pitts, R. F., J. L. Ayer, and W. A. Schiess. 1949. J. Clin. Invest. 28:35.

[20] Pitts, R. F., and W. D. Lotspeich. 1946. Am. J. Physiol. 147:138.

[21] Rawson, A. J., and F. W. Sunderman. 1948. J. Clin. Invest. 27:82.

[22] Sartorius, O. W., J. C. Roemmelt, and R. F. Pitts. 1949. Ibid. 28:423.

[23] Schiess, W. A., et al. 1948. Ibid. 27:57.

[24] Selkurt, E. E. Unpublished. Indiana University, Medical Center, Indianapolis, 1967.

[25] Thompson, D. D., and H. H. Hiatt. 1957. J. Clin. Invest. 36:550.

[26] Wesson, L. G., Jr., and D. P. Lauler. 1961. Ibid. 40:1967.

[27] Yamahiro, H. S., and T. B. Reynolds. 1962. Metab. Clin. Exptl. 11:213.

108. VARIOUS PROTEIN DIETS AND NITROGENOUS CONSTITUENTS OF URINE: MAN

Part I: Average-Protein Diet

Values are mg/kg body wt/day, unless otherwise indicated. Approximate nitrogen content of diet = 10 g N/day. **Method**: An = analytical; I-E = ion-exchange chromatography; MA = microbiological assay; PC = paper chromatography.

	Property or Constituent	Method	Subjects: No. & Sex	Subjects: Wt[1/] kg	Value	Reference
1	Urine volume	An	400♂	70	19.5[2/]	1
2	Water content	An	400♂	70	18.4[2/]	1
3	Nitrogen, total	An	52-54♂	70	164	7
4	allantoin	An	7[3/]	70	0.16	6
5	α-amino	An	....	70	2.0	8
6	ammonia	An	52-54♂	70	6.0	7
7	creatine	An	6♀	46.5-72.2	0.93	12
8	creatinine	An	52-54♂	70	8.1	7
9		An	6♀	46.5-72.2	7.9	12
10	hippuric acid	An	2♀	56	1.2[4/]	3
11	purine	An	....	......	0.6[5/]	4
12	urea	An	52-54♂	70	137	7
13	uric acid	An	52-54♂	70	2.1[5/]	7
	Amino acids and derivatives					
14	Alanine, free	I-E	12♂, 9♀	70	0.44	9,11
15	β-Alanine, free	I-E	6♂, 9♀	70	0.064	9
16	α-Aminoadipic acid, free	I-E	6♂, 9♀	70	0.086	9
17	β-Aminoisobutyric	I-E	6♂, 9♀	70	0.36	9
18	Arginine, total	MA	13♂, 5♀	66.8	0.36	13
19	free	MA	13♂, 5♀	66.8	0.32	13
20		I-E	6♂, 9♀	70	0.071	9
21	Aspartic acid, total	MA	13♂, 5♀	66.8	2.48	13
22		I-E	3♂	70	3.03	11
23	free	MA	13♂, 5♀	66.8	0.017	13
24		I-E	6♂, 9♀	70	0.086	9
25	Citrulline, free	PC[6/]	12♂	70	0.58	2
26	Cystine, total	I-E	3♂	70	0.74	11
27	free	MA	13♂, 5♀	66.8	1.31	13
28		I-E	6♂, 9♀	70	0.14	9
29	Glutamic acid, total	MA	13♂, 5♀	66.8	5.27	13
30		I-E	3♂	70	7.58	11
31	free	MA	13♂, 5♀	66.8	0.54	13
32	Glutamine, free	I-E	6♂, 9♀	70	0.96	9
33	Glycine[7/], total	MA	4♂, 2♀	70	7.25	5
34		I-E	3♂	70	13.4	11
35	free	MA	4♂, 2♀	70	10.0	5
36		I-E	12♂, 9♀	70	1.80	9,11
37	Histidine, total	MA	13♂, 5♀	66.8	3.04	13
38		I-E	2♂	70	5.14	11
39	free	MA	13♂, 5♀	66.8	2.82	13
40		I-E	12♂, 9♀	70	2.30	9,11
41	Isoleucine, total	MA	13♂, 5♀	66.8	0.34	13
42		I-E	3♂	70	0.34	11
43	free	MA	13♂, 5♀	66.8	0.089	13
44		I-E	12♂, 9♀	70	0.20	9,11
45	Leucine, total	MA	13♂, 5♀	66.8	0.32	13
46		I-E	3♂	70	0.38	11
47	free	MA	13♂, 5♀	66.8	0.14	13
48		I-E	12♂, 9♀	70	0.16	9,11
49	Lysine, total	MA	13♂, 5♀	66.8	1.10	13
50		I-E	3♂	70	0.87	11
51	free	MA	13♂, 5♀	66.8	0.50	13
52		I-E	12♂, 9♀	70	0.16	9,11
53	Methionine, total	MA	13♂, 5♀	66.8	0.13	13
54	free	MA	13♂, 5♀	66.8	0.12	13
55		I-E	6♂, 9♀	70	0.086	9
56	1-Methyl histidine, free	I-E	12♂, 9♀	70	1.51	9,11
57	3-Methyl histidine, free	I-E	6♂, 9♀	70	0.81	9
58	Ornithine, free	I-E	6♂, 9♀	70	0.021	9
59	Phenylalanine, total	MA	13♂, 5♀	66.8	0.35	13
60		I-E	3♂	70	0.64	11
61	free	MA	13♂, 5♀	66.8	0.25	13
62		I-E	12♂, 9♀	70	0.21	9,11
63	Proline, total	MA	13♂, 5♀	66.8	0.64	13
64		I-E	3♂	70	1.18	11
65	free	MA	13♂, 5♀	66.8	0.13	13
66	Serine, total	I-E	3♂	70	1.61	11
67	free	MA	4[3/]	61.5	0.44	10
68		I-E	12♂, 9♀	70	0.59	9,11
69	Taurine	I-E	12♂, 9♀	70	1.74	9,11
70	Threonine, total	MA	13♂, 5♀	66.8	0.81	13
71		I-E	3♂	70	1.06	11
72	free	MA	13♂, 5♀	66.8	0.37	13
73		I-E	12♂, 9♀	70	0.33	9,11
74	Tryptophan, total	MA	13♂, 5♀	66.8	0.62[8/]	13
75	free	MA	13♂, 5♀	66.8	0.37[8/]	13
76	Tyrosine, total	MA	13♂, 5♀	66.8	0.79	13
77		I-E	3♂	70	1.08	11
78	free	MA	13♂, 5♀	66.8	0.31	13
79		I-E	12♂, 9♀	70	0.33	9,11
80	Valine, total	MA	13♂, 5♀	66.8	0.30	13
81		I-E	3♂	70	0.43	11
82	free	MA	13♂, 5♀	66.8	0.68	13
83		I-E	6♂, 9♀	70	0.11	9

[1/] 70 and 56 kg are assumed body weights; all others are actual weights. [2/] ml/kg body wt/day. [3/] Sex not specified. [4/] Greatly influenced by specific fruits in diet (i.e., prunes, cranberries); not appreciably affected by dietary protein level. [5/] Influenced by intake of dietary purines which may or may not be associated with protein intake. [6/] Estimated from determinations of creatinine. [7/] Probably occurs in conjugation as hippuric acid. [8/] Obtained from alkali-hydrolyzed urine; basic hydrolysis causes racemization of unknown extent, so that values are probably too low.

Contributors: (a) Pearson, W. N., (b) Swendseid, Marian E., and Vinyard, Elizabeth.

continued

Part I. Average-Protein Diet

References

[1] Beard, H. H. 1935. Human Biol. 7:419.
[2] Beerstecher, E., et al. 1950. Arch. Biochem. 29:27.
[3] Blatherwick, N. R., and M. L. Lond. 1923. J. Biol. Chem. 57:815.
[4] Burian, R., and H. Schur. 1900. Arch. Ges. Physiol. 80:241.
[5] Dunn, M. S., et al. 1947. Arch. Biochem. 13:207.
[6] Fosse, R., A. Brunel, and P.-E. Thomas. 1931. Compt. Rend. 192:1615.
[7] Jellinek, E. M., and J. M. Looney. 1939. J. Biol. Chem. 128:621.
[8] Pearson, W. N. Unpublished. Vanderbilt Univ., Dept. Biochemistry, Nashville, 1967.
[9] Soupart, P. 1959. Clin. Chim. Acta 4:265.
[10] Steele, B. F., et al. 1947. J. Nutr. 33:209.
[11] Stein, W. H. 1953. J. Biol. Chem. 201:45.
[12] Wang, C. C., et al. 1930. J. Nutr. 3:79.
[13] Woodson, H. W., et al. 1948. J. Biol. Chem. 172:613.

Part II. High- and Low-Protein Diets

Values are mg/kg body wt/day, unless otherwise indicated, and were calculated on the basis of an actual or assumed body weight of 70 kg, unless otherwise indicated. Approximate nitrogen content in high-protein diet = 19 g N/day, in low-protein diet = 6 g N/day. Values for total amino acids were obtained from acid-hydrolyzed urine, and those for free amino acids from nonhydrolyzed urine.

	Property or Constituent	No. & Sex of Subjects	High-Protein Diet	Low-Protein Diet	Reference
1	Urine volume[1/]	400♂	24.5	20.6	1
2	Water content[1/]	400♂	19.8	19.1	1
3	Nitrogen, total	400♂	218	114	1
4	ammonia	400♂	9.7	6.2	1
5	creatine	6♀[2/]	1.9	0.45	5
6	creatinine	400♂	9.0	7.7	1
7		6♀[2/]	8.0	7.8	5
8	purine	....	0.7[3/]	....	2
9	urea	400♂	189	88	1
10	uric acid	....	3.4[4/]	....	4
	Amino acids				3
11	Arginine, total	9♂	0.30	0.29	
12	free	9♂	0.29	0.23	
13	Aspartic acid, total	9♂	1.93	1.63	
14	Cystine, free	9♂	3.38	0.94	
15	Glutamic acid, total	9♂	4.57	4.25	
16	free	9♂	0.27	0.34	
17	Glycine[5/], total	9♂	9.85	9.25	
18	free	9♂	14.0	10.70	
19	Histidine, total	9♂	2.32	1.77	
20	free	9♂	2.1	1.3	
21	Isoleucine, total	9♂	0.20	0.19	
22	Leucine, total	9♂	0.30	0.27	
23	Lysine, total	9♂	0.73	0.60	
24	free	9♂	0.39	0.30	
25	Methionine, total	9♂	0.17	0.16	
26	Phenylalanine, total	9♂	0.29	0.23	
27	free	9♂	0.16	0.16	
28	Threonine, total	9♂	0.64	0.54	
29	Tryptophan, free	9♂	0.29	0.20	
30	Tyrosine, free	9♂	0.31	0.25	
31	Valine, total	9♂	0.39	0.33	

[1/] ml/kg body wt/day. [2/] Body weight = 46.5-72.2 kg. [3/] Values influenced by intake of dietary purines which may or may not be associated with protein intake. [4/] Subjects on high purine diet. [5/] Probably occurs in conjugation as hippuric acid.

Contributor: Pearson, W. N.

References

[1] Beard, H. H. 1935. Human Biol. 7:419.
[2] Burian, R., and H. Schur. 1900. Arch. Ges. Physiol. 80:241.
[3] Dunn, M. S., et al. 1949. Am. Rev. Tuberc. 60:439.
[4] Taylor, C. M., and M. S. Rose. 1965. In B. L. Oser, ed. Hawk's Physiological chemistry. Ed. 14. Blakiston. Philadelphia. p. 862.
[5] Wang, C. C., et al. 1930. J. Nutr. 3:79.

continued

108. VARIOUS PROTEIN DIETS AND NITROGENOUS CONSTITUENTS OF URINE: MAN

Part III. Protein-free Diet

Values are mg/kg body wt/day. Diet contained little or no nitrogen. With the exception of tryptophan, values for amino acids were obtained from acid-hydrolyzed urine.

	Constituent	Subjects: No. & Sex	Subjects: Weight[1] kg	Value	Reference
	Nitrogen				
1	Total N	1♂	64.75[2]	25	3
2	Ammonia N	1♂	64.75[2]	3.5	3
3	Creatinine N	1♂	64.75[2]	8.6	3
4		25♀	....	6.3	1
5	Purine N	1♂	65[2]	0.23[3]	5
6	Urea N	1♂	64.75[2]	5.4	3
7	Uric acid N	...	70	1.0[3]	4
	Amino acids				2
8	Arginine	♀	56	0.27	
9	Aspartic acid	♀	56	1.46	
10	Glutamic acid	♀	56	3.00	
11	Histidine	♀	56	1.73	
12	Isoleucine	♀	56	0.16	
13	Leucine	♀	56	0.24	
14	Lysine	♀	56	0.52	
15	Methionine	♀	56	0.07	
16	Phenylalanine	♀	56	0.39	
17	Threonine	♀	56	0.58	
18	Tryptophan[4]	♀	56	0.11	
19	Tyrosine	♀	56	0.75	
20	Valine	♀	56	0.19	

1/ Assumed weight, unless otherwise specified. 2/ Actual weight. 3/ Endogenous value; subjects on purine-free diet. 4/ Obtained from alkali-hydrolyzed urine; basic hydrolysis causes racemization of unknown extent, so that value is probably too low.

Contributor: Pearson, W. N.

References

[1] Bricker, M. L., and J. M. Smith. 1951. J. Nutr. 44: 553.

[2] Hier, S. W. 1948. Trans. N. Y. Acad. Sci., II, 10:280.

[3] Smith, M. 1926. J. Biol. Chem. 68:15.

[4] Taylor, C. M., and M. S. Rose. 1965. In B. L. Oser, ed. Hawk's Physiological chemistry. Ed. 14. Blakiston, Philadelphia. p. 862.

[5] Umeda, N. 1915. Biochem. J. 9:421.

109. NONPROTEIN NITROGEN IN URINE

Values in parentheses are ranges, estimate "c" (*see* Introduction).

Part I. Mammals

Values are percent of nonprotein nitrogen in urine, unless otherwise indicated. **Other Nonprotein N:** U = undetermined N; A = allantoin N; P = purine N.

	Species (Synonym)	No. of Subjects	No. of Observations	Amino N	Ammonia N	Creatinine N	Urea N	Uric Acid N	Other Nonprotein N	Reference
	Mammalia									
1	*Homo sapiens*	6	30	....	4.3(2.7-5.7)	3.6(3.1-4.9)	87.5(84.5-90.1)	0.8(0.5-1.5)	U, 3.8(2.0-6.4)	1
2	*Balaenoptera borealis*[1]	...	...	....	5.7(3.2-9.4)	0.80(0.5-1.2)[2]	87.6(83.2-93.4)	1.8(0.6-4.25)	U, 3.9(2.3-6.1)	5
3	*B. physalus*[1]	...	...	....	(1.9-3.6)	(0.3-3.8)[2]	(85.5-93.0)	(1.6-4.4)	U, (2.7-3.1)	5
4	*Camelus bactrianus*, pregnant	2	6	(1.2-2.1)	(1.7-3.8)	(11.1-13.1)[3]	(65.2-69.0)	(0.8-1.8)	U, (14.0-16.1)	6
5	*C. dromedarius*, ♂	1	2	(0.2-1.7)	(12.3-19.1)	(17.6-18.1)[3]	(32.5-55.5)	0.3	U, (12.7-19.8)	6
6	*Canis familiaris*	2	26	....	(3.5-28.0)	(0.9-10.0)[3]	(71.0-96.5)	....	U, (1.4-21.9)	4
7	Chiroptera[4]	...	...	0.96	6.0	8.5[3]	63.4	0.87	U, 20.3	2

1/ Urine obtained postmortem. 2/ Creatinine N and/or creatine N. 3/ Creatinine N plus creatine N. 4/ Order; species not indicated.

continued

109. NONPROTEIN NITROGEN IN URINE

Part I. Mammals

	Species (Synonym)	No. of Subjects	No. of Observations	Amino N	Ammonia N	Creatinine N	Urea N	Uric Acid N	Other Nonprotein N	Reference
	Felis catus									3
8	Protein-rich diet	1	25	....	(3.5-5.5)	(0.49-1.07)	(77.6-89.4)	(0.10-0.35)	....	
9	Low-protein diet	1	25	....	(5.7-11.1)	(1.40-2.46)	(57.9-80.1)	(0-0.09)	....	
10	Purine-rich diet	1	3	....	(4.0-4.9)	(0.6-0.7)	(68.0-89.5)	0.1	....	
11	Purine-free diet	1	3	....	(3.9-7.9)	(2.5-3.9)	(79.5-85.5)	0.01	....	
12	Hyaenidae[5/]	...	...	0.95	4.0	0.88[2/]	89.3	0.06	A, 1.75; P, 0.23; U, 2.80	2
13	*Lama glama (Auchenia huanocos)*, ♂	1	2	(1.3-1.4)	(1.8-2.2)	(9.1-11.7)[3/]	(60.5-67.7)	(0.7-0.8)	U, (19.0-23.9)	6
14	*L. vicugna (Auchenia vicunna)*, ♂	...	1	....	4.5	7.3[3/]	59.6	0.3	U, 28.3	6
15	*Mustela* sp.	...	...	0.89	2.6	1.67[2/]	91.0	0.16	A, 0.48; P, 0.58; U, 2.60	2
16	*Panthera pardus*	...	...	0.86	3.2	1.32[2/]	87.1	0.06	A, 0.52; P, 0.25; U, 6.70	2
17	*P. tigris*	...	...	0.95	3.3	1.72[2/]	89.1	0.06	P, 0.18; U, 3.40	2
	Phoca vitulina									7
18	Fasting[6/]	1	5	....	(9.9-16.8)	(12.9-30.8)[3/]	(52.4-72.8)	....	....	
19	Nonfasting[6/]	1	20	....	(2-7.5)	(7.1-31.1)[3/]	(61.4-89.8)	....	....	

[2/] Creatinine N and/or creatine N. [3/] Creatinine N plus creatine N. [5/] Family; species not indicated. [6/] Percent of the sum of the N values listed.

Contributors: Scheer, Bradley T., and Ramamurthi, R.

References

[1] Folin, O. 1905. Am. J. Physiol. 13:45.

[2] Fuse, N. 1925. Japan. J. Med. Sci., II, 1:103.

[3] Hammett, F. S. 1915. J. Biol. Chem. 22:551.

[4] Osterberg, E., and C. G. L. Wolf. 1907. Biochem. Z. 5:304.

[5] Schmidt-Nielsen, S., and J. Holmsen. 1921. Arch. Intern. Physiol. 18:128.

[6] Smith, H. W., and H. Silvette. 1928. J. Biol. Chem. 78:409.

[7] Smith, H. W. 1936. J. Cellular Comp. Physiol. 7:465.

Part II. Birds, Reptiles, and Amphibians

Values are percent of nonprotein nitrogen in urine, unless otherwise indicated. **Other Nonprotein** N: C = creatine N; c = creatinine N; Cc = creatine N plus creatinine N; P = purine N; H = hippuric acid N; GX = guanidine N plus xanthine N.

	Species (Synonym)	No. of Subjects [Observations]	Allantoin N	Amino N	Ammonia N	Urea N	Uric Acid N	Undetermined Nonprotein N	Other Nonprotein N	Reference
	Aves									
1	*Anas* sp.	......	......	....	3.2	4.2	71.9	20.7	....	17
2	*Anser* sp.	......	......	....	13.5	....	80.0	6.5	....	17
3	*Cygnus* sp.	......	......	....	15.8	2.6	68.7	13.9	....	17
4	*Gallus domesticus*	5[10-15]	......	....	17.3(14.9-19.5)	10.4(9.2-11.5)	62.9(59.4-69.5)	1.4(0.3-2.9)	Cc, 8.0(7.4-9.1)	7
5		......	......	....	1.5	0.9	70.0	27.6	....	17

continued

Part II. Birds, Reptiles, and Amphibians

	Species (Synonym)	No. of Subjects [Observations]	Allantoin N	Amino N	Ammonia N	Urea N	Uric Acid N	Undetermined Nonprotein N	Other Nonprotein N	Reference
6	Embryo[1]	......	......	....	11.2	11.4	77.1	....	....	3,4
7	Day 1	......	......	....	29	25	46	....	....	3,4
8	Day 10	......	......	....	5	31	64	....	....	3,4
9	Day 21	......	......	....	11	11	78	....	....	3,4
	Reptilia									
10	*Alligator mississippiensis*	......	......	....	65.2	Trace	12.3	....	....	5
11		3 [18]	......	....	(66-81)	(0-17.0)	(7.0-19.8)	(0.2-23.0)	....	8
12	*Caiman crocodilus*	[6[2]]	3-4	....	52.5	5.9	27.3	(7.3-10.8)	Cc, 0.5-3	6
13	*Chalcides ocellatus*	[1]	2.7	2.5	0	0	92.5	....	C, 1.17; c, 0.11; P, 0.33	12
	Chelodina longicollis (Chelonia longicolis)									19
14	Normal	10[3]	......	....	15.44	77.64	3.85	....	....	
15	After catheterization[4]	10[2]	......	....	28.19	51.26	12.02	....	....	
16	Without catheterization[4]	9[2]	......	....	51.56	27.03	16.12	....	....	
17	Control group[5]	8	......	....	43.22	39.21	11.62	....	....	
18	Control group from tank	7[3,6]	......	....	17.08	75.06	6.46	....	....	
19		7[3,7]	......	....	25.23	66.36	7.47	....	....	
20	*Chelonia mydas*	2[8]	......	....	(14.5-17.7)	(31.1-45.1)	(14-19.1)	....	Cc, (3.5-11.3)[9]	9,15
21		3[8]	13.6	7.5	43.0	0.0	2.2	12.2	C, 6.0; c, 1.5; H, 13.8	9
22		4[8,10]	(4.4-25.0)	(5.4-18.4)	(29-51)	(0-12)	(1.4-6.3)	(2.4-22)	Cc, (5.2-11.5)[9]; H, (8.0-23.0)	9
23	*Chrysemys picta*	4[8]	......	3.8	11.1(9.8-21.7)	24.1	13.9(7.4-27.7)	40.6	Cc, 5.5	22
24	*Coluber constrictor constrictor (C. coluber constrictor)*, embryo	......	......	20	....	60	20	....	....	2
25	*Crocodylus niloticus*	[7[2]]	1-2	....	66.2	4.5	20.8	(3.5-7.0)	Cc, (0.5-3)	6
26		[...[11]]	......	....	66.8	12.5	2.3	....	....	14
27		[...[2]]	......	....	25.4	4.5	68.5	....	....	14
28	*Emys orbicularis*	[3]	(0.3-0.9)	19.7(15.8-21.9)	14.4(10.6-18.8)	47.1(26.4-69.0)	2.5(1.4-4.0)	14.8	GX, (0.5-1.2)	16
29	*Eryx thebaicus*	9[12] [1]	......	1.1	5.7	0	62.8	29.1	C, 0.20; c, 0.03; H, 0.95; P, 0.3	11
30	*Kinixys belliana belliana (K. youngii)*	[5]	(0.3-1.3)	15.2(7.7-22.0)	6.0(2.9-12.5)	44.0(30.3-72.7)	5.5(3.4-8.7)	26.4	GX, (0.3-3.8)	16
31	*K. erosa*	[2]	0.4	13.7(12.7-14.7)	6.1(5.7-6.5)	61.0(50-72)	4.2(3.5-5.0)	15.2	GX, 0.4	16
32	*Kinosternon subrubrum*	[1]	1.1	10.0	24.0	22.9	0.7	40.3	GX, 1.0	16
33	*Pelusios subniger (P. derbianus)*	[1]	1.0	20.6	18.5	24.4	4.5	27.2	....	16
34	*Phrynosoma cornutum*	......	......	....	0.4	0	99.5	....	....	21
35	Pythonidae[13]	[1[14]]	......	....	8.7	....	89.0	....	....	1
36	*Scincus scincus (S. officinalis)*	......	1.6	0.7	3.0	....	93.6	....	C, 0.30; c, 0.07; P, 0.60	12

[1] Percent of the total N excreted during entire incubation period. [2] Liquid urine plus deposit. [3] Urine obtained by catheterization. [4] Dehydrated and starved 20 days. [5] Given water but no food. [6] Urine collected at beginning. [7] Urine collected after 30 days' starvation. [8] Bladder urine obtained postmortem. [9] Creatine N, or creatine N plus creatinine N. [10] One animal pregnant. [11] Liquid urine. [12] Pooled samples. [13] Family; species not indicated. [14] Only solid portion of urine analyzed.

continued

109. NONPROTEIN NITROGEN IN URINE

Part II. Birds, Reptiles, and Amphibians

	Species (Synonym)	No. of Subjects [Observations]	Allantoin N	Amino N	Ammonia N	Urea N	Uric Acid N	Undetermined Nonprotein N	Other Nonprotein N	Reference
37	*Spalerosophis diadema* (*Zamenis diadema*)	15[12/] [1]	......	4.5	4.3	2.0	67.0	17.2	C, 0.06; c, 0.03; H, 2.7; P, 2.0	10
38	*Testudo denticulata*	[3]	(6.7-8.6)	15.6(9.4-22.2)	6.0(3.9-8.7)	29.1(26.8-31.2)	6.7(4.9-7.7)	32.1	GX, (1.7-5.0)	16
39	*T. elegans*	[2]	(1.0-1.2)	13.1(10.6-15.5)	6.2(5.9-6.5)	8.5(7.8-9.1)	56.1(54.3-57.8)	12.0	GX, (0.9-5.1)	16
40	*T. graeca*	[2]	(1.4-1.9)	6.6(4.5-8.6)	4.1	22.3(15.3-29.3)	51.9(48.7-55.0)	4.0	GX, (8.7-10.1)	16
41	*T. kleinmanni* (*T. leithii*)	......	......	2.4	4.2	48.7	33.6	8.4	C, 1.80; c, 0.95	13
42	*T. sulcata*	......	......	4.4	2.8	20.2	55	14.9	C, 1.7; c, 0.95	13
	Amphibia									
43	*Bufo bufo*	[7[15/]]	......	0.1	5.3	90.4	....	4.2	....	6
44	*B. calamita*	[9[15/]]	......	0.6	5.9	86.7	0.5	5.6	C, 0.5; c, 0.2	6
45	*Hyla arborea*	[8[15/]]	......	......	4.1	86.0	0.3	9.6	....	6
46	*Rana* sp., 11°C	......	......	......	20.9	68.2	....	10.2	....	18
47	22°C	......	......	......	12.2	77.6	....	10.2	....	
48	*R. esculenta*	[7[15/]]	......	5.8	9.3	76.9	0.05	7.9	....	6
49	*R. pipiens* (*R. virescens*), hibernating	4	......	......	5.1(1.2-7.4)	87.4(81.9-90.5)	0.3(0.2-0.4)	(1.9-13.7)	....	20
50	*R. temporaria*	[6[15/]]	......	3.8	7.4	78.1	0.1	10.6	....	6
51	*Salamandra salamandra*	[5[15/]]	......	......	8.1	81.9	....	10.0	....	6
52	*Siredon mexicanum* (*Ambystoma mexicanum*)	[8[15/]]	......	3.8	42.5	28.3	....	25.4	....	6
53	*Triturus cristatus*	[6[15/]]	......	0.3	3.3	79.6	0.2	14.8	C, 1.3; c, 0.5	6

[12/] Pooled samples. [15/] Urine and washings of the container used for analysis.

Contributors: Ramamurthi, R., and Scheer, Bradley T.

References

[1] Bacon, R. F. 1909. Philippine J. Sci., A, 4:165.

[2] Clark, H. 1953. J. Exptl. Biol. 30:492.

[3] Clark, H., and D. Fischer. 1957. J. Exptl. Zool. 136:1.

[4] Clark, H., D. Fischer, and B. Florio. 1953. Anat. Record 117:524.

[5] Coulson, R. A., T. Hernandez, and F. G. Brazda. 1950. Proc. Soc. Exptl. Biol. Med. 73:203.

[6] Cragg, M. M., J. B. Balinsky, and E. Baldwin. 1961. Comp. Biochem. Physiol. 3:227.

[7] Davis, R. E. 1927. J. Biol. Chem. 74:509.

[8] Hopping, A. 1923. Am. J. Physiol. 66:145.

[9] Khalil, F. 1947. J. Biol. Chem. 171:611.

[10] Khalil, F. 1948. Ibid. 172:101.

[11] Khalil, F. 1948. Ibid. 172:105.

[12] Khalil, F. 1951. Ibid. 189:443.

[13] Khalil, F., and G. Haggag. 1955. J. Exptl. Zool. 130:423.

[14] Khalil, F., and G. Haggag. 1958. J. Exptl. Biol. 35:552.

[15] Lewis, H. B. 1918. Science 48:376.

[16] Moyle, V. 1949. Biochem. J. 44:581.

[17] Needham, J. 1931. Chemical embryology. Macmillan, New York. v. 2, pp. 1055-1145.

[18] Przylecki, S. J., J. Opienska, and H. Giedroyc. 1922. Arch. Intern. Physiol. 20:207.

[19] Rogers, L. J. 1966. Comp. Biochem. Physiol. 18:249.

[20] Van Heyde, H. C. 1921. J. Biol. Chem. 46:421.

[21] Weese, A. O. 1917. Science 46:517.

[22] Wiley, F. H., and H. B. Lewis. 1927. Am. J. Physiol. 81:692.

continued

109. NONPROTEIN NITROGEN IN URINE

Part III. Fishes and Ascidians

Values are percent of nonprotein nitrogen in urine. **Type or Method:** BU = bladder urine; RC = retention catheter.

	Species (Synonym)	No. of Specimens	Type or Method	Amino N	Ammonia N	Creatine N	Creatinine N	Urea N	Uric Acid N	Undetermined Nonprotein N	Reference
	Pisces										
1	*Amia calva,* fasting	1	RC	0.9	32.2	17.4	....	15.6	22.6	....	5
2	*Anguilla rostratus (A. chrysypa),* fasting	2	RC	....	(11.7-23.4)	(20.9-28.0)	(0.9-2.6)	(10.7-23.4)	(1.3-5.4)	(17.1-55.9)	5
3	*Archosargus probatocephalus*	2	RC	(15.0-19.9)	(8.4-9.6)	(6.5-9.2)	(5.9-9.0)	(22.9-23.0)	(6.4-8.4)	(25.1-26.4)	5
4	*Carassius auratus,* fasting	2	RC	....	(6.2-15.7)	(11.9-19.2)	0	Trace	1.1	(71.3-74.5)	5
5	*Cyprinus carpio,* fasting	4	RC	....	(3.3-21.6)	(18.2-65.1)	(0-2.9)	3.7	0.6	(32.0-78.5)	5
6	*Epinephelus morio*	1	RC	6.4	....	14.7	2.4	30.8	....	45.7	5
7	*Gadus morhua (G. callarias),* fasting	2	BU[1]	(14.8-21.4)	....	(51.1-52.6)	(2.2-3.1)	(6.5-11.2)	(1.7-2.4)	(15.2-19.0)	5
8	*Ictalurus furcatus*	1	RC	20.0	27.4	5.1	2.8	24.6	....	16.9	5
9	*Lepisosteus osseus,* fasting	1	RC	4.1	33.9	3.3	0.8	5.0	....	53.0	5
10	*Lophius* sp.	1[2]	BU	5.0	2.0	....	....	28.0	....	65.0	1
11	*L. piscatorius*	4[2]	BU	(5.3-14.3)	(0.3-1.3)	(23.0-61.7)	(1.5-4.1)	(0.1-2.7)	(0.2-0.4)	(28.2-63.4)	4
12	Fasting	1	BU[1]	(2.9-10.0)	(0.8-2.3)	(35.4-55.5)		(0.8-2.9)	(0.8-3.5)	(33.0-51.9)	5
13	Nonfasting	7[2]	BU[1]	(14.9-34.0)	(2.0-5.4)	(21.0-46.5)		(1.5-3.6)	(0.7-1.8)	(20.0-51.0)	5
14	*Myoxocephalus octodecemspinosus*	2	BU[3]	(4.0-4.4)	(1.3-2.0)	(22.4-25.0)		(14.1-15.3)	0.7	(54.2-55.9)	3
15	*Protopterus aethiopicus*	.....	.....	....	61.0	10.2		27.6	1.2	....	6
16	*Pseudopleuronectes americanus*	2	BU[3]	(8.2-9.7)	(1.8-2.6)	(15.0-26.1)		(13.5-21.2)	(1.2-1.3)	(48.3-51.1)	3
17	*Sphaeroides maculatus*	3	BU[1]	20.6	(5.1-6.2)	(12.4-53.7)	(0-5.0)	(1.8-19.1)	(0.8-1.2)	(9.1-84.6)	5
	Chondrichthyes										
18	*Torpedo* sp.	.....	.....	1.7	1.7	....	....	85.3	....	11.3	1
	Ascidiacea										
19	*Ascidiella* sp.	.....	.....	....	95	....	....	....	....	....	2
20	*Ciona* sp.	.....	.....	....	87	....	....	....	....	....	2

1/ Obtained postmortem. 2/ Number of subjects. 3/ Obtained with urinary papilla ligated at least 24 hours.

Contributors: Scheer, Bradley T., and Ramamurthi, R.

References

[1] Delaunay, H. 1929. Compt. Rend. Soc. Biol. 101: 371.

[2] Goodbody, I. 1957. J. Exptl. Biol. 35:297.

[3] Grafflin, A. L., and R. G. Gould. 1936. Biol. Bull. 70:16.

[4] Grollman, A. 1929. J. Biol. Chem. 81:267.

[5] Smith, H. W. 1929. Ibid. 81:727.

[6] Smith, H. W. 1930. Ibid. 88:97.

continued

109. NONPROTEIN NITROGEN IN URINE

Part IV. Invertebrates

Values are percent of nonprotein nitrogen in urine, unless otherwise indicated. **Other Nonprotein N**: U = undetermined nonprotein N; G = guanine N.

	Class and Species	Amino N	Ammonia N	Purine N	Urea N	Uric Acid N	Other Nonprotein N	Reference
	Echinodermata							
	Asteroidea							
1	*Asterias rubens*[1]	(17.3-27.5)	(23.7-48)	(3.6-10)	(8-18.7)	......	U, (16.5-26.7)	7
	Echinoidea							
2	*Paracentrotus lividus*[1]	(25-28.5)	(26.2-30)	11.0	(5-10)	1.0	U, (20.2-24.3)	7
	Holothuroidea							
3	*Holothuria tubulosa*[1]	18.0	39.0	12.0	6.0	......	U, 25.0	7
	Arthropoda							
	Arachnida							
4	*Buthus tamulus typicus*[2,3]	......	......	......	......	12.8	G, 34.8; U, 52.4	18
5	*Galeodes indicus*[2,3]	......	......	......	......	12.3	G, 37.8; U, 49.9	18
6	*Heterometrus fulvipes*[2,3]	......	......	......	......	7.9	G, (90-92); U, (0.1-2.1)	18
7	*Lychas tricarinatus*[2,3]	......	......	......	......	28.7	G, 71.1; U, 0.2	18
8	*Nephila claviceps*[2,3]	......	......	......	......	......	G, 88.8	21
9	*Phrynichus phipsoni*[2,3]	......	......	......	......	......	G, (33.5-54.5); U, (45.5-66.5)	18
10	*Thelyphonus sepiaris*[2,3]	......	......	......	......	......	G, 69.5; U, 30.5	18
	Crustacea							
11	*Armadillidium vulgare*[4]	6	55	......	1	8	U, 30	9
12	*Asellus aquaticus*[1]	10	62	......	......	5	U, 21	9
13	*Astacus* sp.[1]	12	64	4	12	0.8	U, 7.2	8
14	*Cancer pagurus*	20.0	42.9	10.0	12.8	2.8	U, 11.5	8
15	*Carcinus maenas*[1]	4	68	2.5	4	1.2	U, 20.3	8
16	*Eriocheir sinensis*[1]	......	63	......	5	......	U, 31	15
17	*Gammarus locusta*[1]	7	80	......	1	......	U, 12	9
18	*G. pulex*[1]	3	70	......	9	......	U, 18	9
19	*G. zaddachi*[1]	3	83	......	1	......	U, 13	9
20	*Ligia oceanica*[5]	6	83	......	......	......	U, 11	9
21	*Maja squinado*	(16.4-27.9)	(4.0-12.0)	(0-7.4)	(2.1-8.5)	(0-4.7)	U, (51.4-71.1)	6,7
22	*Marinogammarus pirloti*[1]	2	87	......	......	......	U, 11	9
23	*Oniscus asellus*[4]	6	47	......	......	5	U, 42	9
24	*Orchestia* sp.[5]	11	70	......	1	......	U, 18	9
25	*Porcellio laevis*[4]	1	57	......	......	4	U, 38	9
	Insecta							
26	*Aedes aegypti*[2]	4.4	6.4	......	11.9	47.3	U, 19.0	12
	Aeshna cyanea, nymph[2,6]							23
27	Prior to feeding	......	74(41-91)	......	......	8.0(6.2-13.1)[7]	......	
28	1 day after feeding	......	87(78-96)	......	......	2.6(1.5-3.9)[7]	......	
29	*Anopheles quadrimaculatus*[2]	4.7	7.8	......	9.5	42.5	U, 26.4	12
30	*Attacus* sp.	9.5	1-8	......	......	80.8	......	5
31	*Brevicoryne brassicae*[2,8]	94.9	0.2	......	......	......	U, 5	13
32		81	11	......	......	......	U, 8	
33		72	......	......	......	......	U, 28	
34	*Culex pipiens*[2]	5.5	10.0	......	7.9	46.9	U, 20.0	12
35	*Rhodnius prolixus*[9]	......	......	......	......	90-92	U, 8-10	25
36	*Sialis* sp., larva[2]	......	90	......	......	......	......	22

1/ Medium sample. 2/ Percent of total N excreted. 3/ Solid excreta. 4/ Solid fecal pellets and washings. 5/ Washings of the dish and animal. 6/ Excreta collected in acetate buffer. 7/ Percent of uric acid N plus ammonia N. 8/ Honeydew analyzed. 9/ Pooled samples.

continued

109. NONPROTEIN NITROGEN IN URINE

Part IV. Invertebrates

	Class and Species	Amino N	Ammonia N	Purine N	Urea N	Uric Acid N	Other Non-protein N	Reference
	Annelida							
	Hirudinea[1]							7
37	Fed	1.9	74.5	2.9	7.0	....	....	
38	Starved	4.5	78.3	4.3	3.8	....	....	
	Oligochaeta							
	Allolobophora caliginosa[1]							10
39	Before starving	....	42.6	....	22.8	....	....	
40	After starving	....	10.5	....	62.6	....	....	
	Eisenia foetida[1]							16
41	Before starving	25.2	51.2	....	23.6	....	....	
42	After starving	12.6	66.1	....	21.2	....	....	
	Lumbricus sp.							3,4
43	Fed	....	72.0	....	5.0	1.40	U, 16.0	
44	Starved	....	8.6	....	84.4	0.76	U, 7.0	
	L. terrestris							16
45	Before starving	....	56.9	....	43.0	1.5	....	
46	After starving	....	18.9	....	81.1	....	....	
47	*Pheretima posthuma*	....	45.0[10]	....	55.0[10]	....	....	1
	Polychaeta							2
48	*Aphrodite aculeata*	....	80	....	0.2	0.8	....	
	Mollusca							
	Cephalopoda							6,7
49	*Octopus vulgaris*	12.5	(12.5-33.3)	25.0	5.2	1.4	U, 29.2	
50	*Sepia officinalis*	(7.2-8.4)	(64.4-69.6)	(3.2-4.9)	(1.4-2.1)	(2.1-2.2)	U, (18.6-20.2)	
	Bivalvia							
51	*Crassostrea virginica*[1,2]	5.2	65	....	13.2	....	U 16.6	11
	Modiolus demissus[1]							14
52	Beaufort population[11]	37.7[12]	62.3[12]	....	....	....	....	
53	Noank population[13]	25.0[12]	75.0[12]	....	....	....	....	
	Gastropoda							
54	*Aplysia* sp.[1]	13.0	37.0	16.7	7.4	9.2	U, 24.1	7
55	*Arion* sp.	18.0	9.8	16.6	0.2	3.3	U, (17-62)	17
56	*A. rufus*	1.7	4.6	10.8	70.8	4.9	U, 12.0	7
	Helix sp.							7
57	Fed	5.2	13.7	16.5	22.0	10.7	U, 42.6	
58	Starved	7.0	22.2	19.0	16.8	7.0	U, 35.0	
59	*Littorina* sp.[1], summer	7.0	40.0	29.0	12.6	0.8	....	17
60	*Lymnaea* sp.[1], summer	....	42.0	39.0	14.0	5.0	....	17
	Brachiopoda							
	Inarticulata							14
	Lingula reevi[1]							
61	Intact	6.1[12]	93.9[12]	....	....	....	....	
62	Regenerating	5.3[12]	94.7[12]	....	....	....	....	
	Aschelminthes							
	Nematoda							
	Ascaridia sp.							24
63	Aerobic	....	56.0	....	12.0	....	....	
64	Anaerobic	....	59.0	....	15.0	....	....	

[1] Medium sample. [2] Percent of total N excreted. [10] Percent of ammonia N plus urea N. [11] Salinity, 32 ppm; temp, 22-27.5°C. [12] Percent of ammonia N plus amino N. [13] Salinity, 27 ppm; temp, 16.0-21.5°C.

continued

109. NONPROTEIN NITROGEN IN URINE

Part IV. Invertebrates

	Class and Species	Amino N	Ammonia N	Purine N	Urea N	Uric Acid N	Other Non-protein N	Reference
	Ascaris sp.2/							24
65	Aerobic	....	69.0	....	7.0	....	....	
66	Anaerobic	....	71.0	....	6.0	....	....	
67	In moist air in "U" tube	....	27.0	....	51.0	....	....	
68	*Nematodirus* sp.	(33-37)	(40-73)	....	7-11	....	....	19,20
69	Aerobic	....	42.0	....	14.0	3.0	....	24
70	Anaerobic	....	29.0	....	4.0	4.0	....	24
71	*Trichinella* sp., larva, aerobic	28.0	33.0	....	....	....	....	24

2/ Percent of total N excreted.

Contributors: Ramamurthi, R., and Scheer, Bradley T.

References

[1] Bahl, K. N. 1945. Quart. J. Microscop. Sci. 85:343.

[2] Baldwin, E. 1947. Dynamic aspects of biochemistry. Macmillan, New York. p. 250.

[3] Cohen, S., and H. B. Lewis. 1949. J. Biol. Chem. 180:79.

[4] Cohen, S., and H. B. Lewis. 1950. Ibid. 184:479.

[5] Courtois, A. 1929. Compt. Rend. Soc Biol. 101:365.

[6] Delaunay, H. 1927. Bull. Sta. Biol. Arcachon 24:95.

[7] Delaunay, H. 1931. Biol. Rev. Cambridge Phil. Soc. 6:265.

[8] Delaunay, H. 1934. Ann. Physiol. Physicochim. Biol. 10:695.

[9] Dresel, E. I. B., and V. Moyle. 1950. J. Exptl. Biol. 27:210.

[10] Haggag, G., and A. Khaluf el-Duweini. 1959. Proc. Egypt. Acad. Sci. 13:1.

[11] Hammen, C. S., H. F. Miller, Jr., and W. H. Geer. 1966. Comp. Biochem. Physiol. 17:1199.

[12] Irreverre, F., and L. A. Terzian. 1958. Science 129: 1358.

[13] Lamb, K. P. 1959. J. Insect Physiol. 3:1.

[14] Lum, S. C., and C. S. Hammen. 1964. Comp. Biochem. Physiol. 12:185.

[15] Molliter, A. 1937. Zool. Jahrb. Abt. Allgem. Zool. Physiol. Tiere 57:323.

[16] Needham, A. E. 1957. J. Exptl. Biol. 34:425.

[17] Needham, J. 1935. Biochem. J. 29:238.

[18] Rao, K. P., and T. Gopalakrishnareddy. 1962. Comp. Biochem. Physiol. 7:175.

[19] Rogers, W. P. 1952. Australian J. Sci. Res., B, 5: 210.

[20] Rogers, W. P. 1935. Exptl. Parasitol. 4:21.

[21] Schmidt, G., M. Liss, and S. J. Thannhauser. 1955. Biochim. Biophys. Acta 16:533.

[22] Staddon, B. W. 1955. J. Exptl. Biol. 32:84.

[23] Staddon, B. W. 1959. Ibid. 36:566.

[24] Weinstein, P. P. 1960. In L. A. Stauber, ed. Host influence on parasite physiology. Rutgers Univ. Press, New Brunswick, N.J. pp. 65-92.

[25] Wigglesworth, V. B. 1931. J. Exptl. Biol. 8:411.

110. WATER TURNOVER: TABULAR

Part I. Terrestrial Vertebrates

Water turnover is generally estimated by measuring free water consumed, by ascertaining water content of food voluntarily ingested, and by computing the water formed from oxidation of food (0.13 g/kcal) under circumstances where body weight remains constant.

	Species (Synonym)	No. of Observations	Body Weight g	Water Consumption ml/kg/day	Urine Output ml/kg/day	Water Turnover ml/kg/day	Reference
	Mammalia						
1	*Homo sapiens*	5	67,302	....	....	41 1/	32
2		166	65,000	35	19	40	27
3	*Blarina brevicauda*	5	26	223	....	572	13
4	*Bos indicus*, nonlactating	44	409,000	55	....	61	30
5	summer	4	....	....	....	135 1/	24

1/ Measured by use of tritiated water.

continued

110. WATER TURNOVER: TABULAR

Part I. Terrestrial Vertebrates

	Species (Synonym)	No. of Observations	Body Weight g	Water Consumption ml/kg/day	Urine Output ml/kg/day	Water Turnover ml/kg/day	Reference
	B. taurus						
6	Steer	28	584,000	40	9	48	34
7	Holstein, nonlactating	21	745,000	60	…	67	4
8	lactating	44	529,000	148	…	159	30
9	Jersey, lactating	44	403,000	118	…	128	30
10	Shorthorn, summer	4	337,000	…	…	148[1]	26
11	*Camelus bactrianus,* winter	….	513,000	…	8-12[2]	…	31
12	*C. dromedarius,* summer, nonlactating	2	337,000	…	…	61[1]	26
13	lactating	2	…	…	…	93[1]	26
14	winter	….	260,000	15	3[3]	17[4]	37,40
15	*Canis familiaris*	5	10,582	…	…	90[1]	32
16		120	18,600	46	19	60	1
17		240	10,700	…	…	56	33
18	*Cavia porcellus*	37	450	145	…	170	3
19	*Citellus leucurus*	10	94	16[5]	…	…	21
20	*Dipodomys agilis*	….	61	108[5,6]; 190[5,7]	…	…	12
21	*D. deserti*	12	93	0[5]	…	40[1]	32
22	*D. merriami*	….	38	0[5]	…	…	12,39
23	*D. spectabilis*	32	106	55[8]	…	82	5,36
24	Elephantidae[9]	9	3,670,000	42	13	46	7
25	*Equus asinus,* winter	….	100,000	35[10]	10-12[11]	…	37,38
26	*E. caballus*	3	398,533	…	…	54[1]	32
27		34	420,000	55	12	62	42
28	*Felis catus*	42	2900	72	41	84	18
29		50	4490	…	…	72	33
30	*Macaca mulatta (M. rhesus)*	30	4900	70	53	82	22
31	*Macropus rufus (Megaleia rufa),* summer, shaded	4	…	…	…	88[1]	26
32	*Mesocricetus* sp.	54	70	184	…	216	3
33	*Microtus californicus*	3	47	…[12]	…	246[1]	14
34		16	30	…[13]	…	139[1]	14
35	*M. ochrogaster ochrogaster*	5	43	368	335	405	13
36		71	29	211	…	273	16
37	*Mus musculus*	12	21	…	…	337[1]	32
38		34	21	101	43	204	6
39	*Neotoma fuscipes*	7	191	248; 50[5]	…	…	23
40	*N. lepida,* coastal	9	139	132; 30[5]	…	153	23
41	desert	9	111	330; 60[5]	…	352	23
42	*Oryctolagus cuniculus*	4	3159	…	…	107[1]	32
43		59	2400	137	…	…	9
44		105	3670	113	74	130	19
45	*Ovis aries,* Merino, summer	5[14]	52,800	…	…	61[1]	29
46		5[15]	51,300	…	…	44[1]	29
47	dehydrating	3	50,300	…	2-13	…	25
48	winter	5[14]	53,000	…	…	63[1]	29
49		5[15]	43,000	…	…	32[1]	29
50	*Peromyscus leucopus*	5	23	396	296	451	13
51		58	20	90	…	154	16
52	*P. maniculatus*	79	15	124	…	192	16,35
53	*Rattus norvegicus*	11	298	…	…	116[1]	32
54		210	225	139	58	163	2
55	*Sigmodon* sp.	….	130	177	…	…	9

[1] Measured by use of tritiated water. [2] Output fell to 3.5 ml/kg/day during dehydration. [3] Output can fall below 2 ml/kg/day in dehydrated animals or rise to nearly 30 ml/kg/day in animals grazing in winter. [4] Turnover increased to 40-50 ml/kg/day in summer as a result of water expended in heat regulation. [5] Minimal drinking requirement with ingestion of food containing approximately 10% water. [6] At an ambient vapor pressure (water) of 14.6 mm Hg. [7] At an ambient vapor pressure (water) of 9.1 mm Hg. [8] Water obtained entirely from food. [9] Family. [10] Water consumption increased to 95-105 ml/kg/day in midsummer. [11] Output during dehydration fell to 4.5 ml/kg/day. [12] Water *ad lib.* [13] Water one-third *ad lib.* [14] 6 sheep/acre. [15] 9 sheep/acre.

continued

110. WATER TURNOVER: TABULAR

Part I. Terrestrial Vertebrates

	Species (Synonym)	No. of Observations	Body Weight g	Water Consumption ml/kg/day	Urine Output ml/kg/day	Water Turnover ml/kg/day	Reference
	Aves						
56	*Gallus gallus*	6	1604	227	139[16]	......	17
57		43	1550	130	....	161	20
58		3[17]	1559	227	81	......	17
59	*Junco hyemalis*	2	19	185	....	283	41
60	*Melopsittacus undulatus*	....	30	13[8]	22[16]	81	10
61		3	30	63	25[16]	131	10
62	*Passer domesticus*	12	23	200	....	290	41
63	*Taeniopygia castanotis*	....	12	30[18]	45[16]	120	11
64		....	12	269[12]	107[16]	359	11
65	*Zonotrichia albicollis*	3	28	294	....	379	41
	Reptilia						
66	*Amphibolurus ornatus,* 20°C	7	3	....	5	30[19]	15
67	*Dipsosaurus dorsalis,* 40°C	13	40	27[8]	24[16]	30[1]	28
68	*Gehyra variegata,* 20°C	17	3	....	4	48[19]	15
69	*Sphenomorphus labillardieri,* 20°C	7	3	....	20	80[19]	15
70	*Tiliqua rugosa,* 25°C	11	300	....	6	......	8

1/ Measured by use of tritiated water. 8/ Water obtained entirely from food. 12/ Water *ad lib.* 16/ Cloacal water loss, urinary and egestive materials being voided together. 17/ Ureters exteriorized. 18/ Minimum water. 19/ Total water output.

Contributors: (a) Dawson, William R., (b) Adolph, Edward F.

References

[1] Adolph, E. F. 1939. Am. J. Physiol. 125:77.
[2] Adolph, E. F. 1943. Physiological regulations. J. Cattell Press, Lancaster, Penna. p. 198.
[3] Adolph, E. F. Unpublished. Univ. Rochester, School Medicine and Dentistry, Rochester, N.Y., 1967.
[4] Atkeson, F. W., and T. R. Warren. 1934. J. Dairy Sci. 17:265.
[5] Bailey, V. 1923. Sci. Monthly 17:66.
[6] Barbour, H. G., and J. Trace. 1937. Am. J. Physiol. 118:77.
[7] Benedict, F. G. 1936. Carnegie Inst. Wash. Publ. 474.
[8] Bentley, P. J. 1959. J. Physiol. (London) 145:37.
[9] Bruce, H. M. 1950. J. Animal Technicians Assoc. 1:2.
[10] Cade, T. J., and J. A. Dybas, Jr. 1962. Auk 79:345.
[11] Calder, W. A. 1964. Physiol. Zool. 37:400.
[12] Carpenter, R. E. 1966. Univ. Calif. (Berkeley) Publ. Zool. 78:1.
[13] Chew, R. M. 1951. Ecol. Monographs 21:215.
[14] Church, R. L. 1966. Physiol. Zool. 39:326.
[15] Dawson, W. R., V. H. Shoemaker, and P. Licht. 1966. Ecology 47:589.
[16] Dice, L. R. 1922. Ibid. 3:29.
[17] Dixon, J. M. 1958. Poultry Sci. 37:410.
[18] Gasnier, A., and A. Mayer. 1937. Ann. Physiol. Physicochim. Biol. 13:175.
[19] Gompel, M., F. Hamon, and A. Mayer. 1936. Ibid. 12:471.
[20] Hart, W. M., and H. E. Essex. 1942. Am. J. Physiol. 136:657.
[21] Hudson, J. W. 1962. Univ. Calif. (Berkeley) Publ. Zool. 64:1.
[22] Krohn, P. L., and S. Zuckerman. 1937. J. Physiol. (London) 88:369.
[23] Lee, A. K. 1963. Univ. Calif. (Berkeley) Publ. Zool. 64:57.
[24] MacFarlane, W. V. 1964. In D. B. Dill, ed. Handbook of physiology. American Physiological Society, Washington, D.C. sect. 4, pp. 509-539.
[25] MacFarlane, W. V., R. J. Morris, and B. Howard. 1956. Nature 178:304.
[26] MacFarlane, W. V., R. J. H. Morris, and B. Howard. 1963. Ibid. 197:270.
[27] Magee, H. E. 1937. J. Hyg. 37:30.
[28] Minnich, J. Unpublished. Univ. Michigan, Dept. Zoology, Ann Arbor, 1967.
[29] Morris, R. J. H., B. Howard, and W. V. MacFarlane. Australian J. Agr. Res. 13:320.
[30] Ragsdale, A. C., et al. 1950. Missouri Univ. Agr. Exptl. Sta. Res. Bull. 460.
[31] Read, B. E. 1925. J. Biol. Chem. 64:615.
[32] Richmond, C. R., W. H. Langham, and T. T. Trujillo. 1962. J. Cellular Comp. Physiol. 59:45.
[33] Richter, C. P. 1938. Am. J. Physiol. 122:668.
[34] Ritzman, E. G., and F. G. Benedict. 1938. Carnegie Inst. Wash. Publ. 494.
[35] Ross, L. G. 1930. Biol. Bull. 59:326.
[36] Schmidt-Nielsen, B., et al. 1948. J. Cellular Comp. Physiol. 32:331.
[37] Schmidt-Nielsen, B., et al. 1956. Am. J. Physiol. 185:185.
[38] Schmidt-Nielsen, K. 1964. Desert animals. Oxford Univ. Press, London.
[39] Schmidt-Nielsen, K., and B. Schmidt-Nielsen. 1952. Physiol. Rev. 32:135.
[40] Schmidt-Nielsen, K., et al. 1957. Am. J. Physiol. 188:103.
[41] Seibert, H. C. 1949. Auk 66:128.
[42] Zuntz, N., and O. Hagemann. 1898. Landwirtsch. Jahrb. 27(3).

continued

Part II. Aquatic Animals

Water turnover is modified by factors of energy exchange and of excretion (e.g., work, temperature, air humidity, solute excretion, and fecal residues). Values are for resting animals, and were estimated by measuring excretory volumes in steady states of water exchange, usually when no food was available to the animal.

	Class and Species (Synonym)	No. of Observations	Environment	Temperature °C	Body Volume ml	Water Turnover % body volume/day	Reference
	Chordata						
	Amphibia						
1	*Bufo bufo (B. vulgaris)*	5	Freshwater	....	22	117	16
2	*Rana esculenta*	25	Freshwater	....	65	22	16
3	*R. pipiens*	19	Freshwater	20	32	40	2
4	*R. temporaria*	5	Freshwater	....	9	100	16
5	*Salamandra maculosa*	4	Freshwater	....	20	53	16
6	*Triturus marmoratus (Triton marmoratus)*	4	Freshwater	....	5	43	16
	Pisces						
7	*Anguilla* sp.	5	Seawater	....	250	6.5	20
8	*Myoxocephalus* sp.	5	Seawater	....	180	11.5	20
	Arthropoda						
	Crustacea						
9	*Astacus* sp. *(Potamobius* sp.)	6	Freshwater	....	46	4.1	6
10	*Cambarus* sp.	10	Freshwater	....	13	5.3	10
11	*Cancer* sp.	2	Seawater	....	300	6.5	17
12	*Carcinus* sp.	6	Seawater	15	40	10.0	15
13	*Eriocheir* sp.	....	Freshwater	13	60	3.6	19
14	*Maja* sp.	3	Seawater	....	2200	2.7	3
	Insecta						
15	*Chaoborus* sp. (*Corethra* sp.), larva	3	Freshwater	20	6.2	19	18
16	*Chironomus* sp., larva	10	Freshwater	....	0.1	22	5
	Annelida						
	Oligochaeta						
17	*Lumbricus* sp.	68	Freshwater	19	4	60	21
	Protozoa						
	Ciliata						
18	*Cothurnia* sp.	8	Seawater	15	1.2×10^{-8}	700	7,8
19	*Cyclidium* sp.	....	Freshwater	....	0.2×10^{-8}	22,000	14
20	*Euplotes* sp.	....	Freshwater	25	30×10^{-8}	10,000	12
21	*Lembus* sp.	....	Freshwater	26	0.2×10^{-8}	60,000	12
22	*Paramecium* sp.	....	Freshwater	22	19×10^{-8}	6200	4
23	*Rhabdostyla* sp.	1	Freshwater	15	0.8×10^{-8}	11,000	9
24	*Spirostomum* sp.	....	Freshwater	....	220×10^{-8}	550	14
25	*Tetrahymena* sp. (*Leucophrys* sp.)	....	Freshwater	21	47×10^{-8}	3300	13
26	*Zoothamnium* sp.	9	Freshwater	15	1.4×10^{-8}	5500	9
27	*Z. marinum*	1	Seawater	15	12×10^{-8}	750	7
	Rhizopoda						
28	*Amoeba mira*	3	Seawater	....	0.6×10^{-12}	4300	11
29	*A. proteus*	8	Freshwater	23	300×10^{-8}	360	1

Contributor: Adolph, Edward F.

References

[1] Adolph, E. F. 1926. J. Exptl. Zool. 44:355.
[2] Adolph, E. F. 1939. Ann. Physiol. Physicochim. Biol. 15:353.
[3] Bialaszewicz, K. 1932. Arch. Intern. Physiol. 35:98.
[4] Hance, R. T. 1917. J. Exptl. Zool. 23:287.
[5] Harnisch, O. 1934. Z. Vergleich. Physiol. 21:281.
[6] Herrmann, F. 1931. Ibid. 14:479.
[7] Kitching, J. A. 1934. J. Exptl. Biol. 11:364.
[8] Kitching, J. A. 1936. Ibid. 13:11.
[9] Kitching, J. A. 1938. Ibid. 15:143.
[10] Lienemann, L. J. 1938. J. Cellular Comp. Physiol. 11:149.
[11] Mast, S. O., and D. L. Hopkins. 1941. Ibid. 17:31.
[12] Maupas, E. 1883. Arch. Zool. Exptl. Gen., Ser. 2, 1:427.
[13] Maupas, E. 1888. Ibid. 6:165.
[14] Metzner, P. 1927. Tabulae Biol. 4:490.
[15] Nagel, H. 1934. Z. Vergleich. Physiol. 21:468.
[16] Rey, P. 1937. Ann. Physiol. Physicochim. Biol. 13:1081.
[17] Robertson, J. D. 1939. J. Exptl. Biol. 16:387.
[18] Schaller, F. 1949. Z. Vergleich. Physiol. 31:684.
[19] Scholles, W. 1933. Ibid. 19:522.
[20] Smith, H. W. 1930. Am. J. Physiol. 93:480.
[21] Wolf, A. V. 1940. J. Cellular Comp. Physiol. 15:355.

111. WATER TURNOVER: GRAPHIC

Excepting the method of measuring the turnover of tritium, evaporative water loss provides the best base for estimation of total water turnover. The relatively abundant data on this water exchange, together with certain other information are presented in log-log form. Regressions were calculated by the method of least squares in the Coefficient of Correlation Program (No. 01-50-01) of the Mathatron R Computer. Scatter of points results from the varied methods of measurement and treatment of animals, small sample sizes, and inherent differences among species.

Part I. Mammals

Both the obligatory loss of water with urinary solutes and the evaporative water loss determine minimum water turnover in mammals. Total water loss is further a function of the level of water intake, roughage content of the diet, environmental temperature (particularly if sweating occurs), and the degree of activity of the animal above resting level. Graph shows total water turnover (upper regression line, x's) and evaporative water loss (lower regression line, dots) of mammals weighing 16 g to 3630 kg, normally hydrated, and at environmental temperatures of 18-29°C (*see* Part I, Table 110).

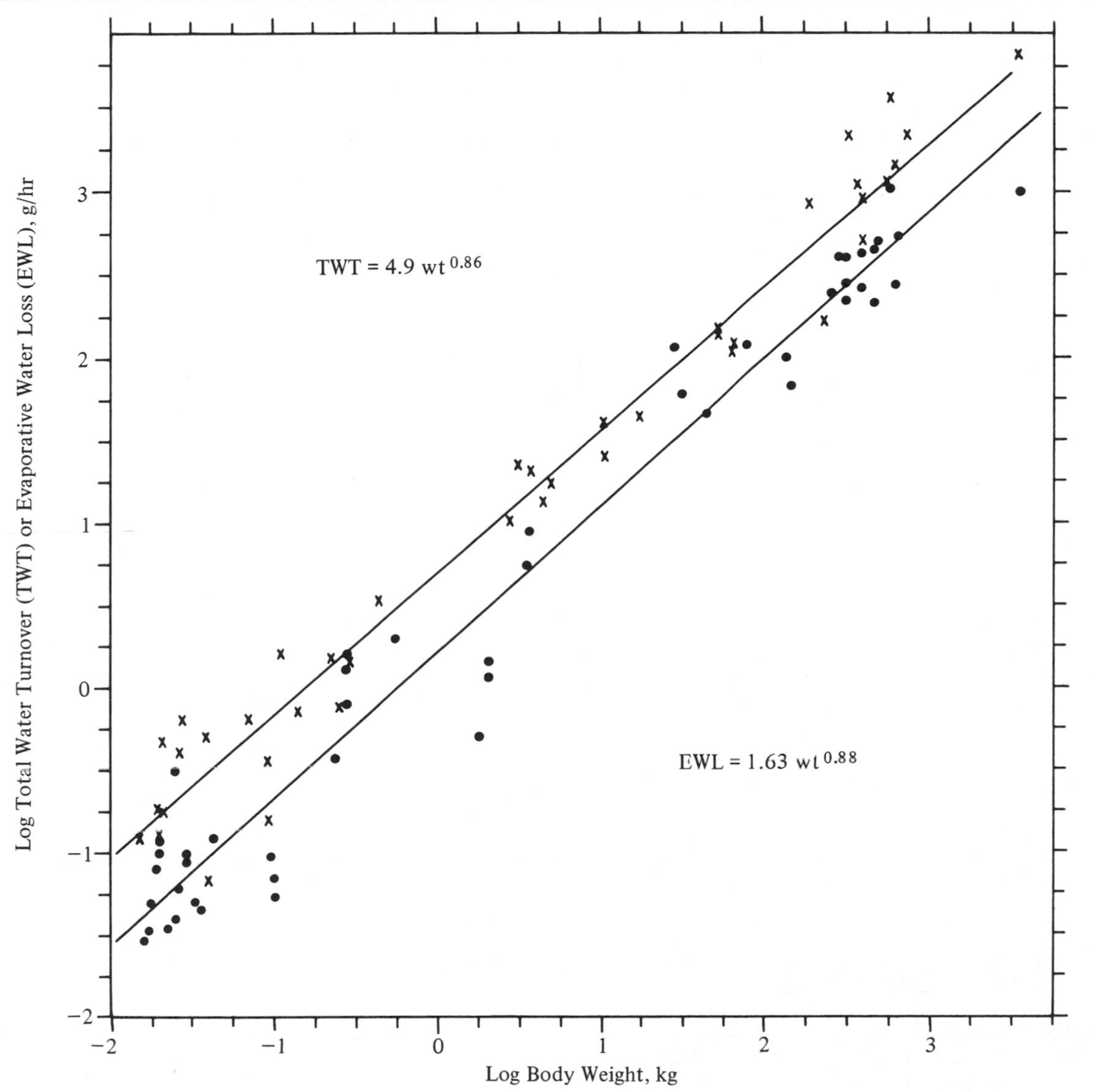

Log Total Water Turnover, g/hr = log 4.892 + 0.862 log wt, kg1/. n = 42, $\bar{x}$ = 0.57730, $\bar{y}$ = 1.1695, Σx^2 = 123.6935, Σy^2 = 96.4431, Σxy = 107.6433.

Log Evaporative Water Loss, g/hr = log 1.632 + 0.883 log wt, kg2/. n = 49, $\bar{x}$ = 0.4772, $\bar{y}$ = 0.6342, Σx^2 = 162.5578, Σy^2 = 131.1381, Σxy = 143. 5684.

1/ Data from Table I of reference 1, and from Part I, Table 110 of this book. 2/ Data from Table IV and Figure 4 of reference 2; regression equation has been recalculated and corrected.

continued

111. WATER TURNOVER: GRAPHIC

Part I. Mammals

Contributor: Chew, Robert M.

References: [1] Chew, R. M. 1965. In W. Mayer and R. VanGelder, ed. Physiological mammalogy. Academic Press, New York. v. 2, pp. 48-49. [2] Chew, R. M. 1965. Ibid. v. 2, pp. 83-85.

Part II. Birds

The level of water turnover is principally determined by the rate of evaporative water loss, particularly when birds are on a minimum water intake and cloacal water loss is reduced to a very low value. Graph shows evaporative water loss of birds weighing 3.0 g to 100 kg, at a median ambient temperature of 25°C (range, 20-35) and median vapor pressure of 6 mm Hg (range, 3.4-16.6). Dots are data for nonpasserine species, and x's are data for passerines. The long regression line is for all species, the short regression line for passerines.

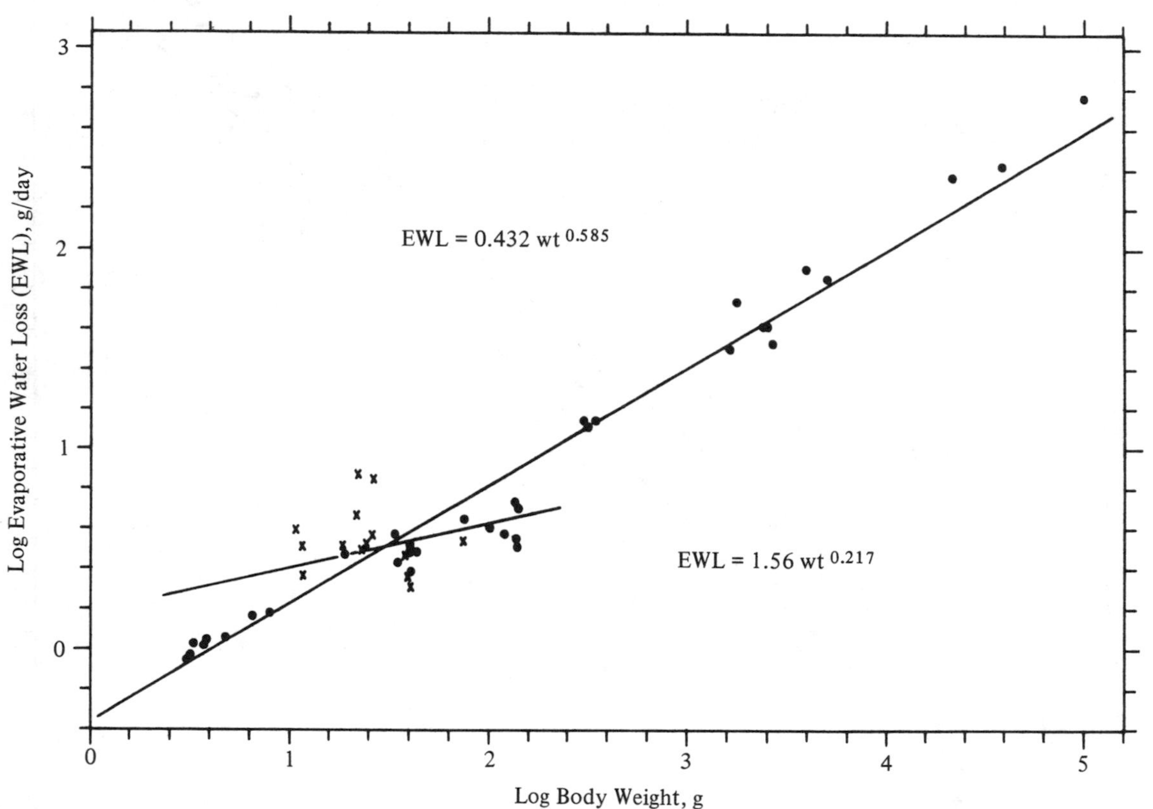

All species: Log Evaporative Water Loss, g/day = log 0.432 + 0.585 log wt, g. $n = 53$, $\bar{x} = 1.8972$, $\bar{y} = 0.7456$, $\Sigma x^2 = 61.3650$, $\Sigma y^2 = 22.6753$, $\Sigma xy = 35.8913$.

Nonpasserine species: Log Evaporative Water Loss, g/day = log 0.351 + 0.613 log wt, g. $n = 35$, $\bar{x} = 2.1764$, $\bar{y} = 0.8783$, $\Sigma x^2 = 51.8223$, $\Sigma y^2 = 20.2042$, $\Sigma xy = 31.7432$.

Passerine species: Log Evaporative Water Loss, g/day = log 1.563 + 0.217 log wt, g. $n = 18$, $\bar{x} = 1.3542$, $\bar{y} = 0.4873$, $\Sigma x^2 = 1.5072$, $\Sigma y^2 = 0.6538$, $\Sigma xy = 0.3266$.

Contributors: Crawford, Eugene C., Lasiewski, Robert C., and Chew, Robert M.

Reference: Crawford, E. C., and R. C. Lasiewski. 1968. Condor, v. 70.

continued

111. WATER TURNOVER: GRAPHIC

Part III. Reptiles

The level of total water turnover is largely determined by evaporative water loss, particularly with animals on minimum water intake when urinary and fecal water losses can be reduced to a very small value. Graph shows evaporative water loss of reptiles in dry air at 25°C, with air movement at 0-400 ml/min. Original data were extrapolated to 25°C as necessary, using a Q_{10} of 3.2 derived from reference 14. Upper regression line (squares) is for snakes, turtles, and crocodilians (read their weights from top x-axis); lower regression line (dots) is for lizards (read their weights from bottom x-axis). Numbers accompanying squares and dots refer to particular species (*see* appended lists).

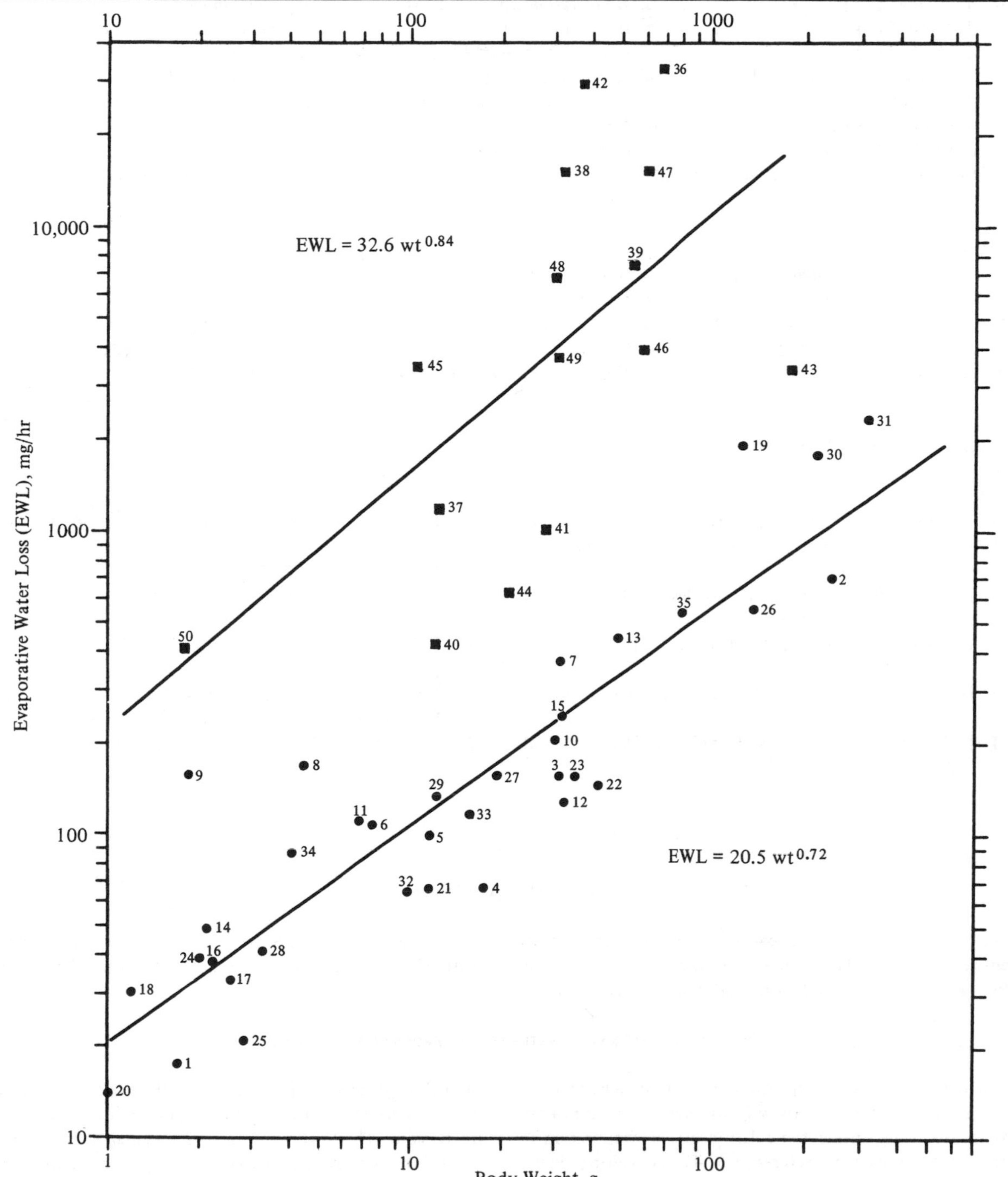

Lizards: Log Evaporative Water Loss, mg/hr = log 20.52 + 0.721 log wt, g. $n = 35, \bar{x} = 1.1234, \bar{y} = 2.1219, \Sigma x^2 = 17.0176, \Sigma y^2 = 10.9097, \Sigma xy = 12.2646$.

Snakes, turtles, and crocodilians: Log Evaporative Water Loss, mg/hr = log 32.55 + 0.839 log wt, g. $n = 15, \bar{x} = 2.4373, \bar{y} = 3.5578, \Sigma x^2 = 3.0575, \Sigma y^2 = 5.5737, \Sigma xy = 2.5658$.

continued

Part III. Reptiles

Lizards:

1. *Ablepharus boutonii metallicum* [14]
2. *Amphibolurus barbatus* [12]
3. *A. cristatus* [13]
4. *A. decresii* [13]
5. *A. fionni* [14]
6. *A. pictus* [13]
7. *A. reticulatus inermis* [13]
8. *Anolis carolinensis* [5]
9. *A. carolinensis* [8]
10. *Crotaphytus collaris* [6]
11. *Diplodactylus strophurus intermedius* [14]
12. *Dipsosaurus dorsalis* [4]
13. *D. dorsalis* [10]
14. *Gehyra variegata* [14]
15. *Gerrhonotus multicarinatus* [7]
16. *Hemiergis decresiense* [14]
17. *H. peronii* [14]
18. *Heteronota bynoei* [14]
19. *Iguana iguana* [2]
20. *Leiolopisma metallicum* [14]
21. *Nephrurus laevis* [14]
22. *Phrynosoma cornutum* [8]
23. *P. solare* [4]
24. *Phyllodactylus marmoratus* [14]
25. *Rhodona planiventrale* [14]
26. *Sauromalus obesus* [2]
27. *Sceloporus undulatus undulatus (S. spinosus floridanus)* [8]
28. *Sphenomorphus leonhardi* [14]
29. *Tiliqua melanops* [13]
30. *T. rugosa* [1]
31. *T. rugosa* [12]
32. *Tympanocryptis lineata lineata* [14]
33. *Uma notata* [4]
34. *Uta stansburiana* [3]
35. *Varanus gouldii* [13]

Snakes, turtles, crocodilians:

36. *Alligator mississippiensis* [3]
37. *Caiman crocodilus sclerops* [2]
38. *Chrysemys picta marginata* [8]
39. *Coluber constrictor* [3]
40. *Crotalus atrox* [4]
41. *C. scutellatus* [4]
42. *Drymarchon corais couperi* [3]
43. *Gopherus agassizii* [9]
44. *G. polyphemus* [3]
45. *Kinosternon subrubrum* [3]
46. *Masticophis flagellum flagellum (Coluber flagellum)* [3]
47. *Pseudemys scripta* [2]
48. *Terrapene carolina* [3]
49. *T. carolina* [2]
50. *Thamnophis sirtalis* [11]

Contributor: Chew, Robert M.

References

[1] Bentley, P. J. 1959. J. Physiol. (London) 145:37.
[2] Bentley, P. J., and K. Schmidt-Nielsen. 1966. Science 151:1547.
[3] Bogert, C. M., and R. B. Cowles. 1947. Am. Museum Novitates 1358:1.
[4] Chew, R. M., and A. E. Dammann. 1961. Science 133:384.
[5] Claussen, E. L. 1967. Comp. Biochem. Physiol. 20:115.
[6] Dawson, W. R., and J. R. Templeton. 1963. Physiol. Zool. 36:219.
[7] Dawson, W. R., and J. R. Templeton. 1966. Ecology 47:759
[8] Hall, F. G. 1922. Biol. Bull. 43:31.
[9] Schmidt-Nielsen, K., and P. J. Bentley. 1966. Science 154:911.
[10] Templeton, J. R. 1960. Physiol. Zool. 33:136.
[11] Thorson, T. B. 1955. Ecology 36:100.
[12] Warburg, M. R. 1965. Australian J. Zool. 13:331.
[13] Warburg, M. R. 1965. Ibid. 13:563.
[14] Warburg, M. R. 1966. Copeia, p. 230.

Part IV. Amphibians

For amphibians in air, the level of water turnover is almost entirely determined by evaporative water loss from the skin. For amphibians partially or totally submerged in water, water turnover depends on the rate of uptake of water through the skin, which is balanced by urine formation.

FIGURE 1. EVAPORATIVE WATER LOSS OF FROGS IN DRY AIR AT 20°C

Original data were extrapolated to 20°C as necessary, assuming a Q_{10} of 1.94 derived from reference 5, and to dry air as necessary, using the relationship of evaporation to relative humidity from reference 1. The dots along the upper regression line are data for frogs in moving air (2 liters/min through animal chamber). The three x's are data for salamanders in moving air; these are not included in the regression. The lower regression line (squares) is for frogs in still dry air. Numbers accompanying squares, dots, and x's refer to particular species (*see* appended lists).

continued

Part IV. Amphibians

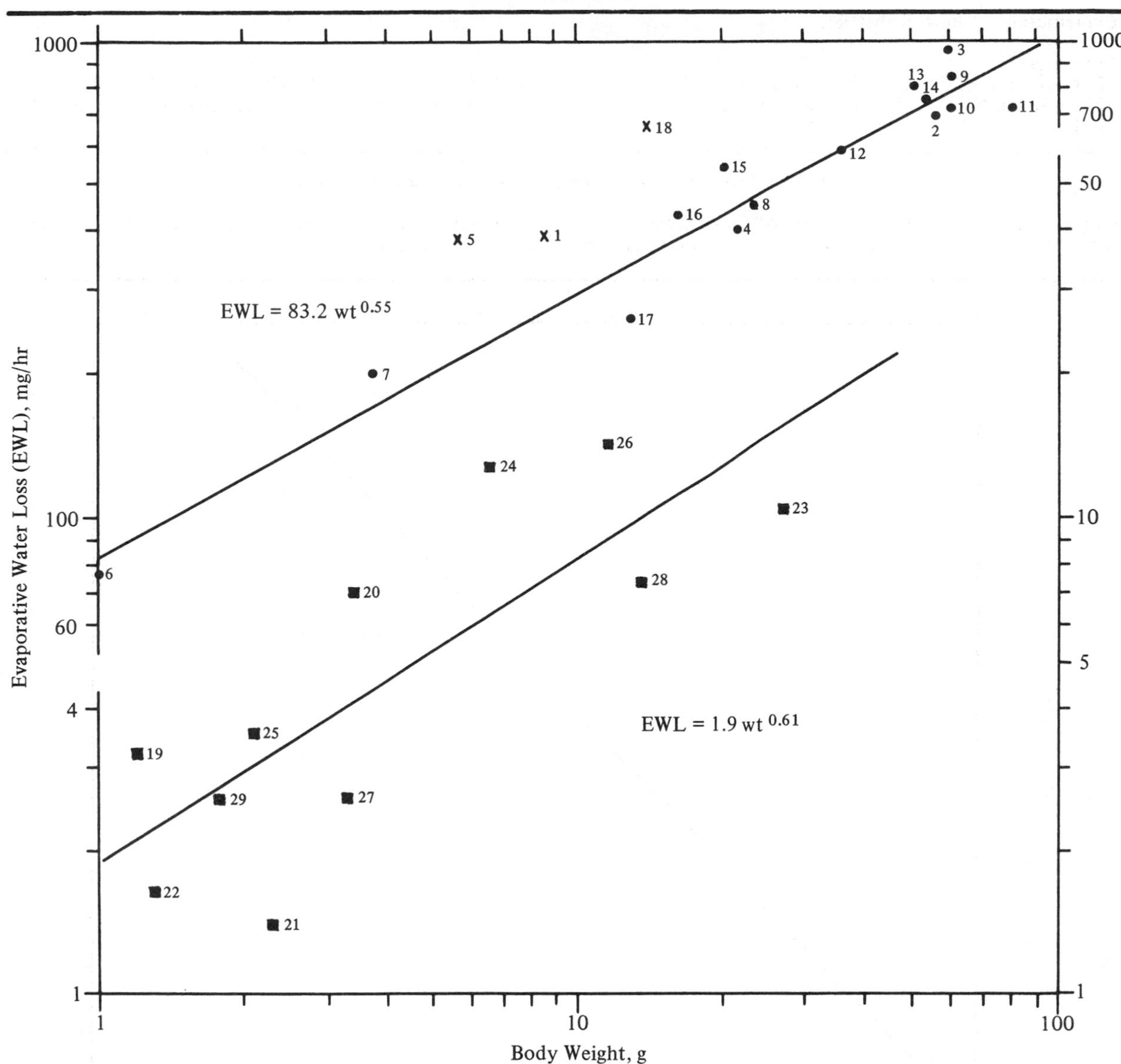

Frogs in moving dry air: Log Evaporative Water Loss, mg/hr = log 83.21 + 0.547 log wt, g. $n = 15$, $\bar{x} = 1.3916$, $\bar{y} = 2.6813$, $\Sigma x^2 = 3.7980$, $\Sigma y^2 = 1.1765$, $\Sigma xy = 2.0773$.

Frogs in still dry air: Log Evaporative Water Loss, mg/hr = log 1.895 + 0.631 log wt, g. $n = 11$, $\bar{x} = 0.6040$, $\bar{y} = 0.6588$, $\Sigma x^2 = 2.0288$, $\Sigma y^2 = 1.2667$, $\Sigma xy = 1.2802$.

Frogs and salamanders in moving dry air:
1. *Aneides lugubris* [2]
2. *Bufo boreas* [4]
3. *B. boreas* [3]
4. *B. terrestris* [4]
5. *Ensatina eschscholtzii xanthoptica (E. ensatina)* [2]
6. *Hyla cinerea* [4]
7. *H. regilla* [4]
8. *Rana aurora* [4]
9. *R. catesbeiana* [3]
10. *R. clamitans* [3]
11. *R. grylio* [4]
12. *R. pipiens* [4]
13. *R. pipiens* [3]
14. *R. sphenocephala* [4]
15. *Scaphiopus hammondi* [3]
16. *S. hammondi* [4]
17. *S. holbrookii* [4]
18. *Triturus torosus* [2]

Frogs in still dry air (all species from reference 5):
19. *Crinia signifera*
20. *Hyla ewingi*
21. *H. rubella*
22. *Limnodynastes dorsalis* [juvenile]
23. *L. dorsalis*
24. *L. ornatus*
25. *L. tasmaniensis* [juvenile]
26. *Neobatrachus centralis*
27. *N. pictus* [juvenile]
28. *N. pictus*
29. *Pseudophryne bibroni*

continued

111. WATER TURNOVER: GRAPHIC

Part IV. Amphibians

Contributor: Chew, Robert M.

References
[1] Adolph, E. F. 1932. Biol. Bull. 62:112.
[2] Cohen, N. W. 1952. Ecology 33:462.
[3] Thorson, T. 1955. Ibid. 36:100
[4] Thorson, T., and A. Svihla. 1943. Ibid. 24:374.
[5] Warburg, M. R. 1965. Australian J. Zool. 13:317.

FIGURE 2. RATE OF URINE FORMATION IN HYDRATED FROGS IN WATER AT 20°C

Original data were extrapolated to 20°C as necessary, on the basis of urine-temperature relationship from reference 1. Numbers accompanying dots refer to particular species (*see* appended list).

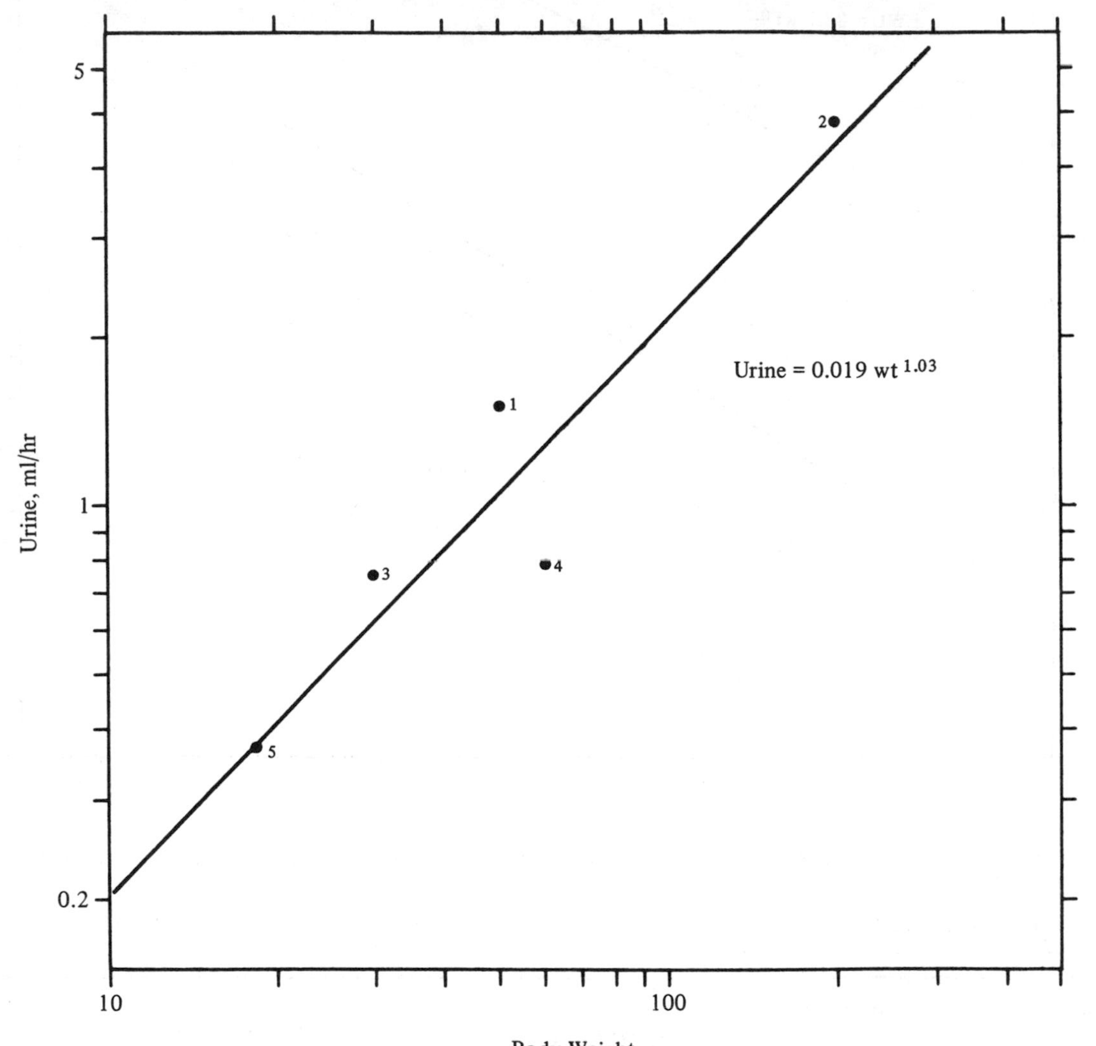

Log Urine, ml/hr = log 0.0191 + 1.028 log wt, g. n = 5, $\bar{x}$ = 1.7045, $\bar{y}$ = 0.03427, Σx^2 = 0.6043, Σy^2 = 0.7092, Σxy = 0.6212.

Frogs:
1. *Bufo cognatus* [4]
2. *B. marinus* [4]
3. *B. valliceps* [4]
4. *Rana clamitans* [3]
5. *R. pipiens* [2]

Contributor: Chew, Robert M.

References
[1] Adolph, E. F. 1927. Am. J. Physiol. 81:315.
[2] Adolph, E. F. 1927. J. Exptl. Zool. 47:1.
[3] Schmidt-Nielsen, B., and R. P. Forster. 1954. J. Cellular Comp. Physiol. 44:233.
[4] Shoemaker, V. H. 1965. Comp. Biochem. Physiol. 15:81.

112. WATER EXCRETION: AQUATIC ANIMALS

Values in parentheses are ranges, estimate "c" (*see* Introduction).

Part I. Mammals, Reptiles, and Amphibians

	Species (Synonym)	Excretion Rate	Remarks	Reference
			Mammalia	
1	*Aplodontia rufa*	(168-192) ml/kg/day	...	10
2		217.2 ml/kg/day	21 measurements	11
3		267 ± 25.7 ml/kg/day	21 subjects	18
4	*Megaptera novaeangliae (M. nodosa)*	11 ml/min	...	3,7
5	*Phoca vitulina*	(0.06-0.1) ml/min	1♀, 18 kg, fasting	14
6		1.0 ml/min	1♀, 18 kg, 4-7 hr after meal of herring	14
7		800 ml/day	Determined by cannulation; 20 young subjects, anesthetized	15,23
8	*Tursiops truncatus*	<50 ml/kg/day	Determined by catheterization; 2♀, 1.5 yr old; 1 measurement each	13
			Reptilia	
9	*Alligator mississippiensis*	(10.2-28.8) ml/kg/day	Determined by catheterization; body weight, 12.5 kg; hydrated	5
10		17 ml/kg/day	Determined by catheterization; 75 measurements; fasting	6
11		30 ml/kg/day	Determined by catheterization; 5 subjects, hydrated	6
12	*Malaclemys terrapin*	4.4 ± 1.8 ml/kg/day	Determined by cannulation; 10 measurements; in seawater	4
13	*centrata*	24 ± 4.6 ml/kg/day	Determined by cannulation; 7 measurements; in tap water	
14	*Natrix* spp.	66.24 ml/kg/day	22 subjects	16
15	*N. sipedon*	61.9 ml/kg/day	21 measurements for each kidney	8
16		69.1 ml/kg/day	Cannula to each kidney	
17	*Pseudemys scripta*	31.92 ml/kg/day	...	9
18	*P. scripta elegans (P. elegans)*	8.0 ml/kg/day	Measured during 4 hr at 6°C	6
			Amphibia	
19	*Ambystoma tigrinum*	249.6 ml/kg/day	9 larvae	2
20		304.8 ml/kg/day	3 larvae	
21		388.8 ml/kg/day	4 adults	
22		561.6 ml/kg/day	3 adults	
23	*Bufo marinus*	72 ml/kg/day	...	21
24	*B. regularis*	3 ml/hr	At 26°C	12
25	*Rana cancrivora*	0.4 ml/kg/hr	Determined by catheterization; temp, 27-31°C; in seawater	20
26		31.0 ml/kg/hr	Determined by catheterization; temp, 27-31°C; in freshwater	
27	*R. catesbeiana*	(36-49) ml/kg/day	...	17
28		54.8 ml/kg/day	4 subjects, fasting	22
29	*R. pipiens*	<17 ml/kg/hr	Determined from weight change; 27 measurements on adult subjects; temp, 18-23°C; water consumption through skin, 13 ml/kg/hr	1,19

Contributors: (a) Giere, Frederic A., (b) Fregley, Melvin J.

References

[1] Adolph, E. F. 1927. J. Exptl. Zool. 47:31.

[2] Alvarado, R. H., and S. P. Johnson. 1965. Comp. Biochem. Physiol. 16:531.

[3] Bentley, P. J. 1963. Ibid. 10:257.

[4] Bentley, P. J., W. L. Bretz, and K. Schmidt-Nielsen. 1967. J. Exptl. Biol. 46:161.

[5] Burgess, W. W., A. M. Harvey, and M. K. Marshall. 1933. J. Pharmacol. Exptl. Therap. 49:237.

[6] Coulson, R. A., and T. Hernandez. 1964. Biochemistry of the alligator. Louisiana State Univ. Press, Baton Rouge.

[7] Dalton, R. G. 1964. Brit. Vet. J. 120:69.

[8] Dantzler, W. H. 1967. Comp. Biochem. Physiol. 22:131.

[9] Dantzler, W. H., and B. Schmidt-Nielsen. 1966. Am. J. Physiol. 210:198.

[10] Dicker, S. E., and M. G. Eggleton. 1963. J. Physiol. (London) 167:35P.

[11] Dicker, S. E., and M. G. Eggleton. 1964. Ibid. 170:186.

[12] Ewer, R. F. 1951. J. Exptl. Biol. 28:374.

continued

112. WATER EXCRETION: AQUATIC ANIMALS

Part I. Mammals, Reptiles, and Amphibians

[13] Fetcher, E. S., and G. W. Fetcher. 1942. J. Cellular Comp. Physiol. 19:123.

[14] Hiatt, E. P., and R. B. Hiatt. 1942. Ibid. 19:221.

[15] Irving, L., K. C. Fisher, and F. C. McIntosh. 1935. Ibid. 6:387.

[16] Lebrie, S. J., and I. D. W. Sutherland. 1962. Am. J. Physiol. 203:995.

[17] Marshall, E. K. 1932. J. Cellular Comp. Physiol. 2:349.

[18] Nungesser, W. C., and E. W. Pfeiffer. 1965. Comp. Biochem. Physiol. 14:289.

[19] Rubenstein, B. B. 1935. J. Cellular Comp. Physiol. 6:85.

[20] Schmidt-Nielsen, K., and P. Lee. 1962. J. Exptl. Biol. 39:167.

[21] Shoemaker, V. H. 1965. Comp. Biochem. Physiol. 15:81.

[22] Smith, H. W. 1929. J. Biol. Chem. 81:727.

[23] Smith, H. W. 1935. J. Cellular Comp. Physiol. 7:465.

Part II. Fishes

	Species (Synonym)	Excretion Rate ml/kg/day[1]	Remarks	Reference
	Pisces			
	Freshwater			
1	*Amia calva*	14.4	Determined by catheterization; 1 subject, fasting	36
2	*Anguilla anguilla*	48.6	...	5
3		84.5(46.2-161)	Catheter into toy balloon; 11 measurements, ♂ and ♀; in freshwater	35
4		15.1 ± 2.07	Catheter into toy balloon; 7 measurements, ♂ and ♀; in seawater	35
5	(*A. vulgaris*)	(0.4-5.0)	Starved	37
6	*A. rostratus*	(0.4-5.0)	Water consumption, 50-200 ml/kg/day	37
7	(*A. chrysypa*)	(15-35)	Determined by catheterization; 2 subjects, fasting	36
8	*Carassius auratus*	(40-110)	...	20
9		52	Determined by catheterization; 4 subjects, fasting	36
10		(60-150)	...	37
11	*Catostomus commersonii*	(7-26)	Determined by catheterization; 8 subjects, fasting	15
12	*Cyprinus carpio*	51	Determined by catheterization; 6 subjects, fasting	36
13		(60-150)	...	37
14	*Fundulus kansae*	9 ± 1	In seawater for 3 days	40
15		21 ± 3	In seawater for 20 days	
16		200 ± 38	In fresh tap water	
17	*Ictalurus* spp. (*Ameiurus* spp.)	300(150-330)	...	23
18	*I. nebulosus* (*Ameiurus nebulosus*)	(51-79)	Determined by catheterization; 5 subjects, fasting	15
19	*Lepisosteus osseus*	19.2	Determined by catheterization; 1 subject, fasting	36
20	*Platichthys stellatus* (*P. flesus*)	24	In 4% saline	16
21	*Protopterus aethiopicus*	(4.9-5.6)	4-day experiment on 2 subjects	31
22	*Salmo gairdneri*	106.6	Determined by cannulation; 10 measurements; presmolt stage	18
23		49.7	Determined by cannulation; 14 measurements; smolt stage	18
24		110	Determined by cannulation; 8 measurements; postsmolt stage	18
25		101.8 ± 8	Determined by catheterization; 32 measurements on 1 subject	12
26	(*S. irideus*)	(60-106)	...	20
27		(75-90)	Determined by catheterization at 10°C	17
	Marine			
28	*Conger* spp.	(3-5)	...	4
29	*Cryptacanthodes maculatus*	(1.5-11.0)	8 subjects	22
30	*Hippocampus* spp.	(80-120)	12 measurements; body weight, 2-5 g	9
31	*Lophius piscatorius*	(12.9-54.4)	11 subjects	22
32		18	...	9
33		(20-30)	Body weight, 2-3 kg	4,37
34		29.4	1 subject	10
35		(1.0-1.5)[2]	After injection of 7.5 g urea in 15 ml water into tail	21

[1] Unless otherwise specified. [2] ml/kg/hr.

continued

Part II. Fishes

	Species (Synonym)	Excretion Rate ml/kg/day	Remarks	Reference
36	*Muraena* spp.	5(1.1-15)	3 measurements; body weight, 2-3 kg	9
37	*Myoxocephalus octodecem-*	(1.0-28.9)	....	13,30
38	*spinosus*	(2.6-23.5)	....	24
39		(11-40)	Starved	37
40		<40	Determined by catheterization; 76 measurements on 16 subjects; water consumption, 50-200 ml/kg/day	22
41		22.0	Indwelling catheter; 12 measurements	10
42		49.5	Indwelling catheter; 12 measurements	10
43		29.2	Indwelling catheter; in isotonic seawater bath for 24 hr	10
44	*M. scorpius*	(16.8-34.5)	Indwelling catheter; 2 subjects	10
45		26.2(9.8-42.0)	4 measurements on 1 subject	30
46	*Opsanus tau*	(0.6-9.4)	15 subjects	22
47		2.5(0.6-9.4)	In brackish water	13
48	*Scorpaena* spp.	(10-12)	....	4
49	*Syngnathus* spp.	80	10 measurements; body weight, 6-8 g	9
	Chondrichthyes			
	Freshwater			
50	*Pristis microdon*	250(150-460)	Body weight, 1.05-8.62 kg	38,39
	Marine			
51	*Mustelus canis*	11.4	Determined by catheterization; 8 subjects; cord severed at level of dorsal fin	8
52		15.4	Determined by catheterization; 8 subjects	8
53		15.8	Determined by catheterization	19
54		21.8	....	32,39
55	*Scyliorhinus caniculus*	1.5	Determined by catheterization; 2♀, fasting	29
56	*(Scyllium catulus)*	(4-5)	....	1
57	*Squalus acanthias*	(9.2-43.7)	Determined by catheterization; ♂	6
58		15.2(7.2-30.0)	Determined by catheterization; 2♂, 3♀	7
59		26.8(23.0-35.7)	Determined by catheterization; 12 measurements on ♂, fasting	33,34
60		32.5; 47.4	Values for 2 subjects, sexes not specified; determined by catheterization	11
61	*S. suckleyi*	1.4	....	38
62		33.6	....	41
	Agnatha			
	Freshwater			
63	*Lampetra fluviatilis*	45 ± 7	Cannula to balloon; in 100 mM NaCl	2
64		125 ± 8	Cannula to balloon; in 50 mM NaCl	2
65		213 ± 34	Cannula to balloon; in distilled water	2
66		245 ± 31	Cannula to balloon; in tap water	2
67		264	....	14
68		362	....	42
69		155.8	Determined by catheterization	25
70		341.9	Determined by membrane method	25
	Marine			
71	*Eptatretus stouti*	(4-10)	Polyethylene cannula implanted for 9 days	28
72	*Myxine* spp.	(1-8)	....	26
73	*M. glutinosa*	(1.0-8.5)	Determined by catheterization	27
74		5.4	....	
75	*Petromyzon marinus*	159	....	3

Contributors: (a) Giere, Frederic A., (b) Fregley, Melvin J.

continued

Part II. Fishes

References

[1] Baglioni, S. 1907. Beitr. Chem. Physiol. Pathol. 9:50.
[2] Bentley, P. J., and B. K. Follett. 1963. J. Physiol. (London) 169:902.
[3] Black, V. S. 1957. In M. E. Brown, ed. The physiology of fishes. Academic Press, New York. v. 1, pp. 163-205.
[4] Burian, R. 1909. Z. Biol. Tech. Methodik 1:383.
[5] Butler, D. G. 1966. Comp. Biochem. Physiol. 18: 773.
[6] Clarke, R. W., and H. W. Smith. 1932. J. Cellular Comp. Physiol. 1:131.
[7] Cohen, J. J., et al. 1959. Am. J. Physiol. 196:93.
[8] Denis, W. 1912. J. Biol. Chem. 13:225.
[9] Edwards, J. S., and L. Condorelli. 1928. Z. Biol. Tech. Methodik 86:383.
[10] Forster, R. P. 1953. J. Cellular Comp. Physiol. 42: 487.
[11] Forster, R. P., and F. Berglund. 1957. Ibid. 49:281.
[12] Fromm, P. O. 1963. Comp. Biochem. Physiol. 10: 121.
[13] Grafflin, A. L. 1931. Z. Biol. Tech. Methodik 97: 602.
[14] Hardisty, M. W. 1954. Nature 174:360.
[15] Haywood, C., and M. J. Clapp. 1942. Biol. Bull. 83:363.
[16] Henschel, J. 1936. Wiss. Meeresuntersuch. Abt. Kiel 22:89.
[17] Holmes, R. M. 1961. Rept. Challenger Soc. Cambridge 3:13,23.
[18] Holmes, W. N., and I. M. Stainer. 1966. J. Exptl. Biol. 44:33.
[19] Kempton, R. T. 1953. Biol. Bull. 104:45.
[20] Krogh, A. 1937. Z. Vergleich. Physiol. 24:656.
[21] Malvin, R., and I. B. Fritz. 1962. J. Cellular Comp. Physiol. 59:111.
[22] Marshall, E. K. 1930. Am. J. Physiol. 94:1.
[23] Marshall, E. K. 1934. Physiol. Rev. 14:133.
[24] Marshall, E. K., and A. L. Grafflin. 1932. J. Cellular Comp. Physiol. 1:161.
[25] Morris, R. 1956. J. Exptl. Biol. 33:325.
[26] Morris, R. 1960. Symp. Zool. Soc. London 1:1.
[27] Morris, R. 1965. J. Exptl. Biol. 42:359.
[28] Munz, F. W., and W. N. McFarland. 1964. Comp. Biochem. Physiol. 13:381.
[29] Perks, A. M. 1959. Ph.D. Thesis. St. Andrews Univ., Scotland.
[30] Pitts, R. F. 1934. J. Cellular Comp. Physiol. 4:389.
[31] Sawyer, W. H. 1966. Am. J. Physiol. 210:191.
[32] Scott, G. G. 1913. Ann. N.Y. Acad. Sci. 23:1.
[33] Shannon, J. A. 1934. J. Cellular Comp. Physiol. 4:211.
[34] Shannon, J. A. 1940. Ibid. 16:285.
[35] Sharratt, B. M., I. C. Jones, and D. Bellamy. 1964. Comp. Biochem. Physiol. 11:9.
[36] Smith, H. W. 1929. J. Biol. Chem. 81:727.
[37] Smith, H. W. 1930. Am. J. Physiol. 93:480.
[38] Smith, H. W. 1931. Ibid. 98:279.
[39] Smith, H. W. 1936. Biol. Rev. Cambridge Phil. Soc. 11:49.
[40] Stanley, J. G., and W. R. Flemming. 1964. Science 144:63.
[41] White, F. D. 1931. Contrib. Can. Biol. Fisheries 6: 343.
[42] Wikgren, B. 1953. Acta Zool. Fennica 71:1.

Part III. Invertebrates

	Species (Synonym)	Excretion Rate	Remarks	Reference
	Arthropoda			
1	*Anabolia nervosa*	(18-114) µl/g/day	In tap water	38
2	*Astacus astacus (A. fluviatilis)*	8.2% body wt/day	At 20°C	5
3	*(Potamobius astacus)*	0.18%,body wt/hr	...	13
4		3.7% body wt/day	At 13-14°C	13
5		4.0% body wt/day	...	33
6	*Cambarus* spp.	0.22% body wt/hr	In freshwater	15
7	*Cancer* sp.	(3-10.0)% body wt/day	In 100% seawater	30
8	*Cancer* spp.	(0.13-0.42)% body wt/hr	In seawater	30
9	*Carcinus maenas*	0.42% body wt/hr	...	22
10		5.0% body wt/day	...	39
11		7.2% body wt/day	In 66% seawater	3
12		10.0% body wt/day	Pores closed by wax	22
13		4.0% body wt/day	In 100% seawater	36
14		6.0% body wt/day	In 90% seawater	36
15		10.8% body wt/day	In 80% seawater	36
16		28.0(20.5-35.2)% body wt/day	In 40% seawater	36

continued

Part III. Invertebrates

	Species (Synonym)	Excretion Rate	Remarks	Reference
17	*Corixa dentipes*	16.6 µl/day	One measurement; body weight, 87 g	37
18	*Dysdercus fasciatus*	(5-20) µl/day	Measured throughout 4th instar; no urine during instars 5-8	2
19	*Eriocheir* spp.	0.18% body wt/hr	....	32
20	*E. sinensis*	4.0% body wt/day	....	33
21	*Gammarus duebeni*	56% body wt/day	....	17
22	*Homarus americanus*	4.8% body wt/day	....	7
23		(4.8-19.2)% body wt/day	Rate higher when subject is injected with fluid	6
24	*Maja* spp.	0.13% body wt/hr	In seawater	4
25	*Orconectes virilis*	3% body wt/day	At 16°C	29
26	*Palaemon longirostris*	68.0% body wt/day	Determined by cannulation; 1 subject; in 7% seawater	24
27	*Palaemonetes antennarius*	45.9% body wt/day	Determined by dye excretion; 49 measurements; in freshwater	24
28		60.6% body wt/day	Determined by dye excretion; 57 measurements; in freshwater	
29	*P. varians*	0.40% body wt/hr	Determined from weight change; 4 measurements	23
30		(0.46-0.55)% body wt/hr	Determined by cannulation; 12 measurements	
31		3.6% body wt/day	In 50% seawater	
32		10.0% body wt/day	In 100% seawater	
33		39.1% body wt/day	In 5% seawater	
34	*Potamon niloticus*	(0.05-0.6)% body wt/day	Determined from weight change	35
35	*Procambarus clarkii*	4.9% body wt/day	Pores in one-third of subjects cemented	19
36	(*Cambarus clarkii*)	5.2% body wt/day	Pores cemented 4-8 hr	15
37	*Rhodnius prolixus*	10.8 µl/hr 1/	At 15°C	18
38		42.0 µl/hr 1/	At 25°C	
39		66.0 µl/hr 1/	At 35°C	
40	*Sialis lutaria*	<3% body wt/day	Determined from weight change	34
			Mollusca	
41	*Achatina fulica*	120.0% body wt/day	Kidney duct catheterized	21
42	*Anodonta* spp.	1.9 ml/hr	At 15°C	27
43		2.37 ml/day	Determined from filtration rate into pericardium; 10 subjects; body weight, 50 g; temp, 17°C	26
44	*A. cygnea*	1.9 ml/hr	Determined from weight change; 4 subjects; temp, 15°C	27
45		470.0/ body wt/day	Pericardium open	25
46	*Haliotis rufescens*	(12.4-50.4)% body wt/day	Determined by catheterization; 11 subjects	11
47	*Octopus dofleini*	4.8% body wt/day	Sacs catheterized	28
48		6.6(2.2-12.5)% body wt/day	Sacs catheterized; 25 subjects	12
49	(*O. hongkongensis*)	6.2% body wt/day	Sacs tied	20
50		10.0% body wt/day	Sacs catheterized	10
51	*O. vulgaris*	2.0% body wt/day	Sacs tied	8
52	*Sepia officinalis*	4.3% body wt/day	Determined by sucrose excretion	31
53	*Viviparus viviparus*	36.0(20.2-53.3)% body wt/day	Determined by catheterization; 10 subjects; in tap water	16
54		131.0(24.5-184.3)% body wt/day	Determined by radioactive inulin; 5 subjects; in tap water	
			Aschelminthes	
55	*Asplanchna* spp.	493 μ^3/sec	In 0.2% saline	9
56		1321 μ^3/sec	In 0.1% saline	
57		1972 μ^3/sec	In freshwater	
58	*Nippostrongylus brasiliensis* (*N. muris*)	246 μ^3/min	In saline	40
59		530 μ^3/min	In distilled water	

1/ Excretion rate is dependent on ambient temperature.

continued

112. WATER EXCRETION: AQUATIC ANIMALS

Part III. Invertebrates

	Species (Synonym)	Excretion Rate	Remarks	Reference
	Protozoa			
60	*Amoeba lacerata*	1.0 μ^3/100 μ^3 protoplast/min	In 50% seawater	14
61		6.5 μ^3/100 μ^3 protoplast/min	In 5% seawater	
62	*A. proteus*	88(11-220) μ^3/sec	....	1

Contributors: (a) Fregley, Melvin J., (b) Giere, Frederic A.

References

[1] Adolph, E. F. 1926. J. Exptl. Zool. 44:355.
[2] Berridge, M. J. 1965. J. Exptl. Biol. 43:511.
[3] Bethe, A., E. von Holst, and E. Huf. 1935. Arch. Ges. Physiol. 235:330.
[4] Bialaszewicz, K. 1932. Arch. Intern. Physiol. 35:98.
[5] Bryan, G. W. 1960. J. Exptl. Biol. 37:83.
[6] Burger, J. W. 1953. Bull. Mt. Desert Isl. Biol. Lab. 37-39.
[7] Burger, J. W. 1957. Biol. Bull. 113:207.
[8] Fürth, O. von. 1900. Z. Physiol. Chem. 31:353.
[9] Green, J. 1957. Nature 179:432.
[10] Harrison, F. L. M. 1954. Ph. D. Thesis. Univ. Washington, Seattle.
[11] Harrison, F. M. 1962. J. Exptl. Biol. 39:179.
[12] Harrison, F. M., and A. W. Martin. 1965. Ibid. 42:71.
[13] Herrmann, F. 1931. Z. Vergleich. Physiol. 14:479.
[14] Hopkins, D. L. 1946. Biol. Bull. 90:158.
[15] Lienemann, L. J. 1938. J. Cellular Comp. Physiol. 11:149.
[16] Little, C. 1965. J. Exptl. Biol. 43:39.
[17] Lockwood, A. P. M. 1961. Ibid. 38:647.
[18] Maddrell, S. H. P. 1964. Ibid. 41:163.
[19] Maluf, N. S. R. 1941. Biol. Bull. 81:235.
[20] Martin, A. W. 1957. Invertebrate physiology. Univ. Oregon Press, Eugene. p. 247.
[21] Martin, A. W., F. M. Harrison, and D. M. Stewart. 1953. Proc. Intern. Physiol. Congr., 19th, p. 592.
[22] Nagel, H. 1934. Z. Vergleich. Physiol. 21:468.
[23] Parry, G. 1955. J. Exptl. Biol. 32:408.
[24] Parry, G. 1957. Ibid. 34:417.
[25] Picken, L. E. R. 1936. Ibid. 13:309.
[26] Picken, L. E. R. 1937. Ibid. 14:20.
[27] Potts, W. T. W. 1954. Ibid. 31:614.
[28] Potts, W. T. W. 1965. Comp. Biochem. Physiol. 14:339.
[29] Riegel, J. A. 1961. J. Exptl. Biol. 38:291.
[30] Robertson, J. D. 1939. Ibid. 16:387.
[31] Robertson, J. D. 1953. Ibid. 30:277.
[32] Scholles, W. 1933. Z. Vergleich. Physiol. 19:183.
[33] Scholles, W. 1933. Ibid. 19:522.
[34] Shaw, J. 1955. J. Exptl. Biol. 32:353.
[35] Shaw, J. 1959. Ibid. 36:157.
[36] Shaw, J. 1961. Ibid. 38:135.
[37] Staddon, B. W. 1964. Ibid. 41:609.
[38] Sutcliffe, D. W. 1962. Ibid. 39:41.
[39] Webb, D. A. 1940. Proc. Roy. Soc. (London), B, 129:107.
[40] Weinstein, P. P. 1952. Exptl. Parasitol. 1:363.

113. RENAL FUNCTION TESTS: VERTEBRATES

Part I. Man

For information on liver function tests, *see* Table 40. Values in parentheses are ranges, estimate "b" unless otherwise indicated (*see* Introduction).

	Specification	Method or Condition	Subjects: Age	Subjects: No.	Value	Reference
1	Renal blood flow, ml/min/ 1.73 m² body surface area	Calculated from renal plasma flow divided by 1 minus hematocrit	16-60 yr	61♂	1209(697-1721)	41,43
2			<20-45 yr	27♂	1076(660-1492)	7
3			20-29 yr	9♂	1077(777-1377)	11
4			30-39 yr	9♂	1181(727-1635)	11
5			40-49 yr	10♂	1008(596-1420)	11
6			50-59 yr	11♂	849(603-1095)	11
7			60-69 yr	10♂	775(497-1053)	11
8			70-79 yr	9♂	589(323-855)	11

continued

113. RENAL FUNCTION TESTS: VERTEBRATES

Part I. Man

	Specification	Method or Condition	Subjects: Age	Subjects: No.	Value	Reference
9			80-89 yr	12♂	475(193-757)	11
10			16-55 yr	17♀	982(614-1350)	41,43
11			<20-45 yr	23♀	973(503-1443)	7
12			<20-45 yr	19♀ 1/	1359(881-1837)	7
13			<20-40 yr	13♀ 2/	919(451-1387)	7
14			Adult	31♀ 3/	962(602-1322)	9
15	Renal plasma flow, ml/min/1.73 m^2 body surface area	Determined by Diodrast clearance without correction for extraction ratio	2-8 days	5	72.7	12
16		Determined by *p*-aminohippurate clearance without correction for extraction ratio	4-28 days	7 4/	148.6	1
17			10-22 days	4	228.5	39
18			37-95 days	8 4/	203.2	2
19			1-5.9 mo	8	326.1	39
20			6-11.7 mo	10	480.3	39
21			12-19 mo	11	518.9(319.9-717.9)	39
22			2-12 yr	19	654(413-895)	39
23		Determined by Diodrast clearance; constant infusion technique	16-60 yr	61♂	697(425-969)	41,43
24			20-29 yr	9♂	613.5(464.3-762.7)	11
25			21-25 yr	10♂	600(388-812)	5
26			30-39 yr	9♂	649.3(414.5-884.1)	11
27			40-49 yr	10♂	573.8(350.6-797.0)	11
28			50-59 yr	11♂	500.4(326.4-674.4)	11
29			60-69 yr	10♂	442.1(281.7-602.5)	11
30			70-79 yr	9♂	354.0(187.2-520.8)	11
31			80-89 yr	12♂	288.8(111.6-466.0)	11
32			16-55 yr	17♀	594(390-798)	41,43
33			19-27 yr	10♀	628(428-828)	5
34			<20-45 yr	19♀ 1/	800(498-1102)	7
35			<20-40 yr	13♀ 2/	571(393-749)	7
36			Adult	34♀ 3/	617(397-837)	9
37		Determined by *p*-aminohippurate clearance; constant infusion technique	16-49 yr	30♂	654(328-980)	42
38			21-32 yr	9♂	613(399-827)	8
39			Adult	8♂	628(538-718)	6
40			Adult	8♂	603(435-771)	8
41			Adult	11♀	592(286-898)	42
42		Determined by *p*-aminohippurate clearance; subcutaneous injection technique	<20-45 yr	27♂	557(251-863)	7
43			<20-45 yr	23♀	557(271-843)	
44	Glomerular filtration rate, ml/min/1.73 m^2 body surface area	Determined by inulin or mannitol clearance	2-8 days	14	38.5(16.7-60.3)	12,32,38,39
45			4-28 days	20 4/	45.1(26.1-64.1)	1,2,46
46			10-22 days	18	50.4(32.2-68.6)	32,39
47			37-95 days	11 4/	58.2(30.2-86.2)	2,46
48			1-5.9 mo	14	76.6(39.4-113.8)	38,39
49			6-11.7 mo	10	103.2(49.4-157.0)	39
50			12-19 mo	11	126.7(62.1-191.3)	39
51			2-12 yr	37	127.0(89.4-164.6)	3,38,39
52		Determined by inulin clearance; constant infusion technique	16-49 yr	34♂	124.0(72.4-175.6)	42
53			16-60 yr	67♂	131(88-174)	41,43
54			18-45 yr	25♂	140(76-204)	27
55			20-29 yr	9♂	122.8(90.0-155.6)	11
56			21-25 yr	10♂	125(116.2-133.8)	5
57			28-60 yr	24♂	136(97.4-174.6)	41,43
58			30-39 yr	9♂	115.0(93.4-136.6)	11
59			40-49 yr	10♂	121.2(74.6-167.8)	11

1/ Pregnant, 2-8 lunar months. 2/ Pregnant, 9 and 10 lunar months. 3/ Pregnant, near term. 4/ Premature infants.

continued

113. RENAL FUNCTION TESTS: VERTEBRATES

Part I. Man

	Specification	Method or Condition	Subjects		Value	Reference
			Age	No.		
60			50-59 yr	11♂	99.3(70.1-128.5)	11
61			60-69 yr	10♂	96(45-147)	11
62			70-79 yr	9♂	89.0(49.4-128.6)	11
63			80-89 yr	12♂	65.3(24.5-106.1)	11
64			Adult	8♂	130(99.2-160.8)	6
65			Adult	26♂	126(91.8-160.2)	4
66			16-55 yr	10♀	115(89.4-140.6)	41,43
67			16-55 yr	21♀	117(85.8-148.2)	41,43
68			19-27 yr	10♀	118(90.2-145.8)	5
69			<20-40 yr	10♀[2]	156(95-217)	7
70			Adult	8♀	119(111-127)	28
71			Adult	16♀	109(82-136)	42
72			Adult	19♀[5]	183(139-227)	28
73			Adult	12♀[6]	129(43-215)	28
74			Adult	57♀[3]	126(68.6-183.4)	9
75			Adult	10♀[3]	131(67-195)	10
76			Adult	8♀[7]	126(94-158)	10
77		Determined by inulin clearance; single intravenous injection technique	<20-45 yr	27♂	118(79-157)	7
78			20-50 yr	36♂	124.0(97.4-150.6)	24
79			<20-45 yr	23♀	122(73.4-170.6)	7
80			<20-45 yr	17♀[1]	170(123.6-216.4)	7
81			20-50 yr	20♀	119(93.4-144.6)	24
82	Filtration fraction, %	Calculated from glomerular filtration rate divided by renal plasma flow	2-8 days	5	0.49	12
83			4-28 days	7[4]	0.34	1
84			10-22 days	3	0.24	39
85			37-95 days	8[4]	0.33	2
86			1-5.9 mo	6	0.24	39
87			6-11.7 mo	10	0.22(0.08-0.36)	39
88			12-19 mo	11	0.25(0.15-0.35)	39
89			2-12 yr	19	0.20(0.12-0.28)	39
90			16-49 yr	31♂	0.192(0.122-0.262)	42
91			16-60 yr	61♂	0.19(0.142-0.238)	41,43
92			<20-45 yr	27♂	0.216(0.152-0.28)	7
93			20-29 yr	9♂	0.201(0.175-0.227)	11
94			21-25 yr	10♂	0.214(0.144-0.284)	5
95			30-39 yr	9♂	0.184(0.112-0.256)	11
96			40-49 yr	10♂	0.213(0.149-0.277)	11
97			50-59 yr	11♂	0.205(0.145-0.265)	11
98			60-69 yr	10♂	0.215(0.147-0.283)	11
99			70-79 yr	9♂	0.262(0.104-0.420)	11
100			80-89 yr	12♂	0.229(0.153-0.305)	11
101			16-55 yr	17♀	0.202(0.140-0.264)	41,43
102			19-27 yr	10♀	0.189(0.155-0.223)	5
103			<20-45 yr	23♀	0.227(0.131-0.323)	7
104			<20-45 yr	17♀[1]	0.221(0.117-0.325)	7
105			<20-40 yr	10♀[2]	0.289(0.211-0.367)	7
106			Adult	26♀[3]	19.5	9
107			Adult	11♀	0.194(0.116-0.272)	42
108	Concentrating capacity (maximal urinary osmolality), milliosmoles/kg H_2O	Determined after 12-18 hr of water deprivation	7-40 days	25	(600-1100)[c]	13,14
109			2 mo-3 yr	42	63[8]	47
110			3-15 yr	16	1069(813-1325)	47
111			2-16 yr	250	1089(870-1309)	15

1/ Pregnant, 2-8 lunar months. 2/ Pregnant, 9 and 10 lunar months. 3/ Pregnant, near term. 4/ Premature infants. 5/ Pregnant less than 38 weeks. 6/ Pregnant more than 37 weeks. 7/ From group of 10 subjects in preceding line of data; second week postpartum. 8/ Milliosmoles/kg = 416 log age (days).

continued

113. RENAL FUNCTION TESTS: VERTEBRATES

Part I. Man

	Specification	Method or Condition	Subjects: Age	Subjects: No.	Value	Reference
112			Adult	63	1027(807-1247)	25
113			Adult	26	1058(762-1354)	26
114			Adult	32	1076(741-1411)	20
115		Determined after 24 hr of water deprivation	Adult	14	1189(967-1342)	30
116	Urinary pH	Determined after 3-5 days of ammonium chloride administration	11-45 days	3[4,9]	4.8(4.7-4.9)[c]	22
117			51-122 days	3[9]	4.9(4.6-5.0)[c]	22
118			3-4 mo	4[10]	4.7(4.3-5.0)[c]	19
119			2-6 mo	4[9]	5.0(4.6-5.4)[c]	19
120			2-12 mo	12[9]	(4.6-6.4)[c]	36
121			2-16 yr	11	(4.7-5.6)[c]	36
122			Adult	20	5.1(4.6-5.6)[c]	18
123		Determined during 5-8 hr after acute administration of ammonium or calcium chloride	7 days	8[10]	5.2	23
124			1-16 mo	11[9]	4.83(4.5-5.05)[c]	16
125			4-15 yr	52	4.8(4.55-5.1)[c]	17
126			Adult	9	4.8(4.6-5.2)[c]	48
127			Adult	8	4.85	23
	Urea clearance, ml/min/1.73 m^2 body surface area					
128	Whole blood	Calculated from urea concentration in urine times urine flow, divided by urea concentration in blood	2-28 days	26	(17-34)[c]	31
129			54-356 days	21	(35-55)[c]	
130			2-13 yr	69	(72-78)[c]	
131		Calculated from urea concentration in urine times urine flow (2 ml/min/1.73 m^2 body surface area), divided by urea concentration in blood	2-8 days	4	23.2	12
132			4-28 days	21[4]	31.5(20.5-42.5)	1
133			10-22 days	6	36.0	39
134			37-95 days	8[4]	40.0	2
135			1-5.9 mo	10	55.4(23.2-87.6)	39,40
136			6-11.7 mo	8	67.9	39,40
137			12-19 mo	8	71.1	39
138			2-12 yr	24	75.0(38.0-112.0)	33,39
139		Calculated as maximal or standard clearance according to Møller, McIntosh, & Van Slyke [35]	40-49 yr	20♂	95(66.2-123.8)	29
140			50-59 yr	20♂	86(44.8-127.2)	
141			60-69 yr	20♂	82(47.2-116.8)	
142			70-79 yr	20♂	65(30-100)	
143			80-89 yr	20♂	61(11-111)	
144	Plasma	Determined simultaneously with inulin clearance; urine flow greater than 2 ml/min	....	10♀[3]	79(21-137)	10
145			....	8♀[7]	77(45-109)	
146	Urinary hydrogen excretion (titratable acid), µEq/min/1.73 m^2 body surface area	Determined after 3-5 days of ammonium chloride administration	11-45 days	3[4,9]	43(36-46)[c]	22
147			51-122 days	3[9]	62(59-64)[c]	22
148			3-4 mo	4[10]	15(9-18)[c]	19
149			2-6 mo	4[9]	79(58-95)[c]	
150			2-12 mo	12[9]	42(21-72)[c]	19
151			2-16 yr	11	27(14-43)[c]	36
152			Adult	20	34(26-47)[c]	18
153		Determined during 5-8 hr after acute administration of ammonium or calcium chloride	7 days	8[10]	3.5(0-8.1)	23
154			1-16 mo	11[9]	62(43-111)[c]	16
155			4-15 yr	52	52(33-71)[c]	17
156			Adult	9	38(24-51)[c]	48
157			Adult	8	29.1(17.5-40.7)	23
158	Urinary hydrogen excretion (ammonium), µEq/min/1.73 m^2 body surface area	Determined after 3-5 days of ammonium chloride administration	11-45 days	3[4,9]	48(44-51)[c]	22
159			51-122 days	3[9]	82(76-92)[c]	22
160			3-4 mo	4[10]	50(37-58)[c]	19
161			2-6 mo	4[9]	118(106-141)[c]	19
162			2-12 mo	12[9]	62(20-111)[c]	36

3/ Pregnant, near term. 4/ Premature infants. 7/ From group of 10 subjects in preceding line of data; second week postpartum. 9/ Cow's milk diet. 10/ Human milk diet.

continued

113. RENAL FUNCTION TESTS: VERTEBRATES

Part I. Man

	Specification	Method or Condition	Subjects		Value	Reference
			Age	No.		
163			2-16 yr	11	59(46-73)[c]	36
164			Adult	20	91(34-154)[c]	18
165		Determined during 5-8 hr after acute	7 days	8[10]	15.0(5.2-24.8)	23
166		administration of ammonium or calcium	1-16 mo	11[9]	57(42-79)[c]	16
167		chloride	4-15 yr	52	73(46-100)[c]	17
168			Adult	9	50(33-75)[c]	48
169			Adult	8	37.5(19.1-55.9)	23
170	*p*-Aminohippurate Tm	Calculated as rate of *p*-aminohippurate	4-28 days	7[4]	12.9	1
171	(excretory), mg/min/1.73	excretion in urine minus rate of *p*-	10-22 days	6	21.4	39
172	m^2 body surface area	aminohippurate filtration	37-95 days	8	17.2	2
173			1-5.9 mo	9	51.4	39
174			6-11.7 mo	8	50.5	39
175			12-19 mo	9	61.2(18.8-103.6)	39
176			2-12 yr	18	73.7(35.9-111.5)	39
177			16-49 yr	35♂	79.8(46.4-113.2)	42
178			20-29 yr	1♂	108.7	45
179			30-39 yr	6♂	87.7(61.9-113.5)	45
180			40-49 yr	11♂	79.4(60.4-98.4)	45
181			50-59 yr	8♂	72.2(40.6-103.8)	45
182			60-69 yr	17♂	66.2(39.6-92.8)	45
183			70-79 yr	17♂	59.4(34.2-84.6)	45
184			80-89 yr	10♂	38.6(11.4-65.8)	45
185			Adult	8♂	65.6(48.2-83.0)	6
186			Adult	43♂	77.2	42
187			Adult	16♀	77.2(55.6-98.8)	42
188	Diodrast Tm (excretory),	Calculated as rate of Diodrast excretion	16-60 yr	40♂	51.8(34.4-69.2)	41,43
189	mg I/min/1.73 m^2 body	in urine minus rate of Diodrast filtration	20-29 yr	9♂	54.6(35.6-73.6)	11
190	surface area		21-25 yr	10♂	50.6(37.6-63.6)	5
191			30 39 yr	9♂	51.0 (33.8-68.2)	11
192			40-49 yr	10♂	49.9(30.3-69.5)	11
193			50-59 yr	11♂	45.3(32.7-57.9)	11
194			60-69 yr	10♂	44.5(26.3-62.7)	11
195			70-79 yr	9♂	39.0(24.4-53.6)	11
196			80-89 yr	12♂	30.8(11.2-50.4)	11
197			Adult	82♂	50	42
198			16-55 yr	14♀	42.6(23.6-61.6)	41,43
199			19-27 yr	10♀	44.2(34.6-53.8)	5
200	Glucose Tm (absorptive),	Calculated as rate of glucose filtration	4-28 days	3[4]	77	46
201	mg/min/1.73 m^2 body	minus rate of glucose excretion in urine	37-95 days	3[4]	104	46
202	surface area		2-12 yr	6	543(285-801)	21
203			20-29 yr	3♂	358.7(324-395)[c]	34
204			28-60 yr	24♂	375(215-535)	41,43
205			30-39 yr	9♂	333.6(221.0-446.2)	34
206			40-49 yr	12♂	315.1(224.7-405.5)	34
207			50-59 yr	14♂	308.2(178.2-438.2)	34
208			60-69 yr	14♂	260.2(131.0-389.4)	34
209			70-79 yr	15♂	239.3(146.5-332.1)	34
210			80-89 yr	9♂	219.2(118.8-319.6)	34
211			16-55 yr	11♀	303(193-413)	41,43
212	Bicarbonate Tm (absorp-	Calculated as rate of bicarbonate filtra-	8-36 days	4[4]	(2.5-2.6)[c]	48
213	tive), mM/100 ml glom-	tion minus rate of bicarbonate excre-	1-12 mo	6	(2.6-2.9)[c]	44
214	erular filtrate	tion in urine	Adult	3	(2.8-3.0)[c]	37
215	Renal bicarbonate thres-	Determined during continuous infusion	8-36 days	4[4]	(22-25)[c]	44
216	hold, mM/liter serum bi-	of sodium bicarbonate	1-12 mo	6	(21.5-22.5)[c]	16
217	carbonate		Adult	3	(26-28)[c]	37

[4] Premature infants. [9] Cow's milk diet. [10] Human milk diet.

continued

113. RENAL FUNCTION TESTS: VERTEBRATES

Part I. Man

Contributors: (a) Lauson, Henry D., (b) Edelmann, Chester M., Jr., and Barnett, Henry L.

References

[1] Barnett, H. L., et al. 1948. J. Clin. Invest. 27:691.
[2] Barnett, H. L., et al. 1948. Proc. Soc. Exptl. Biol. Med. 69:55.
[3] Barnett, H. L., et al. 1949. Pediatrics 3:418.
[4] Berger, E. Y., S. J. Farber, and D. P. Earle, Jr. 1947. Proc. Soc. Exptl. Biol. Med. 66:62.
[5] Brun, C., T. Hilden, and F. Raaschou. 1947. Acta Med. Scand. 127:464.
[6] Brun, C., T. Hilden, and F. Raaschou. 1947. Ibid. 127:471.
[7] Bucht, H. 1951. Scand. J. Clin. Lab. Invest., Suppl. 3.
[8] Chapman, C. B., et al. 1948. J. Clin. Invest. 27:639.
[9] Chesley, L. C. 1951. Med. Clin. N. Am. 35:699.
[10] Chesley, L. C., and L. O. Williams. 1945. Am. J. Obstet. Gynecol. 50:367.
[11] Davies, D. F., and N. W. Shock. 1950. J. Clin. Invest. 29:496.
[12] Dean, R. F. A., and R. A. McCance. 1947. J. Physiol. (London) 106:431.
[13] Edelmann, C. M., Jr., and H. L. Barnett. 1960. J. Pediat. 56:154.
[14] Edelmann, C. M., Jr., H. L. Barnett, and V. Troupkou. 1960. J. Clin. Invest. 39:1062.
[15] Edelmann, C. M., Jr., et al. 1967. Am. J. Diseases Children 114(6):639.
[16] Edelmann, C. M., Jr., et al. 1967. J. Clin. Invest. 46: 1309.
[17] Edelmann, C. M., Jr., et al. 1967. Pediat. Res. 1:452.
[18] Elkinton, J. R., et al. 1960. Am. J. Med. 29:554.
[19] Fomon, S. J., D. M. Harris, and R. L. Jensen. 1959. Pediatrics 23:113.
[20] Frank, M. N., et al. 1957. Am. J. Med. Sci. 233:121.
[21] Galan, E., et al. 1947. Arch. Med. Enfants 26:102.
[22] Gordon, H. H., H. McNamara, and H. R. Benjamin. 1948. Pediatrics 2:290.
[23] Hatemi, N., and R. A. McCance. 1961. Acta Paediat. 50:603.
[24] Hogeman, O. 1948. Acta Med. Scand., Suppl. 216a.
[25] Isaacson, L. C. 1960. Lancet 1:467.
[26] Jacobson, M. H., et al. 1962. Arch. Internal Med. 110:121.
[27] Josephson, B., and O. Lindahl. 1943-44. Acta Med. Scand. 116:20.
[28] Lange, W. A., D. G. Johnson, and R. W. Bonsnes. Unpublished. Cornell Univ. Medical College, New York, 1953.
[29] Lewis, W. H., Jr., and A. S. Alving. 1938. Am. J. Physiol. 123:500.
[30] Lindeman, R. D., H. C. Van Buren, and L. G. Raisz. 1960. New Engl. J. Med. 262:1306.
[31] McCance, R. A., and E. M. Widdowson. 1952. Lancet 263-860.
[32] McCrory, W. W., et al. 1952. J. Clin. Invest. 31:357.
[33] McIntosh, J. F., E. Møller, and D. D. Van Slyke. 1929. Ibid. 6:467.
[34] Miller, J. H., R. K. McDonald, and N. W. Shock. 1952. J. Gerontol. 7:196.
[35] Møller, E., J. F. McIntosh, and D. D. Van Slyke. 1929. J. Clin. Invest. 6:427.
[36] Peonides, A., B. Levin, and W. F. Young. 1965. Arch. Disease Childhood 40:33.
[37] Pitts, R. F., J. L. Ayer, and W. A. Schiess. 1949. J. Clin. Invest. 28:35.
[38] Richmond, J. B., et al. 1951. Proc. Soc. Exptl. Biol. Med. 77:83.
[39] Rubin, M. I., E. Bruck, and M. Rapoport. 1949. J. Clin. Invest. 28:1144.
[40] Schoenthal, L., D. Lurie, and M. Kelly. 1933. Am. J. Diseases Children 45:41.
[41] Smith, H. W. 1943. Lectures on the kidney. Univ. Kansas, Lawrence.
[42] Smith, H. W. 1951. The kidney. Oxford Univ. Press, New York.
[43] Smith, H. W., et al. 1943. J. Mt. Sinai Hosp. N.Y. 10:59.
[44] Tudvad, F., H. McNamara, and H. L. Barnett. 1954. Pediatrics 13:4.
[45] Watkin, D. M. Unpublished. Natl. Institutes of Health, Bethesda, Md., 1953.
[46] Weintraub, D. H., et al. 1952. Proc. Soc. Exptl. Biol. Med. 81:542.
[47] Winberg, J. 1954. Acta Paediat. 48:1.
[48] Wrong, O., and H. E. F. Davies. 1959. Quart J. Med. 28:259.

Part II. Vertebrates Other Than Man

Unit of Measurement: C_C/C_{PAH} = creatinine clearance divided by *p*-aminohippurate clearance; C_C/C_D = creatinine clearance divided by Diodrast clearance; C_I/C_{PAH} = inulin clearance divided by *p*-aminohippurate clearance; C_I/C_D = inulin clearance divided by Diodrast clearance.

	Animal	Specification: Method	Specification: Unit of Measurement	Subjects: Age	Subjects: No.	Value	Reference
1	Cat	Creatinine clearance	ml/min	....	2	18.8(17.6-19.9)	17
2		*p*-Aminohippurate clearance	ml/min	....	2	59.5(59.3-59.8)	17
3		Filtration fraction	C_C/C_{PAH}	....	7	0.31(0.23-0.46)	17
4		Tubular maxima, *p*-aminohippurate	mg/min	....	...	4.2	17

continued

113. RENAL FUNCTION TESTS: VERTEBRATES

Part II. Vertebrates Other Than Man

	Animal	Specification: Method	Specification: Unit of Measurement	Subjects: Age	Subjects: No.	Value	Reference
5	Cattle	Inulin clearance	ml/min	1-2 wk	3♀	112(100-128)	49
6				6-10 wk	4♀	169(139-186)	49
7				1.5-2.5 yr	4♀[1]	151(142-216)	49
8			ml/min/kg	Adult	10♀[2]	1.84(1.30-2.20)	47
9		Creatinine clearance	ml/min	1-2 wk	3♀	129(103-148)	49
10				6-10 wk	4♀	179(160-227)	49
11				1.5-2.5 yr	4♀[1]	189(156-217)	49
12			liters/hr/	Heifer	4	5.51(3.77-7.25)	65
13			100 lb	Heifer	4[2]	4.29(2.13-6.45)	65
14			ml/min	Adult	6♀[3]	191(171-237)	49
15				Adult	6♀[4]	191(140-240)	49
16				Adult	5♀	211(207-255)	49
17			ml/min/kg	Adult	19♀	1.68(1.32-2.23)	47
18		Thiosulfate clearance	ml/min/kg	Adult	15♀	1.45(1.20-2.19)	47
19		*p*-Aminohippurate clearance	ml/min/kg	1-2 wk	3♀	541(501-590)	49
20				6-10 wk	4♀	779(720-909)	49
21				1.5-2.5 yr	4♀[1]	887(701-1108)	49
22				Adult	6♀[2]	892(763-1220)	49
23				Adult	6♀[3]	975(672-1308)	49
24				Adult	5♀[4]	699(613-920)	49
25		Phenol red clearance	ml/min/kg	Calf	28♀	7.48(2.28-13.2)	1
26				Calf	20♀	7.89	2
27				Calf	4♀	7.58	2
28				Adult	24♀	8.00(4.70-10.9)	1
29				Adult	22♀	7.77	2
30				Adult	4♀	8.02	2
31		Diodrast clearance	ml/min/kg	Adult	6♀	9.11(5.82-12.60)	47
32		Urea clearance	ml/min/kg	Adult	3♀	0.84(0.56-1.00)	47
33		Filtration fraction	C_C/C_{PAH}	1-2 wk	3♀	0.24(0.21-0.27)	49
34				6-10 wk	4♀	0.23(0.22-0.25)	49
35				1.5-2.5 yr	4♀[1]	0.20(0.18-0.22)	49
36				Adult	6♀[2]	0.21(0.19-0.23)	49
37				Adult	6♀[3]	0.20(0.18-0.22)	49
38				Adult	5♀[4]	0.30(0.26-0.34)	49
39			C_C/C_D	Adult	6♀	0.16(0.11-0.22)	47
40		Tubular maxima, *p*-aminohippurate	mg/min	Adult	6♀	150(123-174)	49
41				Adult	6♀	153(159-178)	49
42				Adult	5♀	231(180-289)	49
43		Diodrast	mg/min/kg	Adult	3♀	0.94(0.67-1.33)	47
44	Dog	Inulin clearance	ml/min	Adult	9	36.2(24.8-49.6)	8
45				Adult	7	61.2(51-76)	59
46			ml/min/m²	Adult	7	69(40-98)	9
47				Adult	8♀	50(36-64)	5
48			ml/min/kg	Adult	32	3.77(1.74-5.86)	3
49		Creatinine clearance	ml/min	Adult	6	69.3(56-84)	58
50				Adult	5	53.5(32.8-60.9)	27
51			ml/min/m²	Adult	32	88.4(63-119)	37
52				Adult	6	86.5(68-139)	37
53				Adult	5	101(65-128)	31
54			ml/min/kg	Adult	17	4.2(3.2-4.9)	40
55				Adult	75♀	4.3(2.2-8.3)	29
56		*p*-Aminohippurate clearance	ml/min	Adult	7	303(180-370)	59
57				Adult	6	195(150-228)	58
58				Adult	5	148(100-203)	27

1/ Nonpregnant, nonlactating. 2/ Prepartum, nonlactating. 3/ 7-14 days postpartum. 4/ 7-21 days postpartum.

continued

113. RENAL FUNCTION TESTS: VERTEBRATES

Part II. Vertebrates Other Than Man

	Animal	Specification: Method	Specification: Unit of Measurement	Subjects: Age	Subjects: No.	Value	Reference
59			ml/min/m²	Adult	32	286(203-425)	37
60				Adult	6	279(210-420)	37
61			ml/min/kg	Adult	32	12.9(6.3-21.2)	3
62				....	17	11.2(7.8-15.5)	40
63				Adult	75♀	13.5(8.1-22.4)	29
64		Phenol red clearance	ml/min/m²	Adult	7	118(68-168)	9
65				Adult	8♀	300(172-428)	5
66		Urea clearance	ml/min	Adult	23	36.6(20.1-48.4)	60
67				Adult	11	55.6(28.2-83.0)	29
68				Adult	9	19.9(11.7-28.1)	8
69		Filtration fraction	C_I/C_{PAH}	Adult	32	0.31(0.10-0.44)	3
70				Adult	8♀	0.17(0.13-0.21)	5
71			C_C/C_{PAH}	Adult	32	0.31(0.26-0.40)	37
72				Adult	7	0.30(0.20-0.52)	59
73				Adult	6	0.31(0.28-0.34)	37
74				Adult	6	0.35(0.31-0.47)	58
75				Adult	5	0.37(0.33-0.41)	27
76				Adult	75♀	0.32(0.23-0.47)	29
77		Tubular maxima, *p*-aminohippurate	mg/min/kg	Adult	32	1.21(0.43-1.89)	3
78				Adult	12	0.78(0.54-1.03)	40
79	Goat	Inulin clearance	ml/min	Adult	5	105(75-145)	39
80		Creatinine clearance	ml/min	Adult	5	137(115-179)	39
81			ml/min/kg	....	.....	2.2	16
82	Horse	Inulin clearance	ml/min/m²	Adult	.....	69.4(47.2-91.6)	33
83			ml/min/kg	Adult	12	1.66(1.00-2.32)	34
84				Adult	1	1.40	47
85		Creatinine clearance	ml/min/kg	Adult	12	1.46(1.02-1.90)	34
86		Diodrast clearance	ml/min/kg	Adult	1♀[5]	6.91(5.29-8.53)	35
87		Urea clearance	ml/min/kg	Adult	6	0.76(0.56-0.96)	34
88		Filtration fraction	C_I/C_D	Adult	1♀	0.24	35
	Monkey						
89	Baboon	Inulin clearance	ml/min/m²	Adult	2♀	60.5(49.1-71.9)	54
90		Creatinine clearance	ml/min/m²	Adult	2♀	69.3(57.1-81.6)	54
91	Chimpanzee	Inulin clearance	ml/min/m²	Adult	5	76(62-103)	23
92				Adult	2♀	103.0(73.3-132.6)	54
93		Creatinine clearance	ml/min/m²	Adult	5	105(77-156)	23
94				Adult	2♀	124(90-158.3)	54
95		*p*-Aminohippurate clearance	ml/min/m²	Adult	3	254(213-301)	23
96		Filtration fraction	C_I/C_{PAH}	Adult	3	0.26(0.22-0.31)	23
97	Gibbon	Inulin clearance	ml/min/m²	Adult	1♂	78.3	54
98		Creatinine clearance	ml/min/m²	Adult	1♂	95.9	54
99	Macaque	Inulin clearance	ml/min	Adult[6]	12♂	12.9(9.0-15.3)	61
100			ml/min/kg	Immature[7]	6	2.18(1.00-3.60)	44
101				Adult[7]	12	1.96(1.18-3.03)	44
102				Adult[6]	12♂	3.1(2.2-3.8)	61
103		Creatinine clearance	ml/min/kg	Adult[7]	10	3.08(1.73-5.22)	44
104				Adult[7,8]	4	1.1(0.9-1.3)	64
105		*p*-Aminohippurate clearance	ml/min/kg	Adult[7]	4	8.06(6.71-10.90)	44
106	Orangutan	Inulin clearance	ml/min/m²	Adult	1♀	76.2	54
107		Creatinine clearance	ml/min/m²	Adult	1♀	112.5	44
108	Rabbit	Inulin clearance	ml/min/m²	Young adult	♂	50.2(22-70)	32
109			ml/min/kg	....	.....	5.00	14
110				....	.....	7.0(5.0-8.4)	30
111		Creatinine clearance	ml/min	Adult	15♂	10.1(6.3-15.2)	7
112			ml/min/kg	Adult	22♂	3.2(2.2-4.2)	28
113				Adult	2♂	5.3	19

[5] 7 occasions. [6] *Macaca irus (M. cynomolgus).* [7] *M. mulatta.* [8] Left kidney only.

continued

113. RENAL FUNCTION TESTS: VERTEBRATES

Part II. Vertebrates Other Than Man

	Animal	Specification: Method	Specification: Unit of Measurement	Subjects: Age	Subjects: No.	Value	Reference
114		*p*-Aminohippurate clearance	ml/min	Adult	15♂	60.1(21.5-199.0)	7
115		Diodone clearance	ml/min	....	.....	36.2(30.9-45.7)	30
116		Urea clearance	ml/min/m²	....	25	25.5	53
117				Young adult	♂	14.3(3-28)	32
118		Tubular maxima, Diodrast	ml/min/m²	....	.....	33.4(29.1-37.7)	38
119		glucose	ml/min/m²	....	.....	78.7(51.9-105.5)	38
120	Rat	Inulin clearance	ml/min	Adult	14	0.36(0.28-0.44)	22
121			ml/min/kg	Adult[9]	20	3.2(1.1-4.7)	20
122				Adult[10]	19	4.8(3.5-6.5)	20
123				Adult[11]	16	6.1(4.8-7.8)	20
124				Adult[12]	10	6.9(4.7-9.5)	20
125				Adult	134	3.5(2.6-4.3)	15
126				Adult	84	6.0(5.4-6.6)	6
127				Adult	31♂	2.7(1.5-3.9)	21
128		Creatinine clearance	ml/min/kg	Adult[9]	12	3.1(2.0-4.9)	20
129				Adult[10]	27	5.6(3.0-6.5)	20
130				Adult[11]	22	6.5(4.2-11.0)	20
131				Adult[12]	9	7.0(6.0-8.6)	20
132				Adult	39	6.1(2.9-9.3)	11
133		*p*-Aminohippurate clearance	ml/min	Adult	14	2.31(1.95-2.63)	22
134			ml/min/kg	Adult[9]	6	15.7(10.0-24.8)	20
135				Adult[10]	13	21.5(11.8-35.7)	20
136				Adult[11]	15	25.8(16.0-35.3)	20
137				Adult[12]	10	34.8(29.2-40.0)	20
138		Diodone clearance	ml/min/kg	Adult	134	22.2(16.6-27.8)	15
139		Diodrast clearance	ml/min/kg	Adult	31	13.3(6.1-17.1)	10
140		Urea clearance	ml/min/m²	Adult	8	10.9(4.7-17.1)	18
141		Mannitol clearance	ml/min/kg	Adult	20	5.5(3.8-7.2)	10
142		Filtration fraction	C_I/C_{PAH}	....	35	0.17(0.10-0.24)	14
143				Adult	14	0.16(0.11-0.21)	22
144				Adult	31♂	0.20	21
145		Tubular maxima, *p*-aminohippurate	mg/min	Adult	14	0.10(0.08-0.12)	22
146			mg/min/kg	....	39	2.9(2.8-3.0)	11
147				....	20[13]	3.27	10
148				....	20[14]	2.36	10
149		diodone	mg/min/kg	....	134	1.32(0.96-1.68)	15
150				....	30	1.83(1.6-2.1)	6
151	Sheep	Inulin clearance	ml/min	Adult	4♀[15]	78(64-92)	56
152				Adult	4♀[16]	78(65-95)	56
153				Adult	3♀[17]	112(94-139)	26
154				Adult	3♀[18]	49(39-57)	26
155				Adult	6♀	111	24
156				Adult	5♀	101	25
157				Adult	1♀	59	50
158			ml/min/kg	Adult	2♀	1.80(1.72-1.87)	48
159		Creatinine clearance	ml/min	Adult	1♀[19]	30.6	57
160				Adult	1♀[20]	31.3	57
161				Adult	1♀	60.0	48
162			ml/min/kg	Adult	2♀	1.75(1.70-1.79)	48
163		*p*-Aminohippurate clearance	ml/min	Adult	4♀[15]	469(434-534)	56
164				Adult	4♀[16]	489(413-571)	56
165				Adult	3♀[17]	639(479-823)	26
166				Adult	3♀[18]	190(170-228)	26
167		Phenol red clearance	ml/min	Adult	6♀	400(110-704)	41

[9] Urine flow: 0-0.5 ml/hr. [10] Urine flow: 0.5-1.0 ml/hr. [11] Urine flow: 1.0-1.5 ml/hr. [12] Urine flow: 1.5-2.0 ml/hr. [13] Sprague-Dawley strain. [14] Wistar strain. [15] Before feeding. [16] After feeding. [17] High protein intake. [18] Low protein intake. [19] Normal ureter. [20] Exteriorized ureter.

continued

113. RENAL FUNCTION TESTS: VERTEBRATES

Part II. Vertebrates Other Than Man

	Animal	Specification: Method	Specification: Unit of Measurement	Subjects: Age	Subjects: No.	Value	Reference
168		Urea clearance	ml/min	Adult	6♀	62	57
169				Adult	5♀	56	57
170				Adult	1♀	32	50
171	Swine	Inulin clearance	ml/min/kg	Immature	....	3.7	12
172				Adult	4	5.06(4.87-5.32)	42
173		Creatinine clearance	ml/min/kg	Adult	4	4.15(4.07-4.40)	42
174		*p*-Aminohippurate clearance	ml/min/kg	Adult	2	19.5(19.3-19.7)	42
175		Filtration fraction	C_I/C_{PAH}	Adult	2	0.26(24.7-27.5)	42
176		Tubular maxima, *p*-aminohippurate	mg/min/kg	Adult	2	3.11(3.00-3.21)	42
177	Chicken	Inulin clearance	ml/min/kg	Adult	5[21]	2.03	52
178				Adult	...[21]	1.87	51
179				Adult	...[21]	2.45	36
180				Adult	...[22]	1.37	36
181				Adult	...[23]	0.60	36
182				Adult	5[24]	2.04	46
183				Adult	13♀[21]	1.84	45
184				Adult	♀[23]	3.0	55
185				Adult	43♀	1.8(0.2-3.4)	4
186				Adult	11♀	1.84(1.04-2.83)	62
187				Adult	6♀	2.5(1.8-3.5)	43
188		Creatinine clearance	ml/min/kg	Adult	♀[24]	3.90(2.0-6.8)	63
189				Adult	♀[25]	2.25(1.3-2.6)	63
190		*p*-Aminohippurate clearance	ml/min	Adult	7♀	67.6(53.4-104.4)	62
191				Adult	6♀	30.7(20.8-40.6)	43
192		Diodone clearance	ml/min/kg	Adult	6♀	18.0(10.5-25.8)	62
193		Phenol red clearance	....	Adult	13♀	25.0	45
194		Urea clearance	....	....	5	1.50	46
195		Uric acid clearance	ml/min/kg	Adult	43♀	11.3(0-23.0)	4
196				Adult	6♀	19.8(8.7-30.0)	43
197				Adult	5♀	25.1(15.6-35.1)	62
198		Tubular maxima, *p*-aminohippurate	mg/min/kg	Adult	2♀	1.58(1.08-1.93)	13

21/ Normal. 22/ During water loading. 23/ During dehydration. 24/ Exogenous creatinine. 25/ Endogenous creatinine.

Contributors: Osbaldiston, G. W., and Cornelius, C. E.

References

[1] Anderson, R. R., and J. P. Mixner. 1959. J. Dairy Sci. 42:545.

[2] Anderson, R. R., and J. P. Mixner. 1960. Ibid. 43: 1476.

[3] Asheim, A., F. Persson, and S. Persson. 1961. Acta Physiol. Scand. 51:150.

[4] Berger, L., T. F. Yu, and A. B. Gutman. 1960. Am. J. Physiol. 198:575.

[5] Blatteis, C. M., and S. M. Horvath. 1958. Ibid. 192: 353.

[6] Braun-Menendez, E., and H. Chiodi. 1946. Rev. Soc. Arg. Biol. 22:314.

[7] Brod, J., and J. H. Sirota. 1949. Am. J. Physiol. 157:31.

[8] Clapp, J. R. 1965. Proc. Soc. Exptl. Biol. Med. 120: 521.

[9] Corcoran, A. C., and I. H. Page. 1939. Am. J. Physiol. 126:354.

[10] Corcoran, A. C., and I. H. Page. 1947. Federation Proc. 6:91.

[11] Corcoran, A. C., et al. 1948. Am. J. Physiol. 154: 170.

[12] Dalgaard-Mikkelsen, S., E. Poulsen, and B. Simensen. 1953. Nord. Vet. Med. 5:965.

[13] Dantzler, W. H. 1966. Am. J. Physiol. 210:640.

[14] Dicker, S. E., and H. Heller. 1945. J. Physiol. (London) 103:449.

[15] Dicker, S. E., and H. Heller. 1946. Ibid. 104:353.

[16] Dziemian, A. J., P. P. Wilson, and W. P. McShane. 1950. Army Med. Center Chem. Corps. Res. Rept. 29:1.

[17] Eggleton, M. G., and Y. A. Habib. 1950. J. Physiol (London) 110:458.

[18] Farr, L. E., and J. E. Smadel. 1936. Am. J. Physiol. 116:349.

[19] Forster, R. P. 1952. Ibid. 168:666.

[20] Friedman, S. M. 1947. Ibid. 148:387.

[21] Friedman, S. M., and C. A. Livingstone. 1942. Ibid. 137:564.

continued

Part II. Vertebrates Other Than Man

[22] Friedman, S. M., J. R. Polley, and C. L. Friedman. 1947. Ibid. 150:340.
[23] Gagnon, J. A., and R. W. Clarke. 1957. Ibid. 190: 117.
[24] Gans, J. H. 1964. Am. J. Vet. Res. 25:914.
[25] Gans, J. H. 1964. Ibid. 25:924.
[26] Gans, J. H., and P. F. Mercer. 1962. Ibid. 23:230.
[27] Glauser, K. F., and E. E. Selkurt. 1952. Am. J. Physiol. 168:469.
[28] Grant, R. 1953. Ibid. 174:79.
[29] Houck, C. R. 1948. Ibid. 153:169.
[30] Hughes-Jones, N. C., et al. 1949. J. Physiol. (London) 109:288.
[31] Jolliffe, N., and H. W. Smith. 1931. Am. J. Physiol. 98:572.
[32] Kaplan, B., and H. W. Smith. 1935. Ibid. 113:354.
[33] Ketz, H. A., et al. 1956. Monatsh. Veterinaermed. 11:575.
[34] Knudsen, E. 1959. Acta Vet. Scand. 1:52.
[35] Knudsen, E. 1959. Ibid. 1:188.
[36] Korr, I. M. 1939. J. Cellular Comp. Physiol. 13:175.
[37] Kubicek, W. G., et al. 1953. Am. J. Physiol. 174: 397.
[38] Laake, H. 1945. Acta Med. Scand., Suppl. 168.
[39] Ladd, M., et al. 1957. J. Appl. Physiol. 10:249.
[40] Low, D. G., et al. 1956. J. Infect. Diseases 98:260.
[41] Manning, J. P., et al. 1959. Am. J. Vet. Res. 20: 858.
[42] Mundsick, R. A., W. H. Sawyer, and H. V. Van Dyke. 1958. Endocrinology 63:688.
[43] Nechay, B. R., and L. Nechay. 1959. J. Pharmacol. Exptl. Therap. 126:291.
[44] Pickering, D. E., and H. H. Sussman. 1962. Am. J. Vet. Res. 23:667.
[45] Pitts, R. F. 1938. J. Cellular Comp. Physiol. 11:99.
[46] Pitts, R. F., and I. M. Korr. 1938. Ibid. 11:117.
[47] Poulsen, E. 1957. Kgl. Vet. Land-Bohoejskole Arsskr., p. 97.
[48] Schmidt-Nielsen, B., et al. 1958. Am. J. Physiol. 194:221.
[49] Sellers, A. F., et al. 1958. Am. J. Vet. Res. 19:580.
[50] Shannon, J. 1937. Proc. Soc. Exptl. Biol. Med. 37: 379.
[51] Shannon, J. A. 1938. J. Cellular Comp. Physiol. 11: 108.
[52] Shannon, J. A. 1938. Ibid. 11:135.
[53] Smith, H. W. 1951. The kidney. Oxford Univ. Press, New York. p. 541.
[54] Smith, H. W., and R. W. Clarke. 1938. Am. J. Physiol. 122:132.
[55] Sperber, I. 1960. In A. J. Marshall, ed. Biology and comparative physiology of birds. Academic Press, New York. pp. 469-492.
[56] Stacy, B. P., and A. H. Brook. 1964. Australian J. Agr. Res. 15:289.
[57] Stacy, B. P., and A. H. Brook. 1964. Quart. J. Exptl. Physiol. 49:301.
[58] Stamler, J., L. N. Katz, and S. Rodbard. 1949. J. Exptl. Med. 90:511.
[59] Stevens, C. E., A. F. Sellers, and J. J. Clark. 1956. Am. J. Vet. Res. 17:710.
[60] Summerville, W. W., R. F. Hanzal, and H. B. Goldblatt. 1932. Am. J. Physiol. 102:1.
[61] Sweet, A. Y., M. F. Levitt, and H. L. Hodes. 1961. Ibid. 201:975.
[62] Sykes, A. H. 1960. Res. Vet. Sci. 1:308.
[63] Sykes, A. H. 1960. Ibid. 1:315.
[64] Vander, A. J., and E. J. Cafruny. 1962. Am. J. Physiol. 202:1105.
[65] Weeth, H. J., and A. L. Lesperance. 1965. J. Animal Sci. 24:441.

114. GNOTOBIOTIC END PRODUCTS

Condition of Subject: Conv = conventional; Gf = germ-free; Mono = monocontaminated with *Clostridium.*

Part I. Composition of Cecal Contents and Feces: Dutch Rabbit

Values are for three subjects fitted with coprophagy-preventing collars. ± = plus or minus (standard error).

	Constituent	Unit of Measurement	Condition of Subject	Cecal Contents	Feces	
					Hard	Soft
1	Moisture	% in fresh matter	Conv	74.34 ± 0.99	17.54 ± 3.31	44.71 ± 5.15 1/
2			Gf	85.16 ± 0.31	29.88 ± 2.54 2/	74.27 ± 2.53 1,2/
3	Crude ash	% in dry matter	Conv	8.63 ± 0.88	6.20 ± 0.32	7.71 ± 0.32 1/
4			Gf	6.36 ± 0.49 2/	5.80 ± 0.49	6.71 ± 0.49
5	Crude fiber	% in dry matter	Conv	24.43 ± 5.34	47.40 ± 1.88	26.43 ± 3.43 1/
6			Gf	27.18 ± 3.14	44.02 ± 1.26	33.55 ± 0.37 1/
7	Crude fat	% in dry matter	Conv	0.96 ± 0.20	1.40 ± 0.15	1.29 ± 0.08
8			Gf	0.91 ± 0.01	0.93 ± 0.07 2/	0.74 ± 0.01 2/

1/ Difference from hard feces significant at $P<0.05$. 2/ Difference from conventional rabbits significant at $P<0.05$.

continued

114. GNOTOBIOTIC END PRODUCTS

Part I. Composition of Cecal Contents and Feces: Dutch Rabbit

	Constituent	Unit of Measurement	Condition of Subject	Cecal Contents	Feces	
					Hard	Soft
9	Crude protein	% in dry matter	Conv	42.19 ± 6.03	20.26 ± 2.96	39.65 ± 3.61[1/]
10			Gf	26.48 ± 1.82	13.25 ± 0.73	21.82 ± 0.41[1,2/]
11	True protein	% in dry matter	Conv	27.93 ± 5.07	18.33 ± 2.91	31.65 ± 2.99[1/]
12			Gf	7.85 ± 0.70[2/]	7.10 ± 0.25[2/]	6.67 ± 0.82[2/]
13	$\frac{\text{True protein}}{\text{Crude protein}} \times 100$	% in dry matter	Conv	66.2 ± 4.1	90.5 ± 1.3	79.8 ± 0.6[1/]
14			Gf	29.6 ± 0.6[2/]	53.6 ± 1.4[2/]	30.6 ± 3.3[1,2/]
15	Nitrogen-free extract	% in dry matter	Conv	23.80 ± 3.11	24.75 ± 1.36	24.91 ± 1.17
16			Gf	39.07 ± 5.46	36.00 ± 0.85[2/]	37.18 ± 0.46[2/]
17	Calcium	% in dry matter	Conv	0.816 ± 0.013	1.178 ± 0.037	0.956 ± 0.125
18			Gf	0.484 ± 0.054[2/]	0.921 ± 0.075[2/]	0.709 ± 0.052
19	Phosphorus	% in dry matter	Conv	1.435 ± 0.065	1.048 ± 0.096	1.408 ± 0.066[1/]
20			Gf	0.545 ± 0.040[2/]	0.946 ± 0.077	0.885 ± 0.008[2/]

[1/] Difference from hard feces significant at $P<0.05$. [2/] Difference from conventional rabbits significant at $P<0.05$.

Contributors: Wostmann, Bernard S., and Havell, Edward

Reference: Yoshida, T., et al. 1968. Brit. J. Nutr. 22(4).

Part II. Calcium and Phosphorus Intake and Excretion: Dutch Rabbit

Values are for three subjects fitted with coprophagy-preventing collars. ± = plus or minus (standard error).

	Constituent	Unit of Measurement	Condition of Subject	Intake	Excretion				
					Total	Urine	Feces		
							Total	Hard	Soft
1	Calcium	mg/kg body wt/day	Conv	194 ± 12	186 ± 15	65 ± 4	121 ± 11	79 ± 20	42 ± 20
2			Gf	186 ± 8	177 ± 9	90 ± 12	87 ± 3[1/]	33 ± 5	54 ± 1
3		% of intake	Conv	100	96 ± 2	34 ± 0	62 ± 2	41 ± 9	21 ± 10
4			Gf	100	95 ± 1	48 ± 4[1/]	47 ± 4[1/]	18 ± 3	29 ± 0
5	Phosphorus	mg/kg body wt/day	Conv	143 ± 12	136 ± 10	6 ± 2	130 ± 11	72 ± 20	58 ± 22
6			Gf	134 ± 6	127 ± 8	25 ± 6[1/]	102 ± 1	33 ± 5	69 ± 8
7		% of intake	Conv	100	95 ± 2	4 ± 2	91 ± 4	50 ± 13	41 ± 16
8			Gf	100	95 ± 2	19 ± 4[1/]	76 ± 1[1/]	25 ± 5	51 ± 4

[1/] Difference from conventional rabbits significant at $P<0.05$.

Contributors: Wostmann, Bernard S., and Havell, Edward

Reference: Yoshida, T., et al. 1968. Brit. J. Nutr. 22(4).

Part III. Composition of Urine and Feces: Rat

Values in parentheses are ranges, estimate "c" (*see* Introduction).

	Constituent	Unit of Measurement	Condition of Subject	Amount Excreted	Reference
	Urine[1/]				
1	Calcium	$\frac{\text{mM} \times 10}{\text{mM creatinine}}$	Gf	14.5	4
2	Magnesium	$\frac{\text{mM} \times 10}{\text{mM creatinine}}$	Gf	20.5	

[1/] Values are mean daily electrolyte excretions of 3 subjects.

continued

114. GNOTOBIOTIC END PRODUCTS

Part III. Composition of Urine and Feces: Rat

	Constituent	Unit of Measurement	Condition of Subject	Amount Excreted	Reference
3	Potassium	mM × 10 / mM creatinine	Gf	51.2	
4	Sodium	mM × 10 / mM creatinine	Gf	36.2	
5	Citrate	mM × 10 / mM creatinine	Gf	11.75	
6	Phosphate	mM × 10 / mM creatinine	Gf	3	
			Feces		
7	Hexosamines	mg/day	Gf	10-32	6
8	Sugar residues	mg/g feces	Gf	21.9	2
9	Lactic acid	mg/g feces	Gf	0.442	
10	Bile acids	mg/kg body wt/day	Conv	14.2	5
11			Gf	1.82	
12			Mono	2.1	
13	Bilirubin	μM sterobilinogen/kg body wt/24 hr	Conv	1.56(0.92-2.65)2/	3
14			Gf	4.68(2.93-7.80)3/	
15	Urobilin	μM sterobilinogen/kg body wt/24 hr	Conv	3.4(2.1-5.0)4/	
16			Gf	05/	
17	Nitrogen, total	mg/day	Gf	30	6
18	Neutral sterols	mg/kg body wt/day	Conv	7.11	5
19			Gf	5.90	
20			Mono	11.1	
21	Amylase	units/day	Gf	40-100	1
22	Invertase	units/day	Gf	12-25	
23	Trypsin	mg/day	Gf	2-6	

2/ 8 animals, 10 determinations. 3/ 7 animals, 13 determinations. 4/ 9 animals, 15 determinations. 5/ 3 animals, 3 determinations.

Contributors: Wostmann, Bernard S., and Havell, Edward

References

[1] Borgstrom, B., et al. 1959. Proc. Soc. Exptl. Biol. Med. 102:155.

[2] Ducluzeau, R., et al. 1966. Compt. Rend. 262:321.

[3] Gustafsson, B. E., and L. S. Lanke. 1960. J. Exptl. Med. 112:977.

[4] Gustafsson, B. E., and A. Norman. 1962. Ibid. 116: 280.

[5] Kellogg, T. Unpublished. Univ. Notre Dame, Dept. Microbiology, Ind., 1967.

[6] Lindstedt, G., S. Lindstedt, and B. E. Gustafsson. 1965. J. Exptl. Med. 121:201.

115. BACTERIAL AND FUNGAL METABOLIC PRODUCTS USEFUL TO MAN

Data are for representative types of the vast number of microbial reactions used commercially. Most processes are patented, and recent information on yields and process modifications is not generally available. Industry in continually seeking better yielding strains of microorganisms through selection and mutation.

Part I. Antibiotics

Type of Culture: Aer = aerobic; sub = submerged. **Route:** Paren = parenteral; top = topical.

	Product (Synonym)	Microorganism	Substrate	Type of Culture [pH]	Temp °C	No. of Days	Yield	Use: Route	Use: Organisms Affected	Reference
1	Amphotericin B	*Streptomyces nodosus*	Starch, dextrose, soybean meal, $CaCO_3$	Aer, sub [6.5-7.5]	25	5-6	5 g/liter	Paren	Fungi causing various mycoses	10,14
2	Bacitracin	*Bacillus licheniformis*	Starch or sucrose, dextrose, soybean or peanut meal	Aer, sub [6.2-7.7]	37	2-3	1.5 g/liter	Top	Gram-positive bacteria	19,28, 39

continued

115. BACTERIAL AND FUNGAL METABOLIC PRODUCTS USEFUL TO MAN

Part I. Antibiotics

	Product (Synonym)	Microorganism	Substrate	Type of Culture [pH]	Temp °C	No. of Days	Yield	Use: Route	Use: Organisms Affected	Reference
3	Carbomycin (Magnamycin)	*Streptomyces halstedii*	Media of organic composition	Aer, sub [6-8]	28	3-5	100 mg/liter		Rickettsias, gram-positive bacteria	29,37, 39
4	Cephalosporin C	*Cephalosporium* sp.	Beet molasses, animal protein, methionine, $CaCO_3$	Aer, sub [6.5-7.5]	28	4	1.4 g/liter	Oral & paren	Gram-positive bacteria	1,5
5	Chloramphenicol (Chloromycetin)	*Streptomyces venezuelae*	1% maltose, 0.5% casein amino acids, 0.5% distiller's solubles, 0.5% NaCl	Aer, sub [6.7]	23-27	3-6	0.2 g/liter	Oral & paren	Broad spectrum	12
6	Chlortetracycline (Aureomycin)	*S. aureofaciens*	Starch, corn steep liquor, minor metals, $CaCO_3$	Aer, sub [6.0-8.0]	26-28	3-6	10 g/liter	Oral & paren	Broad spectrum	9,26
7	Colistin (Colimycin)	*Bacillus polymyxa*		Aer				Oral & paren	*Pseudomonas*	20,36
8	Cycloheximide (Actidione)	*Streptomyces griseus*	Glucose, soybean meal, salts, distillers' solubles	Aer, sub [6-8]	24	3-5	0.25 g/liter		Fungi, especially plant disease fungi	39
9	Cycloserine	*S. orchidaceous; S. lavendulae*	Starch, soybean meal, corn steep liquor, $NaNO_3$	Aer, sub [6.5-7.5]	28	4		Oral	*Mycobacterium tuberculosis*	16,33
10	Demethyltetracycline	*S. aureofaciens*, mutant	Starch, corn steep liquor, minor metals, $CaCO_3$	Aer, sub [6.0-8.0]	26-28	3-6		Oral	Broad spectrum	22
11	Erythromycin (Ilotycin)	*S. erythreus*	Glucose, soybean meal, corn steep liquor	Aer, sub [6.4-7.2]	26-30	4-5	0.35 g/liter	Oral & paren	Rickettsias, gram-positive bacteria	4,24 39
12	Fumagillin (Phagopedin sigma)	*Aspergillus fumigatus*	Dextrin, corn steep liquor	Aer [6.5-7.5]		2	0.12 g/liter		Amoebas	11,39
13	Griseofulvin	*Penicillium griseofulvum; P. patulum*	Lactose, corn steep liquor, $CaCO_3$, KH_2PO_4	Aer, sub [6.5-8.0]	25-30	9	1 g/liter	Oral	*Microsporum, Trichophyton*	3,27, 31, 44
14	Kanamycin	*Streptomyces kanamyceticus*	Starch, soybean meal, peptone, $MgSO_4$, $NaNO_3$	Aer, sub [6.5-8.0]	27-30	5	0.25 g/liter	Oral & paren	*Mycobacterium tuberculosis*	38,43
15	Lincomycin	*S. lincolnensis*	Molasses, corn steep liquor, animal peptone, $CaCO_3$	Aer, sub [6.5-7.5]	28	4-5	0.8 g/liter	Paren	Gram-positive bacteria	18,21
16	Neomycin	*S. fradiae*	Glucose, soybean meal, animal protein, NaCl, $ZnSO_4$	Aer, sub [6.5-6.8]	26-28	4-6	2-4 g/liter	Oral & paren	Gram-positive & gram-negative bacteria; *Mycobacterium tuberculosis*	39,41
17	Novobiocin (Cathomycin)	*S. griseus; S. niveus; S. spheroides*	Starch, plant proteins	Aer, sub [6.5-7.5]	20-28	4-5	0.4 g/liter	Oral & paren	Gram-positive bacteria	13,29, 40, 42
18	Nystatin	*S. noursei*		Aer, sub				Oral	Intestinal *Candida*	17
19	Oleandomycin	*S. antibioticus*	Glucose, soybean meal, distiller's solubles	Aer, sub [6.5-7.5]	28	4	0.45 g/liter	Oral	Rickettsias, gram-positive bacteria	6,30

continued

115. BACTERIAL AND FUNGAL METABOLIC PRODUCTS USEFUL TO MAN

Part I. Antibiotics

	Product (Synonym)	Microorganism	Substrate	Type of Culture [pH]	Temp °C	No. of Days	Yield	Use		Reference
								Route	Organisms Affected	
20	Oxytetracycline (Terramycin)	*S. rimosus*	Starch, soybean meal, casein hydrolysate, salts	Aer, sub [6.5-8.0]	28	4	1.0 g/liter	Oral & paren	Broad spectrum	29,34, 39
21	Penicillin	*Penicillium chrysogenum*	Glucose, corn steep liquor, salts, phenylacetic acid	Aer, sub [5.5-7.5]	25	4	3000 I.U./ml	Oral & paren	Gram-positive bacteria	2,8, 29, 39
22	Polymyxin	*Bacillus polymyxa*	Glucose, yeast extract, salts	Aer, sub [6.3-7.9]	25	5	350 units/ml	Oral & paren	Gram-negative bacteria	35,39
23	Streptomycin	*Streptomyces griseus*	Glucose, soybean meal, corn steep liquor, distiller's solubles	Aer, sub [6.0-7.5]	24-30	3-6	0.9 g/liter	Oral & paren	Gram-positive & gram-negative bacteria; *Mycobacterium tuberculosis*	29,32, 39
24	Tetracycline	*S. aureofaciens*, mutant	Starch, corn steep liquor, salts, $CaCO_3$	Aer, sub [6.5-7.5]	28-30	5	10 g/liter	Oral & paren	Broad spectrum	15,25, 29, 39
25	Vancomycin	*S. orientalis*	Starch, soybean meal, molasses	Aer, sub [6.0-8.0]	30	5		Oral & paren	Gram-positive bacteria	23
26	Viomycin	*S. floridae*	Glucose, casein hydrolysate, yeast hydrolysate, salts	Aer, sub [6.0-8.0]	24-26	3-6	0.6 g/liter	Paren	*Mycobacterium tuberculosis*	7,39

Contributors: (a) Tanner, Fred W., Jr., (b) Marshall, C. R., (c) Underkofler, L. A.

References

[1] Abraham, E. P., and G. C. F. Newton. 1961. Biochem. J. 79:377.
[2] Anderson, R. F., et al. 1953. Ind. Eng. Chem. 45: 768.
[3] Brian, P. W., et al. 1955. Brit. Mycol. Soc. Trans. 38:305.
[4] Bunch, R. L., and J. M. McGuire. 1953. U.S. Pat. 2,653,899.
[5] Caltrider, P. G., and H. C. Niss. 1966. Appl. Microbiol. 14:746.
[6] Celmar, W. D. 1955-56. Antibiot. Ann., p. 437.
[7] Coffey, G. L., et al. 1951. Antibiot. Chemotherapy 1:203.
[8] Coghill, R. D., and R. S. Koch. 1945. Chem. Eng. News 23:2310.
[9] Dugger, B. M. 1949. U.S. Pat. 2,482,055.
[10] Dutcher, J. D., et al. 1959. U.S. Pat. 2,908,611.
[11] Eble, T. E., and F. R. Hanson. 1951. Antibiot. Chemotherapy 1:54.
[12] Ehrlich, J., et al. 1947. Science 106:417.
[13] Frost, B. M., et al. 1955-56. Antibiot. Ann., p. 918.
[14] Gold, W., et al. 1955-56. Ibid., p. 579.
[15] Growich, J. J., and N. Deduck. 1963. U.S. Pat. 3,092,556.
[16] Harned, R. L., P. H. Hidy, and E. K. LaBaw. 1955. Antibiot. Chemotherapy 5:204.
[17] Hazen, E. L., and R. Brown. 1950. Proc. Soc. Exptl. Biol. Med. 76:93.
[18] Herr, R. R., and M. E. Bergy. 1962. Antimicrobial Agents Chemotherapy, p. 560.
[19] Inskeep, G. C., et al. 1951. Ind. Eng. Chem. 43: 1488.
[20] Koyama, Y. 1952. Chem. Abstr. 47:6097 (Japan. Pat. 1546).
[21] Mason, D. J., et al. 1962. Antimicrobial Agents Chemotherapy, p. 554.
[22] McCormick, J. R. D., et al. 1957. J. Am. Chem. Soc. 79:4561 (U.S. Pat. 2,878,289).
[23] McCormick, M. H., et al. 1955-56. Antibiot. Ann., p. 606.
[24] McGuire, J. M., et al. 1952. Antibiot. Chemotherapy 2:281.
[25] Minieri, P. P., et al. 1953-54. Antibiot. Ann., p. 81.
[26] Niedercorn, J. G. 1952. U.S. Pat. 2,609,329.
[27] Oxford, A. E., et al. 1939. Biochem. J. 33:240.
[28] Prescott, S. C., and C. G. Dunn. 1959. Industrial microbiology. Ed. 3, McGraw-Hill, New York.
[29] Rainbow, C., and A. H. Rose, ed. 1963. Biochemistry of industrial micro-organisms. Academic Press, New York.
[30] Ratajak, E. J., et al. 1958. U.S. Pat. 2,842,481.
[31] Rhodes, A., et al. 1958. U.S. Pat. 2,843,527.
[32] Schatz, A., and S. A. Waksman. 1945. Proc. Natl. Acad. Sci. U.S. 31:129 (U.S. Pat. 2,449,866).
[33] Shull, G. M., et al. 1956. U.S. Pat. 2,773,878.
[34] Sobin, B. A., et al. 1950. U.S. Pat. 2,516,080.

continued

115. BACTERIAL AND FUNGAL METABOLIC PRODUCTS USEFUL TO MAN

Part I. Antibiotics

[35] Stansly, P. G., and N. H. Ananenko. 1949. Arch. Biochem. 23:256.
[36] Takubo, T. 1956. Chem. Abstr. 50:13374.
[37] Tanner, F. W., et al. 1952. Antibiot. Chemotherapy 2:441.
[38] Umezawa, H., et al. 1959. J. Antibiotics (Tokyo), A, 10:181.
[39] Underkofler, L. A., and R. J. Hickey, ed. 1954. Industrial fermentations. Chemical, New York. v. 1 & 2.
[40] Verwey, W. F., et al. 1955-56. Antibiot. Ann., p. 924.
[41] Waksman, S. A., et al. 1949. J. Clin. Invest. 28:934.
[42] Wallick, H., et al. 1955-56. Antibiot. Ann., p. 909.
[43] Whitelock, O. von S., ed. 1958. Ann. N.Y. Acad. Sci. 76:17.
[44] Williams, D. I., et al. 1958. Lancet 2:1212.

Part II. Industrial Fermentation Products

Type of Culture: Aer = aerobic; Anaer = anaerobic; sub = submerged; surf = surface.

	Product	Microorganism (Synonym)	Substrate	Type of Culture [pH]	Temp °C	No. of Days	Yield	Industrial Use	Reference
			Vitamins & Provitamins						
1	Riboflavin	*Ashbya gossypii; Eremothecium ashbyii*	Glucose, corn steep liquor, animal protein	Aer, sub [4.5-7.5]	27-30	5-10	2-10 g/liter	Food & feed supplement	35,36, 51
2	Vitamin B_{12}	*Propionibacterium freudenreichii; Streptomyces olivaceus*	Glucose, distiller's solubles, $CaCO_3$, $CoCl_2$	Aer, sub [6.5-8.0]	27-30	3-5	1.2 mg/liter	Food & feed supplement	15,25, 32, 51
3	β-Carotene	*Blakeslea trispora*	Cornmeal, cottonseed meal, kerosene, β-ionone, vegetable oil	Aer, sub [6-8]	28		1-1.5 g/liter	Food & feed additive	1,7,8
4	Ergosterol	*Saccharomyces carlsbergensis*	Molasses, salts	Aer [7-7.5]	25	1-2	2-2.7% of yeast wt	Manufacture of vitamin D	27,51
			Hormones & Enzymes						
5	Gibberellin	*Gibberella zeae*	Glucose, KH_2PO_4, NH_4Cl	Aer, sub [5-7]	25	5	1 g/liter	Plant growth regulator	36,47, 48
6	11γ-Hydroxyprogesterone	*Rhizopus arrhizus; R. stolonifer (R. nigricans)*	Glucose, corn steep liquor, progesterone	Aer, sub [4.4-6]	24-28	2	10-95%	Intermediate for 17γ-hydroxycorticosterone	14,51
	Amylase								
7	Bacterial	*Bacillus subtilis*	Surface culture: vegetable protein plus sugar Submerged culture: starch, cereal grain, & protein	Aer, surf or sub [6.5-7.0]	30-40	1-3	400-500 g concentrate/100 liters culture	Modified starches, sizing paper; desizing textiles	18,35, 51-53
8	Fungal	*Aspergillus niger*	Cereal grains	Aer, sub [6.0]	34	3-5	12-15 glucoamylase units/ml	Glucose, food syrup	35,44
9	Pectinase	*A. foetidus (A. aureus); A. wentii*	1000 kg bran plus 800 liters H_2O, inoculated with 100 liters spore suspension	Aer, surf	30-37	2-3	Aqueous extract of culture adsorbed on bran from coffee bean husk	Clarifying agents in fruit juice industries	4,51

continued

115. BACTERIAL AND FUNGAL METABOLIC PRODUCTS USEFUL TO MAN

Part II. Industrial Fermentation Products

	Product	Microorganism (Synonym)	Substrate	Type of Culture [pH]	Temp °C	No. of Days	Yield	Industrial Use	Reference
	Protease								
10	Bacterial	*Bacillus subtilis*	6% carbohydrate, 1% protein, salts	Aer, surf [6.5-7.0]	30-40	3-5		Bating hides, desizing fibers, tenderizing meat; spot remover	23,51-53
11	Fungal	*Aspergillus* spp.	Wheat bran, soybean meal, salts	Aer, sub [6.0-7.0]	28-30	3-4		Bating hides, chillproofing beer; digestive acid	42
12	Rennin, microbial	*Endothia parasitica*	Glucose, soybean meal, skim milk	Aer, sub [6-8]	28	2		Replaces animal rennin in cheese making	40
13	Resorcinylic acids	*Gibberella zeae;* others	Starch, molasses, mineral salts	Aer, sub	34			Potential growth hormone	46
	Organic Acids								
14	Amino acids	Bacteria	Glucose, inorganic nitrogen	Aer [7.0]	±30	1-3	10 g/liter	Human & animal food	24,36
15	6-Aminopenicillanic acid	*Bacillus* sp.; *Proteus* sp.; others	Penicillin G	Enzymatic [7]	25-30	1	70-100%	Precursor of synthetic penicillins	3,16,17, 26,39
16	Citric acid	*Aspergillus niger*	Molasses plus nutrients	Aer, surf or sub [3-4]	25-30	3-10	60-90% of sugar	Food acid, medicinal citrates	10,30, 51
17	Fumaric acid	*Rhizopus arrhizus*	10-16% sugar, inorganic salts, $CaCO_3$	Aer, sub [6.0]	33	4-7	65-70% of sugar	Manufacture of alkyd resins, wetting agents	35,37, 51
18		*R. stolonifer (R. nigricans)*	Invert molasses, nutrient salts, $CaCO_3$	Aer, sub [5-6]	33	4	58-64% of sugar	Food acid, alkyd resins	30,35, 51
19	Gluconic acid	*Acetobacter suboxydans; Aspergillus niger*	Glucose, $CaCO_3$, $MgSO_4$, KH_2PO_4, $(NH_4)_2HPO_4$	Aer, sub [2.5-7.0]	30	1-2	93-97% of sugar	Chelating agent as Na salt; food acid	13,36, 51
20	L-Glutamic acid	*Brevibacterium; Micrococcus glutamicus*	Glucose, biotin, urea, salts	Aer, sub [7.4-7.6]	30	3	30 g/liter	Food flavor	20,25
21	Guanylic acid	*M. glutamicus,* auxotrophs	Glucose, thiamine, biotin, casein hydrolysate, salts		30	3		Food flavor, with inosinic acid	9,29
22	Inosinic acid	*M. glutamicus,* auxotrophs	Glucose, thiamine, biotin, casein hydrolysate, salts	Aer, sub [7.4-7.6]	30	3		Food flavor, with glutamic & guanylic acids	9,29
23	Itaconic acid	*Aspergillus terreus*	Sugar or molasses, corn steep liquor, $(NH_4)_2SO_4$, $MgSO_4$	Aer, sub [2]	35-37	3	40% of sugar	Resins	30,31, 51
24	2-Ketogluconic acid	*Pseudomonas* sp.; *Serratia marcescens*	Glucose, salts	Aer, sub [4.5-7]	30-35	1.3-1.5	90% of sugar	Intermediate for erythorbic acid	28,33, 34,36, 51
25	5-Ketogluconic acid	*Acetobacter suboxydans*	Glucose, salts	Aer, sub [4.5-7.0]	30-35	1.5-2.5	90-95% of sugar	No commercial use	36,51

continued

Part II. Industrial Fermentation Products

	Product	Microorganism (Synonym)	Substrate	Type of Culture [pH]	Temp °C	No. of Days	Yield	Industrial Use	Reference
26	2-Ketoglutaric acid	*Pseudomonas* sp.; *Serratia marcescens*	Glucose, salts, $CaCO_3$	Aer, sub [5-7]	28-30	3	33% of sugar	No commercial use	30,36, 41
27	Kojic acid	*Aspergillus flavus*	Sugars, salts	Aer, surf or sub [2.0-3.5]	29-35	4-12	45-60% of sugar	Intermediate to maltol, ethyl maltol	2,35, 51
28	Lactic acid	*Lactobacillus delbrueckii*	Glucose, lactose, salts, $CaCO_3$	Anaer [5.5-6.5]	45	3-5	90-95% of sugar	Food acid; manufacture of chemicals	19,35, 51
29	L-Lysine	*Brevibacterium & Micrococcus,* auxotrophs	Molasses, biotin, urea	Aer, sub [7]	30	3	15 g/liter	Essential amino acid used in food fortification	21,22
	Other Organic Compounds								
30	Acetone-butanol	*Clostridium acetobutylicum*	Molasses diluted to 5-7% sugar, NH_3 compounds, $CaHPO_4$	Anaer [5.0-7.0]	29-34	1.7-2	Mixed solvents[1/], 28-33% of sugar	Industrial solvents	5,35, 45,51
31	2,3-Butanediol	*Aerobacter aerogenes; Bacillus polymyxa*	Starch or sugars plus nutrients; or grain mash	Aer, sub [6.2]	33	1.5-3	26-30% of carbohydrate wt	Potential solvent, humectant	35,50, 51
32	Dextran	*Leuconostoc mesenteroides*	Sucrose, nutrient salts	Anaer	20-30	1-5	10-40% of sucrose	Blood plasma substitute, food products stabilizer	6,51
33	Dihydroxyacetone	*Acetobacter suboxydans*	5% glycerol, 0.5% yeast extract, 0.25% KH_2PO_4	Aer, sub [5.5-7.0]	28-30	2-3	90% of theory	Fine chemical	35,49, 51
34	Ethanol	*Saccharomyces cerevisiae*	Molasses diluted to 12% sugar, NH_4 salts	Anaer [4-4.5]	21-26	2-3	90% of theory	Solvent, chemical intermediate, beverage	35,51
35	Glycerol	*S. cerevisiae; S. ellipsoideus*	Molasses, Na_2CO_3	Anaer [7-8]	30-32	5	20-25% of sugar	Humectant, solvent, explosives	11,51
36	Monosodium glutamate	*Brevibacterium* spp.; *Micrococcus glutamicus*	Glucose, sucrose, limited biotin, urea, NH_4 salts	Aer [7.0]	30	2-5	50% of glucose	Food flavoring	23,27
37	Sorbose	*Acetobacter suboxydans*	Sorbitol, corn steep liquor	Aer, sub [5-7]	27-30	3	90-95% of theory	Manufacture of ascorbic acid	12,35, 51,54
38	Xanthan gum	*Xanthomonas campestris*	Glucose, distiller's solubles	Aer, sub [6.5-7.5]	30-35	3-4	1.5-2.0%	Food & industrial thickener	38,43

[1/] Approximately 74% butanol, 22% acetone, 4% ethanol.

Contributors: (a) Tanner, Fred W., Jr., (b) Van Lanen, J. M., (c) Marshall, C. R., (d) Underkofler, L. A.

References

[1] Anderson, R. F., et al. 1958. J. Agr. Food Chem. 6:543.

[2] Barham, H. N., and B. L. Smits. 1936. Ind. Eng. Chem. 28:567.

[3] Batchelor, F. R., et al. 1959. Nature 183:257.

[4] Bate-Smith, E. C., et al. 1945. Brit. Intelligence Objectives Subcomm. Final Rept. 275, Item 22: P.B. 23808.

continued

Part II. Industrial Fermentation Products

[5] Beesch, S. C. 1952. Ind. Eng. Chem. 44:1677.
[6] Bixler, G. H., et al. 1953. Ibid. 45:692.
[7] Ciegler, A. 1965. Advan. Appl. Microbiol. 7:1.
[8] Ciegler, A., et al. 1959. Appl. Microbiol. 7:94.
[9] Demain, A. L., et al. 1966. Ibid. 14:821.
[10] Doelger, W. P., and S. C. Prescott. 1934. Ind. Eng. Chem. 26:1142.
[11] Eoff, J. R., W. V. Linden, and G. F. Beyer. 1919. Ibid. 11:842.
[12] Fulmer, E. I., et al. 1936. J. Am. Chem. Soc. 58: 1012.
[13] Gastrock, E. A., et al. 1938. Ind. Eng. Chem. 30: 782.
[14] Hanson, F. R., et al. 1953. J. Am. Chem. Soc. 75: 5369.
[15] Hester, A. S., and G. E. Ward. 1954. Ind. Eng. Chem. 46:238.
[16] Huang, H. T. 1963. U.S. Pat. 3,088,880.
[17] Huang, H. T., et al. 1960. J. Am. Chem. Soc. 82: 3790.
[18] Imsenecki, A. A., and L. I. Solnzeva. 1944. Microbiology (USSR) 13:54.
[19] Inskeep, G. C., et al. 1952. Ind. Eng. Chem. 44:1955.
[20] Kinoshita, S. 1961. U.S. Pat. 3,002,889.
[21] Kinoshita, S., et al. 1958. J. Gen. Appl. Microbiol. (Tokyo) 4:128.
[22] Kinoshita, S., et al. 1961. U.S. Pat. 2,979,439.
[23] Kline, L., L. R. MacDonnell, and H. Lineweaver. 1944. Ind. Eng. Chem. 36:1152.
[24] Koda, C. F., ed. 1966. Develop. Ind. Microbiol. 7:3.
[25] Leviton, A., and R. E. Hargrove. 1952. Ind. Eng. Chem. 44:2651.
[26] Licentia Patent-verwaltungs G.m.b.H. 1958. Belg. Pat. 569,728.
[27] Massengale, O. N., C. E. Bills, and P. S. Prickett. 1932. J. Biol. Chem. 94:213.
[28] Misenheimer, T. J., et al. 1965. Appl. Microbiol. 13:393.
[29] Nagayama, K. T., et al. 1966. J. Gen. Appl. Microbiol. (Tokyo) 10:133.
[30] Perlman, D., and C. J. Sih. 1960. Progr. Ind. Microbiol. 2:167.
[31] Pfeiffer, V. F., C. Vojnovich, and E. N. Heger. 1952. Ind. Eng. Chem. 44:2975.
[32] Pfeiffer, V. F., C. Vojnovich, and E. N. Heger. 1954. Ibid. 46:843.
[33] Pfeiffer, V. F., C. Vojnovich, and E. N. Heger. 1958. Ibid. 50:1009.
[34] Pfeiffer, V. F., et al. 1950. Ibid. 42:1776.
[35] Prescott, S. C., and C. G. Dunn. 1959. Industrial microbiology. Ed. 3. McGraw-Hill, New York.
[36] Rainbow, C., and A. H. Rose, ed. 1963. Biochemistry of industrial micro-organisms. Academic Press, New York.
[37] Rhodes, R. A., et al. 1962. Appl. Microbiol. 10:9.
[38] Rogovin, S. P., et al. 1961. J. Biochem. Microbiol. Technol. Eng. 3:51.
[39] Rolison, G. N., et al. 1960. Nature 187:236.
[40] Sardinas, J. L. 1966. U.S. Pat. 3,275,453.
[41] Sharpe, E. S., and J. Corman. 1959. U.S. Pat. 2,776,926.
[42] Sizer, I. W. 1964. Advan. Appl. Microbiol. 6:207.
[43] Smiley, K. L. 1966. Food Technol. 20:112.
[44] Smiley, K. L., et al. 1964. Appl. Microbiol. 12:455.
[45] Speakman, H. B. 1919. J. Soc. Chem. Ind. (London) 38:155.
[46] Stob, M., et al. 1962. Nature 196:1318.
[47] Stodola, F. H., et al. 1955. Arch. Biochem. Biophys. 54:240.
[48] Stodola, F. H., et al. 1957. Ibid. 66:438.
[49] Underkofler, L. A., and E. I. Fulmer. 1937. J. Am. Chem. Soc. 59:301.
[50] Underkofler, L. A., and E. I. Fulmer. 1948. Wallerstein Lab. Commun. 11:41.
[51] Underkofler, L. A., and R. J. Hickey, ed. 1954. Industrial fermentations. Chemical, New York. v. 1 & 2.
[52] Wallerstein, L. 1939. Ind. Eng. Chem. 31:1218.
[53] Wallerstein, L. 1939. Wallerstein Lab. Commun. 7:5.
[54] Wells, P. A., et al. 1937. Ind. Eng. Chem. 29:1385.

Part III. Foods and Beverages

	Product	Microorganism	Method of Preparation	Conditions Influencing Reaction	Reaction Produced by Microorganism	Reference
1	Acidophilus milk	*Lactobacillus acidophilus*	Fresh, whole milk, sterilized at 120°C for 15 min, then cooled and inoculated	Microaerophilic, pH 6.6; 35-37°C; 20-48 hr	Produces lactic acid from milk sugar[1]	7
	Cheese					5
2	Camembert and Brie types	*Penicillium camemberti*; others	Curd, containing 55-60% H_2O, cut into cakes 3-4 cm thick and salted on surface	4 wk at 10-15.6°C, in ripening room at 88% relative humidity	Mold grows on cheese surface, gradually softening whole mass of curd	
3	Roquefort and Gorgonzola types	*P. roqueforti*	Raw curd pressed to leave irregular cracks & channels; inoculated with mold grown on bread	Partially aerobic; aerated during ripening at 9°C by piercing with wires	Produces caproic, caprylic, & other acids imparting characteristic flavor	

[1] Lactic acid, plus large quantities of organism produced, used for disorders of the gastrointestinal tract.

continued

Part III. Foods and Beverages

	Product	Micro-organism	Method of Preparation	Conditions Influencing Reaction	Reaction Produced by Microorganism	Reference
4	Oriental foods, e.g., miso, shoyu, tempeh	*Aspergillus* spp.; *Mucor; Rhizopus;* yeasts	Soybeans, rice, & other cereals crushed, soaked, cooked, and inoculated	Aerobic, surface culture; 28-30°C for days to months	Enhance digestibility, enzyme modification, flavor development	3
5	Pickles	Mixed natural lactic acid organisms, including *Lactobacillus plantarum*	Cucumbers in tanks; spontaneous lactic acid fermentation in salt brine. For dill pickles, dill spices added before fermentation; for others, salt is leached, and pickles packed with vinegar, sugar, & spices.	Salt concentration & availability of O_2 affect rate & kind of fermentation; optimum temp, 21-27°C	Convert fermentable substances, forming particularly lactic acid; final titratable acidity as lactic acid, 0.5-1.0% (pH, 3.5-3.8)	7,9
6	Sauerkraut	Same as for pickles	Shredded cabbage in vats with salt; spontaneous lactic acid fermentation	Anaerobic fermentation; optimum temp, 16-24°C	Convert fermentable substances mainly into lactic acid, plus acetic acid & ethanol; final acidity, as lactic acid, 1.5-2.0%	7,9
7	Vinegar	*Acetobacter aceti, A. pasteurianus;* other *Acetobacter* spp.	Alcoholic solutions (e.g., wine, cider), from fermentation of grapes, apples, or grain, are "acetified" by acetic acid bacteria	Aerobic, requiring 8-10 days at 35-40°C or less, depending on process conditions	Oxidize alcohol to acetic acid; 5% acid formed from approximately 6% alcohol	4
8	Yeast, baker's	*Saccharomyces cerevisiae* (selected baker's strains)	Molasses solutions with ammonium salts, phosphates, & magnesium salts seeded with pure yeast strains; increments of medium added frequently as nutrients are exhausted	Very vigorous aeration throughout process; pH 3.5-4.5; 24-30°C; growth complete in 11 hr	Converts 100 parts molasses to equivalent of 100 parts pressed yeast (27% dry matter)	11
9	Beer	*S. carlsbergensis; S. cerevisiae*	Barley malt & starch adjuncts mixed with warm water; after enzymic starch conversion, wort is filtered, boiled with hops, and fermented with yeast	Aerobic in early stages, but quickly becomes anaerobic; pH at start, 5.0-5.4, at end, 4.2-4.8; 8-12°C[2]; primary fermentation lasts 7-9 days	Convert sugar into alcohol CO_2; produce changes in proteins & other minor constituents which modify flavor	2,6, 7,9
10	Rum	*S. cerevisiae;* other yeasts	Blackstrap molasses containing 12-14% fermentable sugar; ammonium sulfate & occasionally phosphates may be added as nutrients; distilled after fermentation	Optimum pH 4.0-4.7; initial temp, 21°C, rising to final temp of 35.5°C; fermentation lasts 3-7 days	Convert sugar to alcohol which is then removed by distillation	10
11	Whiskey, bourbon	*S. cerevisiae*	Grain mash, consistency of corn (at least 51%); generally with rye, cooked and saccharified with malt, and fermented; distillate, between 110-130 proof, matured in charred oak barrels	Optimum pH 4.0-5.0; initial temp, 25.6°C; fermentation completed in 72 hr	Same as for Scotch whisky, but the flavor is characteristic of bourbon whiskey	9
12	Whisky, Scotch	*S. cerevisiae* (generally a top yeast)	Grain mash cooked, saccharified with peated malt, and fermented; batch distilled and distillate aged in oak casks at least 3 yr, then blended with grain whiskey	Same as for bourbon whiskey	Produces alcohol & congeneric substances (acids, esters, various alcohols) which with the peated malt give characteristic Scotch flavor	8,9

[2] 14-20°C with *Saccharomyces cerevisiae.*

continued

115. BACTERIAL AND FUNGAL METABOLIC PRODUCTS USEFUL TO MAN

Part III. Foods and Beverages

	Product	Micro-organism	Method of Preparation	Conditions Influencing Reaction	Reaction Produced by Microorganism	Reference
13	Wine	*S. ellipsoideus*, various strains	Grape must, with sugar concentration up to 22° Balling, sulfited to reduce rate of fermentation; fermented with special strain of yeast, or with yeast naturally present on the grape; primary fermentation, then stored for maturation	Aerobic in early stages, but mainly anaerobic later; temp below 29.4°C, but varies according to local conditions, yeast strain, & type of wine; fermentation lasts 7-11 days	Convert sugar into alcohol, and also produce changes in minor constituents which modify flavor & bouquet; amount of alcohol varies according to type of wine	1

Contributors: (a) Marshall, C. R., (b) Underkofler, L. A., (c) Van Lanen, J. M.

References

[1] Cruess, W. V. 1947. The principles and practice of wine making. Avi, New York.

[2] Hansen, A., ed. 1948. Jǿrgensen's Micro-organisms and fermentation. Ed. 15. C. Griffin, London.

[3] Hesseltine, C. W. 1965. Mycologia 57:149.

[4] Mitchell, C. A. 1926. Vinegar, its manufacture and examination. C. Griffin, London.

[5] Orla-Jensen, S. C. 1931. Dairy bacteriology. Ed. 2. Blakiston, Philadelphia.

[6] Preece, I. A. 1954. Biochemistry of brewing. Oliver and Boyd, Edinburgh.

[7] Prescott, S. C., and C. G. Dunn. 1959. Industrial microbiology. Ed. 3. McGraw-Hill, New York.

[8] Simmonds, C. 1919. Alcohol. Macmillan, London.

[9] Underkofler, L. A., and R. J. Hickey, ed. 1954. Industrial fermentations. Chemical, New York. v. 1 & 2.

[10] Valaer, P. 1937. Ind. Eng. Chem. 29:988.

[11] White, J. 1954. Yeast technology. Chapman and Hall, London.

116. PRODUCTS OF FUNGAL METABOLISM

Products listed include only compounds (both diffusible and confined to the mycelium) which are produced by the more common fungi on media containing glucose or sucrose and various nitrogen sources--most commonly inorganic, such as $(NH_4)_2SO_4$. The well-known antibiotics have been omitted. The organisms listed are the more common ones or those used industrially, and are not necessarily the only species producing the various compounds. Most figures on yield are approximate, as they are frequently based on weights of the crude product, or of pure material after losses in purification. Strains of one species may differ widely in yield. For information on other fungal products, consult references 190 and 269.

	Metabolic Product (Synonym)	Produced by	Yield	Reference
1	Acetaldehyde	Various *Penicillium* spp., *Aspergillus* spp., *A. niger*, *Mucor* spp., many other genera. Produced by fixation with intercepting agents.	Up to 60% of theory when grown on sucrose with *Aspergillus niger*	39,207,210
2	Acetic acid	*Fomes annosus, Marasmius chordalis, Merulius confluens, M. lacrymans, M. niveus, M. tremellosus*	0.6-0.9% of glucose used for *Merulius lacrymans* & *Marasmius chordalis*	206,207,210, 277
3	Aconitic acid	*Aspergillus niger*	...	36
4	Adenine	*A. niger*	0.05%	180,296
5	Adenosine 5′-triphosphate (ATP)	Several molds	...	170
6	Albidin	*Penicillium albidum*	...	110
7	Alboleersin 1/,2/	*Helminthosporium leersii*	0.4% of mycelial wt	18,234
8	Alloisocitric acid (Lactone)	*Penicillium purpurogenum rubrisclerotium*	20% of glucose substrate	30
9	6-Aminopenicillanic acid	*P. chrysogenum*	...	29

1/ Colorless. 2/ Related to one another: alboleersin, helminthosporin, luteoleersin.

continued

	Metabolic Product (Synonym)	Produced by	Yield	Reference
10	Ascorbic acid	*Aspergillus niger*	0.2% of glucose consumed	132
11	Aspergillic acid	*A. flavus*	1% of carbohydrate added	119,162,309
12	Asperthecin	*A. quadrilineatus, A. nidulans*	....	197
13	Asperxanthone	*A. niger* (mycelium)	....	183
14	Atrovenetin	*Penicillium atrovenetum*	....	198
15	Aurofusarin	*Fusarium culmorum, F. graminearum*	Up to 4.4% of mycelial wt	20,196
16	Auroglaucin	*Aspergillus glaucus, A. mangini,* other *Aspergillus* spp.	>13% of the dry growth	106,137,231, 240
17	Betaine	*A. oryzae* (spores)	....	180,281,289
18	Biotin 1-sulfoxide	*A. niger*	....	318
19	Bromogriseofulvin	*Penicillium griseofulvum*	....	185
20	Byssochlamic acid	*Byssochlamys fulva*	0.5% of glucose consumed	244
21	Caldariomycin	*Caldariomyces fumago*	0.4% of glucose consumed	99,102
22	Canescine	*Penicillium canescens*	30-110 mg/liter	70
23	Capreolinose[3]	*P. capreolinum*	....	101
24	1-Carboxy-2,5-dioxybenzyl methyl ketone	*P. brevi-compactum (P. stoloniferum)*	....	213
25	1-Carboxy-2,5-dioxyphenyl acetyl carbinol	*P. brevi-compactum (P. stoloniferum)*	....	97
26	Carlic acid	*P. charlesii*	Up to 1.1% of sugar consumed	99,100
27	Carlosic acid	*P. charlesii, P. cinerascens*	Up to 0.36% of sugar consumed	68,99,100
28	Carolic acid	*P. charlesii*	Up to 1.54% of sugar consumed	99,100
29	Carolinic acid	*P. charlesii*	Up to 0.9% of sugar consumed	99,100
30	α-Carotene	*Neurospora crassa* mutants, *Penicillium sclerotiorum*	....	135
31	β-Carotene	*Neurospora* spp., *Mucor hiemalis, Phycomyces blakesleeanus*	Traces	262,263,326
32	β-, γ-, δ-, & *n*-Carotene	....	....	136
33	γ-Carotene	*Allomyces* spp.	Traces	121
34	Carviolacin	*Penicillium roseopurpureum (P. carminoviolaceum)*	3.0% of mycelium (crude pigment)	148
35	Carviolin	*P. roseopurpurem (P. carminoviolaceum)*	3.0% of mycelium (crude pigment)	148,226
36	Catenarin (1-Hydroxyemodin)	*Helminthosporium catenarium, H. gramineum, H. velutinum, H. tritici-vulgaris, Penicillium islandicum, Aspergillus amstelodami*	As much as 10-40% of mycelial wt in *Helminthosporium gramineum,* 20% in *H. catenarium*	12,14,89, 233,237, 239,249
37	Cerebrin	*Aspergillus sydowi*	0.1-0.4%	63
38	Cerebronylsphingosine compounds	*A. citromyces*	....	255
39	Chaetomin	*Chaetomium cochliodes*	....	131
40	Choline sulfate	*Aspergillus sydowi.* From hydrolysis of mycelium.	....	316
41	Chrysogenin	*Penicillium chrysogenum*	....	98
42	Chrysophanic acid (Chrysophanol)	*P. islandicum*	0.1% of dried mycelium	153
43	Citric acid	*Penicillium (Citromyces)* spp., *P. luteum, P. citrinum, P. spinulosum, Aspergillus niger, A. clavatus, A. itaconicus, A. wentii, Mucor pyriformis,* many other species. Commercial production on beet and cane molasses. Submerged production possible but not yet commercially successful.	As high as 90% of theory	37,46,72,79, 125,132, 168,186, 273,307
44	Citrinin[4]	*Penicillium citrinum, Aspergillus terreus*	3.4% of sugar consumed	104,150,245
45	Citromycetin	*Penicillium frequentans (Citromyces glabrum)* group	As much as 20% sugar metabolized	149,150
46	Clavatol[5]	*Aspergillus clavatus*	Small amount	32,144
47	Compound T	*Penicillium stipitatum*	....	292

[3] Hydrolysis yields galactose, glucose, mannose, and mannonic acid. [4] Possesses antibiotic properties but is not in clinical use. [5] Minor product with patulin.

continued

	Metabolic Product (Synonym)	Produced by	Yield	Reference
48	Culmorin[1]	*Fusarium culmorum, F. graminearum*	Up to 4.64% of mycelium; isolated along with aurofusarin	20,196
49	Cyclopaldic acid	*Penicillium cyclopium album*	0.97% of dry mycelium	60
50	Cyclopenin	*P. cyclopium*	....	67
51	Cyclopolic acid	*P. cyclopium, P. cyclopium album*	5.45% of dry mycelium in *P. cyclopium;* 1.65% of dry mycelium in *P. cyclopium album*	60
52	Cynodontin	*Helminthosporium cynodontis, H. euchlaenae, H. avenae*	Up to 4.2% of mycelium	13,233,237, 239
53	2-Decene-1,10-dioic acid	*Penicillium notatum*	....	105
54	Dechlorogriseofulvin	*P. griseofulvum, P. janczewski*	....	184
55	Dechloronornidulin (Ustin II)	*Aspergillus nidulans* NRRL No. 2006	....	115
56	Dehydrocarolic acid	*Penicillium cinerascens*	3% of glucose consumed	68
57	14-Dehydroergosterol; also, ergosterol	*Aspergillus niger*	....	26
58	Desthiobiotin (Dethiobiotin)	*Penicillium chrysogenum*	....	293
59	Dihydrogladiolic acid	*P. gladioli*	340 mg/liter of Raulin-Thom medium	241
60	Dihydroxyacetone	*P. brevi-compactum*	....	134
61	α,β-Dihydroxyisovaleric acid	*Neurospora crassa* mutant	....	275
62	α,β-Dihydroxy-β-methylvaleric acid	*N. crassa* mutant	....	275
63	3,5-Dihydroxyphthalic acid	*Penicillium brevi-compactum*	....	212
64	3,5-Dimethyl-6-oxyphthalide	*P. gladioli*	....	241
65	Dimethyl pyruvic acid	*Aspergillus niger.* In presence of sodium sulfite as interceptor.	....	151
66	2,4-Dioxy-6-pyruvylbenzoic acid	*Penicillium brevi-compactum (P. stoloniferum)*	....	213
67	Diphosphopyridine nucleotide (DPN)	Widely distributed	....	179
68	Echinulin	*Aspergillus glaucus* types	200 g/5 kg dry mycelium	230
69	Emodic acid	*Penicillium cyclopium*	0.1% (as acetyl derivative) of glucose supplied	8
70	Erdin[6]	*Aspergillus terreus*	0.6% of sugar consumed	81,94,246
71	Ergochrysin	*Sclerotium clavus*	....	34
72	Ergoflavin	*S. clavus*	....	33
73	Ergosterol	*Aspergillus niger, A. oryzae, Fusarium lycopersici, F. lini, Helminthosporium avenae, H. ravenelii, H. velutinum, Lentinus lepideus, Penicillium expansum, P. puberulum*	0.13-1.7% of mycelium	50,123,229, 239,250, 264,303
74	Ergosterol palmitate	*Penicillium* spp., *Aspergillus fumigatus*	....	123
75	Ergosterol peroxide	*Aspergillus fumigatus* (mycelium)	....	310
76	Ergosteryl palmitate	*Penicillium brevi-compactum, P. italicum*	0.5% of growth, 0.6% of glucose consumed	214
77	Erythritol	*P. brevi-compactum, P. cyclopium*	0.7% of wt of organism	217
78	Erythroglaucin (Catenarin 6-methyl ether)	*Aspergillus glaucus* group, 15 species	0.25% of mycelium (pure)	12,19
79	Ethyl acetate	*Penicillium digitatum*	0.6% of sugar consumed	53,207,210
80	Ethyl alcohol	*Fusarium* spp., *Mucor* spp., *Merulius* spp., various *Penicillium* spp. and *Aspergillus* spp., *Fomes annosus.* Production much slower than by yeast.	Stoichiometric yield with *Fusarium* spp. & *Merulius* spp. *Fomes annosus* grown on hexoses and pentoses.	4,112,125, 138,207, 210
81	Ethylene	*Penicillium digitatum*	....	199
82	L-Ethylene oxide α, β dicarboxylic acid	*Monilia formosa, Penicillium viniferum, Aspergillus fumigatus*	10-15% yield from various substrates: hexoses, hexahydric alcohols, pentoses, pentahydric alcohol, erythritol, butyleneglycol, glycerol, acetate, alcohol	43,257
83	Fat	All organisms	Various	206,276,277

[1] Colorless. [6] Erdin and geodin are closely related compounds.

continued

	Metabolic Product (Synonym)	Produced by	Yield	Reference
84	Flavacol	*A. flavus*	....	118
85	Flavin adenine dinucleotide (FAD)	Several molds	....	90
86	Flaviolin	*A. citricus*	....	113
87	Flavipin	*A. flavipes, A. terreus*	....	242
88	Flavoglaucin	*A. glaucus,* other *Aspergillus* spp.	>25% of dry growth wt	106,137,231, 240
89	Flavoskyrin	*Penicillium islandicum*	....	268
90	Formic acid	*Aspergillus oryzae*	....	288
91	Frequentin	*Penicillium frequentans, P. cyclopium*	....	111
92	Fulvic acid	*P. griseofulvum, P. flexuosum, P. brefeldianum*	15-20% of mycelium, 2.7% of glucose consumed	220
93	Fumagillin (Amebacilin: Fumidil)	*Aspergillus fumigatus*	....	120
94	Fumaric acid	Various *Rhizopus* spp., *Aspergillus fumaricus, Penicillium griseofulvum, Caldariomyces fumago.* Most species in orders other than Mucorales give small amounts.	50% of theoretical yield after 30 days	40,125,126, 243,302
95	Fumaroalanide	*Penicillium resticulosum*	3.3 g from 1750 g glucose furnished	49,102
96	Fumigatin	*Aspergillus fumigatus*	0.35% of glucose consumed (crude material)	10,22
97	Fungal cerebrins	*Penicillium* spp.	....	211
98	Fungisterol	*P. chrysogenum, Rhizopus japonicus*	....	256
99	Funiculosin (Trihydroxymethylanthraquinone)	*Penicillium funiculosum*	....	156
100	Fusarubin	*Fusarium solani*	25 mg/liter of medium on sucrose	254
101	Galactosyl lactose	*Penicillium chrysogenum*	....	23
102	Gentisic acid	*P. griseofulvum, P. jenseni, P. divergens*	0.1% of glucose consumed	66,243
103	Gentisyl alcohol	*P. patulum, P. divergens*	2.3% of glucose added	42,58,66
104	Gentisylquinone	*P. patulum*	....	122
105	Geodin[6]	*Aspergillus terreus*	0.6% of sugar consumed	81,82,94,246
106	Geodoxin	*A. terreus*	....	143
107	Gladiolic acid	*Penicillium gladioli*	94 mg/liter of Raulin-Thom medium	140,241
108	Glaucic acid	*Aspergillus glaucus*	....	286
109	Glauconic acid	Green *Penicillium* sp.	20% of a mixture	323
110	Glauconic acids: I & II	*P. glaucum, P. purpurogenum*	....	311
111	Gliotoxin	*Aspergillus fumigatus, Penicillium terlikowskii,* other fungi	100 mg/liter	160
112	Gliotoxin acetate	*P. terlikowskii*	....	161
113	Gluconic acid	*P. chrysogenum, P. luteum, P. purpurogenum, Aspergillus* spp., *Fusarium lini*	Practically quantitative conversion in 24 hr	132,168,195, 206,254, 283,308
114	Glucose	*Aspergillus niger.* From tartaric acid, lactic acid, mannitol, and quinic acid.	....	177
115	Glucosone	*A. parasiticus, A. flavus*	8% from glucose; 13-17% from sucrose, maltose, starch	64,300
116	D-Glucuronic acid	*Penicillium* sp.	....	260
117	Glutaconic acid	*Aspergillus niger* strains	....	21
118	Glutaric acid	*A. niger* strains	....	21
119	L(−)Glyceric acid	Large variety	....	190
120	Glycerol	*Mucor racemosus, Aspergillus wentii,* white *Aspergillus* spp., *Clasterosporium* spp., *Helminthosporium* spp., *Penicillium* spp.	Usually small amounts; some species, 3% of glucose consumed	52

[6] Erdin and geodin are closely related compounds.

continued

	Metabolic Product (Synonym)	Produced by	Yield	Reference
121	Glycogen[7,8]	White *Aspergillus* spp., *Penicillium digitatum*	....	52-54
122	Glycolic acid	*Aspergillus niger*, from acetate.	Traces	38
123	Glycuronic acid	*Ustulina vulgaris*	....	319
124	Glyoxylic acid	*Aspergillus niger* (from acetate), *Merulius lacrymans*	Traces	38,276,277
125	Granegillin	Mold resembling *Aspergillus flavus*	....	119
126	Griseofulvin[4] (Fulvicin; Grisovin)	*Penicillium griseofulvum, P. janczewski, P. patulum, P. albidum*	2% of mycelium	141,219
127	Gums	*Oidium* sp., *Penicillium lactis, P. guttulosum, Monilia candida, Mucor racemosus*	38% on 10% mannose	258,259
128	Helenine	*Penicillium funiculosum*	....	272
129	Helminthosporin[2]	*Helminthosporium gramineum, H. catenarium, H. tritici-vulgaris, H. cynodontis*	As much as 22-40% of mycelial wt in *H. gramineum*	89,233,237-239, 249
130	Helvolic acid[4] (Fumigacin; Mycocidin)	*Aspergillus fumigatus, A. fumigatus helvola*	0.02-0.15% of glucose added	86,188,298, 299
131	Herquein	*Penicillium herquei*	....	75
132	Herqueinone	*P. herquei*	....	278
133	Hydroxyaspergillic acid	*Aspergillus flavus*	....	119
134	*p*-Hydroxybenzoic acid	*Penicillium patulum*	....	27
135	ω-Hydroxyemodin (Citreorosein)	*P. cyclopium, P. citreo-roseum, P. cyaneofulvum*	0.1% of glucose (tetraacetyl derivative) supplied	8,225,227
136	3-Hydroxy-4-methoxy-toluquinol[9]	*Aspergillus fumigatus*	....	10
137	2-Hydroxymethyl-furane-5-carboxylic acid	*A. glaucus, A. clavatus, A. niger, A. oryzae, A. wentii*	....	282,284,285
138	3-Hydroxyphthalic acid	*Penicillium islandicum, P. patulum*	1-2 mg/liter	129
139	Hypoxanthine	*Aspergillus oryzae, Rhizopus japonicus*	....	180,291
140	Iridoskyrin	*Penicillium islandicum*	....	154
141	Islandicin	*P. islandicum*	3% of mycelium	152
142	Itaconic acid	*Aspergillus terreus, A. itaconicus*	As high as 50% of theoretical yield	80,125,168, 169,182, 192,193, 280
143	Itatartaric acid	*A. terreus* mutant	1.5% of glucose added	200,280
144	Javanicin	*Fusarium javanicum*	0.05% of glucose added (pure)	16,17
145	γ-Ketopentadecoic acid	*Penicillium minio-luteum, P. spiculisporum*	2.5% of glucose consumed	48
146	Kojibiose	*Aspergillus niger*	....	261
147	Kojic acid	*A. flavus, A. oryzae, A. tamarii, A. wentii, A. glaucus*	45-55% in 12 days. 63-66% reported.	133,167,187, 194,320
148	D-Lactic acid	Practically confined to Mucorales. Various *Rhizopus* spp., i.e. *R. stolonifer, R. oryzae, R. japonicus, R. tritici, R. arrhizus.* Fumaric acid produced by altering conditions.	Up to 62% with *R. oryzae;* 39-40% with *R. japonicus*	125,164,302
149	Lecithin	*Aspergillus oryzae* (spores)	....	281
150	Lecithin & cephalin	*A. sydowi*	0.43-0.73%	317
151	Levan[10]	*A. sydowi*, from sucrose only.	....	176
152	Luteic acid[11] (Luteose)	*Penicillium luteum*	10-12%	5,236
153	Luteoleersin[2]	*Helminthosporium leersii*	1.8% of mycelium	18,234
154	Luteoskyrin	*Penicillium islandicum*	....	267
155	Lycomarasmine (Asparagyl-glycyl-hydroxyalanine)	*Fusarium lycopersici*	110 mg/liter of medium on glucose	222,223,315
156	Lycopersin	*F. lycopersici*	....	178
157	Malic acid	White *Aspergillus* spp., *A. flavus, Clasterosporium* sp. Accompanied by succinic and fumaric acids.	Fair yields by submerged growths when growing at low temp	324

[2] Related to one another: alboleersin, helminthosporin, luteoleersin. [4] Possesses antibiotic properties but is not in clinical use. [7] Red-brown iodine color. [8] Hydrolysis yields glucose. [9] Reduced form of fumigatin. [10] Hydrolysis yields fructose. [11] Hydrolysis yields β-glucose-malonic acid (2:1), demalonylated luteic acid.

continued

	Metabolic Product (Synonym)	Produced by	Yield	Reference
158	Malonic acid	*Penicillium funiculosum*	....	155
159	Mannitol	White *Aspergillus* spp., many *Aspergillus* spp., *Byssochlamys fulva, Penicillium griseofulvum.* Not produced from fructose.	45-50% of theory	52,168,243, 284,285
160	Mannonic acid	*P. purpurogenum rubrisclerotium,* on D-mannose	9%	6
161		Certain *Aspergillus niger* strains, on mannose	70%	172
162		Certain *A. niger* strains, on galactose	High yield	172
163	Mellein[12] (Ochracin)	*A. melleus, A. ochraceus*	300 mg/liter of medium on sucrose	76,200,321, 322
164	α-Methyl butyric acid	*Penicillium notatum*	....	105
165	Methyl salicylic acid	*P. griseofulvum, P. flexuosum*	2.4% of glucose consumed	9
166	6-Methyl salicylic acid	*P. griseofulvum, P. flexuosum, P. patulum, P. urticae*	....	28
167	γ-Methyl tetronic acid	*P. charlesii*	Up to 0.52% of sugar consumed	99,100
168		*P. charlesii, P. fellutanum*	14% of glucose consumed	295
169	Methylglyoxal	*Aspergillus niger,* on hexosediphosphate	16% of substrate consumed	287
170	Minioluteic acid[13]	*Penicillium minio-luteum*	2.5% of glucose consumed	48
171	Mold starch[8,14]	*Penicillium* spp.	....	92
172	Monascoflavin	*Monascus purpureus*	....	201
173	Monascorubrin	*M. purpureus*	....	201
174	Mycelianamide	*Penicillium griseofulvum*	....	41
175	Mycodextran[8,15]	*P. expansum, Aspergillus niger*	2% of the growth	116
176	Mycogalactan[16]	*A. niger.* Produced along with mycodextran.	....	117
177	Mycophenolic acid	*Penicillium brevi-compactum (P. stoloniferum)*	0.95% of glucose consumed	3,59,95,97
178	Nalgiolaxin[17]	*P. nalgiovensis*	0.18% of dry mycelium	248
179	Nalgiovensin	*P. nalgiovensis*	1% of dry mycelium	248
180	Neohydroxyaspergillic acid	*Aspergillus sclerotiorum*	300 mg/liter	306
181	Neurosporaxanthin	*Neurospora crassa*	....	325
182	Nidulin	*Aspergillus nidulans* NRRL No. 2006	6 g/126 g of dry mycelium	114
183	β-Nitro propionic acid	*A. flavus, A. oryzae*	....	77
184	Nordin	*Penicillium paxilli echinulatum*	....	175
185	Nornidulin (Ustin)	*Aspergillus nidulans* NRRL No. 2006	....	114
186	Oosporein	*Oospora colorans*	9.5% of substrate added	174
187	Orotidine	*Neurospora crassa* mutant	....	189
188	Orsellinic acid	*Penicillium griseofulvum, Chaetomium cochliodes*	....	191
189	Oryzacidin (Oryzasizine)	*Aspergillus oryzae*	....	271
190	Oxalic acid	*Aspergillus* spp., *Penicillium (Citromyces)* spp., many other genera. Can be produced more economically by other methods.	50% of sugar consumed	35,76,107, 125,208, 209,245
191	Oxy-javanicin	*Fusarium javanicum*	0.02% of glucose added (pure)	16,17
192	Palitantin	*Penicillium palitans, P. frequentans, P. cyclopium*	About 1% of glucose consumed	67,207
193	Palmitoleic acid (Physetolic acid; 9-Hexadecenoic acid)	*P. lilacinum*	....	274
194	Patulin[4] (Clavacin; Clavatin; Claviformin; Penicidin; Expansine; Mycoin)	*P. patulum,* many other *Penicillium* spp., *Aspergillus clavatus, A. terreus, A. giganteus*	2.2% of glucose added	15,31,57,84, 85,124, 297,314
195	Penetrinic acid	*Penicillium notatum*	....	279
196	Penicillic acid[4]	*P. cyclopium, P. puberulum, Aspergillus* spp.	4.2% of glucose consumed	45,55,76,84, 166

[4] Possesses antibiotic properties but is not in clinical use. [8] Hydrolysis yields glucose. [12] Converted to methyl salicylic acid on potassium hydroxide fusion. [13] Minioluteic and spiculisporic acids are related. [14] Blue iodine color. [15] No iodine color. [16] Hydrolysis yields galactose. [17] Mono-chloro-nalgiovensin.

continued

	Metabolic Product (Synonym)	Produced by	Yield	Reference
197	Penicilliopsin	*Penicilliopsis clavariaeformis*	7.5% of mycelium	19,62,73, 218,240
	Penicillium brevicompactum acids			
198	I	*Penicillium brevi-compactum*	0.9% of sugar consumed	97,215
199	II	*P. brevi-compactum*	0.1% of sugar consumed	97,213,215
200	III	*P. brevi-compactum*	0.9% of sugar consumed	97,215
201	IV	*P. brevi-compactum*	0.03% of sugar consumed	97,212,215
202	Phoenicin	*P. phoeniceum, P. rubrum, Bacillus pyocyaneus*	1.2% of mycelium (pure)	127,128,224, 225,228
203	Phosphatides	*Aspergillus oryzae, A. sydowi, A. citromyces*	....	255,290
204	Physcion (Emodin monomethyl ether; Parietin)	*A. glaucus, A. chevalieri, A. ruber, Penicillium herquei*	0.65% of mycelium (pure)	19,171,232, 240
	Physcion anthranol			
205	A: (4,5-Dihydroxy-7-methoxy-2-methyl-9-anthranol)	*Aspergillus glaucus*	Very small amount	19
206	B: (4,5-Dihydroxy-7-methoxy-2-methyl-10-anthranol)	*A. glaucus*	Very small amount	19
207	Phytofluene	*Neurospora crassa*	....	326
208	Pigments B & C (Oxidized skyrins)	*Penicillium islandicum* NRRL No. 1175	....	270
209	Polygalactose[16] (Galactocarolose)	*P. charlesii*	Approx 4% of sugar consumed (crude)	99,146
210	Polymannose[18]	*P. charlesii*	Approx 4% of sugar consumed (crude)	99
211	Prephenic acid	*Neurospora crassa* mutants	....	305
212	Propionic acid	*Botrytis cinerea,* on lactate	....	91
213	Pterin-like substance (2-Amino-4,7-dihydroxypteridine-6-acetic acid ?)	*Aspergillus* spp.	....	163
214	Pteroylhexaglutamylglutamic acid (Vitamin B_c conjugate)	Widely distributed	....	74
215	Puberulic acid[19]	*Penicillium puberulum, P. aurantio-virens, P. cyclopium viridicatum, P. johannioli*	0.66% of glucose consumed (crude)	25,47,103, 235
216	Puberulonic acid[19]	*P. puberulum, P. johannioli,* other *Penicillium* spp.	....	25,47,235, 266
217	Pulvilloric acid	*P. pulvillorum*	....	71
218	Pyridoxal-5′-phosphate	Widely distributed	....	142
219	Pyrocalciferol	*P. notatum*	12 mg/450 g dry mycelium	7
220	Pyrogallol	*P. patulum*	....	27
221	Pyruvic acid	*Aspergillus niger* (in presence of sodium sulfite as interceptor), *Fusarium* spp.	8.2% of glucose consumed	151,253,312
222	Quadrilineatin	*Aspergillus quadrilineatus*	....	44
223	Ravenelin	*Helminthosporium ravenelii, H. turcicum*	10% of mycelium	196,250
224	Rhizopterin (N^{10}-Formylpteroic acid)	*Rhizopus nigricans*	....	251
225	Rhodoviolascin (Spirilloxanthin)	*Neurospora crassa* mutants	....	24
226	Roseopurpurin (Carbiolin)	*Penicillium roseopurpureum*	....	226
227	Rotiorin	*P. sclerotiorum*	100-150 g/8 kg dry mycelium	159
228	Rubrofusarin	*Fusarium culmorum, F. graminearum*	Up to 1.15% of mycelial wt. Crude pigment up to 8.7% of mycelial wt.	20,196,265
229	Rubroskyrin	*Penicillium islandicum*	....	267
230	Rugulose[16]	*P. rugulosum*	....	101
231	Rugulosin (Radicalisin)	*P. rugulosum, P. tardum, P. wortmannii*	20% of dry wt of *P. rugulosum*	69,153

[16] Hydrolysis yields galactose. [18] Hydrolysis yields mannose. [19] Tropolone derivative.

continued

	Metabolic Product (Synonym)	Produced by	Yield	Reference
232	Saccharic acid	*Aspergillus niger*	....	87,88
233	Sclerotiorine	*Penicillium sclerotiorum*	2% of mycelium	108,109
234	Sclerotiose[8]	*P. sclerotiorum*	10% of mycelial wt	2
235	Skyrin (Endothianin)	*P. islandicum, P. wortmannii, P. tardum, P. rugulosum*	....	173
236	Solanione	*Fusarium solani* D_2 purple	....	304
237	Sorbicillin	*Penicillium notatum*	....	105
238	Spermidine	*Neurospora crassa*	....	139
239	Spiculosporic acid[13]	*Penicillium spiculisporum, P. crateriforme, P. minio-luteum*	Approx 2% of sugar utilized	48,96,216
240	Spinulosin (Hydroxyfumigatin)	*P. spinulosum, P. cinerascens, Aspergillus fumigatus*	0.11% of glucose consumed (*A. fumigatus*)	11,46,68
241	Stachydrine (*n*-Methyl-proline-methyl betaine)	*A. oryzae, Rhizopus japonicus*	....	180,281,289
242	Stearyl alcohol	*Penicillium notatum*	0.13 g/300 g dry mycelium	7
243	Sterigmatocystin	*Aspergillus versicolor*	....	61
244	Sterols	*A. fischeri, Penicillium puberulum, Paecilomyces varioti, Fusarium* spp.	0.13-1.0% of dry mycelium	51,123,229
245	Stipitatic acid[19]	*Penicillium stipitatum*	Up to 3% of sugar consumed	56,221,235
246	Stipitatonic acid	*P. stipitatum*	....	266
247	Succinic acid	*Mucor stolonifer, Aspergillus terreus, Ustulina vulgaris, Penicillium aurantio-virens, P. spiculosporum, Fusarium oxysporum, F. heterosporum, F. lini, Fomes annosus, Merulius confluens, M. niveus, M. tremellosus*	Yields very small, except for *Fusarium* spp.	4,78,96,125, 150,181, 207,233, 245
248	Sulochrin	*Oospora sulphureaochracea*	5% of mycelium	202-205
249	Tardin	*Penicillium tardum*	....	65
250	Terrecin	*Aspergillus terreus*	....	158
251	Terreic acid	*A. terreus*	138 g from 200 liters	165
252	Terrein	*A. terreus, Penicillium raistrickii*	2-3% of glucose consumed (crude)	245,247
253	Terrestric acid (Ethyl carolic acid)	*P. terrestre*	2.4% of sugar consumed	247
254	1,4,7,8-Tetrachyroxy-2-methylanthraquinone	*P. islandicum*	....	130
255	Tetracosanoic acid (Lignoceric acid)	*P. chrysogenum*	....	1
256	Tetrahydrophoenicin (Leucophoenicin)	*P. rubrum*	....	225
257	Thiamine	*Fusarium lini*	20 µg/g of mycelium	313
258	Triphosphopyridine nucleotide (TPN)	Widely distributed	....	301
259	Tritisporin	*Helminthosporium tritici-vulgaris, Helminthosporium* spp.	1.4% of mycelium	233,239,249
260	Urea	*Penicillium johannioli, Aspergillus niger, Rhizopus nigricans*	....	93,157
261	Uric acid	*Aspergillus oryzae* (spores)	....	281
262	Uridine diphosphate glucose (UDPG)	Several molds	....	83
263	Ustic acid	*A. ustus*	0.5 g/liter	247
264	Varianose[20]	*Penicillium varians*	Approx 1% of glucose consumed (crude material)	147
265	Versicolorin	*Aspergillus versicolor*	....	145
266	Viridicatic acid (Ethylcarlosic acid)	*Penicillium viricatum*	....	50
267	Vitamin B_6 (Pyridoxine)	*Penicillium* spp.	82-114 µg/g from penicillin broth filtrates	294
268	Wortmannin	*P. wortmannii*	....	71
269	Xanthocillin X & Y	*P. notatum*	....	252

[8] Hydrolysis yields glucose. [13] Minioluteic and spiculisporic acids are related. [19] Tropolone derivative. [20] Hydrolysis yields D-galactose, D-glucose, and D-idose or L-altrose.

continued

116. PRODUCTS OF FUNGAL METABOLISM

Contributors: (a) Snell, J. F., (b) Nord, F. F., (c) Gould, Bernard S.

References

[1] Abe, Y. 1949. Proc. Fac. Eng. Keiogijuku Univ. 2(7):15 (Chem. Abstr. 47:4949i).
[2] Albericci, V. J., T. P. Curtin, and D. Reilly. 1943. Biochem. J. 37:243.
[3] Alsberg, C. L., and O. F. Black. 1913. U.S. Dept. Agr. Bur. Plant Ind. Bull. 270.
[4] Anderson, A. K., and J. J. Willaman. 1922. Proc. Soc. Exptl. Biol. Med. 20:108.
[5] Anderson, C. G., et al. 1939. Biochem. J. 33:272.
[6] Angeletti, A., and C. F. Cerruti. 1930. Ann. Chim. Appl. 20:424.
[7] Angeletti, A., G. Tappi, and G. Biglino. 1952. Ann. Chim. (Rome) 42:502.
[8] Anslow, W. K., J. Breen, and H. Raistrick. 1940. Biochem. J. 34:159.
[9] Anslow, W. K., and H. Raistrick. 1931. Ibid. 25:39.
[10] Anslow, W. K., and H. Raistrick. 1939. Ibid. 32:687.
[11] Anslow, W. K., and H. Raistrick. 1938. Ibid. 32: 803, 2288.
[12] Anslow, W. K., and H. Raistrick. 1940. Ibid. 34: 1124.
[13] Anslow, W. K., and H. Raistrick. 1940. Ibid. 34: 1546.
[14] Anslow, W. K., and H. Raistrick. 1941. Ibid. 35: 1006.
[15] Anslow, W. K., and H. Raistrick. 1943. J. Soc. Chem. Ind. (London) 62:236.
[16] Arnstein, H. R. V., and A. H. Cook. 1947. J. Chem. Soc., p. 1021.
[17] Arnstein, H. R. V., A. H. Cook, and M. S. Lacey. 1946. Brit. J. Exptl. Pathol. 27:349.
[18] Ashley, J. N., and H. Raistrick. 1938. Biochem. J. 32:449.
[19] Ashley, J. N., H. Raistrick, and T. Richards. 1939. Ibid. 33:1291.
[20] Ashley, J. N., et al. 1937. Ibid. 31:385.
[21] Baba, S., and K. Sakaguchi. 1942. Nippon Nogeikagaku Kaishi 18(Abstr.):93.
[22] Baker, W., and H. Raistrick. 1941. J. Chem. Soc., p. 670.
[23] Ballio, A., and S. Russi. 1960. Tetrahedron 9:125.
[24] Barber, M. S., L. M. Jackson, and B. C. L. Weedon. 1959. Proc. Chem. Soc., p. 96.
[25] Barger, G., and O. Dorrer. 1934. Biochem. J. 28:11.
[26] Barton, D. H. R., and T. Buun. 1951. J. Chem. Soc., p. 2728.
[27] Bassett, E. W., and S. W. Tanenbaum. 1958. Biochim. Biophys. Acta 28:247.
[28] Bassett, E. W., and S. W. Tanenbaum. 1958. Experientia 14:38.
[29] Batchelor, F. R., et al. 1959. Nature 183:257.
[30] Beppu, T., S. Abe, and K. Sakaguchi. 1957. Nippon Nogeikagaku Kaishi 21:263.
[31] Bergel, F., et al. 1943. Nature 152:750.
[32] Bergel, F., et al. 1944. J. Chem. Soc., p. 415.
[33] Bergmann, W. 1932. Ber. Deut. Chem. Ges. 65: 1486.
[34] Bergmann, W. 1932. Ibid. 65:1489.
[35] Bernhauer, K. 1950. Ergeb. Enzymforsch. 11:151.
[36] Bernhauer, K., and N. Böckl. 1932. Biochem. Z. 253:16.
[37] Bernhauer, K., N. Böckl, and H. Siebenauger. 1932. Ibid. 253:37.
[38] Bernhauer, K., and Z. Scheuer. 1932. Ibid. 253:11.
[39] Bernhauer, K., and H. Thelen. 1932. Ibid. 253:30.
[40] Bernhauer, K., and H. Thole. 1936. Ibid. 287:167.
[41] Birch, A. J., R. A. Massy-Westropp, and R. W. Rickards. 1956. J. Chem. Soc., p. 3717.
[42] Birkinshaw, J. H., A. Bracken, and H. Raistrick. 1943. Biochem. J. 37:726.
[43] Birkinshaw, J. H., A. Bracken, and H. Raistrick. 1945. Ibid. 39:70.
[44] Birkinshaw, J. H., P. Chaplen, and R. Lahoz-Oliver. 1957. Ibid. 67:155.
[45] Birkinshaw, J. H., A. E. Oxford, and H. Raistrick. 1936. Ibid. 30:394.
[46] Birkinshaw, J. H., and H. Raistrick. 1931. Phil. Trans. Roy. Soc. London, B, 220:245.
[47] Birkinshaw, J. H., and H. Raistrick. 1932. Biochem. J. 26:441.
[48] Birkinshaw, J. H., and H. Raistrick. 1934. Ibid. 28:828.
[49] Birkinshaw, J. H., H. Raistrick, and G. Smith. 1942. Ibid. 36:829.
[50] Birkinshaw, J. H., and M. S. Samant. 1960. Ibid. 74:369.
[51] Birkinshaw, J. H., et al. 1931. Ibid. 25:1977.
[52] Birkinshaw, J. H., et al. 1931. Phil. Trans. Roy. Soc. London, B, 220:153.
[53] Birkinshaw, J. H., et al. 1931. Ibid., B, 220:331.
[54] Birkinshaw, J. H., et al. 1931. Ibid., B, 220:355.
[55] Birkinshaw, J. H., et al. 1936. Biochem. J. 30:801.
[56] Birkinshaw, J. H., et al. 1942. Ibid. 36:242.
[57] Birkinshaw, J. H., et al. 1943. Lancet 245:625.
[58] Birkinshaw, J. H., et al. 1944. Biochem. J. 38:131.
[59] Birkinshaw, J. H., et al. 1948. Ibid. 43:216.
[60] Birkinshaw, J. H., et al. 1952. Ibid. 50:610.
[61] Birkinshaw, J. H., et al. 1957. Ibid. 65:162.
[62] Blochwitz, A. 1931. Ber. Deut. Botan. Ges. 49:319.
[63] Bohonos, N., and W. H. Peterson. 1943. J. Biol. Chem. 149:295.
[64] Bond, C. R., E. C. Knight, and T. K. Walker. 1937. Biochem. J. 31:1033.
[65] Borodin, N., F. J. Philpot, and H. W. Florey. 1947. J. Exptl. Pathol. 28:31.
[66] Brack, A. 1947. Helv. Chim. Acta 30:1.
[67] Bracken, A., A. Pocker, and H. Raistrick. 1954. Biochem. J. 57:587.
[68] Bracken, A., and H. Raistrick. 1947. Ibid. 41:569.
[69] Breen, J., et al. 1955. Ibid. 60:618.
[70] Brian, P. W., et al. 1953. Brit. Mycol. Soc. Trans. 36:243.
[71] Brian, P. W., et al. 1957. Ibid. 40:365.
[72] British Intelligence Objectives Subcommittee. 1946. Final Rept. 220.
[73] Brockmann, H., and H. Effers. 1955. Angew. Chem. 67:706.
[74] Burkholder, P. R., I. McVeigh, and K. Wilson. 1945. Arch. Biochem. 7:287.
[75] Burton, H. S. 1949. Brit. J. Exptl. Pathol. 30:151.
[76] Burton, H. S. 1950. Nature 165:274.
[77] Bush, M. R., O. Touster, and J. E. Brockmann. 1951. J. Biol. Chem. 188:685.
[78] Butkevich, V. S., and M. V. Fedoroff. 1930. Biochem. Z. 219:103.
[79] Butkewitsch, V. S., and M. S. Gaevskaya. 1935. Compt. Rend. Acad. Sci. URSS, N.S.3:405.

continued

[80] Calam, C. T., A. E. Oxford, and H. Raistrick. 1939. Biochem. J. 33:1488.
[81] Calam, C. T., et al. 1939. Ibid. 33:579.
[82] Calam, C. T., et al. 1947. Ibid. 41:458.
[83] Caputto, R., et al. 1950. J. Biol. Chem. 184:333.
[84] Chain, E., H. W. Florey, and M. A. Jennings. 1942. Brit. J. Exptl. Pathol. 23:202.
[85] Chain, E., H. W. Florey, and M. A. Jennings. 1944. Lancet 1:112.
[86] Chain, E., et al. 1943. Brit. J. Exptl. Pathol. 24: 108.
[87] Challenger, F., V. Subramaniam, and T. K. Walker. 1927. J. Chem. Soc., p. 200.
[88] Challenger, F., V. Subramaniam, and T. K. Walker. 1927. Nature 119:674.
[89] Charles, J. H. V., et al. 1933. Biochem. J. 27:499.
[90] Christie, S. M. H., G. W. Kenner, and A. R. Todd. 1952. Nature 170:924.
[91] Chrzaszcz, T., and K. Leonhard. 1936. Biochem. J. 30:1947.
[92] Chrzaszcz, T., and D. Tiukow. 1929. Biochem. Z. 207:39.
[93] Chrzaszcz, T., and M. Zakomorny. 1934. Ibid. 273:31.
[94] Clutterbuck, P. W., W. Koerber, and H. Raistrick. 1937. Biochem. J. 31:1089.
[95] Clutterbuck, P. W., and H. Raistrick. 1933. Ibid. 27:654.
[96] Clutterbuck, P. W., et al. 1931. Phil. Trans. Roy. Soc. London, B, 220:301.
[97] Clutterbuck, P. W., et al. 1932. Biochem. J. 26: 1441.
[98] Clutterbuck, P. W., et al. 1932. Ibid. 26:1907.
[99] Clutterbuck, P. W., et al. 1934. Ibid. 28:94.
[100] Clutterbuck, P. W., et al. 1935. Ibid. 29:1300.
[101] Clutterbuck, P. W., et al. 1936. J. Soc. Chem. Ind. (London) 55:55T.
[102] Clutterbuck, P. W., et al. 1940. Biochem. J. 34: 664.
[103] Corbett, R. E., et al. 1950. J. Chem. Soc., p. 1.
[104] Coyne, F. P., H. Raistrick, and R. Robinson. 1931. Phil. Trans. Roy. Soc. London, B, 220:297.
[105] Cram, D. J. 1948. J. Am. Chem. Soc. 70:4238.
[106] Cruickshank, J. R., H. Raistrick, and R. Robinson. 1938. J. Chem. Soc., p. 2056.
[107] Currie, H. N., and C. Thom. 1915. J. Biol. Chem. 22:287.
[108] Curtin, T. P., and J. Reilly. 1940. Biochem. J. 34: 1419.
[109] Curtin, T. P., and J. Reilly. 1943. Ibid. 37:36.
[110] Curtis, P. J., and J. F. Grove. 1947. Nature 160: 574.
[111] Curtis, P. J., H. G. Hemming, and W. K. Smith. 1951. Ibid. 167:557.
[112] Dammann, E., O. T. Rotini, and F. F. Nord. 1938. Biochem. Z. 297:184.
[113] Davies, J. E., F. E. King, and J. C. Roberts. 1954. Chem. Ind. (London), p. 1110.
[114] Dean, F. M., J. C. Roberts, and A. Robertson. 1954. J. Chem. Soc., p. 1432.
[115] Dean, F. M., J. C. Roberts, and A. Robertson. 1956. Ibid., p. 3545.
[116] Dox, A. W., and R. E. Neidig. 1914. J. Biol. Chem. 18:167.
[117] Dox, A. W., and R. E. Neidig. 1914. Ibid. 19:235.
[118] Dunn, G., G. T. Newbold, and F. S. Spring. 1949. J. Chem. Soc., p. 2586.
[119] Dutcher, J. D. 1958. J. Biol. Chem. 232:785.
[120] Eble, T. E., and F. R. Hanson. 1951. Antibiot. Chemotherapy 1:54.
[121] Emerson, R., and D. L. Fox. 1940. Proc. Roy. Soc. (London), B, 128:275.
[122] Engel, B. G., and W. Brzeski. 1947. Helv. Chim. Acta 30:1472.
[123] Fiore, J. V. 1948. Arch. Biochem. 16:161.
[124] Florey, H. W., et al. 1949. Antibiotics. Oxford Univ. Press, London. pp. 223-272.
[125] Foster, J. W. 1949. Chemical activities of fungi. Academic Press, New York.
[126] Foster, J. W., and S. B. Waksman. 1939. J. Am. Chem. Soc. 61:127.
[127] Friedheim, E. A. H. 1933. Compt. Rend. Soc. Biol. 112:1030.
[128] Friedheim, E. A. H. 1938. Helv. Chim. Acta 21: 1464.
[129] Gatenbeck, S. 1957. Acta Chem. Scand. 11:555.
[130] Gatenbeck, S. 1958. Ibid. 12:1985.
[131] Geiger, W. B. 1949. Arch. Biochem. 21:125.
[132] Geiger-Huber, M., and H. Galli. 1945. Helv. Chim. Acta 28:248.
[133] Gill-Carey, D. 1949. Brit. J. Expt. Pathol. 23:202.
[134] Godin, P. 1953. Biochim. Biophys. Acta 11:114.
[135] Goodwin, T. W. 1953. Biochem. J. 53:538.
[136] Goodwin, T. W. 1955. Ann. Rev. Biochem. 24:497.
[137] Gould, B. S., and H. Raistrick. 1934. Biochem. J. 28:1640.
[138] Gould, B. S., et al. 1942. J. Biol. Chem. 146:219.
[139] Greene, R. C. 1957. J. Am. Chem. Soc. 79:3929.
[140] Grove, J. F. 1952. Biochem. J. 50:648.
[141] Grove, J. F., and J. C. McGowan. 1947. Nature 160:574.
[142] Gunsalus, I. C., et al. 1944. J. Biol. Chem. 155: 685.
[143] Hassall, C. H., and T. C. McMorris. 1959. J. Chem. Soc., p. 2831.
[144] Hassall, C. H., and A. R. Todd. 1947. Ibid., p. 611.
[145] Hatsuda, Y., S. Kuyama, and N. Terashima. 1955. Nippon Nogeikagaku Kaishi 29:11.
[146] Haworth, W. N., et al. 1935. Biochem. J. 29:617.
[147] Haworth, W. N., et al. 1935. Ibid. 29:2668.
[148] Hind, H. G. 1940. Ibid. 34:67.
[149] Hetherington, A. C., and H. Raistrick. 1931. Phil. Trans. Roy. Soc. London, B, 220:209.
[150] Hetherington, A. C., and H. Raistrick. 1931. Ibid., B, 220:269.
[151] Hida, T. 1935. J. Shanghai Sci. Inst., IV, 1:201.
[152] Howard, B. H., and H. Raistrick. 1949. Biochem. J. 44:227.
[153] Howard, B. H., and H. Raistrick. 1950. Ibid. 46:49.
[154] Howard, B. H., and H. Raistrick. 1954. Ibid. 57: 212.
[155] Igarasi, H. 1930. Nippon Nogeikagaku Kaishi 15: 229.
[156] Igarasi, H. 1939. Ibid. 15:225.
[157] Iwanov, N. N. 1925. Biochem. Z. 157:231.
[158] Iwata, K., and I. Yoshioka. 1950. J. Antibiot. (Japan) 3:192.
[159] Jackman, G. B., et al. 1958. J. Chem. Soc., p. 1825.
[160] Johnson, J. R., W. F. Bruce, and J. D. Dutcher. 1943. J. Am. Chem. Soc. 65:2005.
[161] Johnson, J. R., A. R. Kidwai, and J. S. Warner. 1953. Ibid. 75:2110.
[162] Jones, H., G. Rake, and D. M. Hamre. 1943. J. Bacteriol. 45:461.

continued

[163] Kaneko, Y. 1957. Nippon Nogeikagaku Kaishi 31:122.
[164] Kanel, E. 1934. Microbiology (USSR) 3:259.
[165] Kaplan, M. A., I. R. Harper, and B. Heinsmann. 1954. Antibiot. Chemotherapy 4:746.
[166] Karow, E. O., and J. W. Foster. 1944. Arch. Biochem. 5:279.
[167] Katagiri, H., and K. Kitahara. 1937. Mem. Coll. Agr. Kyoto Imp. Univ. 26:1.
[168] Kinoshita, K. 1931. Acta Phytochim. (Japan) 5:271.
[169] Kinoshita, K. 1931. Botan. Mag. (Tokyo) 45:60.
[170] Kita, D. A., and W. H. Peterson. 1953. J. Biol. Chem. 203:861.
[171] Kitamura, J., U. Kurimoto, and M. Yokoyama. 1956. Yakugaku Zasshi 76:972.
[172] Knobloch, H., and H. Mayer. 1941. Biochem. Z. 307:285.
[173] Kogl, F., and F. S. Quackenbush. 1944. Rec. Trav. Chim. 63:251.
[174] Kogl, F., and G. C. van Wessem. 1944. Ibid. 63:5.
[175] Komatsu, E. 1953. Japan. Pat. 4799.
[176] Kopeloff, N., and L. Kopeloff. 1919. J. Agr. Res. 18:195.
[177] Kostychev, S. 1920. Z. Physiol. Chem. 111:236.
[178] Kraitman, G., and F. F. Nord. 1949. Arch. Biochem. 21:457.
[179] LePage, G. A. 1947. J. Biol. Chem. 168:623.
[180] Lim, H. 1935. J. Fac. Agr. Hokkaido Imp. Univ. 37:165.
[181] Lockwood, L. B., J. J. Stubbs, and C. E. Senseman. 1938. Zentr. Bakteriol. Parasitenk., II, 98:167.
[182] Lockwood, L. B., and G. E. Ward. 1945. Ind. Eng. Chem. 37:405 (Chem. Abstr. 39:2174).
[183] Lund, N. A., A. Robertson, and W. B. Whalley. 1953. J. Chem. Soc., p. 2434.
[184] MacMillan. J. 1951. Chem. Ind. (London), p. 719.
[185] MacMillan, J. 1954. J. Chem. Soc., p. 2585.
[186] Martin, S. M., and W. R. Waters. 1952. Ind. Eng. Chem. 44:2229.
[187] May, D. E., et al. 1931. J. Am. Chem. Soc. 53:774.
[188] Menzel, A. E. Q., O. Wintersteiner, and J. C. Hoogerheide. 1944. J. Biol. Chem. 152:419.
[189] Michelson, A. M., W. Drell, and H. K. Mitchell. 1951. Proc. Natl. Acad. Sci. U.S. 37:396.
[190] Miller, M. W., ed. 1961. Pfizer Handbook of microbial metabolites. McGraw-Hill, New York.
[191] Mosbach, K. 1959. Z. Naturforsch. 14b:69.
[192] Moyer, A. J., and R. D. Coghill. 1945. Arch. Biochem. 7:167.
[193] Moyer, A. J., and R. D. Coghill. 1945. Chem. Abstr. 39:5277.
[194] Moyer, A. J., et al. 1931. J. Am. Chem. Soc. 53:774.
[195] Moyer, A. J., et al. 1940. Ind. Eng. Chem. 32:1379.
[196] Mull, R. P., and F. F. Nord. 1944. Arch. Biochem. 4:419.
[197] Neelakantan, S., A. Pocker, and H. Raistrick. 1957. Biochem. J. 66:234.
[198] Neill, K. G., and H. Raistrick. 1957. Ibid. 65:166.
[199] Nickerson, W. J. 1948. Arch. Biochem. 17:225.
[200] Nishikawa, H. 1933. Nippon Nogeikagaku Kaishi 9:772 (Chem. Abstr. 28:2751).
[201] Nishikawa, H. 1934. Proc. Imp. Acad. (Tokyo) 10:414.
[202] Nishikawa, H. 1936. Nippon Nogeikagaku Kaishi 12:1.
[203] Nishikawa, H. 1936. Ibid. 12:47 (Chem. Abstr. 30:7140).
[204] Nishikawa, H. 1937. Ibid. 13:1 (Chem. Abstr. 31:3485).
[205] Nishikawa, H. 1939. Acta Phytochim. (Japan) 11:167.
[206] Nord, F. F., and W. Engel. 1938. Biochem. Z. 296:153.
[207] Nord, F. F., and L. J. Sciarini. 1946. Arch. Biochem. 9:419.
[208] Nord, F. F., and J. C. Vitucci. 1947. Ibid. 14:229.
[209] Nord, F. F., and J. C. Vitucci. 1947. Nature 160:261.
[210] Nord, F. F., et al. 1946. Ibid. 157:335.
[211] Oda, T. 1952. Yakugaku Zasshi 72:136.
[212] Oxford, A. E., and H. Raistrick. 1932. Biochem. J. 26:1902.
[213] Oxford, A. E., and H. Raistrick. 1933. Ibid. 27:634.
[214] Oxford, A. E., and H. Raistrick. 1933. Ibid. 27:1176.
[215] Oxford, A. E., and H. Raistrick. 1933. Ibid. 27:1473.
[216] Oxford, A. E., and H. Raistrick. 1934. Ibid. 28:1321.
[217] Oxford, A. E., and H. Raistrick. 1935. Ibid. 29:1599.
[218] Oxford, A. E., and H. Raistrick. 1940. Ibid. 34:790.
[219] Oxford, A. E., H. Raistrick, and P. Simonart. 1939. Ibid. 33:240.
[220] Oxford, A. E., et al. 1935. Ibid. 29:1102.
[221] Pauson, P. K. 1955. Chem. Rev. 55:9.
[222] Plattner, P. A., and N. Clauson-Kaas. 1945. Experientia 1:195.
[223] Plattner, P. A., and N. Clauson-Kaas. 1945. Helv. Chim. Acta 28:188.
[224] Posternak, T. 1938. Ibid. 21:1326.
[225] Posternak, T. 1939. Compt. Rend. Soc. Phys. Hist. Nat. Geneve 56:28.
[226] Posternak, T. 1940. Helv. Chim. Acta 23:1046.
[227] Posternak, T., and J. P. Jacobs. 1940. Ibid. 23:237.
[228] Posternak, T., H. W. Ruelius, and J. Tscherniak. 1943. Ibid. 26:2031.
[229] Pruess, L. M., et al. 1931. J. Biol. Chem. 90:369.
[230] Quilico, A., and L. Panizzi. 1943. Ber. Deut. Chem. Ges. 76b:348.
[231] Quilico, A., L. Panizzi, and E. Mugnaini. 1949. Nature 164:26.
[232] Raistrick, H. 1937. Enzymologia 4:76.
[233] Raistrick, H. 1940. Ann. Rev. Biochem. 9:571.
[234] Raistrick, H. 1949. Proc. Roy. Soc. (London), A, 199:158.
[235] Raistrick, H. 1950. Ibid., B, 136:481.
[236] Raistrick, H., and M. L. Rintoul. 1931. Phil. Trans. Roy. Soc. London, B, 220:255.
[237] Raistrick, H., R. Robinson, and A. R. Todd. 1933. Biochem. J. 27:1170.
[238] Raistrick, H., R. Robinson, and A. R. Todd. 1933. J. Chem. Soc., p. 488.
[239] Raistrick, H., R. Robinson, and A. R. Todd. 1934. Biochem. J. 28:559.
[240] Raistrick, H., R. Robinson, and A. R. Todd. 1937. J. Chem. Soc., p. 80.

continued

[241] Raistrick, H., and D. J. Ross. 1952. Biochem. J. 50:635.
[242] Raistrick, H., and P. Rudman. 1956. Ibid. 63:395.
[243] Raistrick, H., and P. Simonart. 1933. Ibid. 27:628.
[244] Raistrick, H., and G. Smith. 1933. Ibid. 27:1814.
[245] Raistrick, H., and G. Smith. 1935. Ibid. 29:606.
[246] Raistrick, H., and G. Smith. 1936. Ibid. 30:1315.
[247] Raistrick, H., and C. E. Stickings. 1951. Ibid. 48:53.
[248] Raistrick, H., and J. Ziffer. 1951. Ibid. 49:563.
[249] Raistrick, H., et al. 1934. Brit. Pat. 420,362.
[250] Raistrick, H., et al. 1936. Biochem. J. 30:1303.
[251] Rickes, E. L., L. Chaiet, and J. C. Keresztesy. 1947. J. Am. Chem. Soc. 69:2749.
[252] Rothe, W. 1954. Deut. Med. Wochschr. 79:1080.
[253] Rotini, O. T., E. Dammann, and F. F. Nord. 1936. Biochem. Z. 288:414.
[254] Ruelius, H. W., and A. Gauhe. 1950. Ann. Chem. 569:38.
[255] Ruppol, E. 1943. Bull. Soc. Chim. Biol. 25:57.
[256] Saito, A. 1951. J. Ferment. Technol. (Japan) 29: 310.
[257] Sakaguchi, K., T. Inoue, and S. Tada. 1939. Zentr. Bakteriol. Parasitenk., II, 100:302.
[258] Sanborn, J. R. 1934. Ind. Eng. Chem. 26:532.
[259] Sanborn, J. R. 1936. Ibid. 28:1189.
[260] Sastry, K. S., and P. S. Sarma. 1957. Nature 179:44.
[261] Sato, A., and K. Aso. 1957. Ibid. 180:984.
[262] Schopfer, W. H. 1935. Compt. Rend. Soc. Biol. 118:3.
[263] Schopfer, W. H., and E. C. Grob. 1950. Experientia 6:419.
[264] Schubert, W. J., and F. F. Nord. 1949. Arch. Biochem. 20:465.
[265] Sciarini, L. J., et al. 1943. Proc. Natl. Acad. Sci. U.S. 29:121.
[266] Segal, W. 1957. Chem. Ind. (London), p. 1040.
[267] Shibata, S., and I. Kitagawa. 1956. Pharm. Bull. (Tokyo) 4:309.
[268] Shibata, S., T. Murakami, and M. Takido. 1956. Ibid. 4:303.
[269] Shibata, S., S. Natori, and S. Udagawa. 1964. List of fungal products. C. C. Thomas, Springfield, Ill.
[270] Shibata, S., M. Takido, and T. Nakajima. 1955. Pharm. Bull. (Tokyo) 3:286.
[271] Shimoda, C. 1951. Nippon Nogeikagaku Kaishi 25:254.
[272] Shope, R. E. 1953. J. Exptl. Med. 97:601, 639.
[273] Shu, P., and M. J. Johnson. 1948. Ind. Eng. Chem. 40:1202.
[274] Singh, J., S. Shah, and T. K. Walker. 1956. Biochem. J. 62:222.
[275] Sjolander, J. R., et al. 1954. J. Am. Chem. Soc. 76:1085.
[276] Smith, V. M. 1949. Arch. Biochem. 22:275.
[277] Smith, V. M. 1949. Ibid. 23:446.
[278] Stodola, F. H., K. B. Raper, and D. I. Fennell. 1951. Nature 167:773.
[279] Stodola, F. H., et al. 1945. J. Biol. Chem. 159:67.
[280] Stodola, F. H., et al. 1945. Ibid. 161:739.
[281] Sumi, M. 1928. Biochem. Z. 195:161.
[282] Sumiki, Y. 1929. Nippon Nogeikagaku Kaishi 5:10.
[283] Sumiki, Y. 1930. Ibid. 6:17 (Chem Abstr. 24:3811).
[284] Sumiki, Y. 1931. Ibid. 7:819.
[285] Sumiki, Y. 1932. Chem. Abstr. 26:1008.
[286] Sumiki, Y. 1933. Nippon Nogeikagaku Kaishi 9:914.
[287] Suthers, A. J., and T. K. Walker. 1932. Biochem. J. 26:317.
[288] Tadokoro, T. 1935. Nippon Nogeikagaku Kaishi 11:365.
[289] Takata, R. 1929. J. Soc. Chem. Ind. Japan, Suppl. 32:154B.
[290] Takata, R. 1929. Ibid., Suppl. 32:169B.
[291] Takata, R. 1929. Ibid., Suppl. 32:172.
[292] Tanenbaum, S. W., E. E. Bassett, and M. Kaplan. 1959. Arch. Biochem. Biophys. 81:169.
[293] Tatum, E. L. 1945. J. Biol. Chem. 160:455.
[294] Underkofler, L. A., and R. J. Hickey, ed. 1954. Industrial fermentations. Chemical, New York. v. 2, pp. 191-216.
[295] Vora, V. C. 1954. J. Sci. Ind. Res. (India) 13B:504.
[296] Vorbrodt, W. 1921. Bull. Intern. Acad. Polon. Sci., B, p. 223 (Chem. Abstr. 18:1313).
[297] Waksman, S. A. 1944. Science 99:220.
[298] Waksman, S. A., E. S. Horning, and E. L. Spencer. 1943. J. Bacteriol. 45:233.
[299] Waksman, S. A., et al. 1942. Science 96:202.
[300] Walker, T. K. 1932. Nature 130:582.
[301] Warburg, O., et al. 1935. Biochem. Z. 279:143.
[302] Ward, G. E., et al. 1936. J. Am. Chem. Soc. 58: 1286.
[303] Wehmer, C. 1897. Chem. Ztg. 21:1022.
[304] Weiss, S., J. V. Fiore, and F. F. Nord. 1947. Arch. Biochem. 15:326.
[305] Weiss, U., et al. 1954. Science 119:774.
[306] Weiss, U., et al. 1958. Arch. Biochem. Biophys. 74:150.
[307] Wells, P. A., et al. 1936. J. Am. Chem. Soc. 58:555.
[308] Wells, P. A., et al. 1937. Chem. Met. Eng. 44:188.
[309] White, E. C., and J. H. Hill. 1943. J. Bacteriol. 45: 433.
[310] Wieland, P., and V. Prelog. 1947. Helv. Chim. Acta 30:1028.
[311] Wijkman, N. 1931. Ann. Chem. 485:61.
[312] Wirth, J. C., and F. F. Nord. 1942. Arch. Biochem. 1:143.
[313] Wirth, J. C., and F. F. Nord. 1943. Ibid. 2:463.
[314] Woodward, R. B., and G. Singh. 1949. J. Am. Chem. Soc. 71:758.
[315] Woolley, D. W. 1948. J. Biol. Chem. 176:1291.
[316] Woolley, D. W., and W. H. Peterson. 1937. Ibid. 122:213.
[317] Woolley, D. W., et al. 1935. J. Am. Chem. Soc. 57: 2589.
[318] Wright, L. D., and E. L. Cresson. 1954. Ibid. 76: 4156.
[319] Wunschendorff, H., and C. Killian. 1928. Compt. Rend. 187:572.
[320] Yabuta, T. 1912. J. Coll. Agr. Imp. Univ. Tokyo 5:51.
[321] Yabuta, T., and Y. Sumiki. 1933. Nippon Nogeikagaku Kaishi 9:1264.
[322] Yabuta, T., and Y. Sumiki. 1934. Ibid. 10:703.
[323] Yuill, J. L. 1934. Biochem. J. 28:222.
[324] Yuill, J. L. 1936. J. Soc. Chem. Ind. (London) 55:155.
[325] Zalokar, M. 1957. Arch. Biochem. Biophys. 70: 568.
[326] Zechmeister, L., and F. Haxa. 1946. Arch. Biochem. 11:539.

117. TRACE ELEMENTS AFFECTING PRODUCTION OF BACTERIAL AND FUNGAL METABOLIC PRODUCTS

The elements listed are those having an effect when added to media in trace quantities.

	Species (Synonym)	Element	Metabolic Product	Reference
			Bacteriophyta	
1	*Micromonospora* sp.	Co	Gentamicin	12
2	*M. purpurea*	Cu, Fe, Mn, Zn	Antibiotics	84
3	*Streptomyces antibioticus*	Ca, Fe, Zn	Dactinomycin	37
4	*S. aureofaciens*	Cr, Mn, Zn	Tetracyclines	21
5	*S. azureus*	Co, Fe, Mn, Ni, Sn, V	Thiostrepton	65
6	*S. erythreus*	Co, Cu, Fe, Mn, Zn	Erythromycin	20
7	*S. fradiae*	Ca, Cu, Fe, Mn, Zn	Neomycins	48,86
8	*S. griseus*	Ca, Cr, Cu, Fe, Mg, Mn, Ni, Zn	Mannosidostreptomycinase	72
9		Co	Vitamin B_{12}	34,63
10		Cr, Co, Cu, Fe, Mn, Ni, Se, Zn	Streptomycins	2,13,14,55,73,76, 79,89
11		Fe, Zn	Grisein	33,67
12		Co, Cu, Fe, Mn, Zn	Candicidin	1
13	*S. lavendulae*	Fe, Zn	Streptothricin	85,90
14	*S. nodosus*	Co, Fe, Mn, Ni, Zn	Amphotericins A & B	8
15	*S. olivaceus*	Co	Vitamin B_{12}	32
16	*S. rimosus*	Ca, Fe, Zn	5-Oxytetracycline	91
17	*S. rishiriensis*	Al, Cd, Cr, Co, Cu, Fe, Pb, Mg, Mn	Coumermycin	16
18	*S. roseochromogenus*	Fe	Steroid transformations	31
19	*Thermoactinomyces viridis*	Cu, Fe, Mn, Zn	Thermoviridin	70
			Fungi	
20	*Aspergillus* sp.	Fe, Zn	Citrinin	80
21	*A. flavus*	Zn	Aflatoxins	23
22	*A. fumigatus*	Fe, Zn	Gliotoxin, helvolic acid	49
23	*A. niger*	Al, Sb, Cr, Co, Cu, Fe, Pb, Mn, Mo, Ni, Se, Ag, Te, U, W, Zn	Citric acid	4,5,15,17,18,38,40, 42,52,61,62,64, 74,75,81,82
24		Fe	Gluconic acid	6,41
25	*A. ochraceus*	Zn	Steroid hydroxylation	25
26	*A. terreus*	Al, Nb, Fe, Mo, Zn	Itaconic acid	46,53,88
27	*A. wentii*	Fe, Mn, Zn	Citric acid	36,64
28	*Candida guilliermondii & C. flareri*	Fe	Riboflavin	9,10,44,78
29	*Cephalosporium* sp.	Cu, Fe, Mn, Zn	Cephalosporins C & N	58
30	*Claviceps paspali*	Cu, Fe, Zn	Alkaloids	59,60
31	*Cunninghamella blakesleeana*	Fe	Steroid hydroxylation	57
32	*Curvularia lunata*	Zn	Steroid hydroxylation	24
33	*Fusarium moniliforma*	Ca, Fe, Zn	L-Alanine	11
34		B, Cu, Fe, Mn, Mo, Zn	Steroid-transforming spores	83
35	*Lactarius volema*	Zn	Steroid hydroxylation	71
36	*Lepiota naucina*	Zn	Steroid hydroxylation	71
37	*Morchella crassipes*	Ca, Mn	Cells	69
38	*Naucoria confragosa*	Zn	Steroid hydroxylation	71
39	*Neurospora crassa*	Cu, Fe, Mo	Enzymes	56
40	*Penicillium citrinum*	Fe, Mn	Citrinin	3
41	*P. griseofulvum*	Ca, Cu	Spores	51
42	*P. notatum-chrysogenum* group	Al, Cr, Co, Fe, Mn, Sn, Zn	Penicillin	19,28,35,39,43,54, 66,77
43	*P. patulum*	Cu, Fe, Mn	Patulin or gentisic acid	7
44	*P. roqueforti*	Ca, Cu, Mn, Mo, Zn	Cells	50
45	*Phytophthora fragariae*	Ca, Sr	Cells	22
46	*Rhizopus arrhizus*	Fe, Mg, Zn	Fumaric acid	68
47	*R. delemar*	Al	Amylase	26
48	*R. oryzae*	Zn	Lactic acid	45,87
49	*R. stolonifer*	Fe, Mn, Zn	Cells	30
50	*(R. nigricans)*	Fe	Acetoin	27
51		Cu, Fe, Mn, Zn	Fumaric acid, lactic acid, ethanol	29,47
52	*Septomyxa affinis*	Fe	Steroid-transforming spores	83

continued

117. TRACE ELEMENTS AFFECTING PRODUCTION OF BACTERIAL AND FUNGAL METABOLIC PRODUCTS

Contributor: Perlman D.

References

[1] Acker, R. F., and H. Lechevalier. 1954. Appl. Microbiol. 2:152.
[2] Ainsworth, G. C., et al. 1947. J. Gen. Microbiol. 1:335.
[3] Bailey, J. H., and C. J. Cavallito. 1943. J. Bacteriol. 45:30.
[4] Bernhauer, K., A. Iglauer, and H. Knobloch. 1941. Biochem. Z. 307:298.
[5] Bernhauer, K., and H. Knobloch. 1941. Ibid. 309: 151.
[6] Blom, R. H., et al. 1952. Ind. Eng. Chem. 44:435.
[7] Brack, A. 1947. Helv. Chim. Acta 30:1.
[8] Brewer, G. A., Jr., and W. R. Frazier. 1962. Antimicrobial Agents Chemotherapy 1:212.
[9] Burkholder, P. R. 1943. Arch. Biochem. 3:121.
[10] Burkholder, P. R. 1943. Proc. Natl. Acad. Sci. U.S. 29:166.
[11] Carito, S. L., and M. A. Pisano. 1966. Appl. Microbiol. 14:39.
[12] Charney, W. 1964. Chem. Abstr. 61:4924b (U.S. Pat. 3,136,704).
[13] Chesters, C. G. C., and G. N. Rolinson. 1951. J. Gen. Microbiol. 5:553.
[14] Chesters, C. G. C., and G. N. Rolinson. 1951. Ibid. 5:559.
[15] Choudhary, A. Q., and S. J. Pirt. 1966. Ibid. 43:71.
[16] Claridge, C. A., et al. 1966. Appl. Microbiol. 14: 280.
[17] Clark, D. S., K. Ito, and H. Horitsu. 1966. Biotech. Bioeng. 8:465.
[18] Clark, D. S., K. Ito, and P. Tymchuk. 1965. Ibid. 7:269.
[19] Cook, R. P., W. J. Tulloch, and M. B. Brown. 1945. Biochem. J. 39:314.
[20] Corum, C. J., et al. 1954. Appl. Microbiol. 2:326.
[21] Darken, M. A., et al. 1960. Ibid. 8:46.
[22] Davies, M. E. 1959. Brit. Mycol. Soc. Trans. 42:194.
[23] Davis, N. D., U. L. Diener, and D. W. Eldridge. 1966. Appl. Microbiol. 14:378.
[24] Dulaney, E. L., and E. O. Stapley. 1959. Ibid. 7:276.
[25] Dulaney, E. L., E. O. Stapley, and C. Hlavac. 1955. Mycologia 47:464.
[26] Erb, N. M., and F. M. Hildebrandt. 1946. Ind. Eng. Chem. 38:792.
[27] Fields, M. L. 1964. Appl. Microbiol. 12:141.
[28] Foster, J. W., H. B. Woodruff, and L. E. McDaniel. 1946. J. Bacteriol. 51:465.
[29] Foster, J. W., and S. A. Waksman. 1939. Ibid. 37: 599.
[30] Fothergill, P. G., and M. M. Yeoman. 1957. J. Gen. Microbiol. 17:631.
[31] Goodman, J. J., and L. L. Smith. 1960. Appl. Microbiol. 8:363.
[32] Hall, H. H., et al. 1953. Ibid. 1:124.
[33] Hendlin, D. 1952. Chem. Abstr. 46:7294b (U.S. Pat. 2,596,969).
[34] Hendlin, D., and M. L. Ruger. 1950. Science 111: 541.
[35] Jarvis, F. G., and M. J. Johnson. 1947. J. Am. Chem. Soc. 69:3010.
[36] Karow, E. O., and S. A. Waksman. 1947. Ind. Eng. Chem. 39:821.
[37] Katz, E., P. Pienta, and A. Sivak. 1958. Appl. Microbiol. 6:236.
[38] Kitos, P. A., J. J. R. Campbell, and N. Tomlinson. 1953. Ibid. 1:156.
[39] Knight, S. G., and W. C. Frazier. 1945. Science 102: 617.
[40] Knobloch, H., and J. N. Miksch. 1941. Biochem. Z. 309:90.
[41] Knobloch, H., and H. Moyer. 1941. Ibid. 307:285.
[42] Knobloch, H., and R. Sellmann. 1941. Ibid. 309: 145.
[43] Koffler, H., S. G. Knight, and W. C. Frazier. 1947. J. Bacteriol. 53:115.
[44] Levine, H., et al. 1949. Ind. Eng. Chem. 41:1665.
[45] Lockwood, L. B. 1940. Intern. Congr. Microbiol., 3rd, 1939, Rept. Proc., p. 229.
[46] Lockwood, L. B., and G. E. N. Nelson. 1946. Arch. Biochem. 10:365.
[47] Lockwood, L. B., G. E. Ward, and O. E. May. 1936. J. Agr. Res. 53:849.
[48] Majumdar, M. K., and S. K. Majumdar. 1965. Appl. Microbiol. 13:190.
[49] Menzel, A. E. O., O. Wintersteiner, and J. C. Hoogerheide. 1944. J. Biol. Chem. 152:419.
[50] Meyers, E., and S. G. Knight. 1958. Appl. Microbiol. 6:174.
[51] Morton, A. G., D. J. F. England, and D. A. Towler. 1958. Brit. Mycol. Soc. Trans. 41:39.
[52] Moyer, A. J. 1953. Appl. Microbiol. 1:1.
[53] Moyer, A. J., and R. D. Coghill. 1945. Arch. Biochem. 7:167.
[54] Moyer, A. J., and R. D. Coghill. 1946. J. Bacteriol. 51:79.
[55] Musilek, V. 1963. Appl. Microbiol. 11:28.
[56] Nicholas, D. J. D., and K. Commissiong. 1957. J. Gen. Microbiol. 17:699.
[57] O'Connell, P. W., et al. 1955. Appl. Microbiol. 3:16.
[58] Ott, J. L., et al. 1962. Ibid. 10:515.
[59] Pacifici, L. R., W. J. Kelleher, and A. E. Schwarting. 1962. Lloydia 25:36.
[60] Pacifici, L. R., W. J. Kelleher, and A. E. Schwarting. 1963. Ibid. 26:161.
[61] Perlman, D. 1951. Am. J. Botany 38:652.
[62] Perlman, D., W. W. Dorrell, and M. J. Johnson. 1946. Arch. Biochem. 11:131.
[63] Perlman, D., and E. O'Brien. 1954. J. Bacteriol 68: 167.
[64] Perquin, L. H. C. 1938. Dissertation. Technische Hogeschool, Delft, Netherlands.
[65] Platt, T. B., and W. R. Frazier. 1962. Antimicrobial Agents Chemotherapy 1:205.
[66] Pratt, R., and J. Dufrenoy. 1947. Science 105:574.
[67] Reynolds, D. M., and S. A. Waksman. 1948. J. Bacteriol. 55:739.

continued

[68] Rhodes, R. A., et al. 1959. Appl. Microbiol. 7:74.
[69] Robbins, W. J., and A. Hervey. 1965. Mycologia 57:262.
[70] Schuurmans, D. M., B. H. Olson, and C. L. San Clemente. 1956. Appl. Microbiol. 4:61.
[71] Schuytema, E. C., et al. 1966. Biotech. Bioeng. 8: 275.
[72] Shaw, R. K., R. D. Henderson, and W. J. Seagers. 1960. Appl. Microbiol. 8:12.
[73] Shirato, S., and H. Motoyama. 1966. Ibid. 14:706.
[74] Shu, P., and M. J. Johnson. 1948. Ind. Eng. Chem. 40:1202.
[75] Shu, P., and M. J. Johnson. 1948. J. Bacteriol. 56: 577.
[76] Spilsbury, J. F. 1948. Brit. Mycol. Soc. Trans. 31: 210.
[77] Stone, R. W., and M. A. Farrell. 1946. Science 104:445.
[78] Tanner, F. W., Jr., C. Vojnovich, and J. M. Van Lanen. 1945. Ibid. 100:180.
[79] Thornberry, H. H., and H. W. Anderson. 1948. Arch. Biochem. 16:389.
[80] Timonin, M. I., and J. W. Rouatt. 1944. Can. J. Public Health 35:80.
[81] Tomlinson, N., J. J. R. Campbell, and P. C. Trussell. 1950. J. Bacteriol. 59:217.
[82] Tomlinson, N., J. J. R. Campbell, and P. C. Trussell. 1951. Ibid. 61:17.
[83] Vezina, C., K. Singh, and S. N. Sehgal. 1965. Mycologia 57:722.
[84] Wagman, G. H., and M. J. Weinstein. 1966. Biotech. Bioeng. 8:259.
[85] Waksman, S. A. 1943. J. Bacteriol. 46:299.
[86] Waksman, S. A., H. A. Lechevalier, and D. A. Harris. 1949. J. Clin. Invest. 28:934.
[87] Ward, G. E., et al. 1938. Ind. Eng. Chem. 30:1233.
[88] Westhuizen, G. C. A. van der, C. J. P. Spruit, and H. H. Sephton. 1951. J. Appl. Chem. 1:356.
[89] Woodruff, H. B. 1947. J. Bacteriol. 54:42.
[90] Woodruff, H. B., and J. W. Foster. 1943. Arch. Biochem. 2:301.
[91] Zygmunt, W. A. 1961. Appl. Microbiol. 9:502.

APPENDIXES

Appendix I. SCIENTIFIC NAMES AND CORRESPONDING COMMON NAMES

Protozoa and nonvascular plants have not been included.

Part I. Animals

Scientific Name	Common Name
Ablepharus boutonii metallicum	Bouton's snake-eyed skink
Acanthis cannabina	European linnet
A. hornemanni exilipes	Hoary redpoll
Accipiter nisus nisus	Hawk
A. striatus velox	Sharp-shinned hawk
Achatina fulica	Giant African land snail
Acheta domesticus	House cricket
Achipteria sp.	Oribatid mite
Acinonyx jubatus	Cheetah
Acroloxus laucustris	Lake limpet
Actitis macularia	Spotted sandpiper
Acyrthosiphon pisum	Pea aphid
Aechmophorus occidentalis	Western grebe
Aedes aegypti	Yellow-fever mosquito
A. australis	Mosquito
Aeronautes melanoleucus	White-throated swift
A. saxatilis	White-throated swift
Aeshna cyanea	Southern aeshna
Aethia cristatella	Crested or least auklet
Agelaius phoeniceus	Red-winged blackbird
Aglais urtica	Small tortoiseshell
Agrotis orthogonia	Pale western cutworm
Ailurus fulgens fulgens	Lesser panda
Aimophila cassinii	Cassin's sparrow
A. ruficeps	Rufous-crowned sparrow
Aix sponsa	North American wood duck
Alabama argillacea	Cotton leafworm
Alauda arvensis	Skylark
Alca torda	Razor-billed auk
Alcelaphus buselaphus jacksoni	Jackson hartebeest
Alces alces andersoni	Moose
A. americana	American moose
Alligator mississippiensis	American alligator
Allolobophora caliginosa	Earthworm
Alopex lagopus	Arctic fox
Alouatta seniculus	Red howler monkey
Amazilia fimbriata	Hummingbird
A. leucogaster bahiae	Brazilian hummingbird
Amazona aestiva aestiva	Amazon basin or Brazilian parrot
Ambystoma maculatum	Spotted salamander
A. tigrinum	Tiger salamander
Amia calva	Bowfin
Ammodramus savannarum	Grasshopper sparrow
Ammotragus lervia	Aoudad
Amphibolurus barbatus	Australian bearded lizard
A. cristatus	Crested dragon
A. decresii	Tawny dragon
A. fionni	Peninsula dragon
A. ornatus	Ornate dragon
A. pictus	Painted dragon
A. reticulatus inermis	Reticulated dragon
Anabolia nervosa	Caddisfly
Anagasta kuehniella	Mediterranean flour moth
Anas acuta	Common pintail duck
A. acuta tzitzihoa	Pintail duck
A. carolinensis	Green-winged teal
A. crecca nimia	Common teal
A. cyanoptera	Cinnamon teal
A. platyrhynchos	Mallard duck
A. rubripes	Black duck
A. strepera	Gadwall
Anastrepha ludens	Mexican fruit fly
Ancylus fluviatilis	River limpet
Aneides lugubris	Arboreal salamander
Anemonia sulcata	Sea anemone
Anguilla anguilla	Common European eel
A. rostratus	American eel
Anguis fragilis	Slowworm
Anhinga anhinga	Anhinga
Anoa depressicornis	Anoa
Anodonta cellensis	Freshwater mussel
A. cygnea	Swan mussel
Anolis carolinensis	Green anole
Anopheles quadrimaculatus	Common malaria mosquito
Anser albifrons	White-fronted goose
A. anser	Greylag goose
A. anser domesticus	Domestic goose
A. fabalis	Bean goose
Antechinus flavipes	Marsupial mouse
Antheraea polyphemus	Polyphemus moth
Anthonomus grandis	Boll weevil
Anthropoides paradisea	South African paradise or Stanley crane
A. virgo	Demoiselle crane
Anthus pratensis	Meadow pipit
A. spinoletta	Rock or water pipit
Antilocapra americana	Pronghorn
Antilope cervicapra	Black buck
Antrozous pallidus	Pallid bat
Aotus trivirgatus	Night monkey
Aphantocroa cirrochloris	Brazilian hummingbird
Aphrodite aculeata	Sea mouse
Apis mellifera	Honeybee
Aplodontia rufa	Mountain beaver
Aplysia fasciata	Sea hare
Aptenodytes forsteri	Emperor penguin
A. patagonica	King penguin
A. patagonica patagonica	King penguin
Apteryx australis	Common kiwi
A. australis mantelli	North Island kiwi
A. haasti	Great spotted kiwi
Aquila chrysaetos	Golden eagle
Aramus guarauna	Limpkin
Arapaima gigas	Arapaima
Archilochus alexandri	Black-chinned hummingbird
A. colubris	Ruby-throated hummingbird
Archosargus probatocephalus	Sheepshead

continued

Appendix I. SCIENTIFIC NAMES AND CORRESPONDING COMMON NAMES

Part I. Animals

Scientific Name	Common Name
Arctictis binturong	Binturong
Ardea herodias	Great blue heron
Arenicola marina	Polychaete
Argyrotaenia velutinana	Red-banded leaf roller
Arion ater	Land slug
A. hortensis	Land slug
A. rufus	Land slug
Armadillidium pallasi	Pillbug
A. vulgare	Pillbug
Artemia salina	Brine shrimp
Artibeus lituratus	Greater artibeus fruit bat
Ascaridia galli	Large roundworm of chicken
Ascaris lumbricoides	Large roundworm
Ascidia mentula	Sea squirt
Ascidiella sp.	Sea squirt
Asellia tridens	Trident leaf-nosed bat
Asellus aquaticus	Isopod
A. intermedius	Water slater
Asio flammeus	Short-eared owl
A. flammeus flammeus	Short-eared owl
A. otus	Long-eared owl
A. otus wilsonianus	Long-eared owl
Asplanchna spp.	Rotifer
Astacus astacus	Crayfish
A. leptodactylus	Crayfish
Asterias rubens	Starfish
Astronotus ocellatus	Peacock-eyed cichlid
Asyndesmus lewis	Lewis' woodpecker
Atherurus centralis centralis	Congo brush-tailed porcupine
Attacus sp.	Atlas moth
Attagenus sp.	Carpet beetle
Aurelia aurita	Moon jellyfish
Australorbis glabratus	American bilharzia snail
A. tenagophilus	Snail
Austropotamobius torrentium	Crayfish
Automeris io	Io moth
Axis axis	Axis deer
Aythya affinis	Lesser scaup
A. marila	Greater scaup
Baiomys taylori	Northern pygmy mouse
Balaenoptera borealis	Sei whale
B. musculus	Blue whale
B. physalus	Fin whale
Bassariscus astutus	Cacomistle
Belostoma spp.	Giant water bug
Beroe ovata	Comb jelly
Bettongia sp.	Rat kangaroo
Bison bison	American bison
B. bison bison	American bison
B. bonasus bonasus	Wisent
Bithynia leachi	North American freshwater snail
B. tentaculata	European bithynia
Blarina brevicauda	Short-tailed shrew
B. brevicauda kirtlandi	Short-tailed shrew
Blatta orientalis	Oriental cockroach
Blattella germanica	German cockroach
Bombycilla cedrorum	Cedar waxwing

Scientific Name	Common Name
B. garrulus	Bohemian waxwing
Bombyx mori	Silkworm moth
Bonasa umbellus	Ruffed grouse
B. umbellus togata	Ruffed grouse
Boreogadus saida	Arctic cod
Bos indicus	Brahman cattle
B. taurus	Cattle
Boselaphus tragocamelus	Nilgai
Botaurus lentiginosus	American bittern
Bradypus griseus	Three-toed sloth
B. tridactyla	Three-toed sloth
Branchiostoma lanceolatum	Lancelet
Branta bernicla	Brant
B. canadensis canadensis	Canada goose
B. canadensis hutchinsii	Canada goose
B. canadensis minima	Canada goose
B. leucopsis	Barnacle goose
B. nigricans	Black brant
Brevicoryne brassicae	Cabbage aphid
Brevoortia sp.	Menhaden
Bubalus spp.	Buffalo
Bubo virginianus	Great horned owl
Bucephala clangula	Common goldeneye
B. clangula americana	Common goldeneye
Budorcas taxicolor taxicolor	Takin
Bufo boreas	Northern toad
B. bufo	Common European toad
B. calamita	Natterjack
B. cognatus	Great Plains toad
B. marinus	Marine toad
B. regularis	Square-marked or leopard toad
B. terrestris	Southern toad
B. valliceps	Gulf Coast toad
Buteo jamaicensis borealis	Red-tailed hawk
B. lagopus	Rough-legged hawk
B. lagopus s.johannis	Rough-legged hawk
B. platypterus	Broad-winged hawk
B. swainsoni	Swainson's hawk
Buthus tamulus typicus	Scorpion
Butorides virescens	Little green heron
Cacajao calvus	Bald uakari
Cadra cautella	Almond moth
Caiman crocodilus	Caiman
C. crocodilus sclerops	Common spectacled caiman
Cairina moschata	Muscovy duck
Calanus finmarchicus	Calanoid copepod
Calcarius lapponicus	Lapland longspur
C. ornatus	Chestnut-collared longspur
Callianassa subterranea	Mud shrimp
Callinectes ornatus	Swimming crab
C. sapidus	Blue crab
Calliphora vicina	Bluebottle blowfly
Callithrix geoffroyi	White-faced marmoset
C. jacchus	Marmoset
Callorhinus ursinus	Northern Pacific fur seal
Callosobruchus chinensis	Mung bean weevil
C. maculatus	Cowpea weevil
Calopteryx virgo	Demoiselle agrion
Caluromys sp.	Woolly opossum
Caluromysiops irrupta	Black-shouldered opossum

continued

Appendix I. SCIENTIFIC NAMES AND CORRESPONDING COMMON NAMES

Part I. Animals

Scientific Name	Common Name
Calypte anna	Anna's hummingbird
C. costae	Costa's hummingbird
Cambarellus shufeldtii	Crayfish
Cambarus sp.	Crayfish
Camelus bactrianus	Bactrian camel
C. dromedarius	Dromedary or Arabian camel
Canachites canadensis canadensis	Spruce grouse
Cancer pagurus	Rock crab
Canis aureus indicus	Asiatic jackal
C. dingo	Dingo
C. familiaris	Dog
C. lupus	Wolf
C. lupus nubilis	Timber wolf
Capra ibex sibirica	Siberian ibex
Caprimulgus europaeus	Common nightjar
C. vociferus	Common whippoorwill
Capromys pilorides	Cuban hutia
Carabus nemoralis	Ground beetle
Carassius auratus	Goldfish
C. carassius	Crucian carp
Carcinus maenas	Green crab
C. mediterraneas	Shore crab
Cardisoma guanhumi	West Indies land crab
Carduelis carduelis	European goldfinch
Carmarina hastata	Medusa
Carollia perspicillata	Seba's short-tailed fruit bat
Carpocapsa pomonella	Codling moth
Carpodacus purpureus	Purple finch
Cassiopea frondosa	Jellyfish
Castor fiber	Old World beaver
Casuarius bennetti	Bennett's cassowary
C. casuarius aruensis	Violet-necked cassowary
C. casuarius beccarii	Cassowary
C. bicarunculatus intensus	Cassowary
Catharacta skua	Antarctic skua
Cathartes aura	Turkey vulture
Catoptrophorus semipalmatus	Willet
Catostomus commersonii	White sucker
Cavia porcellus	Guinea pig
Cebuella pygmaea	Pygmy marmoset
Cebus albifrons	White-fronted sapajou
Centurus carolinus	Red-bellied woodpecker
Cepaea nemoralis	Land snail
Cepphus grylle	Black guillemot
Ceratotherium simum	White rhinoceros
C. simum simum	Square-lipped rhinoceros
Cercartetus nanus	Dormouse possum
Cercopithecus albogularis erythrarchus	Beira guenon
C. diana	Diana monkey
C. mona mona	Mona monkey
C. neglectus	Brazza's monkey
C. pygerythrus	Guenon
C. talapoin	Talapoin monkey
Cerdocyon thous	Mountain fox
Certhia familiaris	Brown or tree creeper
Cervus canadensis canadensis	Elk
C. canadensis roosevelti	Roosevelt elk
C. elaphus	Red deer

Scientific Name	Common Name
C. nippon hortulorum	Dybowski sika deer
C. nippon nippon	Japanese sika deer
C. nippon taiouanus	Formosan sika deer
C. unicolor equinus	Sambar deer
Cestum veneris	Venus'-girdle
Chaetophractus villosus	Hairy armadillo
Chaetopterus variopedapus	Polychaete
Chaetura pelagica	Chimney swift
Chalcides ocellatus	Ocellated sand skink
Chamaea fasciata	Wren-tit
Chaoborus sp.	Phantom midge
Charadrius hiaticula	Ringed plover
C. vociferus	Killdeer
Chelodina longicollis	Long-necked turtle
Chelonia mydas	Atlantic green turtle
Chen caerulescens	Blue goose
C. hyperborea	Snow goose
C. hyperborea atlantica	Snow goose
Chilo suppressalis	Asiatic rice borer
Chironomus riparius	Midge
Chlidonias niger	Black tern
Chlorestes notatus cyanogenys	Brazilian hummingbird
Chloris chloris	Greenfinch
Choeropsis liberiensis	Pigmy hippopotamus
Choloepus hoffmanni	Hoffmann's two-toed sloth
Chordeiles minor	Nighthawk
C. minor minor	Nighthawk
Chromis chromis	Blue damselfish
Chrysemys picta	Painted turtle
C. picta marginata	Midland painted turtle
Chrysolophus amherstiae	Lady Amherst pheasant
C. pictus	Golden pheasant
Cichla temensis	Cichlid
Cinachyra cavernosa	Sponge
Cinclus mexicanus	North American dipper
Ciona sp.	Sea squirt
Circus cyaneus hudsonius	Marsh harrier or marsh hawk
Citellus citellus	Souslik
C. franklini	Franklin ground squirrel
C. lateralis	Golden mantled ground squirrel
C. leucurus	White-tailed antelope squirrel
C. pygmaeus	Little souslik
C. tereticaudus	Round-tailed ground squirrel
C. tridecemlineatus	Thirteen-lined ground squirrel
C. undulatus	Arctic ground squirrel
C. undulatus parryii	Parry's ground squirrel
Clethrionomys gapperi	Red-backed vole
C. gapperi gapperi	Red-backed vole
C. gapperi rhoadsi	Red-backed vole
C. rutilus	Northern red-backed mouse
Clibanarius vittatus	Hermit crab
Clonorchis sinensis	Chinese liver fluke
Clytolaema rubricauda	Brazilian hummingbird
Coccyzus americanus	Yellow-billed cuckoo
Cochliomyia hominivorax	Screwworm
Coenagrion puella	Common coenagrion
Coendou prehensilis	Prehensile-tailed porcupine
C. villosus	Prehensile-tailed porcupine

continued

Appendix I. SCIENTIFIC NAMES AND CORRESPONDING COMMON NAMES

Part I. Animals

Scientific Name	Common Name
Colaptes auratus	Yellow-shafted flicker
Colibri serrirostris	Violet-ear
Colinus virginianus	Bobwhite
Colobus guereza kikuyuensis	East African colobus
Coluber constrictor	Black snake
C. constrictor constrictor	Northern black racer
Columba livia	Street pigeon
Condylactis gigantea	Sea anemone
Conger spp.	Conger eel
Connochaetes gnou	White-tailed gnu
C. taurinus albojubatus	White-bearded gnu
Constrictor constrictor	Boa constrictor
Contopus virens	Eastern wood pewee
Corbicula sandai	Edible mussel
Corixa dentipes	Water boatman
Corvus brachyrhynchos	American common crow
C. caurinus	Northwestern crow
C. corax	Common raven
C. corax principalis	Common raven
C. cryptoleucus	White-necked raven
C. monedula	European jackdaw
Coturnix coturnix	European quail
C. coturnix japonica	Japanese quail
Crassostrea angulata	Portuguese oyster
C. gigas	Oyster
C. virginica	Virginia oyster
Crax alector	Black curassow
C. rubra	Great curassow
Crenichthys baileyi	White River killifish
Crenobia alpina	Alpine planarian
Cricetus cricetus	European hamster
Crinia signifera	Leptodactylid
Cristaria plicata	Freshwater mussel
Crocodylus niloticus	African crocodile
Crocuta crocuta	Spotted hyena
C. crocuta germinans	Spotted hyena
Crossarchus obscurus	Cusimanse
Crotalus atrox	Western diamondback rattlesnake
C. scutellatus	Mojave rattlesnake
Crotaphytus collaris	Collared lizard
Cryptacanthodes maculatus	Wrymouth
Culex pipiens	Northern house mosquito
C. pipiens quinquefasciatus	Southern house mosquito
Culiseta incidens	Mosquito
Cyanocitta cristata	American blue jay
C. cristata bromia	Blue jay
C. stelleri	Steller's jay
Cyclopes sp.	South American silky anteater
Cyclosalpa pinnata	Salp
Cygnus atratus	Black swan
C. olor	Mute swan
Cynanthus latirostris	Broad-billed hummingbird
Cynopithecus niger	Celebes crested macaque
Cyprinus carpio	Carp
Dactylopsila trivirgata melampus	New Guinea striped possum
Dacus dorsalis	Oriental fruit fly
Damaliscus dorcas phillipsi	Blesbok

Scientific Name	Common Name
Daption capense	Cape petrel
Dasycercus cristicauda	Marsupial mouse
Dasyprocta aguti	Agouti
D. azarae	Agouti
D. paraguayensis	Paraguayan agouti
D. pyrmnolopha	Agouti
Dasypus novemcinctus	Nine-banded armadillo
D. sexcinctus	Armadillo
Dasyurus maculatus	Tiger cat
Dendrocopos pubescens	Downy woodpecker
D. villosus septentrionalis	Northern hairy woodpecker
Dendrocygna autumnalis	Black-bellied tree duck
Dendroica auduboni	Audubon's warbler
D. caerulescens	Black-throated blue warbler
D. magnolia	Magnolia warbler
D. tigrina	Cape May warbler
Dermestes maculatus	Hide beetle
Deroceras agreste	Slug
D. reticulatum	Slug
Desmodus rotundus	Common vampire bat
Diceros bicornis	Black rhinoceros
Dicrostonyx groenlandicus	Collared lemming
D. groenlandicus rubricatus	Varying lemming
Didelphis marsupialis	Large American opossum
D. marsupialis virginiana	Common opossum
Diomedea chlororhynchos	Yellow-nosed albatross
D. exulans	Wandering albatross
D. immutabilis	Laysan albatross
D. nigripes	Black-footed albatross
Diphyllobothrium latum	Fish tapeworm
Diplodactylus strophurus intermedius	Gecko
Diplodus sargus	European porgy
Dipodomys agilis	Agile kangaroo rat
D. deserti	Desert kangaroo rat
D. merriami	Merriam's kangaroo rat
D. spectabilis	Bannertailed kangaroo rat
Dipsosaurus dorsalis	Desert iguana
Dolichonyx oryzivorus	Bobolink
Dreissena polymorpha	Zebra mussel
Dromia vulgaris	Sponge crab
Dromiceius novaehollandiae	Emu
Drosophila melanogaster	Fruit fly
D. pachea	Fruit fly
D. repleta	Fruit fly
Drymarchon corais couperi	Eastern indigo snake
Dryocopus pileatus	Pileated woodpecker
Dugesia gonocephala	Freshwater planarian
D. polychroa	Freshwater planarian
D. tigrina	Freshwater planarian
Dumetella carolinensis	American catbird
Dysdercus fasciatus	Cotton stainer
Dysidea crawshayi	Horny sponge
Echinococcus granulosus	Hydatid tapeworm
Echinops telfairi	Small hedgehog tenrec
Egretta thula candidissima	Snowy heron
Eisenia foetida	Manure worm or brandling
Elaphurus davidianus	Pere David's deer
Eledone moschata	Mediterranean musk octopus
Elephas maximus	Indian elephant

continued

Appendix I. SCIENTIFIC NAMES AND CORRESPONDING COMMON NAMES

Part I. Animals

Scientific Name	Common Name
E. maximus indicus	Indian elephant
Eliomys quercinus	Garden dormouse
Emberiza calandra	Corn bunting
E. citrinella	Yellowhammer
Emerita talpoida	Sand crab
Empidonax flaviventris	Yellow-bellied flycatcher
E. minimus	Least flycatcher
E. traillii	Traill's flycatcher
Emys orbicularis	European pond turtle
Enallagma cyathigerum	Common blue damselfly
Enhydra lutris	Sea otter
Enoplus communis	Roundworm
Ensatina eschscholtzii	Redwood salamander
E. eschscholtzii xanthoptica	Yellow-eyed salamander
Ephestia elutella	Tobacco moth
Epinephelus morio	Red grouper
Epiperipatus brasiliensis	Onychophoran
Epomophorus anurus	Fruit bat
Eptatretus stouti	Pacific hagfish
Eptesicus fuscus	Big brown bat
E. serotinus	Serotine, or brown bat
E. tenuipinnis	White-winged serotine
Equus asinus	Donkey
E. caballus	Horse
E. grevyi	Grevy's zebra
Eremophila alpestris	Horned lark
E. alpestris alpestris	Horned lark
Erethizon dorsatum	North American porcupine
Ereunetes mauri	Western sandpiper
Erignathus barbatus	Bearded seal
Erinaceus europaeus	European hedgehog
Eriocheir sinensis	Mitten crab
Eriphia spinifrons	Sponge crab
Erithacus rubecula	European robin
Erolia alpina	Dunlin
E. bairdii	Baird's sandpiper
E. ferruginea	Dunlin
Erpobdella octoculata	Leech
E. testacea	Leech
Erythrocebus patas	Patas monkey
Eryx thebaicus	Theban sand boa
Eschrichtius gibbosus	Gray whale
Esox lucius	Northern pike
Estrilda troglodytes	Tropical black-rumped waxbill
Eudyptes crestatus	Rockhopper
Eudyptula minor	Little blue penguin
Eudocimus albus	White ibis
Eumeces obsoletus	Great Plains skink
Eumetopias jubata	Steller's or northern sea lion
Eumops perotis	Mastiff bat
Eupetomena macroura	Swallowtail hummingbird
Euphagus carolinus	Rusty blackbird
E. cyanocephalus	Brewer's blackbird
Eurycea bislineata bislineata	Two-lined salamander
E. nana	San Marcos salamander
E. neotenes	Neotenic salamander
E. pterophila	Fern bank salamander
Eurytium limosum	Mud crab
Eustrongylides ignotus	Roundworm of birds & fish
Eutamias minimus	Least chipmunk
Exeristes comstockii	Ichneumon wasp

Scientific Name	Common Name
Falco mexicanus	American prairie falcon
F. peregrinus	Peregrine
F. sparverius	Sparrow hawk
Fasciola hepatica	Liver fluke
Felis bengalensis	Leopard cat
F. canadensis	Yukon lynx
F. catus	Cat
F. chaus	Jungle cat
F. chaus fulvidina	Jungle cat
F. concolor	Puma
F. concolor missoulensis	Mountain puma
F. jagouaroundi fossata	Jaguarundi
F. libyca	Steppe cat
F. manul	Pallas cat
F. nigripes	Black-footed cat
Fennecus zerda	Fennec fox
Formica polyctena	Ant
Francolinus natalensis	African Franklin partridge
Fridericia sp.	Microdrilid, or enchytraeid worm
Fringilla coelebs	Chaffinch
Fulica americana	American coot
F. atra	European coot
Fulmarus glacialis	Fulmar
Fundulus heteroclitus	Mummichog
F. kansae	Plains killifish
F. parvipinnis	California killifish
Gadus morhua	Cod
Galago senegalensis	Galago
Galathea squamifera	Crab
Galeodes indicus	False or sun spider, or wind scorpion
Galleria mellonella	Greater wax moth
Gallus domesticus	Chicken
G. gallus	Red jungle fowl
Gammarus duebeni	Scud
G. locusta	Beachflea
G. pulex	Beachflea
G. zaddachi	Beachflea
Gasterophilus intestinalis	Horse botfly
Gastrothylax crumenifer	Rumen fluke
Gavia arctica pacifica	Arctic loon
Gazella thomsoni	Thomson gazelle
Gecarcinus lateralis	Purple land crab
Gehyra variegata	Gecko
Gennaeus nycthemerus nycthemerus	Silver pheasant
Geococcyx californianus	Roadrunner
Geodia gibberosa	Sponge
Geomys bursarius	Pocket gopher
G. pinetis	Southeastern pocket gopher
Geothlypis trichas	Yellowthroat
Geotrupes sp.	Common European dung beetle
Geranoaetus melanoleucus	Black-chested buzzard eagle
Gerrhonotus multicarinatus	Southern alligator lizard
Gillichthys sp.	Goby
Giraffa camelopardalis	Giraffe
G. camelopardalis rothschildi	Uganda giraffe
Glaucomys volans	Southern flying squirrel

continued

Appendix I. SCIENTIFIC NAMES AND CORRESPONDING COMMON NAMES

Part I. Animals

Scientific Name	Common Name
G. volans volans	Southern flying squirrel
Glis glis	Fat dormouse
Glossiphonia complanata	Leech
Glossoscolex sp.	Oligochaete
Glycera siphonostoma	Burrowing marine polychaete
Glyptocephalus sp.	Righteye flounder
Gnathostoma spinigerum	Roundworm
Gopherus agassizii	Western gopher turtle
G. polyphemus	Gopher tortoise
Gorgoderina attenuata	Digenetic fluke
Gorgonia flabellum	Sea fan
Gorilla gorilla	Gorilla
G. gorilla beringei	Mountain gorilla
G. gorilla gorilla	Lowland gorilla
Grison furox	Grison
Grus canadensis	Sandhill crane
G. canadensis canadensis	Sandhill crane
Guiraca caerulea	Blue grosbeak
Gymnorhinus cyanocephala	Piñon jay
Gynaecotyla adunca	Bird fluke
Gypaetus barbatus	Bearded vulture
Haemonchus contortus	Twisted stomach worm
Haemopis sanguisuga	Leech
Haliaeetus leucocephalus	Bald eagle
H. leucocephalus alascanus	Northern bald eagle
Halichoerus grypus	Gray seal
Haliotis rufescens	Abalone
Hedymeles ludovicianus	Red-breasted grosbeak
Helarctos malayanus	Malayan sun bear
Helicella candicans	Sheep snail
Heliophobius argenteocinereus kapiti	Sand rat
Helix aspersa	Dented garden snail or petit-gris
H. pisana	Little edible land snail
H. pomatia	Edible snail
H. vermiculata	White-lipped edible land snail
Helobdella stagnalis	Leech
Hemiechinus auritus	Long-eared hedgehog
Hemiergis decresiense	Three-toed skink
H. peronii	Four-toed skink
Hemigrapsus nudus	Purple shore crab
H. oregonensis	Yellow shore crab
Hemitragus jemlahicus	Himalayan tahr
H. jemlahicus jemlahicus	Tahr goat
Hermissenda crassicornis	Sea slug
Herpestes edwardsi	Indian mongoose
Hesperiphona vespertina	Evening grosbeak
Heterakis spumosa	Poultry cecal worm
Heterocephalus glaber	Naked mole-rat
Heterometrus fulvipes	Whip scorpion
Heteronota bynoei	Bynoe's gecko
Himantopus mexicanus	Black-necked stilt
Himasthla quissetensis	Fluke
Hippocampus spp.	Seahorse
Hippopotamus amphibius	Nile hippopotamus
Hipposideros bicolor	Bicolored leaf-nosed bat
H. caffer	Old World leaf-nosed bat
H. cyclops	Cyclops bat
H. speoris	Leaf-nosed bat
Hippotragus niger roosevelti	Sable antelope
Hirudo medicinalis	Leech
Hirundo rustica erythrogaster	Barn swallow
Holothuria impatiens	Sea cucumber
H. stellati	Sea cucumber
H. tubulosa	Sea cucumber
Homarus americanus	American lobster
Homo sapiens	Man
Hyalophora cecropia	Cecropia moth
Hydrochoerus hydrochaeris	Capybara
Hydromys chrysogaster	Water rat
Hydrophilus ater	Water scavenger beetle
Hydropsyche sp.	Caddis fly
Hyla arborea	European green tree frog
H. cinerea	Green tree frog
H. ewingi	Ewing's tree frog
H. regilla	Pacific tree frog
H. rubella	Red tree frog
Hylemya antiqua	Onion maggot
Hylobates lar	Gibbon
Hylocharis cyanus cyanus	Brazilian hummingbird
Hylocichla guttata	Hermit thrush
H. mustelina	Wood thrush
Hymenolepis diminuta	Rat tapeworm
Hyriopsis schlegelii	Freshwater mussel
Hystrix indica	Indian crested porcupine
Ictalurus furcatus	Blue catfish
I. nebulosus	Brown bullhead
Icteria virens	Yellow-breasted chat
Icterus bullockii	Bullock's oriole
I. galbula	Baltimore oriole
Idus idus	Golden orfe
Iguana iguana	Common iguana
I. tuberculata	Tuberculate iguana
Ilia nucleus	Crab
Ircinia fasciculata	Stinker sponge
Iridoprocne bicolor	Tree swallow
Isognomon alata	Tree oyster
Isoodon obesulus	Short-nosed bandicoot
Isostichopus badionotus	Sea cucumber
Jabiru mycteria	Jabiru
Jaculus jaculus	Jerboa
Julus sp.	Millipede
Junco hyemalis	Slate-colored junco
J. oreganus	Oregon junco
Kinixys belliana belliana	Bell's African turtle
K. erosa	Forest hinge-back tortoise
Kinosternum subrubrum	Eastern mud turtle
Lacerta agilis	European fence lizard
L. viridis	Green lacerta
Lagodon rhomboides	Pinfish
Lagopus lagopus	Willow ptarmigan
L. leucurus leucurus	White-tailed ptarmigan

continued

Appendix I. SCIENTIFIC NAMES AND CORRESPONDING COMMON NAMES

Part I. Animals

Scientific Name	Common Name
L. mutus nelsoni	Rock ptarmigan
Lagothrix lagotricha	Woolly monkey
Lagurus curtatus	Sagebrush vole
Lama glama	Llama
L. guanicoe	Guanaco
L. pacos	Alpaca
L. vicugna	Vicuña
Lampetra fluviatilis	Pacific American lamprey
Lampornis clemenciae	Blue-throated hummingbird
Lanius ludovicianus	Migrant or loggerhead shrike
Larus argentatus	Herring gull
L. argentatus smithsonianus	Herring gull
L. atricilla	Laughing gull
L. canus brachyrhynchus	Mew gull
L. dominicanus	Kelp or southern black-backed gull
L. fuscus	Lesser black-backed gull
L. glaucescens	Glaucous-winged gull
L. hyperboreus	Glaucous gull
L. hyperboreus barrovianus	Glaucous gull
L. marinus	Great black-backed gull
L. pipixcan	Franklin's gull
L. ridibundus	Black-headed gull
Lasioderma serricorne	Cigarette beetle
Leiolopisma metallicum	Metallic skink
Leiostomus xanthurus	Spot
Lemmus lemmus	Brown lemming
Lemur cattus	Ring-tailed lemur
L. variegatus	Ruffed or black and white lemur
Lepidosiren paradoxa	South American lungfish
Lepisosteus osseus	Longnose gar
Lepomis macrochirus	Common bluegill
Leptasterias pusilla	Starfish
Leptoptilos crumeniferus	Marabou stork
L. dubius	Indian adjutant stork
L. javanicus	Lesser adjutant stork
Lepus americanus	Snowshoe rabbit or American hare
L. timidus	Blue or varying hare
L. townsendii townsendii	White-tailed jackrabbit
Leucophaea maderae	Madeira cockroach
Libinia dubia	Spider crab
L. emarginata	Spider crab
Ligia oceanica	Rock slater or wharf louse
Limanda ferruginea	Yellowtail flounder
Limax flavus	Slug
Limnephilus vittatus	Caddis fly
Limnodrilus claparedianus	Tubificid oligochaete
L. hoffmeisteri	Tubificid oligochaete
Limnodromus griseus	Short-billed dowitcher
Limnodynastes dorsalis	Australian frog
L. ornatus	Ornate frog
L. tasmaniensis	Marbled frog
Limosa fedoa	Marbled godwit
Limulus polyphemus	King crab
Lingula reevii	Tongue shell
Liomys irroratus	Pocket mouse
L. salvini	Pocket mouse
Lissodendoryx isodictyalis	Sponge
Littorina littorea	Periwinkle
Lobipes lobatus	Northern phalarope
Locusta migratoria	Locust
Loligo pealeii	Common American squid
Lophius piscatorius	Monkfish
Lophodytes culcullatus	Hooded merganser
Lophornis magnifica	Frilled coquette
Lophortyx californicus	California quail
L. gambelii	Desert or Gambel's quail
Loxia curvirostra	Red crossbill
L. curvirostra pusilla	Red crossbill
L. leucoptera leucoptera	White-winged crossbill
Loxodonta africana cxyotis	African bush elephant
Lullula arborea	Wood lark
Lumbricus terrestris	Earthworm
Lunda cirrhata	Tufted puffin
Lutragale perspicillata perspicillata	Smooth otter
Lutreolina crassicaudata	Thick-tailed opossum
Lychas tricarinatus	Scorpion
Lycosa sp.	Wolf spider
Lyctus sp.	Powder post beetle
Lymnaea auricularia	Freshwater snail
L. ovata	Oval lymnaea
L. palustris	Freshwater snail
L. peregra	Exotic lymnaea
L. stagnalis	Freshwater snail
Lynx rufus baileyi	Bailey's bobcat
Macaca cyclopis	Formosan rock macaque
M. fuscata yakui	Japanese macaque
M. irus	Philippine or crab-eating monkey
M. maurus ochreatus	Gray-armed macaque
M. mulatta	Rhesus monkey
M. nemestrina leonina	Burmese pig-tailed macaque
M. silenus	Wanderoo
M. sylvana	Barbary ape
Macrocentrus ancylivorus	Braconid
Macropus giganteus	Great gray kangaroo
M. major	Great grey kangaroo
M. robustus robustus	Wallaroo
M. rufus	Red kangaroo
Macrosiphum rosae	Rose aphid
Maja squinado	Spider crab
M. verrucosa	Spider crab
Malaclemys terrapin centrata	Diamondback terrapin
Malacosoma neustria	Lackey
Malacothrix typica	Long-eared mouse
Mandrillus sphinx	Mandrill
Manis tricuspis	Pangolin or scaly anteater
Mareca americana	American widgeon
M. penelope	European widgeon
Marinogammarus pirloti	Scud
Marmosa cinerea	Mouse opossum
M. mexicana	Mexican opossum
Marmota caligata	Hoary marmot
M. marmota	Eurasian marmot
Martes americana actuosa	American marten
M. penanti	Fisher
Masticophis flagellum flagellum	Eastern coachwhip snake
Megaceryle alcyon	Belted kingfisher

continued

Appendix I. SCIENTIFIC NAMES AND CORRESPONDING COMMON NAMES

Part I. Animals

Scientific Name	Common Name
Megaderma lyra	Indian false vampire bat
Megadyptes antipodes	Yellow-eyed penguin
Megaloscolex mauritii	Oligochaete
Megaptera novaeanglia	Humpback whale
Melanerpes erythrocephalus	Acorn woodpecker
Melanoides tuberculata	Marine snail
Melanoplus bivittatus	Two-striped grasshopper
M. differentialis	Differential grasshopper
Melanotrochilus fuscus	Black jacobin
Melanotus communis	Corn wireworm
Meleagris gallopavo	Turkey
Mellivora capensis leuconota	Ratel
Melolontha sp.	Cockchafer
Melomys littoralis	Mosaic-tailed rat
Melopsittacus undulatus	Budgerigar
Melospiza lincolnii	Lincoln's sparrow
M. melodia	Song sparrow
M. melodia melodia	Song sparrow
Menippe mercenaria	Stone crab
Mephitis mephitis mesomelas	Striped skunk
Mercenaria mercenaria	Northern quahog
Mergus serrator	Red-breasted merganser
Meriones unguiculatus	Clawed jird
Merluccius bilinearis	American Atlantic silver hake
Merodon equestris	Narcissus bulb fly
Mesocricetus auratus	Golden or Syrian hamster
Metachirus nudicaudatus	Brown "four-eyed" opossum
Metapenaeus monocerus	Shrimp
Microciona prolifera	Red oyster sponge
Microdipodops megacephalus nasutus	Kangaroo mouse
M. pallidus	Pale kangaroo mouse
Microsorex hoyi	Pygmy shrew
Microtus arvalis	Common vole
M. californicus	California vole
M. longicaudus	Long-tailed vole
M. ochrogaster ochrogaster	Prairie vole
M. pennsylvanicus	Meadow mouse
M. pennsylvanicus pennsylvanicus	Meadow vole
Mimus polyglottos	Mockingbird
Miniopterus blepotis	Long-winged bat
Mirounga angustirostris	Elephant seal
Misgurnus fossilis	European loach or European weatherfish
Modiolus demissus	Horse mussel
Molothrus ater	Brown-headed cowbird
Moniezia expansa	Double-pored ruminant tapeworm
Morus bassanus	Northern gannet
Motacilla alba	White wagtail
Mugil sp.	Mullet
Mungos mungo	East African banded mongoose
Muntiacus muntjac	Muntjac or barking deer
M. reevesi	Reeves' muntjac
Muraena spp.	Moray eel
Mus musculus	House mouse
Musca domestica	House fly
M. domestica vicina	Oriental house fly
Muscardinus avellanarius	Common dormouse
Muscicapa striata	Spotted flycatcher
Musculium lacustre	Fingernail clam
Mustela putorius	European polecat
M. rixosa	Least weasel
Mustelus canis	Smooth dogfish
Myadestes townsendi	Townsend's solitaire
Mycteria americana	Wood ibis or wood stork
Myocastor coypus	Coypu
Myoprocta acouchy	Long-tailed agouti
Myotis lucifugus	Little brown bat
M. myotis	Common brown bat
M. mystacinus	Little brown bat
M. nattereri	Brown bat
M. sodalis	Brown bat
M. yumanensis	Brown bat
Myoxocephalus octodecemspinosus	Longhorn sculpin
M. scorpius	Shorthorn sculpin
Myrmecophaga tridactyla	Giant anteater
Mytilus crassitesta	Sea mussel
M. edulis	Edible mussel
M. galloprovincialis	Mediterranean sea mussel
Myxas glutinosa	North American pond snail
Myxine glutinosa	Common Atlantic hagfish
Myzus persicae	Green peach aphid
Nandinia binotata	African palm civet
Napaeozapus insignis	Woodland jumping mouse
N. insignis insignis	Woodland jumping mouse
Nasalis larvatus	Proboscis monkey
Nasua narica	Coati
N. nasua	Coati
Natrix natrix	Common European water snake
N. sipedon	North American water snake
Nematodirus spp.	Strongyle
Nemobius sylvestris	Wood cricket
Neoaplectana glaseri	Japanese beetle parasite
Neobatrachus centralis	Central Australian frog
N. pictus	Painted frog
Neotoma fuscipes	Dusky-footed wood rat
N. lepida	Desert wood rat
Nephila claviceps	Tropical silk spider
Nephrurus laevis	Knob-tailed gecko
Nereis virens	Clam worm
Nippostrongylus brasiliensis	Strongylin
Noctilio labialis	Bulldog bat
N. leporinus	Fisherman bat
Noetia ponderosa	Ark shell
Nosopsyllus fasciatus	Rat flea
Nothura maculosa	Tinamou
Nucifraga columbiana	Clark's nutcracker
Numenius americanus	Long-billed curlew
Numida meleagris	Common guinea hen
Nuttallornis borealis	Olive-sided flycatcher
Nyctalus noctula	Noctule
Nyctea scandiaca	Snowy owl
Nyctereutes procyonoides	Raccoon dog

continued

Appendix I. SCIENTIFIC NAMES AND CORRESPONDING COMMON NAMES

Part I. Animals

Scientific Name	Common Name
Nycticorax nycticorax	Black-crowned night heron
N. nycticorax hoactli	Black-crowned night heron
Nyctidromus albicollis	Pauraque
Nymphalis io	Brush-footed butterfly
N. urtica	Brush-footed butterfly
Oceanodroma leuchorhoa	Leach's petrel
Ochotona collaris	Alaskan pika
Octopus dofleini	Octopus
O. macropus	Octopus
O. vulgaris	Octopus
Ocypode albicans	Sand crab
O. quadrata	Ghost crab
Odobenus rosmarus divergens	North Pacific walrus
Odocoileus hemionus	Mule deer
Oidemia nigra	Common scoter
Okapia johnstoni	Okapi
Olor buccinator	Trumpeter swan
Oncomelania nosophora	Marine snail
Oncopeltus fasciatus	Milkweed bug
Ondatra zibethicus	Muskrat
Oniscus asellus	Sow bug
Onychiurus procampatus	Springtail
Ophioderma longicauda	Brittle star
Oporornis agilis	Connecticut warbler
O. philadelphia	Mourning warbler
O. tolmiei	MacGillivray's warbler
Opsanus tau	Oyster toadfish
Orchestia sp.	Amphipod
Orchomenella chilensis	Amphipod
Orconectes immunis	Crayfish
O. nais	Crayfish
O. propinquus	Freshwater crayfish
O. virilis	Freshwater crayfish
Oreamnos americanus	North American mountain goat
Oreortyx pictus	Mountain quail
Oreotrochilus estella	Estella hummingbird
Ornithorhynchus anatinus	Platypus
Orycteropus afer ruvanensis	Kenya aardvark
Oryctolagus cuniculus	European rabbit
Oryx beisa	Gemsbok
O. gazella gazella	Gemsbok
Oryzaephilus surinamensis	Saw-toothed grain beetle
Ostertagia circumcincta	Brown stomach worm of sheep
Ostrea circumpicta	Oyster
Ostrinia nubilalis	European corn borer
Otocyon megalotis	Bat-eared fox
Otus asio	Screech owl
O. asio naevius	Screech owl
O. flammeolus	Flammulated owl
Ovibos moschatus	Musk ox
Ovis aries	Sheep
O. canadensis canadensis	Mountain sheep
O. musimon	Mouflon
Oxyura jamaicensis	Ruddy duck
Pachygrapsus crassipes	Striped rock crab
P. marmoratus	Shore crab

Scientific Name	Common Name
Pachyptila turtur	Fairy prion
Pagodroma nivea	Snow petrel
Pagophila eburnea	Ivory gull
Paguristes maculata	Decapod
Palaemon longirostris	Shrimp
P. serratus	Prawn
P. squilla	Prawn
Palaemonetes antennarius	Freshwater shrimp
P. varians	Shrimp
Palinurus vulgaris	Spiny lobster
Palorus ratzeburgi	Small-eyed flour beetle
Pan troglodytes	Chimpanzee
P. troglodytes schweinfurthii	Chimpanzee
Pandalina brevirostris	Decapod
Pandalus borealis	Prawn
P. montagui	Prawn or pink shrimp
Panopeus herbstii	Mud crab
Panthera leo	Lion
P. nebulosa	Clouded leopard
P. onca	Jaguar
P. pardus	Leopard
P. tigris	Tiger
P. tigris longipilis	Siberian tiger
P. tigris tigris	Bengal tiger
P. uncia	Snow leopard
Panulirus argus	Spiny lobster
Papio hamadryas	Baboon
Paracentrotus lividus	Sea urchin
Paraechinus aethiopicus	Ethiopian hedgehog
P. hypomelas	Brandt hedgehog
Paragonimus westermani	Lung fluke
Paramphistomum cervi	Cattle rumen fluke
Parascaris equorum	Roundworm of horse
Parus atricapillus	Black-capped chickadee
P. atricapillus atricapillus	Black-capped chickadee
P. atricapillus turneri	Black-capped chickadee
P. carolinensis	Carolina chickadee
P. cinctus	Gray-headed chickadee
P. major	Great tit
Passer domesticus	House sparrow
P. montanus	European tree sparrow
Passerculus sandwichensis	Savannah sparrow
Passerella iliaca	Fox sparrow
Passerherbulus caudacutus	Le Conte's sparrow
Passerina amoena	Lazuli bunting
Patella vulgata	Common European limpet
Pavo cristatus	Peacock
Pecari tajacu	Collared peccary
Pecten irradians	Scallop
Pectinophora gossypiella	Pink bollworm
Pedetes cafer	Springhaas
Pelagia noctiluca	Jellyfish
Pelecanus conspicillatus	Black-backed pelican
P. erythrorhynchos	American white pelican
P. occidentalis	Brown pelican
P. onocrotalus	European white pelican
Pelobates fuscus	European frog
Pelusios subniger	Dark pelomedusa turtle
Penaeus japonicus	Shrimp
Pergamasus crassipes	Parasitic mite or tick

continued

Appendix I. SCIENTIFIC NAMES AND CORRESPONDING COMMON NAMES

Part I. Animals

Scientific Name	Common Name
Peripatus accacioi	Peripatus
Periplaneta americana	American cockroach
Perisoreus canadensis	Canada or gray jay
P. canadensis pacificus	Alaska or gray jay
Perla burmeisteriana	European stone fly
Perodicticus potto	West African lemur or potto
P. potto edwardsi	Cameroon potto
Perognathus hispidus	Plains or pale pocket mouse
P. longimembris	Little pocket mouse
P. penicillatus penicillatus	Desert pocket mouse
Peromyscus californicus	California mouse
P. crinitus	Canyon mouse
P. eremicus	Cactus mouse
P. leucopus	White-footed mouse
P. maniculatus	Deer mouse
P. maniculatus artemisiae	Deer mouse
P. maniculatus austerus	Deer mouse
P. maniculatus gracilis	Deer mouse
P. maniculatus nebrascensis	Deer mouse
P. maniculatus oreas	Deer mouse
P. maniculatus sonoriensis	Deer mouse
P. polionotus	Beach mouse
P. sitkensis	Sitka mouse
P. thomasi	Thomas' deer mouse
P. truei	Piñon mouse
Petaurus breviceps	Sugar glider
Petrochelidon pyrrhonota	Cliff swallow
Petrogale xanthopus	Ring-tailed rock wallaby
Petromyzon marinus	Sea lamprey
Phaenicia sericata	Blowfly
Phaethon rubricauda	Red-tailed tropic bird
Phainopepla nitens	Phainopepla
Phalacrocorax aristotelis	Shag or cormorant
P. auritus	Double-crested cormorant
P. carbo	Common cormorant
P. pelagicus resplendens	Pelagic cormorant
Phalaenoptilus nuttalli	Poorwill
Phalera bucephala	Buff-tip moth
Phascogale tapoatafa	Marsupial rat
Phascolarctos cinereus	Koala
Phasianus colchicus	Ring-necked pheasant
P. colchicus mongolicus	Ring-necked pheasant
P. torquatus	Pheasant
Pheretima hawayana	Earthworm
P. posthuma	Earthworm
Philacte canagica	Emperor goose
Philomachus pugnax	Ruff
Phloeomys cumingi	Slender-tailed cloud rat
Phoca vitulina	Harbor seal
P. vitulina concolor	Atlantic harbor seal
Phocoena phocoena	Harbor porpoise
Phoenicopterus chilensis	Flamingo
P. ruber roseus	European flamingo
Phoenicurus phoenicurus	European redstart
Phormia regina	Black blowfly
Phrynichus phipsoni	Whip scorpion
Phrynosoma cornutum	Horned lizard
P. coronatum	Coast horned toad
P. solare	Regal horned lizard
Phyllodactylus marmoratus	Marbled gecko
Phylloscopus trochilus	Willow warbler
Phyllostomus hastatus hastatus	Trinidad spear-nosed bat
Physa acuta	Pond snail
P. fontinalis	North American pond snail
Physalia physalis	Portuguese man-of-war
Physeter catodon	Sperm whale
Pica pica	Black-billed magpie
P. pica hudsonia	Black-billed magpie
Picoides arcticus	Black-backed three-toed woodpecker
P. tridactylus	Three-toed woodpecker
P. tridactylus fasciatus	Northern three-toed woodpecker
Pieris brassicae	European cabbageworm
Pilumnus hirtellus	Decapod
Pinctada martensii	Pearl oyster
Pinicola enculeator alascensis	Pine grosbeak
P. enucleator leucura	Pine grosbeak
Pinna muricata	Pen shell
P. nobilis	Pen shell
Pipilo aberti	Abert's towhee
P. fuscus	Brown towhee
Pipistrellus pipistrellus	European brown bat
Pipra mentalis	Yellow-thighed manakin
Piranga ludovicians	Western tanager
Piscicola geometra	Leech
Pitymys pinetorum scalopsoides	Pine mouse
P. subterraneus	European pine vole
Planorbis corneus	Ramshorn snail
Platichthys stellatus	Flounder
Platybunus triangularis	Daddy longlegs
Plecotus auritus	Long-eared bat
Plectrophenax nivalis	Snow bunting
P. nivalis nivalis	Snow bunting
Plectus sp.	Roundworm
Plegadis falcinellus	Glossy ibis
Pleolophus basizonus	Parasitic wasp
Plethodon cinereus cinereus	Red-backed salamander
Pleurobranchaea meckelii	Nudibranch
Pleurogonius malaclemys	Fluke
Plexaura flexuosa	Purple gorgonian
Plodia interpunctella	Indian meal moth
Podargus strigoides	Tawny frogmouth
Podiceps auritus	Horned grebe
P. caspicus	Eared or black-necked grebe
Podilymbus podiceps	Pied-billed grebe
Poephagus grunniens	Yak
Poephila castanotis	Zebra finch
Polioptila caerulea	Blue-gray gnatcatcher
Polytmus guainumbi	Goldthroat
Pongo pygmaeus	Orangutan
Pontoscolex sp.	Oligochaete
Popilius disjunctus	Horned passalus beetle, or bessbug
Porcellio laevis	Sow bug
P. scaber	Scabby sow bug or wood louse
Poroaria coronata	Red-crested cardinal
Potamon niloticus	Freshwater crab
Potamopyrgus jenkinsi	Marine snail
Potorous tridactylus	Rat kangaroo
Potos caudiovolvus	Kinkajou
P. flavus	Kinkajou
Primnoa lepadifera	Indian Ocean octocoral

continued

Appendix I. SCIENTIFIC NAMES AND CORRESPONDING COMMON NAMES

Part I. Animals

Scientific Name	Common Name
Pristis microdon	Sawfish
Procambarus alleni	Dwarf crayfish
P. clarkii	Louisiana red crayfish
Procavia capensis	Rock hyrax
Procyon cancrivorus	Crab-eating raccoon
P. lotor	Raccoon
Prodenia eridania	Southern armyworm
Proechimys semispinosus	Spiny rat
Progne subis	Purple martin
Protemnodon agilis	Agile wallaby
Protopterus aethiopicus	African lungfish
Psaltriparus minimus	Common bush tit
Pseudaxinella rosacea	Sponge
Pseudemys scripta	Red-eared terrapin
P. scripta elegans	Red-eared turtle
Pseudophryne bibroni	False toad
Pseudopleuronectes americanus	Winter flounder
Pseudosarcophaga sp.	Flesh fly
Pterodroma leucoptera hypoleuca	Bonin Island petrel
Pteronura brasiliensis brasiliensis	Northern giant otter
Pteropus geddiei	Flying fox
P. giganteus	Flying fox, or Indian fruit bat
P. poliocephalus	Grey-headed fruit bat
P. scapulatus	Little reddish fruit bat
Pterotrachea coronata	Heteropod
Ptinus tectus	Spider beetle
Puffinus nativitatis	Christmas Island shearwater
P. pacificus	Wedge-tailed shearwater
P. tenuirostris	Slender-billed shearwater
Pugettia producta	Kelp crab
Purpura aperta	Rock snail
Pygoscelis adeliae	Adelie penguin
P. papua	Gentoo penguin
Pyrrhula pyrrhula	Bullfinch
Python molurus	Indian python
P. reticulatus	Reticulated python
P. sebae	African python
Quiscalus quiscula	Common grackle
Q. quiscula aeneus	Common grackle
Rallus limicola	Virginia rail
R. longirostris crepitans	Clapper rail
Rana aurora	Red-legged frog
R. cancrivora	Crab-eating frog
R. catesbeiana	Bullfrog
R. clamitans	Bronze frog
R. esculenta	European edible frog
R. grylio	Pig frog
R. pipiens	Leopard frog
R. sphenocephala	Southern leopard frog
R. temporaria	Common European frog
Rangifer tarandus	Reindeer
R. tarandus arcticus	Caribou
R. tarandus stonei	Caribou
Rattus conatus	Rat
R. norvegicus	Norway rat

Scientific Name	Common Name
R. rattus	Rat
Recurvirostra americana	Old World avocet
Redunca arundinum	Reedbuck
Regulus satrapa	Golden-crowned kinglet
Reithrodontomys megalotis	Western harvest mouse
R. megalotis longicaudus	Western harvest mouse
Rhabdomys pumilio	Four-striped grass mouse
Rhinoceros sp.	Rhinoceros
Rhinolophus ferrum-equinum	Horseshoe bat
R. hipposideros	Lesser horseshoe bat
R. landeri	Horseshoe bat
Rhinopoma hardwickei	Rat-tailed bat
R. microphyllum	Rat-tailed bat
Rhizostoma pulmo	Jellyfish
Rhodnius prolixus	Assassin bug
Rhodona planiventrale	Flat-bellied skink
Rhynocops nigra	Black skimmer
Richmondena cardinalis	Cardinal
Riparia riparia	Bank swallow
Rissa tridactyla	Black-legged kittiwake
Rivulogammarus pulex	Side-swimmer
Rousettus aegyptiacus	Dog-faced bat
R. angolensis	Fruit bat
Sabella penicillus	Feather duster
Saccocoelium beauforti	Parasitic fluke
Saguinus geoffroyi	Geoffroy's marmoset
S. oedipus	Cottonhead marmoset
Saimiri sciurea	Squirrel monkey
Salamandra maculosa	European spotted salamander
S. salamandra	Common fire salamander
Salmo gairdneri	Rainbow trout
S. salar	Atlantic salmon
S. trutta	Brown trout
Salpa maxima africana	Salp
Sarcophaga argyrostoma	Flesh fly
S. bullata	Flesh fly
Sarcophilus harrisii	Tasmanian devil
Satanellus hallucatus	Little northern native cat
Sauromalus obesus	Chuckwalla
Saxostrea commercialis	Australian rock oyster
Sayornis phoebe	Eastern phoebe
Scalopus aquaticus	Eastern American mole
Scaphiopus hammondi	Western spadefoot toad
S. holbrookii	Eastern spadefoot toad
Scardafella inca	Inca dove
Sceloporus occidentalis	Iguana or Pacific fence lizard
S. undulatus undulatus	Southern fence lizard
Schistocerca gregaria	Desert locust
S. infumata	South American locust
Schistosoma japonicum	Blood fluke
S. mansoni	Manson's blood fluke
Schizobranchia insignis	Polychaete
Scincus scincus	North African sand skink
Sciurus granatensis	Tropical red squirrel
S. variegatoides dorsalis	Variegated squirrel
Scomber scombrus	Atlantic mackerel
Scorpaena spp.	Scorpion fish
Scyliorhinus caniculus	Cat shark

continued

Appendix I. SCIENTIFIC NAMES AND CORRESPONDING COMMON NAMES

Part I. Animals

Scientific Name	Common Name
Seiurus aurocapillus	Ovenbird
Selasphorus platycercus	Broad-tailed hummingbird
S. rufus	Rufous hummingbird
S. sasin	Allen's hummingbird
Sepia officinalis	Common cuttlefish
Serinus canarius	Canary
Serranus scriba	Sea bass
Sesarma cinereum	Wood crab
S. reticulatum	Marsh crab
Setonix brachyurus	Scrub wallaby
Setophaga ruticilla	American redstart
Sialia sialis	Eastern bluebird
Sialis lutaria	Common alderfly
Sicista betulina	Birch mouse
Sicyonia carinata	Shrimp
Sigmodon sp.	Cotton rat
Sipunculus nudus	Marine worm
Siredon mexicanum	Axolotl
Sitta carolinensis	White-breasted nuthatch
Sminthopsis crassicaudata	Narrow-footed marsupial mouse
S. larapinta	Narrow-footed marsupial mouse
Somateria mollissima dresseri	Common eider
Sorex cinereus	Masked shrew
S. cinereus cinereus	European shrew
S. trowbridgii montereyensis	Trowbridge's shrew
S. vagrans sonomae	Wandering shrew
S. vagrans vagrans	Wandering shrew
Spalax leucodon	Lesser mole rat
Spalerosophis diadema	Rat snake
Sparus auratus	European porgy
Spatula clypeata	Shoveler
Speotyto cunicularia	Burrowing owl
Sphaeroides maculatus	Northern puffer
Spheciospongia sp.	Sponge
Sphenomorphus labillardieri	Skink
S. leonhardi	Skink
Sphyrapicus varius	Yellow-bellied sapsucker
Spinus pinus	Pine siskin
Spirographis spallanzanii	Peacock fan worm
Spirontocaris liljeborgi	Shrimp
Spiza americana	Dickcissel
Spizella arborea	Tree sparrow
S. passerina passerina	Chipping sparrow
Squalus acanthias	Common spiny dogfish
S. suckleyi	Spiny dogfish
Squatarola squatarola	Black-bellied plover
Steganopus tricolor	Wilson's phalarope
Stegobium paniceum	Drugstore beetle
Stelgidopteryx ruficollis	New World rough-winged swallow
Stellula calliope	Calliope hummingbird
Stenotomus chrysops	Scup
Stercorarius parasiticus	Parasitic jaeger
Sterna forsteri	Forster's tern
S. fuscata	Sooty tern
Storeria dekayi	Brown snake
Streptopelia decaocto	Collared turtledove
Strix varia	Barred owl
Strongylocentrotus purpuratus	Western purple sea urchin
Strongylus equinus	Double-tooth strongyle
S. vulgaris	Single-tooth strongyle
Struthio camelus	African ostrich
S. camelus camelus	North African ostrich
S. camelus massaicus	Masai ostrich
Sturnella neglecta	Western meadowlark
Sturnira lilium	Fruit bat
Sturnus vulgaris	Common starling
Suberites massa	Sponge
Sula dactylatra	Blue-faced booby
S. sula	Red-footed booby
Suricata suricatta	Suricate
Sus scrofa	Swine
Syconycteris australis	Fruit bat
Sylvicapra grimmia	Gray duiker
Sylvilagus floridanus	Eastern cottontail rabbit
Symphalangus syndactylus	Siamang gibbon
Syncerus caffer	African or cape buffalo
S. caffer nanus	Forest buffalo
Syngnathus sp.	Pipefish
Syphacia obvelata	Cecal worm of rodents
Tachycines asynamorus	Greenhouse stone cricket
Tachycineta thalassina	Violet-green swallow
Tachyglossus aculeatus	Spiny anteater
Tachyoryctes splendens	African mole rat
Tadarida condylura	Free-tailed bat
T. hindei	Free-tailed bat
T. pumila	Free-tailed bat
T. teniotis	Free-tailed bat
Tadorna tadorna	Sheldrake
Taenia crassiceps	Tapeworm of red fox
T. taeniaeformis	Cyclophyllidean tapeworm
Talitrus sylvaticus	Sand hopper
Talorchestia longicornis	Beach flea
Tamandua tetradactyla	Tamandua or collared anteater
Tamias striatus	Eastern chipmunk
Tamiasciurus hudsonicus	Alaska red squirrel
Taphozous melanopogon	Tomb bat
Tapirus terrestris	South American tapir
Taurotragus oryx	Common eland
Tautoga onitis	Tautog
Tautogolabrus adspersus	Cunner
Tayassu tajacu angulatus	Collared peccary
Tayra barbara	Tayra
Tedania ignis	Fire sponge
Telmatodytes palustris	Long-billed marsh wren
Tenebrio molitor	Yellow mealworm
Tenebroides mauritanicus	Cadelle
Tenrec ecaudatus	Tenrec
Terpios fugax	Sponge
Terrapene carolina	Eastern box turtle
Testudo denticulata	South American tortoise
T. elegans	Star tortoise
T. elephantopus elephantopus	Elephant-footed Galapagos turtle
T. graeca	European tortoise
T. kleinmanni	Egyptian land turtle
T. sulcata	Spurred turtle

continued

Appendix I. SCIENTIFIC NAMES AND CORRESPONDING COMMON NAMES

Part I. Animals

Scientific Name	Common Name
Tethya aurantia	Sponge
Tethys leporina	Sea hare
Tetrameres confusa	Poultry stomach worm
Thalarctos maritimus	Polar bear
Thalurania furcata	Wood nymph
T. glaucopis	Wood nymph
Thamnophis sirtalis	Common garter snake
Thelyphonus sepiaris	Whip scorpion
Theodoxus fluviatilis	River neritina
Theropithecus gelada	Gelada baboon
Thetys vagina	Salp
Thoralus cranchi	Shrimp
Thryomanes bewickii	Bewick's wren
Thylacomys lagotis	Rabbit bandicoot
Tiliqua melanops	Skink
T. rugosa	Stump-tailed skink
Tinca tinca	Golden tench
Tineola bisselliella	Webbing clothes moth
Tipula sp.	Crane fly
Torpedo sp.	Electric ray
Totanus flavipes	Lesser yellowlegs
T. melanoleucus	Greater yellowlegs
Toxostoma curvirostre	Curve-billed thrasher
Tragelaphus angasi	Nyala
Tragulus napu	Large Malayan mouse deer
Tremarctos ornatus	Spectacled bear
Tribolium castaneum	Red flour beetle
T. confusum	Confused flour beetle
Trichechus manatus latirostris	Manatee
Trichinella spiralis	Trichina worm
Trichodactylus petropolitanus	Freshwater crab
Trichoplusia ni	Cabbage looper
Trichosurus sp.	Common phalanger
T. caninus	Brush-tailed possum
T. vulpecula	Brush-tailed possum
Triturus cristatus	Warty newt
T. marmoratus	Marbled salamander
T. torosus	Giant or California newt
T. vulgaris	Smooth newt
Troglodytes aedon	Northern house wren
T. aedon aedon	Eastern house wren
T. troglodytes	Winter wren
Trogoderma granarium	Khapra beetle
Tubifex tubifex	Tubificid oligochaete
Turdus migratorius	Robin
T. musicus	Redwing
Tursiops truncatus	Atlantic bottle-nosed porpoise
Tympanocryptis lineata lineata	Earless dragon
Typhlonectes compressicauda	Caecilian
Tyrannus tyrannus	Eastern kingbird
Tyto alba	Common barn owl
Uca minax	Fiddler crab
U. mordax	Fiddler crab
U. pugilator	Fiddler crab
U. pugnax	Fiddler crab
U. rapax	Fiddler crab
U. uruguayensis	Fiddler crab
Uma notata	Fringe-footed iguana
Unio pictorum	Painted unio
Uria aalge	Common murre
U. lomvia	Thick-billed murre
Uromys sherrini	Giant naked-tailed rat
Ursus americanus	Black bear
U. arctos	Alaskan brown bear
U. arctos arctos	Eurasian brown bear
U. horribilis horribilis	Grizzly bear
Uta stansburiana	Ground uta
Valvata piscinalis	North American freshwater snail
Vanessa sp.	Brush-footed butterfly
Varanus gouldii	Gould's monitor
V. varius	Lace monitor
Vermivora celata	Orange-crowned warbler
V. peregrina	Tennessee warbler
Vicugna vicugna mensalis	Vicuña
Vireo gilvus	Warbling vireo
V. olivaceus	Red-eyed vireo
V. solitarius	Blue-headed vireo
Viviparus viviparus	River snail
Vulpes fulva	Red fox
V. fulva fulva	Red fox
V. macrotis neomexicana	Kit fox
V. pallidus	Pale fox
V. vulpes	Red fox
V. vulpes alascensis	Arctic red fox
Vultur gryphus	Andean condor
Wallabia dorsalis	Scrub wallaby
W. rufogrisea	Red-necked wallaby
Wilsonia pusilla	Wilson's warbler
Xanthocephalus xanthocephalus	Yellow-headed blackbird
Zaglossus sp.	Spiny anteater
Zapus hudsonius	Meadow jumping mouse
Z. hudsonius americanus	Meadow jumping mouse
Zebrina detrita	Land slug
Zenaida asiatica	White-winged dove
Zenaidura macroura	Mourning dove
Zonotrichia albicollis	White-throated sparrow
Z. leucophrys	White-crowned sparrow
Z. leucophrys gambelii	White-crowned sparrow
Zoogonus lasius	Fluke
Zootermopsis angusticollis	Pacific coast rotten wood termite
Z. nevadensis	Dark Pacific coast rotten wood termite

continued

Appendix I. SCIENTIFIC NAMES AND CORRESPONDING COMMON NAMES

Part II. Plants

Scientific Name	Common Name
Abelia spp.	Abelia
Abies sp.	Fir
Acacia farnesiana	Sweet acacia
A. melanoxylon	Blackwood acacia
Acer negundo	Box elder
A. platanoides	Norway maple
A. pseudoplatanus	Plane-tree maple
A. rubrum	Red maple
A. saccharum	Sugar maple
A. spicatum	Mountain maple
Aesculus glabra	Ohio buckeye
A. hippocastanum	Common horsechestnut
A. pavia	Red buckeye
Agropyron repens	Quack grass
Agrostis alba	Redtop
Ailanthus altissima	Tree of heaven
Allium cepa	Garden onion
Alnus crispa	American green alder
Alopecurus pratensis	Meadow foxtail
Althaea spp.	Hollyhock
Alyssum spp.	Alyssum
Amaranthus retroflexus	Redroot amaranth
Amelanchier sp.	Serviceberry
Ananas comosus	Pineapple
Anthyllis vulneraria	Anthyllis
Antirrhinum majus	Common snapdragon
Apium graveolens dulce	Garden celery
Arachis hypogaea	Peanut
Artemisia tridentata	Big sagebrush
Arum maculatum	Lords-and-ladies
Asparagus albus	White asparagus
A. officinalis	Garden asparagus
Asplenium adiantum nigrum	Black spleenwort
Avena sativa	Common oat
Begonia rex	Assam king begonia
B. tuberhybrida	Begonia
Berula erecta	Stalky berula
Beta saccharifera	Sugar beet
B. vulgaris	Common beet
Betula lenta	Sweet birch
B. nana	Dwarf arctic birch
Brassica campestris	Bird rape
B. napobrassica	Rutabaga
B. nigra	Black mustard
B. oleracea	Wild cabbage
B. oleracea botrytis	Cauliflower
B. oleracea capitata	Cabbage
B. oleracea gemmifera	Brussels sprout
B. oleracea italica	Broccoli
B. rapa	Turnip
Bryonia dioica	Red berry bryony
Buddleia spp.	Butterfly bush
Buxus sempervirens	Common box
Calendula spp.	Calendula
Callistephus chinensis	China aster
Calonyction aculeatum	Large moonflower
Camellia japonica	Common camellia
C. sinensis	Common tea
Canna indica	India canna
Cannabis sativa	Hemp
Capsicum frutescens	Bush red pepper
Carica papaya	Papaya
Carpinus spp.	Hornbeam
Carya ovata	Shagbark hickory
Castanea dentata	American chestnut
C. pumila	Allegheny chinquapin
Casuarina equisetifolia	Horsetail beefwood
Catalpa bignonioides	Southern catalpa
Ceanothus spp.	Ceanothus
Celtis spp.	Hackberry
Ceratozamia spp.	Horncorn
Cercis canadensis	Eastern redbud
Cercocarpus spp.	Mountain mahogany
Chamaecyparis thyoides	Southern white cedar
Chenopodium album	Lamb's-quarter
Chrysanthemum morifolium	Florist's chrysanthemum
Chrysothamnus graveolens	Green plume rabbit brush
Citrullus vulgaris	Watermelon
Citrus aurantium	Sour orange
C. grandis	Pomelo
C. limetioides	Sweet lime
C. limon	Lemon
C. paradisi	Grapefruit
C. sinensis	Sweet orange
Clematis spp.	Clematis
Cocos nucifera	Coconut
Coleus blumei	Common coleus
Comptonia spp.	Sweet fern
Coriaria spp.	Coriaria
Cornus florida	Flowering dogwood
Cucumis melo	Muskmelon
C. sativus	Cucumber
Cucurbita maxima	Winter squash
C. pepo	Pumpkin
Cuscuta indecora	Big seed alfalfa dodder
Cycas spp.	Cycas
Cynodon dactylon	Bermuda grass
Dahlia pinnata	Garden dahlia
Datura stramonium	Jimsonweed
Daucus carota	Carrot
Delphinium spp.	Larkspur
Dianthus caryophyllus	Clove pink
Discaria spp.	Discaria
Distichlis spicata	Seashore salt grass
Dryas spp.	Dryad
Dryopteris austriaca	Wood fern
Echinochloa sp.	Cockspur
E. crusgalli	Barnyard grass
Elaeagnus spp.	Elaeagnus
Elaeis guineensis	African oil palm
Elodea canadensis	Canada waterweed
Encephalartos spp.	Kafir bread
Equisetum telmateia	Giant horsetail
Eucalyptus spp.	Eucalyptus

continued

Appendix I. SCIENTIFIC NAMES AND CORRESPONDING COMMON NAMES

Part II. Plants

Scientific Name	Common Name
Fagopyrum sagittatum	Buckwheat
Fagus grandifolia	American beech
F. sylvatica	European beech
Festuca elatior	Meadow fescue
F. rubra	Red fescue
Ficus carica	Fig
Fragaria sp.	Strawberry
Fraxinus excelsior	European ash
F. nigra	Black ash
Gaillardia spp.	Gaillardia
Gardenia jasminoides	Cape jasmine
Geranium robertianum	Herb Robert geranium
Ginkgo biloba	Ginkgo
Gladiolus gandavensis	Breeder's gladiolus
Gleditsia triacanthos	Common honey locust
Glycine max	Soybean
Gossypium hirsutum	Upland cotton
G. roseum	Indian cotton
Gymnocladus dioicus	Kentucky coffee tree
Hedera helix	English ivy
Helianthus annuus	Common sunflower
H. tuberosus	Jerusalem artichoke
Heliotropium spp.	Heliotrope
Hemerocallis spp.	Day lily
Hibiscus esculentus	Okra
H. rosa-sinensis	Chinese hibiscus
Hippophae rhamnoides	Common sea buckthorn
Hordeum hexastichum	Six-rowed barley
H. vulgare	Barley
Hyacinthus orientalis	Common hyacinth
Iberis spp.	Candytuft
Ilex aquifolium	English holly
I. cornuta	Chinese holly
I. opaca	American holly
I. vomitoria	Yaupon
Impatiens sp.	Snapweed
I. balsamina	Garden balsam
Ipomoea batatas	Sweet potato
Iris germanica	German iris
Isatis djurjaedae	Woad
Iva axillaris	Poverty sump weed
Juglans regia	Persian walnut
Juniperus communis	Common juniper
J. communis saxatilis	Mountain juniper
J. virginiana	Eastern red cedar
Kalanchoe blossfeldiana	Kalanchoe
Kalmia latifolia	Mountain laurel
Lactuca sativa	Lettuce
L. virosa	Bitter lettuce
Larix spp.	Larch
Lathyrus odoratus	Sweet pea
Lepidium sativum	Garden cress
Lespedeza stipulacea	Korean lespedeza
Ligustrum spp.	Privet
Lilium bulbiferum	Bulbil lily
L. longiflorum	Easter lily
Linum usitatissimum	Common flax
Liquidambar styraciflua	American sweet gum
Liriodendron tulipifera	Yellow poplar
Lolium perenne	Perennial rye
Lupinus angustifolius	Tree lupine
Lycopersicon esculentum	Common tomato
Macrozamia spp.	Macrozamia
Magnolia grandiflora	Southern magnolia
Malus pumila	Apple
M. sylvestris	Apple
Matthiola incana	Common stock
Medicago sativa	Alfalfa
Melilotus alba	White sweet clover
M. indica	Annual yellow sweet clover
Mercurialis annua	Annual mercurialis
Morus spp.	Mulberry
Musa paradisiaca	Plantain banana
M. sapientum	Common banana
Myrica spp.	Bayberry or waxmyrtle
M. gale	Sweet gale
Narcissus spp.	Narcissus
Nicotiana glauca	Tree tobacco
N. langsdorffi	Tobacco
N. tabacum	Common tobacco
Nyssa sylvatica	Black tupelo
Oenothera biennis	Common evening primrose
Olea europaea	Common olive
Onopordum acanthium	Scotch cotton thistle
Oryza sativa	Rice
Ostrya virginiana	American hop hornbeam
Paspalum dilatatum	Dallis grass
Pastinaca sativa	Parsnip
Paulownia tomentosa	Royal paulownia
Pelargonium domesticum	Lady Washington pelargonium
Pennisetum glaucum	Pearl millet
Persea americana	American avocado
Petroselinum crispum	Common garden parsley
Petunia spp.	Petunia
Phaseolus limensis	Lima bean
P. vulgaris	Kidney bean
Phleum pratense	Timothy
Phoenix dactylifera	Date
Phyllitis scolopendrium	Hart's-tongue
Picea abies	Norway spruce
P. pungens	Colorado spruce
P. sitchensis	Sitka spruce
Pinus contorta	Shore pine
P. densiflora	Japanese red pine
P. palustris	Longleaf pine

continued

Appendix I. SCIENTIFIC NAMES AND CORRESPONDING COMMON NAMES

Part II. Plants

Scientific Name	Common Name
P. pinea	Italian stone pine
P. radiata	Monterey pine
P. resinosa	Red pine
P. sylvestris	Scotch pine
P. taeda	Loblolly pine
Pisum sativum	Garden pea
Platanus spp.	Plane tree
Poa pratensis	Kentucky bluegrass
P. trivalis	Rough-stalked bluegrass
Polypodium vulgare	Common polypody
Populus deltoides	Eastern poplar
P. nigra	Black poplar
P. tremuloides	Quaking aspen
Prasium majus	Prasium
Prosopis juliflora	Mesquite tree
Prunus amygdalus	Almond
P. cerasus	Sour cherry
P. domestica	Garden plum
P. glandulosa	Almond cherry
P. laurocerasus	Common laurel cherry
P. persica	Peach
P. virginiana	Common chokecherry
Pseudotsuga taxifolia	Douglas fir
Psoralea bituminosa	Arabian scurf pea
Psychotria spp.	Psychotria
Pteridium aquilinum	Bracken
Purshia tridentata	Antelope bitterbrush
Pyrus communis	Pear
Quercus alba	White oak
Q. borealis	Northern red oak
Q. coccifera	Kermes oak
Q. coccinea	Scarlet oak
Q. falcata	Southern red oak
Q. ilicifolia	Scrub oak
Q. laevis	Turkey oak
Q. marilandica	Blackjack oak
Q. palustris	Pin oak
Q. phellos	Willow oak
Q. prinus	Swamp chestnut oak
Q. robur	English oak
Q. stellata	Post oak
Q. velutina	Black oak
Ranunculus macrophyllus	Large-leaf buttercup
R. pseudofluitans	Floating water crowfoot
Raphanus raphanistrum	Wild radish
R. sativus	Garden radish
Rheum rhaponticum	Garden rhubarb
Rhododendron fargesi	Pere Farges rhododendron
R. obtusum amoenum	Amoena azalea
Ribes nigrum	European black currant
R. rubrum	Northern red currant
Ricinus communis	Castor bean
Robinia pseudoacacia	Black locust
Rosa sempervirens	Evergreen rose
Rubus spp.	Blackberry, boysenberry, or raspberry
R. idaeus	Red raspberry
Rumex crispus	Curly dock
R. pulcher	Fiddleleaf dock
Saccharum officinarum	Sugarcane
Saintpaulia ionantha	Common African violet
Salix glauca	Gray-leaf willow
S. herbacea	Pygmy willow
S. koriyanagi	Salix
S. repens	Creeping willow
Salvia mellifera	Black sage
Sambucus sp.	Elder
Sarcobatus vermiculatus	Black greasewood
Saxifraga cernua	Saxifrage
S. oppositifolia	Twin-leaf saxifrage
Secale cereale	Rye
Sedum acre	Goldmoss stonecrop
S. hybridum	Evergreen stonecrop
S. reflexum	Jenny stonecrop
Setaria italica	Foxtail millet
Shepherdia spp.	Buffalo berry
Solanum tuberosum	Potato
Sorbus americana	American mountain ash
S. aucuparia	European mountain ash
Sorghum halepense	Johnson grass
S. vulgare	Sorghum
S. vulgare caffrorum	Kafir
S. vulgare sudanense	Sudan grass
Spinacia oleracea	Spinach
Stangeria spp.	Fern cycad
Symphoricarpos albus	Common snowberry
Syringa vulgaris	Common lilac
Tamarix sp.	Tamarisk
Taraxacum officinale	Dandelion
Taxodium distichum	Bald cypress
Taxus baccata	English yew
Thuja occidentalis	Eastern arborvitae
Tilia spp.	Linden
Torilis nodosa	Knotted hedge parsley
Tradescantia virginiana	Virginia spiderwort
T. viridis	Wandering Jew
Trifolium pratense	Red clover
T. repens	White clover
T. subterraneum	Subterraneum clover
Triticum aestivum	Wheat
Tropaeolum majus	Common nasturtium
Tsuga canadensis	Eastern hemlock
Tulipa gesneriana	Common tulip
Ulmus americana	American elm
U. glabra	Scotch elm
U. parvifolia	Chinese elm
Vaccinium spp.	Blueberry or cranberry
V. stamineum	Common deerberry
Vicia faba	Broad bean
V. faba equina	Horsebean
V. villosa	Hairy vetch
Vigna sinensis	Common cowpea

continued

Appendix I. SCIENTIFIC NAMES AND CORRESPONDING COMMON NAMES

Part II. Plants

Scientific Name	Common Name
Viola sp.	Violet
Vitis vinifera	European grape
Xanthium sp.	Cocklebur
Yucca gloriosa	Mound lily yucca
Zea mays	Corn

Appendix II. COMMON NAMES AND CORRESPONDING SCIENTIFIC NAMES

Protozoa and nonvascular plants have not been included.

Part I. Animals

Common Name	Scientific Name
Aardvark, Kenya	*Orycteropus afer ruvanensis*
Abalone	*Haliotis rufescens*
Aeshna, southern	*Aeshna cyanea*
Agouti	*Dasyprocta aguti*
	D. azarae
	D. pyrmnolopha
long-tailed	*Myoprocta acouchy*
Paraguayan	*Dasyprocta paraguayensis*
Agrion, demoiselle	*Calopteryx virgo*
Albatross, black-footed	*Diomedea nigripes*
Laysan	*D. immutabilis*
wandering	*D. exulans*
yellow-nosed	*D. chlororhynchos*
Alderfly, common	*Sialis lutaria*
Alligator, American	*Alligator mississippiensis*
Alpaca	*Lama pacos*
Amphipod	*Orchestia* sp.
	Orchomenella chilensis
Anhinga	*Anhinga anhinga*
Anoa	*Anoa depressicornis*
Anole, green	*Anolis carolinensis*
Ant	*Formica polyctena*
Anteater, giant	*Myrmecophaga tridactyla*
South American silky	*Cyclopes* sp.
spiny	*Tachyglossus aculeatus*
	Zaglossus sp.
Antelope, sable	*Hippotragus niger roosevelti*
Aoudad	*Ammotragus lervia*
Ape, Barbary	*Macaca sylvana*
Aphid, cabbage	*Brevicoryne brassicae*
green peach	*Myzus persicae*
pea	*Acyrthosiphon pisum*
rose	*Macrosiphum rosae*
Arapaima	*Arapaima gigas*
Ark shell	*Noetia ponderosa*
Armadillo	*Dasypus sexcinctus*
hairy	*Chaetophractus villosus*
nine-banded	*Dasypus novemcinctus*
Armyworm, southern	*Prodenia eridania*
Assassin bug	*Rhodnius prolixus*
Auk, razor-billed	*Alca torda*
Auklet, crested or least	*Aethia cristatella*
Avocet, Old World	*Recurvirostra americana*
Axolotl	*Siredon mexicanum*
Baboon	*Papio hamadryas*
gelada	*Theropithecus gelada*
Bandicoot, rabbit	*Thylacomys lagotis*
short-nosed	*Isoodon obesulus*
Bass, sea	*Serranus scriba*
Bat, bicolored leaf-nosed	*Hipposideros bicolor*
big brown	*Eptesicus fuscus*
brown	*Myotis nattereri*
	M. sodalis
	M. yumanensis
bulldog	*Noctilio labialis*
common brown	*Myotis myotis*
common vampire	*Desmodus rotundus*
cyclops	*Hipposideros cyclops*
dog-faced	*Rousettus aegyptiacus*
European brown	*Pipistrellus pipistrellus*
fisherman	*Noctilio leporinus*
free-tailed	*Tadarida condylura*
	T. hindei
	T. pumila
	T. teniotis
fruit	*Epomophorus anurus*
	Rousettus angolensis
	Sturnira lilium
	Syconycteris australis
greater artibeus fruit	*Artibeus lituratus*
grey-headed fruit	*Pteropus poliocephalus*
horseshoe	*Rhinolophus ferrum-equinum*
	R. landeri
Indian false vampire	*Megaderma lyra*
leaf-nosed	*Hipposideros speoris*
lesser horseshoe	*Rhinolophus hipposideros*
little brown	*Myotis lucifugus*
	M. mystacinus
little reddish fruit	*Pteropus scapulatus*
long-eared	*Plecotus auritus*
long-winged	*Miniopterus blepotis*
mastiff	*Eumops perotis*
Old World leaf-nosed	*Hipposideros caffer*
pallid	*Antrozous pallidus*
rat-tailed	*Rhinopoma hardwickei*
	R. microphyllum
Seba's short-tailed fruit	*Carollia perspicillata*
tomb	*Taphozous melanopogon*

continued

Appendix II. COMMON NAMES AND CORRESPONDING SCIENTIFIC NAMES

Part I. Animals

Common Name	Scientific Name
trident leaf-nosed	*Asellia tridens*
Trinidad spear-nosed	*Phyllostomus hastatus hastatus*
Beachflea	*Gammarus locusta*
	G. pulex
	G. zaddachi
	Talorchestia longicornis
Bear, Alaskan brown	*Ursus arctos*
black	*U. americanus*
Eurasian brown	*U. arctos arctos*
grizzly	*U. horribilis horribilis*
Malayan sun	*Helarctos malayanus*
polar	*Thalarctos maritimus*
spectacled	*Tremarctos ornatus*
Beaver, mountain	*Aplodontia rufa*
Old World	*Castor fiber*
Bee, honey-	*Apis mellifera*
Beetle, carpet	*Attagenus* sp.
cigarette	*Lasioderma serricorne*
common European dung	*Geotrupes* sp.
confused flour	*Tribolium confusum*
drugstore	*Stegobium paniceum*
ground	*Carabus nemoralis*
hide	*Dermestes maculatus*
horned passalus, or bessbug	*Popilius disjunctus*
khapra	*Trogoderma granarium*
powder post	*Lyctus* sp.
red flour	*Tribolium castaneum*
saw-toothed grain	*Oryzaephilus surinamensis*
small-eyed flour	*Palorus ratzeburgi*
spider	*Ptinus tectus*
water scavenger	*Hydrophilus ater*
Beetle parasite, Japanese	*Neoaplectana glaseri*
Binturong	*Arctictis binturong*
Bison, American	*Bison bison*
	B. bison bison
Bithynia, European	*Bithynia tentaculata*
Bittern, American	*Botaurus lentiginosus*
Blackbird, Brewer's	*Euphagus cyanocephalus*
red-winged	*Agelaius phoeniceus*
rusty	*Euphagus carolinus*
yellow-headed	*Xanthocephalus xanthocephalus*
Black buck	*Antilope cervicapra*
Blesbok	*Damaliscus dorcas phillipsi*
Bluebird, eastern	*Sialia sialis*
Bluegill, common	*Lepomis macrochirus*
Boa, Theban sand	*Eryx thebaicus*
Boa constrictor	*Constrictor constrictor*
Bobcat, Bailey's	*Lynx rufus baileyi*
Bobolink	*Dolichonyx oryzivorus*
Bobwhite	*Colinus virginianus*
Bollworm, pink	*Pectinophora gossypiella*
Booby, blue-faced	*Sula dactylatra*
red-footed	*S. sula*
Borer, Asiatic rice	*Chilo suppressalis*
European corn	*Ostrinia nubilalis*
Bowfin	*Amia calva*
Braconid	*Macrocentrus ancylivorus*
Brant	*Branta bernicla*
black	*B. nigricans*

Common Name	Scientific Name
Brine shrimp	*Artemia salina*
Brittle star	*Ophioderma longicauda*
Budgerigar	*Melopsittacus undulatus*
Buffalo	*Bubalus* spp.
African or cape	*Syncerus caffer*
forest	*S. caffer nanus*
Bullhead, brown	*Ictalurus nebulosus*
Bunting, corn	*Emberiza calandra*
lazuli	*Passerina amoena*
snow	*Plectrophenax nivalis*
	P. nivalis nivalis
Butterfly, brush-footed	*Nymphalis io*
	N. urtica
	Vanessa sp.
Buzzard eagle, black-chested	*Geranoaetus melanoleucus*
Cabbageworm, European	*Pieris brassicae*
Cacomistle	*Bassariscus astutus*
Caddisfly	*Anabolia nervosa*
	Hydropsyche sp.
	Limnephilus vittatus
Cadelle	*Tenebroides mauritanicus*
Caecilian	*Typhlonectes compressicauda*
Caiman	*Caiman crocodilus*
common spectacled	*C. crocodilus sclerops*
Camel, Bactrian	*Camelus bactrianus*
dromedary or Arabian	*C. dromedarius*
Canary	*Serinus canarius*
Capybara	*Hydrochoerus hydrochaeris*
Cardinal	*Richmondena cardinalis*
red-crested	*Poroaria coronata*
Caribou	*Rangifer tarandus arcticus*
	R. tarandus stonei
Carp	*Cyprinus carpio*
crucian	*Carassius carassius*
Cassowary	*Casuarius casuarius beccarii*
	C. bicarunculatus intensus
Bennett's	*C. bennetti*
violet-necked	*C. casuarius aruensis*
Cat	*Felis catus*
black-footed	*F. nigripes*
jungle	*F. chaus*
	F. chaus fulvidina
leopard	*F. bengalensis*
Pallas	*F. manul*
steppe	*F. libyca*
Catbird, American	*Dumetella carolinensis*
Catfish, blue	*Ictalurus furcatus*
Cattle	*Bos taurus*
Brahman	*B. indicus*
Cecal worm of poultry	*Heterakis spumosa*
Cecal worm of rodents	*Syphacia obvelata*
Chaffinch	*Fringilla coelebs*
Chat, yellow-breasted	*Icteria virens*
Cheetah	*Acinonyx jubatus*
Chickadee, black-capped	*Parus atricapillus*
	P. atricapillus atricapillus
	P. atricapillus turneri

continued

Appendix II. COMMON NAMES AND CORRESPONDING SCIENTIFIC NAMES

Part I. Animals

Common Name	Scientific Name
Carolina	*P. carolinensis*
Gray-headed	*P. cinctus*
Chicken	*Gallus domesticus*
Chimpanzee	*Pan troglodytes*
	P. troglodytes schweinfurthii
Chipmunk, eastern	*Tamias striatus*
least	*Eutamias minimus*
Chuckwalla	*Sauromalus obesus*
Cichlid	*Cichla temensis*
peacock-eyed	*Astronotus ocellatus*
Civet, African palm	*Nandinia binotata*
Clam, fingernail	*Musculium lacustre*
Clam worm	*Nereis virens*
Coati	*Nasua narica*
	N. nasua
Cockchafer	*Melolontha* sp.
Cockroach, American	*Periplaneta americana*
German	*Blattella germanica*
Madeira	*Leucophaea maderae*
oriental	*Blatta orientalis*
Cod	*Gadus morhua*
Arctic	*Boreogadus saida*
Coenagrion, common	*Coenagrion puella*
Colobus, East African	*Colobus guereza kikuyuensis*
Comb jelly	*Beroe ovata*
Condor, Andean	*Vultur gryphus*
Coot, American	*Fulica americana*
European	*F. atra*
Copepod, calanoid	*Calanus finmarchicus*
Coquette, frilled	*Lophornis magnifica*
Cormorant, common	*Phalacrocorax carbo*
double-crested	*P. auritus*
pelagic	*P. pelagicus resplendens*
Cowbird, brown-headed	*Molothrus ater*
Coypu	*Myocastor coypus*
Crab	*Galathea squamifera*
	Ilia nucleus
blue	*Callinectes sapidus*
fiddler	*Uca minax*
	U. mordax
	U. pugilator
	U. pugnax
	U. rapax
	U. uruguayensis
freshwater	*Potamon niloticus*
	Trichodactylus petropolitanus
ghost	*Ocypode quadrata*
green	*Carcinus maenas*
hermit	*Clibanarius vittatus*
kelp	*Pugettia producta*
marsh	*Sesarma reticulatum*
mitten	*Eriocheir sinensis*
mud	*Eurytium limosum*
	Panopeus herbstii
purple land	*Gecarcinus lateralis*
purple shore	*Hemigrapsus nudus*
rock	*Cancer pagurus*
sand	*Emerita talpoida*
	Ocypode albicans

Common Name	Scientific Name
shore	*Carcinus mediterraneas*
	Pachygrapsus marmoratus
spider	*Libinia dubia*
	L. emarginata
	Maja squinado
	M. verrucosa
sponge	*Dromia vulgaris*
	Eriphia spinifrons
stone	*Menippe mercenaria*
striped rock	*Pachygrapsus crassipes*
swimming	*Callinectes ornatus*
West Indies land	*Cardisoma guanhumi*
wood	*Sesarma cinereum*
yellow shore	*Hemigrapsus oregonensis*
Crane, demoiselle	*Anthropoides virgo*
sandhill	*Grus canadensis*
	G. canadensis canadensis
South African paradise or Stanley	*Anthropoides paradisea*
Crane fly	*Tipula* sp.
Crayfish	*Astacus astacus*
	A. leptodactylus
	Austropotamobius torrentium
	Cambarellus shufeldtii
	Cambarus sp.
	Orconectes immunis
	O. nais
dwarf	*Procambarus alleni*
freshwater	*Orconectes propinquus*
	O. virilis
Louisiana red	*Procambarus clarkii*
Creeper, brown or tree	*Certhia familiaris*
Cricket, greenhouse stone	*Tachycines asynamorus*
house	*Acheta domesticus*
wood	*Nemobius sylvestris*
Crocodile, African	*Crocodylus niloticus*
Crossbill, red	*Loxia curvirostra*
	L. curvirostra pusilla
white-winged	*L. leucoptera leucoptera*
Crow, American common	*Corvus brachyrhynchos*
northwestern	*C. caurinus*
Cuckoo, yellow-billed	*Coccyzus americanus*
Cunner	*Tautogolabrus adspersus*
Curassow, black	*Crax alector*
great	*C. rubra*
Curlew, long-billed	*Numenius americanus*
Cusimanse	*Crossarchus obscurus*
Cuttlefish, common	*Sepia officinalis*
Cutworm, pale western	*Agrotis orthogonia*
Daddy longlegs	*Platybunus triangularis*
Damselfish, blue	*Chromis chromis*
Damselfly, common blue	*Enallagma cyathigerum*
Decapod	*Paguristes maculata*
	Pandalina brevirostris
	Pilumnus hirtellus
Deer, axis	*Axis axis*
Dybowski sika	*Cervus nippon hortulorum*
Formosan sika	*C. nippon taiouanus*
Japanese sika	*C. nippon nippon*

continued

Appendix II. COMMON NAMES AND CORRESPONDING SCIENTIFIC NAMES

Part I. Animals

Common Name	Scientific Name
large Malayan mouse	*Tragulus napu*
mule	*Odocoileus hemionus*
Pere David's	*Elaphurus davidianus*
red	*Cervus elaphus*
sambar	*C. unicolor equinus*
Dickcissel	*Spiza americana*
Dingo	*Canis dingo*
Dipper, North American	*Cinclus mexicanus*
Dog	*Canis familiaris*
raccoon	*Nyctereutes procyonoides*
Dogfish, common spiny	*Squalus acanthias*
smooth	*Mustelus canis*
spiny	*Squalus suckleyi*
Donkey	*Equus asinus*
Dormouse, common	*Muscardinus avellanarius*
fat	*Glis glis*
garden	*Eliomys quercinus*
Dove, collared turtle-	*Streptopelia decaocto*
Inca	*Scardafella inca*
mourning	*Zenaidura macroura*
white-winged	*Zenaida asiatica*
Dowitcher, short-billed	*Limnodromus griseus*
Dragon, crested	*Amphibolurus cristatus*
earless	*Tympanocryptis lineata lineata*
ornate	*Amphibolurus ornatus*
painted	*A. pictus*
peninsula	*A. fionni*
reticulated	*A. reticulatus inermis*
tawny	*A. decresii*
Duck, black	*Anas rubripes*
black-bellied tree	*Dendrocygna autumnalis*
common pintail	*Anas acuta*
mallard	*A. platyrhynchos*
muscovy	*Cairina moschata*
North American wood	*Aix sponsa*
pintail	*Anas acuta tzitzihoa*
ruddy	*Oxyura jamaicensis*
Duiker, gray	*Sylvicapra grimmia*
Dunlin	*Erolia alpina*
	E. ferruginea
Eagle, bald	*Haliaeetus leucocephalus*
golden	*Aquila chrysaetos*
northern bald	*Haliaeetus leucocephalus alascanus*
Earthworm	*Allolobophora caliginosa*
	Lumbricus terrestris
	Pheretima hawayana
	P. posthuma
Eel, American	*Anguilla rostratus*
common European	*A. anguilla*
conger	*Conger* spp.
moray	*Muraena* spp.
Eider, common	*Somateria mollissima dresseri*
Eland, common	*Taurotragus oryx*
Elephant, African bush	*Loxodonta africana cxyotis*
Indian	*Elephas maximus*
	E. maximus indicus

Common Name	Scientific Name
Elk	*Cervus canadensis canadensis*
Roosevelt	*C. canadensis roosevelti*
Emu	*Dromiceius novaehollandiae*
Falcon, American prairie	*Falco mexicanus*
Fan worm, peacock	*Spirographis spallanzanii*
Feather duster	*Sabella penicillus*
Finch, bull-	*Pyrrhula pyrrhula*
European gold-	*Carduelis carduelis*
green	*Chloris chloris*
purple	*Carpodacus purpureus*
zebra	*Poephila castanotis*
Fisher	*Martes penanti*
Flamingo	*Phoenicopterus chilensis*
European	*P. ruber roseus*
Flea, rat	*Nosopsyllus fasciatus*
Flicker, yellow-shafted	*Colaptes auratus*
Flounder	*Platichthys stellatus*
righteye	*Glyptocephalus* sp.
winter	*Pseudopleuronectes americanus*
yellowtail	*Limanda ferruginea*
Fluke	*Himasthla quissetensis*
	Pleurogonius malaclemys
	Zoogonus lasius
bird	*Gynaecotyla adunca*
blood	*Schistosoma japonicum*
cattle rumen	*Paramphistomum cervi*
Chinese liver	*Clonorchis sinensis*
digenetic	*Gorgoderina attenuata*
liver	*Fasciola hepatica*
lung	*Paragonimus westermani*
Manson's blood	*Schistosoma mansoni*
parasitic	*Saccocoelium beauforti*
rumen	*Gastrothylax crumenifer*
Fly, black blow-	*Phormia regina*
blow-	*Phaenicia sericata*
bluebottle blow-	*Calliphora vicina*
flesh	*Pseudosarcophaga* sp.
	Sarcophaga argyrostoma
	S. bullata
fruit	*Drosophila melanogaster*
	D. pachea
	D. repleta
horse bot-	*Gasterophilus intestinalis*
house	*Musca domestica*
Mexican fruit	*Anastrepha ludens*
narcissus bulb	*Merodon equestris*
oriental fruit	*Dacus dorsalis*
oriental house	*Musca domestica vicina*
Flycatcher, least	*Empidonax minimus*
olive-sided	*Nuttallornis borealis*
spotted	*Muscicapa striata*
Traill's	*Empidonax traillii*
yellow-bellied	*E. flaviventris*
Flying fox	*Pteropus geddiei*
Flying fox, or Indian fruit bat	*P. giganteus*
Fox, Arctic	*Alopex lagopus*
Arctic red	*Vulpes vulpes alascensis*

continued

Appendix II. COMMON NAMES AND CORRESPONDING SCIENTIFIC NAMES

Part I. Animals

Common Name	Scientific Name
bat-eared	*Otocyon megalotis*
fennec	*Fennecus zerda*
kit	*Vulpes macrotis neomexicana*
mountain	*Cerdocyon thous*
pale	*Vulpes pallidus*
red	*V. fulva*
	V. fulva fulva
	V. vulpes
Fowl, red jungle	*Gallus gallus*
Frog, Australian	*Limnodynastes dorsalis*
bronze	*Rana clamitans*
bull-	*R. catesbeiana*
Central Australian	*Neobatrachus centralis*
common European	*Rana temporaria*
crab-eating	*R. cancrivora*
European	*Pelobates fuscus*
European edible	*Rana esculenta*
European green tree	*Hyla arborea*
Ewing's tree	*H. ewingi*
green tree	*H. cinerea*
leopard	*Rana pipiens*
marbled	*Limnodynastes tasmaniensis*
ornate	*L. ornatus*
Pacific tree	*Hyla regilla*
painted	*Neobatrachus pictus*
pig	*Rana grylio*
red-legged	*R. aurora*
red tree	*Hyla rubella*
southern leopard	*Rana sphenocephala*
Frogmouth, tawny	*Podargus strigoides*
Fulmar	*Fulmarus glacialis*
Gadwall	*Anas strepera*
Galago	*Galago senegalensis*
Gannet, northern	*Morus bassanus*
Gar, longnose	*Lepisosteus osseus*
Gazelle, Thomson	*Gazella thomsoni*
Gecko	*Diplodactylus strophurus intermedius*
	Gehyra variegata
Bynoe's	*Heteronota bynoei*
knob-tailed	*Nephrurus laevis*
marbled	*Phyllodactylus marmoratus*
Gemsbok	*Oryx beisa*
	O. gazella gazella
Gibbon	*Hylobates lar*
siamang	*Symphalangus syndactylus*
Giraffe	*Giraffa camelopardalis*
Uganda	*G. camelopardalis rothschildi*
Glider, sugar	*Petaurus breviceps*
Gnatcatcher, blue-gray	*Polioptila caerulea*
Gnu, white-bearded	*Connochaetes taurinus albojubatus*
white-tailed	*C. gnou*
Goat, North American mountain	*Oreamnos americanus*
Goby	*Gillichthys* sp.
Godwit, marbled	*Limosa fedoa*
Goldeneye, common	*Bucephala clangula*
	B. clangula americana

Common Name	Scientific Name
Goldfish	*Carassius auratus*
Goldthroat	*Polytmus guainumbi*
Goose, barnacle	*Branta leucopsis*
bean	*Anser fabalis*
blue	*Chen caerulescens*
Canada	*Branta canadensis canadensis*
	B. canadensis hutchinsii
	B. canadensis minima
domestic	*Anser anser domesticus*
emperor	*Philacte canagica*
greylag	*Anser anser*
snow	*Chen hyperborea*
	C. hyperborea atlantica
white-fronted	*Anser albifrons*
Goosefish or monkfish	*Lophius* sp.
Gopher, pocket	*Geomys bursarius*
southeastern pocket	*G. pinetis*
Gorgonian, purple	*Plexaura flexuosa*
Gorilla	*Gorilla gorilla*
lowland	*G. gorilla gorilla*
mountain	*G. gorilla beringei*
Grackle, common	*Quiscalus quiscula*
	Q. quiscula aeneus
Grasshopper, differential	*Melanoplus differentialis*
two-striped	*M. bivittatus*
Grebe, eared or black-necked	*Podiceps caspicus*
horned	*P. auritus*
pied-billed	*Podilymbus podiceps*
western	*Aechmophorus occidentalis*
Grison	*Grison furox*
Grosbeak, blue	*Guiraca caerulea*
evening	*Hesperiphona vespertina*
pine	*Pinicola enucleator alascensis*
	P. enucleator leucura
red-breasted	*Hedymeles ludovicianus*
Grouper, red	*Epinephelus morio*
Grouse, ruffed	*Bonasa umbellus*
	B. umbellus togata
spruce	*Canachites canadensis canadensis*
Guanaco	*Lama guanicoe*
Guenon	*Cercopithecus pygerythrus*
Beira	*C. albogularis erythrarchus*
Guillemot, black	*Cepphus grylle*
Guinea hen, common	*Numida meleagris*
Guinea pig	*Cavia porcellus*
Gull, black-headed	*Larus ridibundus*
Franklin's	*L. pipixcan*
glaucous	*L. hyperboreus*
	L. hyperboreus barrovianus
glaucous-winged	*L. glaucescens*
great black-backed	*L. marinus*
herring	*L. argentatus*
	L. argentatus smithsonianus
ivory	*Pagophila eburnea*
kelp, or southern black-backed	*Larus dominicanus*
laughing	*L. atricilla*
lesser black-backed	*L. fuscus*

continued

Appendix II. COMMON NAMES AND CORRESPONDING SCIENTIFIC NAMES

Part I. Animals

Common Name	Scientific Name
mew	*L. canus brachyrhynchus*
Hagfish, common Atlantic	*Myxine glutinosa*
Pacific	*Eptatretus stouti*
Hake, American Atlantic	*Merluccius bilinearis*
silver	
Hamster, European	*Cricetus cricetus*
golden or Syrian	*Mesocricetus auratus*
Hare, blue or varying	*Lepus timidus*
Harrier, marsh, or marsh hawk	*Circus cyaneus hudsonius*
Hartebeest, Jackson	*Alcelaphus buselaphus jacksoni*
Hawk	*Accipiter nisus nisus*
broad-winged	*Buteo platypterus*
red-tailed	*B. jamaicensis borealis*
rough-legged	*B. lagopus*
	B. lagopus s.johannis
sharp-shinned	*Accipiter striatus velox*
sparrow	*Falco sparverius*
Swainson's	*Buteo swainsoni*
Hedgehog, Brandt	*Parechinus hypomelas*
Ethiopian	*P. aethiopicus*
European	*Erinaceus europaeus*
long-eared	*Hemiechinus auritus*
Hedgehog tenrec, small	*Echinops telfairi*
Heron, black-crowned night	*Nycticorax nycticorax*
	N. nycticorax hoactli
great blue	*Ardea herodias*
little green	*Butorides virescens*
snowy	*Egretta thula candidissima*
Heteropod	*Pterotrachea coronata*
Hippopotamus, Nile	*Hippopotamus amphibius*
pigmy	*Choeropsis liberiensis*
Horse	*Equus caballus*
Hummingbird	*Amazilia fimbriata*
Allen's	*Selasphorus sasin*
Anna's	*Calypte anna*
black-chinned	*Archilochus alexandri*
blue-throated	*Lampornis clemenciae*
Brazilian	*Amazilia leucogaster bahiae*
	Aphantocroa cirrochloris
	Chlorestes notatus cyanogenys
	Clytolaema rubricauda
	Hylocharis cyanus cyanus
broad-billed	*Cynanthus latirostris*
broad-tailed	*Selasphorus platycercus*
calliope	*Stellula calliope*
Costa's	*Calypte costae*
Estella	*Oreotrochilus estella*
ruby-throated	*Archilochus colubris*
rufous	*Selasphorus rufus*
swallowtail	*Eupetomena macroura*
Hutia, Cuban	*Capromys pilorides*
Hyena, spotted	*Crocuta crocuta*
	C. crocuta germinans
Hyrax, rock	*Procavia capensis*
Ibex, Siberian	*Capra ibex sibirica*
Ibis, glossy	*Plegadis falcinellus*
white	*Eudocimus albus*

Common Name	Scientific Name
Ibis, wood, or wood stork	*Mycteria americana*
Iguana, common	*Iguana iguana*
desert	*Dipsosaurus dorsalis*
fringe-footed	*Uma notata*
tuberculate	*Iguana tuberculata*
Isopod	*Asellus aquaticus*
Jabiru	*Jabiru mycteria*
Jackal, Asiatic	*Canis aureus indicus*
Jackdaw, European	*Corvus monedula*
Jacobin, black	*Melanotrochilus fuscus*
Jaeger, parasitic	*Stercorarius parasiticus*
Jaguar	*Panthera onca*
Jaguarundi	*Felis jagouaroundi fossata*
Jay, Alaska or gray	*Perisoreus canadensis pacificus*
American blue	*Cyanocitta cristata*
blue	*C. cristata bromia*
Canada or gray	*Perisoreus canadensis*
piñon	*Gymnorhinus cyanocephala*
Steller's	*Cyanocitta stelleri*
Jellyfish	*Cassiopea frondosa*
	Pelagia noctiluca
	Rhizostoma pulmo
moon	*Aurelia aurita*
Jerboa	*Jaculus jaculus*
Jird, clawed	*Meriones unguiculatus*
Junco, Oregon	*Junco oreganus*
slate-colored	*J. hyemalis*
Kangaroo, great gray	*Macropus giganteus*
	M. major
rat	*Bettongia* sp.
	Potorous tridactylus
red	*Macropus rufus*
Killdeer	*Charadrius vociferus*
Killifish, California	*Fundulus parvipinnis*
plains	*F. kansae*
White River	*Crenichthys baileyi*
Kingbird, eastern	*Tyrannus tyrannus*
King crab	*Limulus polyphemus*
Kingfisher, belted	*Megaceryle alcyon*
Kinglet, golden-crowned	*Regulus satrapa*
Kinkajou	*Potos caudiovolvus*
	P. flavus
Kittiwake, black-legged	*Rissa tridactyla*
Kiwi, common	*Apteryx australis*
great spotted	*A. haasti*
North Island	*A. australis mantelli*
Koala	*Phascolarctos cinereus*
Lacerta, green	*Lacerta viridis*
Lackey	*Malacosoma neustria*
Lamprey, Pacific American	*Lampetra fluviatilis*
sea	*Petromyzon marinus*
Lancelet	*Branchiostoma lanceolatum*
Lark, horned	*Eremophila alpestris*
	E. alpestris alpestris
wood	*Lullula arborea*
Leaf roller, red-banded	*Argyrotaenia velutinana*

continued

Appendix II. COMMON NAMES AND CORRESPONDING SCIENTIFIC NAMES

Part I. Animals

Common Name	Scientific Name
Leafworm, cotton	*Alabama argillacea*
Leech	*Erpobdella octuculata*
	E. testacea
	Glossiphonia complanata
	Haemopis sanguisuga
	Helobdella stagnalis
	Hirudo medicinalis
	Piscicola geometra
Lemming, brown	*Lemmus lemmus*
collared	*Dicrostonyx groenlandicus*
varying	*D. groenlandicus rubricatus*
Lemur, ring-tailed	*Lemur cattus*
ruffed or black and white	*L. variegatus*
West African, or potto	*Perodicticus potto*
Leopard	*Panthera pardus*
clouded	*P. nebulosa*
snow	*P. uncia*
Leptodactylid	*Crinia signifera*
Limpet, common European	*Patella vulgata*
lake	*Acroloxus lacustris*
river	*Ancylus fluviatilis*
Limpkin	*Aramus guarauna*
Linnet, European	*Acanthis cannabina*
Lion	*Panthera leo*
Lizard, Australian bearded	*Amphibolurus barbatus*
collared	*Crotaphytus collaris*
European fence	*Lacerta agilis*
horned	*Phrynosoma cornutum*
iguana or Pacific fence	*Sceloporus occidentalis*
regal horned	*Phrynosoma solare*
southern alligator	*Gerrhonotus multicarinatus*
southern fence	*Sceloporus undulatus undulatus*
Llama	*Lama glama*
Loach, European, or European weatherfish	*Misgurnus fossilis*
Lobster, American	*Homarus americanus*
spiny	*Palinurus vulgaris*
	Panulirus argus
Locust	*Locusta migratoria*
desert	*Schistocerca gregaria*
South American	*S. infumata*
Longspur, chestnut-collared	*Calcarius ornatus*
Lapland	*C. lapponicus*
Loon, Arctic	*Gavia arctica pacifica*
Looper, cabbage	*Trichoplusia ni*
Lungfish, African	*Protopterus aethiopicus*
South American	*Lepidosiren paradoxa*
Lymnaea, exotic	*Lymnaea peregra*
oval	*L. ovata*
Lynx, Yukon	*Felis canadensis*
Macaque, Burmese pig-tailed	*Macaca nemestrina leonina*
Celebes crested	*Cynopithecus niger*
Formosan rock	*Macaca cyclopis*
gray-armed	*M. maurus ochreatus*
Japanese	*M. fuscata yakui*
Mackerel, Atlantic	*Scomber scombrus*
Maggot, onion	*Hylemya antiqua*
Magpie, black-billed	*Pica pica*
	P. pica hudsonia
Man	*Homo sapiens*
Manakin, yellow-thighed	*Pipra mentalis*
Manatee	*Trichechus manatus latirostris*
Mandrill	*Mandrillus sphinx*
Manure worm or brandling	*Eisenia foetida*
Marine worm	*Sipunculus nudus*
Marmoset	*Callithrix jacchus*
cottonhead	*Saguinus oedipus*
Geoffroy's	*S. geoffroyi*
pygmy	*Cebuella pygmaea*
white-faced	*Callithrix geoffroyi*
Marmot, Eurasian	*Marmota marmota*
hoary	*M. caligata*
Marsupial mouse	*Antechinus flavipes*
	Dasycercus cristicauda
narrow-footed	*Sminthopsis crassicaudata*
	S. larapinta
Marsupial rat	*Phascogale tapoatafa*
Marten, American	*Martes americana actuosa*
Martin, purple	*Progne subis*
Meadowlark, western	*Sturnella neglecta*
Mealworm, yellow	*Tenebrio molitor*
Medusa	*Carmarina hastata*
Menhaden	*Brevoortia* sp.
Merganser, hooded	*Lophodytes cucullatus*
red-breasted	*Mergus serrator*
Microdrilid, or enchytraeid worm	*Fridericia* sp.
Midge	*Chironomus riparius*
phantom	*Chaoborus* sp.
Milkweed bug	*Oncopeltus fasciatus*
Millipede	*Julus* sp.
Mite, oribatid	*Achipteria* sp.
Mite or tick, parasitic	*Pergamasus crassipes*
Mockingbird	*Mimus polyglottos*
Mole, eastern American	*Scalopus aquaticus*
Mongoose, East African banded	*Mungos mungo*
Indian	*Herpestes edwardsi*
Monitor, Gould's	*Varanus gouldii*
lace	*V. varius*
Monkey, Brazza's	*Cercopithecus neglectus*
diana	*C. diana*
mona	*C. mona mona*
night	*Aotus trivirgatus*
Patas	*Erythrocebus patas*
Philippine or crab-eating	*Macaca irus*
proboscis	*Nasalis larvatus*
red howler	*Alouatta seniculus*
rhesus	*Macaca mulatta*
squirrel	*Saimiri sciurea*
talapoin	*Cercopithecus talapoin*
woolly	*Lagothrix lagotricha*
Monkfish	*Lophius piscatorius*
Moose	*Alces alces andersoni*
American	*A. americana*
Mosquito	*Aedes australis*
	Culiseta incidens
common malaria	*Anopheles quadrimaculatus*

continued

Appendix II. COMMON NAMES AND CORRESPONDING SCIENTIFIC NAMES

Part I. Animals

Common Name	Scientific Name
northern house	*Culex pipiens*
southern house	*C. pipiens quinquefasciatus*
yellow-fever	*Aedes aegypti*
Moth, almond	*Cadra cautella*
atlas	*Attacus* sp.
buff-tip	*Phalera bucephala*
cecropia	*Hyalophora cecropia*
codling	*Carpocapsa pomonella*
greater wax	*Galleria mellonella*
Indian meal	*Plodia interpunctella*
io	*Automeris io*
Mediterranean flour	*Anagasta kuehniella*
polyphemus	*Antheraea polyphemus*
silkworm	*Bombyx mori*
tobacco	*Ephestia elutella*
webbing clothes	*Tineola bisselliella*
Mouflon	*Ovis musimon*
Mouse, beach	*Peromyscus polionotus*
birch	*Sicista betulina*
cactus	*Peromyscus eremicus*
California	*P. californicus*
canyon	*P. crinitus*
deer	*P. maniculatus*
	P. maniculatus artemisiae
	P. maniculatus austerus
	P. maniculatus gracilis
	P. maniculatus nebrascensis
	P. maniculatus oreas
	P. maniculatus sonoriensis
desert pocket	*Perognathus penicillatus penicillatus*
four-striped grass	*Rhabdomys pumilio*
house	*Mus musculus*
kangaroo	*Microdipodops megacephalus nasutus*
little pocket	*Perognathus longimembris*
long-eared	*Malacothrix typica*
meadow	*Microtus pennsylvanicus*
meadow jumping	*Zapus hudsonius*
	Z. hudsonius americanus
northern pygmy	*Baiomys taylori*
northern red-backed	*Clethrionomys rutilus*
pale kangaroo	*Microdipodops pallidus*
pine	*Pitymys pinetorum scalopsoides*
piñon	*Peromyscus truei*
plains or pale pocket	*Perognathus hispidus*
pocket	*Liomys irroratus*
	L. salvini
sitka	*Peromyscus sitkensis*
Thomas' deer	*P. thomasi*
western harvest	*Reithrodontomys megalotis*
	R. megalotis longicaudus
white-footed	*Peromyscus leucopus*
woodland jumping	*Napaeozapus insignis*
	N. insignis insignis
Mud shrimp	*Callianassa subterranea*
Mullet	*Mugil* sp.
Mummichog	*Fundulus heteroclitus*
Muntjac or barking deer	*Muntiacus muntjac*
Muntjac, Reeves'	*M. reevesi*
Murre, common	*Uria aalge*
thick-billed	*U. lomvia*
Musk ox	*Ovibos moschatus*
Muskrat	*Ondatra zibethicus*
Mussel, edible	*Corbicula sandai*
	Mytilus edulis
freshwater	*Anodonta cellensis*
	Cristaria plicata
	Hyriopsis schlegelii
horse	*Modiolus demissus*
Mediterranean sea	*Mytilus galloprovincialis*
sea	*M. crassitesta*
swan	*Anodonta cygnea*
zebra	*Dreissena polymorpha*
Native cat, little northern	*Satanellus hallucatus*
Natterjack	*Bufo calamita*
Neritina, river	*Theodoxus fluviatilis*
Newt, giant or California	*Triturus torosus*
smooth	*T. vulgaris*
warty	*T. cristatus*
Nighthawk	*Chordeiles minor*
	C. minor minor
Nightjar, common	*Caprimulgus europaeus*
Nilgai	*Boselaphus tragocamelus*
Noctule	*Nyctalus noctula*
Nudibranch	*Pleurobranchaea meckelii*
Nutcracker, Clark's	*Nucifraga columbiana*
Nuthatch, white-breasted	*Sitta carolinensis*
Nyala	*Tragelaphus angasi*
Octocoral, Indian Ocean	*Primnoa lepadifera*
Octopus	*Octopus dofleini*
	O. macropus
	O. vulgaris
Mediterranean musk	*Eledone moschata*
Okapi	*Okapia johnstoni*
Oligochaete	*Glossoscolex* sp.
	Megaloscolex mauritii
	Pontoscolex sp.
tubificid	*Limnodrilus claparedianus*
	L. hoffmeisteri
	Tubifex tubifex
Onychophoran	*Epiperipatus brasiliensis*
Opossum, black-shouldered	*Caluromysiops irrupta*
brown "four-eyed"	*Metachirus nudicaudatus*
common	*Didelphis marsupialis virginiana*
large American	*D. marsupialis*
Mexican	*Marmosa mexicana*
mouse	*M. cinerea*
thick-tailed	*Lutreolina crassicaudata*
woolly	*Caluromys* sp.
Orangutan	*Pongo pygmaeus*
Orfe, golden	*Idus idus*
Oriole, Baltimore	*Icterus galbula*
Bullock's	*I. bullockii*
Ostrich, African	*Struthio camelus*
Masai	*S. camelus massaicus*
North African	*S. camelus camelus*
Otter, northern giant	*Pteronura brasiliensis brasiliensis*

continued

Appendix II. COMMON NAMES AND CORRESPONDING SCIENTIFIC NAMES

Part I. Animals

Common Name	Scientific Name
sea	*Enhydra lutris*
smooth	*Lutragale perspicillata perspicillata*
Ovenbird	*Seiurus aurocapillus*
Owl, barred	*Strix varia*
burrowing	*Speotyto cunicularia*
common barn	*Tyto alba*
flammulated	*Otus flammeolus*
great horned	*Bubo virginianus*
long-eared	*Asio otus*
	A. otus wilsonianus
screech	*Otus asio*
	O. asio naevius
short-eared	*Asio flammeus*
	A. flammeus flammeus
snowy	*Nyctea scandiaca*
Oyster	*Crassostrea gigas*
	Ostrea circumpicta
Australian rock	*Saxostrea commercialis*
pearl	*Pinctada martensii*
Portuguese	*Crassostrea angulata*
tree	*Isognomon alata*
Virginia	*Crassostrea virginica*
Panda, lesser	*Ailurus fulgens fulgens*
Pangolin or scaly anteater	*Manis tricuspis*
Parrot, Amazon basin or Brazilian	*Amazona aestiva aestiva*
Partridge, African Franklin	*Francolinus natalensis*
Pauraque	*Nyctidromus albicollis*
Peacock	*Pavo cristatus*
Peccary, collared	*Pecari tajacu*
	Tayassu tajacu angulatus
Pelican, American white	*Pelecanus erythrorhynchos*
black-backed	*P. conspicillatus*
brown	*P. occidentalis*
European white	*P. onocrotalus*
Pen shell	*Pinna muricata*
	P. nobilis
Penguin, Adelie	*Pygoscelis adeliae*
emperor	*Aptenodytes forsteri*
Gentoo	*Pygoscelis papua*
king	*Aptenodytes patagonica*
	A. patagonica patagonica
little blue	*Eudyptula minor*
yellow-eyed	*Megadyptes antipodes*
Peregrine	*Falco peregrinus*
Peripatus	*Peripatus accacioi*
Periwinkle	*Littorina littorea*
Petrel, Bonin Island	*Pterodroma leucoptera hypoleuca*
cape	*Daption capense*
Leach's	*Oceanodroma leuchorhoa*
snow	*Pagodroma nivea*
Pewee, eastern wood	*Contopus virens*
Phainopepla	*Phainopepla nitens*
Phalanger, common	*Trichosurus* sp.
Phalarope, northern	*Lobipes lobatus*
Wilson's	*Steganopus tricolor*
Pheasant	*Phasianus torquatus*
golden	*Chrysolophus pictus*
Lady Amherst	*C. amherstiae*
ring-necked	*Phasianus colchicus*
	P. colchicus mongolicus
silver	*Gennaeus nycthemerus nycthemerus*
Phoebe, eastern	*Sayornis phoebe*
Pigeon, street	*Columba livia*
Pika, Alaskan	*Ochotona collaris*
Pike, northern	*Esox lucius*
Pillbug	*Armadillidium pallasi*
	A. vulgare
Pinfish	*Lagodon rhomboides*
Pipefish	*Syngnathus* sp.
Pipit, meadow	*Anthus pratensis*
rock or water	*A. spinoletta*
Planarian, alpine	*Crenobia alpina*
freshwater	*Dugesia gonocephala*
	D. polychroa
	D. tigrina
Platypus	*Ornithorhynchus anatinus*
Plover, black-bellied	*Squatarola squatarola*
ringed	*Charadrius hiaticula*
Polecat, European	*Mustela putorius*
Polychaete	*Arenicola marina*
	Chaetopterus variopedapus
	Schizobranchia insignis
burrowing marine	*Glycera siphonostoma*
Poorwill	*Phalaenoptilus nuttalli*
Porcupine, Congo brush-tailed	*Atherurus centralis centralis*
Indian crested	*Hystrix indica*
North American	*Erethizon dorsatum*
prehensile-tailed	*Coendou prehensilis*
	C. villosus
Porgy, European	*Diplodus sargus*
	Sparus auratus
Porpoise, Atlantic bottle-nosed	*Tursiops truncatus*
harbor	*Phocoena phocoena*
Portuguese man-of-war	*Physalia physalis*
Possum, dormouse	*Cercartetus nanus*
brush-tailed	*Trichosurus caninus*
	T. vulpecula
New Guinea striped	*Dactylopsila trivirgata melampus*
Potto, Cameroon	*Perodicticus potto edwardsi*
Prawn	*Palaemon serratus*
	P. squilla
	Pandalus borealis
Prawn or pink shrimp	*P. montagui*
Prion, fairy	*Pachyptila turtur*
Pronghorn	*Antilocapra americana*
Ptarmigan, rock	*Lagopus mutus nelsoni*
white-tailed	*L. leucurus leucurus*
willow	*L. lagopus*
Puffer, northern	*Sphaeroides maculatus*
Puffin, tufted	*Lunda cirrhata*
Puma	*Felis concolor*
mountain	*F. concolor missoulensis*
Python, African	*Python sebae*
Indian	*P. molurus*
reticulated	*P. reticulatus*

continued

Appendix II. COMMON NAMES AND CORRESPONDING SCIENTIFIC NAMES

Part I. Animals

Common Name	Scientific Name
Quahog, northern	*Mercenaria mercenaria*
Quail, California	*Lophortyx californicus*
desert or Gambel's	*L. gambelii*
European	*Coturnix coturnix*
Japanese	*C. coturnix japonica*
mountain	*Oreortyx pictus*
Rabbit, eastern cottontail	*Sylvilagus floridanus*
European	*Oryctolagus cuniculus*
snowshoe, or American hare	*Lepus americanus*
white-tailed jack-	*L. townsendii townsendii*
Raccoon	*Procyon lotor*
crab-eating	*P. cancrivorus*
Racer, northern black	*Coluber constrictor constrictor*
Rail, clapper	*Rallus longirostris crepitans*
Virginia	*R. limicola*
Rat	*Rattus conatus*
	R. rattus
African mole	*Tachyoryctes splendens*
agile kangaroo	*Dipodomys agilis*
bannertailed kangaroo	*D. spectabilis*
cotton	*Sigmodon* sp.
desert kangaroo	*Dipodomys deserti*
desert wood	*Neotoma lepida*
dusky-footed wood	*N. fuscipes*
giant naked-tailed	*Uromys sherrini*
lesser mole	*Spalax leucodon*
Merriam's kangaroo	*Dipodomys merriami*
mosaic-tailed	*Melomys littoralis*
naked mole-	*Heterocephalus glaber*
Norway	*Rattus norvegicus*
sand	*Heliophobius argenteocinereus kapiti*
slender-tailed cloud	*Phloeomys cumingi*
spiny	*Proechimys semispinosus*
water	*Hydromys chrysogaster*
Ratel	*Mellivora capensis leuconota*
Raven, common	*Corvus corax*
	C. corax principalis
white-necked	*C. cryptoleucus*
Ray, electric	*Torpedo* sp.
Redpoll, hoary	*Acanthis hornemanni exilipes*
Redstart, American	*Setophaga ruticilla*
European	*Phoenicurus phoenicurus*
Redwing	*Turdus musicus*
Reedbuck	*Redunca arundinum*
Reindeer	*Rangifer tarandus*
Rhinoceros	*Rhinoceros* sp.
black	*Diceros bicornis*
square-lipped	*Ceratotherium simum simum*
white	*C. simum*
Roadrunner	*Geococcyx californianus*
Robin	*Turdus migratorius*
European	*Erithacus rubecula*
Rockhopper	*Eudyptes crestatus*
Rotifer	*Asplanchna* spp.

Common Name	Scientific Name
Roundworm	*Enoplus communis*
	Gnathostoma spinigerum
	Plectus sp.
large	*Ascaris lumbricoides*
Roundworm of birds & fish	*Eustrongylides ignotus*
Roundworm of chicken, large	*Ascaridia galli*
Roundworm of horse	*Parascaris equorum*
Ruff	*Philomachus pugnax*
Salamander, arboreal	*Aneides lugubris*
common fire	*Salamandra salamandra*
European spotted	*S. maculosa*
fern bank	*Eurycea pterophila*
marbled	*Triturus marmoratus*
neotenic	*Eurycea neotenes*
red-backed	*Plethodon cinereus cinereus*
redwood	*Ensatina eschscholtzii*
San Marcos	*Eurycea nana*
spotted	*Ambystoma maculatum*
tiger	*A. tigrinum*
two-lined	*Eurycea bislineata bislineata*
yellow-eyed	*Ensatina eschscholtzii xanthoptica*
Salmon, Atlantic	*Salmo salar*
Salp	*Cyclosalpa pinnata*
	Salpa maxima africana
	Thetys vagina
Sand hopper	*Talitrus sylvaticus*
Sandpiper, Baird's	*Erolia bairdii*
spotted	*Actitis macularia*
western	*Ereunetes mauri*
Sapajou, white-fronted	*Cebus albifrons*
Sapsucker, yellow-bellied	*Sphyrapicus varius*
Sawfish	*Pristis microdon*
Scallop	*Pecten irradians*
Scaup, greater	*Aythya marila*
lesser	*A. affinis*
Scorpion	*Buthus tamulus typicus*
	Lychas tricarinatus
whip	*Heterometrus fulvipes*
	Phrynichus phipsoni
	Thelyphonus sepiaris
Scorpion fish	*Scorpaena* spp.
Scoter, common	*Oidemia nigra*
Screwworm	*Cochliomyia hominivorax*
Scud	*Gammarus duebeni*
	Marinogammarus pirloti
Sculpin, longhorn	*Myoxocephalus octodecemspinosus*
shorthorn	*M. scorpius*
Scup	*Stenotomus chrysops*
Sea anemone	*Anemonia sulcata*
	Condylactis gigantea
Sea cucumber	*Holothuria impatiens*
	H. stellati
	H. tubulosa
	Isostichopus badionotus
Sea fan	*Gorgonia flabellum*

continued

Appendix II. COMMON NAMES AND CORRESPONDING SCIENTIFIC NAMES

Part I. Animals

Common Name	Scientific Name
Sea hare	*Aplysia fasciata*
	Tethys leporina
Sea lion, Steller's or northern	*Eumetopias jubata*
Sea mouse	*Aphrodite aculeata*
Sea squirt	*Ascidia mentula*
	Ascidiella sp.
	Ciona sp.
Sea urchin	*Paracentrotus lividus*
western purple	*Strongylocentrotus purpuratus*
Seahorse	*Hippocampus* spp.
Seal, Atlantic harbor	*Phoca vitulina concolor*
bearded	*Erignathus barbatus*
elephant	*Mirounga angustirostris*
gray	*Halichoerus grypus*
harbor	*Phoca vitulina*
northern Pacific fur	*Callorhinus ursinus*
Serotine, or brown bat	*Eptesicus serotinus*
Serotine, white-winged	*E. tenuipinnis*
Shag or cormorant	*Phalacrocorax aristotelis*
Shark, cat	*Scyliorhinus caniculus*
Shearwater, Christmas Island	*Puffinus nativitatis*
slender-billed	*P. tenuirostris*
wedge-tailed	*P. pacificus*
Sheep	*Ovis aries*
mountain	*O. canadensis canadensis*
Sheepshead	*Archosargus probatocephalus*
Sheldrake	*Tadorna tadorna*
Shoveler	*Spatula clypeata*
Shrew, European	*Sorex cinereus cinereus*
masked	*S. cinereus*
pygmy	*Microsorex hoyi*
short-tailed	*Blarina brevicauda*
	B. brevicauda kirtlandi
Trowbridge's	*Sorex trowbridgii montereyensis*
wandering	*S. vagrans sonomae*
	S. vagrans vagrans
Shrike, migrant or loggerhead	*Lanius ludovicianus*
Shrimp	*Metapenaeus monocerus*
	Palaemon longirostris
	Palaemonetes varians
	Penaeus japonicus
	Sicyonia carinata
	Spirontocaris liljeborgi
	Thoralus cranchi
freshwater	*Palaemonetes antennarius*
Side-swimmer	*Rivulogammarus pulex*
Siskin, pine	*Spinus pinus*
Skimmer, black	*Rhynocops nigra*
Skink	*Sphenomorphus labillardieri*
	S. leonhardi
	Tiliqua melanops
Bouton's snake-eyed	*Ablepharus boutonii metallicum*
flat-bellied	*Rhodona planiventrale*
four-toed	*Hemiergis peronii*
Great Plains	*Eumeces obsoletus*
metallic	*Leiolopisma metallicum*
North African sand	*Scincus scincus*
ocellated sand	*Chalcides ocellatus*

Common Name	Scientific Name
stump-tailed	*Tiliqua rugosa*
three-toed	*Hemiergis decresiense*
Skua, Antarctic	*Catharacta skua*
Skunk, striped	*Mephitis mephitis mesomelas*
Skylark	*Alauda arvensis*
Slater, rock, or wharf louse	*Ligia oceanica*
water	*Asellus intermedius*
Sloth, Hoffmann's two-toed	*Choloepus hoffmanni*
three-toed	*Bradypus griseus*
	B. tridactyla
Slowworm	*Anguis fragilis*
Slug	*Deroceras agreste*
	D. reticulatum
	Limax flavus
land	*Arion ater*
	A. hortensis
	A. rufus
	Zebrina detrita
sea	*Hermissenda crassicornis*
Snail	*Australorbis tenagophilus*
American bilharzia	*A. glabratus*
dented garden, or petit-gris	*Helix aspersa*
edible	*H. pomatia*
freshwater	*Lymnaea auricularia*
	L. palustris
	L. stagnalis
giant African land	*Achatina fulica*
land	*Cepaea nemoralis*
little edible land	*Helix pisana*
marine	*Melanoides tuberculata*
	Oncomelania nosphora
	Potamopyrgus jenkinsi
North American freshwater	*Bithynia leachi*
	Valvata piscinalis
North American pond	*Myxas glutinosa*
	Physa fontinalis
pond	*P. acuta*
ramshorn	*Planorbis corneus*
river	*Viviparus viviparus*
rock	*Purpura aperta*
sheep	*Helicella candicans*
white-lipped edible land	*Helix vermiculata*
Snake, black	*Coluber constrictor*
brown	*Storeria dekayi*
common European water	*Natrix natrix*
common garter	*Thamnophis sirtalis*
eastern coachwhip	*Masticophis flagellum flagellum*
eastern indigo	*Drymarchon corais couperi*
Mojave rattle-	*Crotalus scutellatus*
North American water	*Natrix sipedon*
rat	*Spalerosophis diadema*
western diamond-back rattle-	*Crotalus atrox*
Solitaire, Townsend's	*Myadestes townsendi*
Souslik	*Citellus citellus*
little	*C. pygmaeus*
Sow bug	*Oniscus asellus*
	Porcellio laevis
scabby, or wood louse	*P. scaber*

continued

Appendix II. COMMON NAMES AND CORRESPONDING SCIENTIFIC NAMES

Part I. Animals

Common Name	Scientific Name
Sparrow, Cassin's	*Aimophila cassinii*
chipping	*Spizella passerina passerina*
European tree	*Passer montanus*
fox	*Passerella iliaca*
grasshopper	*Ammodramus savannarum*
house	*Passer domesticus*
Le Conte's	*Passerherbulus caudacutus*
Lincoln's	*Melospiza lincolnii*
rufous-crowned	*Aimophila ruficeps*
savannah	*Passerculus sandwichensis*
song	*Melospiza melodia*
	M. melodia melodia
tree	*Spizella arborea*
white-crowned	*Zonotrichia leucophrys*
	Z. leucophrys gambelii
white-throated	*Z. albicollis*
Spider, false or sun, or wind scorpion	*Galeodes indicus*
tropical silk	*Nephila claviceps*
wolf	*Lycosa* sp.
Sponge	*Cinachyra cavernosa*
	Geodia gibberosa
	Lissodendoryx isodictyalis
	Pseudaxinella rosacea
	Spheciospongia sp.
	Suberites massa
	Terpios fugax
	Tethya aurantia
fire	*Tedania ignis*
horny	*Dysidea crawshayi*
red oyster	*Microciona prolifera*
stinker	*Ircinia fasciculata*
Spot	*Leiostomus xanthurus*
Springhaas	*Pedetes cafer*
Springtail	*Onychiurus procampatus*
Squid, common American	*Loligo pealeii*
Squirrel, Alaska red	*Tamiasciurus hudsonicus*
Arctic ground	*Citellus undulatus*
Franklin ground	*C. franklini*
golden mantled ground	*C. lateralis*
Parry's ground	*C. undulatus parryii*
round-tailed ground	*C. tereticaudus*
southern flying	*Glaucomys volans*
	G. volans volans
thirteen-lined ground	*Citellus tridecemlineatus*
tropical red	*Sciurus granatensis*
variegated	*S. variegatoides dorsalis*
white-tailed antelope	*Citellus leucurus*
Stainer, cotton	*Dysdercus fasciatus*
Starfish	*Asterias rubens*
	Leptasterias pusilla
Starling, common	*Sturnus vulgaris*
Stilt, black-necked	*Himantopus mexicanus*
Stomach worm, twisted	*Haemonchus contortus*
Stomach worm of poultry	*Tetrameres confusa*
Stomach worm of sheep, brown	*Ostertagia circumcincta*
Stone fly, European	*Perla burmeisteriana*
Stork, Indian adjutant	*Leptoptilos dubius*
lesser adjutant	*L. javanicus*
marabou	*L. crumeniferus*

Common Name	Scientific Name
Strongyle	*Nematodirus* spp.
double-tooth	*Strongylus equinus*
single-tooth	*S. vulgaris*
Strongylin	*Nippostrongylus brasiliensis*
Sucker, white	*Catostomus commersonii*
Suricate	*Suricata suricatta*
Swallow, bank	*Riparia riparia*
	Hirundo rustica erythrogaster
cliff	*Petrochelidon pyrrhonota*
New World rough-winged	*Stelgidopteryx ruficollis*
tree	*Iridoprocne bicolor*
violet-green	*Tachycineta thalassina*
Swan, black	*Cygnus atratus*
mute	*C. olor*
trumpeter	*Olor buccinator*
Swift, chimney	*Chaetura pelagica*
white-throated	*Aeronautes melanoleucus*
	A. saxatilis
Swine	*Sus scrofa*
Tahr, Himalayan	*Hemitragus jemlahicus*
Tahr goat	*H. jemlahicus jemlahicus*
Takin	*Budorcas taxicolor taxicolor*
Tamandua, or collared anteater	*Tamandua tetradactyla*
Tanager, western	*Piranga ludoviciana*
Tapeworm, cyclophyllidean	*Taenia taeniaeformis*
double-pored ruminant	*Moniezia expansa*
fish	*Diphyllobothrium latum*
hydatid	*Echinococcus granulosus*
rat	*Hymenolepis diminuta*
Tapeworm of red fox	*Taenia crassiceps*
Tapir, South American	*Tapirus terrestris*
Tasmanian devil	*Sarcophilus harrisii*
Tautog	*Tautoga onitis*
Tayra	*Tayra barbara*
Teal, cinnamon	*Anas cyanoptera*
common	*A. crecca nimia*
green-winged	*A. carolinensis*
Tench, golden	*Tinca tinca*
Tenrec	*Tenrec ecaudatus*
Termite, dark Pacific coast rotten wood	*Zootermopsis nevadensis*
Pacific coast rotten wood	*Z. angusticollis*
Tern, black	*Chlidonias niger*
Forster's	*Sterna forsteri*
sooty	*S. fuscata*
Terrapin, diamondback	*Malaclemys terrapin centrata*
red-eared	*Pseudemys scripta*
Thrasher, curve-billed	*Toxostoma curvirostre*
Thrush, hermit	*Hylocichla guttata*
wood	*H. mustelina*
Tiger	*Panthera tigris*
Bengal	*P. tigris tigris*
Siberian	*P. tigris longipilis*
Tiger cat	*Dasyurus maculatus*
Tinamou	*Nothura maculosa*

continued

Appendix II. COMMON NAMES AND CORRESPONDING SCIENTIFIC NAMES

Part I. Animals

Common Name	Scientific Name
Tit, common bush	*Psaltriparus minimus*
great	*Parus major*
Toad, coast horned	*Phrynosoma coronatum*
common European	*Bufo bufo*
eastern spadefoot	*Scaphiopus holbrookii*
false	*Pseudophryne bibroni*
Great Plains	*Bufo cognatus*
Gulf Coast	*B. valliceps*
marine	*B. marinus*
northern	*B. boreas*
southern	*B. terrestris*
square-marked or leopard	*B. regularis*
western spadefoot	*Scaphiopus hammondi*
Toadfish, oyster	*Opsanus tau*
Tongue shell	*Lingula reevii*
Tortoise, European	*Testudo graeca*
forest hinge-back	*Kinixys erosa*
gopher	*Gopherus polyphemus*
South American	*Testudo denticulata*
star	*T. elegans*
Tortoiseshell, small	*Aglais urtica*
Towhee, Abert's	*Pipilo aberti*
brown	*P. fuscus*
Trichina worm	*Trichinella spiralis*
Tropic bird, red-tailed	*Phaethon rubricauda*
Trout, brown	*Salmo trutta*
rainbow	*S. gairdneri*
Turkey	*Meleagris gallopavo*
Turtle, Atlantic green	*Chelonia mydas*
Bell's African	*Kinixys belliana belliana*
dark pelomedusa	*Pelusios subniger*
eastern box	*Terrapene carolina*
eastern mud	*Kinosternum subrubrum*
Egyptian land	*Testudo kleinmanni*
elephant-footed Galapagos	*T. elephantopus elephantopus*
European pond	*Emys orbicularis*
long-necked	*Chelodina longicollis*
midland painted	*Chrysemys picta marginata*
painted	*C. picta*
red-eared	*Pseudemys scripta elegans*
spurred	*Testudo sulcata*
western gopher	*Gopherus agassizii*
Uakari, bald	*Cacajao calvus*
Unio, painted	*Unio pictorum*
Uta, ground	*Uta stansburiana*
Venus's-girdle	*Cestum veneris*
Vicuña	*Lama vicugna*
	Vicugna vicugna mensalis
Violet-ear	*Colibri serrirostris*
Vireo, blue-headed	*Vireo solitarius*
red-eyed	*V. olivaceus*
warbling	*V. gilvus*
Vole, California	*Microtus californicus*
common	*M. arvalis*
European pine	*Pitymys subterraneus*
long-tailed	*Microtus longicaudus*
meadow	*M. pennsylvanicus pennsylvanicus*

Common Name	Scientific Name
prairie	*M. ochrogaster ochrogaster*
red-backed	*Clethrionomys gapperi*
	C. gapperi gapperi
	C. gapperi rhoadsi
sagebrush	*Lagurus curtatus*
Vulture, bearded	*Gypaetus barbatus*
turkey	*Cathartes aura*
Wagtail, white	*Motacilla alba*
Wallaby, agile	*Protemnodon agilis*
red-necked	*Wallabia rufogrisea*
ring-tailed rock	*Petrogale xanthopus*
scrub	*Setonix brachyurus*
	Wallabia dorsalis
Wallaroo	*Macropus robustus robustus*
Walrus, North Pacific	*Odobenus rosmarus divergens*
Wanderoo	*Macaca silenus*
Warbler, Audubon's	*Dendroica auduboni*
black-throated blue	*D. caerulescens*
Cape May	*D. tigrina*
Connecticut	*Oporornis agilis*
MacGillivray's	*O. tolmiei*
magnolia	*Dendroica magnolia*
mourning	*Oporornis philadelphia*
orange-crowned	*Vermivora celata*
Tennessee	*V. peregrina*
willow	*Phylloscopus trochilus*
Wilson's	*Wilsonia pusilla*
Wasp, ichneumon	*Exeristes comstockii*
parasitic	*Pleolophus basizonus*
Water boatman	*Corixa dentipes*
Water bug, giant	*Belostoma* spp.
Waxbill, tropical black-rumped	*Estrilda troglodytes*
Waxwing, Bohemian	*Bombycilla garrulus*
cedar	*B. cedrorum*
Weasel, least	*Mustela rixosa*
Weevil, boll	*Anthonomus grandis*
cowpea	*Callosobruchus maculatus*
mung bean	*C. chinensis*
Whale, blue	*Balaenoptera musculus*
fin	*B. physalus*
gray	*Eschrichtius gibbosus*
humpback	*Megaptera novaeanglia*
sei	*Balaenoptera borealis*
sperm	*Physeter catodon*
Whippoorwill, common	*Caprimulgus vociferus*
Widgeon, American	*Mareca americana*
European	*M. penelope*
Willet	*Catoptrophorus semipalmatus*
Wireworm, corn	*Melanotus communis*
Wisent	*Bison bonasus bonasus*
Wolf	*Canis lupus*
timber	*C. lupus nubilus*
Wood nymph	*Thalurania furcata*
	T. glaucopis
Woodpecker, acorn	*Melanerpes erythrocephalus*
black-backed three-toed	*Picoides arcticus*
downy	*Dendrocopos pubescens*
Lewis'	*Asyndesmus lewis*

continued

Appendix II. COMMON NAMES AND CORRESPONDING SCIENTIFIC NAMES

Part I. Animals

Common Name	Scientific Name
northern hairy	*Dendrocopos villosus septentrionalis*
northern three-toed	*Picoides tridactylus fasciatus*
pileated	*Dryocopus pileatus*
red-bellied	*Centurus carolinus*
three-toed	*Picoides tridactylus*
Wren, Bewick's	*Thryomanes bewickii*
eastern house	*Troglodytes aedon aedon*
long-billed marsh	*Telmatodytes palustris*
northern house	*Troglodytes aedon*
winter	*T. troglodytes*

Common Name	Scientific Name
Wren-tit	*Chamaea fasciata*
Wrymouth	*Cryptacanthodes maculatus*
Yak	*Poephagus grunniens*
Yellowhammer	*Emberiza citrinella*
Yellowlegs, greater	*Totanus melanoleucus*
lesser	*T. flavipes*
Yellowthroat	*Geothlypis trichas*
Zebra, Grevy's	*Equus grevyi*

Part II. Plants

Common Name	Scientific Name
Abelia	*Abelia* spp.
Acacia, blackwood	*Acacia melanoxylon*
sweet	*A. farnesiana*
African violet, common	*Saintpaulia ionantha*
Alder, American green	*Alnus crispa*
Alfalfa	*Medicago sativa*
Almond	*Prunus amygdalus*
Alyssum	*Alyssum* spp.
Amaranth, redroot	*Amaranthus retroflexus*
Anthyllis	*Anthyllis vulneraria*
Apple	*Malus pumila*
	M. sylvestris
Arborvitae, eastern	*Thuja occidentalis*
Artichoke, Jerusalem	*Helianthus tuberosus*
Ash, black	*Fraxinus nigra*
European	*F. excelsior*
Asparagus, garden	*Asparagus officinalis*
white	*A. albus*
Aspen, quaking	*Populus tremuloides*
Aster, China	*Callistephus chinensis*
Avocado, American	*Persea americana*
Azalea, amoena	*Rhododendron obtusum amoenum*
Balsam, garden	*Impatiens balsamina*
Banana, common	*Musa sapientum*
plantain	*M. paradisiaca*
Barley	*Hordeum vulgare*
six-rowed	*H. hexastichum*
Bayberry or waxmyrtle	*Myrica* spp.
Bean, broad	*Vicia faba*
horse-	*V. faba equina*
kidney	*Phaseolus vulgaris*
lima	*P. limensis*
Beech, American	*Fagus grandifolia*
European	*F. sylvatica*
Beefwood, horsetail	*Casuarina equisetifolia*
Beet, common	*Beta vulgaris*
sugar	*B. saccharifera*
Begonia	*Begonia tuberhybrida*
Assam king	*B. rex*
Berula, stalky	*Berula erecta*

Common Name	Scientific Name
Birch, dwarf arctic	*Betula nana*
sweet	*B. lenta*
Bitterbrush, antelope	*Purshia tridentata*
Blackberry, boysenberry, or raspberry	*Rubus* spp.
Blueberry or cranberry	*Vaccinium* spp.
Box, common	*Buxus sempervirens*
Box elder	*Acer negundo*
Bracken	*Pteridium aquilinum*
Broccoli	*Brassica oleracea italica*
Brussels sprout	*B. oleracea gemmifera*
Bryony, red berry	*Bryonia dioica*
Buckeye, Ohio	*Aesculus glabra*
red	*A. pavia*
Buckwheat	*Fagopyrum sagittatum*
Buffalo berry	*Shepherdia* spp.
Buttercup, large-leaf	*Ranunculus macrophyllus*
Butterfly bush	*Buddleia* spp.
Cabbage	*Brassica oleracea capitata*
wild	*B. oleracea*
Calendula	*Calendula* spp.
Camellia, common	*Camellia japonica*
Candytuft	*Iberis* spp.
Canna, India	*Canna indica*
Carrot	*Daucus carota*
Castor bean	*Ricinus communis*
Catalpa, southern	*Catalpa bignonioides*
Cauliflower	*Brassica oleracea botrytis*
Ceanothus	*Ceanothus* spp.
Celery, garden	*Apium graveolens dulce*
Cherry, almond	*Prunus glandulosa*
common laurel	*P. laurocerasus*
sour	*P. cerasus*
Chestnut, American	*Castanea dentata*
Chinquapin, Allegheny	*C. pumila*
Chokecherry, common	*Prunus virginiana*
Chrysanthemum, florist's	*Chrysanthemum morifolium*
Clematis	*Clematis* spp.
Clover, annual yellow sweet	*Melilotus indica*
red	*Trifolium pratense*
subterraneum	*T. subterraneum*

continued

Appendix II. COMMON NAMES AND CORRESPONDING SCIENTIFIC NAMES

Part II. Plants

Common Name	Scientific Name
white	*T. repens*
white sweet	*Melilotus alba*
Cocklebur	*Xanthium* sp.
Cockspur	*Echinochloa* sp.
Coconut	*Cocos nucifera*
Coffee tree, Kentucky	*Gymnocladus dioicus*
Coleus, common	*Coleus blumei*
Coriaria	*Coriaria* spp.
Corn	*Zea mays*
Cotton, Indian	*Gossypium roseum*
upland	*G. hirsutum*
Cowpea, common	*Vigna sinensis*
Cress, garden	*Lepidium sativum*
Crowfoot, floating water	*Ranunculus pseudofluitans*
Cucumber	*Cucumis sativus*
Currant, European black	*Ribes nigrum*
northern red	*R. rubrum*
Cycas	*Cycas* spp.
Cypress, bald	*Taxodium distichum*
Dahlia, garden	*Dahlia pinnata*
Dandelion	*Taraxacum officinale*
Date	*Phoenix dactylifera*
Deerberry, common	*Vaccinium stamineum*
Discaria	*Discaria* spp.
Dock, curly	*Rumex crispus*
fiddleleaf	*R. pulcher*
Dodder, big seed alfalfa	*Cuscuta indecora*
Dogwood, flowering	*Cornus florida*
Douglas fir	*Pseudotsuga taxifolia*
Dryad	*Dryas* spp.
Elaeagnus	*Elaeagnus* spp.
Elder	*Sambucus* sp.
Elm, American	*Ulmus americana*
Chinese	*U. parvifolia*
Scotch	*U. glabra*
Eucalyptus	*Eucalyptus* spp.
Evening primrose, common	*Oenothera biennis*
Fern, wood	*Dryopteris austriaca*
Fern cycad	*Stangeria* spp.
Fescue, meadow	*Festuca elatior*
red	*F. rubra*
Fig	*Ficus carica*
Fir	*Abies* sp.
Flax, common	*Linum usitatissimum*
Foxtail, meadow	*Alopecurus pratensis*
Gaillardia	*Gaillardia* spp.
Geranium, Herb Robert	*Geranium robertianum*
Ginkgo	*Ginkgo biloba*
Gladiolus, breeder's	*Gladiolus gandavensis*
Grape, European	*Vitis vinifera*

Common Name	Scientific Name
Grapefruit	*Citrus paradisi*
Grass, barnyard	*Echinochloa crusgalli*
Bermuda	*Cynodon dactylon*
Dallis	*Paspalum dilatatum*
Johnson	*Sorghum halepense*
Kentucky blue-	*Poa pratensis*
quack	*Agropyron repens*
rough-stalked blue-	*Poa trivalis*
seashore salt	*Distichlis spicata*
Sudan	*Sorghum vulgare sudanense*
Greasewood, black	*Sarcobatus vermiculatus*
Hackberry	*Celtis* spp.
Hart's-tongue	*Phyllitis scolopendrium*
Heliotrope	*Heliotropium* spp.
Hemlock, eastern	*Tsuga canadensis*
Hemp	*Cannabis sativa*
Hibiscus, Chinese	*Hibiscus rosa-sinensis*
Hickory, shagbark	*Carya ovata*
Holly, American	*Ilex opaca*
Chinese	*I. cornuta*
English	*I. aquifolium*
Hollyhock	*Althaea* spp.
Honey locust, common	*Gleditsia triacanthos*
Hornbeam	*Carpinus* spp.
American hop	*Ostrya virginiana*
Horncorn	*Ceratozamia* spp.
Horsechestnut, common	*Aesculus hippocastanum*
Horsetail, giant	*Equisetum telmateia*
Hyacinth, common	*Hyacinthus orientalis*
Iris, German	*Iris germanica*
Ivy, English	*Hedera helix*
Jasmine, cape	*Gardenia jasminoides*
Jimsonweed	*Datura stramonium*
Juniper, common	*Juniperus communis*
mountain	*J. communis saxatilis*
Kafir	*Sorghum vulgare caffrorum*
Kafir bread	*Encephalartos* spp.
Kalanchoe	*Kalanchoe blossfeldiana*
Lamb's-quarter	*Chenopodium album*
Larch	*Larix* spp.
Larkspur	*Delphinium* spp.
Laurel, mountain	*Kalmia latifolia*
Lemon	*Citrus limon*
Lespedeza, Korean	*Lespedeza stipulacea*
Lettuce	*Lactuca sativa*
bitter	*L. virosa*
Lilac, common	*Syringa vulgaris*
Lily, bulbil	*Lilium bulbiferum*

continued

Appendix II. COMMON NAMES AND CORRESPONDING SCIENTIFIC NAMES

Part II. Plants

Common Name	Scientific Name
day	*Hemerocallis* spp.
Easter	*Lilium longiflorum*
Lime, sweet	*Citrus limetioides*
Linden	*Tilia* spp.
Locust, black	*Robinia pseudoacacia*
Lords-and-ladies	*Arum maculatum*
Lupine, tree	*Lupinus angustifolius*
Macrozamia	*Macrozamia* spp.
Magnolia, southern	*Magnolia grandiflora*
Maple, mountain	*Acer spicatum*
Norway	*A. platanoides*
plane-tree	*A. pseudoplatanus*
red	*A. rubrum*
sugar	*A. saccharum*
Mercurialis, annual	*Mercurialis annua*
Mesquite tree	*Prosopis juliflora*
Millet, foxtail	*Setaria italica*
pearl	*Pennisetum glaucum*
Moonflower, large	*Calonyction aculeatum*
Mountain ash, American	*Sorbus americana*
European	*S. aucuparia*
Mountain mahogany	*Cercocarpus* spp.
Mulberry	*Morus* spp.
Muskmelon	*Cucumis melo*
Mustard, black	*Brassica nigra*
Narcissus	*Narcissus* spp.
Nasturtium, common	*Tropaeolum majus*
Oak, black	*Quercus velutina*
blackjack	*Q. marilandica*
English	*Q. robur*
kermes	*Q. coccifera*
northern red	*Q. borealis*
pin	*Q. palustris*
post	*Q. stellata*
scarlet	*Q. coccinea*
scrub	*Q. ilicifolia*
southern red	*Q. falcata*
swamp chestnut	*Q. prinus*
turkey	*Q. laevis*
white	*Q. alba*
willow	*Q. phellos*
Oat, common	*Avena sativa*
Okra	*Hibiscus esculentus*
Olive, common	*Olea europaea*
Onion, garden	*Allium cepa*
Orange, sour	*Citrus aurantium*
sweet	*C. sinensis*
Palm, African oil	*Elaeis guineensis*
Papaya	*Carica papaya*
Parsley, common garden	*Petroselinum crispum*
knotted hedge	*Torilis nodosa*
Parsnip	*Pastinaca sativa*
Paulownia, royal	*Paulownia tomentosa*
Pea, garden	*Pisum sativum*
sweet	*Lathyrus odoratus*

Common Name	Scientific Name
Peach	*Prunus persica*
Peanut	*Arachis hypogaea*
Pear	*Pyrus communis*
Pelargonium, Lady Washington	*Pelargonium domesticum*
Pepper, bush red	*Capsicum frutescens*
Petunia	*Petunia* spp.
Pine, Italian stone	*Pinus pinea*
Japanese red	*P. densiflora*
loblolly	*P. taeda*
longleaf	*P. palustris*
Monterey	*P. radiata*
red	*P. resinosa*
Scotch	*P. sylvestris*
shore	*P. contorta*
Pineapple	*Ananas comosus*
Pink, clove	*Dianthus caryophyllus*
Plane tree	*Platanus* spp.
Plum, garden	*Prunus domestica*
Polypody, common	*Polypodium vulgare*
Pomelo	*Citrus grandis*
Poplar, black	*Populus nigra*
eastern	*P. deltoides*
yellow	*Liriodendron tulipifera*
Potato	*Solanum tuberosum*
Prasium	*Prasium majus*
Privet	*Ligustrum* spp.
Psychotria	*Psychotria* spp.
Pumpkin	*Cucurbita pepo*
Rabbit brush, green plume	*Chrysothamnus graveolens*
Radish, garden	*Raphanus sativus*
wild	*R. raphanistrum*
Rape, bird	*Brassica campestris*
Raspberry, red	*Rubus idaeus*
Redbud, eastern	*Cercis canadensis*
Red cedar, eastern	*Juniperus virginiana*
Redtop	*Agrostis alba*
Rhododendron, Pere Farges	*Rhododendron fargesi*
Rhubarb, garden	*Rheum rhaponticum*
Rice	*Oryza sativa*
Rose, evergreen	*Rosa sempervirens*
Rutabaga	*Brassica napobrassica*
Rye	*Secale cereale*
perennial	*Lolium perenne*
Sage, black	*Salvia mellifera*
Sagebrush, big	*Artemisia tridentata*
Salix	*Salix koriyanagi*
Saxifrage	*Saxifraga cernua*
twin-leaf	*S. oppositifolia*
Scurf pea, Arabian	*Psoralea bituminosa*
Sea buckthorn, common	*Hippophae rhamnoides*
Serviceberry	*Amelanchier* sp.
Snapdragon, common	*Antirrhinum majus*
Snapweed	*Impatiens* sp.
Snowberry, common	*Symphoricarpos albus*
Sorghum	*Sorghum vulgare*
Soybean	*Glycine max*
Spiderwort, Virginia	*Tradescantia virginiana*
Spinach	*Spinacia oleracea*

continued

Appendix II. COMMON NAMES AND CORRESPONDING SCIENTIFIC NAMES

Part II. Plants

Common Name	Scientific Name
Spleenwort, black	*Asplenium adiantum nigrum*
Spruce, Colorado	*Picea pungens*
Norway	*P. abies*
Sitka	*P. sitchensis*
Squash, winter	*Cucurbita maxima*
Stock, common	*Matthiola incana*
Stonecrop, evergreen	*Sedum hybridum*
goldmoss	*S. acre*
jenny	*S. reflexum*
Strawberry	*Fragaria* sp.
Sugarcane	*Saccharum officinarum*
Sump weed, poverty	*Iva axillaris*
Sunflower, common	*Helianthus annuus*
Sweet fern	*Comptonia* spp.
Sweet gale	*Myrica gale*
Sweet gum, American	*Liquidambar styraciflua*
Sweet potato	*Ipomoea batatas*
Tamarisk	*Tamarix* sp.
Tea, common	*Camellia sinensis*
Thistle, Scotch cotton	*Onopordum acanthium*
Timothy	*Phleum pratense*
Tobacco	*Nicotiana langsdorffi*
common	*N. tabacum*
tree	*N. glauca*
Tomato, common	*Lycopersicon esculentum*
Tree of heaven	*Ailanthus altissima*
Tulip, common	*Tulipa gesneriana*
Tupelo, black	*Nyssa sylvatica*
Turnip	*Brassica rapa*
Vetch, hairy	*Vicia villosa*
Violet	*Viola* sp.
Walnut, Persian	*Juglans regia*
Wandering Jew	*Tradescantia viridis*
Watermelon	*Citrullus vulgaris*
Waterweed, Canada	*Elodea canadensis*
Wheat	*Triticum aestivum*
White cedar, southern	*Chamaecyparis thyoides*
Willow, creeping	*Salix repens*
gray-leaf	*S. glauca*
pygmy	*S. herbacea*
Woad	*Isatis djurjaedae*
Yaupon	*Ilex vomitoria*
Yew, English	*Taxus baccata*
Yucca, mound lily	*Yucca gloriosa*

INDEX

To facilitate identification, the index includes the taxonomic order for animals and the family for plants, unless otherwise specified. As a further aid, the index lists the animals and plants as they are presented in the tables. Entries for a particular organism may therefore be found under the common name, under the scientific name, or under both. Where information is available under both, cross-references (and Appendixes I and II if more than one genus is applicable to a common name) make the data easily accessible. In some tables, only the formula for a chemical compound appears. When this occurs, the compound name in the index is followed by the formula in brackets.

*	indicates diagram or graph
fn	indicates footnote material
hn	indicates headnote material

† Class

† Class

‡ Subphylum

■ Order

† Class

† Class

† Class

† Class

† Class

† Class

† Class

† Class

† Class

† Class

† Class

■ Order

† Class

† Class

† Class

† Class

■ Order

■ Order

† Class

† Class
■ Order

† Class

† Class

† Class